ALGEBRA

Exponents and Radicals

$x^a x^b = x^{a+b}$ $\qquad \dfrac{x^a}{x^b} = x^{a-b}$ $\qquad x^{-a} = \dfrac{1}{x^a}$ $\qquad (x^a)^b = x^{ab}$ $\qquad \left(\dfrac{x}{y}\right)^a = \dfrac{x^a}{y^a}$

$x^{1/n} = \sqrt[n]{x}$ $\qquad x^{m/n} = \sqrt[n]{x^m} = (\sqrt[n]{x})^m$ $\qquad \sqrt[n]{xy} = \sqrt[n]{x}\sqrt[n]{y}$ $\qquad \sqrt[n]{x/y} = \sqrt[n]{x}/\sqrt[n]{y}$

Factoring Formulas

$a^2 - b^2 = (a-b)(a+b)$ $\qquad a^2 + b^2$ does not factor over real numbers.

$a^3 - b^3 = (a-b)(a^2+ab+b^2)$ $\qquad a^3 + b^3 = (a+b)(a^2-ab+b^2)$

$a^n - b^n = (a-b)(a^{n-1} + a^{n-2}b + a^{n-3}b^2 + \cdots + ab^{n-2} + b^{n-1})$

Binomials

$(a \pm b)^2 = a^2 \pm 2ab + b^2$

$(a \pm b)^3 = a^3 \pm 3a^2b + 3ab^2 \pm b^3$

Binomial Theorem

$$(a+b)^n = a^n + \binom{n}{1}a^{n-1}b + \binom{n}{2}a^{n-2}b^2 + \cdots + \binom{n}{n-1}ab^{n-1} + b^n,$$

where $\dbinom{n}{k} = \dfrac{n(n-1)(n-2)\cdots(n-k+1)}{k(k-1)(k-2)\cdots 3\cdot 2\cdot 1} = \dfrac{n!}{k!(n-k)!}$

Quadratic Formula

The solutions of $ax^2 + bx + c = 0$ are

$$x = \frac{-b \pm \sqrt{b^2 - 4ac}}{2a}.$$

GEOMETRY

Parallelogram

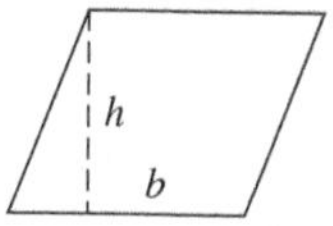

$A = bh$

Triangle

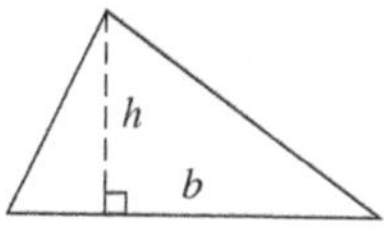

$A = \frac{1}{2}bh$

Trapezoid

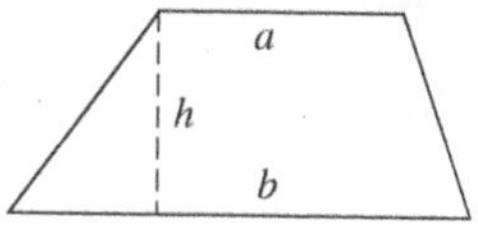

$A = \frac{1}{2}(a+b)h$

Circle

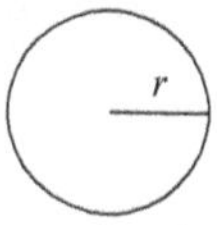

$A = \pi r^2$

$C = 2\pi r$

Sector

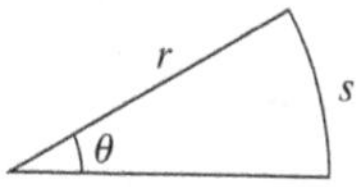

$A = \frac{1}{2}r^2\theta$

$s = r\theta$ (θ in radians)

Cylinder

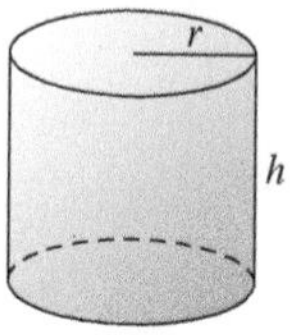

$V = \pi r^2 h$

$S = 2\pi rh$

(lateral surface area)

Cone

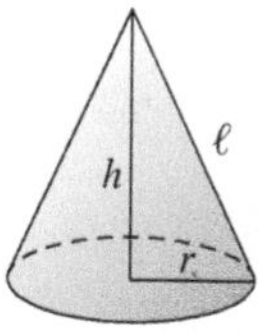

$V = \frac{1}{3}\pi r^2 h$

$S = \pi r\ell$

(lateral surface area)

Sphere

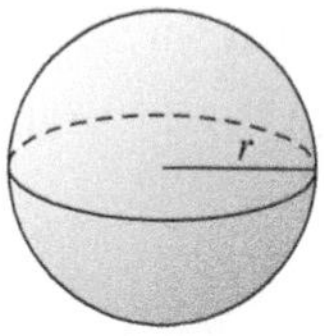

$V = \frac{4}{3}\pi r^3$

$S = 4\pi r^2$

Equations of Lines and Circles

$m = \dfrac{y_2 - y_1}{x_2 - x_1}$ — slope of line through (x_1, y_1) and (x_2, y_2)

$y - y_1 = m(x - x_1)$ — point–slope form of line through (x_1, y_1) with slope m

$y = mx + b$ — slope–intercept form of line with slope m and y-intercept $(0, b)$

$(x-h)^2 + (y-k)^2 = r^2$ — circle of radius r with center (h, k)

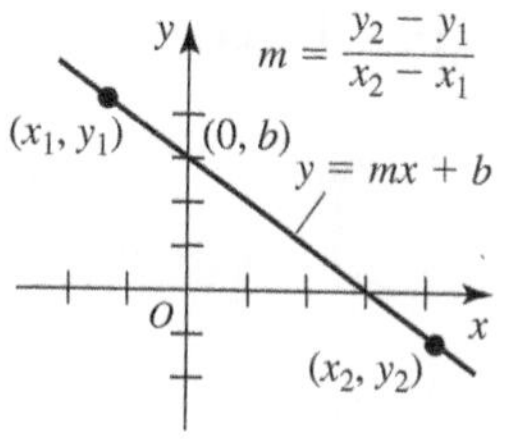

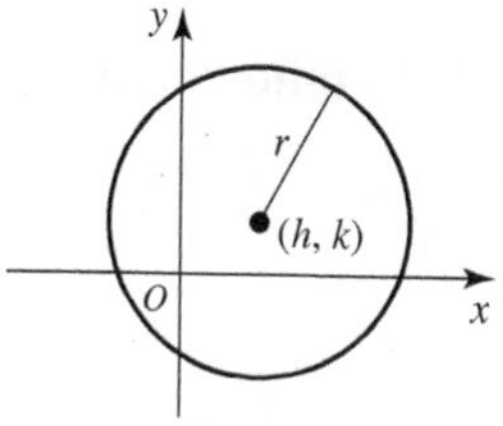

$(x-h)^2 + (y-k)^2 = r^2$

TRIGONOMETRY

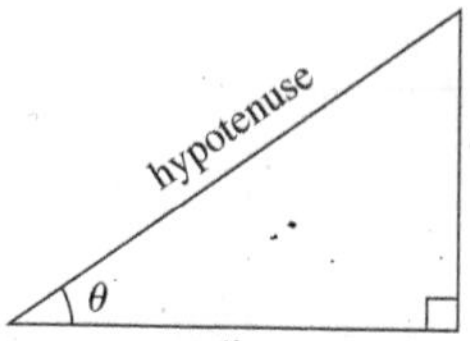

$\cos\theta = \dfrac{\text{adj}}{\text{hyp}}$ $\qquad \sin\theta = \dfrac{\text{opp}}{\text{hyp}}$ $\qquad \tan\theta = \dfrac{\text{opp}}{\text{adj}}$

$\sec\theta = \dfrac{\text{hyp}}{\text{adj}}$ $\qquad \csc\theta = \dfrac{\text{hyp}}{\text{opp}}$ $\qquad \cot\theta = \dfrac{\text{adj}}{\text{opp}}$

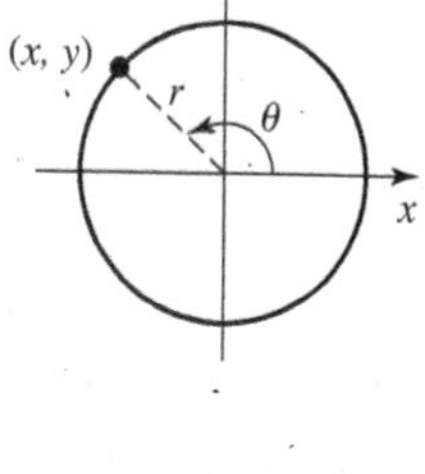

$\cos\theta = \dfrac{x}{r}$ $\qquad \sec\theta = \dfrac{r}{x}$

$\sin\theta = \dfrac{y}{r}$ $\qquad \csc\theta = \dfrac{r}{y}$

$\tan\theta = \dfrac{y}{x}$ $\qquad \cot\theta = \dfrac{x}{y}$

(Continued)

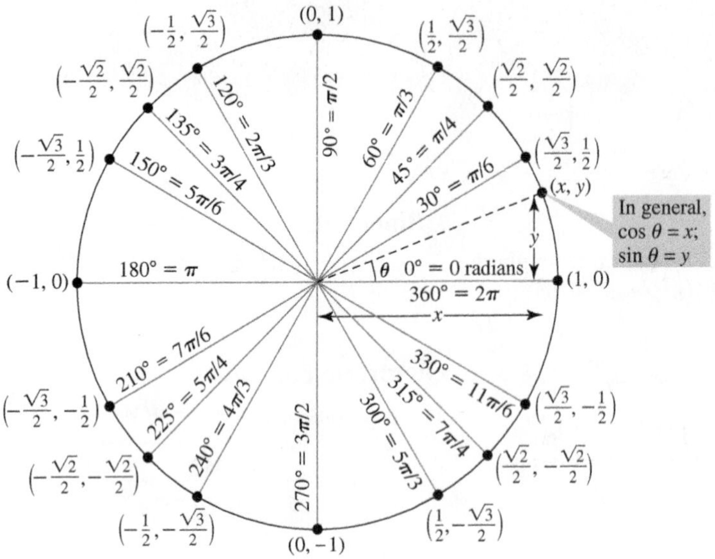

Reciprocal Identities

$$\tan\theta = \frac{\sin\theta}{\cos\theta} \quad \cot\theta = \frac{\cos\theta}{\sin\theta} \quad \sec\theta = \frac{1}{\cos\theta} \quad \csc\theta = \frac{1}{\sin\theta}$$

Pythagorean Identities

$$\sin^2\theta + \cos^2\theta = 1 \quad \tan^2\theta + 1 = \sec^2\theta \quad 1 + \cot^2\theta = \csc^2\theta$$

Sign Identities

$$\sin(-\theta) = -\sin\theta \quad \cos(-\theta) = \cos\theta \quad \tan(-\theta) = -\tan\theta$$
$$\csc(-\theta) = -\csc\theta \quad \sec(-\theta) = \sec\theta \quad \cot(-\theta) = -\cot\theta$$

Double-Angle Identities

$$\sin 2\theta = 2\sin\theta\cos\theta$$
$$\cos 2\theta = \cos^2\theta - \sin^2\theta = 2\cos^2\theta - 1 = 1 - 2\sin^2\theta$$
$$\tan 2\theta = \frac{2\tan\theta}{1 - \tan^2\theta}$$

Half-Angle Formulas

$$\cos^2\theta = \frac{1 + \cos 2\theta}{2} \quad \sin^2\theta = \frac{1 - \cos 2\theta}{2}$$

Addition Formulas

$$\sin(\alpha + \beta) = \sin\alpha\cos\beta + \cos\alpha\sin\beta$$
$$\cos(\alpha + \beta) = \cos\alpha\cos\beta - \sin\alpha\sin\beta$$
$$\tan(\alpha + \beta) = \frac{\tan\alpha + \tan\beta}{1 - \tan\alpha\tan\beta}$$
$$\sin(\alpha - \beta) = \sin\alpha\cos\beta - \cos\alpha\sin\beta$$
$$\cos(\alpha - \beta) = \cos\alpha\cos\beta + \sin\alpha\sin\beta$$
$$\tan(\alpha - \beta) = \frac{\tan\alpha - \tan\beta}{1 + \tan\alpha\tan\beta}$$

Law of Sines

$$\frac{\sin\alpha}{a} = \frac{\sin\beta}{b} = \frac{\sin\gamma}{c}$$

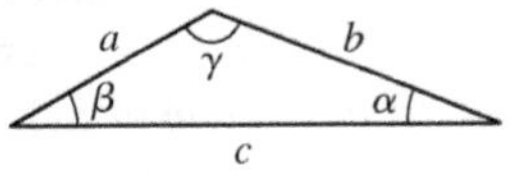

Law of Cosines

$$a^2 = b^2 + c^2 - 2bc\cos\alpha$$

Graphs of Trigonometric Functions and Their Inverses

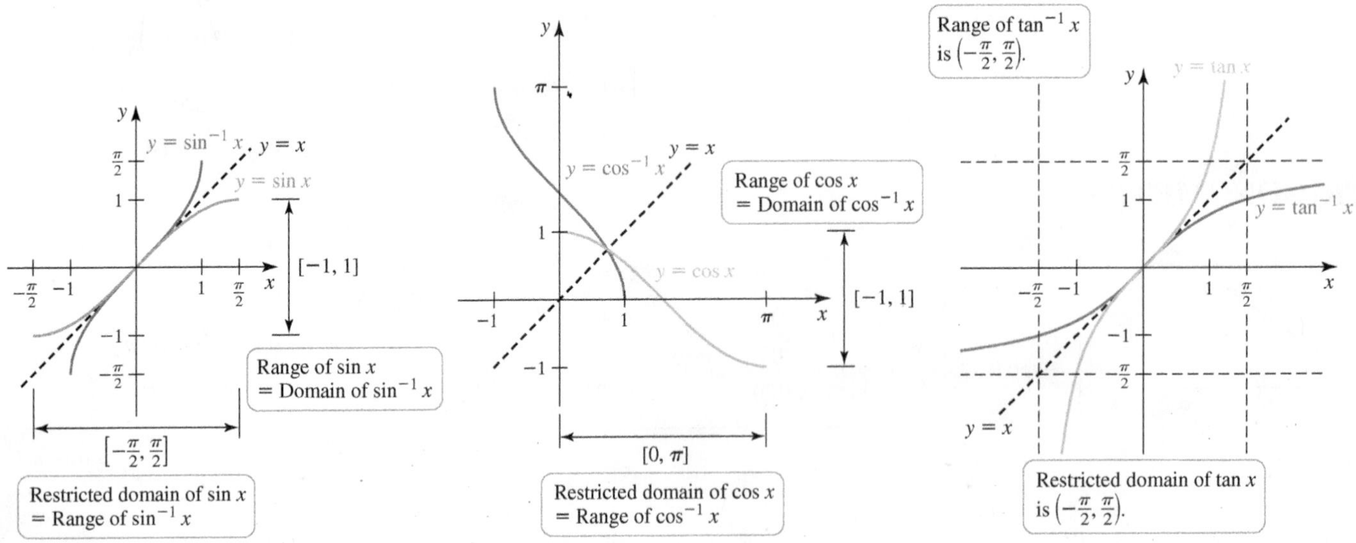

PEARSON ALWAYS LEARNING

William Briggs • Lyle Cochran • Bernard Gillett

Calculus

Early Transcendentals

Volume I

Custom Edition for Oakton Community College

Taken from:
Calculus: Early Transcendentals, Second Edition
by William Briggs, Lyle Cochran, and Bernard Gillett

Cover Art: Courtesy of Photodisc/Getty Images.

Taken from:

Calculus: Early Transcendentals, Second Edition
by William Briggs, Lyle Cochran, and Bernard Gillett

Boston, Massachusetts 02116

This special edition published in cooperation with Pearson Learning Solutions.

Pearson Learning Solutions, 501 Boylston Street, Suite 900, Boston, MA 02116
A Pearson Education Company
www.pearsoned.com

Printed in the United States of America

1 2 3 4 5 6 7 8 9 10 V092 15 14

000200010271885389

SK

PEARSON

ISBN 10: 1-269-86812-8
ISBN 13: 978-1-269-86812-9

Contents

Preface

The second edition of *Calculus: Early Transcendentals* supports a three-semester or four-quarter calculus sequence typically taken by students studying mathematics, engineering, the natural sciences, or economics. The second edition has the same goals as the first edition:

- to motivate the essential ideas of calculus with a lively narrative, demonstrating the utility of calculus with applications in diverse fields;
- to introduce new topics through concrete examples, applications, and analogies, appealing to students' intuition and geometric instincts to make calculus natural and believable; and
- once this intuitive foundation is established, to present generalizations and abstractions and to treat theoretical matters in a rigorous way.

The second edition both builds on the success and addresses the inevitable deficiencies of the first edition. We have listened to and learned from the instructors who used the first edition. They have given us wise guidance about how to make the second edition an even more effective learning tool for students and a more powerful resource for instructors. Users of the book continue to tell us that it mirrors the course they teach—and more importantly, that students actually read it! Of course, the second edition also benefits from our own experiences using the book, as well as our experiences teaching mathematics at diverse institutions over the past 30 years.

We are grateful to users of the first edition—for their courage in adopting a first edition book, for their enthusiastic response to the book, and for their invaluable advice and feedback. They deserve much of the credit for the improvements that we have made in the second edition.

New in the Second Edition

Narrative

The second edition of this book has undergone a thorough cover-to-cover polishing of the narrative, making the presentation of material even more concise and lucid. Occasionally, we discovered new ways to present material to make the exposition clearer for students and more efficient for instructors.

Figures

The figures—already dynamic and informative in the first edition—were thoroughly reviewed and revised when necessary. The figures enrich the overall spirit of the book and tell as much of the calculus story as the words do. The path-breaking interactive figures in the companion eBook have been refined, and they still represent a revolutionary way to communicate mathematics. See page xii, eBook with Interactive Figures, for more information.

Exercises

The comprehensive 7656 exercises in the first edition were thoroughly reviewed and refined. Then 19% more basic skills and mid-level exercises were added. The exercises at the end of each section are still efficiently organized in the following categories.

- *Review Questions* begin each exercise set and check students' conceptual understanding of the essential ideas from the section.
- *Basic Skills* exercises are confidence-building problems that provide a solid foundation for the more challenging exercises to follow. Each example in the narrative is linked directly to a block of *Basic Skills* exercises via *Related Exercises* references at the end of the example solution.
- *Further Explorations* exercises expand on the *Basic Skills* exercises by challenging students to think creatively and to generalize newly acquired skills.
- *Applications* exercises connect skills developed in previous exercises to applications and modeling problems that demonstrate the power and utility of calculus.
- *Additional Exercises* are generally the most difficult and challenging problems; they include proofs of results cited in the narrative.

Each chapter concludes with a comprehensive set of *Review Exercises*.

Answers

The answers in the back of the book have been reviewed and thoroughly checked for accuracy. The reliability that we achieved in the first edition has been maintained—if not improved.

New Topics

We have added new material on Newton's method, surface area of solids of revolution, hyperbolic functions, and TNB frames. Based on our own teaching experience, we also added a brief new introductory section to the chapter on Techniques of Integration. We felt it makes sense to introduce students to some general integration strategies before diving into the standard techniques of integration by parts, partial fraction, and various substitutions.

MyMathLab

We (together with the team at Pearson) have made many improvements to the MyMathLab course for the second edition. Hundreds of new algorithmic exercises that correspond to those in the text were added to the course. Cumulative review exercises have been added, providing an opportunity for students to get "mixed practice" with important skills such as finding derivatives. New step-by-step exercises for key skills provide support for students in their first attempts at new and important problems. Real-world exerciess now require that students provide units with their answer. We've added more exercises that call for student manipulation and analysis of the Interactive Figures. We have greatly increased the number of instructional videos. The graphing functionality in MyMathLab has become more sophisticated and the answer-checking algorithms are more refined.

Differential Equations

This book has a single robust section devoted to an overview of differential equations. However, for schools that require more expansive coverage of differential equations, we provide complete online chapters on both first- and second-order differential equations, available in MyMathLab as well as through the Pearson Math and Stats Resource page at **www.pearsonhighered.com/mathstatsresources**.

Pedagogical Features

Figures

Given the power of graphics software and the ease with which many students assimilate visual images, we devoted considerable time and deliberation to the figures in this book. Whenever possible, we let the figures communicate essential ideas using annotations

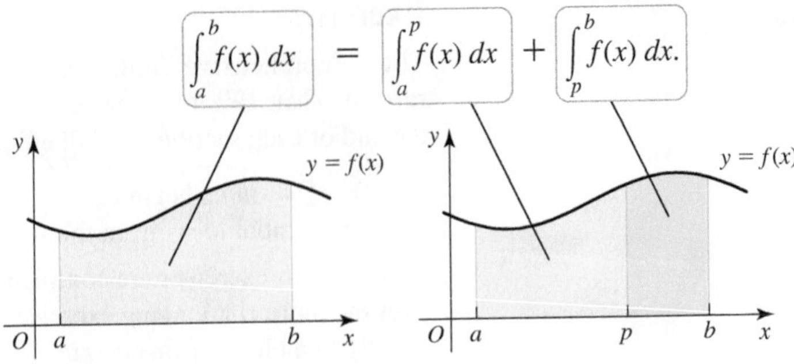

Figure 5.29

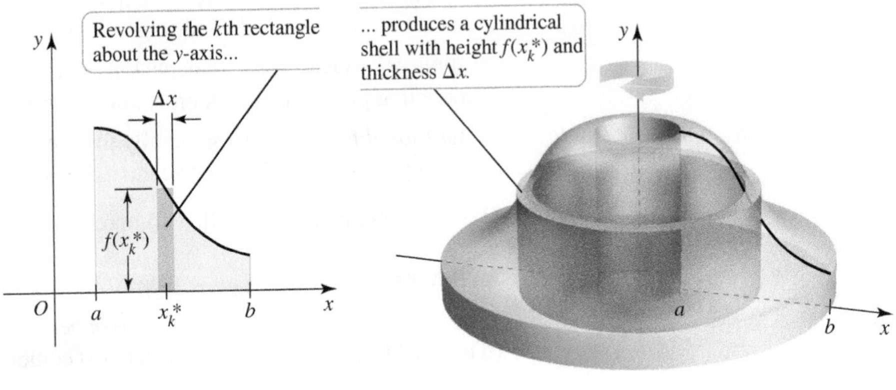

Figure 6.40

reminiscent of an instructor's voice at the board. Readers will quickly find that the figures facilitate learning in new ways.

Quick Check and *Margin Notes*

The narrative is interspersed with *Quick Check* questions that encourage students to read with pencil in hand. These questions resemble the kinds of questions instructors pose in class. Answers to the *Quick Check* questions are found at the end of the section in which they occur. *Margin Notes* offer reminders, provide insight, and clarify technical points.

Guided Projects

The *Instructor's Resource Guide and Test Bank* contains 78 *Guided Projects*. These projects allow students to work in a directed, step-by-step fashion, with various objectives: to carry out extended calculations, to derive physical models, to explore related theoretical topics, or to investigate new applications of calculus. The *Guided Projects* vividly demonstrate the breadth of calculus and provide a wealth of mathematical excursions that go beyond the typical classroom experience. A list of suggested *Guided Projects* is included at the end of each chapter. Students may access the *Guided Projects* within MyMathLab.

Technology

We believe that a calculus text should help students strengthen their analytical skills and demonstrate how technology can extend (not replace) those skills. Calculators and graphing utilities are additional tools in the kit, and students must learn when and when not to use them. Our goal is to accommodate the different policies about technology that various instructors may use.

Throughout the book, exercises marked with T indicate that the use of technology— ranging from plotting a function with a graphing calculator to carrying out a calculation using a computer algebra system—may be needed. See page xiv for information regarding our technology resource manuals covering Maple, Mathematica and Texas Instruments graphing calculators.

eBook with Interactive Figures

The textbook is supported by a groundbreaking and award-winning electronic book, created by Eric Schulz of Walla Walla Community College. This "live book" contains the complete text of the print book plus interactive versions of approximately 700 figures. Instructors can use these interactive figures in the classroom to illustrate the important ideas of calculus, and students can explore them while they are reading the textbook. Our experience confirms that the interactive figures help build students' geometric intuition of calculus. The authors have written Interactive Figure Exercises that can be assigned via MyMathLab so that students can engage with the figures outside of class in a directed way. Additionally, the authors have created short videos, accessed through the eBook, that tell the story of key Interactive Figures. Available only within MyMathLab, the eBook provides instructors with powerful new teaching tools that expand and enrich the learning experience for students.

Content Highlights

In writing this text, we identified content in the calculus curriculum that consistently presents challenges to our students. We made organizational changes to the standard presentation of these topics or slowed the pace of the narrative to facilitate students' comprehension of material that is traditionally difficult. Two noteworthy modifications to the traditional table of contents for this course appear in the material for Calculus II and Calculus III.

Often appearing near the end of the term, the topics of sequences and series are the most challenging in Calculus II. By splitting this material into two chapters, we have given these topics a more deliberate pace and made them more accessible without adding significantly to the length of the narrative.

There is a clear and logical path through multivariate calculus, which is not apparent in many textbooks. We have carefully separated functions of several variables from vector-valued functions, so that these ideas are distinct in the minds of students. The book culminates when these two threads are joined in the last chapter, which is devoted to vector calculus.

Additional Resources

Instructor's Resource Guide and Test Bank

ISBN 0-321-95429-7 | 978-0-321-95429-9
Bernard Gillett, University of Colorado at Boulder

This guide represents significant contributions by the textbook authors and contains a variety of classroom support materials for instructors.

- Seventy-eight *Guided Projects*, correlated to specific chapters of the text, can be assigned to students for individual or group work. The *Guided Projects* vividly demonstrate the breadth of calculus and provide a wealth of mathematical excursions that go beyond the typical classroom experience.
- *Lecture Support Notes* give an *Overview* of the material to be taught in each section of the text, and helpful classroom *Teaching Tips*. *Connections* among various sections of the text are also pointed out, and *Additional Activities* are provided.
- *Quick Quizzes* for each section in the text consist of multiple-choice questions that can be used as in-class quiz material or as Active Learning Questions. These Quick Quizzes can also be found at the end of each section in the interactive eBook.
- *Chapter Reviews* provide a list of key concepts from each chapter, followed by a set of chapter review questions.
- *Chapter Test Banks* consist of between 25 and 30 questions that can be used for in-class exams, take-home exams, or additional review material.
- *Learning Objectives Lists* and an *Index of Applications* are tools to help instructors gear the text to their course goals and students' interests.
- *Student Study Cards*, consisting of key concepts for both single-variable and multivariable calculus, are included for instructors to photocopy and distribute to their students as convenient study tools.
- *Answers* are provided for all exercises in the manual, including the *Guided Projects*.

Instructor's Solutions Manuals

Mark Woodard, Furman University
Single Variable Calculus (Chapters 1–10) ISBN 0-321-95422-X | 978-0-321-95422-0
Multivariable Calculus (Chapters 8–14) ISBN 0-321-95430-0 | 978-0-321-95430-5

The *Instructor's Solutions Manual* contains complete solutions to all the exercises in the text.

Student's Solutions Manuals

Mark Woodard, Furman University
Single Variable Calculus (Chapters 1–10) ISBN 0-321-95432-7 | 978-0-321-95432-9
Multivariable Calculus (Chapters 8–14) ISBN 0-321-95431-9 | 978-0-321-95431-2

The *Student's Solutions Manual* is designed for the student and contains complete solutions to all the odd-numbered exercises in the text.

Just-in-Time Algebra and Trigonometry for Early Transcendentals Calculus, Fourth Edition

ISBN 0-321-67103-1 | 978-0-321-67103-5
Guntram Mueller and Ronald I. Brent, University of Massachusetts—Lowell

Sharp algebra and trigonometry skills are critical to mastering calculus, and *Just-in-Time Algebra and Trigonometry for Early Transcendentals Calculus* is designed to bolster these skills while students study calculus. As students make their way through calculus, this text is with them every step of the way, showing them the necessary algebra or trigonometry topics and pointing out potential problem spots. The easy-to-use table of contents has algebra and trigonometry topics arranged in the order in which students will need them as they study calculus.

Technology Resource Manuals

Maple Manual by Marie Vanisko, Carroll College
Mathematica Manual by Marie Vanisko, Carroll College
TI-Graphing Calculator Manual by Elaine McDonald-Newman, Sonoma State University

These manuals cover Maple™ 17, Mathematica® 8, and the TI-83 Plus/TI-84 Plus and TI-89, respectively. Each manual provides detailed guidance for integrating a specific software package or graphing calculator throughout the course, including syntax and commands. These manuals are available to instructors and students through the Pearson Math and Stats Resources page, **www.pearsonhighered.com/mathstatsresources**, and MyMathLab®.

MyMathLab® Online Course (access code required)

MyMathLab from Pearson is the world's leading online resource in mathematics, integrating interactive homework, assessment, and media in a flexible, easy-to-use format. MyMathLab delivers **proven results** in helping individual students succeed. It provides **engaging experiences** that personalize, stimulate, and measure learning for each student. And it comes from an **experienced partner** with educational expertise and an eye on the future.

MyMathLab for *Calculus: Early Transcendentals* contains the groundbreaking **eBook featuring over 700 Interactive Figures** that can be manipulated to illuminate difficult-to-convey concepts. Instructors can use these interactive figures in the classroom to illustrate the important ideas of calculus, and students can manipulate the interactive figures while they are using MyMathLab. In each case, these interactive figures help build geometric intuition of calculus. Exercises for the Interactive Figures can be assigned as homework to encourage students to explore the concepts presented.

The MyMathLab course for this text contains over 7500 assignable algorithmic exercises. To learn more about how MyMathLab combines proven learning applications with powerful assessment, visit **www.mymathlab.com** or contact your Pearson representative.

MathXL® Online Course (access code required)

MathXL® is the homework and assessment engine that runs MyMathLab. (MyMathLab is MathXL plus a learning management system.)

With MathXL, instructors can:

- Create, edit, and assign online homework and tests using algorithmically generated exercises correlated at the objective level to the textbook.
- Create and assign their own online exercises.
- Maintain records of all student work tracked in MathXL's online gradebook.

With MathXL, students can:

- Work through the **Getting Ready for Calculus** chapter, which includes hundreds of exercises that address prerequisite skills in algebra and trigonometry, and receive remediation for those skills with which they need help.
- Take chapter tests in MathXL and receive personalized study plans and/or personalized homework assignments based on their test results.
- Use the study plan and/or the homework to link directly to tutorial exercises for the objectives they need to study.
- Access supplemental animations and video clips directly from selected exercises.

MathXL is available to qualified adopters. For more information, visit our website at **www.mathxl.com** or contact your Pearson representative.

TestGen®

TestGen® (**www.pearsoned.com/testgen**) enables instructors to build, edit, print, and administer tests using a computerized bank of questions developed to cover all the objectives of the text. TestGen is algorithmically based, allowing instructors to create multiple but equivalent versions of the same question or test with the click of a button. Instructors can also modify test bank questions or add new questions. The software and testbank are available for download from Pearson Education's online catalog, **www.pearsonhighered.com/irc**.

Video Resources

The Video Lectures With Optional Captioning feature an engaging team of mathematics instructors who present comprehensive coverage of topics in the text. The lecturers' presentations include illustrative examples and exercises and support an approach that emphasizes visualization and problem solving. Available only through MyMathLab and MathXL.

PowerPoint® Lecture Slides

These PowerPoint slides contain key concepts, definitions, figures, and tables from the textbook. These files are available to qualified instructors through the Pearson Instructor Resource Center, **www.pearsonhighered.com/irc**, and MyMathLab.

Acknowledgments

We would like to express our thanks to the people who made many valuable contributions to this edition as it evolved through its many stages:

Accuracy Checkers

Lisa Collette
Blaise DeSesa
Patricia Espinoza-Toro
David Grinstein
Ebony Harvey
Michele Jean-Louis
Nickolas Mavrikidis
Renato Mirollo
Patricia Nelson
John Samons
Joan Saniuk
Tom Wegleitner
Gary Williams

Reviewers

Jay Paul Abramson, *Arizona State University*

Anthony Barcellos, *American River College*

Maurino Bautista, *Rochester Institute of Technology*

Nick Belloit, *Florida State College at Jacksonville, Kent Campus*

Patrice D. Benson, *The United States Military Academy*

Nadine Bluett, *Front Range Community College, Westminster*

Maritza M. Branker, *Niagara College*

Tim Britt, *Jackson State Community College*

Zhixiong Chen, *New Jersey City University*

Marcela Chiorescu, *Georgia College and State University*

Ray E. Collins, *Georgia Perimeter College*

Robert Diaz, *Fullerton College*

Vincent D. Dimiceli, *Oral Roberts University*

Paul Drelles, *West Shore Community College*

Lori Dunlop-Pyle, *University of Central Florida*

Keith Erickson, *Georgia Highlands College*

Justin Fitzpatrick, *Vanderbilt University*

Laurie Huffman, *Georgia College and State University*

Michelle Knox, *Midwestern State University*

Christy Koelling, *Davidson County Community College*

John M. Livermore, *Cazenovia College*

Mike Long, *Shippensburg University*

Gabriel Melendez, *Mohawk Valley Community College*

Susan Miller, *Richland College*

Renato Mirollo, *Boston College*

Val Mohanakumar, *Hillsborough Community College*

Nathan T. Moyer, *Whitworth University*

Lloyd Moyo, *Henderson State University*

Mihai Putinar, *University of California at Santa Barbara*

Marc Renault, *Shippensburg University*

Michael Rosenthal, *Florida International University*

Jennifer Strehler, *Oakton Community College*

V. Lee Turner, *Southern Nazarene University*

Larissa Williamson, *University of Florida*

Deborah Ziegler, *Hannibal-LaGrange University*

Calculus MyMathLab Advisory Board

Maria Capursi, *University Central Florida*

Jacqueline Donofrio, *Monroe Community College*

Allen Guest, *Clemson University*

Debbie Korth, *University of Arkansas*

Nela Lakos, *Ohio State University*

Elizabeth Miller, *Ohio State University*

Stephen Scarborough, *Oregon State University*

German Vargas, *College of Coastal Georgia*

Janet Woodland, *University of Arkansas*

Class Testers, Focus Group Participants

Martha Gady, *Whitworth University*

Nathan T. Moyer, *Whitworth University*

Donna M. Pierce, *Whitworth University*

Michael J. Rempe, *Whitworth University*

Anne A. Trefry, *Whitworth University*

Credits

Chapter opener art: Petr Vaclavek/Shutterstock

Chapter 1

Page 25, The Journal of Experimental Biology 203: 3745–3754, Dec. 2000. **Page 25,** The College Mathematics Journal 38, No. 1, Jan. 2007. **Page 25,** U.S. Fish and Wildlife Service. **Page 49,** The College Mathematics Journal 27, No. 4, Jan. 1996.

Chapter 2

Page 111, Arthur Koestler, The Act of Creation.

Chapter 3

Page 134, U.S. Bureau of Census. **Page 180,** J. Perloff MICROECONOMICS, Prentice Hall, 2012. **Page 206,** E.G. Hook and A. Lindsjo, Down Syndrome in Live Births by Single Year Maternal Age. **Page 213,** H. Ska la, The College Mathematics Journal, 28 Mar. 1997. **Page 223,** The College Mathematics Journal, 32, 4 Sept. 2001. **Page 228,** Calculus, Tom M. Apostol, Vol. 1, John Wiley & Sons, New York, 1967.

Chapter 4

Pages 237, 238, 239, 251, and 256, Thomas, George B.; Weir, Maurice D.; Hass, Joel; Giordano, Frank R., THOMAS' CALCULUS, EARLY TRANSCENDENTALS, MEDIA UPGRADE, 11th edition, © 2008 Printed and Electronically reproduced by permission of Pearson Education, Inc., Upper Saddle River, New Jersey. **Page 276,** Mathematics Teacher, Nov. 2002. **Page 278,** PROBLEMS FOR MATHEMATICIANS, YOUNG AND OLD by Paul R. Halmos. Copyright © 1991 Mathematical Association of America. Reprinted by permission. All rights reserved. **Page 279,** "Do Dogs Know Calculus?" by Tim Pennings from The College Mathematics Journal, Vol. 34, No. 3. Copyright © 2003 Mathematical Association of America. Reprinted by permission. All rights reserved. **Page 280,** "Energetic Savings and The Body Size Distributions of Gliding Mammals" Roman Dial, Evolutionary Ecology Research 5 2003: 1151–1162. **Page 280,** Calculus, Vol. 1, Tom M Apostol, John Wiley & Sons, 1967.

Chapter 5

Page 361, The College Mathematics Journal 32, 4 Sept. 2001. **Page 383,** Mathematics Magazine 78, 5 Dec. 2005. **Page 384,** The College Mathematics Journal 33, 5, Nov. 2002. **Page 397,** Mathematics Magazine 81, 5, Dec. 2008.

Chapter 6

Page 414, Thomas, George B; Weir, Maurice D; Hass, Joel; Giordano, Frank R., THOMAS' CALCULUS, EARLY TRANSCENDENTALS, MEDIA UPGRADE, 11th edition © 2008. Printed and Electronically reproduced by permission of Pearson Education, Inc., Upper Saddle River, New Jersey. **Page 419,** Mathematics Magazine 81, No. 2, Apr. 2008. **Pages 421, 425, 426, 433, 435,** Thomas, George B.; Weir, Maurice D.; Hass Joel; Giordano, Frank R., THOMAS' CALCULUS, EARLY TRANSCENDENTALS, MEDIA UP. GRADE, 11th edition, © 2008. Printed and Electronically reproduced by permission of Pearson Education, Inc., Upper Saddle River, New Jersey. **Page 490,** Adapted from Putnam Exam 1939. **Page 490,** "A Theory of Competitive Running," Joe Keller, Physics Today 26 Sept. 1973.

1

Functions

Chapter Preview Mathematics is a language with an alphabet, a vocabulary, and many rules. Before beginning your calculus journey, you should be familiar with the elements of this language. Among these elements are algebra skills; the notation and terminology for various sets of real numbers; and the descriptions of lines, circles, and other basic sets in the coordinate plane. A review of this material is found in Appendix A. This chapter begins with the fundamental concept of a function and then presents the entire cast of functions needed for calculus: polynomials, rational functions, algebraic functions, exponential and logarithmic functions, and the trigonometric functions, along with their inverses. Before you begin studying calculus, it is important that you master the ideas in this chapter.

1.1 Review of Functions

Everywhere around us we see relationships among quantities, or **variables**. For example, the consumer price index changes in time and the temperature of the ocean varies with latitude. These relationships can often be expressed by mathematical objects called *functions*. Calculus is the study of functions, and because we use functions to describe the world around us, calculus is a universal language for human inquiry.

> DEFINITION **Function**
>
> A **function** f is a rule that assigns to each value x in a set D a *unique* value denoted $f(x)$. The set D is the **domain** of the function. The **range** is the set of all values of $f(x)$ produced as x varies over the entire domain (Figure 1.1).

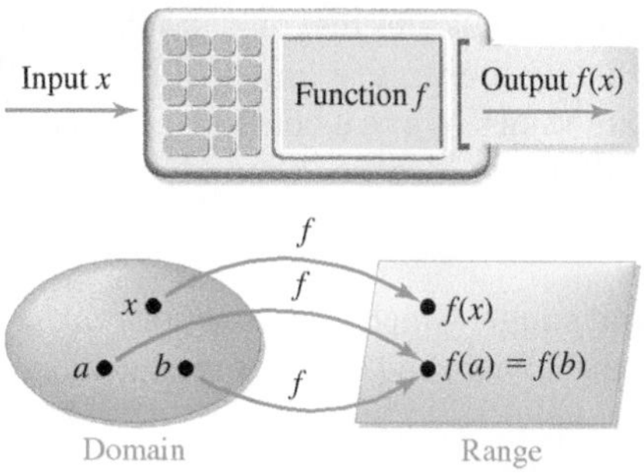

Figure 1.1

The **independent variable** is the variable associated with the domain; the **dependent variable** belongs to the range. The **graph** of a function f is the set of all points (x, y) in the xy-plane that satisfy the equation $y = f(x)$. The **argument** of a function is the expression on which the function works. For example, x is the argument when we write $f(x)$. Similarly, 2 is the argument in $f(2)$ and $x^2 + 4$ is the argument in $f(x^2 + 4)$.

QUICK CHECK 1 If $f(x) = x^2 - 2x$, find $f(-1)$, $f(x^2)$, $f(t)$, and $f(p - 1)$. ◄

The requirement that a function assigns a *unique* value of the dependent variable to each value in the domain is expressed in the vertical line test (Figure 1.2a). For example, the outside temperature as it varies over the course of a day is a function of time (Figure 1.2b).

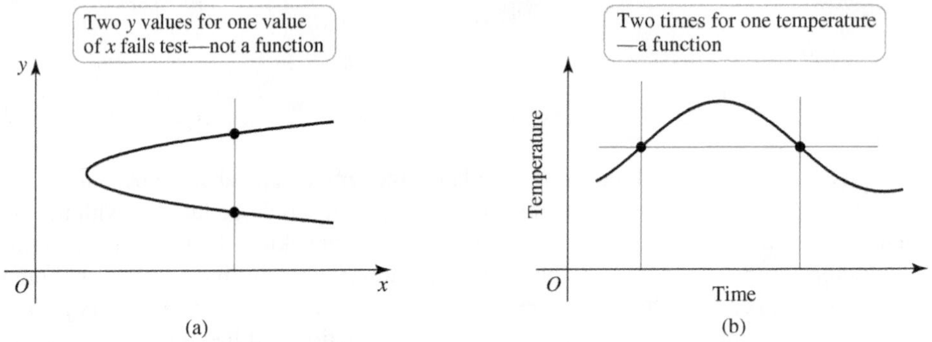

Figure 1.2

➤ If the domain is not specified, we take it to be the set of all values of x for which f is defined. We will see shortly that the domain and range of a function may be restricted by the context of the problem.

➤ A set of points or a graph that does *not* correspond to a function represents a **relation** between the variables. All functions are relations, but not all relations are functions.

Vertical Line Test

A graph represents a function if and only if it passes the **vertical line test**: Every vertical line intersects the graph at most once. A graph that fails this test does not represent a function.

EXAMPLE 1 **Identifying functions** State whether each graph in Figure 1.3 represents a function.

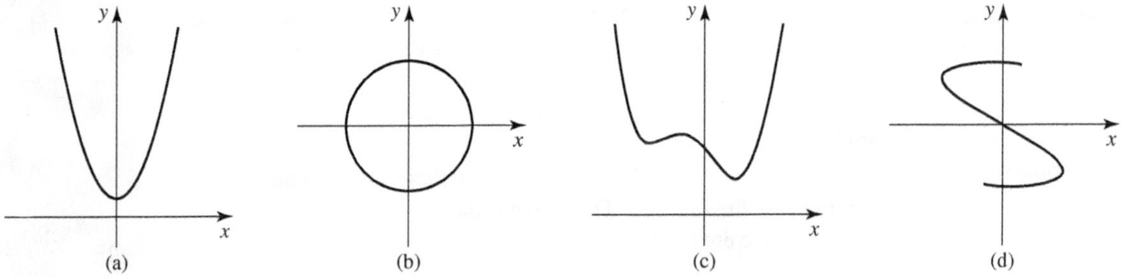

Figure 1.3

SOLUTION The vertical line test indicates that only graphs (a) and (c) represent functions. In graphs (b) and (d), there are vertical lines that intersect the graph more than once. Equivalently, there are values of x that correspond to more than one value of y. Therefore, graphs (b) and (d) do not pass the vertical line test and do not represent functions.

Related Exercises 11–12 ◄

➤ A window of $[a, b] \times [c, d]$ means $a \le x \le b$ and $c \le y \le d$.

EXAMPLE 2 **Domain and range** Graph each function with a graphing utility using the given window. Then state the domain and range of the function.

a. $y = f(x) = x^2 + 1$; $[-3, 3] \times [-1, 5]$

b. $z = g(t) = \sqrt{4 - t^2}$; $[-3, 3] \times [-1, 3]$

c. $w = h(u) = \dfrac{1}{u - 1}$; $[-3, 5] \times [-4, 4]$

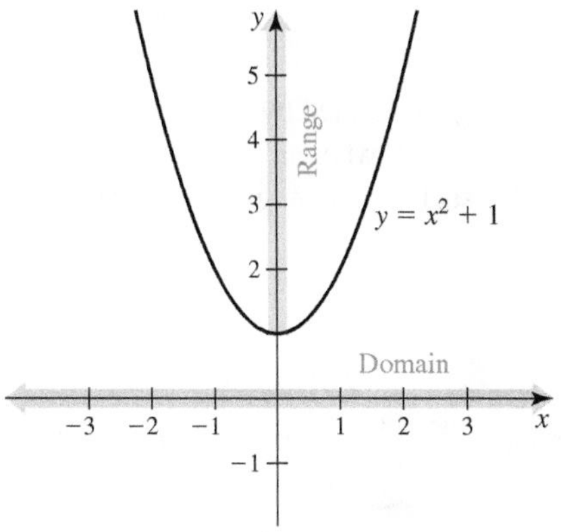

Figure 1.4

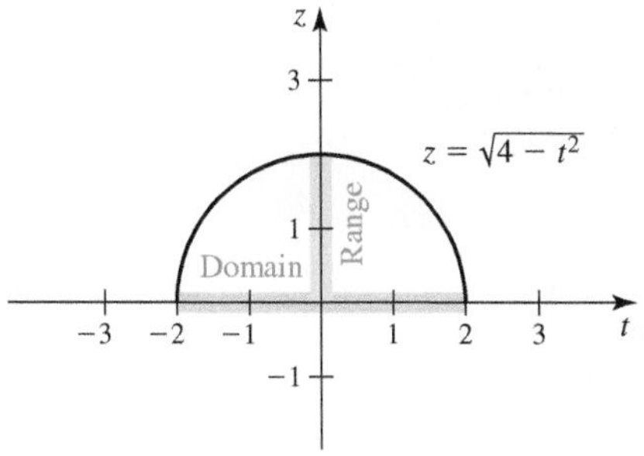

Figure 1.5

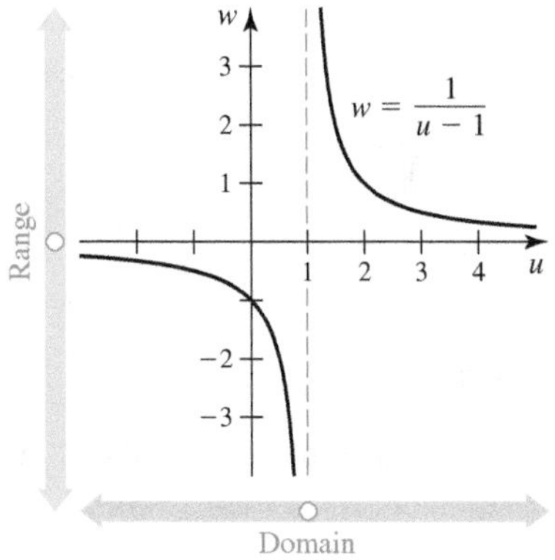

Figure 1.6

➤ The dashed vertical line $u = 1$ in Figure 1.6 indicates that the graph of $w = h(u)$ approaches a *vertical asymptote* as u approaches 1 and that w becomes large in magnitude for u near 1.

SOLUTION

a. Figure 1.4 shows the graph of $f(x) = x^2 + 1$. Because f is defined for all values of x, its domain is the set of all real numbers, written $(-\infty, \infty)$ or $\mathbb{R}$. Because $x^2 \geq 0$ for all x, it follows that $x^2 + 1 \geq 1$ and the range of f is $[1, \infty)$.

b. When n is even, functions involving nth roots are defined provided the quantity under the root is nonnegative (additional restrictions may also apply). In this case, the function g is defined provided $4 - t^2 \geq 0$, which means $t^2 \leq 4$, or $-2 \leq t \leq 2$. Therefore, the domain of g is $[-2, 2]$. By the definition of the square root, the range consists only of nonnegative numbers. When $t = 0$, z reaches its maximum value of $g(0) = \sqrt{4} = 2$, and when $t = \pm 2$, z attains its minimum value of $g(\pm 2) = 0$. Therefore, the range of g is $[0, 2]$ (Figure 1.5).

c. The function h is undefined at $u = 1$, so its domain is $\{u: u \neq 1\}$, and the graph does not have a point corresponding to $u = 1$. We see that w takes on all values except 0; therefore, the range is $\{w: w \neq 0\}$. A graphing utility does *not* represent this function accurately if it shows the vertical line $u = 1$ as part of the graph (Figure 1.6).

Related Exercises 13–20 ◄

EXAMPLE 3 Domain and range in context At time $t = 0$, a stone is thrown vertically upward from the ground at a speed of 30 m/s. Its height above the ground in meters (neglecting air resistance) is approximated by the function $h = f(t) = 30t - 5t^2$, where t is measured in seconds. Find the domain and range of f in the context of this particular problem.

SOLUTION Although f is defined for all values of t, the only relevant times are between the time the stone is thrown ($t = 0$) and the time it strikes the ground, when $h = f(t) = 0$. Solving the equation $h = 30t - 5t^2 = 0$, we find that

$$30t - 5t^2 = 0$$
$$5t(6 - t) = 0 \qquad \text{Factor.}$$
$$5t = 0 \quad \text{or} \quad 6 - t = 0 \qquad \text{Set each factor equal to 0.}$$
$$t = 0 \quad \text{or} \quad t = 6. \qquad \text{Solve.}$$

Therefore, the stone leaves the ground at $t = 0$ and returns to the ground at $t = 6$. An appropriate domain that fits the context of this problem is $\{t: 0 \leq t \leq 6\}$. The range consists of all values of $h = 30t - 5t^2$ as t varies over $[0, 6]$. The largest value of h occurs when the stone reaches its highest point at $t = 3$ (halfway through its flight), which is $h = f(3) = 45$. Therefore, the range is $[0, 45]$. These observations are confirmed by the graph of the height function (Figure 1.7). Note that this graph is *not* the trajectory of the stone; the stone moves vertically.

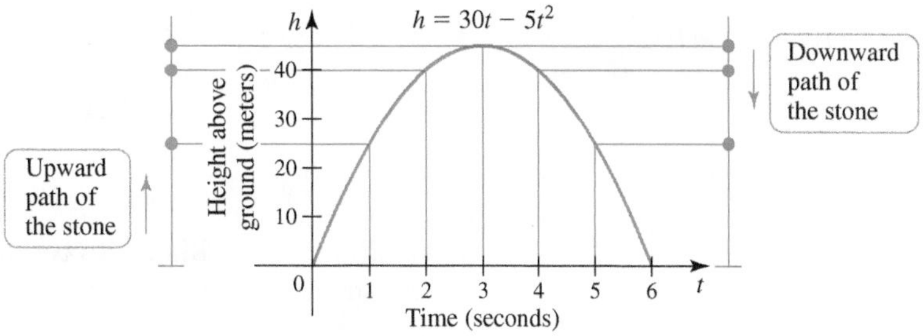

Figure 1.7

Related Exercises 21–24 ◄

QUICK CHECK 2 State the domain and range of $f(x) = (x^2 + 1)^{-1}$. ◄

Composite Functions

Functions may be combined using sums $(f + g)$, differences $(f - g)$, products (fg), or quotients (f/g). The process called *composition* also produces new functions.

➤ In the composition $y = f(g(x))$, f is the *outer function* and g is the *inner function*.

DEFINITION Composite Functions

Given two functions f and g, the composite function $f \circ g$ is defined by $(f \circ g)(x) = f(g(x))$. It is evaluated in two steps: $y = f(u)$, where $u = g(x)$. The domain of $f \circ g$ consists of all x in the domain of g such that $u = g(x)$ is in the domain of f (Figure 1.8).

➤ You have now seen three different notations for intervals on the real number line, all of which will be used throughout the book:
- $[-2, 3)$ is an example of interval notation,
- $-2 \le x < 3$ is inequality notation, and
- $\{x: -2 \le x < 3\}$ is set notation.

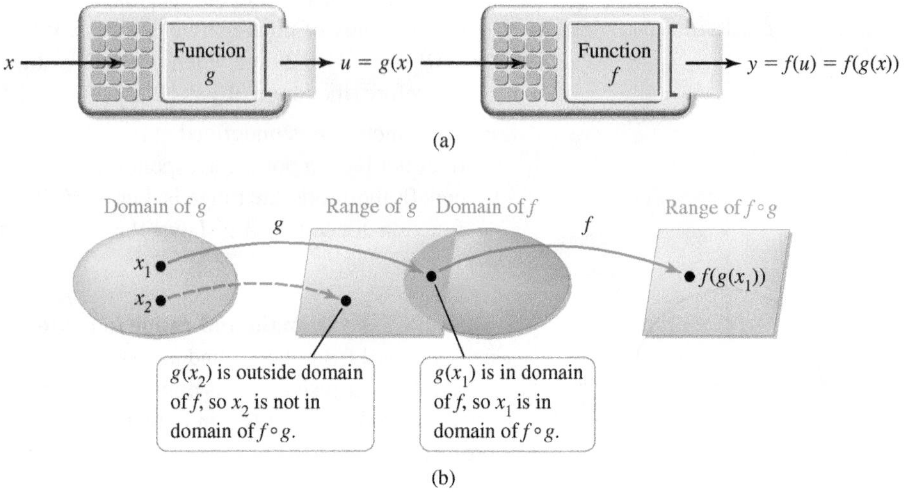

Figure 1.8

EXAMPLE 4 Composite functions and notation Let $f(x) = 3x^2 - x$ and $g(x) = 1/x$. Simplify the following expressions.

a. $f(5p + 1)$ **b.** $g(1/x)$ **c.** $f(g(x))$ **d.** $g(f(x))$

SOLUTION In each case, the functions work on their arguments.

a. The argument of f is $5p + 1$, so

$$f(5p + 1) = 3(5p + 1)^2 - (5p + 1) = 75p^2 + 25p + 2.$$

b. Because g requires taking the reciprocal of the argument, we take the reciprocal of $1/x$ and find that $g(1/x) = 1/(1/x) = x$.

c. The argument of f is $g(x)$, so

$$f(g(x)) = f\left(\frac{1}{x}\right) = 3\left(\frac{1}{x}\right)^2 - \left(\frac{1}{x}\right) = \frac{3}{x^2} - \frac{1}{x} = \frac{3 - x}{x^2}.$$

➤ Examples 4c and 4d demonstrate that, in general,

$$f(g(x)) \neq g(f(x)).$$

d. The argument of g is $f(x)$, so

$$g(f(x)) = g(3x^2 - x) = \frac{1}{3x^2 - x}.$$

Related Exercises 25–36 ◀

EXAMPLE 5 Working with composite functions Identify possible choices for the inner and outer functions in the following composite functions. Give the domain of the composite function.

a. $h(x) = \sqrt{9x - x^2}$ **b.** $h(x) = \dfrac{2}{(x^2 - 1)^3}$

SOLUTION

➤ Techniques for solving inequalities are discussed in Appendix A.

a. An obvious outer function is $f(x) = \sqrt{x}$, which works on the inner function $g(x) = 9x - x^2$. Therefore, h can be expressed as $h = f \circ g$ or $h(x) = f(g(x))$. The domain of $f \circ g$ consists of all values of x such that $9x - x^2 \ge 0$. Solving this inequality gives $\{x: 0 \le x \le 9\}$ as the domain of $f \circ g$.

b. A good choice for an outer function is $f(x) = 2/x^3 = 2x^{-3}$, which works on the inner function $g(x) = x^2 - 1$. Therefore, h can be expressed as $h = f \circ g$ or $h(x) = f(g(x))$. The domain of $f \circ g$ consists of all values of $g(x)$ such that $g(x) \neq 0$, which is $\{x: x \neq \pm 1\}$.

Related Exercises 37–40 ◀

EXAMPLE 6 More composite functions Given $f(x) = \sqrt[3]{x}$ and $g(x) = x^2 - x - 6$, find (a) $g \circ f$ and (b) $g \circ g$, and their domains.

SOLUTION

a. We have

$$(g \circ f)(x) = g(f(x)) = g(\sqrt[3]{x}) = (\underbrace{\sqrt[3]{x}}_{f(x)})^2 - \underbrace{\sqrt[3]{x}}_{f(x)} - 6 = x^{2/3} - x^{1/3} - 6.$$

Because the domains of f and g are $(-\infty, \infty)$, the domain of $f \circ g$ is also $(-\infty, \infty)$.

b. In this case, we have the composition of two polynomials:

$$\begin{aligned}(g \circ g)(x) &= g(g(x)) \\ &= g(x^2 - x - 6) \\ &= \underbrace{(x^2 - x - 6)^2}_{g(x)} - \underbrace{(x^2 - x - 6)}_{g(x)} - 6 \\ &= x^4 - 2x^3 - 12x^2 + 13x + 36.\end{aligned}$$

The domain of the composition of two polynomials is $(-\infty, \infty)$.

Related Exercises 41–54 ◀

QUICK CHECK 3 If $f(x) = x^2 + 1$ and $g(x) = x^2$, find $f \circ g$ and $g \circ f$. ◀

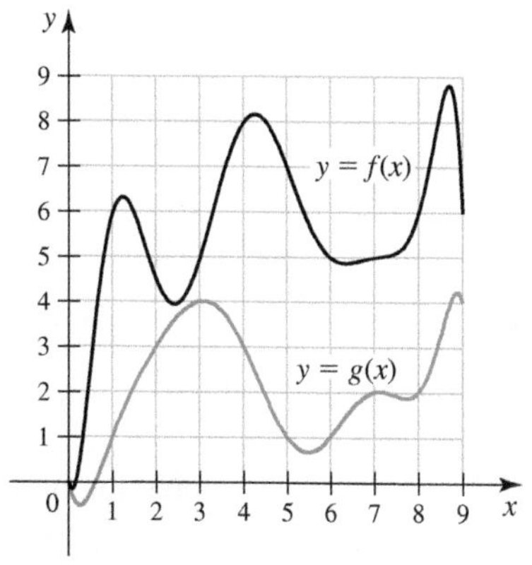

Figure 1.9

EXAMPLE 7 Using graphs to evaluate composite functions Use the graphs of f and g in Figure 1.9 to find the following values.

a. $f(g(3))$ **b.** $g(f(3))$ **c.** $f(f(4))$ **d.** $f(g(f(8)))$

SOLUTION

a. The graphs indicate that $g(3) = 4$ and $f(4) = 8$, so $f(g(3)) = f(4) = 8$.

b. We see that $g(f(3)) = g(5) = 1$. Observe that $f(g(3)) \neq g(f(3))$.

c. In this case, $f(\underbrace{f(4)}_{8}) = f(8) = 6$.

d. Starting on the inside,

$$f(g(\underbrace{f(8)}_{6})) = f(\underbrace{g(6)}_{1}) = f(1) = 6.$$

Related Exercises 55–56 ◀

EXAMPLE 8 Using a table to evaluate composite functions Use the function values in the table to evaluate the following composite functions.

a. $(f \circ g)(0)$ **b.** $g(f(-1))$ **c.** $f(g(g(-1)))$

x	-2	-1	0	1	2
$f(x)$	0	1	3	4	2
$g(x)$	-1	0	-2	-3	-4

SOLUTION

a. Using the table, we see that $g(0) = -2$ and $f(-2) = 0$. Therefore, $(f \circ g)(0) = 0$.

b. Because $f(-1) = 1$ and $g(1) = -3$, it follows that $g(f(-1)) = -3$.

c. Starting with the inner function,

$$f(g(\underbrace{g(-1)}_{0})) = f(\underbrace{g(0)}_{-2}) = f(-2) = 0.$$

Related Exercises 55–56

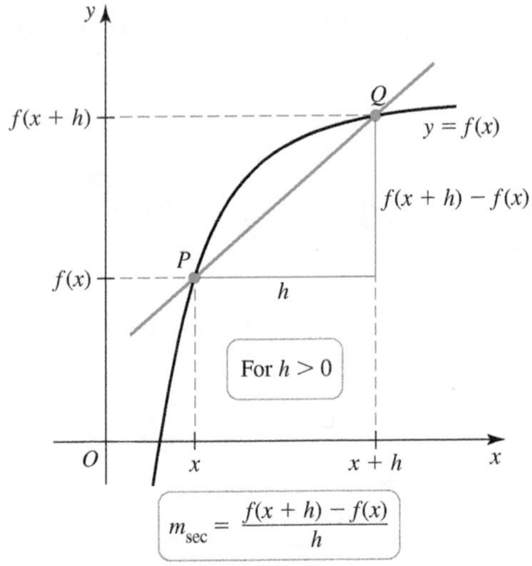

Figure 1.10

Secant Lines and the Difference Quotient

As you will see shortly, slopes of lines and curves play a fundamental role in calculus. Figure 1.10 shows two points $P(x, f(x))$ and $Q(x + h, f(x + h))$ on the graph of $y = f(x)$ in the case that $h > 0$. A line through any two points on a curve is called a **secant line**; its importance in the study of calculus is explained in Chapters 2 and 3. For now, we focus on the slope of the secant line through P and Q, which is denoted m_{sec} and is given by

$$m_{\text{sec}} = \frac{\text{change in } y}{\text{change in } x} = \frac{f(x + h) - f(x)}{(x + h) - x} = \frac{f(x + h) - f(x)}{h}.$$

The slope formula $\dfrac{f(x + h) - f(x)}{h}$ is also known as a **difference quotient**, and it can be expressed in several ways depending on how the coordinates of P and Q are labeled. For example, given the coordinates $P(a, f(a))$ and $Q(x, f(x))$ (Figure 1.11), the difference quotient is

$$m_{\text{sec}} = \frac{f(x) - f(a)}{x - a}.$$

We interpret the slope of the secant line in this form as the **average rate of change** of f over the interval $[a, x]$.

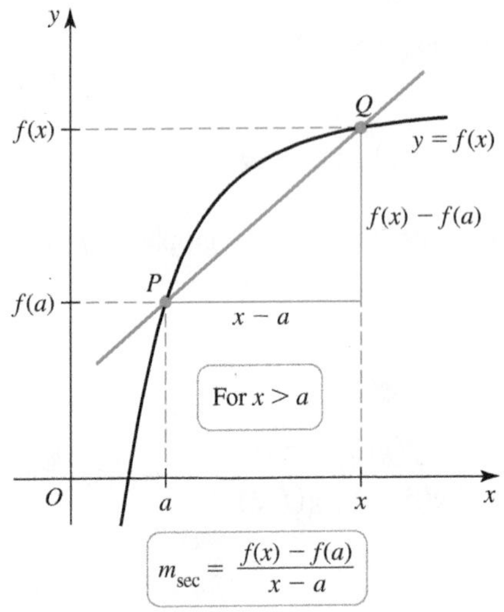

Figure 1.11

EXAMPLE 9 Working with difference quotients

a. Simplify the difference quotient $\dfrac{f(x + h) - f(x)}{h}$, for $f(x) = 3x^2 - x$.

b. Simplify the difference quotient $\dfrac{f(x) - f(a)}{x - a}$, for $f(x) = x^3$.

SOLUTION

a. First note that $f(x + h) = 3(x + h)^2 - (x + h)$. We substitute this expression into the difference quotient and simplify:

$$\frac{f(x + h) - f(x)}{h} = \frac{\overbrace{3(x + h)^2 - (x + h)}^{f(x+h)} - \overbrace{(3x^2 - x)}^{f(x)}}{h}$$

$$= \frac{3(x^2 + 2xh + h^2) - (x + h) - (3x^2 - x)}{h} \quad \text{Expand } (x + h)^2.$$

$$= \frac{3x^2 + 6xh + 3h^2 - x - h - 3x^2 + x}{h} \quad \text{Distribute.}$$

$$= \frac{6xh + 3h^2 - h}{h} \quad \text{Simplify.}$$

$$= \frac{h(6x + 3h - 1)}{h} = 6x + 3h - 1. \quad \text{Factor and simplify.}$$

➤ Treat $f(x + h)$ like the composition $f(g(x))$, where $x + h$ plays the role of $g(x)$. It may help to establish a pattern in your mind before evaluating $f(x + h)$. For instance, using the function in Example 9a, we have

$$f(x) = 3x^2 - x;$$
$$f(12) = 3 \cdot 12^2 - 12;$$
$$f(b) = 3b^2 - b;$$
$$f(\text{math}) = 3 \cdot \text{math}^2 - \text{math};$$

therefore,

$$f(x + h) = 3(x + h)^2 - (x + h).$$

➤ Some useful factoring formulas:

1. Difference of perfect squares: $x^2 - y^2 = (x - y)(x + y)$.
2. Sum of perfect squares: $x^2 + y^2$ does not factor over the real numbers.
3. Difference of perfect cubes: $x^3 - y^3 = (x - y)(x^2 + xy + y^2)$.
4. Sum of perfect cubes: $x^3 + y^3 = (x + y)(x^2 - xy + y^2)$.

b. The factoring formula for the difference of perfect cubes is needed:

$$\frac{f(x) - f(a)}{x - a} = \frac{x^3 - a^3}{x - a}$$

$$= \frac{(x - a)(x^2 + ax + a^2)}{x - a} \quad \text{Factoring formula}$$

$$= x^2 + ax + a^2. \quad \text{Simplify.}$$

Related Exercises 57–66 ◄

EXAMPLE 10 Interpreting the slope of the secant line Sound intensity I, measured in watts per square meter (W/m^2), at a point r meters from a sound source with acoustic power P is given by $I(r) = \frac{P}{4\pi r^2}$.

a. Find the sound intensity at two points $r_1 = 10$ m and $r_2 = 15$ m from a sound source with power $P = 100$ W. Then find the slope of the secant line through the points $(10, I(10))$ and $(15, I(15))$ on the graph of the intensity function and interpret the result.

b. Find the slope of the secant line through any two points $(r_1, I(r_1))$ and $(r_2, I(r_2))$ on the graph of the intensity function with acoustic power P.

SOLUTION

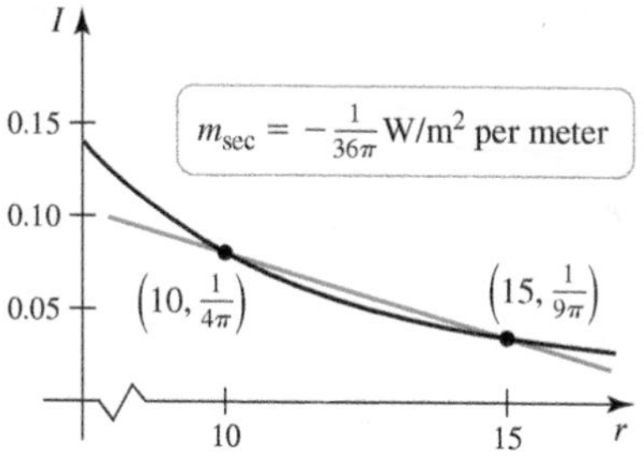

Figure 1.12

a. The sound intensity 10 m from the source is $I(10) = \frac{100\text{ W}}{4\pi(10\text{ m})^2} = \frac{1}{4\pi}\text{ W/m}^2$. At 15 m, the intensity is $I(15) = \frac{100\text{ W}}{4\pi(15\text{ m})^2} = \frac{1}{9\pi}\text{ W/m}^2$. To find the slope of the secant line (Figure 1.12), we compute the change in intensity divided by the change in distance:

$$m_{sec} = \frac{I(15) - I(10)}{15 - 10} = \frac{\frac{1}{9\pi} - \frac{1}{4\pi}}{5} = -\frac{1}{36\pi} \approx -0.0088\text{ W/m}^2\text{ per meter.}$$

The units provide a clue to the physical meaning of the slope: It measures the average rate at which the intensity changes as one moves from 10 m to 15 m away from the sound source. In this case, because the slope of the secant line is negative, the intensity *decreases* (slowly) at an average rate of $1/(36\pi)$ W/m² per meter.

b.

$$m_{sec} = \frac{I(r_2) - I(r_1)}{r_2 - r_1} = \frac{\frac{P}{4\pi r_2^2} - \frac{P}{4\pi r_1^2}}{r_2 - r_1} \quad \text{Evaluate } I(r_2) \text{ and } I(r_1).$$

$$= \frac{\frac{P}{4\pi}\left(\frac{1}{r_2^2} - \frac{1}{r_1^2}\right)}{r_2 - r_1} \quad \text{Factor.}$$

$$= \frac{P}{4\pi}\left(\frac{r_1^2 - r_2^2}{r_1^2 r_2^2}\right)\frac{1}{r_2 - r_1} \quad \text{Simplify.}$$

$$= \frac{P}{4\pi} \cdot \frac{(r_1 - r_2)(r_1 + r_2)}{r_1^2 r_2^2} \cdot \frac{1}{-(r_1 - r_2)} \quad \text{Factor.}$$

$$= -\frac{P(r_1 + r_2)}{4\pi r_1^2 r_2^2} \quad \text{Cancel and simplify.}$$

This result is the average rate at which the sound intensity changes over an interval $[r_1, r_2]$. Because $r_1 > 0$ and $r_2 > 0$, we see that m_{sec} is always negative. Therefore, the sound intensity $I(r)$ decreases as r increases, for $r > 0$.

Related Exercises 67–70 ◄

Symmetry

The word *symmetry* has many meanings in mathematics. Here we consider symmetries of graphs and the relations they represent. Taking advantage of symmetry often saves time and leads to insights.

> **DEFINITION Symmetry in Graphs**
>
> A graph is **symmetric with respect to the y-axis** if whenever the point (x, y) is on the graph, the point $(-x, y)$ is also on the graph. This property means that the graph is unchanged when reflected across the y-axis (Figure 1.13a).
>
> A graph is **symmetric with respect to the x-axis** if whenever the point (x, y) is on the graph, the point $(x, -y)$ is also on the graph. This property means that the graph is unchanged when reflected across the x-axis (Figure 1.13b).
>
> A graph is **symmetric with respect to the origin** if whenever the point (x, y) is on the graph, the point $(-x, -y)$ is also on the graph (Figure 1.13c). Symmetry about both the x- and y-axes implies symmetry about the origin, but not vice versa.

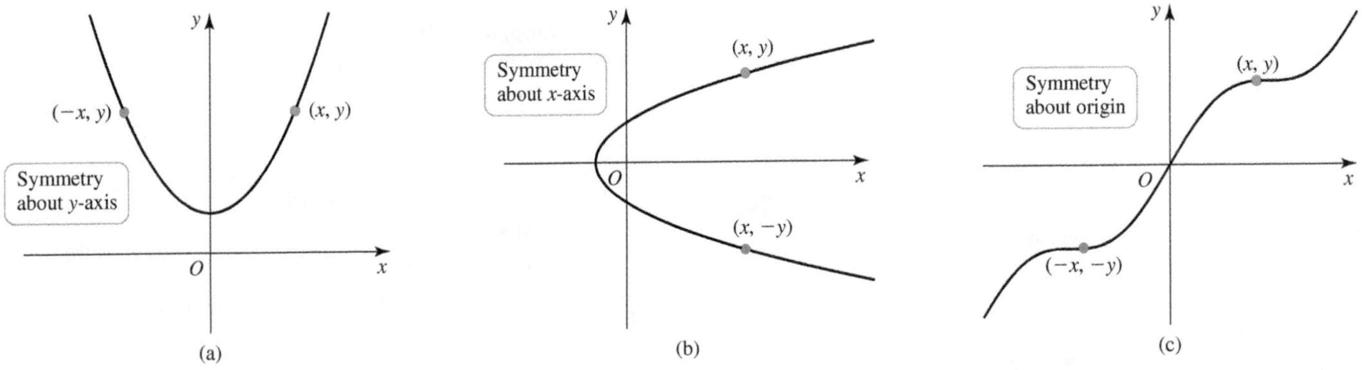

Figure 1.13

> **DEFINITION Symmetry in Functions**
>
> An **even function** f has the property that $f(-x) = f(x)$, for all x in the domain. The graph of an even function is symmetric about the y-axis.
>
> An **odd function** f has the property that $f(-x) = -f(x)$, for all x in the domain. The graph of an odd function is symmetric about the origin.

Polynomials consisting of only even powers of the variable (of the form x^{2n}, where n is a nonnegative integer) are even functions. Polynomials consisting of only odd powers of the variable (of the form x^{2n+1}, where n is a nonnegative integer) are odd functions.

QUICK CHECK 4 Explain why the graph of a nonzero function is never symmetric with respect to the x-axis. ◀

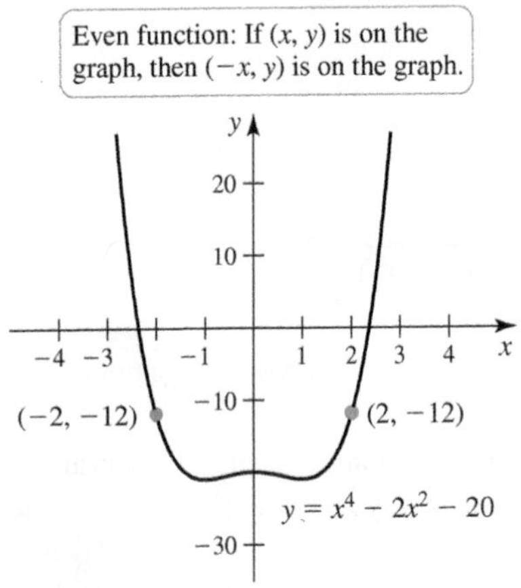

Figure 1.14

EXAMPLE 11 Identifying symmetry in functions Identify the symmetry, if any, in the following functions.

a. $f(x) = x^4 - 2x^2 - 20$ **b.** $g(x) = x^3 - 3x + 1$ **c.** $h(x) = \dfrac{1}{x^3 - x}$

SOLUTION

a. The function f consists of only even powers of x (where $20 = 20 \cdot 1 = 20x^0$ and x^0 is considered an even power). Therefore, f is an even function (Figure 1.14). This fact is verified by showing that $f(-x) = f(x)$:

$$f(-x) = (-x)^4 - 2(-x)^2 - 20 = x^4 - 2x^2 - 20 = f(x).$$

No symmetry: neither an even nor odd function.

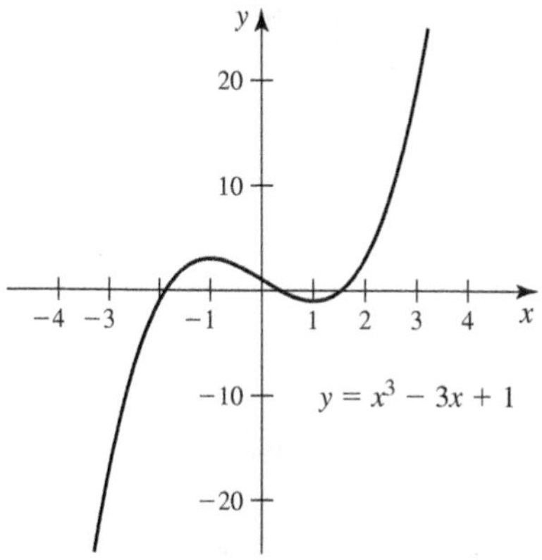

Figure 1.15

➤ The symmetry of compositions of even and odd functions is considered in Exercises 95–101.

b. The function g consists of two odd powers and one even power (again, $1 = x^0$ is an even power). Therefore, we expect that g has no symmetry about the y-axis or the origin (Figure 1.15). Note that

$$g(-x) = (-x)^3 - 3(-x) + 1 = -x^3 + 3x + 1,$$

so $g(-x)$ equals neither $g(x)$ nor $-g(x)$; therefore, g has no symmetry.

c. In this case, h is a composition of an odd function $f(x) = 1/x$ with an odd function $g(x) = x^3 - x$. Note that

$$h(-x) = \frac{1}{(-x)^3 - (-x)} = -\frac{1}{x^3 - x} = -h(x).$$

Because $h(-x) = -h(x)$, h is an odd function (Figure 1.16).

Odd function: If (x, y) is on the graph, then $(-x, -y)$ is on the graph.

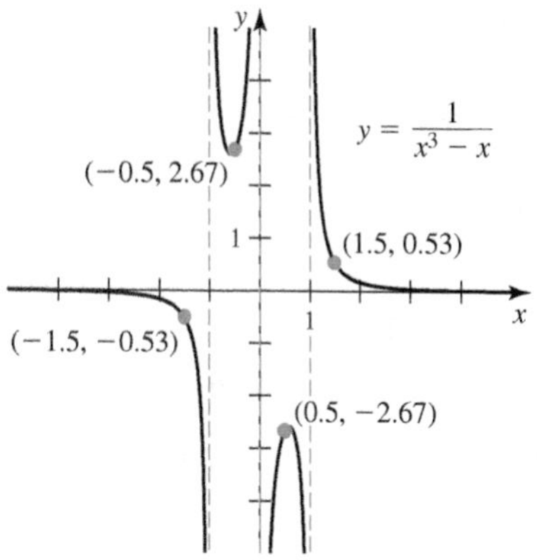

Figure 1.16

Related Exercises 71–80 ◀

SECTION 1.1 EXERCISES

Review Questions

1. Use the terms *domain, range, independent variable*, and *dependent variable* to explain how a function relates one variable to another variable.

2. Is the independent variable of a function associated with the domain or range? Is the dependent variable associated with the domain or range?

3. Explain how the vertical line test is used to detect functions.

4. If $f(x) = 1/(x^3 + 1)$, what is $f(2)$? What is $f(y^2)$?

5. Which statement about a function is true? (i) For each value of x in the domain, there corresponds one unique value of y in the range; (ii) for each value of y in the range, there corresponds one unique value of x in the domain. Explain.

6. If $f(x) = \sqrt{x}$ and $g(x) = x^3 - 2$, find the compositions $f \circ g$, $g \circ f$, $f \circ f$, and $g \circ g$.

7. Suppose f and g are even functions with $f(2) = 2$ and $g(2) = -2$. Evaluate $f(g(2))$ and $g(f(-2))$.

8. Explain how to find the domain of $f \circ g$ if you know the domain and range of f and g.

9. Sketch a graph of an even function f and state how $f(x)$ and $f(-x)$ are related.

10. Sketch a graph of an odd function f and state how $f(x)$ and $f(-x)$ are related.

Basic Skills

11–12. Vertical line test *Decide whether graphs A, B, or both represent functions.*

11.

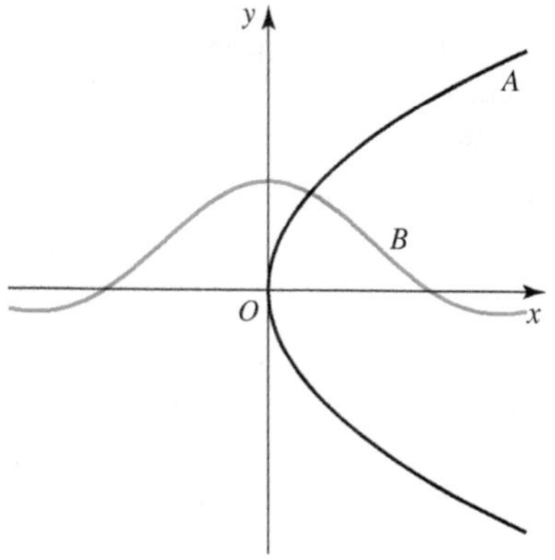

12.

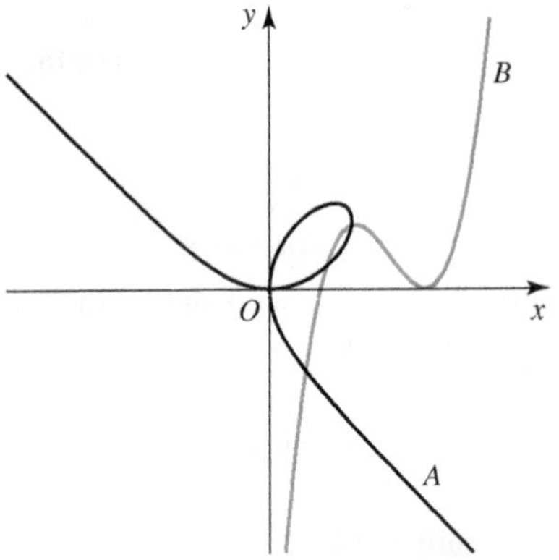

13–20. Domain and range *Graph each function with a graphing utility using the given window. Then state the domain and range of the function.*

13. $f(x) = 3x^4 - 10;\quad [-2, 2] \times [-10, 15]$

14. $g(y) = \dfrac{y + 1}{(y + 2)(y - 3)};\quad [-4, 6] \times [-3, 3]$

15. $f(x) = \sqrt{4 - x^2};\quad [-4, 4] \times [-4, 4]$

16. $F(w) = \sqrt[4]{2 - w};\quad [-3, 2] \times [0, 2]$

17. $h(u) = \sqrt[3]{u - 1};\quad [-7, 9] \times [-2, 2]$

18. $g(x) = (x^2 - 4)\sqrt{x + 5};\quad [-5, 5] \times [-10, 50]$

19. $f(x) = (9 - x^2)^{3/2};\quad [-4, 4] \times [0, 30]$

20. $g(t) = \dfrac{1}{1 + t^2};\quad [-7, 7] \times [0, 1.5]$

21–24. Domain in context *Determine an appropriate domain of each function. Identify the independent and dependent variables.*

21. A stone is thrown vertically upward from the ground at a speed of 40 m/s at time $t = 0$. Its distance d (in meters) above the ground (neglecting air resistance) is approximated by the function $f(t) = 40t - 5t^2$.

22. A stone is dropped off a bridge from a height of 20 m above a river. If t represents the elapsed time (in seconds) after the stone is released, then its distance d (in meters) above the river is approximated by the function $f(t) = 20 - 5t^2$.

23. A cylindrical water tower with a radius of 10 m and a height of 50 m is filled to a height of h. The volume V of water (in cubic meters) is given by the function $g(h) = 100\pi h$.

24. The volume V of a balloon of radius r (in meters) filled with helium is given by the function $f(r) = \frac{4}{3}\pi r^3$. Assume the balloon can hold up to 1 m^3 of helium.

25–36. Composite functions and notation *Let $f(x) = x^2 - 4$, $g(x) = x^3$, and $F(x) = 1/(x - 3)$. Simplify or evaluate the following expressions.*

25. $f(10)$ 26. $f(p^2)$ 27. $g(1/z)$

28. $F(y^4)$ 29. $F(g(y))$ 30. $f(g(w))$

31. $g(f(u))$ 32. $\dfrac{f(2 + h) - f(2)}{h}$ 33. $F(F(x))$

34. $g(F(f(x)))$ 35. $f(\sqrt{x + 4})$ 36. $F\left(\dfrac{3x + 1}{x}\right)$

37–40. Working with composite functions *Find possible choices for the outer and inner functions f and g such that the given function h equals $f \circ g$. Give the domain of h.*

37. $h(x) = (x^3 - 5)^{10}$

38. $h(x) = \dfrac{2}{(x^6 + x^2 + 1)^2}$

39. $h(x) = \sqrt{x^4 + 2}$

40. $h(x) = \dfrac{1}{\sqrt{x^3 - 1}}$

41–48. More composite functions *Let $f(x) = |x|$, $g(x) = x^2 - 4$, $F(x) = \sqrt{x}$, and $G(x) = 1/(x - 2)$. Determine the following composite functions and give their domains.*

41. $f \circ g$ 42. $g \circ f$ 43. $f \circ G$

44. $f \circ g \circ G$ 45. $G \circ g \circ f$ 46. $F \circ g \circ g$

47. $g \circ g$ 48. $G \circ G$

49–54. Missing piece *Let $g(x) = x^2 + 3$. Find a function f that produces the given composition.*

49. $(f \circ g)(x) = x^2$ 50. $(f \circ g)(x) = \dfrac{1}{x^2 + 3}$

51. $(f \circ g)(x) = x^4 + 6x^2 + 9$ 52. $(f \circ g)(x) = x^4 + 6x^2 + 20$

53. $(g \circ f)(x) = x^4 + 3$ 54. $(g \circ f)(x) = x^{2/3} + 3$

55. **Composite functions from graphs** Use the graphs of f and g in the figure to determine the following function values.

a. $(f \circ g)(2)$ b. $g(f(2))$ c. $f(g(4))$
d. $g(f(5))$ e. $f(f(8))$ f. $g(f(g(5)))$

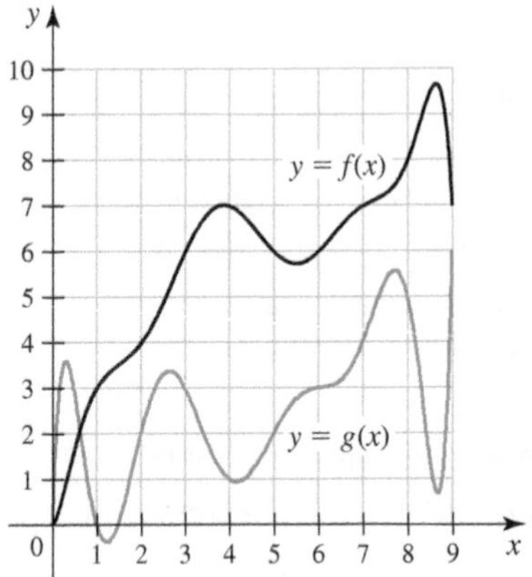

56. **Composite functions from tables** Use the table to evaluate the given compositions.

x	−1	0	1	2	3	4
$f(x)$	3	1	0	−1	−3	−1
$g(x)$	−1	0	2	3	4	5
$h(x)$	0	−1	0	3	0	4

a. $h(g(0))$ b. $g(f(4))$ c. $h(h(0))$
d. $g(h(f(4)))$ e. $f(f(f(1)))$ f. $h(h(h(0)))$
g. $f(h(g(2)))$ h. $g(f(h(4)))$ i. $g(g(g(1)))$
j. $f(f(h(3)))$

57–61. Working with difference quotients *Simplify the difference quotient* $\frac{f(x+h)-f(x)}{h}$ *for the following functions.*

57. $f(x) = x^2$

58. $f(x) = 4x - 3$

59. $f(x) = 2/x$

60. $f(x) = 2x^2 - 3x + 1$

61. $f(x) = \frac{x}{x+1}$

62–66. Working with difference quotients *Simplify the difference quotient* $\frac{f(x)-f(a)}{x-a}$ *for the following functions.*

62. $f(x) = x^4$

63. $f(x) = x^3 - 2x$

64. $f(x) = 4 - 4x - x^2$

65. $f(x) = -\frac{4}{x^2}$

66. $f(x) = \frac{1}{x} - x^2$

67–70. Interpreting the slope of secant lines *In each exercise, a function and an interval of its independent variable are given. The endpoints of the interval are associated with the points P and Q on the graph of the function.*

a. Sketch a graph of the function and the secant line through P and Q.

b. Find the slope of the secant line in part (a), and interpret your answer in terms of an average rate of change over the interval. Include units in your answer.

67. After t seconds, an object dropped from rest falls a distance $d = 16t^2$, where d is measured in feet and $2 \le t \le 5$.

68. After t seconds, the second hand on a clock moves through an angle $D = 6t$, where D is measured in degrees and $5 \le t \le 20$.

69. The volume V of an ideal gas in cubic centimeters is given by $V = 2/p$, where p is the pressure in atmospheres and $0.5 \le p \le 2$.

70. The speed of a car prior to hard braking can be estimated by the length of the skid mark. One model claims that the speed S in mi/hr is $S = \sqrt{30\ell}$, where ℓ is the length of the skid mark in feet and $50 \le \ell \le 150$.

T **71–78. Symmetry** *Determine whether the graphs of the following equations and functions are symmetric about the x-axis, the y-axis, or the origin. Check your work by graphing.*

71. $f(x) = x^4 + 5x^2 - 12$

72. $f(x) = 3x^5 + 2x^3 - x$

73. $f(x) = x^5 - x^3 - 2$

74. $f(x) = 2|x|$

75. $x^{2/3} + y^{2/3} = 1$

76. $x^3 - y^5 = 0$

77. $f(x) = x|x|$

78. $|x| + |y| = 1$

79. Symmetry in graphs State whether the functions represented by graphs A, B, and C in the figure are even, odd, or neither.

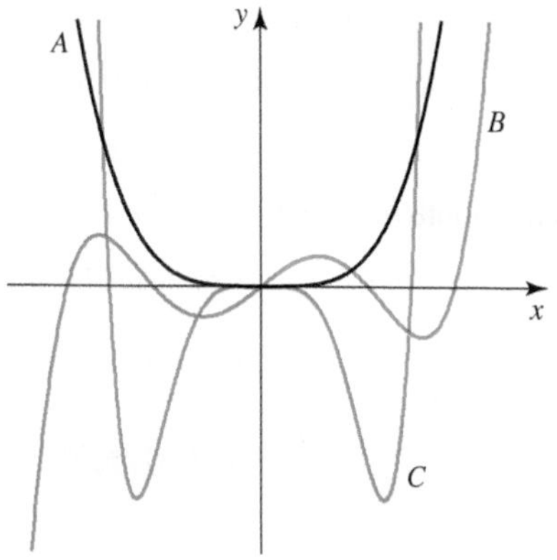

80. Symmetry in graphs State whether the functions represented by graphs A, B, and C in the figure are even, odd, or neither.

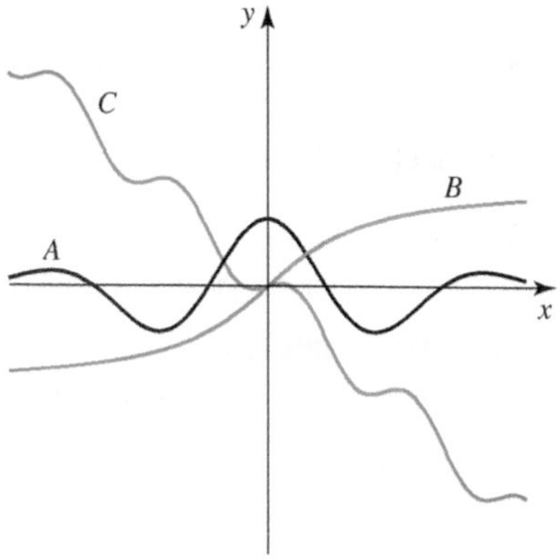

Further Explorations

81. Explain why or why not Determine whether the following statements are true and give an explanation or counterexample.

a. The range of $f(x) = 2x - 38$ is all real numbers.

b. The relation $y = x^6 + 1$ is *not* a function because $y = 2$ for both $x = -1$ and $x = 1$.

c. If $f(x) = x^{-1}$, then $f(1/x) = 1/f(x)$.

d. In general, $f(f(x)) = (f(x))^2$.

e. In general, $f(g(x)) = g(f(x))$.

f. By definition, $f(g(x)) = (f \circ g)(x)$.

g. If $f(x)$ is an even function, then $cf(ax)$ is an even function, where a and c are nonzero real numbers.

h. If $f(x)$ is an odd function, then $f(x) + d$ is an odd function, where d is a nonzero real number.

i. If f is both even *and* odd, then $f(x) = 0$ for all x.

82. Range of power functions Using words and figures, explain why the range of $f(x) = x^n$, where n is a positive odd integer, is all real numbers. Explain why the range of $g(x) = x^n$, where n is a positive even integer, is all nonnegative real numbers.

T **83. Absolute value graph** Use the definition of absolute value to graph the equation $|x| - |y| = 1$. Use a graphing utility to check your work.

84. Even and odd at the origin

a. If $f(0)$ is defined and f is an even function, is it necessarily true that $f(0) = 0$? Explain.

b. If $f(0)$ is defined and f is an odd function, is it necessarily true that $f(0) = 0$? Explain.

T 85–88. Polynomial calculations *Find a polynomial f that satisfies the following properties. (Hint: Determine the degree of f; then substitute a polynomial of that degree and solve for its coefficients.)*

85. $f(f(x)) = 9x - 8$ **86.** $(f(x))^2 = 9x^2 - 12x + 4$

87. $f(f(x)) = x^4 - 12x^2 + 30$ **88.** $(f(x))^2 = x^4 - 12x^2 + 36$

89–92. Difference quotients *Simplify the difference quotients* $\dfrac{f(x+h) - f(x)}{h}$ *and* $\dfrac{f(x) - f(a)}{x - a}$ *by rationalizing the numerator.*

89. $f(x) = \sqrt{x}$ **90.** $f(x) = \sqrt{1 - 2x}$

91. $f(x) = -\dfrac{3}{\sqrt{x}}$ **92.** $f(x) = \sqrt{x^2 + 1}$

Applications

T 93. Launching a rocket A small rocket is launched vertically upward from the edge of a cliff 80 ft off the ground at a speed of 96 ft/s. Its height (in feet) above the ground is given by $h(t) = -16t^2 + 96t + 80$, where t represents time measured in seconds.

a. Assuming the rocket is launched at $t = 0$, what is an appropriate domain for h?

b. Graph h and determine the time at which the rocket reaches its highest point. What is the height at that time?

94. Draining a tank (Torricelli's law) A cylindrical tank with a cross-sectional area of 100 cm^2 is filled to a depth of 100 cm with water. At $t = 0$, a drain in the bottom of the tank with an area of 10 cm^2 is opened, allowing water to flow out of the tank. The depth of water in the tank at time $t \geq 0$ is $d(t) = (10 - 2.2t)^2$.

a. Check that $d(0) = 100$, as specified.

b. At what time is the tank empty?

c. What is an appropriate domain for d?

Additional Exercises

95–101. Combining even and odd functions *Let E be an even function and O be an odd function. Determine the symmetry, if any, of the following functions.*

95. $E + O$ **96.** $E \cdot O$ **97.** E/O **98.** $E \circ O$

99. $E \circ E$ **100.** $O \circ O$ **101.** $O \circ E$

102. Composition of even and odd functions from tables Assume f is an even function and g is an odd function. Use the (incomplete) table to evaluate the given compositions.

x	1	2	3	4
$f(x)$	2	-1	3	-4
$g(x)$	-3	-1	-4	-2

a. $f(g(-1))$ b. $g(f(-4))$ c. $f(g(-3))$
d. $f(g(-2))$ e. $g(g(-1))$ f. $f(g(0) - 1)$
g. $f(g(g(-2)))$ h. $g(f(f(-4)))$ i. $g(g(g(-1)))$

103. Composition of even and odd functions from graphs Assume f is an even function and g is an odd function. Use the (incomplete) graphs of f and g in the figure to determine the following function values.

a. $f(g(-2))$ b. $g(f(-2))$ c. $f(g(-4))$
d. $g(f(5) - 8)$ e. $g(g(-7))$ f. $f(1 - f(8))$

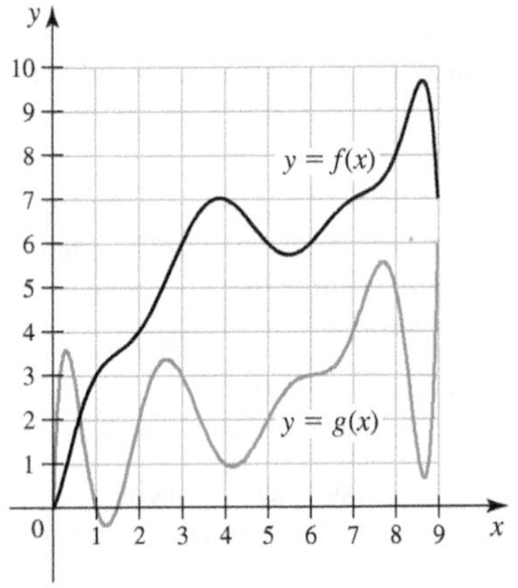

QUICK CHECK ANSWERS

1. $3, x^4 - 2x^2, t^2 - 2t, p^2 - 4p + 3$ **2.** Domain is all real numbers; range is $\{y: 0 < y \leq 1\}$. **3.** $(f \circ g)(x) = x^4 + 1$ and $(g \circ f)(x) = (x^2 + 1)^2$ **4.** If the graph were symmetric with respect to the x-axis, it would not pass the vertical line test. ◄

1.2 Representing Functions

We consider four approaches to defining and representing functions: formulas, graphs, tables, and words.

Using Formulas

The following list is a brief catalog of the families of functions that are introduced in this chapter and studied systematically throughout this book; they are all defined by *formulas*.

➤ One version of the Fundamental Theorem of Algebra states that a nonzero polynomial of degree n has exactly n (possibly complex) roots, counting each root up to its multiplicity.

1. Polynomials are functions of the form

$$p(x) = a_n x^n + a_{n-1}x^{n-1} + \cdots + a_1 x + a_0,$$

where the **coefficients** $a_0, a_1, \ldots, a_n$ are real numbers with $a_n \neq 0$ and the nonnegative integer n is the **degree** of the polynomial. The domain of any polynomial is the set of all real numbers. An nth-degree polynomial can have as many as n real **zeros** or **roots**—values of x at which $p(x) = 0$; the zeros are points at which the graph of p intersects the x-axis.

2. **Rational functions** are ratios of the form $f(x) = p(x)/q(x)$, where p and q are polynomials. Because division by zero is prohibited, the domain of a rational function is the set of all real numbers except those for which the denominator is zero.
3. **Algebraic functions** are constructed using the operations of algebra: addition, subtraction, multiplication, division, and roots. Examples of algebraic functions are $f(x) = \sqrt{2x^3 + 4}$ and $g(x) = x^{1/4}(x^3 + 2)$. In general, if an even root (square root, fourth root, and so forth) appears, then the domain does not contain points at which the quantity under the root is negative (and perhaps other points).

➤ Exponential and logarithmic functions are introduced in Section 1.3.

4. **Exponential functions** have the form $f(x) = b^x$, where the base $b \neq 1$ is a positive real number. Closely associated with exponential functions are **logarithmic functions** of the form $f(x) = \log_b x$, where $b > 0$ and $b \neq 1$. Exponential functions have a domain consisting of all real numbers. Logarithmic functions are defined for positive real numbers.

   The **natural exponential function** is $f(x) = e^x$, with base $b = e$, where $e \approx 2.71828\ldots$ is one of the fundamental constants of mathematics. Associated with the natural exponential function is the **natural logarithm function** $f(x) = \ln x$, which also has the base $b = e$.

➤ Trigonometric functions and their inverses are introduced in Section 1.4.

5. The **trigonometric functions** are $\sin x$, $\cos x$, $\tan x$, $\cot x$, $\sec x$, and $\csc x$; they are fundamental to mathematics and many areas of application. Also important are their relatives, the **inverse trigonometric functions**.
6. Trigonometric, exponential, and logarithmic functions are a few examples of a large family called **transcendental functions.** Figure 1.17 shows the organization of these functions, which are explored in detail in upcoming chapters.

QUICK CHECK 1 Are all polynomials rational functions? Are all algebraic functions polynomials? ◄

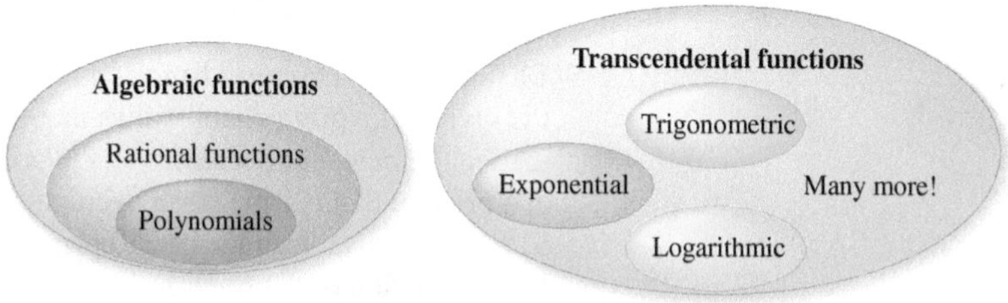

Figure 1.17

Using Graphs

Although formulas are the most compact way to represent many functions, graphs often provide the most illuminating representations. Two of countless examples of functions and their graphs are shown in Figure 1.18. Much of this book is devoted to creating and analyzing graphs of functions.

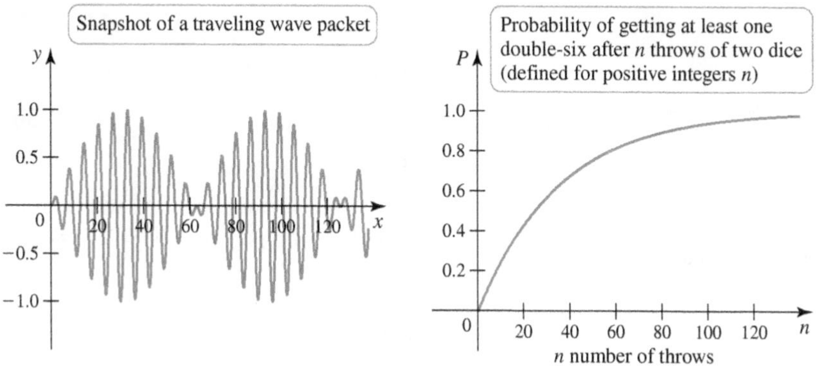

Figure 1.18

There are two approaches to graphing functions.

- Graphing calculators, tablets, and software are easy to use and powerful. Such **technology** easily produces graphs of most functions encountered in this book. We assume you know how to use a graphing utility.
- Graphing utilities, however, are not infallible. Therefore, you should also strive to master **analytical methods** (pencil-and-paper methods) in order to analyze functions and make accurate graphs by hand. Analytical methods rely heavily on calculus and are presented throughout this book.

The important message is this: Both technology and analytical methods are essential and must be used together in an integrated way to produce accurate graphs.

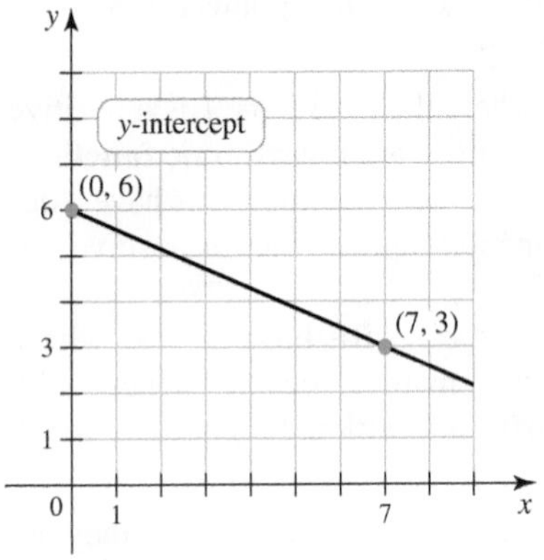

Figure 1.19

Linear Functions One form of the equation of a line (see Appendix A) is $y = mx + b$, where m and b are constants. Therefore, the function $f(x) = mx + b$ has a straight-line graph and is called a **linear function**.

EXAMPLE 1 **Linear functions and their graphs** Determine the function represented by the line in Figure 1.19.

SOLUTION From the graph, we see that the y-intercept is $(0, 6)$. Using the points $(0, 6)$ and $(7, 3)$, the slope of the line is

$$m = \frac{3 - 6}{7 - 0} = -\frac{3}{7}.$$

Therefore, the line is described by the function $f(x) = -3x/7 + 6$.

Related Exercises 11–14 ◄

EXAMPLE 2 **Demand function for pizzas** After studying sales for several months, the owner of a pizza chain knows that the number of two-topping pizzas sold in a week (called the *demand*) decreases as the price increases. Specifically, her data indicate that at a price of \$14 per pizza, an average of 400 pizzas are sold per week, while at a price of \$17 per pizza, an average of 250 pizzas are sold per week. Assume that the demand d is a *linear* function of the price p.

a. Find the constants m and b in the demand function $d = f(p) = mp + b$. Then graph f.

b. According to this model, how many pizzas (on average) are sold per week at a price of \$20?

SOLUTION

a. Two points on the graph of the demand function are given: $(p, d) = (14, 400)$ and $(17, 250)$. Therefore, the slope of the demand line is

$$m = \frac{400 - 250}{14 - 17} = -50 \text{ pizzas per dollar.}$$

It follows that the equation of the linear demand function is

$$d - 250 = -50(p - 17).$$

Expressing d as a function of p, we have $d = f(p) = -50p + 1100$ (Figure 1.20).

b. Using the demand function with a price of \$20, the average number of pizzas that could be sold per week is $f(20) = 100$.

Related Exercises 15–18 ◄

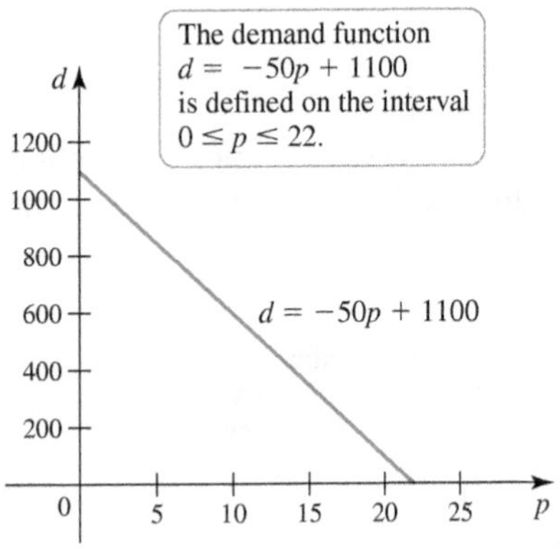

Figure 1.20

➤ The units of the slope have meaning: For every dollar the price is reduced, an average of 50 more pizzas can be sold.

Piecewise Functions A function may have different definitions on different parts of its domain. For example, income tax is levied in tax brackets that have different tax rates. Functions that have different definitions on different parts of their domain are called **piecewise functions**. If all the pieces are linear, the function is **piecewise linear**. Here are some examples.

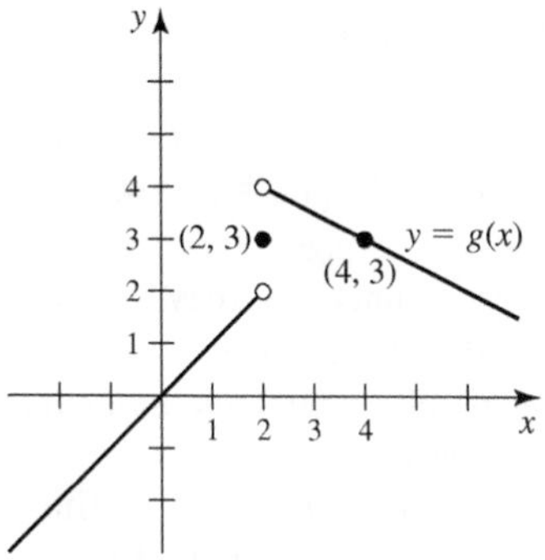

Figure 1.21

EXAMPLE 3 Defining a piecewise function The graph of a piecewise linear function g is shown in Figure 1.21. Find a formula for the function.

SOLUTION For $x < 2$, the graph is linear with a slope of 1 and a y-intercept of $(0, 0)$; its equation is $y = x$. For $x > 2$, the slope of the line is $-\frac{1}{2}$ and it passes through $(4, 3)$; so an equation of this piece of the function is

$$y - 3 = -\frac{1}{2}(x - 4) \quad \text{or} \quad y = -\frac{1}{2}x + 5.$$

For $x = 2$, we have $g(2) = 3$. Therefore,

$$g(x) = \begin{cases} x & \text{if } x < 2 \\ 3 & \text{if } x = 2 \\ -\frac{1}{2}x + 5 & \text{if } x > 2. \end{cases}$$

Related Exercises 19–22 ◀

EXAMPLE 4 Graphing piecewise functions Graph the following functions.

a. $f(x) = \begin{cases} \dfrac{x^2 - 5x + 6}{x - 2} & \text{if } x \neq 2 \\ 1 & \text{if } x = 2 \end{cases}$

b. $f(x) = |x|$, the **absolute value** function

SOLUTION

a. The function f is simplified by factoring and then canceling $x - 2$, assuming $x \neq 2$:

$$\frac{x^2 - 5x + 6}{x - 2} = \frac{(x - 2)(x - 3)}{x - 2} = x - 3.$$

Therefore, the graph of f is identical to the graph of the line $y = x - 3$ when $x \neq 2$. We are given that $f(2) = 1$ (Figure 1.22).

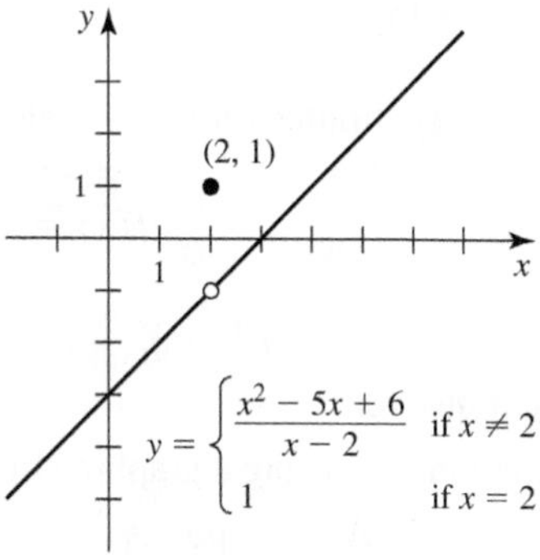

Figure 1.22

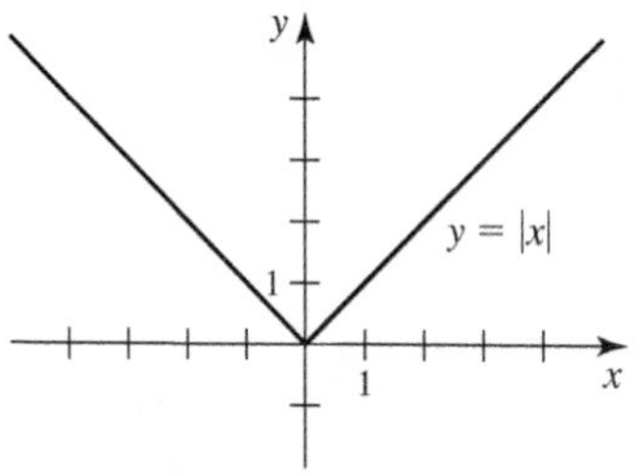

Figure 1.23

b. The absolute value of a real number is defined as

$$f(x) = |x| = \begin{cases} x & \text{if } x \geq 0 \\ -x & \text{if } x < 0. \end{cases}$$

Graphing $y = -x$, for $x < 0$, and $y = x$, for $x \geq 0$, produces the graph in Figure 1.23.

Related Exercises 23–28 ◀

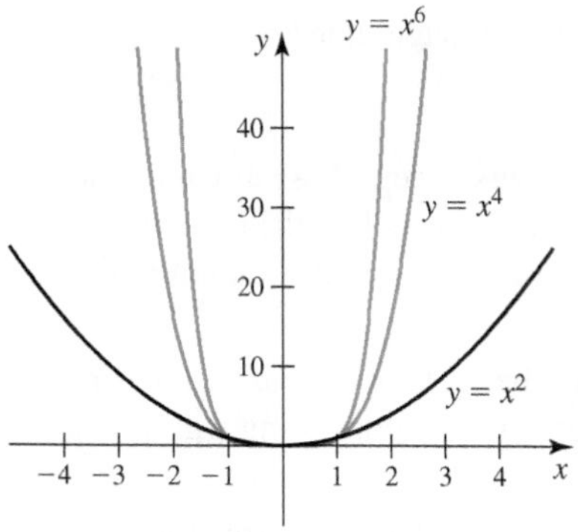

Figure 1.24

Power Functions Power functions are a special case of polynomials; they have the form $f(x) = x^n$, where n is a positive integer. When n is an even integer, the function values are nonnegative and the graph passes through the origin, opening upward (Figure 1.24). For odd integers, the power function $f(x) = x^n$ has values that are positive when x is positive and negative when x is negative (Figure 1.25).

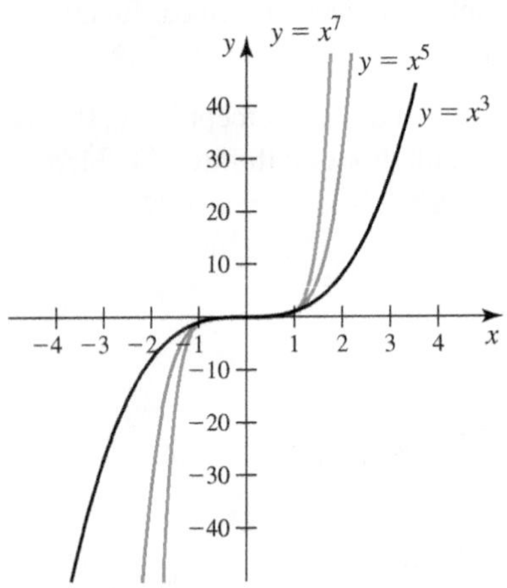

Figure 1.25

QUICK CHECK 2 What is the range of $f(x) = x^7$? What is the range of $f(x) = x^8$? ◀

Root Functions Root functions are a special case of algebraic functions; they have the form $f(x) = x^{1/n}$, where $n > 1$ is a positive integer. Notice that when n is even (square roots, fourth roots, and so forth), the domain and range consist of nonnegative numbers. Their graphs begin steeply at the origin and flatten out as x increases (Figure 1.26).

By contrast, the odd root functions (cube roots, fifth roots, and so forth) are defined for all real values of x and their range is all real numbers. Their graphs pass through the origin, open upward for $x < 0$ and downward for $x > 0$, and flatten out as x increases in magnitude (Figure 1.27).

➤ Recall that if n is a positive integer, then $x^{1/n}$ is the nth root of x; that is, $f(x) = x^{1/n} = \sqrt[n]{x}$.

QUICK CHECK 3 What are the domain and range of $f(x) = x^{1/7}$? What are the domain and range of $f(x) = x^{1/10}$? ◀

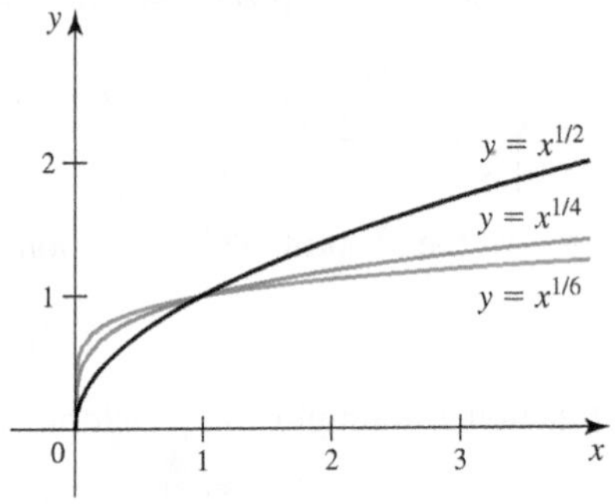

Figure 1.26

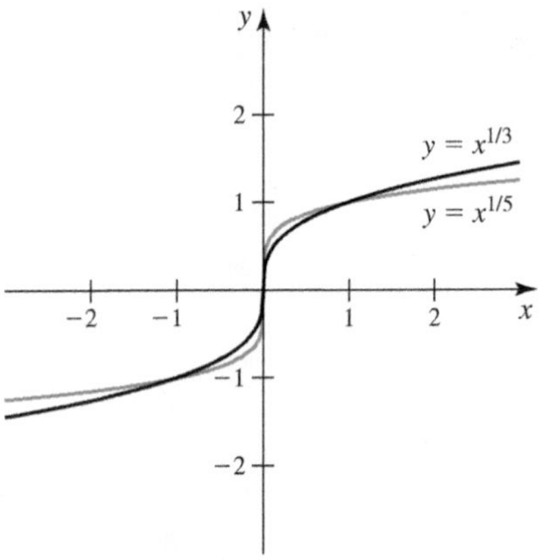

Figure 1.27

Rational Functions Rational functions appear frequently in this book, and much is said later about graphing rational functions. The following example illustrates how analysis and technology work together.

EXAMPLE 5 **Technology and analysis** Consider the rational function

$$f(x) = \frac{3x^3 - x - 1}{x^3 + 2x^2 - 6}.$$

a. What is the domain of f?

b. Find the roots (zeros) of f.

c. Graph the function using a graphing utility.

d. At what points does the function have peaks and valleys?

e. How does f behave as x grows large in magnitude?

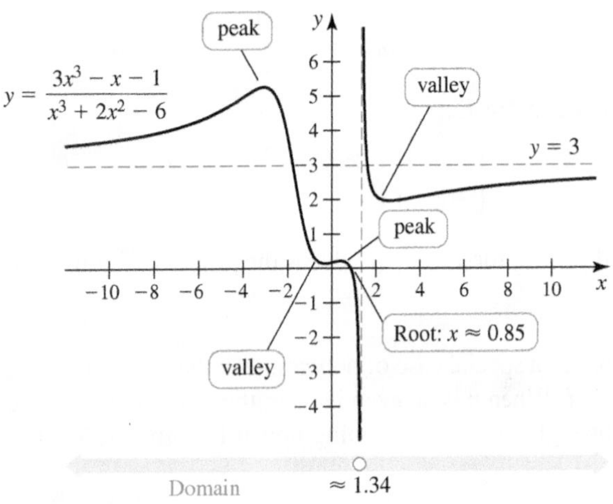

Figure 1.28

SOLUTION

a. The domain consists of all real numbers except those at which the denominator is zero. A graphing utility shows that the denominator has one real zero at $x \approx 1.34$ and therefore, the domain of f is $\{x: x \neq 1.34\}$.

b. The roots of a rational function are the roots of the numerator, provided they are not also roots of the denominator. Using a graphing utility, the only real root of the numerator is $x \approx 0.85$.

c. After experimenting with the graphing window, a reasonable graph of f is obtained (Figure 1.28). At the point $x \approx 1.34$, where the denominator is zero, the function becomes large in magnitude and f has a *vertical asymptote*.

➤ In Chapter 3, we show how calculus is used to locate the local maximum and local minimum values of a function.

d. The function has two peaks (soon to be called *local maxima*), one near $x = -3.0$ and one near $x = 0.4$. The function also has two valleys (soon to be called *local minima*), one near $x = -0.3$ and one near $x = 2.6$.

e. By zooming out, it appears that as x increases in the positive direction, the graph approaches the *horizontal asymptote* $y = 3$ from below, and as x becomes large and negative, the graph approaches $y = 3$ from above.

Related Exercises 29–34 ◄

Using Tables

Sometimes functions do not originate as formulas or graphs; they may start as numbers or data. For example, suppose you do an experiment in which a marble is dropped into a cylinder filled with heavy oil and is allowed to fall freely. You measure the total distance d, in centimeters, that the marble falls at times $t = 0, 1, 2, 3, 4, 5, 6$, and 7 seconds after it is dropped (Table 1.1). The first step might be to plot the data points (Figure 1.29).

Table 1.1

t (s)	d (cm)
0	0
1	2
2	6
3	14
4	24
5	34
6	44
7	54

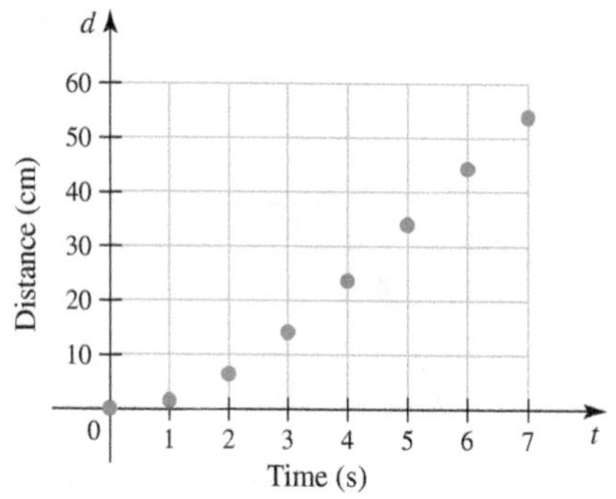

Figure 1.29

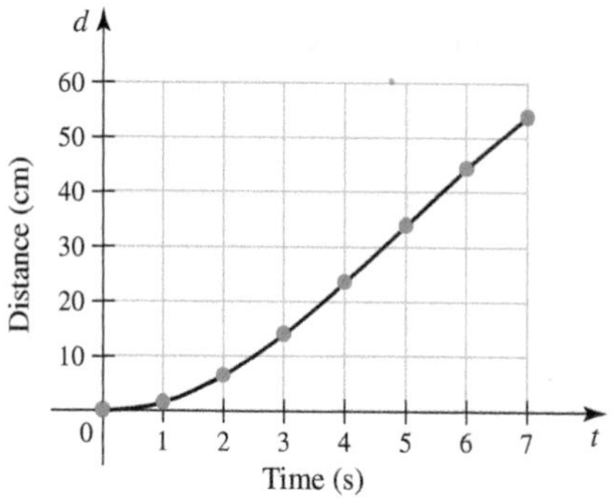

Figure 1.30

The data points suggest that there is a function $d = f(t)$ that gives the distance that the marble falls at *all* times of interest. Because the marble falls through the oil without abrupt changes, a smooth graph passing through the data points (Figure 1.30) is reasonable. Finding the best function that fits the data is a more difficult problem, which we discuss later in the text.

Using Words

Using words may be the least mathematical way to define functions, but it is often the way in which functions originate. Once a function is defined in words, it can often be tabulated, graphed, or expressed as a formula.

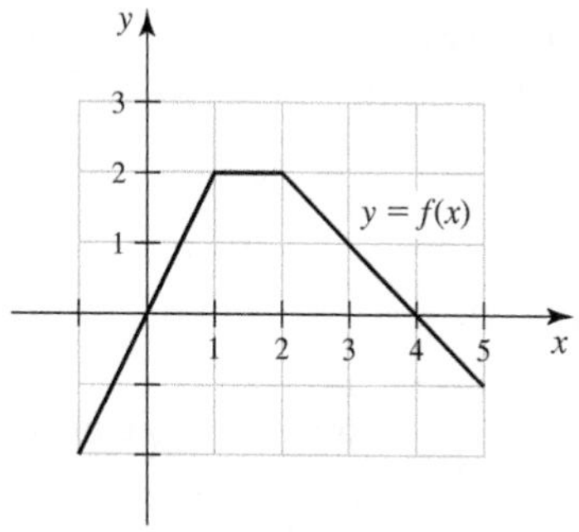

Figure 1.31

EXAMPLE 6 A slope function Let g be the **slope function** for a given function f. In words, this means that $g(x)$ is the slope of the curve $y = f(x)$ at the point $(x, f(x))$. Find and graph the slope function for the function f in Figure 1.31.

SOLUTION For $x < 1$, the slope of $y = f(x)$ is 2. The slope is 0 for $1 < x < 2$, and the slope is -1 for $x > 2$. At $x = 1$ and $x = 2$, the graph of f has a corner, so the slope is undefined at these points. Therefore, the domain of g is the set of all real numbers except $x = 1$ and $x = 2$, and the slope function (Figure 1.32) is defined by the piecewise function

$$g(x) = \begin{cases} 2 & \text{if } x < 1 \\ 0 & \text{if } 1 < x < 2 \\ -1 & \text{if } x > 2. \end{cases}$$

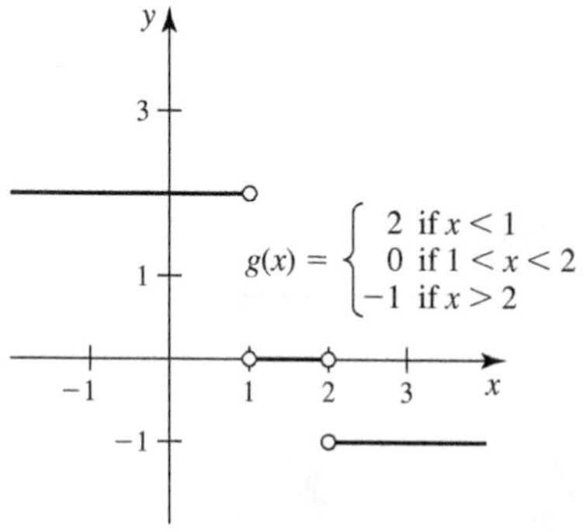

Figure 1.32

Related Exercises 35–38 ◄

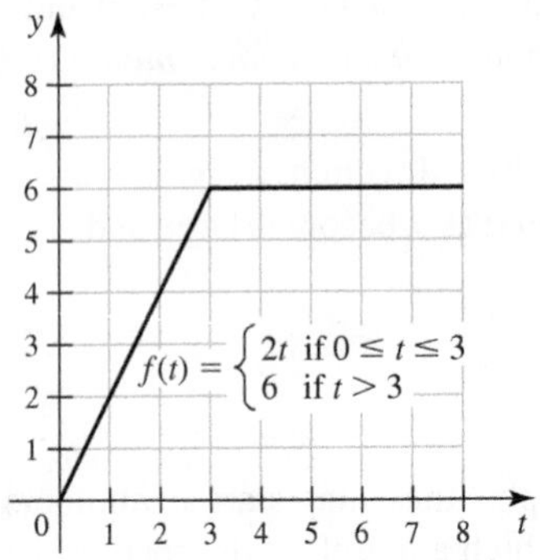

Figure 1.33

EXAMPLE 7 **An area function** Let A be an **area function** for a positive function f. In words, this means that $A(x)$ is the area of the region bounded by the graph of f and the t-axis from $t = 0$ to $t = x$. Consider the function (Figure 1.33)

$$f(t) = \begin{cases} 2t & \text{if } 0 \le t \le 3 \\ 6 & \text{if } t > 3. \end{cases}$$

a. Find $A(2)$ and $A(5)$.

b. Find a piecewise formula for the area function for f.

SOLUTION

a. The value of $A(2)$ is the area of the shaded region between the graph of f and the t-axis from $t = 0$ to $t = 2$ (Figure 1.34a). Using the formula for the area of a triangle,

$$A(2) = \frac{1}{2}(2)(4) = 4.$$

➤ Slope functions and area functions reappear in upcoming chapters and play an essential part in calculus.

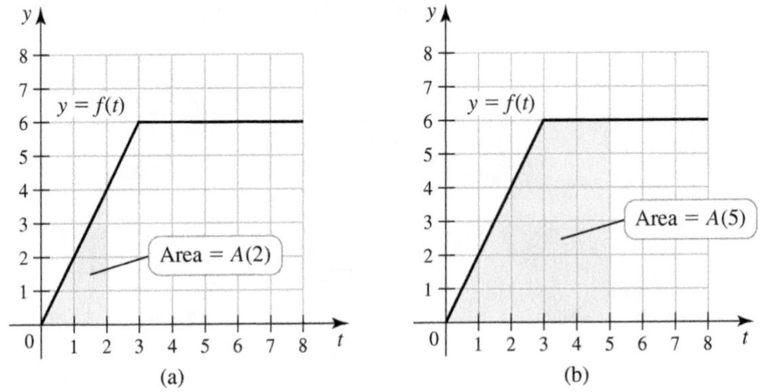

Figure 1.34

The value of $A(5)$ is the area of the shaded region between the graph of f and the t-axis on the interval $[0, 5]$ (Figure 1.34b). This area equals the area of the triangle whose base is the interval $[0, 3]$ plus the area of the rectangle whose base is the interval $[3, 5]$:

$$A(5) = \underbrace{\frac{1}{2}(3)(6)}_{\text{area of the triangle}} + \underbrace{(2)(6)}_{\text{area of the rectangle}} = 21.$$

b. For $0 \le x \le 3$ (Figure 1.35a), $A(x)$ is the area of the triangle whose base is the interval $[0, x]$. Because the height of the triangle at $t = x$ is $f(x)$,

$$A(x) = \frac{1}{2}xf(x) = \frac{1}{2}x\underbrace{(2x)}_{f(x)} = x^2.$$

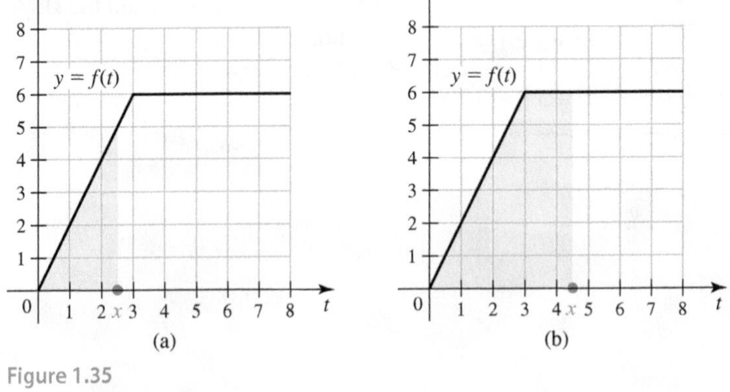

Figure 1.35

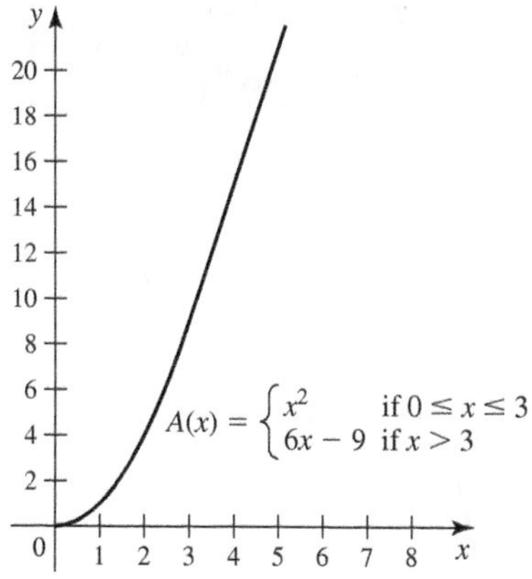

Figure 1.36

For $x > 3$ (Figure 1.35b), $A(x)$ is the area of the triangle on the interval $[0, 3]$ plus the area of the rectangle on the interval $[3, x]$:

$$A(x) = \underbrace{\frac{1}{2}(3)(6)}_{\text{area of the triangle}} + \underbrace{(x-3)(6)}_{\text{area of the rectangle}} = 6x - 9.$$

Therefore, the area function A (Figure 1.36) has the piecewise definition

$$y = A(x) = \begin{cases} x^2 & \text{if } 0 \le x \le 3 \\ 6x - 9 & \text{if } x > 3. \end{cases}$$

Related Exercises 39–42 ◀

Transformations of Functions and Graphs

There are several ways to transform the graph of a function to produce graphs of new functions. Four transformations are common: *shifts* in the x- and y-directions and *scalings* in the x- and y-directions. These transformations, summarized in Figures 1.37–1.42, can save time in graphing and visualizing functions.

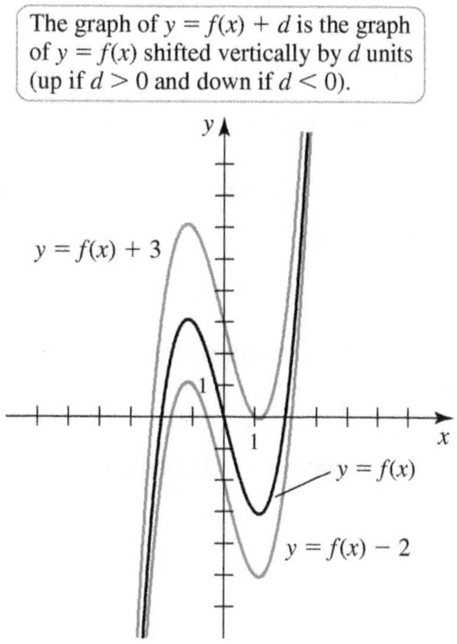

Figure 1.37

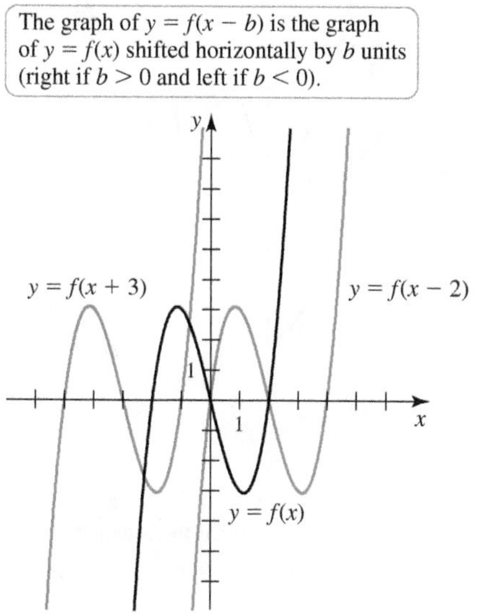

Figure 1.38

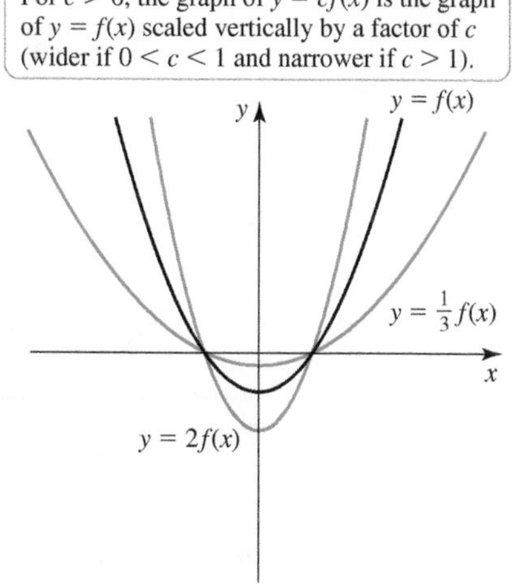

Figure 1.39

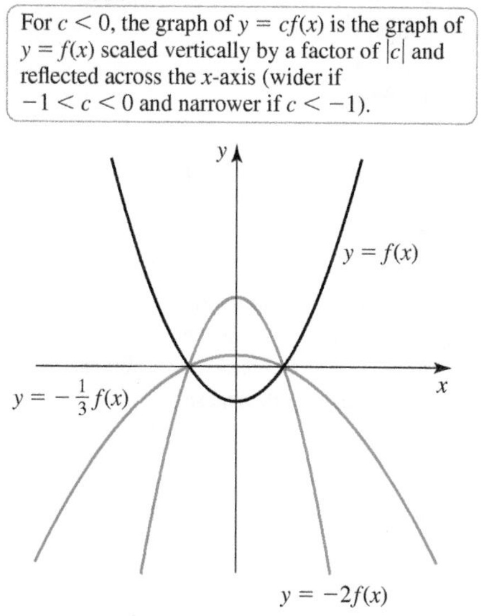

Figure 1.40

For $a > 0$, the graph of $y = f(ax)$ is the graph of $y = f(x)$ scaled horizontally by a factor of a (wider if $0 < a < 1$ and narrower if $a > 1$).

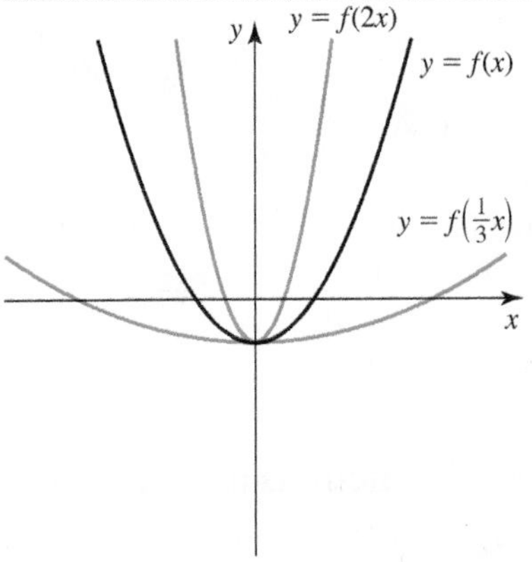

Figure 1.41

For $a < 0$, the graph of $y = f(ax)$ is the graph of $y = f(x)$ scaled horizontally by a factor of $|a|$ and reflected across the y-axis (wider if $-1 < a < 0$ and narrower if $a < -1$).

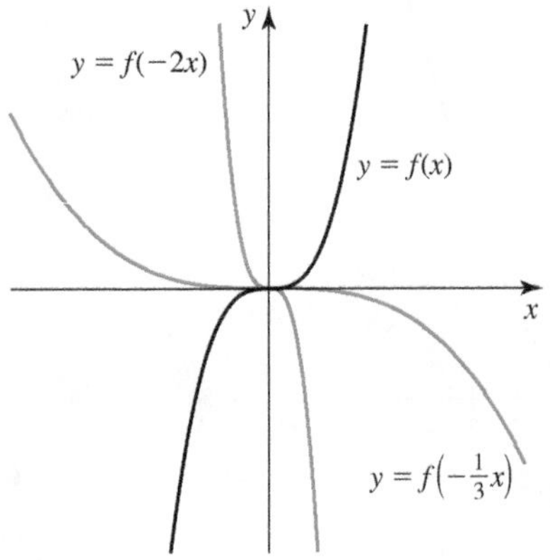

Figure 1.42

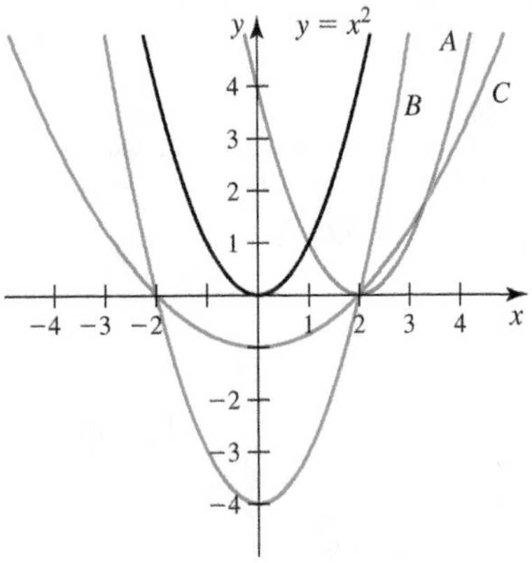

Figure 1.43

➤ You should verify that graph C also corresponds to a horizontal scaling and a vertical shift. It has the equation $y = f(ax) - 1$, where $a = \frac{1}{2}$.

EXAMPLE 8 **Shifting parabolas** The graphs A, B, and C in Figure 1.43 are obtained from the graph of $f(x) = x^2$ using shifts and scalings. Find the function that describes each graph.

SOLUTION

a. Graph A is the graph of f shifted to the right by 2 units. It represents the function

$$f(x - 2) = (x - 2)^2 = x^2 - 4x + 4.$$

b. Graph B is the graph of f shifted down by 4 units. It represents the function

$$f(x) - 4 = x^2 - 4.$$

c. Graph C is a wider version of the graph of f shifted down by 1 unit. Therefore, it represents $cf(x) - 1 = cx^2 - 1$, for some value of c, with $0 < c < 1$ (because the graph is widened). Using the fact that graph C passes through the points $(\pm 2, 0)$, we find that $c = \frac{1}{4}$. Therefore, the graph represents

$$y = \frac{1}{4} f(x) - 1 = \frac{1}{4} x^2 - 1.$$

Related Exercises 43–54 ◄

QUICK CHECK 4 How do you modify the graph of $f(x) = 1/x$ to produce the graph of $g(x) = 1/(x + 4)$? ◄

EXAMPLE 9 **Scaling and shifting** Graph $g(x) = |2x + 1|$.

SOLUTION We write the function as $g(x) = \left|2\left(x + \frac{1}{2}\right)\right|$. Letting $f(x) = |x|$, we have $g(x) = f\left(2\left(x + \frac{1}{2}\right)\right)$. Therefore, the graph of g is obtained by scaling (steepening) the graph of f horizontally and shifting it $\frac{1}{2}$ unit to the left (Figure 1.44).

➤ Note that we can also write $g(x) = 2\left|x + \frac{1}{2}\right|$, which means the graph of g may also be obtained by a vertical scaling and a horizontal shift.

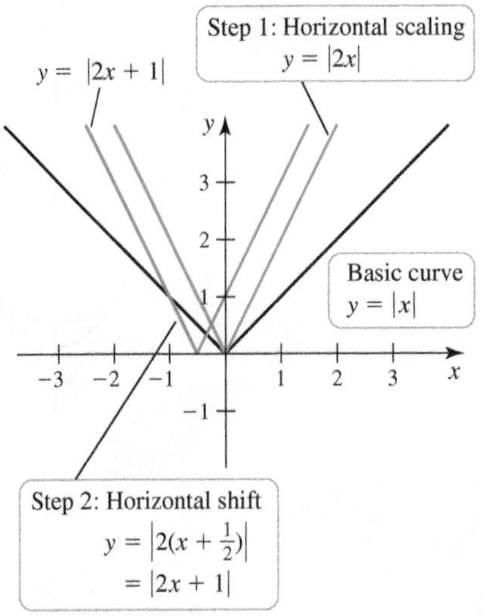

Figure 1.44

Related Exercises 43–54 ◄

SUMMARY Transformations

Given the real numbers a, b, c, and d and the function f, the graph of $y = cf(a(x - b)) + d$ can be obtained from the graph of $y = f(x)$ in the following steps.

$$y = f(x) \xrightarrow[\text{by a factor of } |a|]{\text{horizontal scaling}} y = f(ax)$$

$$\xrightarrow[\text{by } b \text{ units}]{\text{horizontal shift}} y = f(a(x - b))$$

$$\xrightarrow[\text{by a factor of } |c|]{\text{vertical scaling}} y = cf(a(x - b))$$

$$\xrightarrow[\text{by } d \text{ units}]{\text{vertical shift}} y = cf(a(x - b)) + d$$

SECTION 1.2 EXERCISES

Review Questions

1. Give four ways that functions may be defined and represented.
2. What is the domain of a polynomial?
3. What is the domain of a rational function?
4. Describe what is meant by a piecewise linear function.
5. Sketch a graph of $y = x^5$.
6. Sketch a graph of $y = x^{1/5}$.
7. How do you obtain the graph of $y = f(x + 2)$ from the graph of $y = f(x)$?
8. How do you obtain the graph of $y = -3f(x)$ from the graph of $y = f(x)$?
9. How do you obtain the graph of $y = f(3x)$ from the graph of $y = f(x)$?
10. How do you obtain the graph of $y = 4(x + 3)^2 + 6$ from the graph of $y = x^2$?

Basic Skills

11–12. Graphs of functions *Find the linear functions that correspond to the following graphs.*

11.

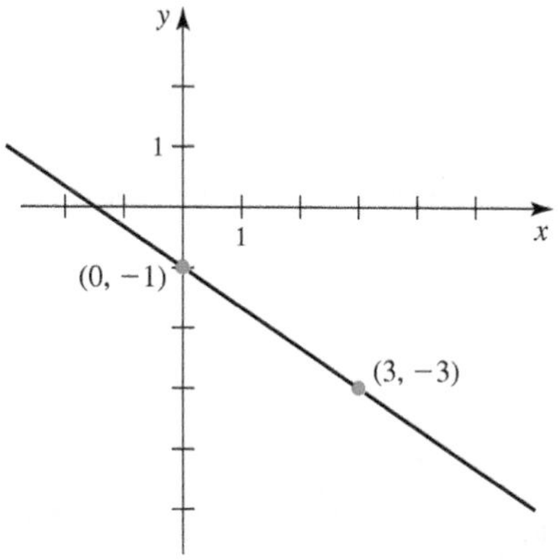

12.

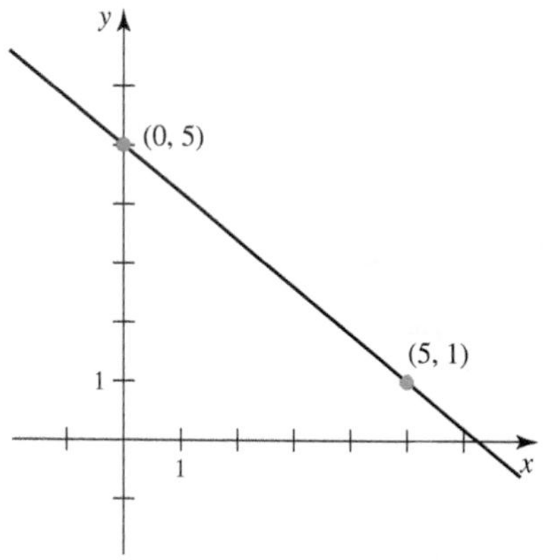

13. **Graph of a linear function** Find and graph the linear function that passes through the points $(1, 3)$ and $(2, 5)$.
14. **Graph of a linear function** Find and graph the linear function that passes through the points $(2, -3)$ and $(5, 0)$.
15. **Demand function** Sales records indicate that if Blu-ray players are priced at \$250, then a large store sells an average of 12 units per day. If they are priced at \$200, then the store sells an average of 15 units per day. Find and graph the linear demand function for Blu-ray sales. For what prices is the demand function defined?
16. **Fundraiser** The Biology Club plans to have a fundraiser for which \$8 tickets will be sold. The cost of room rental and refreshments is \$175. Find and graph the function $p = f(n)$ that gives the profit from the fundraiser when n tickets are sold. Notice that $f(0) = -\$175$; that is, the cost of room rental and refreshments must be paid regardless of how many tickets are sold. How many tickets must be sold to break even (zero profit)?
17. **Population function** The population of a small town was 500 in 2015 and is growing at a rate of 24 people per year. Find and graph the linear population function $p(t)$ that gives the population of the town t years after 2015. Then use this model to predict the population in 2030.

18. Taxicab fees A taxicab ride costs \$3.50 plus \$2.50 per mile. Let m be the distance (in miles) from the airport to a hotel. Find and graph the function $c(m)$ that represents the cost of taking a taxi from the airport to the hotel. Also determine how much it costs if the hotel is 9 miles from the airport.

19–20. Graphs of piecewise functions *Write a definition of the functions whose graphs are given.*

19.

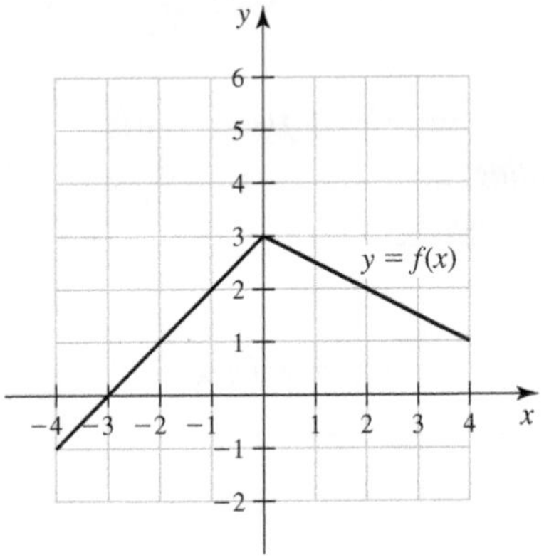

20.

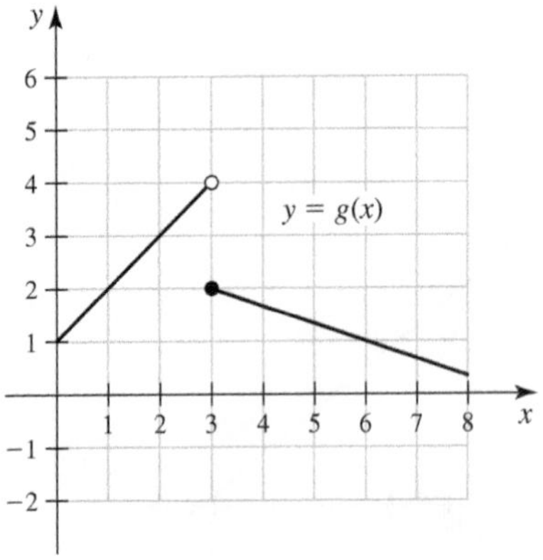

21. Parking fees Suppose that it costs 5¢ per minute to park at the airport with the rate dropping to 3¢ per minute after 9 P.M. Find and graph the cost function $c(t)$ for values of t satisfying $0 \le t \le 120$. Assume that t is the number of minutes after 8 P.M.

22. Taxicab fees A taxicab ride costs \$3.50 plus \$2.50 per mile for the first 5 miles, with the rate dropping to \$1.50 per mile after the fifth mile. Let m be the distance (in miles) from the airport to a hotel. Find and graph the piecewise linear function $c(m)$ that represents the cost of taking a taxi from the airport to a hotel m miles away.

23–28. Piecewise linear functions *Graph the following functions.*

23. $f(x) = \begin{cases} \dfrac{x^2 - x}{x - 1} & \text{if } x \ne 1 \\ 2 & \text{if } x = 1 \end{cases}$

24. $f(x) = \begin{cases} \dfrac{x^2 - x - 2}{x - 2} & \text{if } x \ne 2 \\ 4 & \text{if } x = 2 \end{cases}$

25. $f(x) = \begin{cases} 3x - 1 & \text{if } x \le 0 \\ -2x + 1 & \text{if } x > 0 \end{cases}$

26. $f(x) = \begin{cases} 3x - 1 & \text{if } x < 1 \\ x + 1 & \text{if } x \ge 1 \end{cases}$

27. $f(x) = \begin{cases} -2x - 1 & \text{if } x < -1 \\ 1 & \text{if } -1 \le x \le 1 \\ 2x - 1 & \text{if } x > 1 \end{cases}$

28. $f(x) = \begin{cases} 2x + 2 & \text{if } x < 0 \\ x + 2 & \text{if } 0 \le x \le 2 \\ 3 - x/2 & \text{if } x > 2 \end{cases}$

T **29–34. Graphs of functions**

a. *Use a graphing utility to produce a graph of the given function. Experiment with different windows to see how the graph changes on different scales. Sketch an accurate graph by hand after using the graphing utility.*
b. *Give the domain of the function.*
c. *Discuss interesting features of the function, such as peaks, valleys, and intercepts (as in Example 5).*

29. $f(x) = x^3 - 2x^2 + 6$

30. $f(x) = \sqrt[3]{2x^2 - 8}$

31. $g(x) = \left| \dfrac{x^2 - 4}{x + 3} \right|$

32. $f(x) = \dfrac{\sqrt{3x^2 - 12}}{x + 1}$

33. $f(x) = 3 - |2x - 1|$

34. $f(x) = \begin{cases} \dfrac{|x - 1|}{x - 1} & \text{if } x \ne 1 \\ 0 & \text{if } x = 1 \end{cases}$

35–38. Slope functions *Determine the slope function for the following functions.*

35. $f(x) = 2x + 1$

36. $f(x) = |x|$

37. Use the figure for Exercise 19.

38. Use the figure for Exercise 20.

39–42. Area functions *Let $A(x)$ be the area of the region bounded by the t-axis and the graph of $y = f(t)$ from $t = 0$ to $t = x$. Consider the following functions and graphs.*

a. *Find $A(2)$.*
b. *Find $A(6)$.*
c. *Find a formula for $A(x)$.*

39. $f(t) = 6$

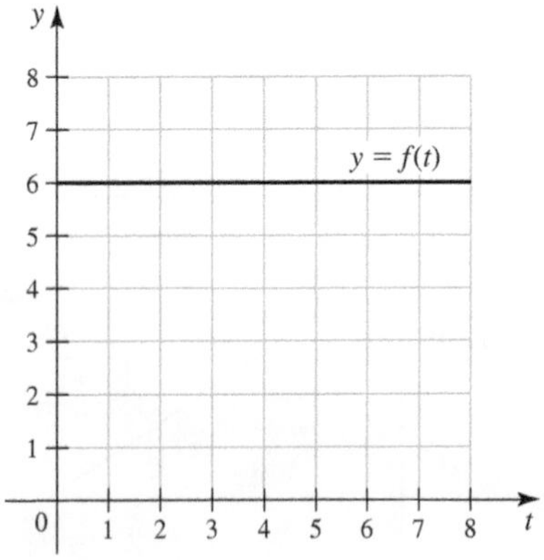

40. $f(t) = \frac{t}{2}$

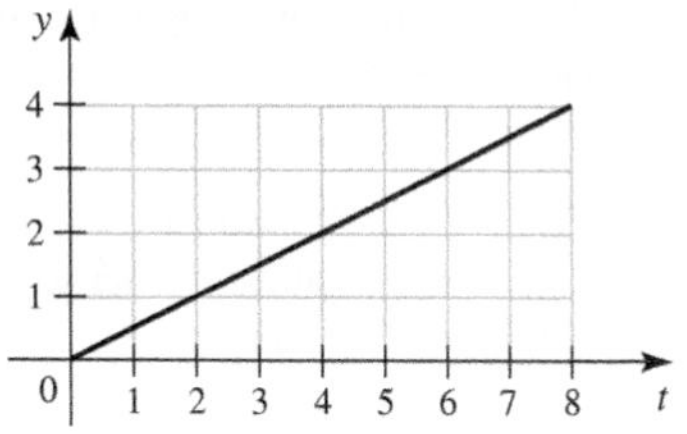

41. $f(t) = \begin{cases} -2t + 8 & \text{if } t \le 3 \\ 2 & \text{if } t > 3 \end{cases}$

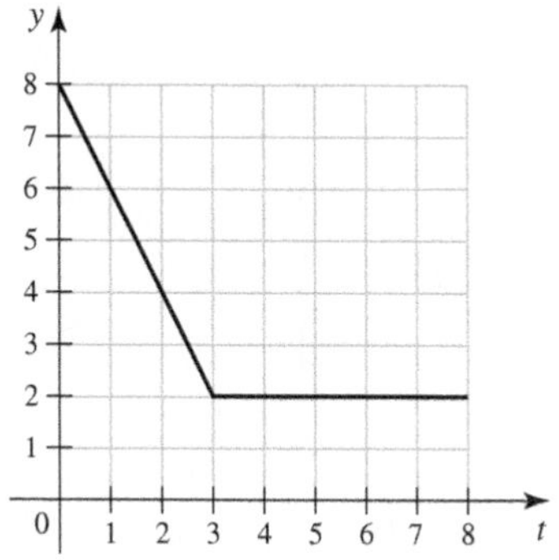

42. $f(t) = |t - 2| + 1$

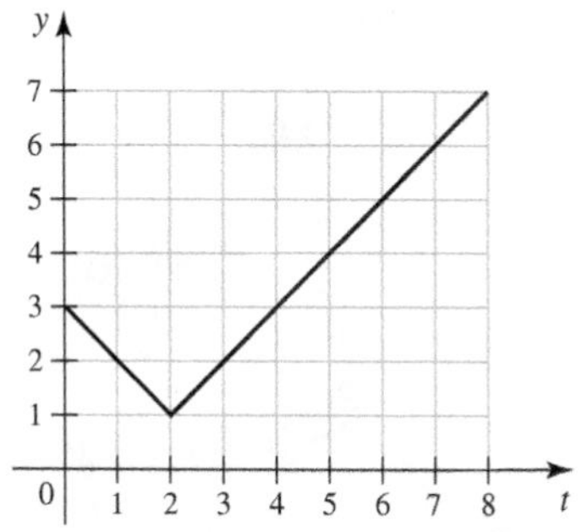

43. Transformations of $y = |x|$ The functions f and g in the figure are obtained by vertical and horizontal shifts and scalings of $y = |x|$. Find formulas for f and g. Verify your answers with a graphing utility.

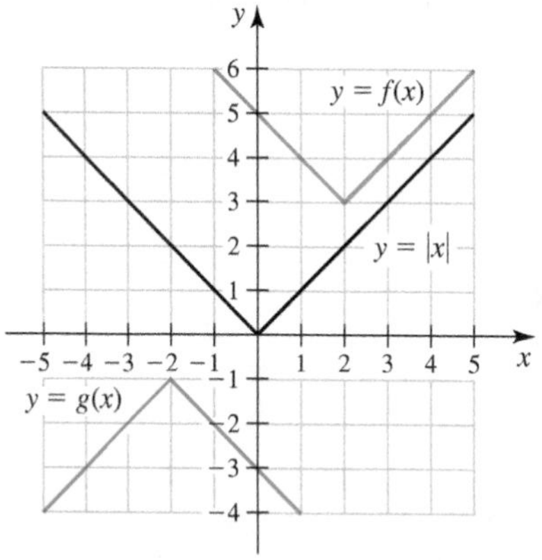

44. Transformations Use the graph of f in the figure to plot the following functions.

a. $y = -f(x)$ **b.** $y = f(x + 2)$
c. $y = f(x - 2)$ **d.** $y = f(2x)$
e. $y = f(x - 1) + 2$ **f.** $y = 2f(x)$

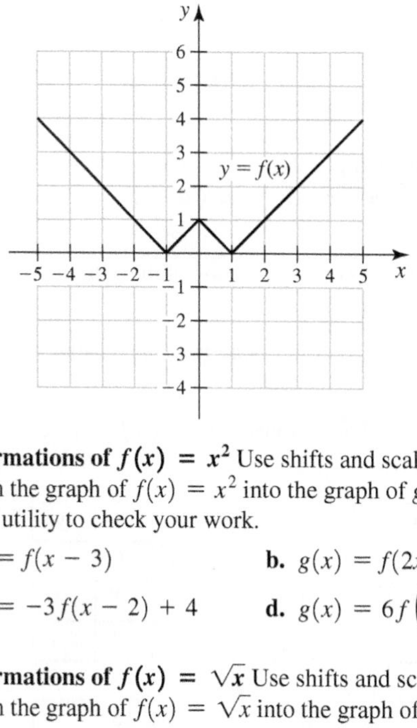

45. Transformations of $f(x) = x^2$ Use shifts and scalings to transform the graph of $f(x) = x^2$ into the graph of g. Use a graphing utility to check your work.

a. $g(x) = f(x - 3)$ **b.** $g(x) = f(2x - 4)$
c. $g(x) = -3f(x - 2) + 4$ **d.** $g(x) = 6f\left(\frac{x - 2}{3}\right) + 1$

46. Transformations of $f(x) = \sqrt{x}$ Use shifts and scalings to transform the graph of $f(x) = \sqrt{x}$ into the graph of g. Use a graphing utility to check your work.

a. $g(x) = f(x + 4)$ **b.** $g(x) = 2f(2x - 1)$
c. $g(x) = \sqrt{x - 1}$ **d.** $g(x) = 3\sqrt{x - 1} - 5$

47–54. Shifting and scaling *Use shifts and scalings to graph the given functions. Then check your work with a graphing utility. Be sure to identify an original function on which the shifts and scalings are performed.*

47. $f(x) = (x - 2)^2 + 1$

48. $f(x) = x^2 - 2x + 3$ (*Hint:* Complete the square first.)

49. $g(x) = -3x^2$

50. $g(x) = 2x^3 - 1$

51. $g(x) = 2(x + 3)^2$

52. $p(x) = x^2 + 3x - 5$

53. $h(x) = -4x^2 - 4x + 12$

54. $h(x) = |3x - 6| + 1$

Further Explorations

55. Explain why or why not Determine whether the following statements are true and give an explanation or counterexample.

a. All polynomials are rational functions, but not all rational functions are polynomials.
b. If f is a linear polynomial, then $f \circ f$ is a quadratic polynomial.
c. If f and g are polynomials, then the degrees of $f \circ g$ and $g \circ f$ are equal.
d. To graph $g(x) = f(x + 2)$, shift the graph of f 2 units to the right.

56–57. Intersection problems *Use analytical methods to find the following points of intersection. Use a graphing utility to check your work.*

56. Find the point(s) of intersection of the parabola $y = x^2 + 2$ and the line $y = x + 4$.

57. Find the point(s) of intersection of the parabolas $y = x^2$ and $y = -x^2 + 8x$.

58–59. Functions from tables *Find a simple function that fits the data in the tables.*

58.

x	y
-1	0
0	1
1	2
2	3
3	4

59.

x	y
0	-1
1	0
4	1
9	2
16	3

60–63. Functions from words *Find a formula for a function describing the given situation. Graph the function and give a domain that makes sense for the problem. Recall that with constant speed, distance = speed · time elapsed.*

60. A function $y = f(x)$ such that y is 1 less than the cube of x

61. Two cars leave a junction at the same time, one traveling north at 30 mi/hr, the other one traveling east at 60 mi/hr. The function $s(t)$ is the distance between the cars t hours after they leave the junction.

62. A function $y = f(x)$ such that if you ride a bike for 50 mi at x miles per hour, you arrive at your destination in y hours

63. A function $y = f(x)$ such that if your car gets 32 mi/gal and gasoline costs $\$x$/gallon, then \$100 is the cost of taking a y-mile trip

64. Floor function The floor function, or greatest integer function, $f(x) = \lfloor x \rfloor$, gives the greatest integer less than or equal to x. Graph the floor function, for $-3 \le x \le 3$.

65. Ceiling function The ceiling function, or smallest integer function, $f(x) = \lceil x \rceil$, gives the smallest integer greater than or equal to x. Graph the ceiling function, for $-3 \le x \le 3$.

66. Sawtooth wave Graph the sawtooth wave defined by

$$f(x) = \begin{cases} \vdots & \\ x + 1 & \text{if } -1 \le x < 0 \\ x & \text{if } 0 \le x < 1 \\ x - 1 & \text{if } 1 \le x < 2 \\ x - 2 & \text{if } 2 \le x < 3 \\ \vdots & \end{cases}$$

67. Square wave Graph the square wave defined by

$$f(x) = \begin{cases} 0 & \text{if } x < 0 \\ 1 & \text{if } 0 \le x < 1 \\ 0 & \text{if } 1 \le x < 2 \\ 1 & \text{if } 2 \le x < 3 \\ \vdots & \end{cases}$$

68–70. Roots and powers *Make a sketch of the given pairs of functions. Be sure to draw the graphs accurately relative to each other.*

68. $y = x^4$ and $y = x^6$

69. $y = x^3$ and $y = x^7$

70. $y = x^{1/3}$ and $y = x^{1/5}$

71. Features of a graph Consider the graph of the function f shown in the figure. Answer the following questions by referring to the points A–I.

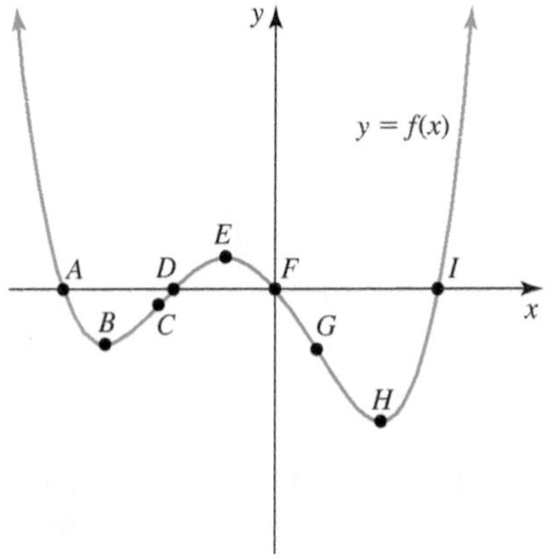

a. Which points correspond to the roots (zeros) of f?
b. Which points on the graph correspond to high points or peaks (soon to be called *local maximum* values of f)?
c. Which points on the graph correspond to low points or valleys (soon to be called *local minimum* values of f)?
d. As you move along the curve in the positive x-direction, at which point is the graph rising most rapidly?
e. As you move along the curve in the positive x-direction, at which point is the graph falling most rapidly?

72. Features of a graph Consider the graph of the function g shown in the figure.

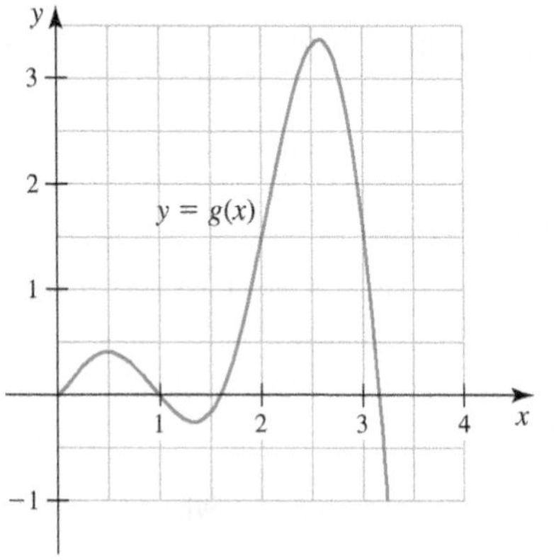

a. Give the approximate roots (zeros) of g.
b. Give the approximate coordinates of the high points or peaks (soon to be called *local maximum* values of f).
c. Give the approximate coordinates of the low points or valleys (soon to be called *local minimum* values of f).
d. Imagine moving along the curve in the positive x-direction on the interval $[0, 3]$. Give the approximate coordinates of the point at which the graph is rising most rapidly.
e. Imagine moving along the curve in the positive x-direction on the interval $[0, 3]$. Give the approximate coordinates of the point at which the graph is falling most rapidly.

Applications

T **73. Relative acuity of the human eye** The **fovea centralis** (or **fovea**) is responsible for the sharp central vision that humans use for reading and other detail-oriented eyesight. The relative acuity of a human eye, which measures the sharpness of vision, is modeled by the function

$$R(\theta) = \frac{0.568}{0.331|\theta| + 0.568},$$

where θ (in degrees) is the angular deviation of the line of sight from the center of the fovea (see figure).

a. Graph R, for $-15 \le \theta \le 15$.
b. For what value of θ is R maximized? What does this fact indicate about our eyesight?
c. For what values of θ do we maintain at least 90% of our maximum relative acuity? (*Source: The Journal of Experimental Biology*, 203, Dec 2000)

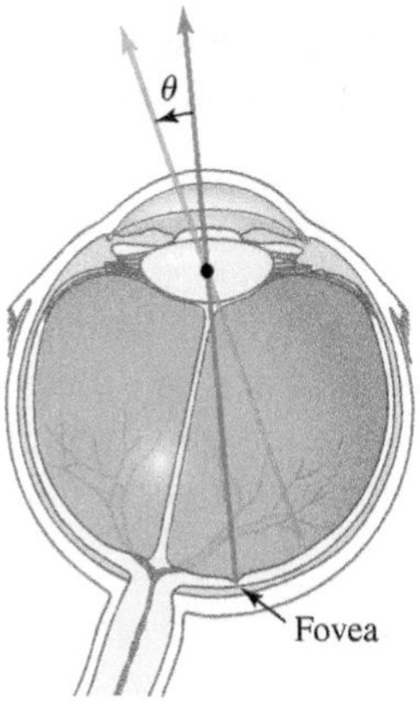

74. Tennis probabilities Suppose the probability of a server winning any given point in a tennis match is a constant p, with $0 \le p \le 1$. Then the probability of the server winning a game when serving from deuce is

$$f(p) = \frac{p^2}{1 - 2p(1 - p)}.$$

a. Evaluate $f(0.75)$ and interpret the result.
b. Evaluate $f(0.25)$ and interpret the result.
(*Source: The College Mathematics Journal* 38, 1, Jan 2007).

75. Bald eagle population Since DDT was banned and the Endangered Species Act was passed in 1973, the number of bald eagles in the United States has increased dramatically (see figure). In the lower 48 states, the number of breeding pairs of bald eagles increased at a nearly linear rate from 1875 pairs in 1986 to 6471 pairs in 2000.

a. Use the data points for 1986 and 2000 to find a linear function p that models the number of breeding pairs from 1986 to 2000 $(0 \le t \le 14)$.
b. Using the function in part (a), approximately how many breeding pairs were in the lower 48 states in 1995?

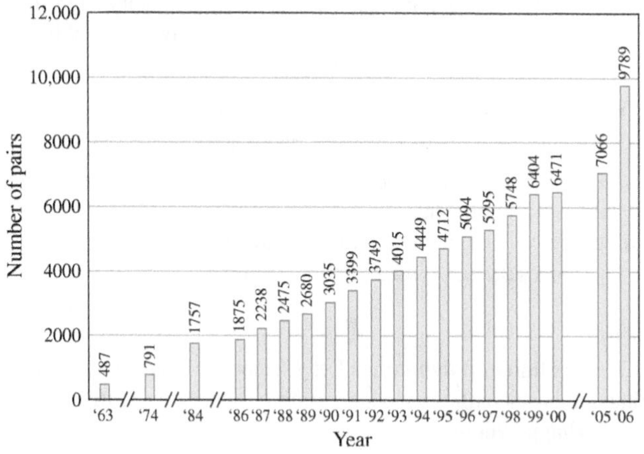

(*Source:* U.S. Fish and Wildlife Service)

76. Temperature scales

a. Find the linear function $C = f(F)$ that gives the reading on the Celsius temperature scale corresponding to a reading on the Fahrenheit scale. Use the facts that $C = 0$ when $F = 32$ (freezing point) and $C = 100$ when $F = 212$ (boiling point).
b. At what temperature are the Celsius and Fahrenheit readings equal?

77. Automobile lease vs. purchase A car dealer offers a purchase option and a lease option on all new cars. Suppose you are interested in a car that can be bought outright for \$25,000 or leased for a start-up fee of \$1200 plus monthly payments of \$350.

a. Find the linear function $y = f(m)$ that gives the total amount you have paid on the lease option after m months.
b. With the lease option, after a 48-month (4-year) term, the car has a residual value of \$10,000, which is the amount that you could pay to purchase the car. Assuming no other costs, should you lease or buy?

78. Surface area of a sphere The surface area of a sphere of radius r is $S = 4\pi r^2$. Solve for r in terms of S and graph the radius function for $S \ge 0$.

T **79. Volume of a spherical cap** A single slice through a sphere of radius r produces a *cap* of the sphere. If the thickness of the cap is h, then its volume is $V = \frac{1}{3}\pi h^2(3r - h)$. Graph the volume as a function of h for a sphere of radius 1. For what values of h does this function make sense?

80. Walking and rowing Kelly has finished a picnic on an island that is 200 m off shore (see figure). She wants to return to a beach house that is 600 m from the point P on the shore closest to the island. She plans to row a boat to a point on shore x meters from P and then jog along the (straight) shore to the house.

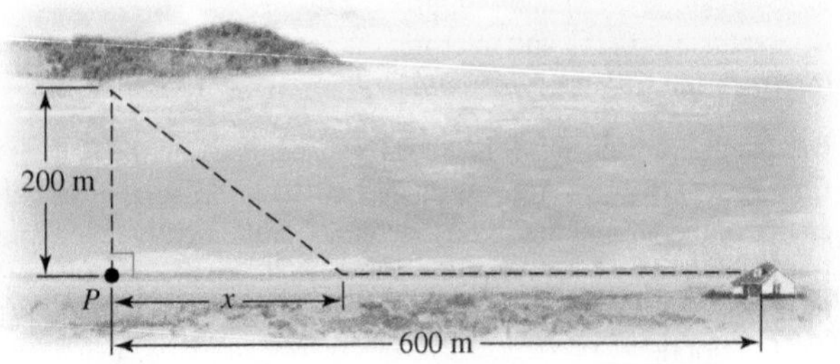

a. Let $d(x)$ be the total length of her trip as a function of x. Find and graph this function.
b. Suppose that Kelly can row at 2 m/s and jog at 4 m/s. Let $T(x)$ be the total time for her trip as a function of x. Find and graph $y = T(x)$.
c. Based on your graph in part (b), estimate the point on the shore at which Kelly should land to minimize the total time of her trip. What is that minimum time?

81. Optimal boxes Imagine a lidless box with height h and a square base whose sides have length x. The box must have a volume of 125 ft^3.

a. Find and graph the function $S(x)$ that gives the surface area of the box, for all values of $x > 0$.
b. Based on your graph in part (a), estimate the value of x that produces the box with a minimum surface area.

Additional Exercises

82. Composition of polynomials Let f be an nth-degree polynomial and let g be an mth-degree polynomial. What is the degree of the following polynomials?

a. $f \cdot f$ b. $f \circ f$ c. $f \cdot g$ d. $f \circ g$

83. Parabola vertex property Prove that if a parabola crosses the x-axis twice, the x-coordinate of the vertex of the parabola is halfway between the x-intercepts.

84. Parabola properties Consider the general quadratic function $f(x) = ax^2 + bx + c$, with $a \neq 0$.

a. Find the coordinates of the vertex in terms of a, b, and c.
b. Find the conditions on a, b, and c that guarantee that the graph of f crosses the x-axis twice.

85. Factorial function The factorial function is defined for positive integers as $n! = n(n-1)(n-2)\cdots 3\cdot 2\cdot 1$.

a. Make a table of the factorial function, for $n = 1, 2, 3, 4, 5$.
b. Graph these data points and then connect them with a smooth curve.
c. What is the least value of n for which $n! > 10^6$?

86. Sum of integers Let $S(n) = 1 + 2 + \cdots + n$, where n is a positive integer. It can be shown that $S(n) = n(n+1)/2$.

a. Make a table of $S(n)$, for $n = 1, 2, \ldots, 10$.
b. How would you describe the domain of this function?
c. What is the least value of n for which $S(n) > 1000$?

87. Sum of squared integers Let $T(n) = 1^2 + 2^2 + \cdots + n^2$, where n is a positive integer. It can be shown that $T(n) = n(n+1)(2n+1)/6$.

a. Make a table of $T(n)$, for $n = 1, 2, \ldots, 10$.
b. How would you describe the domain of this function?
c. What is the least value of n for which $T(n) > 1000$?

QUICK CHECK ANSWERS

1. Yes; no **2.** $(-\infty, \infty)$; $[0, \infty)$ **3.** Domain and range are $(-\infty, \infty)$. Domain and range are $[0, \infty)$. **4.** Shift the graph of f horizontally 4 units to the left. ◄

1.3 Inverse, Exponential, and Logarithmic Functions

Exponential functions are fundamental to all of mathematics. Many processes in the world around us are modeled by *exponential functions*—they appear in finance, medicine, ecology, biology, economics, anthropology, and physics (among other disciplines). Every exponential function has an inverse function, which is a member of the family of *logarithmic functions*, also discussed in this section.

Exponential Functions

Exponential functions have the form $f(x) = b^x$, where the base $b \neq 1$ is a positive real number. An important question arises immediately: For what values of x can b^x be evaluated? We certainly know how to compute b^x when x is an integer. For example, $2^3 = 8$ and $2^{-4} = 1/2^4 = 1/16$. When x is rational, the numerator and denominator are interpreted as a power and root, respectively:

$$16^{3/4} = 16^{3/4} = (\sqrt[4]{16})^3 = 8.$$

(In $16^{3/4}$, the numerator 3 is labeled "power", the denominator 4 is labeled "root", and $\sqrt[4]{16}$ is marked as 2.)

➤ $16^{3/4}$ can also be computed as $\sqrt[4]{16^3} = \sqrt[4]{4096} = 8$.

➤ **Exponent Rules**

For any base $b > 0$ and real numbers x and y, the following relations hold:

E1. $b^x b^y = b^{x+y}$

E2. $\dfrac{b^x}{b^y} = b^{x-y}$

$\left(\text{which includes } \dfrac{1}{b^y} = b^{-y}\right)$

E3. $(b^x)^y = b^{xy}$

E4. $b^x > 0$, for all x

QUICK CHECK 1 Is it possible to raise a positive number b to a power and obtain a negative number? Is it possible to obtain zero? ◄

But what happens when x is irrational? For example, how should 2^π be understood? Your calculator provides an approximation to 2^π, but where does the approximation come from? These questions will be answered eventually. For now, we assume that b^x can be defined for all real numbers x and that it can be approximated as closely as desired by using rational numbers as close to x as needed. In Section 6.8, we prove that the domain of an exponential function is all real numbers.

Properties of Exponential Functions $f(x) = b^x$

1. Because b^x is defined for all real numbers, the domain of f is $\{x: -\infty < x < \infty\}$. Because $b^x > 0$ for all values of x, the range of f is $\{y: 0 < y < \infty\}$.
2. For all $b > 0$, $b^0 = 1$, and therefore $f(0) = 1$.
3. If $b > 1$, then f is an increasing function of x (Figure 1.45). For example, if $b = 2$, then $2^x > 2^y$ whenever $x > y$.
4. If $0 < b < 1$, then f is a decreasing function of x. For example, if $b = \frac{1}{2}$,

$$f(x) = \left(\frac{1}{2}\right)^x = \frac{1}{2^x} = 2^{-x},$$

and because 2^x increases with x, 2^{-x} decreases with x (Figure 1.46).

QUICK CHECK 2 Explain why $f(x) = \left(\dfrac{1}{3}\right)^x$ is a decreasing function. ◄

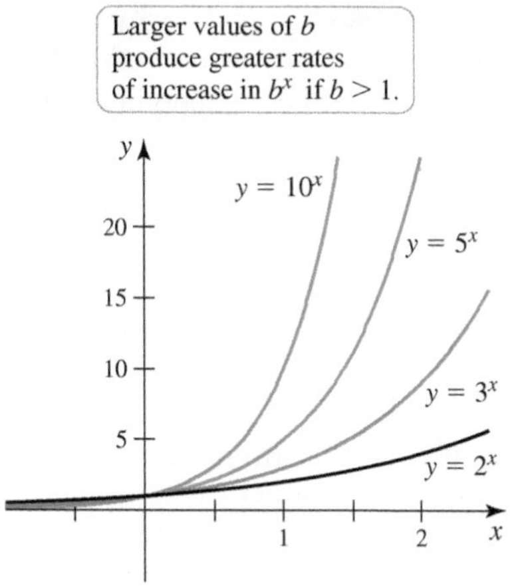

Figure 1.45

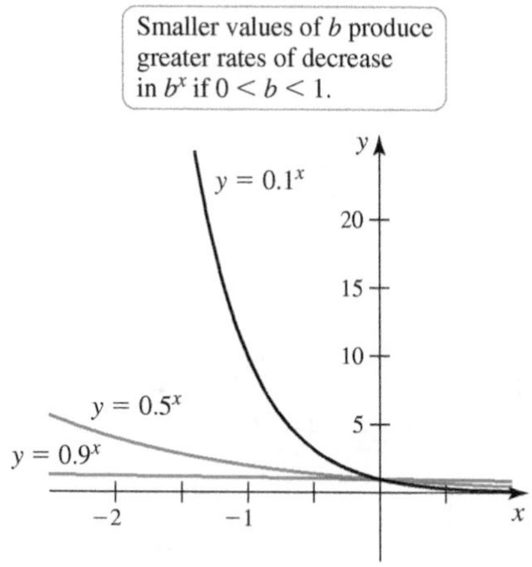

Figure 1.46

➤ The notation e was proposed by the Swiss mathematician Leonhard Euler (pronounced *oiler*) (1707–1783).

The Natural Exponential Function One of the bases used for exponential functions is special. For reasons that will become evident in upcoming chapters, the special base is e, one of the fundamental constants of mathematics. It is an irrational number with a value of $e = 2.718281828459\ldots$.

> DEFINITION **The Natural Exponential Function**
> The **natural exponential function** is $f(x) = e^x$, which has the base $e = 2.718281828459\ldots$.

The base e gives an exponential function that has a valuable property. As shown in Figure 1.47a, the graph of $y = e^x$ lies between the graphs of $y = 2^x$ and $y = 3^x$ (because $2 < e < 3$). At every point on the graph of $y = e^x$, it is possible to draw a *tangent line* (discussed in Chapters 2 and 3) that touches the graph only at that point. The natural exponential function is the only exponential function with the property that the slope of the tangent line at $x = 0$ is 1 (Figure 1.47b); therefore, e^x has both value and slope equal to 1 at $x = 0$. This property—minor as it may seem—leads to many simplifications when we do calculus with exponential functions.

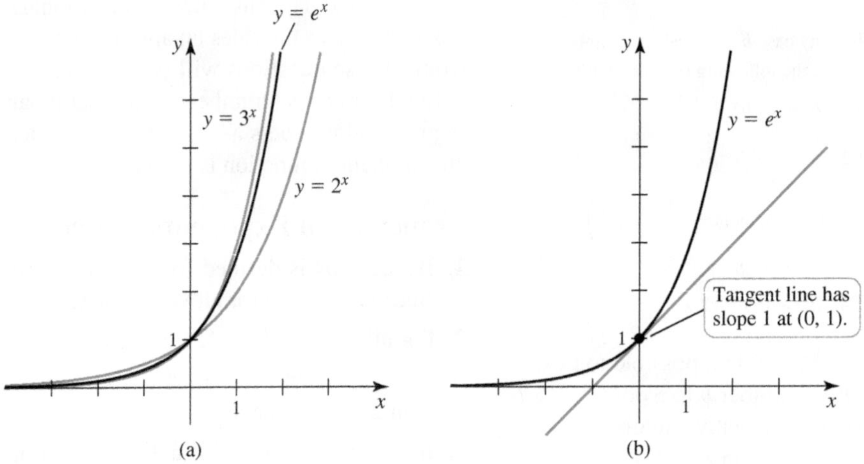

Figure 1.47

Inverse Functions

Consider the linear function $f(x) = 2x$, which takes any value of x and doubles it. The function that reverses this process by taking any value of $f(x) = 2x$ and mapping it back to x is called the *inverse function* of f, denoted f^{-1}. In this case, the inverse function is $f^{-1}(x) = x/2$. The effect of applying these two functions in succession looks like this:

$$x \xrightarrow{f} 2x \xrightarrow{f^{-1}} x$$

We now generalize this idea.

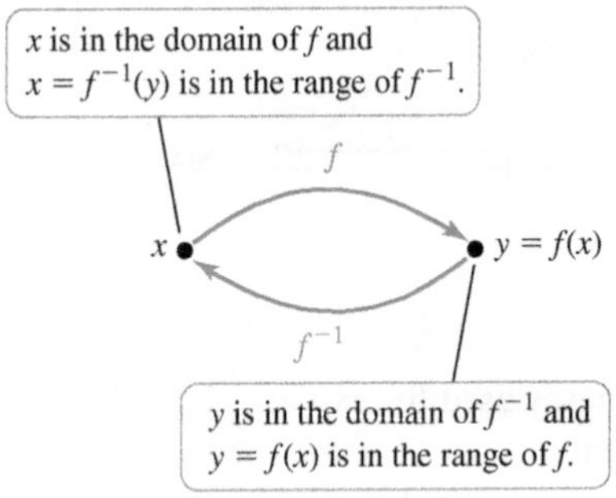

Figure 1.48

> The notation f^{-1} for the inverse can be confusing. The inverse is not the reciprocal; that is, $f^{-1}(x)$ is not $1/f(x) = (f(x))^{-1}$. We adopt the common convention of using simply *inverse* to mean *inverse function*.

DEFINITION Inverse Function

Given a function f, its inverse (if it exists) is a function f^{-1} such that whenever $y = f(x)$, then $f^{-1}(y) = x$ (Figure 1.48).

QUICK CHECK 3 What is the inverse of $f(x) = \frac{1}{3}x$? What is the inverse of $f(x) = x - 7$? ◀

Because the inverse "undoes" the original function, if we start with a value of x, apply f to it, and then apply f^{-1} to the result, we recover the original value of x; that is,

$$f^{-1}(f(x)) = x.$$

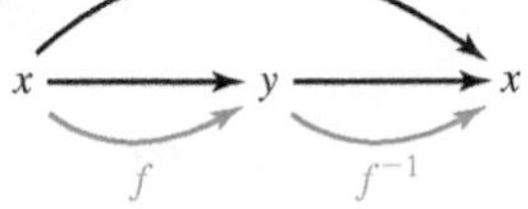

Similarly, if we apply f^{-1} to a value of y and then apply f to the result, we recover the original value of y; that is,

$$f(f^{-1}(y)) = y.$$

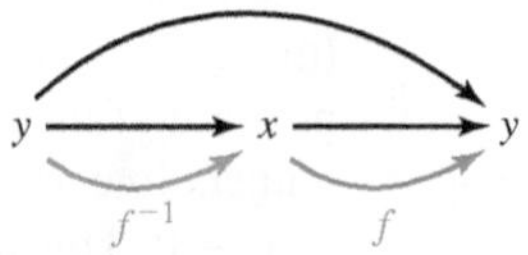

One-to-One Functions We have defined the inverse of a function, but said nothing about when it exists. To ensure that f has an inverse on a domain, f must be *one-to-one* on that domain. This property means that every output of the function f must correspond to exactly one input. The one-to-one property is checked graphically by using the *horizontal line test*.

DEFINITION One-to-One Functions and the Horizontal Line Test

A function f is **one-to-one** on a domain D if each value of $f(x)$ corresponds to exactly one value of x in D. More precisely, f is one-to-one on D if $f(x_1) \neq f(x_2)$ whenever $x_1 \neq x_2$, for x_1 and x_2 in D. The **horizontal line test** says that every horizontal line intersects the graph of a one-to-one function at most once (Figure 1.49).

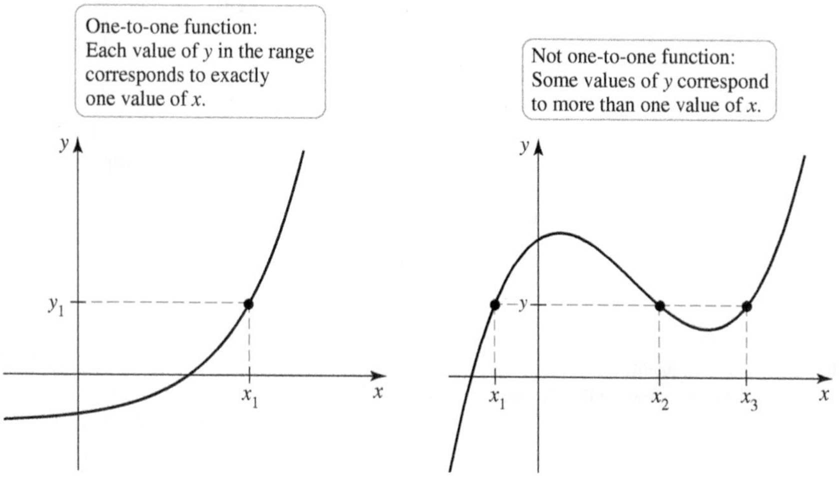

Figure 1.49

For example, in Figure 1.50, some horizontal lines intersect the graph of $f(x) = x^2$ twice. Therefore, f does not have an inverse function on the interval $(-\infty, \infty)$. However, if the domain of f is restricted to one of the intervals $(-\infty, 0]$ or $[0, \infty)$, then the graph of f passes the horizontal line test and f is one-to-one on these intervals.

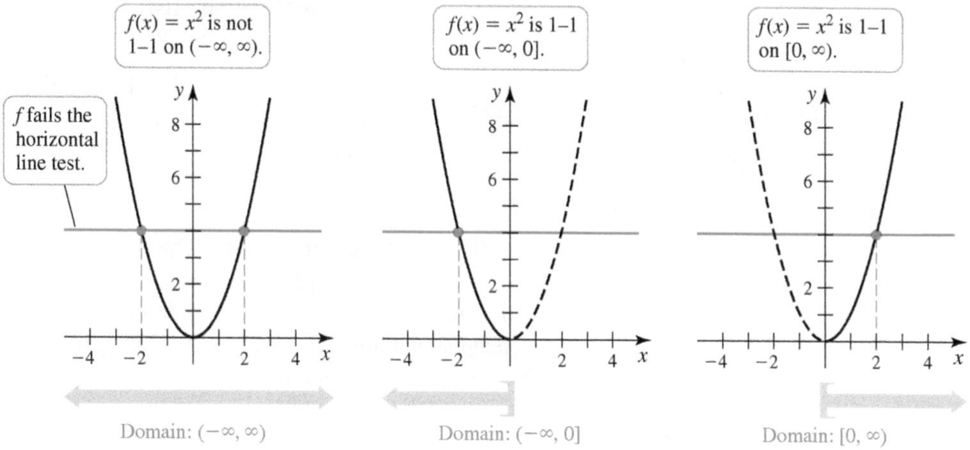

Figure 1.50

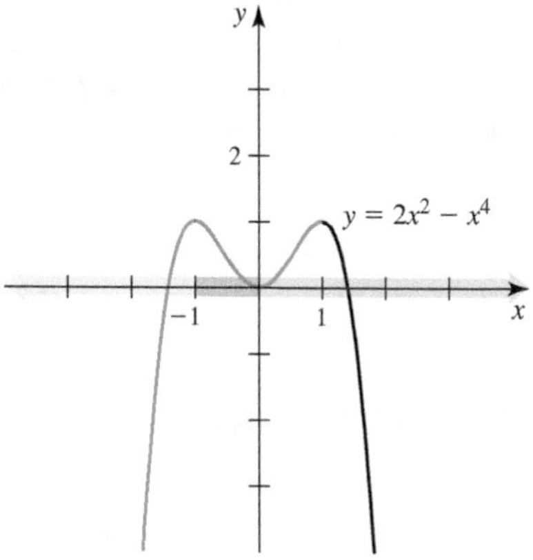

Figure 1.51

EXAMPLE 1 One-to-one functions Determine the (largest possible) intervals on which the function $f(x) = 2x^2 - x^4$ (Figure 1.51) is one-to-one.

SOLUTION The function is not one-to-one on the entire real line because it fails the horizontal line test. However, on the intervals $(-\infty, -1]$, $[-1, 0]$, $[0, 1]$, and $[1, \infty)$, f is one-to-one. The function is also one-to-one on any subinterval of these four intervals.

Related Exercises 11–14 ◀

Existence of Inverse Functions Figure 1.52a illustrates the actions of a one-to-one function f and its inverse f^{-1}. We see that f maps a value of x to a unique value of y. In turn, f^{-1} maps that value of y back to the original value of x. This procedure cannot be carried out if f is *not* one-to-one (Figure 1.52b).

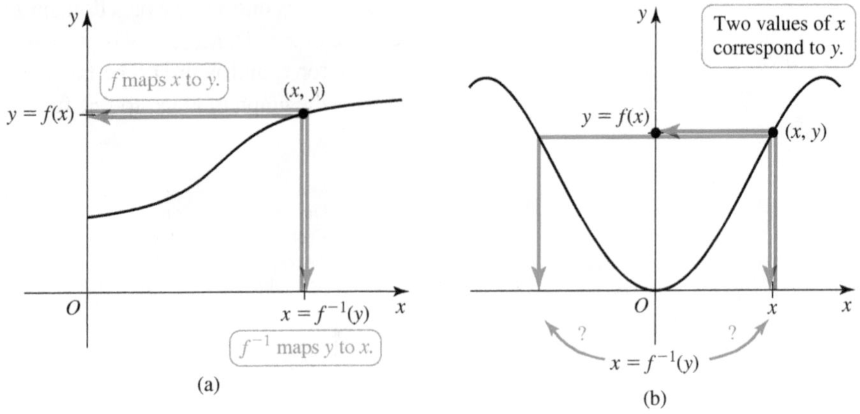

Figure 1.52

➤ The statement that a one-to-one function has an inverse is plausible based on its graph. However, the proof of this theorem is fairly technical and is omitted.

THEOREM 1.1 Existence of Inverse Functions
Let f be a one-to-one function on a domain D with a range R. Then f has a unique inverse f^{-1} with domain R and range D such that

$$f^{-1}(f(x)) = x \quad \text{and} \quad f(f^{-1}(y)) = y,$$

where x is in D and y is in R.

QUICK CHECK 4 The function that gives degrees Fahrenheit in terms of degrees Celsius is $F = 9C/5 + 32$. Why does this function have an inverse? ◄

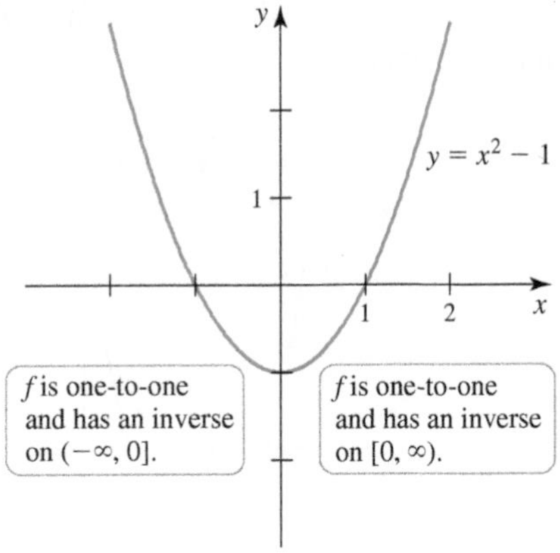

Figure 1.53

EXAMPLE 2 Does an inverse exist? Determine the largest intervals on which $f(x) = x^2 - 1$ has an inverse function.

SOLUTION On the interval $(-\infty, \infty)$ the function does not pass the horizontal line test and is not one-to-one (Figure 1.53). However, if the domain of f is restricted to the interval $(-\infty, 0]$ or $[0, \infty)$, then f is one-to-one and an inverse exists.

Related Exercises 15–20 ◄

Finding Inverse Functions The crux of finding an inverse for a function f is solving the equation $y = f(x)$ for x in terms of y. If it is possible to do so, then we have found a relationship of the form $x = f^{-1}(y)$. Interchanging x and y in $x = f^{-1}(y)$ so that x is the independent variable (which is the customary role for x), the inverse has the form $y = f^{-1}(x)$. Notice that if f is not one-to-one, this process leads to more than one inverse function.

PROCEDURE Finding an Inverse Function
Suppose f is one-to-one on an interval I. To find f^{-1}:

1. Solve $y = f(x)$ for x. If necessary, choose the function that corresponds to I.
2. Interchange x and y and write $y = f^{-1}(x)$.

➤ Once you find a formula for f^{-1}, you can check your work by verifying that $f^{-1}(f(x)) = x$ and $f(f^{-1}(x)) = x$.

EXAMPLE 3 **Finding inverse functions** Find the inverse(s) of the following functions. Restrict the domain of f if necessary.

a. $f(x) = 2x + 6$

b. $f(x) = x^2 - 1$

SOLUTION

➤ A constant function (whose graph is a horizontal line) fails the horizontal line test and does not have an inverse.

a. Linear functions (except constant linear functions) are one-to-one on the entire real line. Therefore, an inverse function for f exists for all values of x.

Step 1: Solve $y = f(x)$ for x: We see that $y = 2x + 6$ implies that $2x = y - 6$, or $x = \frac{1}{2}y - 3$.

Step 2: Interchange x and y and write $y = f^{-1}(x)$:

$$y = f^{-1}(x) = \frac{1}{2}x - 3.$$

It is instructive to verify that the inverse relations $f(f^{-1}(x)) = x$ and $f^{-1}(f(x)) = x$ are satisfied:

$$f(f^{-1}(x)) = f\left(\frac{1}{2}x - 3\right) = \underbrace{2\left(\frac{1}{2}x - 3\right) + 6}_{f(x) = 2x + 6} = x - 6 + 6 = x,$$

$$f^{-1}(f(x)) = f^{-1}(2x + 6) = \underbrace{\frac{1}{2}(2x + 6) - 3}_{f^{-1}(x) = \frac{1}{2}x - 3} = x + 3 - 3 = x.$$

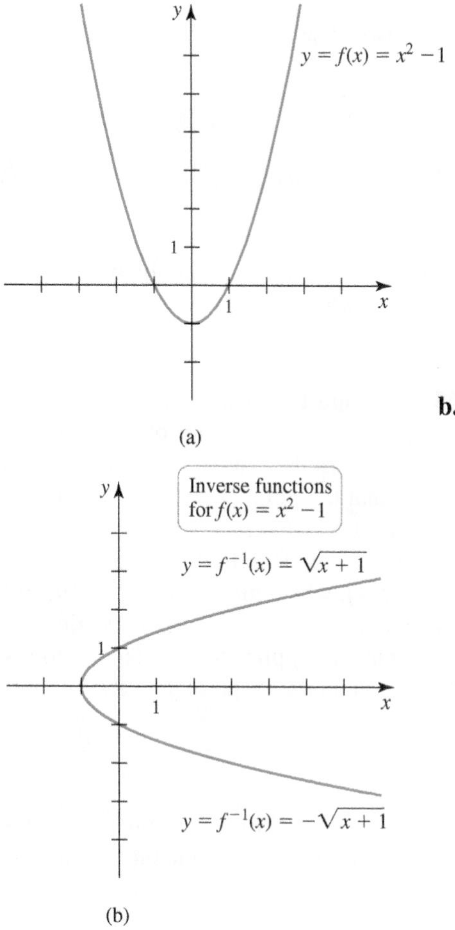

Figure 1.54

b. As shown in Example 2, the function $f(x) = x^2 - 1$ is not one-to-one on the entire real line; however, it is one-to-one on $(-\infty, 0]$ and on $[0, \infty)$ (Figure 1.54a). If we restrict our attention to either of these intervals, then an inverse function can be found.

Step 1: Solve $y = f(x)$ for x:

$$y = x^2 - 1$$
$$x^2 = y + 1$$
$$x = \begin{cases} \sqrt{y+1} \\ -\sqrt{y+1}. \end{cases}$$

Each branch of the square root corresponds to an inverse function.

Step 2: Interchange x and y and write $y = f^{-1}(x)$:

$$y = f^{-1}(x) = \sqrt{x+1} \quad \text{or} \quad y = f^{-1}(x) = -\sqrt{x+1}.$$

The interpretation of this result is important. Taking the positive branch of the square root, the inverse function $y = f^{-1}(x) = \sqrt{x+1}$ gives positive values of y; it corresponds to the branch of $f(x) = x^2 - 1$ on the interval $[0, \infty)$ (Figure 1.54b). The negative branch of the square root, $y = f^{-1}(x) = -\sqrt{x+1}$, is another inverse function that gives negative values of y; it corresponds to the branch of $f(x) = x^2 - 1$ on the interval $(-\infty, 0]$. *Related Exercises 21–30* ◄

QUICK CHECK 5 On what interval(s) does the function $f(x) = x^3$ have an inverse? ◄

Graphing Inverse Functions

The graphs of a function and its inverse have a special relationship, which is illustrated in the following example.

EXAMPLE 4 **Graphing inverse functions** Plot f and f^{-1} on the same coordinate axes.

a. $f(x) = 2x + 6$

b. $f(x) = \sqrt{x - 1}$

SOLUTION

a. The inverse of $f(x) = 2x + 6$, found in Example 3, is

$$y = f^{-1}(x) = \frac{1}{2}x - 3.$$

The graphs of f and f^{-1} are shown in Figure 1.55. Notice that both f and f^{-1} are increasing linear functions that intersect at $(-6, -6)$.

The function $f(x) = 2x + 6$ and its inverse $f^{-1}(x) = \frac{x}{2} - 3$ are symmetric about the line $y = x$.

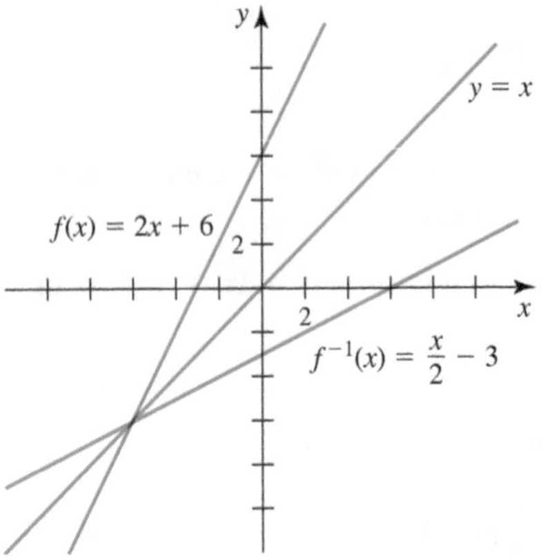

Figure 1.55

b. The domain of $f(x) = \sqrt{x - 1}$ is $[1, \infty)$ and its range is $[0, \infty)$. On this domain, f is one-to-one and has an inverse. It can be found in two steps:

Step 1: Solve $y = \sqrt{x - 1}$ for x:

$$y^2 = x - 1 \quad \text{or} \quad x = y^2 + 1.$$

Step 2: Interchange x and y and write $y = f^{-1}(x)$:

$$y = f^{-1}(x) = x^2 + 1.$$

The graphs of f and f^{-1} are shown in Figure 1.56. Notice that the domain of f^{-1}(which is $x \geq 0$) corresponds to the range of f(which is $y \geq 0$).

Related Exercises 31–40

The function $f(x) = \sqrt{x - 1}$ $(x \geq 1)$ and its inverse $f^{-1}(x) = x^2 + 1$ $(x \geq 0)$ are symmetric about $y = x$.

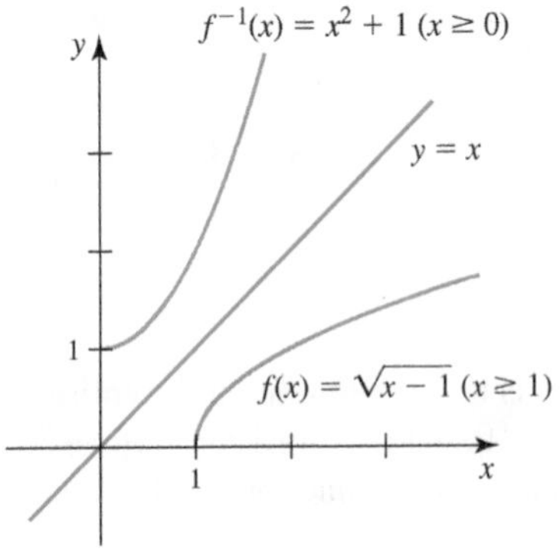

Figure 1.56

Looking closely at the graphs in Figure 1.55 and Figure 1.56, you see a symmetry that always occurs when a function and its inverse are plotted on the same set of axes. In each figure, one curve is the reflection of the other curve across the line $y = x$. These curves have *symmetry about the line* $y = x$, which means that the point (a, b) is on one curve whenever the point (b, a) is on the other curve (Figure 1.57).

The explanation for the symmetry comes directly from the definition of the inverse. Suppose that the point (a, b) is on the graph of $y = f(x)$, which means that $b = f(a)$. By the definition of the inverse function, we know that $a = f^{-1}(b)$, which means that the point (b, a) is on the graph of $y = f^{-1}(x)$. This argument applies to all relevant points (a, b), so whenever (a, b) is on the graph of f, (b, a) is on the graph of f^{-1}. As a consequence, the graphs are symmetric about the line $y = x$.

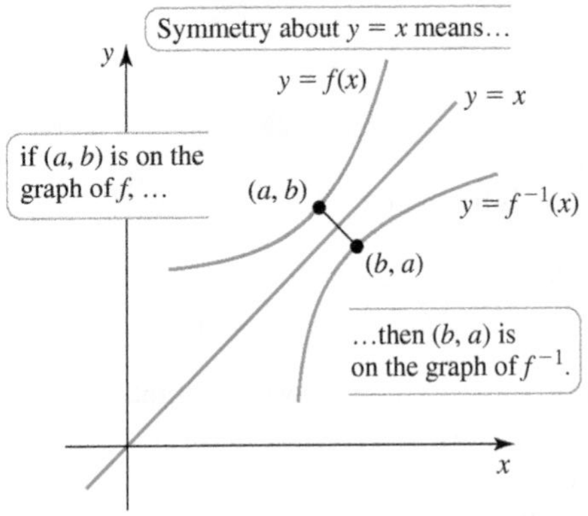

Figure 1.57

Logarithmic Functions

Everything we learned about inverse functions is now applied to the exponential function $f(x) = b^x$. For any $b > 0$, with $b \neq 1$, this function is one-to-one on the interval $(-\infty, \infty)$. Therefore, it has an inverse.

> **DEFINITION** **Logarithmic Function Base b**
>
> For any base $b > 0$, with $b \neq 1$, the **logarithmic function base b**, denoted $y = \log_b x$, is the inverse of the exponential function $y = b^x$. The inverse of the natural exponential function with base $b = e$ is the **natural logarithm function**, denoted $y = \ln x$.

The inverse relationship between logarithmic and exponential functions may be stated concisely in several ways. First, we have

$$y = \log_b x \quad \text{if and only if} \quad b^y = x.$$

➤ Logarithms were invented around 1600 for calculating purposes by the Scotsman John Napier and the Englishman Henry Briggs. Unfortunately, the word *logarithm*, derived from the Greek for reasoning (*logos*) with numbers (*arithmos*), doesn't help with the meaning of the word. **When you see *logarithm*, you should think *exponent*.**

Combining these two conditions results in two important relations.

Inverse Relations for Exponential and Logarithmic Functions

For any base $b > 0$, with $b \neq 1$, the following inverse relations hold.

I1. $b^{\log_b x} = x$, for $x > 0$

I2. $\log_b b^x = x$, for real values of x

➤ **Logarithm Rules**

For any base $b > 0$ $(b \neq 1)$, positive real numbers x and y, and real numbers z, the following relations hold:

L1. $\log_b xy = \log_b x + \log_b y$

L2. $\log_b \frac{x}{y} = \log_b x - \log_b y$

$\left(\text{includes } \log_b \frac{1}{y} = -\log_b y\right)$

L3. $\log_b x^z = z \log_b x$

L4. $\log_b b = 1$

Specifically, these properties hold with $b = e$, in which case $\log_b x = \log_e x = \ln x$.

Properties of Logarithmic Functions The graph of the logarithmic function is generated using the symmetry of the graphs of a function and its inverse. Figure 1.58 shows how the graph of $y = b^x$, for $b > 1$, is reflected across the line $y = x$ to obtain the graph of $y = \log_b x$.

The graphs of $y = \log_b x$ are shown (Figure 1.59) for several bases $b > 1$. Logarithms with bases $0 < b < 1$, although well defined, are generally not used (and they can be expressed in terms of bases with $b > 1$).

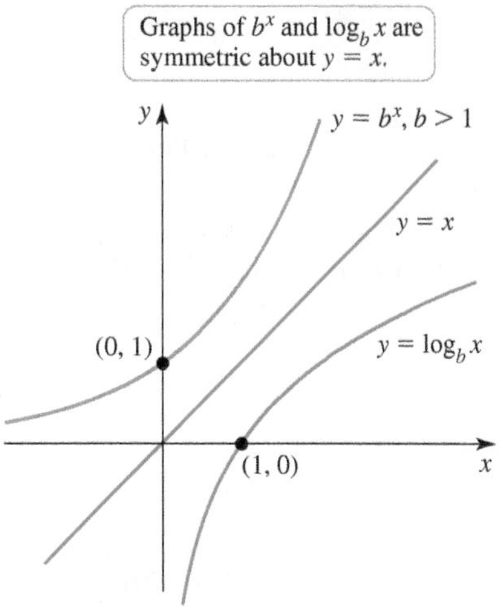

Figure 1.58

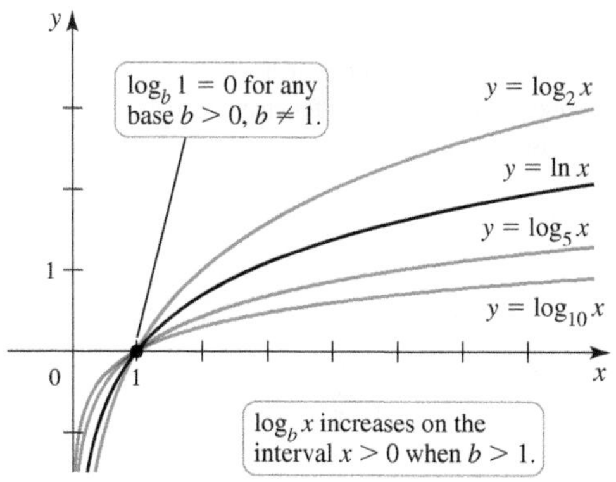

Figure 1.59

Logarithmic functions with base $b > 0$ satisfy properties that parallel the properties of the exponential functions on p. 27.

1. Because the range of b^x is $(0, \infty)$ the domain of $\log_b x$ is $(0, \infty)$.
2. The domain of b^x is $(-\infty, \infty)$, which implies that the range of $\log_b x$ is $(-\infty, \infty)$.
3. Because $b^0 = 1$, it follows that $\log_b 1 = 0$.
4. If $b > 1$, then $\log_b x$ is an increasing function of x. For example, if $b = e$, then $\ln x > \ln y$ whenever $x > y$ (Figure 1.59).

QUICK CHECK 6 What is the domain of $f(x) = \log_b (x^2)$? What is the range of $f(x) = \log_b (x^2)$? ◄

EXAMPLE 5 **Using inverse relations** One thousand grams of a particular radioactive substance decays according to the function $m(t) = 1000e^{-t/850}$, where $t \geq 0$ measures time in years. When does the mass of the substance reach the safe level deemed to be 1 g?

SOLUTION Setting $m(t) = 1$, we solve $1000e^{-t/850} = 1$ by dividing both sides by 1000 and taking the natural logarithm of both sides:

➤ Provided the arguments are positive, we can take the $\log_b$ of both sides of an equation and produce an equivalent equation.

$$\ln (e^{-t/850}) = \ln \left(\frac{1}{1000}\right).$$

This equation is simplified by calculating $\ln(1/1000) \approx -6.908$ and observing that $\ln(e^{-t/850}) = -\frac{t}{850}$ (inverse property I2). Therefore,

$$-\frac{t}{850} \approx -6.908.$$

Solving for t, we find that $t \approx (-850)(-6.908) \approx 5872$ years.

Related Exercises 41–58 ◀

Change of Base

When working with logarithms and exponentials, it doesn't matter *in principle* which base is used. However, there are practical reasons for switching between bases. For example, most calculators have built-in logarithmic functions in just one or two bases. If you need to use a different base, then the change-of-base rules are essential.

Consider changing bases with exponential functions. Specifically, suppose you want to express b^x (base b) in the form e^y (base e), where y must be determined. Taking the natural logarithm of both sides of $e^y = b^x$, we have

$$\underbrace{\ln e^y}_{y} = \underbrace{\ln b^x}_{x \ln b} \quad \text{which implies that } y = x \ln b.$$

It follows that $b^x = e^y = e^{x \ln b}$. For example, $4^x = e^{x \ln 4}$. This result is derived rigorously in Section 6.8.

➤ A similar argument is used to derive more general formulas for changing from base b to any other positive base c.

The formula for changing from $\log_b x$ to $\ln x$ is derived in a similar way. We let $y = \log_b x$, which implies that $x = b^y$. Taking the natural logarithm of both sides of $x = b^y$ gives $\ln x = \ln b^y = y \ln b$. Solving for y gives

$$y = \log_b x = \frac{\ln x}{\ln b}.$$

Change-of-Base Rules

Let b be a positive real number with $b \neq 1$. Then

$$b^x = e^{x \ln b}, \text{ for all } x \quad \text{and} \quad \log_b x = \frac{\ln x}{\ln b}, \text{ for } x > 0.$$

More generally, if c is a positive real number with $c \neq 1$, then

$$b^x = c^{x \log_c b}, \text{ for all } x \quad \text{and} \quad \log_b x = \frac{\log_c x}{\log_c b}, \text{ for } x > 0.$$

EXAMPLE 6 Changing bases

a. Express 2^{x+4} as an exponential function with base e.

b. Express $\log_2 x$ using base e and base 32.

SOLUTION

a. Using the change-of-base rule for exponential functions, we have

$$2^{x+4} = e^{(x+4)\ln 2}.$$

b. Using the change-of-base rule for logarithmic functions, we have

$$\log_2 x = \frac{\ln x}{\ln 2}.$$

To change from base 2 to base 32, we use the general change-of-base formula:

$$\log_2 x = \frac{\log_{32} x}{\log_{32} 2} = \frac{\log_{32} x}{1/5} = 5 \log_{32} x.$$

The second step follows from the fact that $2 = 32^{1/5}$, so $\log_{32} 2 = \frac{1}{5}$.

Related Exercises 59–68 ◀

SECTION 1.3 EXERCISES

Review Questions

1. For $b > 0$, what are the domain and range of $f(x) = b^x$?

2. Give an example of a function that is one-to-one on the entire real number line.

3. Explain why a function that is not one-to-one on an interval I cannot have an inverse function on I.

4. Explain with pictures why (a, b) is on the graph of f whenever (b, a) is on the graph of f^{-1}.

5. Sketch a function that is one-to-one and positive for $x \geq 0$. Make a rough sketch of its inverse.

6. Express the inverse of $f(x) = 3x - 4$ in the form $y = f^{-1}(x)$.

7. Explain the meaning of $\log_b x$.

8. How is the property $b^{x+y} = b^x b^y$ related to the property $\log_b (xy) = \log_b x + \log_b y$?

9. For $b > 0$ with $b \neq 1$, what are the domain and range of $f(x) = \log_b x$ and why?

10. Express 2^5 using base e.

Basic Skills

11–14. One-to-one functions

11. Find three intervals on which f is one-to-one, making each interval as large as possible.

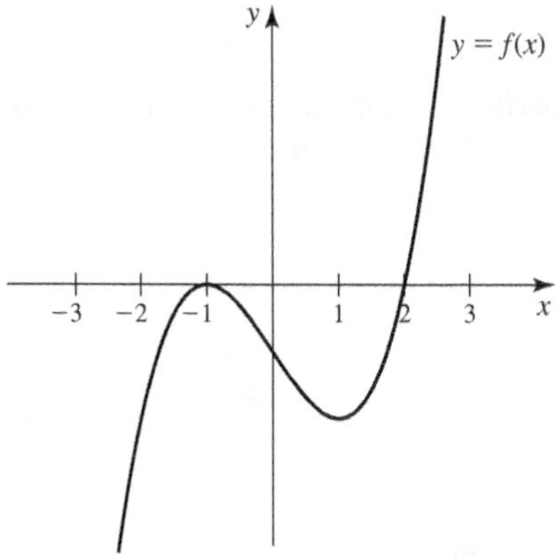

12. Find four intervals on which f is one-to-one, making each interval as large as possible.

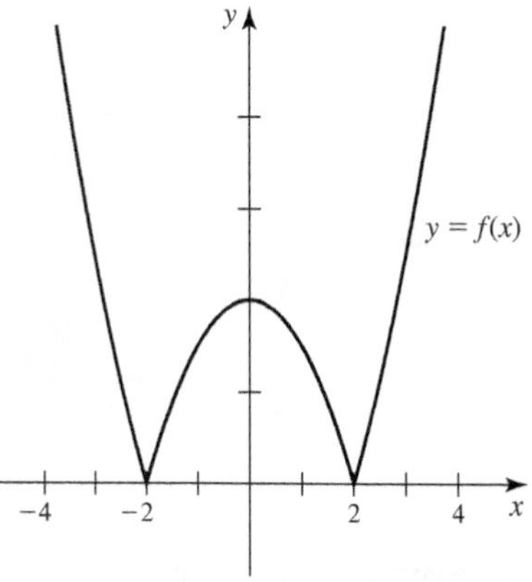

13. Sketch a graph of a function that is one-to-one on the interval $(-\infty, 0]$ but is not one-to-one on $(-\infty, \infty)$.

14. Sketch a graph of a function that is one-to-one on the intervals $(-\infty, -2]$, and $[-2, \infty)$ but is not one-to-one on $(-\infty, \infty)$.

15–20. Where do inverses exist? *Use analytical and/or graphical methods to determine the largest possible sets of points on which the following functions have an inverse.*

15. $f(x) = 3x + 4$

16. $f(x) = |2x + 1|$

17. $f(x) = 1/(x - 5)$

18. $f(x) = -(6 - x)^2$

19. $f(x) = 1/x^2$

20. $f(x) = x^2 - 2x + 8$ (*Hint:* Complete the square.)

21–28. Finding inverse functions

a. Find the inverse of each function (on the given interval, if specified) and write it in the form $y = f^{-1}(x)$.

b. Verify the relationships $f(f^{-1}(x)) = x$ and $f^{-1}(f(x)) = x$.

21. $f(x) = 2x$

22. $f(x) = \frac{1}{4}x + 1$

23. $f(x) = 6 - 4x$

24. $f(x) = 3x^3$

25. $f(x) = 3x + 5$

26. $f(x) = x^2 + 4$, for $x \geq 0$

27. $f(x) = \sqrt{x + 2}$, for $x \geq -2$

28. $f(x) = 2/(x^2 + 1)$, for $x \geq 0$

29. Splitting up curves The unit circle $x^2 + y^2 = 1$ consists of four one-to-one functions, $f_1(x)$, $f_2(x)$, $f_3(x)$, and $f_4(x)$ (see figure).

a. Find the domain and a formula for each function.
b. Find the inverse of each function and write it as $y = f^{-1}(x)$.

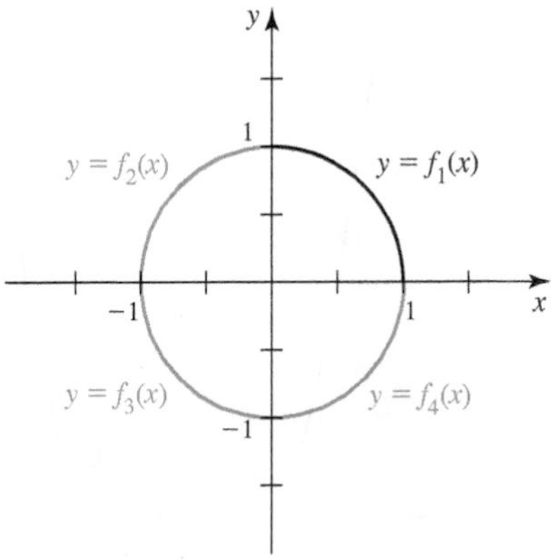

30. Splitting up curves The equation $y^4 = 4x^2$ is associated with four one-to-one functions $f_1(x)$, $f_2(x)$, $f_3(x)$, and $f_4(x)$ (see figure).

a. Find the domain and a formula for each function.
b. Find the inverse of each function and write it as $y = f^{-1}(x)$.

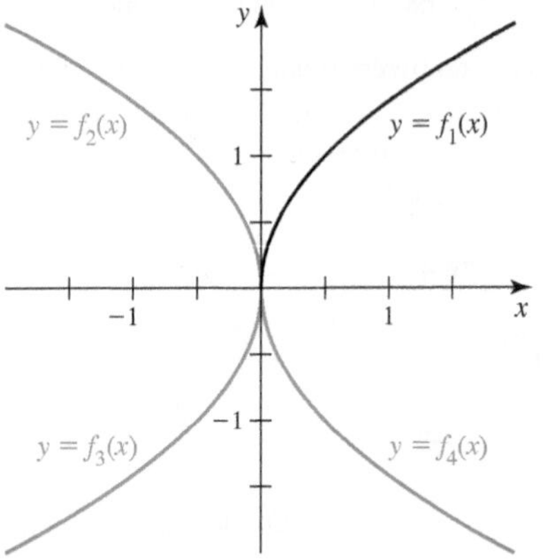

31–38. Graphing inverse functions *Find the inverse function (on the given interval, if specified) and graph both f and f^{-1} on the same set of axes. Check your work by looking for the required symmetry in the graphs.*

31. $f(x) = 8 - 4x$

32. $f(x) = 4x - 12$

33. $f(x) = \sqrt{x}$, for $x \geq 0$

34. $f(x) = \sqrt{3 - x}$, for $x \leq 3$

35. $f(x) = x^4 + 4$, for $x \geq 0$

T **36.** $f(x) = 6/(x^2 - 9)$, for $x > 3$

37. $f(x) = x^2 - 2x + 6$, for $x \geq 1$ (*Hint:* Complete the square first.)

38. $f(x) = -x^2 - 4x - 3$, for $x \leq -2$ (*Hint:* Complete the square first.)

39–40. Graphs of inverses *Sketch the graph of the inverse function.*

39.

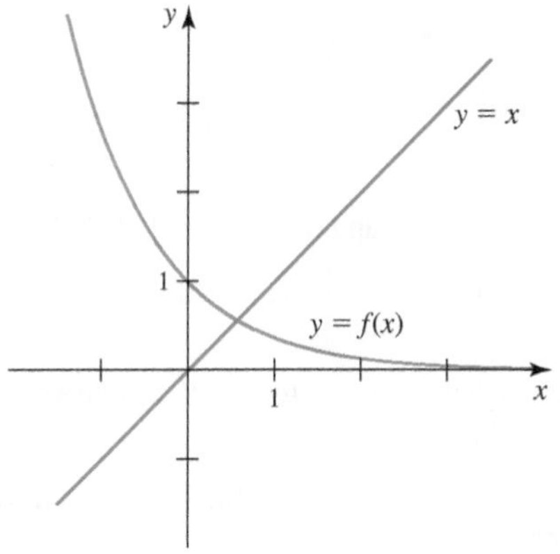

40.

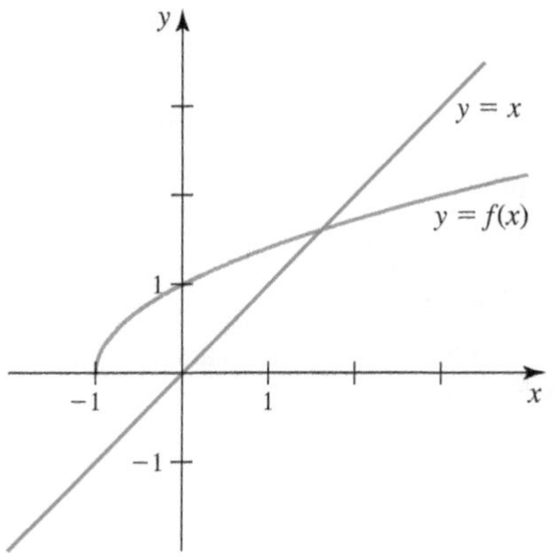

41–46. Solving logarithmic equations *Solve the following equations.*

41. $\log_{10} x = 3$

42. $\log_5 x = -1$

43. $\log_8 x = \frac{1}{3}$

44. $\log_b 125 = 3$

45. $\ln x = -1$

46. $\ln y = 3$

47–52. Properties of logarithms *Assume $\log_b x = 0.36$, $\log_b y = 0.56$, and $\log_b z = 0.83$. Evaluate the following expressions.*

47. $\log_b \frac{x}{y}$

48. $\log_b x^2$

49. $\log_b xz$

50. $\log_b \frac{\sqrt{xy}}{z}$

51. $\log_b \frac{\sqrt{x}}{\sqrt[3]{z}}$

52. $\log_b \frac{b^2 x^{5/2}}{\sqrt{y}}$

53–56. Solving equations *Solve the following equations.*

53. $7^x = 21$

54. $2^x = 55$

55. $3^{3x-4} = 15$

56. $5^{3x} = 29$

T 57. Using inverse relations One hundred grams of a particular radioactive substance decays according to the function $m(t) = 100\,e^{-t/650}$, where $t > 0$ measures time in years. When does the mass reach 50 grams?

T 58. Using inverse relations The population P of a small town grows according to the function $P(t) = 100\,e^{t/50}$, where t measures the number of years after 2010. How long does it take the population to double?

T 59–62. Calculator base change *Write the following logarithms in terms of the natural logarithm. Then use a calculator to find the value of the logarithm, rounding your result to four decimal places.*

59. $\log_2 15$ **60.** $\log_3 30$ **61.** $\log_4 40$ **62.** $\log_6 60$

63–68. Changing bases *Convert the following expressions to the indicated base.*

63. 2^x using base e

64. $3^{\sin x}$ using base e

65. $\ln |x|$ using base 5

66. $\log_2 (x^2 + 1)$ using base e

67. $a^{1/\ln a}$ using base e, for $a > 0$ and $a \neq 1$

68. $a^{1/\log_{10} a}$ using base 10, for $a > 0$ and $a \neq 1$

Further Explorations

69. Explain why or why not Determine whether the following statements are true and give an explanation or counterexample.

a. If $y = 3^x$, then $x = \sqrt[3]{y}$.
b. $\dfrac{\log_b x}{\log_b y} = \log_b x - \log_b y$
c. $\log_5 4^6 = 4 \log_5 6$
d. $2 = 10^{\log_{10} 2}$
e. $2 = \ln 2^e$
f. If $f(x) = x^2 + 1$, then $f^{-1}(x) = 1/(x^2 + 1)$.
g. If $f(x) = 1/x$, then $f^{-1}(x) = 1/x$.

70. Graphs of exponential functions The following figure shows the graphs of $y = 2^x$, $y = 3^x$, $y = 2^{-x}$, and $y = 3^{-x}$. Match each curve with the correct function.

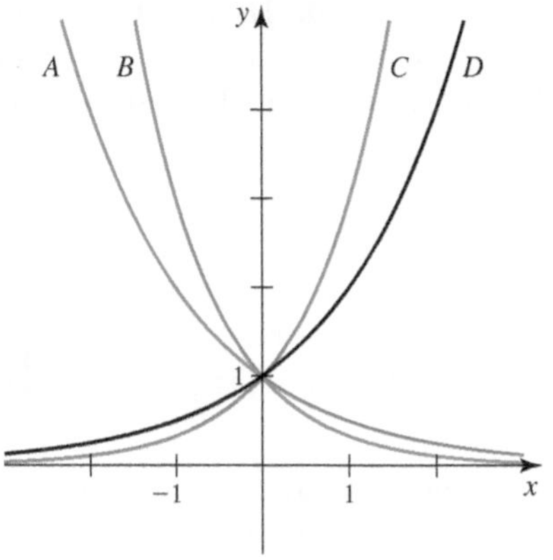

71. Graphs of logarithmic functions The following figure shows the graphs of $y = \log_2 x$, $y = \log_4 x$, and $y = \log_{10} x$. Match each curve with the correct function.

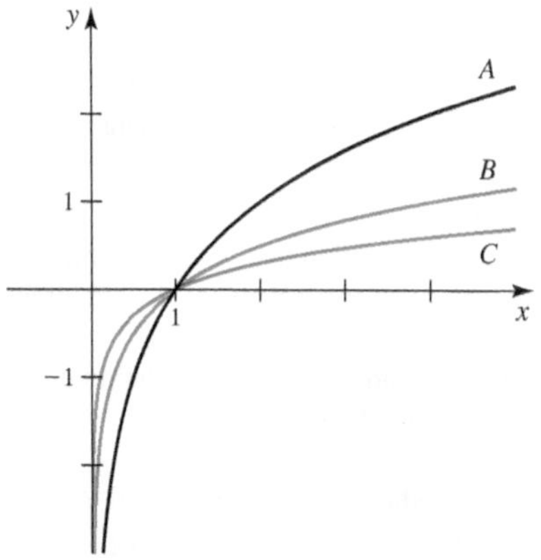

72. Graphs of modified exponential functions Without using a graphing utility, sketch the graph of $y = 2^x$. Then on the same set of axes, sketch the graphs of $y = 2^{-x}$, $y = 2^{x-1}$, $y = 2^x + 1$, and $y = 2^{2x}$.

73. Graphs of modified logarithmic functions Without using a graphing utility, sketch the graph of $y = \log_2 x$. Then on the same set of axes, sketch the graphs of $y = \log_2 (x - 1)$, $y = \log_2 x^2$, $y = (\log_2 x)^2$, and $y = \log_2 x + 1$.

T 74. Large intersection point Use any means to approximate the intersection point(s) of the graphs of $f(x) = e^x$ and $g(x) = x^{123}$. (*Hint:* Consider using logarithms.)

75–78. Finding all inverses *Find all the inverses associated with the following functions and state their domains.*

75. $f(x) = (x + 1)^3$ **76.** $f(x) = (x - 4)^2$

77. $f(x) = 2/(x^2 + 2)$ **78.** $f(x) = 2x/(x + 2)$

Applications

79. Population model A culture of bacteria has a population of 150 cells when it is first observed. The population doubles every 12 hr, which means its population is governed by the function $p(t) = 150 \cdot 2^{t/12}$, where t is the number of hours after the first observation.

a. Verify that $p(0) = 150$, as claimed.
b. Show that the population doubles every 12 hr, as claimed.
c. What is the population 4 days after the first observation?
d. How long does it take the population to triple in size?
e. How long does it take the population to reach 10,000?

T 80. Charging a capacitor A capacitor is a device that stores electrical charge. The charge on a capacitor accumulates according to the function $Q(t) = a(1 - e^{-t/c})$, where t is measured in seconds, and a and $c > 0$ are physical constants. The *steady-state charge* is the value that $Q(t)$ approaches as t becomes large.

a. Graph the charge function for $t \geq 0$ using $a = 1$ and $c = 10$. Find a graphing window that shows the full range of the function.
b. Vary the value of a while holding c fixed. Describe the effect on the curve. How does the steady-state charge vary with a?

c. Vary the value of c while holding a fixed. Describe the effect on the curve. How does the steady-state charge vary with c?
d. Find a formula that gives the steady-state charge in terms of a and c.

T **81. Height and time** The height in feet of a baseball hit straight up from the ground with an initial velocity of 64 ft/s is given by $h = f(t) = 64t - 16t^2$, where t is measured in seconds after the hit.

a. Is this function one-to-one on the interval $0 \le t \le 4$?
b. Find the inverse function that gives the time t at which the ball is at height h as the ball travels *upward*. Express your answer in the form $t = f^{-1}(h)$.
c. Find the inverse function that gives the time t at which the ball is at height h as the ball travels *downward*. Express your answer in the form $t = f^{-1}(h)$.
d. At what time is the ball at a height of 30 ft on the way up?
e. At what time is the ball at a height of 10 ft on the way down?

T **82. Velocity of a skydiver** The velocity of a skydiver (in m/s) t seconds after jumping from a plane is $v(t) = 600(1 - e^{-kt/60})/k$, where $k > 0$ is a constant. The *terminal velocity* of the skydiver is the value that $v(t)$ approaches as t becomes large. Graph v with $k = 11$ and estimate the terminal velocity.

Additional Exercises

83. Reciprocal bases Assume that $b > 0$ and $b \ne 1$. Show that $\log_{1/b} x = -\log_b x$.

84. Proof of rule L1 Use the following steps to prove that $\log_b xy = \log_b x + \log_b y$.

a. Let $x = b^p$ and $y = b^q$. Solve these expressions for p and q, respectively.
b. Use property E1 for exponents to express xy in terms of b, p, and q.
c. Compute $\log_b xy$ and simplify.

85. Proof of rule L2 Modify the proof outlined in Exercise 84 and use property E2 for exponents to prove that $\log_b (x/y) = \log_b x - \log_b y$.

86. Proof of rule L3 Use the following steps to prove that $\log_b x^z = z \log_b x$.

a. Let $x = b^p$. Solve this expression for p.
b. Use property E3 for exponents to express x^z in terms of b and p.
c. Compute $\log_b x^z$ and simplify.

T **87. Inverses of a quartic** Consider the quartic polynomial $y = f(x) = x^4 - x^2$.

a. Graph f and estimate the largest intervals on which it is one-to-one. The goal is to find the inverse function on each of these intervals.
b. Make the substitution $u = x^2$ to solve the equation $y = f(x)$ for x in terms of y. Be sure you have included all possible solutions.
c. Write each inverse function in the form $y = f^{-1}(x)$ for each of the intervals found in part (a).

88. Inverse of composite functions

a. Let $g(x) = 2x + 3$ and $h(x) = x^3$. Consider the composite function $f(x) = g(h(x))$. Find f^{-1} directly and then express it in terms of g^{-1} and h^{-1}.
b. Let $g(x) = x^2 + 1$ and $h(x) = \sqrt{x}$. Consider the composite function $f(x) = g(h(x))$. Find f^{-1} directly and then express it in terms of g^{-1} and h^{-1}.
c. Explain why if g and h are one-to-one, the inverse of $f(x) = g(h(x))$ exists.

T **89–90. Inverses of (some) cubics** *Finding the inverse of a cubic polynomial is equivalent to solving a cubic equation. A special case that is simpler than the general case is the cubic $y = f(x) = x^3 + ax$. Find the inverse of the following cubics using the substitution (known as Vieta's substitution) $x = z - a/(3z)$. Be sure to determine where the function is one-to-one.*

89. $f(x) = x^3 + 2x$

90. $f(x) = x^3 + 4x - 1$

91. Nice property Prove that $(\log_b c)(\log_c b) = 1$, for $b > 0$, $c > 0$, $b \ne 1$, and $c \ne 1$.

QUICK CHECK ANSWERS

1. b^x is always positive (and never zero) for all x and for positive bases b. **2.** Because $(1/3)^x = 1/3^x$ and 3^x increases as x increases, it follows that $(1/3)^x$ decreases as x increases. **3.** $f^{-1}(x) = 3x; f^{-1}(x) = x + 7$. **4.** For every Fahrenheit temperature, there is exactly one Celsius temperature, and vice versa. The given relation is also a linear function. It is one-to-one, so it has an inverse function. **5.** The function $f(x) = x^3$ is one-to-one on $(-\infty, \infty)$, so it has an inverse for all values of x. **6.** The domain of $\log_b x^2$ is all real numbers except zero (because x^2 is positive for $x \ne 0$). The range of $\log_b x^2$ is all real numbers. ◀

1.4 Trigonometric Functions and Their Inverses

This section is a review of what you need to know in order to study the calculus of trigonometric functions. Once the trigonometric functions are on stage, it makes sense to present the inverse trigonometric functions and their basic properties.

Degrees	Radians
0	0
30	$\pi/6$
45	$\pi/4$
60	$\pi/3$
90	$\pi/2$
120	$2\pi/3$
135	$3\pi/4$
150	$5\pi/6$
180	π

Radian Measure

Calculus typically requires that angles be measured in **radians** (rad). Working with a circle of radius r, the radian measure of an angle θ is the length of the arc associated with θ, denoted s, divided by the radius of the circle r (Figure 1.60a). Working on a unit circle $(r = 1)$, the radian measure of an angle is simply the length of the arc associated with θ (Figure 1.60b). For example, the length of a full unit circle is 2π; therefore, an angle with a radian measure of π corresponds to a half circle $(\theta = 180°)$ and an angle with a radian measure of $\pi/2$ corresponds to a quarter circle $(\theta = 90°)$.

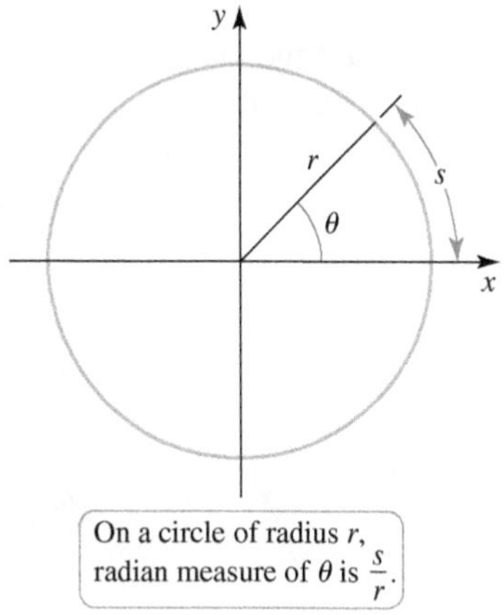

(a)

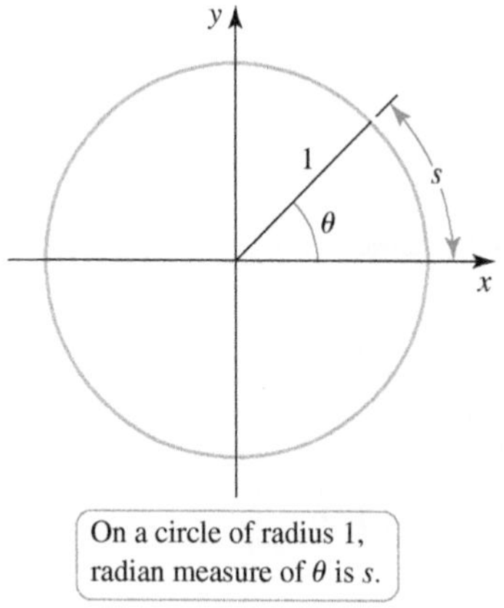

(b)

Figure 1.60

QUICK CHECK 1 What is the radian measure of a 270° angle? What is the degree measure of a $5\pi/4$-rad angle? ◄

Trigonometric Functions

For acute angles, the trigonometric functions are defined as ratios of the lengths of the sides of a right triangle (Figure 1.61). To extend these definitions to include all angles, we work in an xy-coordinate system with a circle of radius r centered at the origin. Suppose that $P(x, y)$ is a point on the circle. An angle θ is in **standard position** if its initial side is on the positive x-axis and its terminal side is the line segment OP between the origin and P. An angle is positive if it is obtained by a counterclockwise rotation from the positive x-axis (Figure 1.62). When the right-triangle definitions of Figure 1.61 are used with the right triangle in Figure 1.62, the trigonometric functions may be expressed in terms of x, y, and the radius of the circle, $r = \sqrt{x^2 + y^2}$.

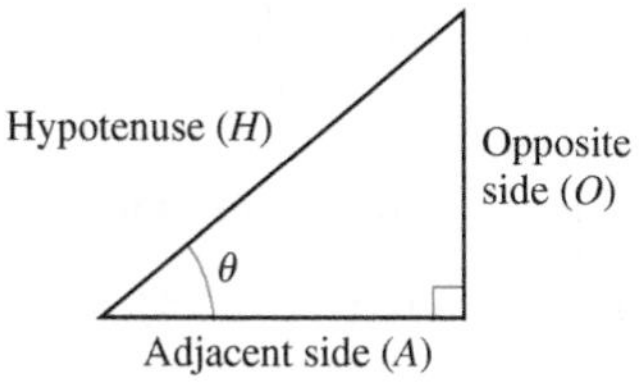

$$\sin\theta = \frac{O}{H} \quad \cos\theta = \frac{A}{H}$$

$$\tan\theta = \frac{O}{A} \quad \cot\theta = \frac{A}{O}$$

$$\sec\theta = \frac{H}{A} \quad \csc\theta = \frac{H}{O}$$

Figure 1.61

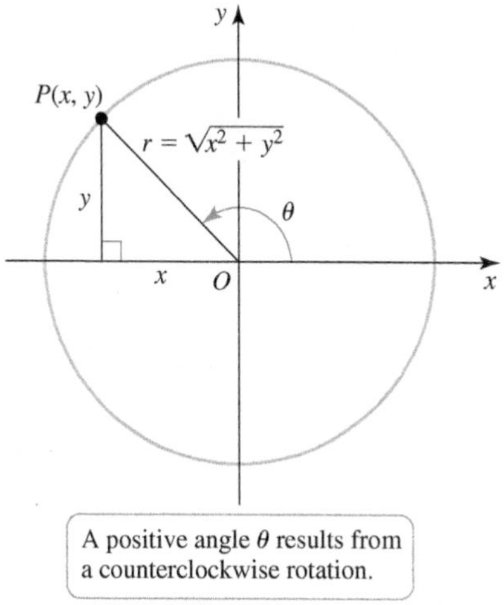

Figure 1.62

➤ When working on a unit circle ($r = 1$), these definitions become

$\sin\theta = y \quad \cos\theta = x$

$\tan\theta = \frac{y}{x} \quad \cot\theta = \frac{x}{y}$

$\sec\theta = \frac{1}{x} \quad \csc\theta = \frac{1}{y}$

DEFINITION Trigonometric Functions

Let $P(x, y)$ be a point on a circle of radius r associated with the angle θ. Then

$$\sin\theta = \frac{y}{r}, \quad \cos\theta = \frac{x}{r}, \quad \tan\theta = \frac{y}{x},$$

$$\cot\theta = \frac{x}{y}, \quad \sec\theta = \frac{r}{x}, \quad \csc\theta = \frac{r}{y}.$$

To find the trigonometric functions of the standard angles (multiples of 30° and 45°), it is helpful to know the radian measure of those angles and the coordinates of the associated points on the unit circle (Figure 1.63).

➤ **Standard triangles**

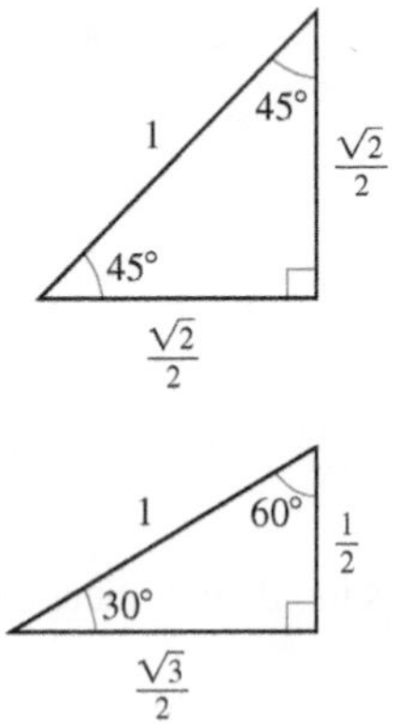

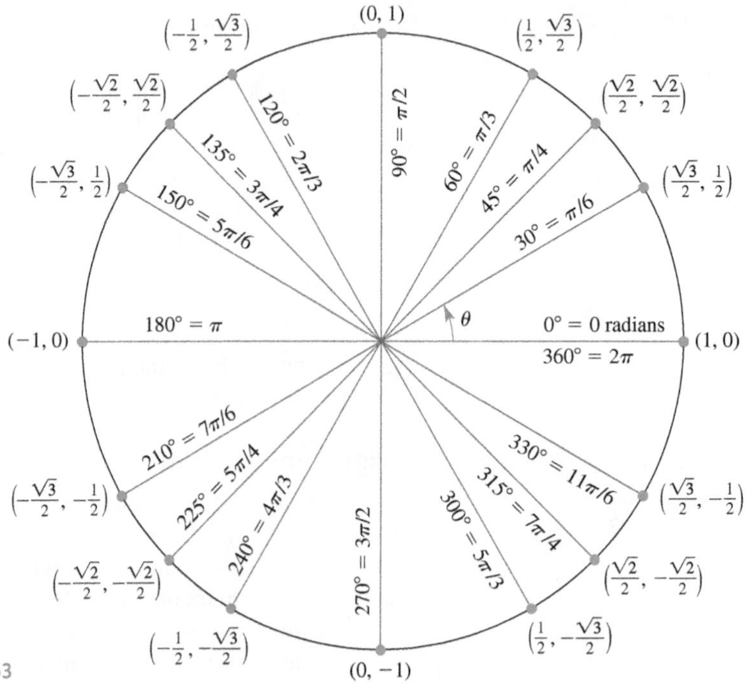

Figure 1.63

Combining the definitions of the trigonometric functions with the coordinates shown in Figure 1.63, we may evaluate these functions at any standard angle. For example,

$$\sin\frac{2\pi}{3} = \frac{\sqrt{3}}{2}, \quad \cos\frac{5\pi}{6} = -\frac{\sqrt{3}}{2}, \quad \tan\frac{7\pi}{6} = \frac{1}{\sqrt{3}}, \quad \tan\frac{3\pi}{2} \text{ is undefined,}$$

$$\cot\frac{5\pi}{3} = -\frac{1}{\sqrt{3}}, \quad \sec\frac{7\pi}{4} = \sqrt{2}, \quad \csc\frac{3\pi}{2} = -1, \quad \sec\frac{\pi}{2} \text{ is undefined.}$$

EXAMPLE 1 Evaluating trigonometric functions Evaluate the following expressions.

a. $\sin(8\pi/3)$ **b.** $\csc(-11\pi/3)$

SOLUTION

a. The angle $8\pi/3 = 2\pi + 2\pi/3$ corresponds to a *counterclockwise* revolution of one full circle (2π radians) plus an additional $2\pi/3$ radians (Figure 1.64). Therefore, this angle has the same terminal side as the angle $2\pi/3$, and the corresponding point on the unit circle is $(-1/2, \sqrt{3}/2)$. It follows that $\sin(8\pi/3) = y = \sqrt{3}/2$.

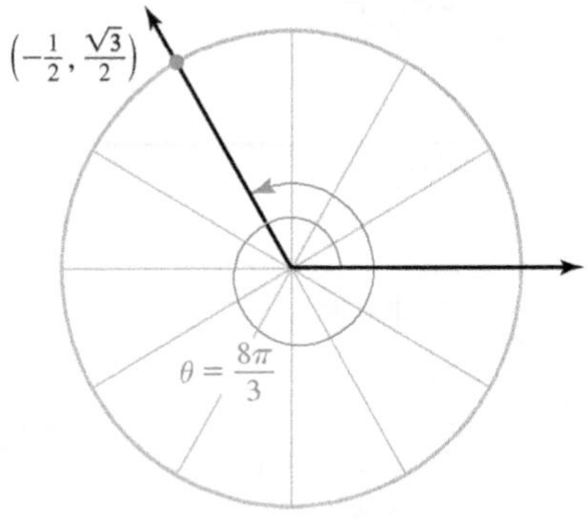

Figure 1.64

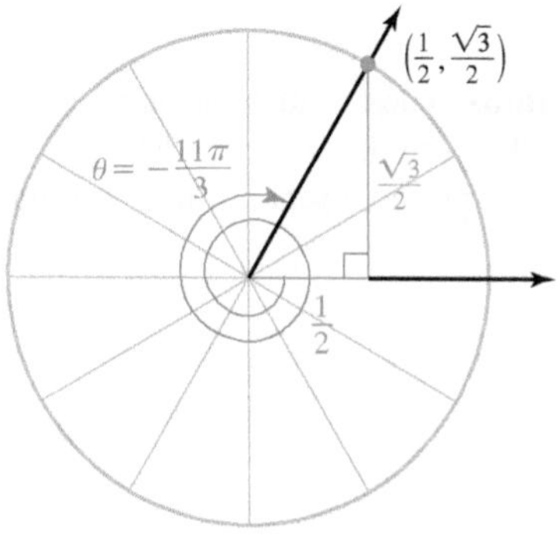

Figure 1.65

b. The angle $\theta = -11\pi/3 = -2\pi - 5\pi/3$ corresponds to a *clockwise* revolution of one full circle (2π radians) plus an additional $5\pi/3$ radians (Figure 1.65). Therefore, this angle has the same terminal side as the angle $\pi/3$. The coordinates of the corresponding point on the unit circle are $(1/2, \sqrt{3}/2)$, so $\csc(-11\pi/3) = 1/y = 2/\sqrt{3}$.

Related Exercises 15–28 ◀

QUICK CHECK 2 Evaluate $\cos(11\pi/6)$ and $\sin(5\pi/4)$. ◀

Trigonometric Identities

Trigonometric functions have a variety of properties, called identities, that are true for all angles in their domain. Here is a list of some commonly used identities.

➤ In addition, to these identities, you should be familiar with the Law of Sines and the Law of Cosines. See Exercises 108 and 109.

Trigonometric Identities

Reciprocal Identities

$$\tan\theta = \frac{\sin\theta}{\cos\theta} \qquad \cot\theta = \frac{1}{\tan\theta} = \frac{\cos\theta}{\sin\theta}$$

$$\csc\theta = \frac{1}{\sin\theta} \qquad \sec\theta = \frac{1}{\cos\theta}$$

Pythagorean Identities

$$\sin^2\theta + \cos^2\theta = 1 \qquad 1 + \cot^2\theta = \csc^2\theta \qquad \tan^2\theta + 1 = \sec^2\theta$$

Double- and Half-Angle Formulas

$$\sin 2\theta = 2\sin\theta\cos\theta \qquad \cos 2\theta = \cos^2\theta - \sin^2\theta$$

$$\cos^2\theta = \frac{1 + \cos 2\theta}{2} \qquad \sin^2\theta = \frac{1 - \cos 2\theta}{2}$$

QUICK CHECK 3 Use $\sin^2\theta + \cos^2\theta = 1$ to prove that $1 + \cot^2\theta = \csc^2\theta$. ◀

EXAMPLE 2 Solving trigonometric equations Solve the following equations.

a. $\sqrt{2}\sin x + 1 = 0$ **b.** $\cos 2x = \sin 2x$, where $0 \le x < 2\pi$

SOLUTION

➤ By rationalizing the denominator, observe that $\frac{1}{\sqrt{2}} = \frac{1}{\sqrt{2}} \cdot \frac{\sqrt{2}}{\sqrt{2}} = \frac{\sqrt{2}}{2}$.

a. First, we solve for $\sin x$ to obtain $\sin x = -1/\sqrt{2} = -\sqrt{2}/2$. From the unit circle (Figure 1.63), we find that $\sin x = -\sqrt{2}/2$ if $x = 5\pi/4$ or $x = 7\pi/4$. Adding integer multiples of 2π produces additional solutions. Therefore, the set of all solutions is

$$x = \frac{5\pi}{4} + 2n\pi \quad \text{and} \quad x = \frac{7\pi}{4} + 2n\pi, \qquad \text{for } n = 0, \pm 1, \pm 2, \pm 3, \ldots.$$

b. Dividing both sides of the equation by $\cos 2x$ (assuming $\cos 2x \ne 0$), we obtain $\tan 2x = 1$. Letting $\theta = 2x$ gives us the equivalent equation $\tan\theta = 1$. This equation is satisfied by

$$\theta = \frac{\pi}{4}, \frac{5\pi}{4}, \frac{9\pi}{4}, \frac{13\pi}{4}, \frac{17\pi}{4}, \ldots.$$

➤ Notice that the assumption $\cos 2x \ne 0$ is valid for these values of x.

Dividing by two and using the restriction $0 \le x < 2\pi$ gives the solutions

$$x = \frac{\theta}{2} = \frac{\pi}{8}, \frac{5\pi}{8}, \frac{9\pi}{8}, \text{ and } \frac{13\pi}{8}.$$

Related Exercises 29–46 ◀

Graphs of the Trigonometric Functions

Trigonometric functions are examples of **periodic functions**: Their values repeat over every interval of some fixed length. A function f is said to be periodic if $f(x + P) = f(x)$, for all x in the domain, where the **period** P is the smallest positive real number that has this property.

> **Period of Trigonometric Functions**
>
> The functions $\sin \theta$, $\cos \theta$, $\sec \theta$, and $\csc \theta$ have a period of 2π:
>
> $$\sin(\theta + 2\pi) = \sin \theta \qquad \cos(\theta + 2\pi) = \cos \theta$$
> $$\sec(\theta + 2\pi) = \sec \theta \qquad \csc(\theta + 2\pi) = \csc \theta,$$
>
> for all θ in the domain.
>
> The functions $\tan \theta$ and $\cot \theta$ have a period of π:
>
> $$\tan(\theta + \pi) = \tan \theta \qquad \cot(\theta + \pi) = \cot \theta,$$
>
> for all θ in the domain.

The graph of $y = \sin \theta$ is shown in Figure 1.66a. Because $\csc \theta = 1/\sin \theta$, these two functions have the same sign, but $y = \csc \theta$ is undefined with vertical asymptotes at $\theta = 0, \pm\pi, \pm 2\pi, \ldots$. The functions $\cos \theta$ and $\sec \theta$ have a similar relationship (Figure 1.66b).

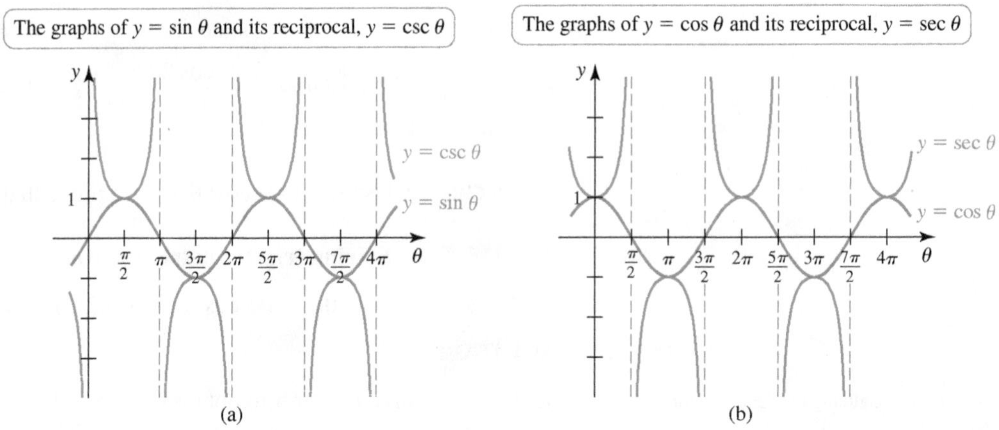

Figure 1.66

The graphs of $\tan \theta$ and $\cot \theta$ are shown in Figure 1.67. Each function has points, separated by π units, at which it is undefined.

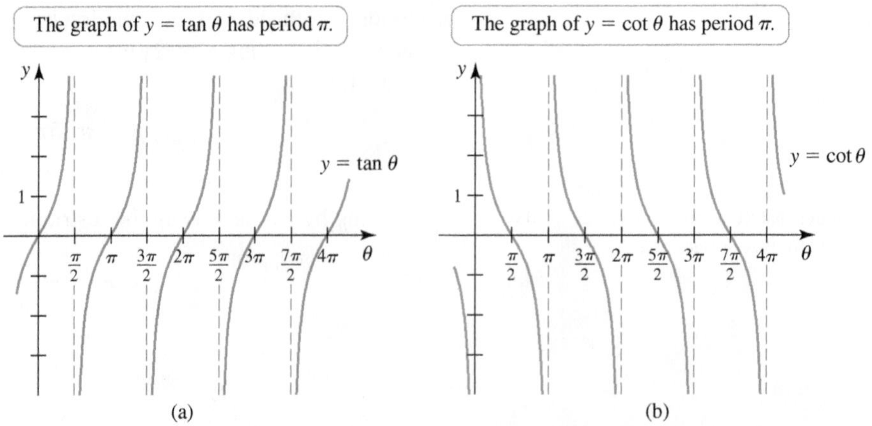

Figure 1.67

Transforming Graphs

Many physical phenomena, such as the motion of waves or the rising and setting of the sun, can be modeled using trigonometric functions; the sine and cosine functions are especially useful. Using the transformation methods introduced in Section 1.2, we can show that the functions

$$y = A \sin (B(\theta - C)) + D \quad \text{and} \quad y = A \cos (B(\theta - C)) + D,$$

when compared to the graphs of $y = \sin \theta$ and $y = \cos \theta$, have a vertical stretch (or **amplitude**) of $|A|$, a period of $2\pi/|B|$, a horizontal shift (or **phase shift**) of C, and a **vertical shift** of D (Figure 1.68).

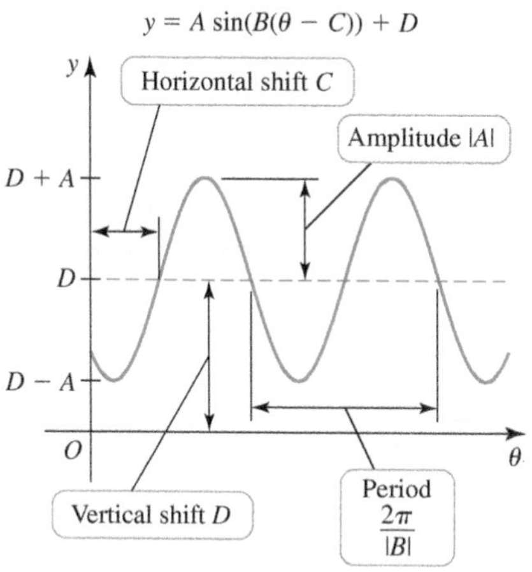

Figure 1.68

For example, at latitude 40° north (Beijing, Madrid, Philadelphia), there are 12 hours of daylight on the equinoxes (approximately March 21 and September 21), with a maximum of 14.8 hours of daylight on the summer solstice (approximately June 21) and a minimum of 9.2 hours of daylight on the winter solstice (approximately December 21). Using this information, it can be shown that the function

$$D(t) = 2.8 \sin \left(\frac{2\pi}{365}(t - 81) \right) + 12$$

models the number of daylight hours t days after January 1 (Figure 1.69; Exercise 100). The graph of this function is obtained from the graph of $y = \sin t$ by (1) a horizontal scaling by a factor of $2\pi/365$, (2) a horizontal shift of 81, (3) a vertical scaling by a factor of 2.8, and (4) a vertical shift of 12.

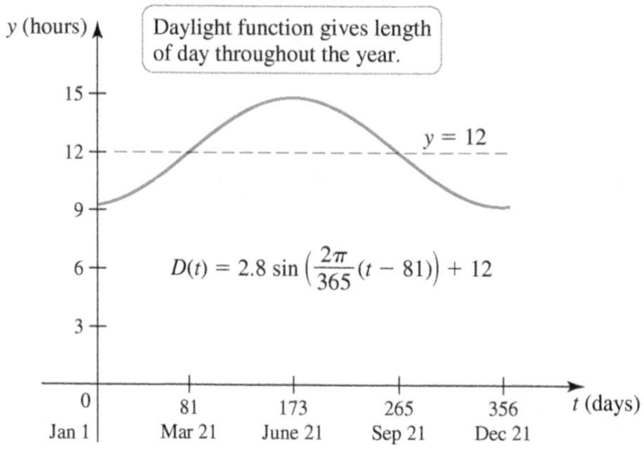

Figure 1.69

Inverse Trigonometric Functions

The notion of inverse functions led from exponential functions to logarithmic functions (Section 1.3). We now carry out a similar procedure—this time with trigonometric functions.

Inverse Sine and Cosine Our goal is to develop the inverses of the sine and cosine in detail. The inverses of the other four trigonometric functions then follow in an analogous way. So far, we have asked this question: Given an angle x, what is $\sin x$ or $\cos x$? Now we ask the opposite question: Given a number y, what is the angle x such that $\sin x = y$? Or what is the angle x such that $\cos x = y$? These are inverse questions.

There are a few things to notice right away. First, these questions don't make sense if $|y| > 1$, because $-1 \le \sin x \le 1$ and $-1 \le \cos x \le 1$. Next, let's select an acceptable value of y, say, $y = \frac{1}{2}$, and find the angle x that satisfies $\sin x = y = \frac{1}{2}$. It is apparent that infinitely many angles satisfy $\sin x = \frac{1}{2}$; all angles of the form $\pi/6 \pm 2n\pi$ and $5\pi/6 \pm 2n\pi$, where n is an integer, answer the inverse question (Figure 1.70). A similar situation occurs with the cosine function.

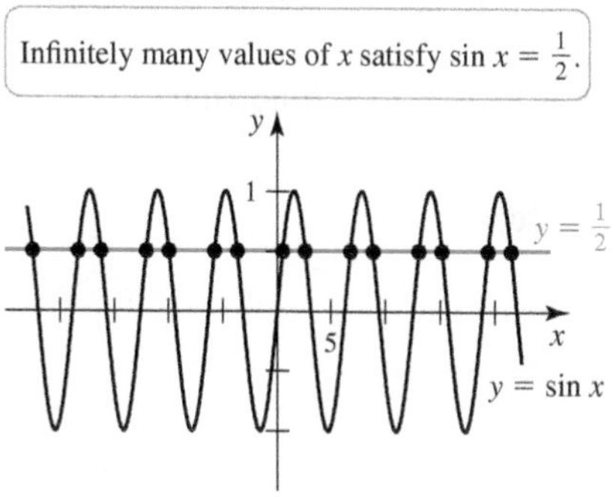

Figure 1.70

These inverse questions do not have unique answers because $\sin x$ and $\cos x$ are not one-to-one on their domains. To define their inverses, these functions are restricted to intervals on which they are one-to-one. For the sine function, the standard choice is $[-\pi/2, \pi/2]$; for cosine, it is $[0, \pi]$ (Figure 1.71). Now when we ask for the angle x on the interval $[-\pi/2, \pi/2]$ such that $\sin x = \frac{1}{2}$, there is one answer: $x = \pi/6$. When we ask for the angle x on the interval $[0, \pi]$ such that $\cos x = -\frac{1}{2}$, there is one answer: $x = 2\pi/3$.

➤ The notation for the inverse trigonometric functions invites confusion: $\sin^{-1} x$ and $\cos^{-1} x$ do not mean the reciprocals of $\sin x$ and $\cos x$. The expression $\sin^{-1} x$ should be read "*angle whose sine is x*," and $\cos^{-1} x$ should be read "*angle whose cosine is x*." The values of $\sin^{-1} x$ and $\cos^{-1} x$ are angles.

We define the **inverse sine**, or **arcsine**, denoted $y = \sin^{-1} x$ or $y = \arcsin x$, such that y is the angle whose sine is x, with the provision that y lies in the interval $[-\pi/2, \pi/2]$. Similarly, we define the **inverse cosine**, or **arccosine**, denoted $y = \cos^{-1} x$ or $y = \arccos x$, such that y is the angle whose cosine is x, with the provision that y lies in the interval $[0, \pi]$.

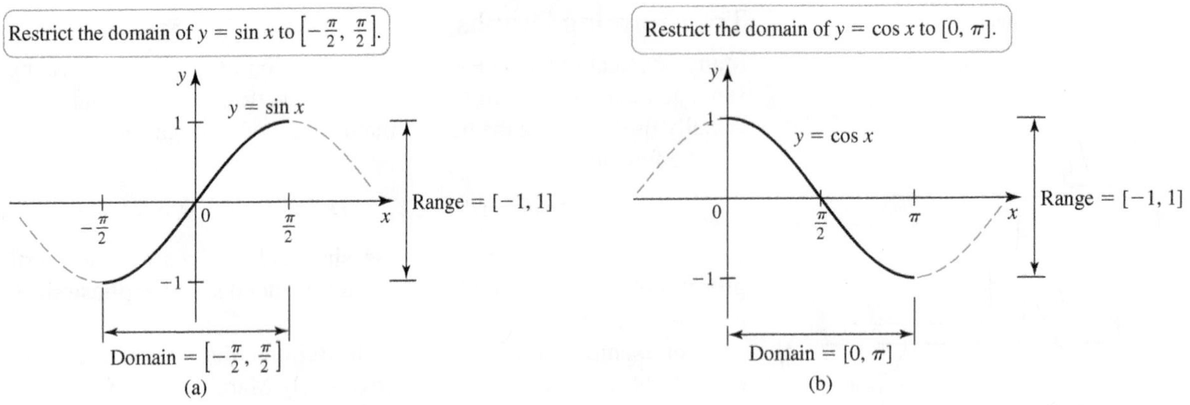

Figure 1.71

DEFINITION Inverse Sine and Cosine

$y = \sin^{-1} x$ is the value of y such that $x = \sin y$, where $-\pi/2 \le y \le \pi/2$.
$y = \cos^{-1} x$ is the value of y such that $x = \cos y$, where $0 \le y \le \pi$.
The domain of both $\sin^{-1} x$ and $\cos^{-1} x$ is $\{x: -1 \le x \le 1\}$.

Recall that any invertible function and its inverse satisfy the properties

$$f(f^{-1}(y)) = y \quad \text{and} \quad f^{-1}(f(x)) = x.$$

These properties apply to the inverse sine and cosine, as long as we observe the restrictions on the domains. Here is what we can say:

- $\sin(\sin^{-1} x) = x$ and $\cos(\cos^{-1} x) = x$, for $-1 \le x \le 1$.
- $\sin^{-1}(\sin y) = y$, for $-\pi/2 \le y \le \pi/2$.
- $\cos^{-1}(\cos y) = y$, for $0 \le y \le \pi$.

QUICK CHECK 4 Explain why $\sin^{-1}(\sin 0) = 0$, but $\sin^{-1}(\sin 2\pi) \ne 2\pi$. ◀

EXAMPLE 3 Working with inverse sine and cosine Evaluate the following expressions.

a. $\sin^{-1}(\sqrt{3}/2)$ **b.** $\cos^{-1}(-\sqrt{3}/2)$ **c.** $\cos^{-1}(\cos 3\pi)$ **d.** $\sin^{-1}\left(\sin \frac{3\pi}{4}\right)$

SOLUTION

a. $\sin^{-1}(\sqrt{3}/2) = \pi/3$ because $\sin(\pi/3) = \sqrt{3}/2$ and $\pi/3$ is in the interval $[-\pi/2, \pi/2]$.

b. $\cos^{-1}(-\sqrt{3}/2) = 5\pi/6$ because $\cos(5\pi/6) = -\sqrt{3}/2$ and $5\pi/6$ is in the interval $[0, \pi]$.

c. It's tempting to conclude that $\cos^{-1}(\cos 3\pi) = 3\pi$, but the result of an inverse cosine operation must lie in the interval $[0, \pi]$. Because $\cos(3\pi) = -1$ and $\cos^{-1}(-1) = \pi$, we have

$$\cos^{-1}(\underbrace{\cos 3\pi}_{-1}) = \cos^{-1}(-1) = \pi.$$

d. $$\sin^{-1}\underbrace{\left(\sin \frac{3\pi}{4}\right)}_{\sqrt{2}/2} = \sin^{-1}\frac{\sqrt{2}}{2} = \frac{\pi}{4}$$

Related Exercises 47–56 ◀

Graphs and Properties Recall from Section 1.3 that the graph of f^{-1} is obtained by reflecting the graph of f about the line $y = x$. This operation produces the graphs of the inverse sine (Figure 1.72) and inverse cosine (Figure 1.73). The graphs make it easy to compare the domain and range of each function and its inverse.

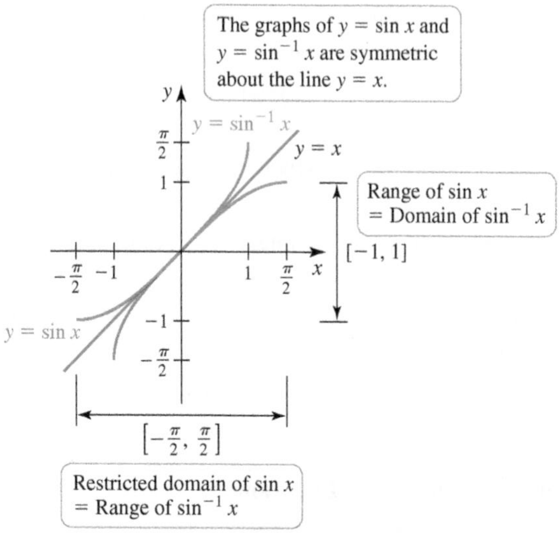

Figure 1.72

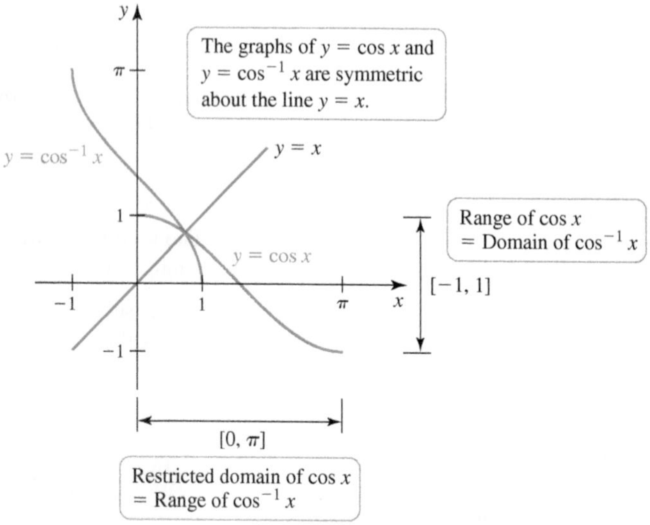

Figure 1.73

EXAMPLE 4 Right-triangle relationships

a. Suppose $\theta = \sin^{-1}(2/5)$. Find $\cos\theta$ and $\tan\theta$.

b. Find an alternative form for $\cot(\cos^{-1}(x/4))$ in terms of x.

SOLUTION

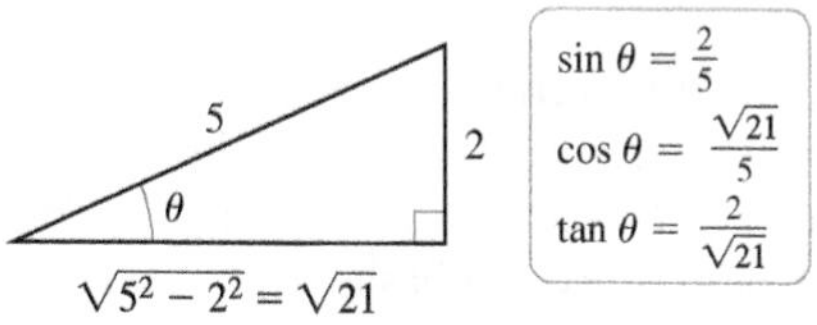

Figure 1.74

a. Relationships between the trigonometric functions and their inverses can often be simplified using a right-triangle sketch. Notice that $0 < \theta < \pi/2$. The right triangle in Figure 1.74 satisfies the relationship $\sin\theta = \frac{2}{5}$, or, equivalently, $\theta = \sin^{-1}\frac{2}{5}$. We label the angle θ and the lengths of two sides; then the length of the third side is $\sqrt{21}$ (by the Pythagorean theorem). Now it is easy to read directly from the triangle:

$$\cos\theta = \frac{\sqrt{21}}{5} \quad \text{and} \quad \tan\theta = \frac{2}{\sqrt{21}}.$$

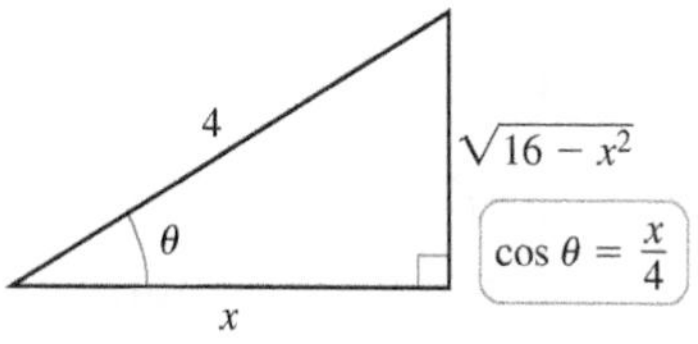

Figure 1.75

b. We draw a right triangle with an angle θ satisfying $\cos\theta = x/4$, or, equivalently, $\theta = \cos^{-1}(x/4)$, where $x > 0$ (Figure 1.75). The length of the third side of the triangle is $\sqrt{16 - x^2}$. It now follows that

$$\cot\underbrace{\left(\cos^{-1}\frac{x}{4}\right)}_{\theta} = \frac{x}{\sqrt{16 - x^2}};$$

this relationship is valid for $|x| < 4$. *Related Exercises 57–62*

EXAMPLE 5 A useful identity Use right triangles to explain why $\cos^{-1}x + \sin^{-1}x = \pi/2$.

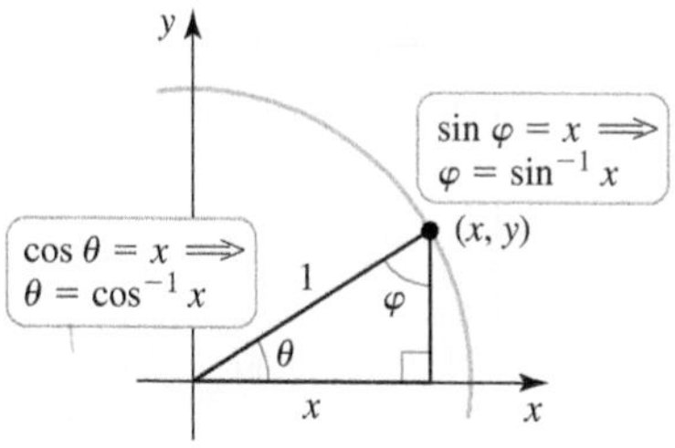

Figure 1.76

SOLUTION We draw a right triangle in a unit circle and label the acute angles θ and φ (Figure 1.76). These angles satisfy $\cos\theta = x$, or $\theta = \cos^{-1}x$, and $\sin\varphi = x$, or $\varphi = \sin^{-1}x$. Because θ and φ are complementary angles, we have

$$\frac{\pi}{2} = \theta + \varphi = \cos^{-1}x + \sin^{-1}x.$$

This result holds for $0 \le x \le 1$. An analogous argument extends the property to $-1 \le x \le 1$. *Related Exercises 63–66* ◀

Other Inverse Trigonometric Functions

The procedures that led to the inverse sine and inverse cosine functions can be used to obtain the other four inverse trigonometric functions. Each of these functions carries a restriction that must be imposed to ensure that an inverse exists.

- The tangent function is one-to-one on $(-\pi/2, \pi/2)$, which becomes the range of $y = \tan^{-1} x$.
- The cotangent function is one-to-one on $(0, \pi)$, which becomes the range of $y = \cot^{-1} x$.
- The secant function is one-to-one on $[0, \pi]$, excluding $x = \pi/2$; this set becomes the range of $y = \sec^{-1} x$.
- The cosecant function is one-to-one on $[-\pi/2, \pi/2]$, excluding $x = 0$; this set becomes the range of $y = \csc^{-1} x$.

The inverse tangent, cotangent, secant, and cosecant are defined as follows.

➤ Tables, books, and computer algebra systems differ on the definition of the inverse secant and cosecant. In some books, $\sec^{-1} x$ is defined to lie in the interval $[-\pi, -\pi/2)$ when $x < 0$.

DEFINITION Other Inverse Trigonometric Functions

$y = \tan^{-1} x$ is the value of y such that $x = \tan y$, where $-\pi/2 < y < \pi/2$.
$y = \cot^{-1} x$ is the value of y such that $x = \cot y$, where $0 < y < \pi$.

The domain of both $\tan^{-1} x$ and $\cot^{-1} x$ is $\{x: -\infty < x < \infty\}$.

$y = \sec^{-1} x$ is the value of y such that $x = \sec y$, where $0 \le y \le \pi$, with $y \ne \pi/2$.
$y = \csc^{-1} x$ is the value of y such that $x = \csc y$, where $-\pi/2 \le y \le \pi/2$, with $y \ne 0$.

The domain of both $\sec^{-1} x$ and $\csc^{-1} x$ is $\{x: |x| \ge 1\}$.

The graphs of these inverse functions are obtained by reflecting the graphs of the original trigonometric functions about the line $y = x$ (Figures 1.77–1.80). The inverse secant and cosecant are somewhat irregular. The domain of the secant function (Figure 1.79) is restricted to the set $[0, \pi]$, excluding $x = \pi/2$, where the secant has a vertical asymptote. This asymptote splits the range of the secant into two disjoint intervals $(-\infty, -1]$ and $[1, \infty)$, which, in turn, splits the domain of the inverse secant into the same two intervals. A similar situation occurs with the cosecant function.

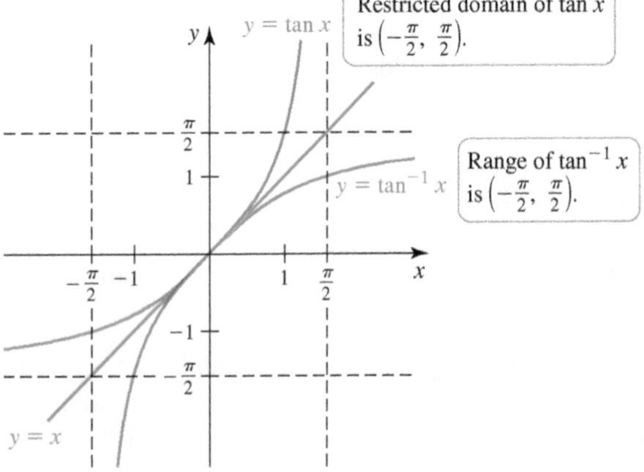

Figure 1.77

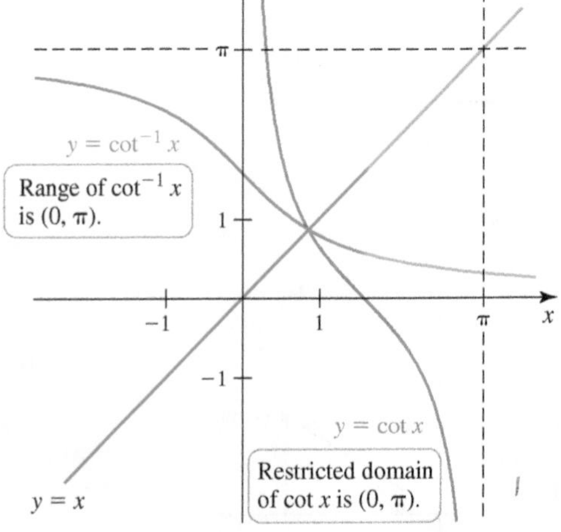

Figure 1.78

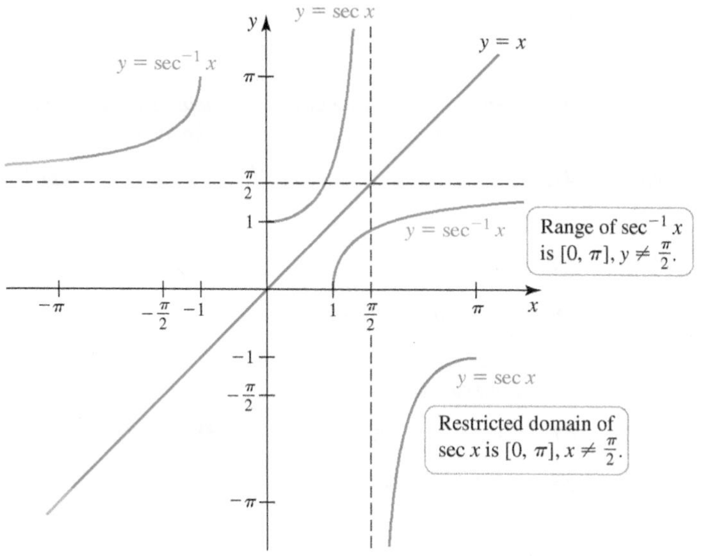

Figure 1.79

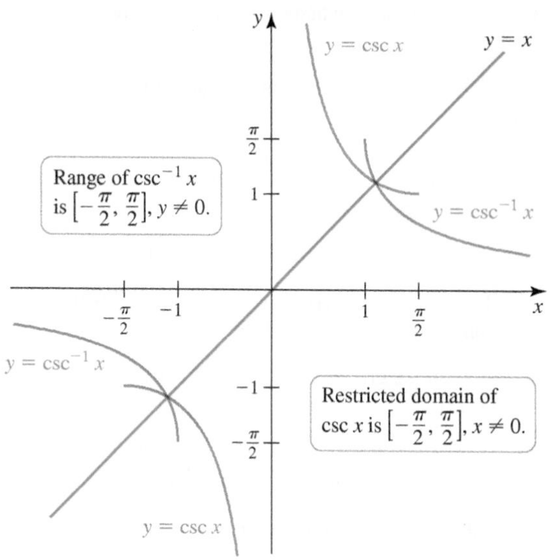

Figure 1.80

EXAMPLE 6 Working with inverse trigonometric functions Evaluate or simplify the following expressions.

a. $\tan^{-1}(-1/\sqrt{3})$ **b.** $\sec^{-1}(-2)$ **c.** $\sin(\tan^{-1} x)$

SOLUTION

a. The result of an inverse tangent operation must lie in the interval $(-\pi/2, \pi/2)$. Therefore,

$$\tan^{-1}\left(-\frac{1}{\sqrt{3}}\right) = -\frac{\pi}{6} \quad \text{because} \quad \tan\left(-\frac{\pi}{6}\right) = -\frac{1}{\sqrt{3}}.$$

b. The result of an inverse secant operation when $x \le -1$ must lie in the interval $(\pi/2, \pi]$. Therefore,

$$\sec^{-1}(-2) = \frac{2\pi}{3} \quad \text{because} \quad \sec\frac{2\pi}{3} = -2.$$

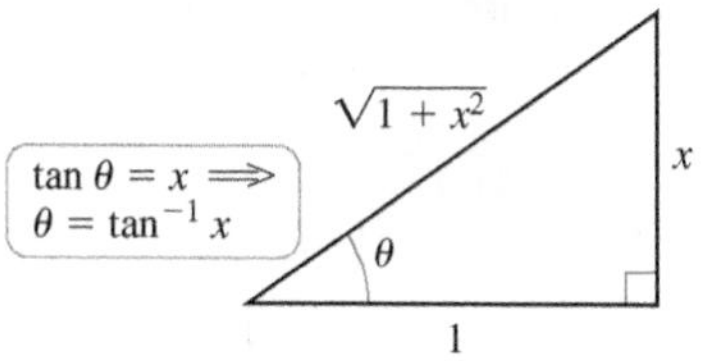

Figure 1.81

c. Figure 1.81 shows a right triangle with the relationship $x = \tan\theta$ or $\theta = \tan^{-1} x$, in the case that $0 \le \theta < \pi/2$. We see that

$$\underbrace{\sin(\tan^{-1} x)}_{\theta} = \frac{x}{\sqrt{1 + x^2}}.$$

The same result follows if $-\pi/2 < \theta < 0$, in which case $x < 0$ and $\sin\theta < 0$.

Related Exercises 67–82 ◀

QUICK CHECK 5 Evaluate $\sec^{-1} 1$ and $\tan^{-1} 1$. ◀

SECTION 1.4 EXERCISES

Review Questions

1. Define the six trigonometric functions in terms of the sides of a right triangle.
2. Explain how a point $P(x, y)$ on a circle of radius r determines an angle θ and the values of the six trigonometric functions at θ.
3. How is the radian measure of an angle determined?
4. Explain what is meant by the period of a trigonometric function. What are the periods of the six trigonometric functions?
5. What are the three Pythagorean identities for the trigonometric functions?

6. How are the sine and cosine functions related to the other four trigonometric functions?

7. Where is the tangent function undefined?

8. What is the domain of the secant function?

9. Explain why the domain of the sine function must be restricted in order to define its inverse function.

10. Why do the values of $\cos^{-1} x$ lie in the interval $[0, \pi]$?

11. Is it true that $\tan(\tan^{-1} x) = x$ for all x? Is it true that $\tan^{-1}(\tan x) = x$ for all x?

12. Sketch the graphs of $y = \cos x$ and $y = \cos^{-1} x$ on the same set of axes.

13. The function $\tan x$ is undefined at $x = \pm\pi/2$. How does this fact appear in the graph of $y = \tan^{-1} x$?

14. State the domain and range of $\sec^{-1} x$.

Basic Skills

15–22. Evaluating trigonometric functions *Evaluate the following expressions using a unit circle. Use a calculator to check your work. All angles are in radians.*

15. $\cos(2\pi/3)$ **16.** $\sin(2\pi/3)$ **17.** $\tan(-3\pi/4)$

18. $\tan(15\pi/4)$ **19.** $\cot(-13\pi/3)$ **20.** $\sec(7\pi/6)$

21. $\cot(-17\pi/3)$ **22.** $\sin(16\pi/3)$

23–28. Evaluating trigonometric functions *Evaluate the following expressions or state that the quantity is undefined. Use a calculator to check your work.*

23. $\cos 0$ **24.** $\sin(-\pi/2)$ **25.** $\cos(-\pi)$

26. $\tan 3\pi$ **27.** $\sec(5\pi/2)$ **28.** $\cot \pi$

29–36. Trigonometric identities

29. Prove that $\sec\theta = \dfrac{1}{\cos\theta}$.

30. Prove that $\tan\theta = \dfrac{\sin\theta}{\cos\theta}$.

31. Prove that $\tan^2\theta + 1 = \sec^2\theta$.

32. Prove that $\dfrac{\sin\theta}{\csc\theta} + \dfrac{\cos\theta}{\sec\theta} = 1$.

33. Prove that $\sec(\pi/2 - \theta) = \csc\theta$.

34. Prove that $\sec(x + \pi) = -\sec x$.

35. Find the exact value of $\cos(\pi/12)$.

36. Find the exact value of $\tan(3\pi/8)$.

37–46. Solving trigonometric equations *Solve the following equations.*

37. $\tan x = 1$ **38.** $2\theta\cos\theta + \theta = 0$

39. $\sin^2\theta = \frac{1}{4}, 0 \le \theta < 2\pi$ **40.** $\cos^2\theta = \frac{1}{2}, 0 \le \theta < 2\pi$

41. $\sqrt{2}\sin x - 1 = 0$ **42.** $\sin 3x = \frac{\sqrt{2}}{2}, 0 \le x < 2\pi$

43. $\cos 3x = \sin 3x, 0 \le x < 2\pi$

44. $\sin^2\theta - 1 = 0$

45. $\sin\theta\cos\theta = 0, 0 \le \theta < 2\pi$

46. $\tan^2 2\theta = 1, 0 \le \theta < \pi$

47–56. Inverse sines and cosines *Without using a calculator, evaluate the following expressions or state that the quantity is undefined.*

47. $\sin^{-1} 1$ **48.** $\cos^{-1}(-1)$ **49.** $\tan^{-1} 1$

50. $\cos^{-1}\left(-\frac{\sqrt{2}}{2}\right)$ **51.** $\sin^{-1}\frac{\sqrt{3}}{2}$ **52.** $\cos^{-1} 2$

53. $\cos^{-1}\left(-\frac{1}{2}\right)$ **54.** $\sin^{-1}(-1)$ **55.** $\cos(\cos^{-1}(-1))$

56. $\cos^{-1}(\cos(7\pi/6))$

57–62. Right-triangle relationships *Draw a right triangle to simplify the given expressions. Assume $x > 0$.*

57. $\cos(\sin^{-1} x)$ **58.** $\cos(\sin^{-1}(x/3))$

59. $\sin(\cos^{-1}(x/2))$

60. $\sin^{-1}(\cos\theta)$, for $0 \le \theta \le \pi/2$

61. $\sin(2\cos^{-1} x)$ (*Hint:* Use $\sin 2\theta = 2\sin\theta\cos\theta$.)

62. $\cos(2\sin^{-1} x)$ (*Hint:* Use $\cos 2\theta = \cos^2\theta - \sin^2\theta$.)

63–64. Identities *Prove the following identities.*

63. $\cos^{-1} x + \cos^{-1}(-x) = \pi$

64. $\sin^{-1} y + \sin^{-1}(-y) = 0$

T **65–66. Verifying identities** *Sketch a graph of the given pair of functions to conjecture a relationship between the two functions. Then verify the conjecture.*

65. $\sin^{-1} x; \dfrac{\pi}{2} - \cos^{-1} x$ **66.** $\tan^{-1} x; \dfrac{\pi}{2} - \cot^{-1} x$

67–74. Evaluating inverse trigonometric functions *Without using a calculator, evaluate or simplify the following expressions.*

67. $\tan^{-1}\sqrt{3}$ **68.** $\cot^{-1}(-1/\sqrt{3})$

69. $\sec^{-1} 2$ **70.** $\csc^{-1}(-1)$

71. $\tan^{-1}(\tan(\pi/4))$ **72.** $\tan^{-1}(\tan(3\pi/4))$

73. $\csc^{-1}(\sec 2)$ **74.** $\tan(\tan^{-1} 1)$

75–80. Right-triangle relationships *Use a right triangle to simplify the given expressions. Assume $x > 0$.*

75. $\cos(\tan^{-1} x)$ **76.** $\tan(\cos^{-1} x)$

77. $\cos(\sec^{-1} x)$ **78.** $\cot(\tan^{-1} 2x)$

79. $\sin\left(\sec^{-1}\left(\dfrac{\sqrt{x^2+16}}{4}\right)\right)$ **80.** $\cos\left(\tan^{-1}\left(\dfrac{x}{\sqrt{9-x^2}}\right)\right)$

81–82. Right-triangle pictures *Express θ in terms of x using the inverse sine, inverse tangent, and inverse secant functions.*

81.

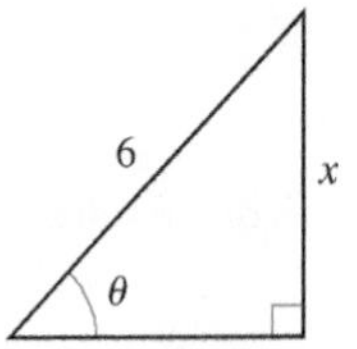

82.

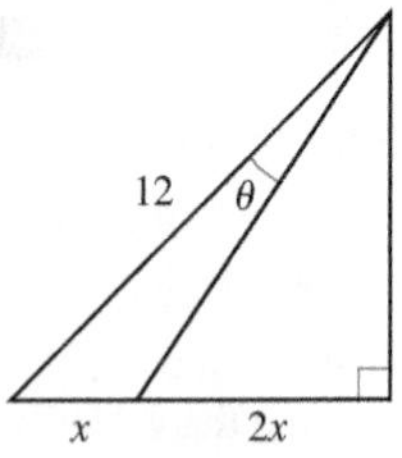

Further Explorations

83. Explain why or why not Determine whether the following statements are true and give an explanation or counterexample.

a. $\sin(a + b) = \sin a + \sin b$.
b. The equation $\cos\theta = 2$ has multiple real solutions.
c. The equation $\sin\theta = \frac{1}{2}$ has exactly one solution.
d. The function $\sin(\pi x/12)$ has a period of 12.
e. Of the six basic trigonometric functions, only tangent and cotangent have a range of $(-\infty, \infty)$.
f. $\dfrac{\sin^{-1} x}{\cos^{-1} x} = \tan^{-1} x$.
g. $\cos^{-1}(\cos(15\pi/16)) = 15\pi/16$.
h. $\sin^{-1} x = 1/\sin x$.

84–87. One function gives all six *Given the following information about one trigonometric function, evaluate the other five functions.*

84. $\sin\theta = -\dfrac{4}{5}$ and $\pi < \theta < 3\pi/2$

85. $\cos\theta = \dfrac{5}{13}$ and $0 < \theta < \pi/2$

86. $\sec\theta = \dfrac{5}{3}$ and $3\pi/2 < \theta < 2\pi$

87. $\csc\theta = \dfrac{13}{12}$ and $0 < \theta < \pi/2$

88–91. Amplitude and period *Identify the amplitude and period of the following functions.*

88. $f(\theta) = 2\sin 2\theta$

89. $g(\theta) = 3\cos(\theta/3)$

90. $p(t) = 2.5\sin\left(\frac{1}{2}(t - 3)\right)$

91. $q(x) = 3.6\cos(\pi x/24)$

92–95. Graphing sine and cosine functions *Beginning with the graphs of $y = \sin x$ or $y = \cos x$, use shifting and scaling transformations to sketch the graph of the following functions. Use a graphing utility to check your work.*

92. $f(x) = 3\sin 2x$

93. $g(x) = -2\cos(x/3)$

94. $p(x) = 3\sin(2x - \pi/3) + 1$

95. $q(x) = 3.6\cos(\pi x/24) + 2$

96–97. Designer functions *Design a sine function with the given properties.*

96. It has a period of 12 hr with a minimum value of -4 at $t = 0$ hr and a maximum value of 4 at $t = 6$ hr.

97. It has a period of 24 hr with a minimum value of 10 at $t = 3$ hr and a maximum value of 16 at $t = 15$ hr.

T **98. Field goal attempt** Near the end of the 1950 Rose Bowl football game between the University of California and Ohio State University, Ohio State was preparing to attempt a field goal from a distance of 23 yd from the endline at point A on the edge of the kicking region (see figure). But before the kick, Ohio State committed a penalty and the ball was backed up 5 yd to point B on the edge of the kicking region. After the game, the Ohio State coach claimed that his team deliberately committed a penalty to improve the kicking angle. Given that a successful kick must go between the uprights of the goal posts G_1 and G_2, is $\angle G_1BG_2$ greater than $\angle G_1AG_2$? (In 1950, the uprights were 23 ft 4 in apart, equidistant from the origin on the end line. The boundaries of the kicking region are 53 ft 4 in apart and are equidistant from the y-axis. (*Source: The College Mathematics Journal* 27, 4, Sep 1996)

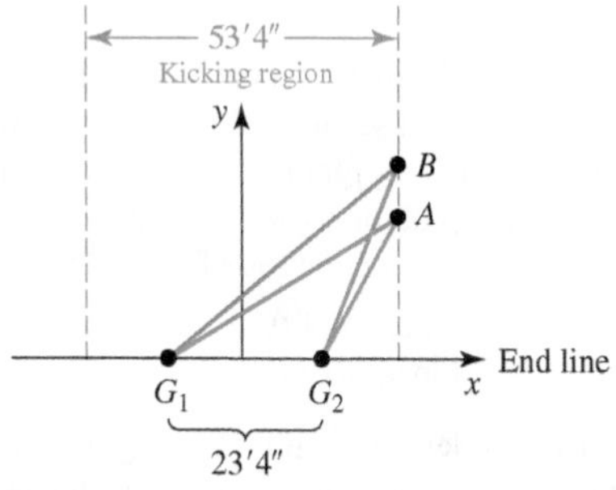

T **99. A surprising result** The Earth is approximately circular in cross section, with a circumference at the equator of 24,882 miles. Suppose we use two ropes to create two concentric circles: one by wrapping a rope around the equator and another using a rope 38 ft longer (see figure). How much space is between the ropes?

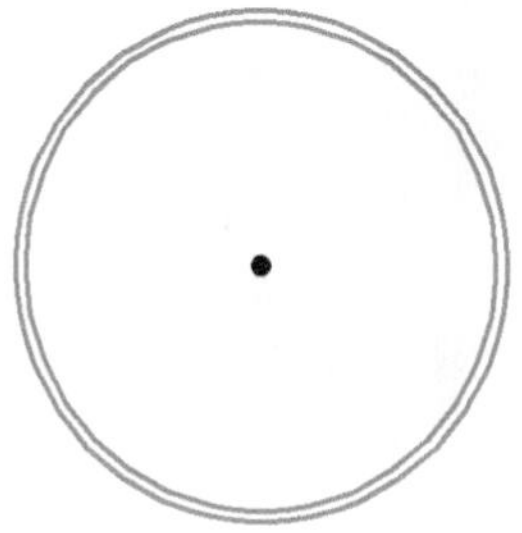

Applications

100. Daylight function for 40° N Verify that the function

$$D(t) = 2.8\sin\left(\frac{2\pi}{365}(t - 81)\right) + 12$$

has the following properties, where t is measured in days and D is the number of hours between sunrise and sunset.

a. It has a period of 365 days.
b. Its maximum and minimum values are 14.8 and 9.2, respectively, which occur approximately at $t = 172$ and $t = 355$, respectively (corresponding to the solstices).
c. $D(81) = 12$ and $D(264) \approx 12$ (corresponding to the equinoxes).

101. Block on a spring A light block hangs at rest from the end of a spring when it is pulled down 10 cm and released. Assume the block oscillates with an amplitude of 10 cm on either side of its rest position with a period of 1.5 s. Find a trigonometric function

$d(t)$ that gives the displacement of the block t seconds after it is released, where $d(t) > 0$ represents downward displacement.

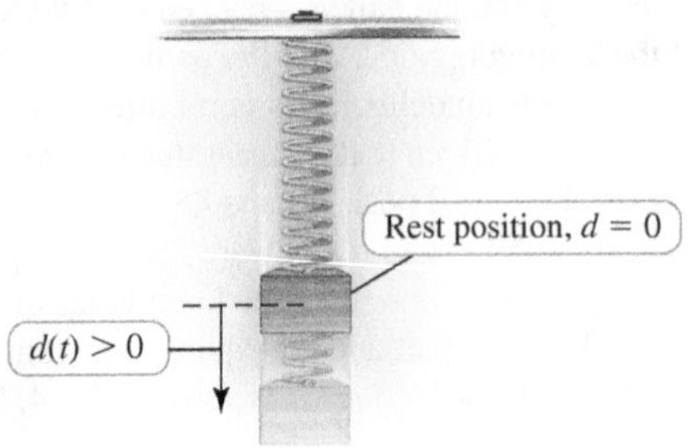

102. Approaching a lighthouse A boat approaches a 50-ft-high lighthouse whose base is at sea level. Let d be the distance between the boat and the base of the lighthouse. Let L be the distance between the boat and the top of the lighthouse. Let θ be the angle of elevation between the boat and the top of the lighthouse.

a. Express d as a function of θ.
b. Express L as a function of θ.

103. Ladders Two ladders of length a lean against opposite walls of an alley with their feet touching (see figure). One ladder extends h feet up the wall and makes a 75° angle with the ground. The other ladder extends k feet up the opposite wall and makes a 45° angle with the ground. Find the width of the alley in terms of h. Assume the ground is horizontal and perpendicular to both walls.

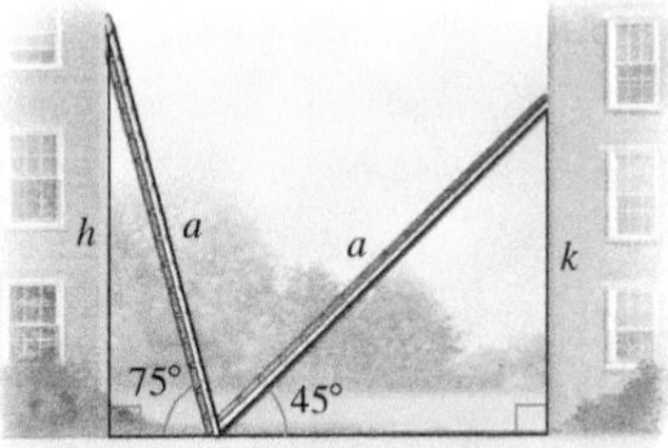

T **104. Pole in a corner** A pole of length L is carried horizontally around a corner where a 3-ft-wide hallway meets a 4-ft-wide hallway. For $0 < \theta < \pi/2$, find the relationship between L and θ at the moment when the pole simultaneously touches both walls and the corner P. Estimate θ when $L = 10$ ft.

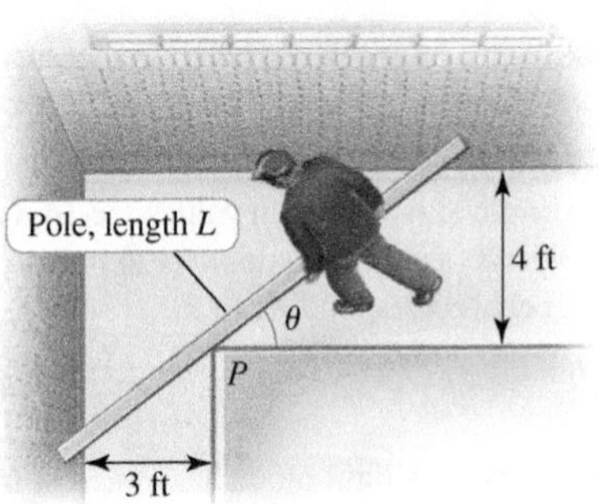

105. Little-known fact The shortest day of the year occurs on the winter solstice (near December 21) and the longest day of the year occurs on the summer solstice (near June 21). However, the latest sunrise and the earliest sunset do not occur on the winter solstice, and the earliest sunrise and the latest sunset do not occur on the summer solstice. At latitude 40° north, the latest sunrise occurs on January 4 at 7:25 A.M. (14 days after the solstice), and the earliest sunset occurs on December 7 at 4:37 P.M. (14 days before the solstice). Similarly, the earliest sunrise occurs on July 2 at 4:30 A.M. (14 days after the solstice) and the latest sunset occurs on June 7 at 7:32 P.M. (14 days before the solstice). Using sine functions, devise a function $s(t)$ that gives the time of sunrise t days after January 1 and a function $S(t)$ that gives the time of sunset t days after January 1. Assume that s and S are measured in minutes and $s = 0$ and $S = 0$ correspond to 4:00 A.M. Graph the functions. Then graph the length of the day function $D(t) = S(t) - s(t)$ and show that the longest and shortest days occur on the solstices.

106. Viewing angles An auditorium with a flat floor has a large flat-panel television on one wall. The lower edge of the television is 3 ft above the floor, and the upper edge is 10 ft above the floor (see figure). Express θ in terms of x.

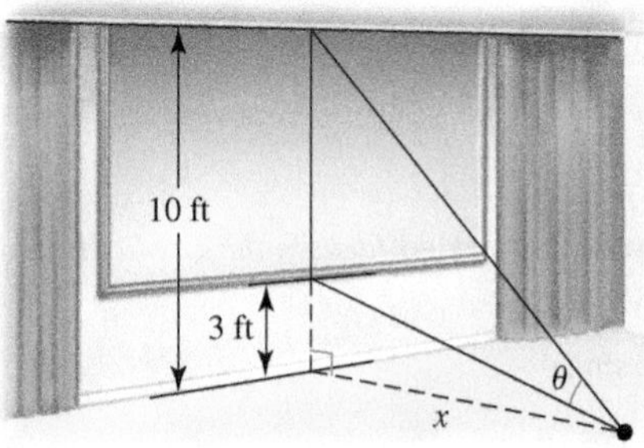

Additional Exercises

107. Area of a circular sector Prove that the area of a sector of a circle of radius r associated with a central angle θ (measured in radians) is $A = \frac{1}{2}r^2\theta$.

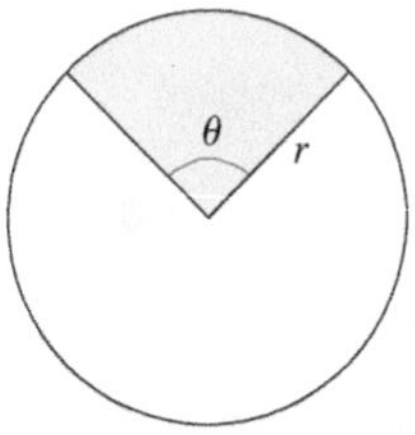

108. Law of cosines Use the figure to prove the law of cosines (which is a generalization of the Pythagorean theorem): $c^2 = a^2 + b^2 - 2ab\cos\theta$.

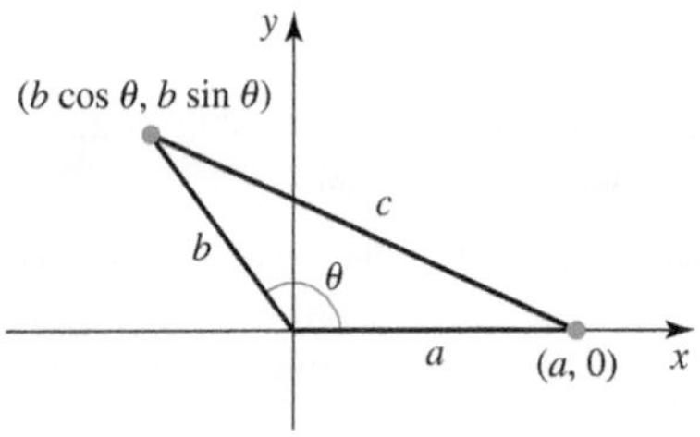

109. Law of sines Use the figure to prove the law of sines:

$$\frac{\sin A}{a} = \frac{\sin B}{b} = \frac{\sin C}{c}.$$

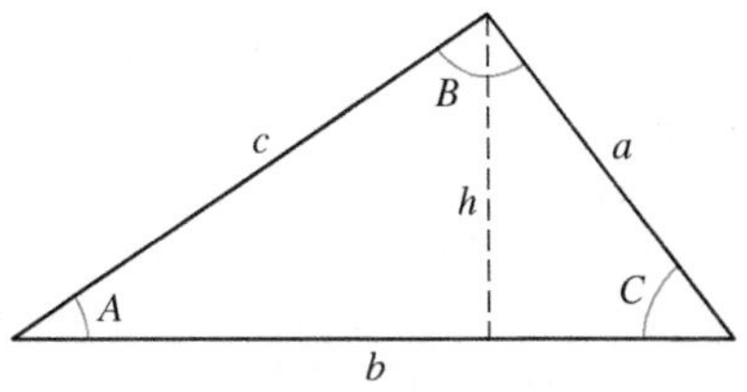

QUICK CHECK ANSWERS

1. $3\pi/2$; $225°$ **2.** $\sqrt{3}/2$; $-\sqrt{2}/2$ **3.** Divide both sides of $\sin^2\theta + \cos^2\theta = 1$ by $\sin^2\theta$. **4.** $\sin^{-1}(\sin 0) = \sin^{-1} 0 = 0$ and $\sin^{-1}(\sin(2\pi)) = \sin^{-1} 0 = 0$
5. $0, \pi/4$ ◀

CHAPTER 1 REVIEW EXERCISES

1. **Explain why or why not** Determine whether the following statements are true and give an explanation or counterexample.
   a. A function could have the property that $f(-x) = f(x)$, for all x.
   b. $\cos(a + b) = \cos a + \cos b$, for all a and b in $[0, 2\pi]$.
   c. If f is a linear function of the form $f(x) = mx + b$, then $f(u + v) = f(u) + f(v)$, for all u and v.
   d. The function $f(x) = 1 - x$ has the property that $f(f(x)) = x$.
   e. The set $\{x: |x + 3| > 4\}$ can be drawn on the number line without lifting your pencil.
   f. $\log_{10}(xy) = (\log_{10} x)(\log_{10} y)$
   g. $\sin^{-1}(\sin(2\pi)) = 0$

2. **Domain and range** Find the domain and range of the following functions.
   a. $f(x) = x^5 + \sqrt{x}$ **b.** $g(y) = \dfrac{1}{y - 2}$
   c. $h(z) = \sqrt{z^2 - 2z - 3}$

3. **Equations of lines** In each part below, find an equation of the line with the given properties. Graph the line.
   a. The line passing through the points $(2, -3)$ and $(4, 2)$
   b. The line with slope $\frac{3}{4}$ and x-intercept $(-4, 0)$
   c. The line with intercepts $(4, 0)$ and $(0, -2)$

4. **Piecewise linear functions** The parking costs in a city garage are \$2 for the first half hour and \$1 for each additional half hour. Graph the function $C = f(t)$ that gives the cost of parking for t hours, where $0 \le t \le 3$.

T 5. **Graphing absolute value** Consider the function $f(x) = 2(x - |x|)$. Express the function in two pieces without using the absolute value. Then graph the function by hand. Use a graphing utility to check your work.

6. **Function from words** Suppose you plan to take a 500-mile trip in a car that gets 35 mi/gal. Find the function $C = f(p)$ that gives the cost of gasoline for the trip when gasoline costs \$$p$ per gallon.

T 7. **Graphing equations** Graph the following equations. Use a graphing utility to check your work.
   a. $2x - 3y + 10 = 0$
   b. $y = x^2 + 2x - 3$
   c. $x^2 + 2x + y^2 + 4y + 1 = 0$
   d. $x^2 - 2x + y^2 - 8y + 5 = 0$

8. **Root functions** Graph the functions $f(x) = x^{1/3}$ and $g(x) = x^{1/4}$. Find all points where the two graphs intersect. For $x > 1$, is $f(x) > g(x)$ or is $g(x) > f(x)$?

9. **Root functions** Find the domain and range of the functions $f(x) = x^{1/7}$ and $g(x) = x^{1/4}$.

10. **Intersection points** Graph the equations $y = x^2$ and $x^2 + y^2 - 7y + 8 = 0$. At what point(s) do the curves intersect?

11. **Boiling-point function** Water boils at 212° F at sea level and at 200° F at an elevation of 6000 ft. Assume that the boiling point B varies linearly with altitude a. Find the function $B = f(a)$ that describes the dependence. Comment on whether a linear function is a realistic model.

12. **Publishing costs** A small publisher plans to spend \$1000 for advertising a paperback book and estimates the printing cost is \$2.50 per book. The publisher will receive \$7 for each book sold.
   a. Find the function $C = f(x)$ that gives the cost of producing x books.
   b. Find the function $R = g(x)$ that gives the revenue from selling x books.
   c. Graph the cost and revenue functions; then find the number of books that must be sold for the publisher to break even.

T 13. **Shifting and scaling** Starting with the graph of $f(x) = x^2$, plot the following functions. Use a graphing calculator to check your work.
   a. $f(x + 3)$ **b.** $2f(x - 4)$ **c.** $-f(3x)$ **d.** $f(2(x - 3))$

14. **Shifting and scaling** The graph of f is shown in the figure. Graph the following functions.
   a. $f(x + 1)$ **b.** $2f(x - 1)$ **c.** $-f(x/2)$ **d.** $f(2(x - 1))$

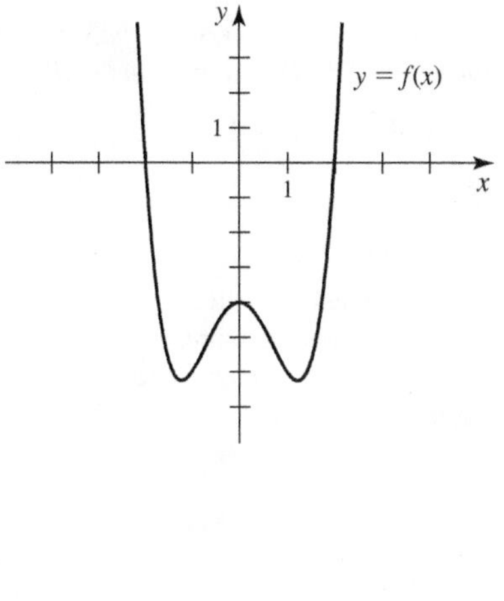

15. **Composite functions** Let $f(x) = x^3$, $g(x) = \sin x$, and $h(x) = \sqrt{x}$.

   a. Evaluate $h(g(\pi/2))$. b. Find $h(f(x))$.
   c. Find $f(g(h(x)))$. d. Find the domain of $g \circ f$.
   e. Find the range of $f \circ g$.

16. **Composite functions** Find functions f and g such that $h = f \circ g$.

   a. $h(x) = \sin(x^2 + 1)$ b. $h(x) = (x^2 - 4)^{-3}$
   c. $h(x) = e^{\cos 2x}$

17–20. Simplifying difference quotients *Evaluate and simplify the difference quotients* $\dfrac{f(x + h) - f(x)}{h}$ *and* $\dfrac{f(x) - f(a)}{x - a}$ *for each function.*

17. $f(x) = x^2 - 2x$
18. $f(x) = 4 - 5x$
19. $f(x) = x^3 + 2$
20. $f(x) = \dfrac{7}{x + 3}$

21. **Symmetry** Identify the symmetry (if any) in the graphs of the following equations.

   a. $y = \cos 3x$ b. $y = 3x^4 - 3x^2 + 1$
   c. $y^2 - 4x^2 = 4$

22–23. Properties of logarithms and exponentials *Use properties of logarithms and exponentials, not a calculator, for the following exercises.*

22. Solve the equation $48 = 6e^{4k}$ for k.

23. Solve the equation $\log_{10} x^2 + 3 \log_{10} x = \log_{10} 32$ for x. Does the answer depend on the base of the log in the equation?

24. **Graphs of logarithmic and exponential functions** The figure shows the graphs of $y = 2^x$, $y = 3^{-x}$, and $y = -\ln x$. Match each curve with the correct function.

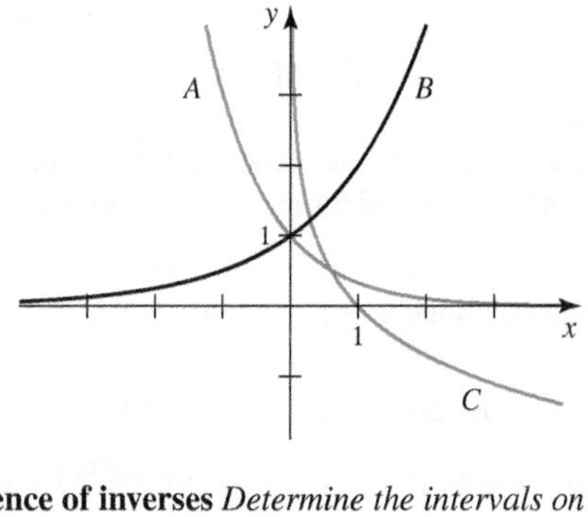

T 25–26. Existence of inverses *Determine the intervals on which the following functions have an inverse.*

25. $f(x) = x^3 - 3x^2$
26. $g(t) = 2\sin(t/3)$

T 27–28. Finding inverses *Find the inverse on the specified interval and express it in the form* $y = f^{-1}(x)$. *Then graph f and* f^{-1}.

27. $f(x) = x^2 - 4x + 5$, for $x > 2$

28. $f(x) = 1/x^2$, for $x > 0$

29. **Degrees and radians**

   a. Convert 135° to radian measure.
   b. Convert $4\pi/5$ to degree measure.
   c. What is the length of the arc on a circle of radius 10 associated with an angle of $4\pi/3$ (radians)?

30. **Graphing sine and cosine functions** Use shifts and scalings to graph the following functions, and identify the amplitude and period.

   a. $f(x) = 4\cos(x/2)$ b. $g(\theta) = 2\sin(2\pi\theta/3)$
   c. $h(\theta) = -\cos(2(\theta - \pi/4))$

31. **Designing functions** Find a trigonometric function f that satisfies each set of properties. Answers are not unique.

   a. It has a period of 6 with a minimum value of -2 at $t = 0$ and a maximum value of 2 at $t = 3$.
   b. It has a period of 24 with a maximum value of 20 at $t = 6$ and a minimum value of 10 at $t = 18$.

32. **Graph to function** Find a trigonometric function f represented by the graph in the figure.

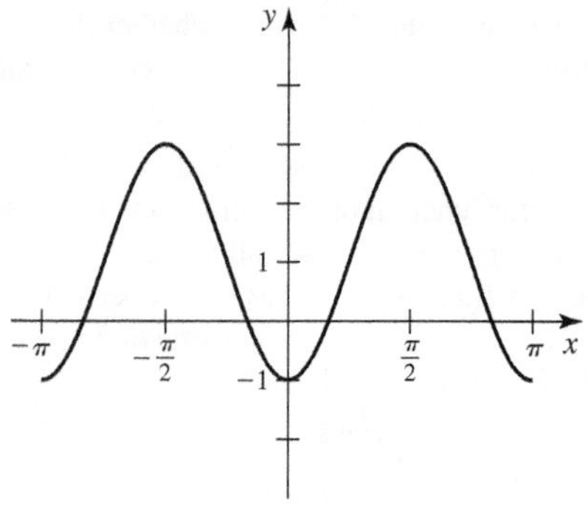

33. **Matching** Match each function a–f with the corresponding graphs A–F.

   a. $f(x) = -\sin x$ b. $f(x) = \cos 2x$
   c. $f(x) = \tan(x/2)$ d. $f(x) = -\sec x$
   e. $f(x) = \cot 2x$ f. $f(x) = \sin^2 x$

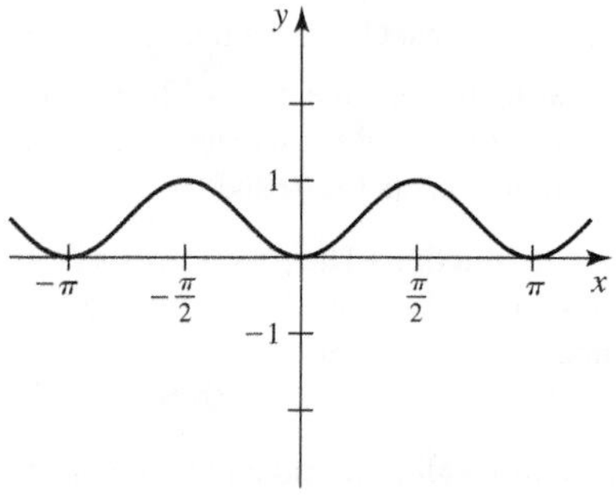

(A)

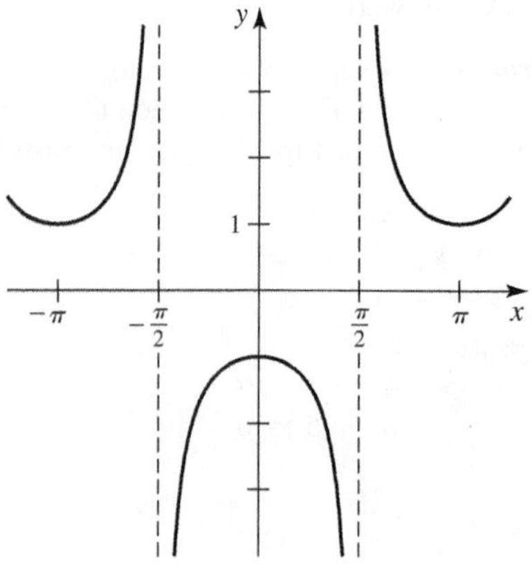

(B)

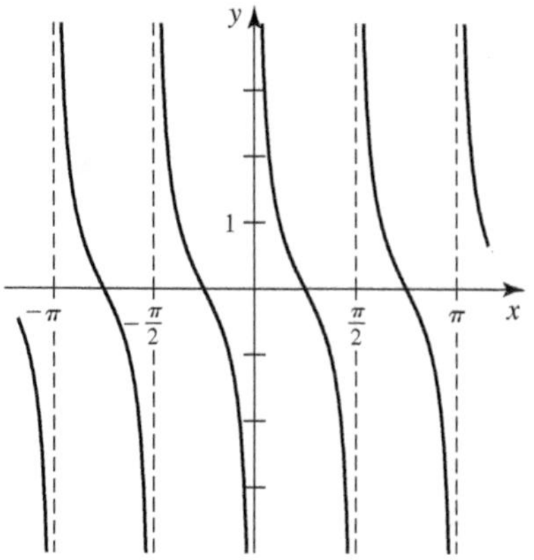

(C)

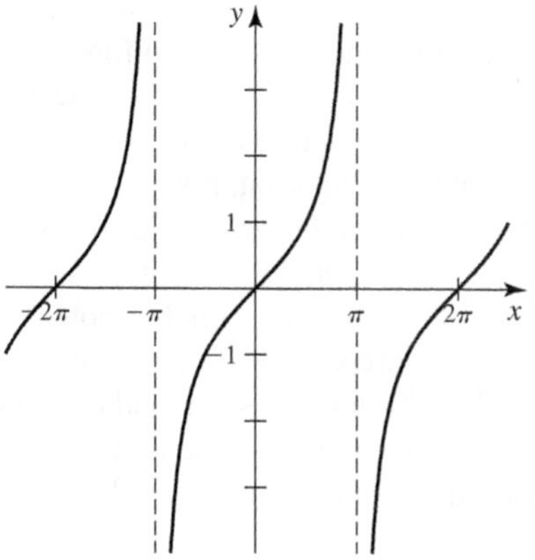

(D)

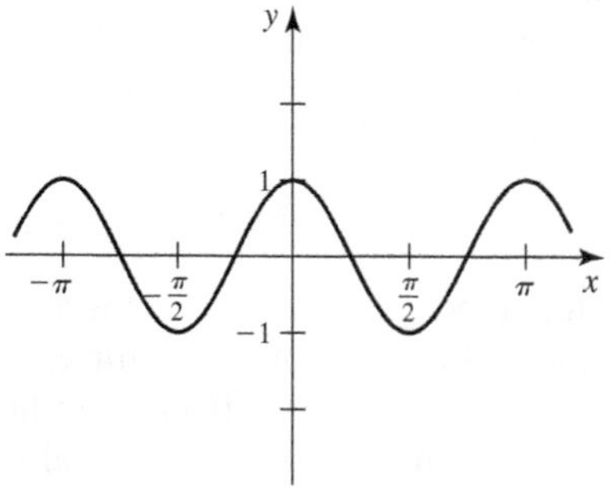

(E)

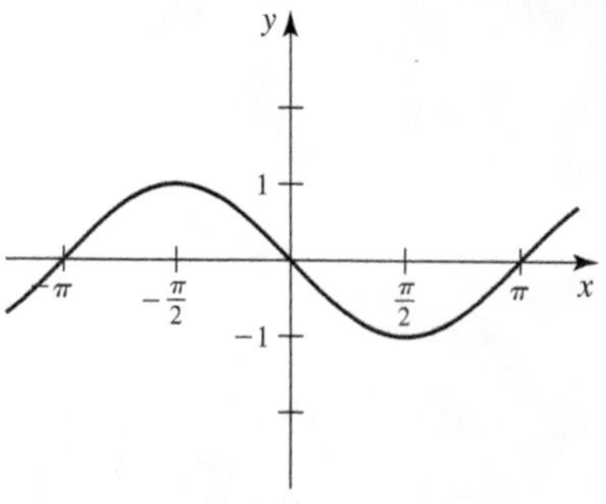

(F)

34–35. Intersection points *Find the points at which the curves intersect on the given interval.*

34. $y = \sec x$ and $y = 2$ on $(-\pi/2, \pi/2)$

35. $y = \sin x$ and $y = -\frac{1}{2}$ on $(0, 2\pi)$

36–42. Inverse sines and cosines *Evaluate or simplify the following expressions without using a calculator.*

36. $\sin^{-1} \frac{\sqrt{3}}{2}$ **37.** $\cos^{-1} \frac{\sqrt{3}}{2}$ **38.** $\cos^{-1}\left(-\frac{1}{2}\right)$

39. $\sin^{-1}(-1)$ **40.** $\cos(\cos^{-1}(-1))$ **41.** $\sin(\sin^{-1} x)$

42. $\cos^{-1}(\sin 3\pi)$

43. Right triangles Given that $\theta = \sin^{-1}\frac{12}{13}$, evaluate $\cos\theta$, $\tan\theta$, $\cot\theta$, $\sec\theta$, and $\csc\theta$.

44–51. Right-triangle relationships *Draw a right triangle to simplify the given expression. Assume $x > 0$ and $0 \le \theta \le \pi/2$.*

44. $\cos(\tan^{-1} x)$ **45.** $\sin(\cos^{-1}(x/2))$

46. $\tan(\sec^{-1}(x/2))$ **47.** $\cot^{-1}(\tan\theta)$

48. $\csc^{-1}(\sec\theta)$ **49.** $\sin^{-1} x + \sin^{-1}(-x)$

50. $\sin(2\cos^{-1} x)$ (*Hint:* Use $\sin 2\theta = 2\sin\theta\cos\theta$.)

51. $\cos(2\sin^{-1} x)$ (*Hint:* Use $\cos 2\theta = \cos^2\theta - \sin^2\theta$.)

52. Stereographic projections A common way of displaying a sphere (such as Earth) on a plane (such as a map) is to use a *stereographic projection.* Here is the two-dimensional version of the method, which maps a circle to a line. Let P be a point on the right half of a circle of radius R identified by the angle φ. Find the function $x = F(\varphi)$ that gives the x-coordinate $(x \ge 0)$ corresponding to φ for $0 < \varphi \le \pi$.

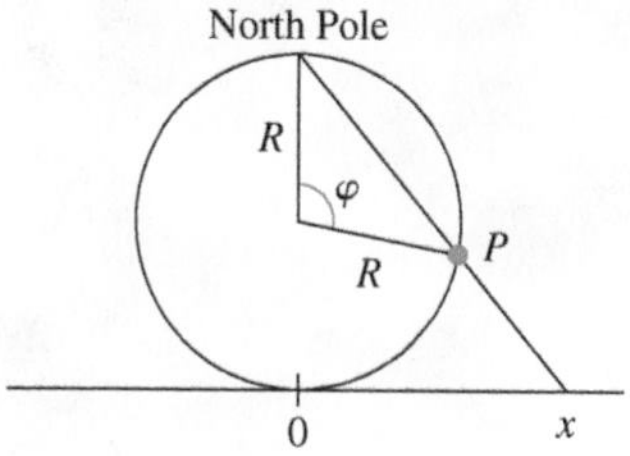

Chapter 1 Guided Projects

Applications of the material in this chapter and related topics can be found in the following Guided Projects. For additional information, see the Preface.

- Problem-solving skills
- Constant rate problems
- Functions in action I
- Functions in action II
- Supply and demand
- Phase and amplitude
- Atmospheric CO_2
- Acid, noise, and earthquakes

2

Limits

Chapter Preview All of calculus is based on the idea of a *limit*. Not only are limits important in their own right but they also underlie the two fundamental operations of calculus: differentiation (calculating derivatives) and integration (evaluating integrals). Derivatives enable us to talk about the instantaneous rate of change of a function, which, in turn, leads to concepts such as velocity and acceleration, population growth rates, marginal cost, and flow rates. Integrals enable us to compute areas under curves, surface areas, and volumes. Because of the incredible reach of this single idea, it is essential to develop a solid understanding of limits. We first present limits intuitively by showing how they arise in computing instantaneous velocities and finding slopes of tangent lines. As the chapter progresses, we build more rigor into the definition of the limit and examine the different ways in which limits arise. The chapter concludes by introducing the important property of *continuity* and by giving the formal definition of a limit.

2.1 The Idea of Limits

This brief opening section illustrates how limits arise in two seemingly unrelated problems: finding the instantaneous velocity of a moving object and finding the slope of a line tangent to a curve. These two problems provide important insights into limits on an intuitive level. In the remainder of the chapter, we develop limits carefully and fill in the mathematical details.

Average Velocity

Suppose you want to calculate your average velocity as you travel along a straight highway. If you pass milepost 100 at noon and milepost 130 at 12:30 P.M., you travel 30 miles in a half hour, so your **average velocity** over this time interval is $(30 \text{ mi})/(0.5 \text{ hr}) = 60 \text{ mi/hr}$. By contrast, even though your average velocity may be 60 mi/hr, it's almost certain that your **instantaneous velocity**, the speed indicated by the speedometer, varies from one moment to the next.

EXAMPLE 1 **Average velocity** A rock is launched vertically upward from the ground with a speed of 96 ft/s. Neglecting air resistance, a well-known formula from physics states that the position of the rock after t seconds is given by the function

$$s(t) = -16t^2 + 96t.$$

The position s is measured in feet with $s = 0$ corresponding to the ground. Find the average velocity of the rock between each pair of times.

a. $t = 1$ s and $t = 3$ s **b.** $t = 1$ s and $t = 2$ s

SOLUTION Figure 2.1 shows the position function of the rock on the time interval $0 \le t \le 3$. The graph is *not* the path of the rock. The rock travels up and down on a vertical line.

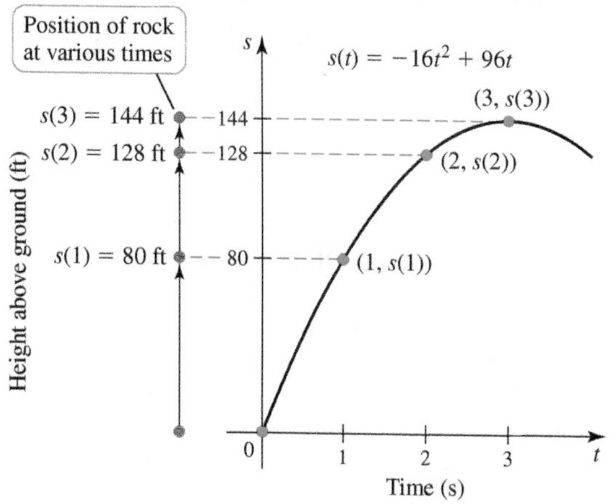

Figure 2.1

a. The average velocity of the rock over any time interval $[t_0, t_1]$ is the change in position divided by the elapsed time:

$$v_{av} = \frac{s(t_1) - s(t_0)}{t_1 - t_0}.$$

Therefore, the average velocity over the interval $[1, 3]$ is

$$v_{av} = \frac{s(3) - s(1)}{3 - 1} = \frac{144\text{ ft} - 80\text{ ft}}{3\text{ s} - 1\text{ s}} = \frac{64\text{ ft}}{2\text{ s}} = 32\text{ ft/s}.$$

Here is an important observation: As shown in Figure 2.2a, the average velocity is simply the slope of the line joining the points $(1, s(1))$ and $(3, s(3))$ on the graph of the position function.

b. The average velocity of the rock over the interval $[1, 2]$ is

$$v_{av} = \frac{s(2) - s(1)}{2 - 1} = \frac{128\text{ ft} - 80\text{ ft}}{2\text{ s} - 1\text{ s}} = \frac{48\text{ ft}}{1\text{ s}} = 48\text{ ft/s}.$$

Again, the average velocity is the slope of the line joining the points $(1, s(1))$ and $(2, s(2))$ on the graph of the position function (Figure 2.2b).

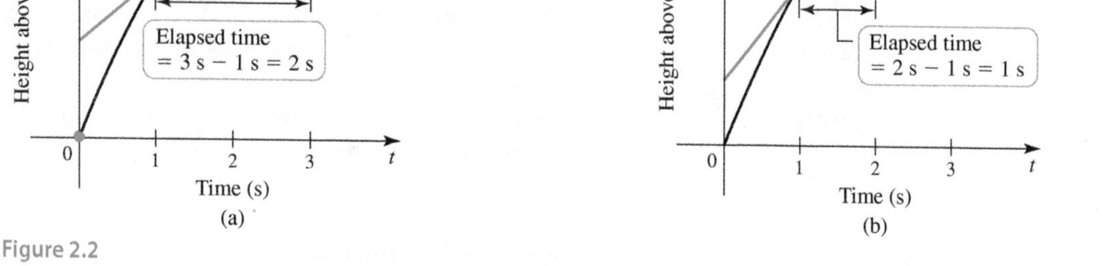

Figure 2.2

Related Exercises 7–14 ◄

QUICK CHECK 1 In Example 1, what is the average velocity between $t = 2$ and $t = 3$? ◄

➤ See Section 1.1 for a discussion of secant lines.

In Example 1, we computed slopes of lines passing through two points on a curve. Any such line joining two points on a curve is called a **secant line**. The slope of the secant line, denoted m_{sec}, for the position function in Example 1 on the interval $[t_0, t_1]$ is

$$m_{sec} = \frac{s(t_1) - s(t_0)}{t_1 - t_0}.$$

Example 1 demonstrates that the average velocity is the slope of a secant line on the graph of the position function; that is, $v_{av} = m_{sec}$ (Figure 2.3).

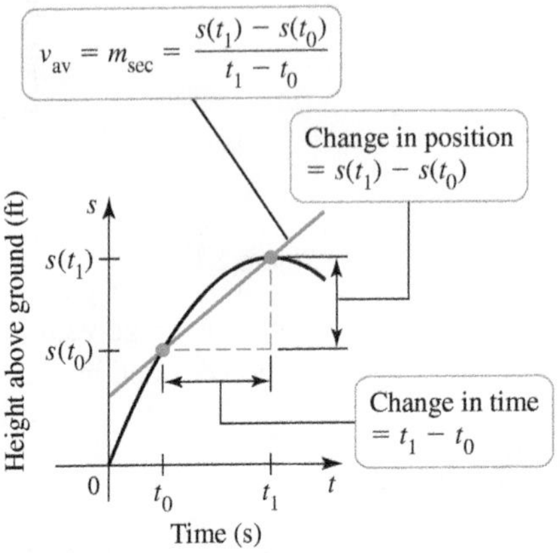

Figure 2.3

Instantaneous Velocity

To compute the average velocity, we use the position of the object at *two* distinct points in time. How do we compute the instantaneous velocity at a *single* point in time? As illustrated in Example 2, the instantaneous velocity at a point $t = t_0$ is determined by computing average velocities over intervals $[t_0, t_1]$ that decrease in length. As t_1 approaches t_0, the average velocities typically approach a unique number, which is the instantaneous velocity. This single number is called a **limit**.

QUICK CHECK 2 Explain the difference between average velocity and instantaneous velocity. ◄

EXAMPLE 2 **Instantaneous velocity** Estimate the instantaneous velocity of the rock in Example 1 at the *single* point $t = 1$.

SOLUTION We are interested in the instantaneous velocity at $t = 1$, so we compute the average velocity over smaller and smaller time intervals $[1, t]$ using the formula

$$v_{av} = \frac{s(t) - s(1)}{t - 1}.$$

Table 2.1

Time interval	Average velocity
$[1, 2]$	48 ft/s
$[1, 1.5]$	56 ft/s
$[1, 1.1]$	62.4 ft/s
$[1, 1.01]$	63.84 ft/s
$[1, 1.001]$	63.984 ft/s
$[1, 1.0001]$	63.9984 ft/s

Notice that these average velocities are also slopes of secant lines, several of which are shown in Table 2.1. For example, the average velocity on the interval $[1, 1.0001]$ is 63.9984 ft/s. Because this time interval is so short, the average velocity gives a good approximation to the instantaneous velocity at $t = 1$. We see that as t approaches 1, the average velocities appear to approach 64 ft/s. In fact, we could make the average velocity as close to 64 ft/s as we like by taking t sufficiently close to 1. Therefore, 64 ft/s is a reasonable estimate of the instantaneous velocity at $t = 1$.

Related Exercises 15–20 ◄

➤ The same instantaneous velocity is obtained as t approaches 1 from the left (with $t < 1$) and as t approaches 1 from the right (with $t > 1$).

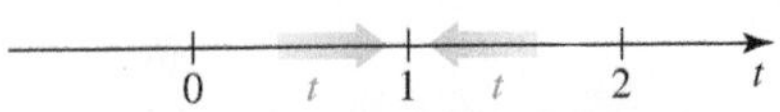

In language to be introduced in Section 2.2, we say that the limit of v_{av} as t approaches 1 equals the instantaneous velocity v_{inst}, which is 64 ft/s. This statement is illustrated in Figure 2.4 and written compactly as

$$v_{inst} = \lim_{t \to 1} v_{av} = \lim_{t \to 1} \frac{s(t) - s(1)}{t - 1} = 64 \text{ ft/s}.$$

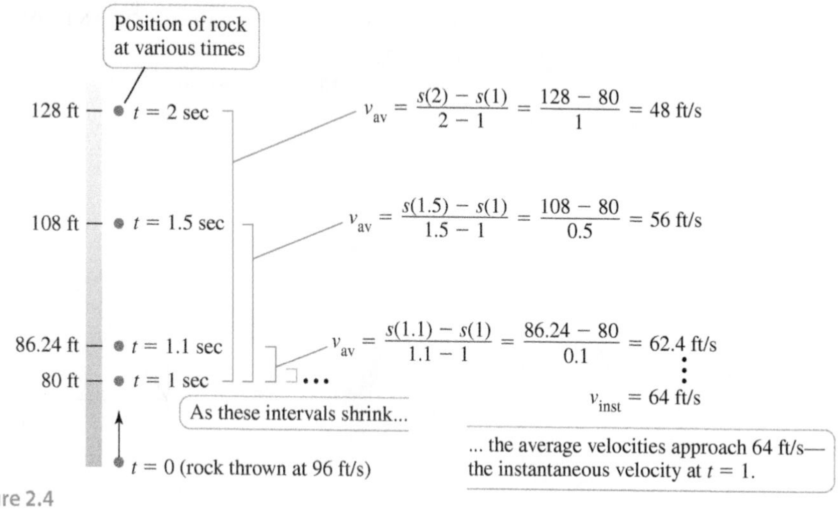

Figure 2.4

Slope of the Tangent Line

Several important conclusions follow from Examples 1 and 2. Each average velocity in Table 2.1 corresponds to the slope of a secant line on the graph of the position function (Figure 2.5). Just as the average velocities approach a limit as t approaches 1, the slopes of the secant lines approach the same limit as t approaches 1. Specifically, as t approaches 1, two things happen:

1. The secant lines approach a unique line called the **tangent line**.
2. The slopes of the secant lines m_{sec} approach the slope of the tangent line m_{tan} at the point $(1, s(1))$. Therefore, the slope of the tangent line is also expressed as a limit:

$$m_{tan} = \lim_{t \to 1} m_{sec} = \lim_{t \to 1} \frac{s(t) - s(1)}{t - 1} = 64.$$

This limit is the same limit that defines the instantaneous velocity. Therefore, the instantaneous velocity at $t = 1$ is the slope of the line tangent to the position curve at $t = 1$.

➤ We define tangent lines carefully in Section 3.1. For the moment, imagine zooming in on a point P on a smooth curve. As you zoom in, the curve appears more and more like a line passing through P. This line is the *tangent line* at P. Because a smooth curve approaches a line as we zoom in on a point, a smooth curve is said to be *locally linear* at any given point.

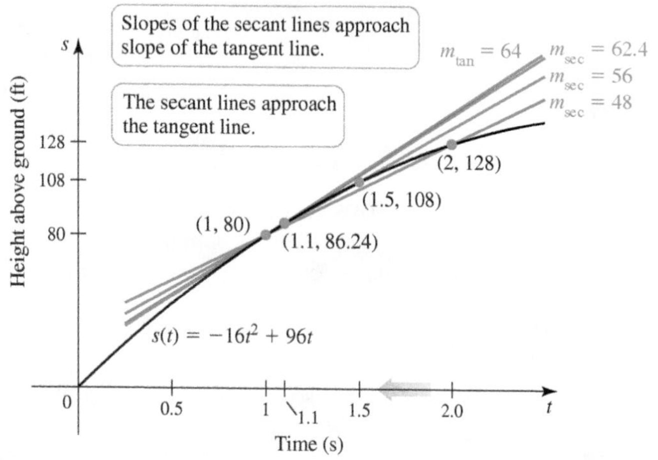

Figure 2.5

QUICK CHECK 3 In Figure 2.5, is m_{tan} at $t = 2$ greater than or less than m_{tan} at $t = 1$? ◄

The parallels between average and instantaneous velocities, on one hand, and between slopes of secant lines and tangent lines, on the other, illuminate the power behind the idea of a limit. As $t \to 1$, slopes of secant lines approach the slope of a tangent line. And as $t \to 1$, average velocities approach an instantaneous velocity. Figure 2.6 summarizes these two parallel limit processes. These ideas lie at the foundation of what follows in the coming chapters.

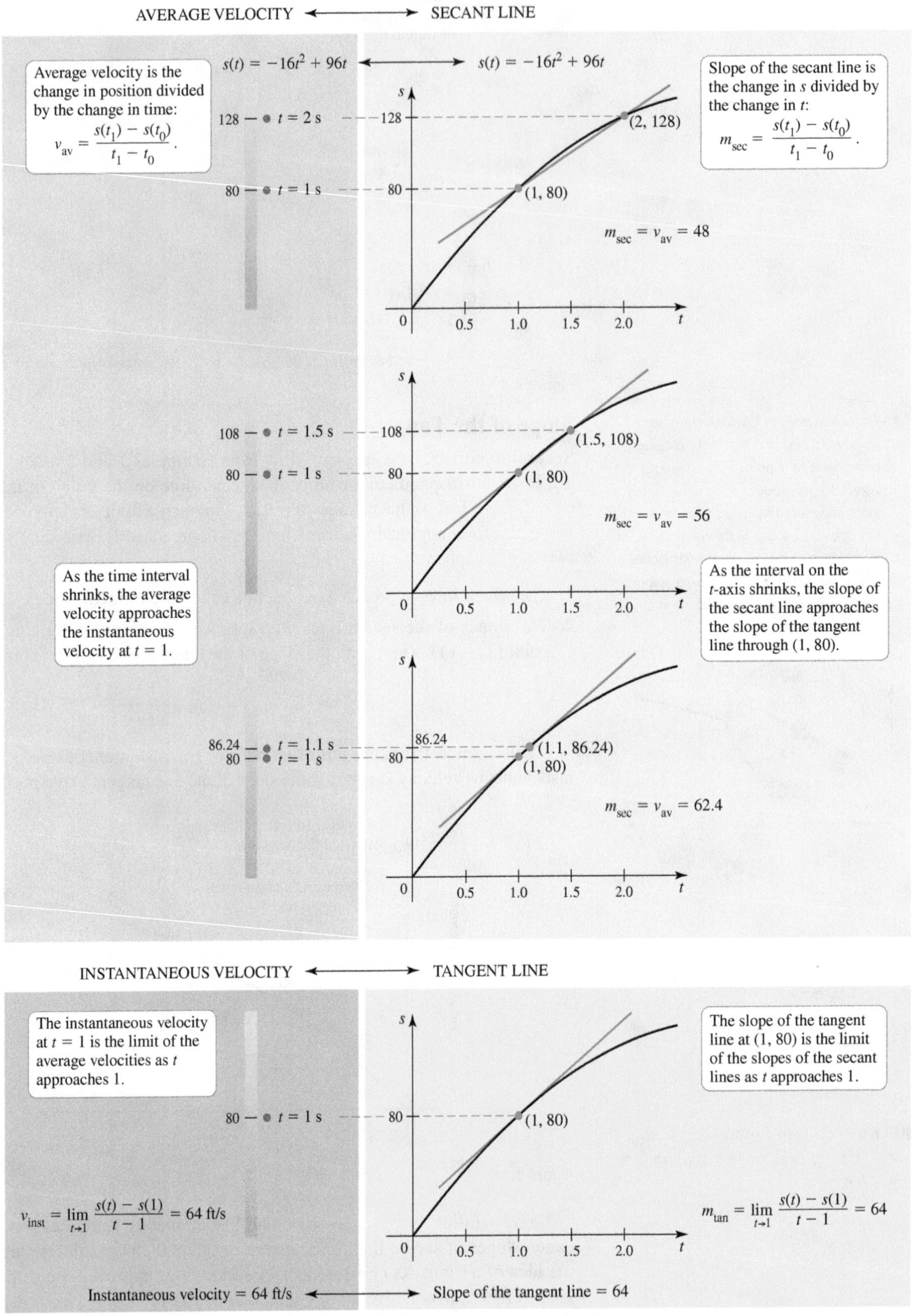
AVERAGE VELOCITY
SECANT LINE
s(t) = −16t² + 96t
s(t) = −16t² + 96t
Average velocity is the change in position divided by the change in time: $v_{av} = \frac{s(t_1) - s(t_0)}{t_1 - t_0}$.
Slope of the secant line is the change in s divided by the change in t: $m_{sec} = \frac{s(t_1) - s(t_0)}{t_1 - t_0}$.
128 — t = 2 s
80 — t = 1 s
(2, 128)
(1, 80)
$m_{sec} = v_{av} = 48$
108 — t = 1.5 s
80 — t = 1 s
(1.5, 108)
(1, 80)
$m_{sec} = v_{av} = 56$
As the time interval shrinks, the average velocity approaches the instantaneous velocity at t = 1.
As the interval on the t-axis shrinks, the slope of the secant line approaches the slope of the tangent line through (1, 80).
86.24 — t = 1.1 s
80 — t = 1 s
86.24
(1.1, 86.24)
(1, 80)
$m_{sec} = v_{av} = 62.4$
INSTANTANEOUS VELOCITY
TANGENT LINE
The instantaneous velocity at t = 1 is the limit of the average velocities as t approaches 1.
The slope of the tangent line at (1, 80) is the limit of the slopes of the secant lines as t approaches 1.
80 — t = 1 s
(1, 80)
$v_{inst} = \lim_{t \to 1} \frac{s(t) - s(1)}{t - 1} = 64$ ft/s
$m_{tan} = \lim_{t \to 1} \frac{s(t) - s(1)}{t - 1} = 64$
Instantaneous velocity = 64 ft/s
Slope of the tangent line = 64
s
t
0
0.5
1.0
1.5
2.0

Figure 2.6

SECTION 2.1 EXERCISES

Review Questions

1. Suppose $s(t)$ is the position of an object moving along a line at time $t \geq 0$. What is the average velocity between the times $t = a$ and $t = b$?

2. Suppose $s(t)$ is the position of an object moving along a line at time $t \geq 0$. Describe a process for finding the instantaneous velocity at $t = a$.

3. What is the slope of the secant line that passes through the points $(a, f(a))$ and $(b, f(b))$ on the graph of f?

4. Describe a process for finding the slope of the line tangent to the graph of f at $(a, f(a))$.

5. Describe the parallels between finding the instantaneous velocity of an object at a point in time and finding the slope of the line tangent to the graph of a function at a point on the graph.

6. Graph the parabola $f(x) = x^2$. Explain why the secant lines between the points $(-a, f(-a))$ and $(a, f(a))$ have zero slope. What is the slope of the tangent line at $x = 0$?

Basic Skills

7. **Average velocity** The function $s(t)$ represents the position of an object at time t moving along a line. Suppose $s(2) = 136$ and $s(3) = 156$. Find the average velocity of the object over the interval of time $[2, 3]$.

8. **Average velocity** The function $s(t)$ represents the position of an object at time t moving along a line. Suppose $s(1) = 84$ and $s(4) = 144$. Find the average velocity of the object over the interval of time $[1, 4]$.

T 9. **Average velocity** The position of an object moving vertically along a line is given by the function $s(t) = -16t^2 + 128t$. Find the average velocity of the object over the following intervals.

a. $[1, 4]$ **b.** $[1, 3]$
c. $[1, 2]$ **d.** $[1, 1 + h]$, where $h > 0$ is a real number

T 10. **Average velocity** The position of an object moving vertically along a line is given by the function $s(t) = -4.9t^2 + 30t + 20$. Find the average velocity of the object over the following intervals.

a. $[0, 3]$ **b.** $[0, 2]$
c. $[0, 1]$ **d.** $[0, h]$, where $h > 0$ is a real number

11. **Average velocity** The table gives the position $s(t)$ of an object moving along a line at time t, over a two-second interval. Find the average velocity of the object over the following intervals.

a. $[0, 2]$ **b.** $[0, 1.5]$
c. $[0, 1]$ **d.** $[0, 0.5]$

t	0	0.5	1	1.5	2
$s(t)$	0	30	52	66	72

12. **Average velocity** The graph gives the position $s(t)$ of an object moving along a line at time t, over a 2.5-second interval. Find the average velocity of the object over the following intervals.

a. $[0.5, 2.5]$ **b.** $[0.5, 2]$
c. $[0.5, 1.5]$ **d.** $[0.5, 1]$

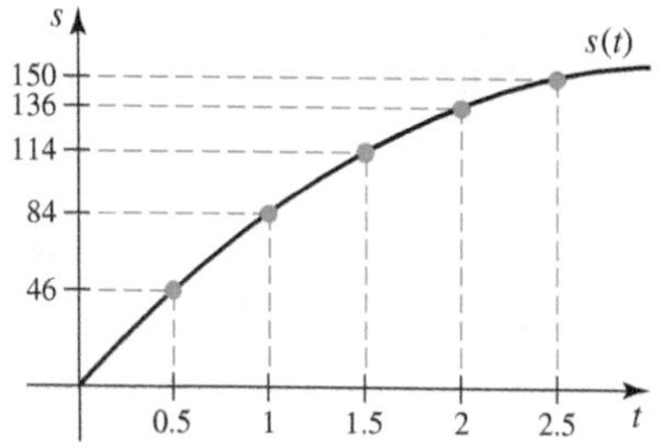

T 13. **Average velocity** Consider the position function $s(t) = -16t^2 + 100t$ representing the position of an object moving vertically along a line. Sketch a graph of s with the secant line passing through $(0.5, s(0.5))$ and $(2, s(2))$. Determine the slope of the secant line and explain its relationship to the moving object.

T 14. **Average velocity** Consider the position function $s(t) = \sin \pi t$ representing the position of an object moving along a line on the end of a spring. Sketch a graph of s together with a secant line passing through $(0, s(0))$ and $(0.5, s(0.5))$. Determine the slope of the secant line and explain its relationship to the moving object.

T 15. **Instantaneous velocity** Consider the position function $s(t) = -16t^2 + 128t$ (Exercise 9). Complete the following table with the appropriate average velocities. Then make a conjecture about the value of the instantaneous velocity at $t = 1$.

Time interval	$[1, 2]$	$[1, 1.5]$	$[1, 1.1]$	$[1, 1.01]$	$[1, 1.001]$
Average velocity					

T 16. **Instantaneous velocity** Consider the position function $s(t) = -4.9t^2 + 30t + 20$ (Exercise 10). Complete the following table with the appropriate average velocities. Then make a conjecture about the value of the instantaneous velocity at $t = 2$.

Time interval	$[2, 3]$	$[2, 2.5]$	$[2, 2.1]$	$[2, 2.01]$	$[2, 2.001]$
Average velocity					

T 17. **Instantaneous velocity** The following table gives the position $s(t)$ of an object moving along a line at time t. Determine the average velocities over the time intervals $[1, 1.01]$, $[1, 1.001]$, and $[1, 1.0001]$. Then make a conjecture about the value of the instantaneous velocity at $t = 1$.

t	1	1.0001	1.001	1.01
$s(t)$	64	64.00479984	64.047984	64.4784

T 18. Instantaneous velocity The following table gives the position $s(t)$ of an object moving along a line at time t. Determine the average velocities over the time intervals $[2, 2.01]$, $[2, 2.001]$, and $[2, 2.0001]$. Then make a conjecture about the value of the instantaneous velocity at $t = 2$.

t	2	2.0001	2.001	2.01
$s(t)$	56	55.99959984	55.995984	55.9584

T 19. Instantaneous velocity Consider the position function $s(t) = -16t^2 + 100t$. Complete the following table with the appropriate average velocities. Then make a conjecture about the value of the instantaneous velocity at $t = 3$.

Time interval	Average velocity
$[2, 3]$	
$[2.9, 3]$	
$[2.99, 3]$	
$[2.999, 3]$	
$[2.9999, 3]$	

T 20. Instantaneous velocity Consider the position function $s(t) = 3 \sin t$ that describes a block bouncing vertically on a spring. Complete the following table with the appropriate average velocities. Then make a conjecture about the value of the instantaneous velocity at $t = \pi/2$.

Time interval	Average velocity
$[\pi/2, \pi]$	
$[\pi/2, \pi/2 + 0.1]$	
$[\pi/2, \pi/2 + 0.01]$	
$[\pi/2, \pi/2 + 0.001]$	
$[\pi/2, \pi/2 + 0.0001]$	

Further Explorations

T 21–24. Instantaneous velocity *For the following position functions, make a table of average velocities similar to those in Exercises 19–20 and make a conjecture about the instantaneous velocity at the indicated time.*

21. $s(t) = -16t^2 + 80t + 60$ at $t = 3$

22. $s(t) = 20 \cos t$ at $t = \pi/2$

23. $s(t) = 40 \sin 2t$ at $t = 0$

24. $s(t) = 20/(t + 1)$ at $t = 0$

T 25–28. Slopes of tangent lines *For the following functions, make a table of slopes of secant lines and make a conjecture about the slope of the tangent line at the indicated point.*

25. $f(x) = 2x^2$ at $x = 2$

26. $f(x) = 3 \cos x$ at $x = \pi/2$

27. $f(x) = e^x$ at $x = 0$

28. $f(x) = x^3 - x$ at $x = 1$

T 29. Tangent lines with zero slope

a. Graph the function $f(x) = x^2 - 4x + 3$.

b. Identify the point $(a, f(a))$ at which the function has a tangent line with zero slope.

c. Confirm your answer to part (b) by making a table of slopes of secant lines to approximate the slope of the tangent line at this point.

30. Tangent lines with zero slope

a. Graph the function $f(x) = 4 - x^2$.

b. Identify the point $(a, f(a))$ at which the function has a tangent line with zero slope.

c. Consider the point $(a, f(a))$ found in part (b). Is it true that the secant line between $(a - h, f(a - h))$ and $(a + h, f(a + h))$ has slope zero for any value of $h \neq 0$?

T 31. Zero velocity A projectile is fired vertically upward and has a position given by $s(t) = -16t^2 + 128t + 192$, for $0 \le t \le 9$.

a. Graph the position function, for $0 \le t \le 9$.

b. From the graph of the position function, identify the time at which the projectile has an instantaneous velocity of zero; call this time $t = a$.

c. Confirm your answer to part (b) by making a table of average velocities to approximate the instantaneous velocity at $t = a$.

d. For what values of t on the interval $[0, 9]$ is the instantaneous velocity positive (the projectile moves upward)?

e. For what values of t on the interval $[0, 9]$ is the instantaneous velocity negative (the projectile moves downward)?

T 32. Impact speed A rock is dropped off the edge of a cliff, and its distance s (in feet) from the top of the cliff after t seconds is $s(t) = 16t^2$. Assume the distance from the top of the cliff to the ground is 96 ft.

a. When will the rock strike the ground?

b. Make a table of average velocities and approximate the velocity at which the rock strikes the ground.

T 33. Slope of tangent line Given the function $f(x) = 1 - \cos x$ and the points $A(\pi/2, f(\pi/2))$, $B(\pi/2 + 0.05, f(\pi/2 + 0.05))$, $C(\pi/2 + 0.5, f(\pi/2 + 0.5))$, and $D(\pi, f(\pi))$ (see figure), find the slopes of the secant lines through A and D, A and C, and A and B. Then use your calculations to make a conjecture about the slope of the line tangent to the graph of f at $x = \pi/2$.

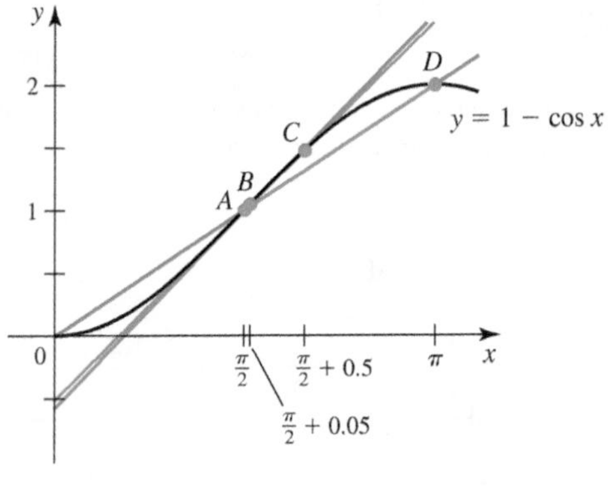

QUICK CHECK ANSWERS

1. 16 ft/s **2.** Average velocity is the velocity over an interval of time. Instantaneous velocity is the velocity at one point of time. **3.** Less than ◀

2.2 Definitions of Limits

Computing slopes of tangent lines and instantaneous velocities (Section 2.1) are just two of many important calculus problems that rely on limits. We now put these two problems aside until Chapter 3 and begin with a preliminary definition of the limit of a function.

➤ The terms *arbitrarily close* and *sufficiently close* will be made precise when rigorous definitions of limits are given in Section 2.7.

> DEFINITION **Limit of a Function (Preliminary)**
>
> Suppose the function f is defined for all x near a except possibly at a. If $f(x)$ is arbitrarily close to L (as close to L as we like) for all x sufficiently close (but not equal) to a, we write
>
> $$\lim_{x \to a} f(x) = L$$
>
> and say the limit of $f(x)$ as x approaches a equals L.

Informally, we say that $\lim_{x \to a} f(x) = L$ if $f(x)$ gets closer and closer to L as x gets closer and closer to a from both sides of a. The value of $\lim_{x \to a} f(x)$ (if it exists) depends on the values of f near a, but it does not depend on the value of $f(a)$. In some cases, the limit $\lim_{x \to a} f(x)$ equals $f(a)$. In other instances, $\lim_{x \to a} f(x)$ and $f(a)$ differ, or $f(a)$ may not even be defined.

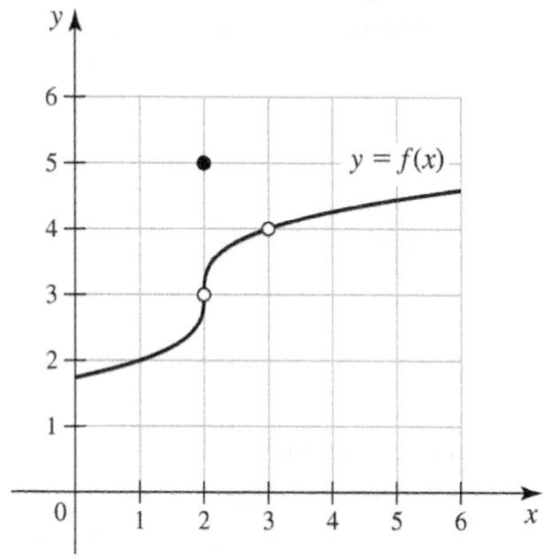

Figure 2.7

EXAMPLE 1 **Finding limits from a graph** Use the graph of f (Figure 2.7) to determine the following values, if possible.

a. $f(1)$ and $\lim_{x \to 1} f(x)$ **b.** $f(2)$ and $\lim_{x \to 2} f(x)$ **c.** $f(3)$ and $\lim_{x \to 3} f(x)$

SOLUTION

a. We see that $f(1) = 2$. As x approaches 1 from either side, the values of $f(x)$ approach 2 (Figure 2.8). Therefore, $\lim_{x \to 1} f(x) = 2$.

b. We see that $f(2) = 5$. However, as x approaches 2 from either side, $f(x)$ approaches 3 because the points on the graph of f approach the open circle at $(2, 3)$ (Figure 2.9). Therefore, $\lim_{x \to 2} f(x) = 3$ even though $f(2) = 5$.

c. In this case, $f(3)$ is undefined. We see that $f(x)$ approaches 4 as x approaches 3 from either side (Figure 2.10). Therefore, $\lim_{x \to 3} f(x) = 4$ even though $f(3)$ does not exist.

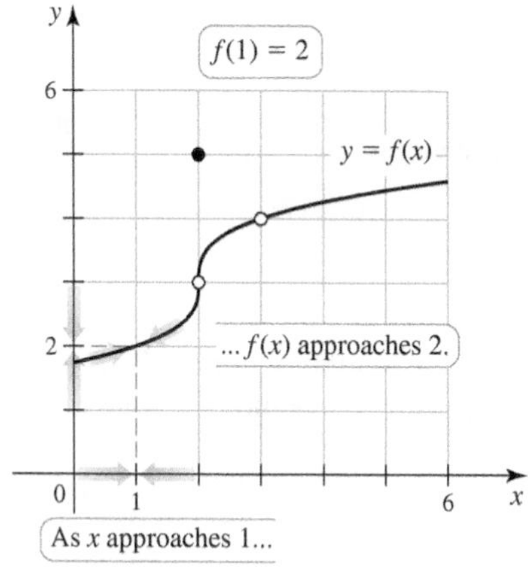

Figure 2.8

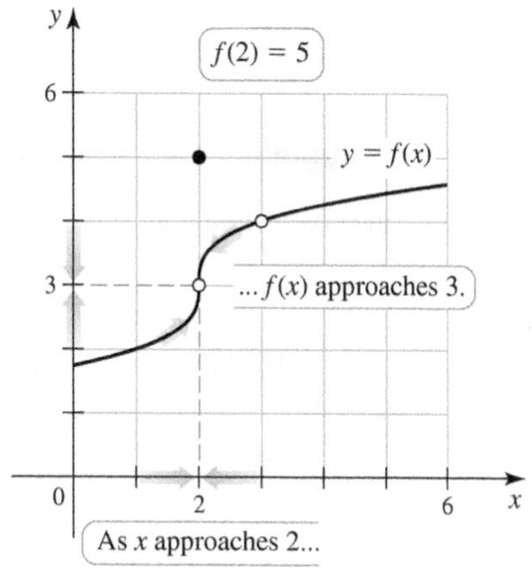

Figure 2.9

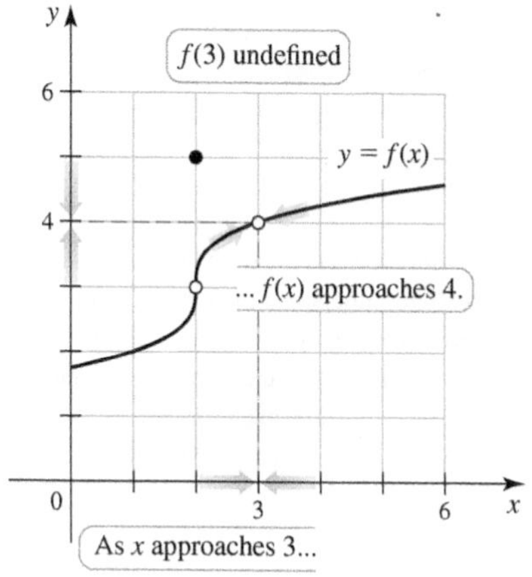

Figure 2.10

Related Exercises 7–10 ◀

QUICK CHECK 1 In Example 1, suppose we redefine the function at one point so that $f(1) = 1$. Does this change the value of $\lim_{x \to 1} f(x)$? ◀

In Example 1, we worked with the graph of a function to estimate limits. Let's now estimate limits using tabulated values of a function.

➤ In Example 2, we have not stated with certainty that $\lim_{x \to 1} f(x) = 0.5$. But this is a reasonable conjecture based on the numerical evidence. Methods for calculating limits precisely are introduced in Section 2.3.

EXAMPLE 2 Finding limits from a table Create a table of values of $f(x) = \dfrac{\sqrt{x} - 1}{x - 1}$ corresponding to values of x near 1. Then make a conjecture about the value of $\lim_{x \to 1} f(x)$.

SOLUTION Table 2.2 lists values of f corresponding to values of x approaching 1 from both sides. The numerical evidence suggests that $f(x)$ approaches 0.5 as x approaches 1. Therefore, we make the conjecture that $\lim_{x \to 1} f(x) = 0.5$.

Table 2.2

	→	→	→	→ 1 ←	←	←	←	←
x	0.9	0.99	0.999	0.9999	1.0001	1.001	1.01	1.1
$f(x) = \dfrac{\sqrt{x} - 1}{x - 1}$	0.5131670	0.5012563	0.5001251	0.5000125	0.4999875	0.4998751	0.4987562	0.4880885

Related Exercises 11–14 ◀

One-Sided Limits

The limit $\lim_{x \to a} f(x) = L$ is referred to as a *two-sided* limit because $f(x)$ approaches L as x approaches a for values of x less than a *and* for values of x greater than a. For some functions, it makes sense to examine *one-sided* limits called *right-sided* and *left-sided* limits.

➤ As with two-sided limits, the value of a one-sided limit (if it exists) depends on the values of $f(x)$ near a but not on the value of $f(a)$.

DEFINITION One-Sided Limits

1. **Right-sided limit** Suppose f is defined for all x near a with $x > a$. If $f(x)$ is arbitrarily close to L for all x sufficiently close to a with $x > a$, we write

$$\lim_{x \to a^+} f(x) = L$$

and say the limit of $f(x)$ as x approaches a from the right equals L.

2. **Left-sided limit** Suppose f is defined for all x near a with $x < a$. If $f(x)$ is arbitrarily close to L for all x sufficiently close to a with $x < a$, we write

$$\lim_{x \to a^-} f(x) = L$$

and say the limit of $f(x)$ as x approaches a from the left equals L.

➤ Computer-generated graphs and tables help us understand the idea of a limit. Keep in mind, however, that computers are not infallible and they may produce incorrect results, even for simple functions (see Example 5).

EXAMPLE 3 Examining limits graphically and numerically Let $f(x) = \dfrac{x^3 - 8}{4(x - 2)}$. Use tables and graphs to make a conjecture about the values of $\lim_{x \to 2^+} f(x)$, $\lim_{x \to 2^-} f(x)$, and $\lim_{x \to 2} f(x)$, if they exist.

SOLUTION Figure 2.11a shows the graph of f obtained with a graphing utility. The graph is misleading because $f(2)$ is undefined, which means there should be a hole in the graph at $(2, 3)$ (Figure 2.11b).

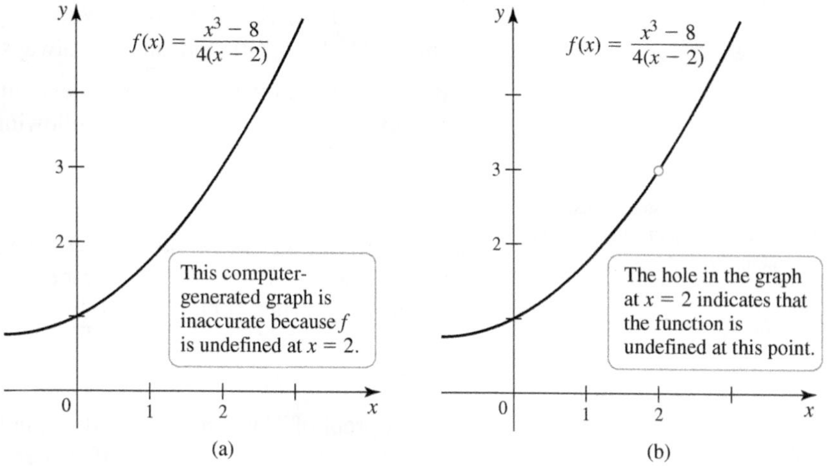

Figure 2.11

The graph in Figure 2.12a and the function values in Table 2.3 suggest that $f(x)$ approaches 3 as x approaches 2 from the right. Therefore, we write the right-sided limit

$$\lim_{x \to 2^+} f(x) = 3,$$

which says the limit of $f(x)$ as x approaches 2 from the right equals 3.

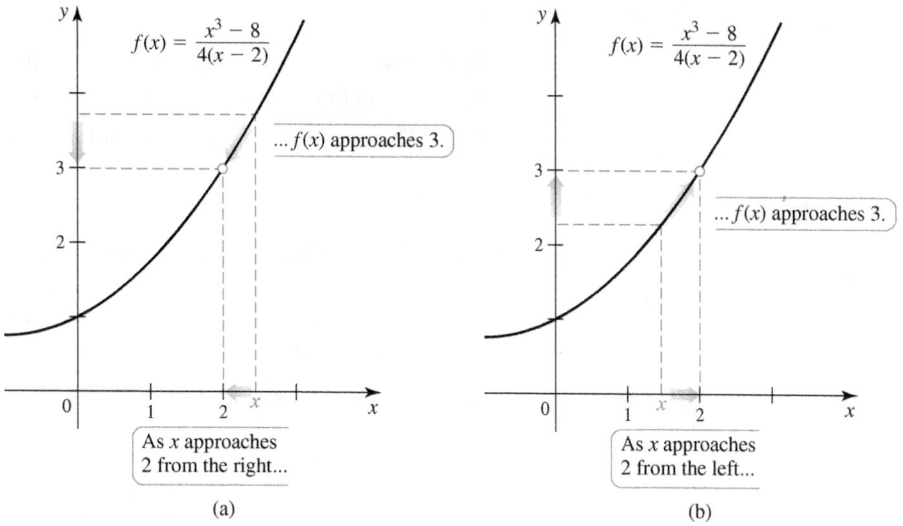

Figure 2.12

Table 2.3

	→				2	←			
x	1.9	1.99	1.999	1.9999		2.0001	2.001	2.01	2.1
$f(x) = \dfrac{x^3 - 8}{4(x - 2)}$	2.8525	2.985025	2.99850025	2.99985000		3.00015000	3.00150025	3.015025	3.1525

➤ Remember that the value of the limit does not depend on the value of $f(2)$. In Example 3, $\lim_{x \to 2} f(x) = 3$ despite the fact that $f(2)$ is undefined.

Similarly, Figure 2.12b and Table 2.3 suggest that as x approaches 2 from the left, $f(x)$ approaches 3. So we write the left-sided limit

$$\lim_{x \to 2^-} f(x) = 3,$$

which says the limit of $f(x)$ as x approaches 2 from the left equals 3. Because $f(x)$ approaches 3 as x approaches 2 from either side, we write the two-sided limit $\lim_{x \to 2} f(x) = 3$.

Related Exercises 15–18 ◀

Based on the previous example, you might wonder whether the limits $\lim_{x\to a^-} f(x)$, $\lim_{x\to a^+} f(x)$, and $\lim_{x\to a} f(x)$ always exist and are equal. The remaining examples demonstrate that these limits may have different values, and in some cases, one or more of these limits may not exist. The following theorem is useful when comparing one-sided and two-sided limits.

➤ Suppose P and Q are statements. We write P *if and only if* Q when P implies Q *and* Q implies P.

THEOREM 2.1 Relationship Between One-Sided and Two-Sided Limits
Assume f is defined for all x near a except possibly at a. Then $\lim_{x\to a} f(x) = L$ if and only if $\lim_{x\to a^+} f(x) = L$ and $\lim_{x\to a^-} f(x) = L$.

A proof of Theorem 2.1 is outlined in Exercise 44 of Section 2.7. Using this theorem, it follows that $\lim_{x\to a} f(x) \neq L$ if either $\lim_{x\to a^+} f(x) \neq L$ or $\lim_{x\to a^-} f(x) \neq L$ (or both). Furthermore, if either $\lim_{x\to a^+} f(x)$ or $\lim_{x\to a^-} f(x)$ does not exist, then $\lim_{x\to a} f(x)$ does not exist. We put these ideas to work in the next two examples.

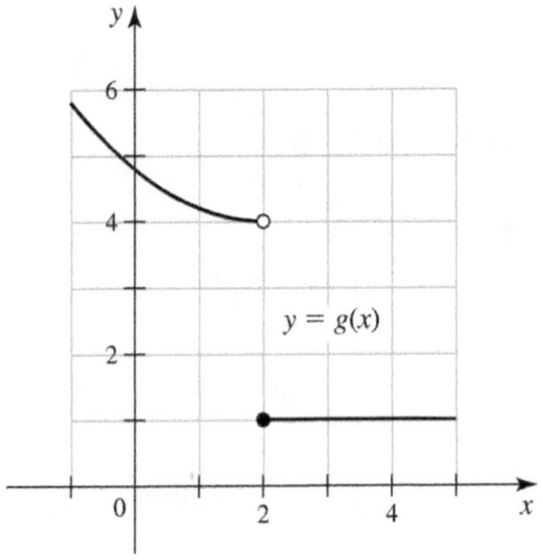

Figure 2.13

EXAMPLE 4 A function with a jump Given the graph of g in Figure 2.13, find the following limits, if they exist.

a. $\lim_{x\to 2^-} g(x)$ **b.** $\lim_{x\to 2^+} g(x)$ **c.** $\lim_{x\to 2} g(x)$

SOLUTION

a. As x approaches 2 from the left, $g(x)$ approaches 4. Therefore, $\lim_{x\to 2^-} g(x) = 4$.

b. Because $g(x) = 1$ for all $x \geq 2$, $\lim_{x\to 2^+} g(x) = 1$.

c. By Theorem 2.1, $\lim_{x\to 2} g(x)$ does not exist because $\lim_{x\to 2^-} g(x) \neq \lim_{x\to 2^+} g(x)$.

Related Exercises 19–24 ◀

EXAMPLE 5 Some strange behavior Examine $\lim_{x\to 0} \cos(1/x)$.

SOLUTION From the first three values of $\cos(1/x)$ in Table 2.4, it is tempting to conclude that $\lim_{x\to 0^+} \cos(1/x) = -1$. But this conclusion is not confirmed when we evaluate $\cos(1/x)$ for values of x closer to 0.

Table 2.4

x	$\cos(1/x)$
0.001	0.56238
0.0001	−0.95216
0.00001	−0.99936
0.000001	0.93675
0.0000001	−0.90727
0.00000001	−0.36338

We might *incorrectly* conclude that $\cos(1/x)$ approaches -1 as x approaches 0 from the right.

The behavior of $\cos(1/x)$ near 0 is better understood by letting $x = 1/(n\pi)$, where n is a positive integer. By making this substitution, we can sample the function at discrete points that approach zero. In this case,

$$\cos\frac{1}{x} = \cos n\pi = \begin{cases} 1 & \text{if } n \text{ is even} \\ -1 & \text{if } n \text{ is odd.} \end{cases}$$

QUICK CHECK 2 Why is the graph of $y = \cos(1/x)$ difficult to plot near $x = 0$, as suggested by Figure 2.14? ◄

As n increases, the values of $x = 1/(n\pi)$ approach zero, while the values of $\cos(1/x)$ oscillate between -1 and 1 (Figure 2.14). Therefore, $\cos(1/x)$ does not approach a single number as x approaches 0 from the right. We conclude that $\lim_{x\to 0^+} \cos(1/x)$ does *not* exist, which implies that $\lim_{x\to 0} \cos(1/x)$ does not exist.

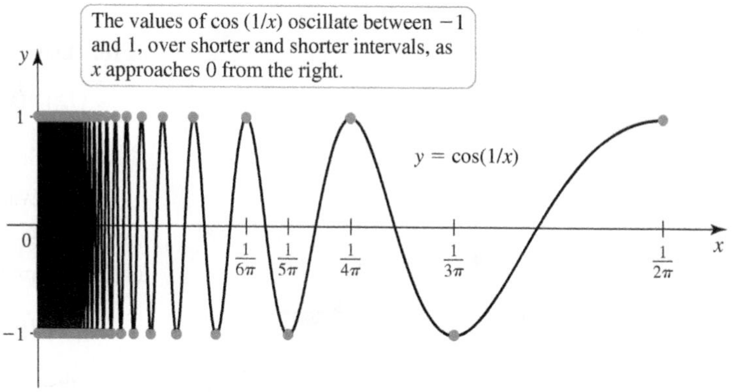

Figure 2.14

Related Exercises 25–26 ◄

Using tables and graphs to make conjectures for the values of limits worked well until Example 5. The limitation of technology in this example is not an isolated incident. For this reason, analytical techniques (paper-and-pencil methods) for finding limits are developed in the next section.

SECTION 2.2 EXERCISES

Review Questions

1. Explain the meaning of $\lim_{x\to a} f(x) = L$.
2. True or false: When $\lim_{x\to a} f(x)$ exists, it always equals $f(a)$. Explain.
3. Explain the meaning of $\lim_{x\to a^+} f(x) = L$.
4. Explain the meaning of $\lim_{x\to a^-} f(x) = L$.
5. If $\lim_{x\to a^-} f(x) = L$ and $\lim_{x\to a^+} f(x) = M$, where L and M are finite real numbers, then how are L and M related if $\lim_{x\to a} f(x)$ exists?
6. What are the potential problems of using a graphing utility to estimate $\lim_{x\to a} f(x)$?

Basic Skills

7. **Finding limits from a graph** Use the graph of h in the figure to find the following values or state that they do not exist.

   a. $h(2)$ **b.** $\lim_{x\to 2} h(x)$ **c.** $h(4)$ **d.** $\lim_{x\to 4} h(x)$ **e.** $\lim_{x\to 5} h(x)$

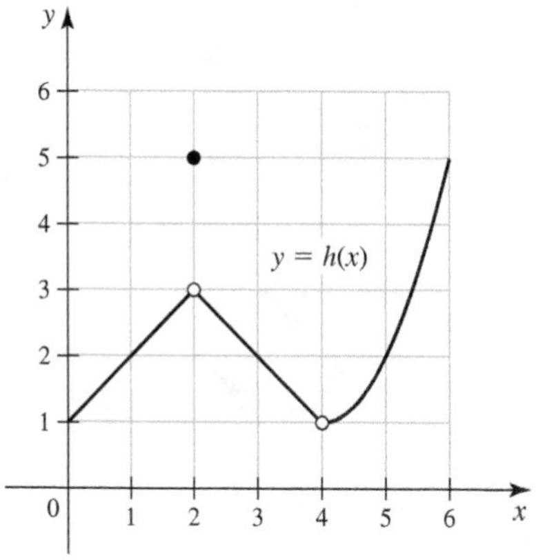

8. **Finding limits from a graph** Use the graph of g in the figure to find the following values or state that they do not exist.

   a. $g(0)$ **b.** $\lim_{x\to 0} g(x)$ **c.** $g(1)$ **d.** $\lim_{x\to 1} g(x)$

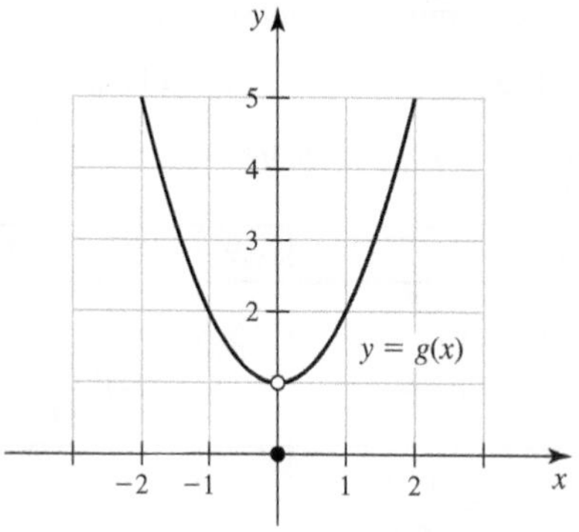

9. **Finding limits from a graph** Use the graph of f in the figure to find the following values or state that they do not exist.

   a. $f(1)$ **b.** $\lim_{x\to 1} f(x)$ **c.** $f(0)$ **d.** $\lim_{x\to 0} f(x)$

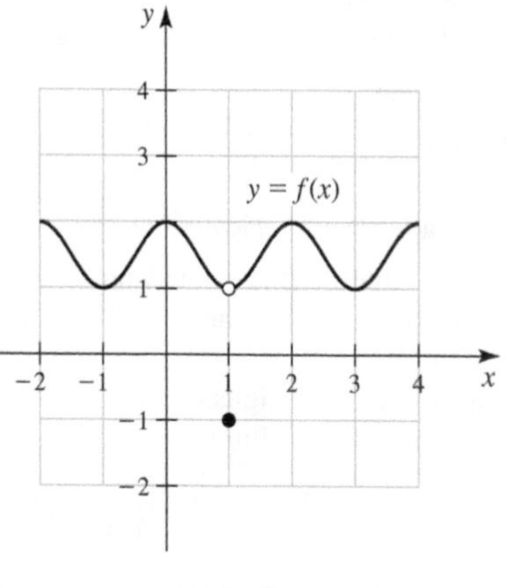

10. **Finding limits from a graph** Use the graph of f in the figure to find the following values or state that they do not exist.

a. $f(2)$ **b.** $\lim_{x\to 2} f(x)$ **c.** $\lim_{x\to 4} f(x)$ **d.** $\lim_{x\to 5} f(x)$

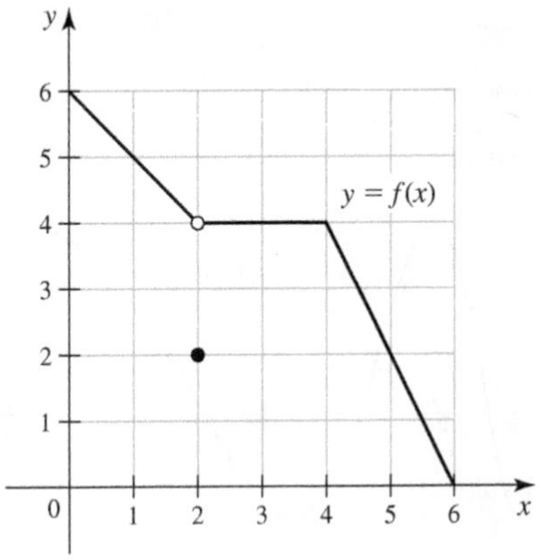

T 11. Estimating a limit from tables Let $f(x) = \dfrac{x^2 - 4}{x - 2}$.

a. Calculate $f(x)$ for each value of x in the following table.

b. Make a conjecture about the value of $\lim_{x\to 2} \dfrac{x^2 - 4}{x - 2}$.

x	1.9	1.99	1.999	1.9999
$f(x) = \dfrac{x^2 - 4}{x - 2}$				
x	2.1	2.01	2.001	2.0001
$f(x) = \dfrac{x^2 - 4}{x - 2}$				

T 12. Estimating a limit from tables Let $f(x) = \dfrac{x^3 - 1}{x - 1}$.

a. Calculate $f(x)$ for each value of x in the following table.

b. Make a conjecture about the value of $\lim_{x\to 1} \dfrac{x^3 - 1}{x - 1}$.

x	0.9	0.99	0.999	0.9999
$f(x) = \dfrac{x^3 - 1}{x - 1}$				
x	1.1	1.01	1.001	1.0001
$f(x) = \dfrac{x^3 - 1}{x - 1}$				

T 13. Estimating a limit numerically Let $g(t) = \dfrac{t - 9}{\sqrt{t} - 3}$.

a. Make two tables, one showing values of g for $t = 8.9, 8.99$, and 8.999 and one showing values of g for $t = 9.1, 9.01$, and 9.001.

b. Make a conjecture about the value of $\lim_{t\to 9} \dfrac{t - 9}{\sqrt{t} - 3}$.

T 14. Estimating a limit numerically Let $f(x) = (1 + x)^{1/x}$.

a. Make two tables, one showing values of f for $x = 0.01, 0.001, 0.0001$, and 0.00001 and one showing values of f for $x = -0.01, -0.001, -0.0001$, and -0.00001. Round your answers to five digits.

b. Estimate the value of $\lim_{x\to 0} (1 + x)^{1/x}$.

c. What mathematical constant does $\lim_{x\to 0} (1 + x)^{1/x}$ appear to equal?

T 15. Estimating a limit graphically and numerically
Let $f(x) = \dfrac{x - 2}{\ln |x - 2|}$.

a. Graph f to estimate $\lim_{x\to 2} f(x)$.

b. Evaluate $f(x)$ for values of x near 2 to support your conjecture in part (a).

T 16. Estimating a limit graphically and numerically
Let $g(x) = \dfrac{e^{2x} - 2x - 1}{x^2}$.

a. Graph g to estimate $\lim_{x\to 0} g(x)$.

b. Evaluate $g(x)$ for values of x near 0 to support your conjecture in part (a).

T 17. Estimating a limit graphically and numerically
Let $f(x) = \dfrac{1 - \cos(2x - 2)}{(x - 1)^2}$.

a. Graph f to estimate $\lim_{x\to 1} f(x)$.

b. Evaluate $f(x)$ for values of x near 1 to support your conjecture in part (a).

T 18. Estimating a limit graphically and numerically
Let $g(x) = \dfrac{3 \sin x - 2 \cos x + 2}{x}$.

a. Graph of g to estimate $\lim_{x\to 0} g(x)$.

b. Evaluate $g(x)$ for values of x near 0 to support your conjecture in part (a).

T 19. One-sided and two-sided limits Let $f(x) = \dfrac{x^2 - 25}{x - 5}$. Use tables and graphs to make a conjecture about the values of $\lim_{x\to 5^+} f(x)$, $\lim_{x\to 5^-} f(x)$, and $\lim_{x\to 5} f(x)$ or state that they do not exist.

T 20. One-sided and two-sided limits Let $g(x) = \dfrac{x - 100}{\sqrt{x} - 10}$. Use tables and graphs to make a conjecture about the values of $\lim_{x\to 100^+} g(x)$, $\lim_{x\to 100^-} g(x)$, and $\lim_{x\to 100} g(x)$ or state that they do not exist.

T 21. One-sided and two-sided limits Use the graph of f in the figure to find the following values or state that they do not exist. If a limit does not exist, explain why.

a. $f(1)$ **b.** $\lim_{x\to 1^-} f(x)$

c. $\lim_{x\to 1^+} f(x)$ **d.** $\lim_{x\to 1} f(x)$

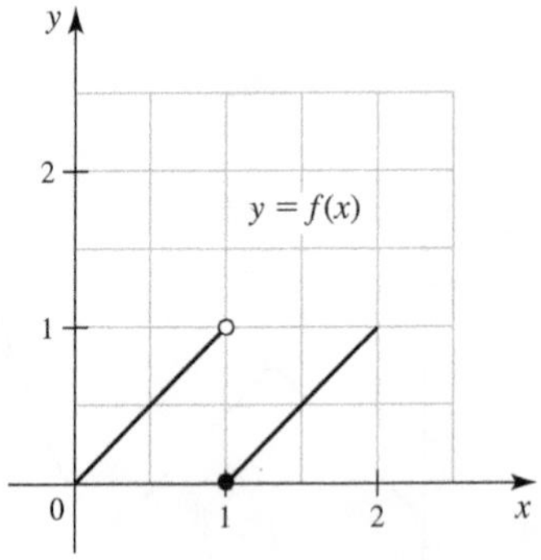

22. One-sided and two-sided limits Use the graph of g in the figure to find the following values or state that they do not exist. If a limit does not exist, explain why.

a. $g(2)$ **b.** $\lim_{x \to 2^-} g(x)$ **c.** $\lim_{x \to 2^+} g(x)$

d. $\lim_{x \to 2} g(x)$ **e.** $g(3)$ **f.** $\lim_{x \to 3^-} g(x)$

g. $\lim_{x \to 3^+} g(x)$ **h.** $g(4)$ **i.** $\lim_{x \to 4} g(x)$

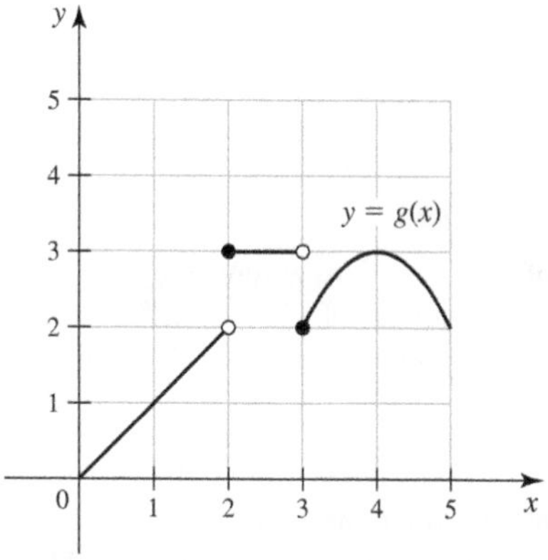

23. Finding limits from a graph Use the graph of f in the figure to find the following values or state that they do not exist. If a limit does not exist, explain why.

a. $f(1)$ **b.** $\lim_{x \to 1^-} f(x)$ **c.** $\lim_{x \to 1^+} f(x)$

d. $\lim_{x \to 1} f(x)$ **e.** $f(3)$ **f.** $\lim_{x \to 3^-} f(x)$

g. $\lim_{x \to 3^+} f(x)$ **h.** $\lim_{x \to 3} f(x)$ **i.** $f(2)$

j. $\lim_{x \to 2^-} f(x)$ **k.** $\lim_{x \to 2^+} f(x)$ **l.** $\lim_{x \to 2} f(x)$

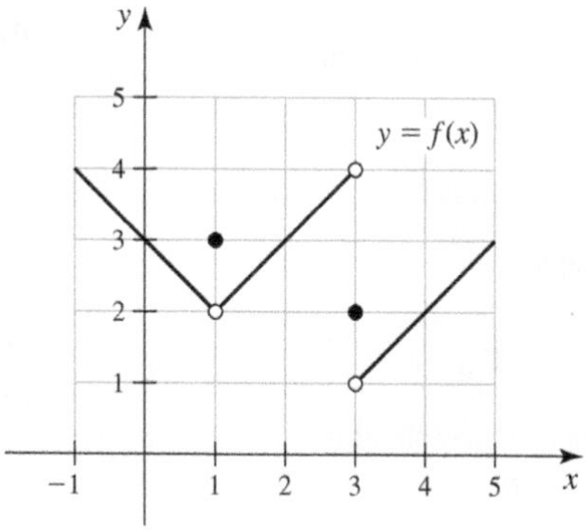

24. Finding limits from a graph Use the graph of g in the figure to find the following values or state that they do not exist. If a limit does not exist, explain why.

a. $g(-1)$ **b.** $\lim_{x \to -1^-} g(x)$ **c.** $\lim_{x \to -1^+} g(x)$

d. $\lim_{x \to -1} g(x)$ **e.** $g(1)$ **f.** $\lim_{x \to 1} g(x)$

g. $\lim_{x \to 3} g(x)$ **h.** $g(5)$ **i.** $\lim_{x \to 5^-} g(x)$

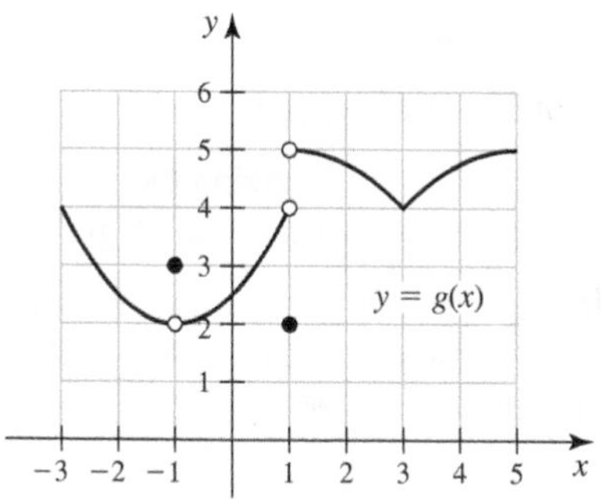

T 25. Strange behavior near $x = 0$

a. Create a table of values of $\sin(1/x)$, for $x = \frac{2}{\pi}, \frac{2}{3\pi}, \frac{2}{5\pi}, \frac{2}{7\pi}, \frac{2}{9\pi}$, and $\frac{2}{11\pi}$. Describe the pattern of values you observe.

b. Why does a graphing utility have difficulty plotting the graph of $y = \sin(1/x)$ near $x = 0$ (see figure)?

c. What do you conclude about $\lim_{x \to 0} \sin(1/x)$?

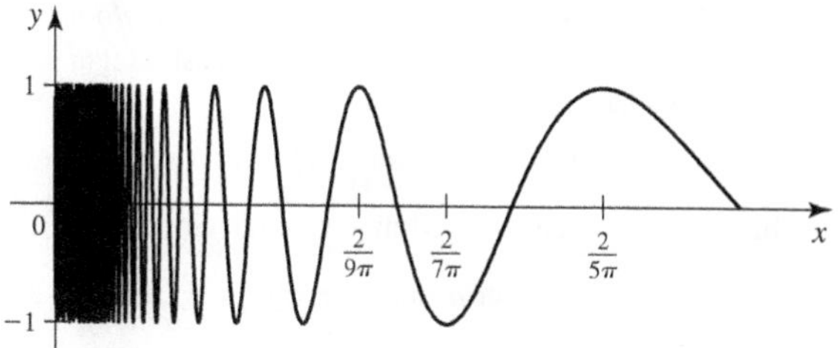

T 26. Strange behavior near $x = 0$

a. Create a table of values of $\tan(3/x)$ for $x = 12/\pi, 12/(3\pi), 12/(5\pi), \ldots, 12/(11\pi)$. Describe the general pattern in the values you observe.

b. Use a graphing utility to graph $y = \tan(3/x)$. Why do graphing utilities have difficulty plotting the graph near $x = 0$?

c. What do you conclude about $\lim_{x \to 0} \tan(3/x)$?

Further Explorations

27. Explain why or why not Determine whether the following statements are true and give an explanation or counterexample.

a. The value of $\lim_{x \to 3} \frac{x^2 - 9}{x - 3}$ does not exist.

b. The value of $\lim_{x \to a} f(x)$ is always found by computing $f(a)$.

c. The value of $\lim_{x \to a} f(x)$ does not exist if $f(a)$ is undefined.

d. $\lim_{x \to 0} \sqrt{x} = 0$.

e. $\lim_{x \to \pi/2} \cot x = 0$.

28–31. Sketching graphs of functions *Sketch the graph of a function with the given properties. You do not need to find a formula for the function.*

28. $f(1) = 0, f(2) = 4, f(3) = 6, \lim_{x \to 2^-} f(x) = -3, \lim_{x \to 2^+} f(x) = 5$

29. $g(1) = 0, g(2) = 1, g(3) = -2, \lim_{x \to 2} g(x) = 0,$
$\lim_{x \to 3^-} g(x) = -1, \lim_{x \to 3^+} g(x) = -2$

30. $h(-1) = 2, \lim_{x \to -1^-} h(x) = 0, \lim_{x \to -1^+} h(x) = 3,$
$h(1) = \lim_{x \to 1^-} h(x) = 1, \lim_{x \to 1^+} h(x) = 4$

31. $p(0) = 2, \lim_{x \to 0} p(x) = 0, \lim_{x \to 2} p(x)$ does not exist,
$p(2) = \lim_{x \to 2^+} p(x) = 1$

T 32–35. Calculator limits *Estimate the value of the following limits by creating a table of function values for $h = 0.01, 0.001$, and 0.0001, and $h = -0.01, -0.001$, and -0.0001.*

32. $\lim_{h \to 0} (1 + 2h)^{1/h}$ **33.** $\lim_{h \to 0} (1 + 3h)^{2/h}$

34. $\lim_{h\to 0} \frac{2^h - 1}{h}$

35. $\lim_{h\to 0} \frac{\ln(1+h)}{h}$

36. A step function Let $f(x) = \frac{|x|}{x}$, for $x \neq 0$.

a. Sketch a graph of f on the interval $[-2, 2]$.

b. Does $\lim_{x\to 0} f(x)$ exist? Explain your reasoning after first examining $\lim_{x\to 0^-} f(x)$ and $\lim_{x\to 0^+} f(x)$.

37. The floor function For any real number x, the *floor function* (or *greatest integer function*) $\lfloor x \rfloor$ is the greatest integer less than or equal to x (see figure).

a. Compute $\lim_{x\to -1^-} \lfloor x \rfloor$, $\lim_{x\to -1^+} \lfloor x \rfloor$, $\lim_{x\to 2^-} \lfloor x \rfloor$, and $\lim_{x\to 2^+} \lfloor x \rfloor$.

b. Compute $\lim_{x\to 2.3^-} \lfloor x \rfloor$, $\lim_{x\to 2.3^+} \lfloor x \rfloor$, and $\lim_{x\to 2.3} \lfloor x \rfloor$.

c. For a given integer a, state the values of $\lim_{x\to a^-} \lfloor x \rfloor$ and $\lim_{x\to a^+} \lfloor x \rfloor$.

d. In general, if a is not an integer, state the values of $\lim_{x\to a^-} \lfloor x \rfloor$ and $\lim_{x\to a^+} \lfloor x \rfloor$.

e. For what values of a does $\lim_{x\to a} \lfloor x \rfloor$ exist? Explain.

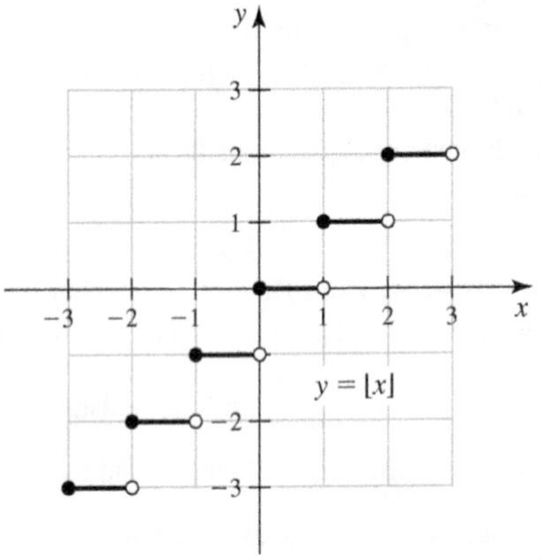

38. The ceiling function For any real number x, the *ceiling function* $\lceil x \rceil$ is the smallest integer greater than or equal to x.

a. Graph the ceiling function $y = \lceil x \rceil$, for $-2 \le x \le 3$.

b. Evaluate $\lim_{x\to 2^-} \lceil x \rceil$, $\lim_{x\to 1^+} \lceil x \rceil$, and $\lim_{x\to 1.5} \lceil x \rceil$.

c. For what values of a does $\lim_{x\to a} \lceil x \rceil$ exist? Explain.

T 39–42. Limits by graphing *Use the zoom and trace features of a graphing utility to approximate the following limits.*

39. $\lim_{x\to 0} x \sin\frac{1}{x}$

40. $\lim_{x\to 1} \frac{18(\sqrt[3]{x} - 1)}{x^3 - 1}$

41. $\lim_{x\to 1} \frac{9(\sqrt{2x - x^4} - \sqrt[3]{x})}{1 - x^{3/4}}$

42. $\lim_{x\to 0} \frac{6^x - 3^x}{x \ln 2}$

Applications

43. Postage rates Assume that postage for sending a first-class letter in the United States is \$0.44 for the first ounce (up to and including 1 oz) plus \$0.17 for each additional ounce (up to and including each additional ounce).

a. Graph the function $p = f(w)$ that gives the postage p for sending a letter that weighs w ounces, for $0 < w \le 5$.

b. Evaluate $\lim_{w\to 3.3} f(w)$.

c. Interpret the limits $\lim_{w\to 1^+} f(w)$ and $\lim_{w\to 1^-} f(w)$.

d. Does $\lim_{w\to 4} f(w)$ exist? Explain.

44. The Heaviside function The Heaviside function is used in engineering applications to model flipping a switch. It is defined as

$$H(x) = \begin{cases} 0 & \text{if } x < 0 \\ 1 & \text{if } x \ge 0. \end{cases}$$

a. Sketch a graph of H on the interval $[-1, 1]$.

b. Does $\lim_{x\to 0} H(x)$ exist? Explain your reasoning after first examining $\lim_{x\to 0^-} H(x)$ and $\lim_{x\to 0^+} H(x)$.

Additional Exercises

45. Limits of even functions A function f is even if $f(-x) = f(x)$, for all x in the domain of f. Suppose f is even, with $\lim_{x\to 2^+} f(x) = 5$ and $\lim_{x\to 2^-} f(x) = 8$. Evaluate the following limits.

a. $\lim_{x\to -2^+} f(x)$

b. $\lim_{x\to -2^-} f(x)$

46. Limits of odd functions A function g is odd if $g(-x) = -g(x)$, for all x in the domain of g. Suppose g is odd, with $\lim_{x\to 2^+} g(x) = 5$ and $\lim_{x\to 2^-} g(x) = 8$. Evaluate the following limits.

a. $\lim_{x\to -2^+} g(x)$

b. $\lim_{x\to -2^-} g(x)$

T 47. Limits by graphs

a. Use a graphing utility to estimate $\lim_{x\to 0} \frac{\tan 2x}{\sin x}$, $\lim_{x\to 0} \frac{\tan 3x}{\sin x}$, and $\lim_{x\to 0} \frac{\tan 4x}{\sin x}$.

b. Make a conjecture about the value of $\lim_{x\to 0} \frac{\tan px}{\sin x}$, for any real constant p.

T 48. Limits by graphs Graph $f(x) = \frac{\sin nx}{x}$, for $n = 1, 2, 3$, and 4 (four graphs). Use the window $[-1, 1] \times [0, 5]$.

a. Estimate $\lim_{x\to 0} \frac{\sin x}{x}$, $\lim_{x\to 0} \frac{\sin 2x}{x}$, $\lim_{x\to 0} \frac{\sin 3x}{x}$, and $\lim_{x\to 0} \frac{\sin 4x}{x}$.

b. Make a conjecture about the value of $\lim_{x\to 0} \frac{\sin px}{x}$, for any real constant p.

T 49. Limits by graphs Use a graphing utility to plot $y = \frac{\sin px}{\sin qx}$ for at least three different pairs of nonzero constants p and q of your choice. Estimate $\lim_{x\to 0} \frac{\sin px}{\sin qx}$ in each case. Then use your work to make a conjecture about the value of $\lim_{x\to 0} \frac{\sin px}{\sin qx}$ for any nonzero values of p and q.

QUICK CHECK ANSWERS

1. The value of $\lim_{x\to 1} f(x)$ depends on the value of f only *near* 1, not at 1. Therefore, changing the value of $f(1)$ will not change the value of $\lim_{x\to 1} f(x)$. **2.** A graphing device has difficulty plotting $y = \cos(1/x)$ near 0 because values of the function vary between −1 and 1 over shorter and shorter intervals as x approaches 0. ◄

2.3 Techniques for Computing Limits

Graphical and numerical techniques for estimating limits, like those presented in the previous section, provide intuition about limits. These techniques, however, occasionally lead to incorrect results. Therefore, we turn our attention to analytical methods for evaluating limits precisely.

Limits of Linear Functions

The graph of $f(x) = mx + b$ is a line with slope m and y-intercept b. From Figure 2.15, we see that $f(x)$ approaches $f(a)$ as x approaches a. Therefore, if f is a linear function, we have $\lim_{x \to a} f(x) = f(a)$. It follows that for linear functions, $\lim_{x \to a} f(x)$ is found by direct substitution of $x = a$ into $f(x)$. This observation leads to the following theorem, which is proved in Exercise 28 of Section 2.7.

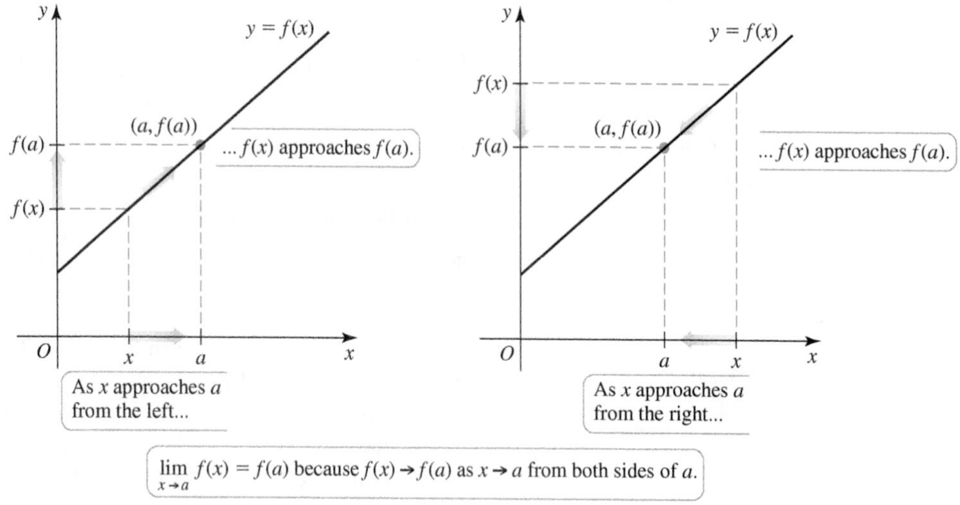

Figure 2.15

> **THEOREM 2.2 Limits of Linear Functions**
> Let a, b, and m be real numbers. For linear functions $f(x) = mx + b$,
> $$\lim_{x \to a} f(x) = f(a) = ma + b.$$

EXAMPLE 1 Limits of linear functions Evaluate the following limits.

a. $\lim_{x \to 3} f(x)$, where $f(x) = \frac{1}{2}x - 7$

b. $\lim_{x \to 2} g(x)$, where $g(x) = 6$

SOLUTION

a. $\lim_{x \to 3} f(x) = \lim_{x \to 3} \left(\frac{1}{2}x - 7\right) = f(3) = -\frac{11}{2}$

b. $\lim_{x \to 2} g(x) = \lim_{x \to 2} 6 = g(2) = 6$

Related Exercises 11–16 ◀

Limit Laws

The following limit laws greatly simplify the evaluation of many limits.

THEOREM 2.3 Limit Laws

Assume $\lim_{x\to a} f(x)$ and $\lim_{x\to a} g(x)$ exist. The following properties hold, where c is a real number, and $m > 0$ and $n > 0$ are integers.

1. **Sum** $\lim_{x\to a}(f(x) + g(x)) = \lim_{x\to a} f(x) + \lim_{x\to a} g(x)$
2. **Difference** $\lim_{x\to a}(f(x) - g(x)) = \lim_{x\to a} f(x) - \lim_{x\to a} g(x)$
3. **Constant multiple** $\lim_{x\to a}(cf(x)) = c\lim_{x\to a} f(x)$
4. **Product** $\lim_{x\to a}(f(x)g(x)) = \left(\lim_{x\to a} f(x)\right)\left(\lim_{x\to a} g(x)\right)$
5. **Quotient** $\lim_{x\to a}\left(\dfrac{f(x)}{g(x)}\right) = \dfrac{\lim_{x\to a} f(x)}{\lim_{x\to a} g(x)}$, provided $\lim_{x\to a} g(x) \neq 0$
6. **Power** $\lim_{x\to a}(f(x))^n = \left(\lim_{x\to a} f(x)\right)^n$
7. **Fractional power** $\lim_{x\to a}(f(x))^{n/m} = \left(\lim_{x\to a} f(x)\right)^{n/m}$, provided $f(x) \geq 0$, for x near a, if m is even and n/m is reduced to lowest terms

➤ Law 6 is a special case of Law 7. Letting $m = 1$ in Law 7 gives Law 6.

A proof of Law 1 is outlined in Section 2.7. Laws 2–5 are proved in Appendix B. Law 6 is proved from Law 4 as follows.

For a positive integer n, if $\lim_{x\to a} f(x)$ exists, we have

$$\begin{aligned}\lim_{x\to a}(f(x))^n &= \lim_{x\to a}\underbrace{(f(x)f(x)\cdots f(x))}_{n \text{ factors of } f(x)} \\ &= \underbrace{\left(\lim_{x\to a} f(x)\right)\left(\lim_{x\to a} f(x)\right)\cdots\left(\lim_{x\to a} f(x)\right)}_{n \text{ factors of } \lim_{x\to a} f(x)} \quad \text{Repeated use of Law 4} \\ &= \left(\lim_{x\to a} f(x)\right)^n.\end{aligned}$$

➤ Recall that to take even roots of a number (for example, square roots or fourth roots), the number must be nonnegative if the result is to be real.

In Law 7, the limit of $(f(x))^{n/m}$ involves the mth root of $f(x)$ when x is near a. If the fraction n/m is in lowest terms and m is even, this root is undefined unless $f(x)$ is nonnegative for all x near a, which explains the restrictions shown.

EXAMPLE 2 Evaluating limits Suppose $\lim_{x\to 2} f(x) = 4$, $\lim_{x\to 2} g(x) = 5$, and $\lim_{x\to 2} h(x) = 8$. Use the limit laws in Theorem 2.3 to compute each limit.

a. $\lim_{x\to 2}\dfrac{f(x) - g(x)}{h(x)}$ **b.** $\lim_{x\to 2}(6f(x)g(x) + h(x))$ **c.** $\lim_{x\to 2}(g(x))^3$

SOLUTION

a.
$$\begin{aligned}\lim_{x\to 2}\frac{f(x) - g(x)}{h(x)} &= \frac{\lim_{x\to 2}(f(x) - g(x))}{\lim_{x\to 2} h(x)} \quad \text{Law 5} \\ &= \frac{\lim_{x\to 2} f(x) - \lim_{x\to 2} g(x)}{\lim_{x\to 2} h(x)} \quad \text{Law 2} \\ &= \frac{4 - 5}{8} = -\frac{1}{8}\end{aligned}$$

b. $\lim_{x\to2}(6f(x)g(x) + h(x)) = \lim_{x\to2}(6f(x)g(x)) + \lim_{x\to2} h(x)$ Law 1

$= 6\cdot\lim_{x\to2}(f(x)g(x)) + \lim_{x\to2} h(x)$ Law 3

$= 6\left(\lim_{x\to2} f(x)\right)\left(\lim_{x\to2} g(x)\right) + \lim_{x\to2} h(x)$ Law 4

$= 6\cdot4\cdot5 + 8 = 128$

c. $\lim_{x\to2}(g(x))^3 = \left(\lim_{x\to2} g(x)\right)^3 = 5^3 = 125$ Law 6

Related Exercises 17–24 ◀

Limits of Polynomial and Rational Functions

The limit laws are now used to find the limits of polynomial and rational functions. For example, to evaluate the limit of the polynomial $p(x) = 7x^3 + 3x^2 + 4x + 2$ at an arbitrary point a, we proceed as follows:

$$\begin{aligned}
\lim_{x\to a} p(x) &= \lim_{x\to a}(7x^3 + 3x^2 + 4x + 2) \\
&= \lim_{x\to a}(7x^3) + \lim_{x\to a}(3x^2) + \lim_{x\to a}(4x + 2) && \text{Law 1} \\
&= 7\lim_{x\to a}(x^3) + 3\lim_{x\to a}(x^2) + \lim_{x\to a}(4x + 2) && \text{Law 3} \\
&= 7\Big(\underbrace{\lim_{x\to a} x}_{a}\Big)^3 + 3\Big(\underbrace{\lim_{x\to a} x}_{a}\Big)^2 + \underbrace{\lim_{x\to a}(4x + 2)}_{4a+2} && \text{Law 6} \\
&= 7a^3 + 3a^2 + 4a + 2 = p(a). && \text{Theorem 2.2}
\end{aligned}$$

As in the case of linear functions, the limit of a polynomial is found by direct substitution; that is, $\lim_{x\to a} p(x) = p(a)$ (Exercise 91).

It is now a short step to evaluating limits of rational functions of the form $f(x) = p(x)/q(x)$, where p and q are polynomials. Applying Law 5, we have

$$\lim_{x\to a}\frac{p(x)}{q(x)} = \frac{\lim_{x\to a} p(x)}{\lim_{x\to a} q(x)} = \frac{p(a)}{q(a)}, \quad \text{provided } q(a) \neq 0,$$

which shows that limits of rational functions are also evaluated by direct substitution.

➤ The conditions under which direct substitution $\left(\lim_{x\to a} f(x) = f(a)\right)$ can be used to evaluate a limit become clear in Section 2.6, when we discuss the important property of *continuity*.

THEOREM 2.4 Limits of Polynomial and Rational Functions
Assume p and q are polynomials and a is a constant.

a. Polynomial functions: $\lim_{x\to a} p(x) = p(a)$

b. Rational functions: $\lim_{x\to a}\frac{p(x)}{q(x)} = \frac{p(a)}{q(a)}$, provided $q(a) \neq 0$

QUICK CHECK 1 Evaluate $\lim_{x\to2}(2x^4 - 8x - 16)$ and $\lim_{x\to-1}\frac{x-1}{x}$. ◀

EXAMPLE 3 Limit of a rational function Evaluate $\lim_{x\to2}\frac{3x^2 - 4x}{5x^3 - 36}$.

SOLUTION Notice that the denominator of this function is nonzero at $x = 2$. Using Theorem 2.4b,

$$\lim_{x\to2}\frac{3x^2 - 4x}{5x^3 - 36} = \frac{3(2^2) - 4(2)}{5(2^3) - 36} = 1.$$

Related Exercises 25–27 ◀

QUICK CHECK 2 Use Theorem 2.4b to compute $\lim_{x\to1}\frac{5x^4 - 3x^2 + 8x - 6}{x + 1}$. ◀

EXAMPLE 4 **An algebraic function** Evaluate $\lim_{x\to 2} \frac{\sqrt{2x^3 + 9} + 3x - 1}{4x + 1}$.

SOLUTION Using Theorems 2.3 and 2.4, we have

$$\begin{aligned}
\lim_{x\to 2} \frac{\sqrt{2x^3 + 9} + 3x - 1}{4x + 1} &= \frac{\lim_{x\to 2} (\sqrt{2x^3 + 9} + 3x - 1)}{\lim_{x\to 2} (4x + 1)} && \text{Law 5} \\
&= \frac{\sqrt{\lim_{x\to 2} (2x^3 + 9)} + \lim_{x\to 2} (3x - 1)}{\lim_{x\to 2} (4x + 1)} && \text{Laws 1 and 7} \\
&= \frac{\sqrt{(2(2)^3 + 9)} + (3(2) - 1)}{(4(2) + 1)} && \text{Theorem 2.4} \\
&= \frac{\sqrt{25} + 5}{9} = \frac{10}{9}.
\end{aligned}$$

Notice that the limit at $x = 2$ equals the value of the function at $x = 2$.

Related Exercises 28–32 ◀

One-Sided Limits

Theorem 2.2, Limit Laws 1–6, and Theorem 2.4 also hold for left-sided and right-sided limits. In other words, these laws remain valid if we replace $\lim_{x\to a}$ with $\lim_{x\to a^+}$ or $\lim_{x\to a^-}$. Law 7 must be modified slightly for one-sided limits, as shown in the next theorem.

> **THEOREM 2.3 (CONTINUED)** **Limit Laws for One-Sided Limits**
> Laws 1–6 hold with $\lim_{x\to a}$ replaced with $\lim_{x\to a^+}$ or $\lim_{x\to a^-}$. Law 7 is modified as follows. Assume $m > 0$ and $n > 0$ are integers.
>
> **7. Fractional power**
>
> **a.** $\lim_{x\to a^+} (f(x))^{n/m} = \left(\lim_{x\to a^+} f(x)\right)^{n/m}$, provided $f(x) \geq 0$, for x near a with $x > a$, if m is even and n/m is reduced to lowest terms
>
> **b.** $\lim_{x\to a^-} (f(x))^{n/m} = \left(\lim_{x\to a^-} f(x)\right)^{n/m}$, provided $f(x) \geq 0$, for x near a with $x < a$, if m is even and n/m is reduced to lowest terms

EXAMPLE 5 **Calculating left- and right-sided limits** Let

$$f(x) = \begin{cases} -2x + 4 & \text{if } x \leq 1 \\ \sqrt{x - 1} & \text{if } x > 1. \end{cases}$$

Find the values of $\lim_{x\to 1^-} f(x)$, $\lim_{x\to 1^+} f(x)$, and $\lim_{x\to 1} f(x)$, or state that they do not exist.

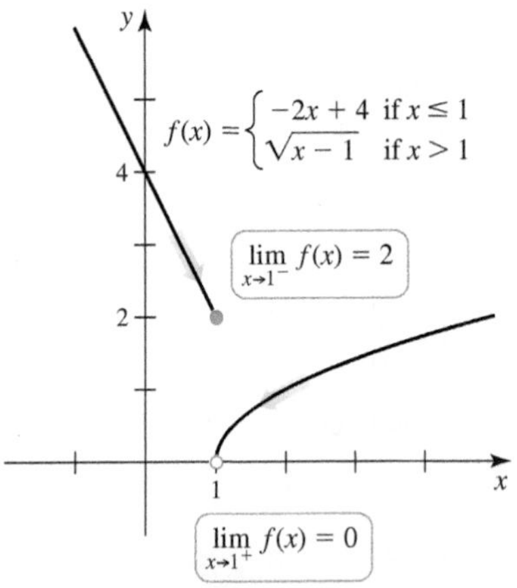

Figure 2.16

SOLUTION The graph of f (Figure 2.16) suggests that $\lim_{x\to 1^-} f(x) = 2$ and $\lim_{x\to 1^+} f(x) = 0$. We verify this observation analytically by applying the limit laws. For $x \leq 1$, $f(x) = -2x + 4$; therefore,

$$\lim_{x\to 1^-} f(x) = \lim_{x\to 1^-} (-2x + 4) = 2. \quad \text{Theorem 2.2}$$

For $x > 1$, note that $x - 1 > 0$; it follows that

$$\lim_{x\to 1^+} f(x) = \lim_{x\to 1^+} \sqrt{x - 1} = 0. \quad \text{Law 7}$$

Because $\lim_{x\to 1^-} f(x) = 2$ and $\lim_{x\to 1^+} f(x) = 0$, $\lim_{x\to 1} f(x)$ does not exist by Theorem 2.1.

Related Exercises 33–38 ◀

Other Techniques

So far, we have evaluated limits by direct substitution. A more challenging problem is finding $\lim_{x \to a} f(x)$ when the limit exists, but $\lim_{x \to a} f(x) \neq f(a)$. Two typical cases are shown in Figure 2.17. In the first case, $f(a)$ is defined, but it is not equal to $\lim_{x \to a} f(x)$; in the second case, $f(a)$ is not defined at all. In both cases, direct substitution does not work—we need a new strategy. One way to evaluate a challenging limit is to replace it with an equivalent limit that *can* be evaluated by direct substitution. Example 6 illustrates two common scenarios.

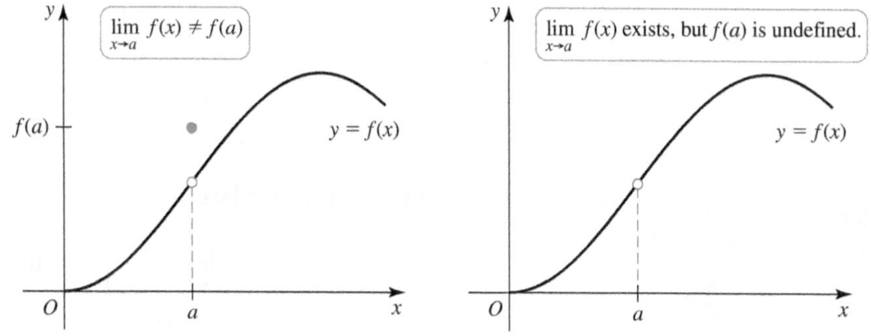

Figure 2.17

EXAMPLE 6 Other techniques Evaluate the following limits.

a. $\displaystyle\lim_{x \to 2} \frac{x^2 - 6x + 8}{x^2 - 4}$ **b.** $\displaystyle\lim_{x \to 1} \frac{\sqrt{x} - 1}{x - 1}$

SOLUTION

a. Factor and cancel This limit cannot be found by direct substitution because the denominator is zero when $x = 2$. Instead, the numerator and denominator are factored; then, assuming $x \neq 2$, we cancel like factors:

$$\frac{x^2 - 6x + 8}{x^2 - 4} = \frac{(x - 2)(x - 4)}{(x - 2)(x + 2)} = \frac{x - 4}{x + 2}.$$

➤ The argument used in Example 6 relies on the fact that in the limit process, x approaches 2, but $x \neq 2$. Therefore, we may cancel like factors.

Because $\dfrac{x^2 - 6x + 8}{x^2 - 4} = \dfrac{x - 4}{x + 2}$ whenever $x \neq 2$, the two functions have the same limit as x approaches 2 (Figure 2.18). Therefore,

$$\lim_{x \to 2} \frac{x^2 - 6x + 8}{x^2 - 4} = \lim_{x \to 2} \frac{x - 4}{x + 2} = \frac{2 - 4}{2 + 2} = -\frac{1}{2}.$$

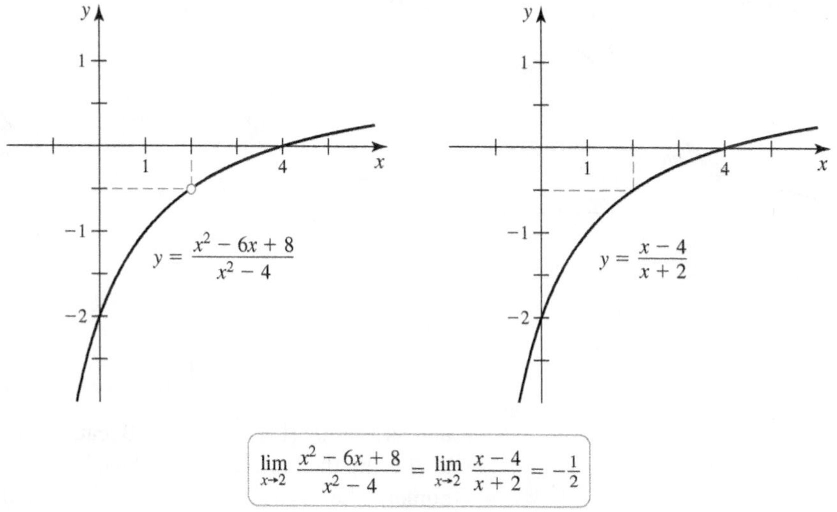

Figure 2.18

b. Use conjugates This limit was approximated numerically in Example 2 of Section 2.2; we conjectured that the value of the limit is $\frac{1}{2}$. Direct substitution fails in this case because the denominator is zero at $x = 1$. Instead, we first simplify the function by multiplying the numerator and denominator by the *algebraic conjugate* of the numerator. The conjugate of $\sqrt{x} - 1$ is $\sqrt{x} + 1$; therefore,

➤ We multiply the given function by
$$1 = \frac{\sqrt{x}+1}{\sqrt{x}+1}.$$

$$\begin{aligned}\frac{\sqrt{x}-1}{x-1} &= \frac{(\sqrt{x}-1)(\sqrt{x}+1)}{(x-1)(\sqrt{x}+1)} && \text{Rationalize the numerator; multiply by 1.}\\ &= \frac{x+\sqrt{x}-\sqrt{x}-1}{(x-1)(\sqrt{x}+1)} && \text{Expand the numerator.}\\ &= \frac{x-1}{(x-1)(\sqrt{x}+1)} && \text{Simplify.}\\ &= \frac{1}{\sqrt{x}+1}. && \text{Cancel like factors assuming } x \neq 1.\end{aligned}$$

The limit can now be evaluated:

$$\lim_{x\to1}\frac{\sqrt{x}-1}{x-1} = \lim_{x\to1}\frac{1}{\sqrt{x}+1} = \frac{1}{1+1} = \frac{1}{2}.$$

Related Exercises 39–52 ◀

QUICK CHECK 3 Evaluate $\lim_{x\to5}\frac{x^2-7x+10}{x-5}$. ◀

An Important Limit

Despite our success in evaluating limits using direct substitution, algebraic manipulation, and the limit laws, there are important limits for which these techniques do not work. One such limit arises when investigating the slope of a line tangent to the graph of an exponential function.

EXAMPLE 7 Slope of a line tangent to $f(x) = 2^x$ Estimate the slope of the line tangent to the graph of $f(x) = 2^x$ at the point $P(0, 1)$.

SOLUTION In Section 2.1, the slope of a tangent line was obtained by finding the limit of slopes of secant lines; the same strategy is employed here. We begin by selecting a point Q near P on the graph of f with coordinates $(x, 2^x)$. The secant line joining the points $P(0, 1)$ and $Q(x, 2^x)$ is an approximation to the tangent line. To estimate the slope of the tangent line (denoted $m_{\tan}$) at $x = 0$, we compute the slope of the secant line $m_{\sec} = (2^x - 1)/x$ and then let x approach 0.

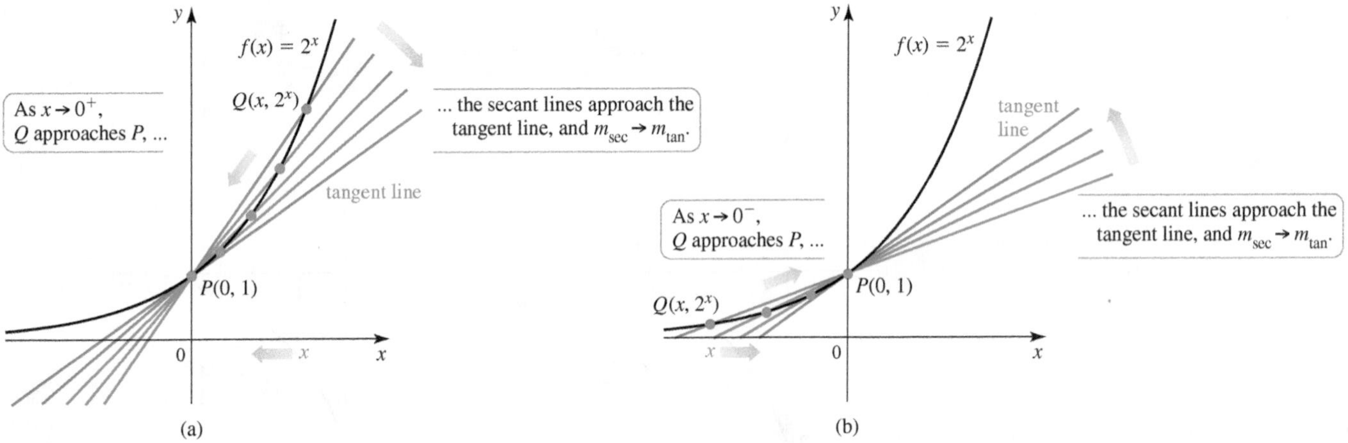

Figure 2.19

The limit $\lim_{x\to0}\frac{2^x-1}{x}$ exists only if it has the same value as $x \to 0^+$ (Figure 2.19a) and as $x \to 0^-$ (Figure 2.19b). Because it is not an elementary limit, it cannot be evaluated using the limit laws introduced in this section. Instead, we investigate the limit using numerical evidence. Choosing positive values of x near 0 results in Table 2.5.

Table 2.5

x	1.0	0.1	0.01	0.001	0.0001	0.00001
$m_{\text{sec}} = \dfrac{2^x - 1}{x}$	1.000000	0.7177	0.6956	0.6934	0.6932	0.6931

We see that as x approaches 0 from the right, the slopes of the secant lines approach the slope of the tangent line, which is approximately 0.693. A similar calculation (Exercise 53) gives the same approximation for the limit as x approaches 0 from the left.

Because the left-sided and right-sided limits are the same, we conclude that $\lim_{x\to 0} (2^x - 1)/x \approx 0.693$ (Theorem 2.1). Therefore, the slope of the line tangent to $f(x) = 2^x$ at $x = 0$ is approximately 0.693.

Related Exercises 53–54 ◀

➤ Example 7 shows that $\lim_{x\to 0} \dfrac{2^x - 1}{x} \approx 0.693$. The exact value of the limit is ln 2. The connection between the natural logarithm and slopes of lines tangent to exponential curves is made clear in Chapters 3 and 6.

➤ The Squeeze Theorem is also called the Pinching Theorem or the Sandwich Theorem.

The Squeeze Theorem

The *Squeeze Theorem* provides another useful method for calculating limits. Suppose the functions f and h have the same limit L at a and assume the function g is trapped between f and h (Figure 2.20). The Squeeze Theorem says that g must also have the limit L at a. A proof of this theorem is outlined in Exercise 54 of Section 2.7.

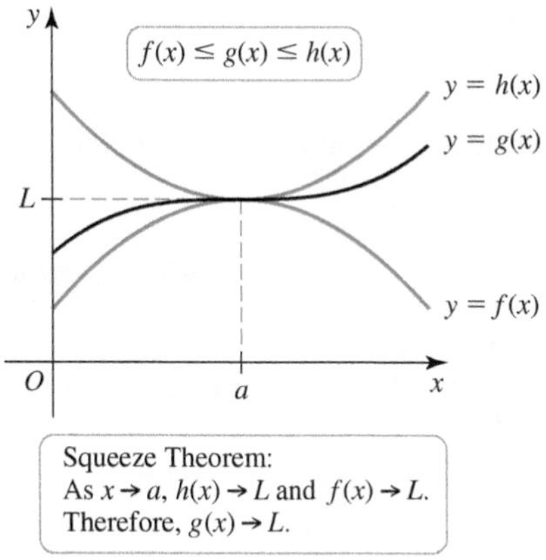

Figure 2.20

THEOREM 2.5 The Squeeze Theorem

Assume the functions f, g, and h satisfy $f(x) \le g(x) \le h(x)$ for all values of x near a, except possibly at a. If $\lim_{x\to a} f(x) = \lim_{x\to a} h(x) = L$, then $\lim_{x\to a} g(x) = L$.

EXAMPLE 8 Sine and cosine limits A geometric argument (Exercise 90) may be used to show that for $-\pi/2 < x < \pi/2$,

$$-|x| \le \sin x \le |x| \quad \text{and} \quad 0 \le 1 - \cos x \le |x|.$$

Use the Squeeze Theorem to confirm the following limits.

a. $\lim_{x\to 0} \sin x = 0$ **b.** $\lim_{x\to 0} \cos x = 1$

➤ The two limits in Example 8 play a crucial role in establishing fundamental properties of the trigonometric functions. The limits reappear in Section 2.6.

SOLUTION

a. Letting $f(x) = -|x|$, $g(x) = \sin x$, and $h(x) = |x|$, we see that g is trapped between f and h on $-\pi/2 < x < \pi/2$ (Figure 2.21a). Because $\lim_{x\to 0} f(x) = \lim_{x\to 0} h(x) = 0$ (Exercise 37), the Squeeze Theorem implies that $\lim_{x\to 0} g(x) = \lim_{x\to 0} \sin x = 0$.

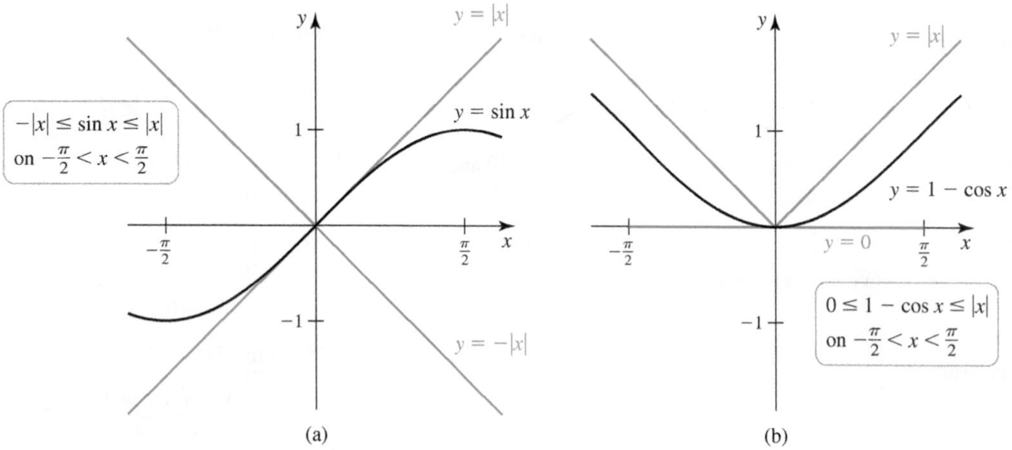

Figure 2.21

b. In this case, we let $f(x) = 0$, $g(x) = 1 - \cos x$, and $h(x) = |x|$ (Figure 2.21b). Because $\lim_{x\to 0} f(x) = \lim_{x\to 0} h(x) = 0$, the Squeeze Theorem implies that $\lim_{x\to 0} g(x) = \lim_{x\to 0} (1 - \cos x) = 0$. By the limit laws of Theorem 2.3, it follows that $\lim_{x\to 0} 1 - \lim_{x\to 0} \cos x = 0$, or $\lim_{x\to 0} \cos x = 1$.

Related Exercises 55–58 ◀

EXAMPLE 9 Applying the Squeeze Theorem Use the Squeeze Theorem to verify that $\lim_{x\to 0} x^2 \sin(1/x) = 0$.

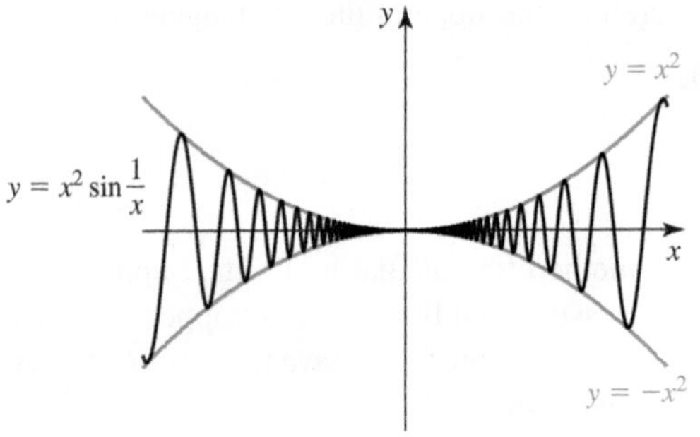

Figure 2.22

SOLUTION For any real number θ, $-1 \le \sin\theta \le 1$. Letting $\theta = 1/x$ for $x \ne 0$, it follows that

$$-1 \le \sin\frac{1}{x} \le 1.$$

Noting that $x^2 > 0$ for $x \ne 0$, each term in this inequality is multiplied by x^2:

$$-x^2 \le x^2 \sin\frac{1}{x} \le x^2.$$

These inequalities are illustrated in Figure 2.22. Because $\lim_{x\to 0} x^2 = \lim_{x\to 0} (-x^2) = 0$, the Squeeze Theorem implies that $\lim_{x\to 0} x^2 \sin(1/x) = 0$.

Related Exercises 55–58 ◀

QUICK CHECK 4 Suppose f satisfies $1 \le f(x) \le 1 + \frac{x^2}{6}$ for all values of x near zero. Find $\lim_{x\to 0} f(x)$, if possible. ◀

SECTION 2.3 EXERCISES

Review Questions

1. How is $\lim_{x\to a} f(x)$ calculated if f is a polynomial function?
2. How are $\lim_{x\to a^-} f(x)$ and $\lim_{x\to a^+} f(x)$ calculated if f is a polynomial function?
3. For what values of a does $\lim_{x\to a} r(x) = r(a)$ if r is a rational function?
4. Assume $\lim_{x\to 3} g(x) = 4$ and $f(x) = g(x)$ whenever $x \ne 3$. Evaluate $\lim_{x\to 3} f(x)$, if possible.
5. Explain why $\lim_{x\to 3} \frac{x^2 - 7x + 12}{x - 3} = \lim_{x\to 3} (x - 4)$.
6. If $\lim_{x\to 2} f(x) = -8$, find $\lim_{x\to 2} (f(x))^{2/3}$.
7. Suppose p and q are polynomials. If $\lim_{x\to 0} \frac{p(x)}{q(x)} = 10$ and $q(0) = 2$, find $p(0)$.
8. Suppose $\lim_{x\to 2} f(x) = \lim_{x\to 2} h(x) = 5$. Find $\lim_{x\to 2} g(x)$, where $f(x) \le g(x) \le h(x)$, for all x.
9. Evaluate $\lim_{x\to 5} \sqrt{x^2 - 9}$.
10. Suppose

$$f(x) = \begin{cases} 4 & \text{if } x \le 3 \\ x + 2 & \text{if } x > 3. \end{cases}$$

Compute $\lim_{x\to 3^-} f(x)$ and $\lim_{x\to 3^+} f(x)$.

Basic Skills

11–16. Limits of linear functions *Evaluate the following limits.*

11. $\lim_{x\to 4} (3x - 7)$
12. $\lim_{x\to 1} (-2x + 5)$
13. $\lim_{x\to -9} 5x$
14. $\lim_{x\to 2} (-3x)$
15. $\lim_{x\to 6} 4$
16. $\lim_{x\to -5} \pi$

17–24. Applying limit laws *Assume* $\lim_{x\to 1} f(x) = 8$, $\lim_{x\to 1} g(x) = 3$, *and* $\lim_{x\to 1} h(x) = 2$. *Compute the following limits and state the limit laws used to justify your computations.*

17. $\lim_{x\to 1} (4f(x))$
18. $\lim_{x\to 1} \frac{f(x)}{h(x)}$
19. $\lim_{x\to 1} (f(x) - g(x))$
20. $\lim_{x\to 1} (f(x)h(x))$
21. $\lim_{x\to 1} \frac{f(x)g(x)}{h(x)}$
22. $\lim_{x\to 1} \frac{f(x)}{g(x) - h(x)}$
23. $\lim_{x\to 1} (h(x))^5$
24. $\lim_{x\to 1} \sqrt[3]{f(x)g(x) + 3}$

25–32. Evaluating limits *Evaluate the following limits.*

25. $\lim_{x\to 1} (2x^3 - 3x^2 + 4x + 5)$
26. $\lim_{t\to -2} (t^2 + 5t + 7)$
27. $\lim_{x\to 1} \frac{5x^2 + 6x + 1}{8x - 4}$
28. $\lim_{t\to 3} \sqrt[3]{t^2 - 10}$
29. $\lim_{b\to 2} \frac{3b}{\sqrt{4b + 1} - 1}$
30. $\lim_{x\to 2} (x^2 - x)^5$

31. $\lim_{x \to 3} \dfrac{-5x}{\sqrt{4x - 3}}$

32. $\lim_{h \to 0} \dfrac{3}{\sqrt{16 + 3h} + 4}$

33. One-sided limits Let

$$f(x) = \begin{cases} x^2 + 1 & \text{if } x < -1 \\ \sqrt{x + 1} & \text{if } x \geq -1. \end{cases}$$

Compute the following limits or state that they do not exist.

a. $\lim_{x \to -1^-} f(x)$ **b.** $\lim_{x \to -1^+} f(x)$ **c.** $\lim_{x \to -1} f(x)$

34. One-sided limits Let

$$f(x) = \begin{cases} 0 & \text{if } x \leq -5 \\ \sqrt{25 - x^2} & \text{if } -5 < x < 5 \\ 3x & \text{if } x \geq 5. \end{cases}$$

Compute the following limits or state that they do not exist.

a. $\lim_{x \to -5^-} f(x)$ **b.** $\lim_{x \to -5^+} f(x)$ **c.** $\lim_{x \to -5} f(x)$

d. $\lim_{x \to 5^-} f(x)$ **e.** $\lim_{x \to 5^+} f(x)$ **f.** $\lim_{x \to 5} f(x)$

35. One-sided limits

a. Evaluate $\lim_{x \to 2^+} \sqrt{x - 2}$.

b. Explain why $\lim_{x \to 2^-} \sqrt{x - 2}$ does not exist.

36. One-sided limits

a. Evaluate $\lim_{x \to 3^-} \sqrt{\dfrac{x - 3}{2 - x}}$.

b. Explain why $\lim_{x \to 3^+} \sqrt{\dfrac{x - 3}{2 - x}}$ does not exist.

37. Absolute value limit Show that $\lim_{x \to 0} |x| = 0$ by first evaluating $\lim_{x \to 0^-} |x|$ and $\lim_{x \to 0^+} |x|$. Recall that

$$|x| = \begin{cases} x & \text{if } x \geq 0 \\ -x & \text{if } x < 0. \end{cases}$$

38. Absolute value limit Show that $\lim_{x \to a} |x| = |a|$, for any real number. (*Hint:* Consider the cases $a < 0$ and $a \geq 0$.)

39–52. Other techniques *Evaluate the following limits, where a and b are fixed real numbers.*

39. $\lim_{x \to 1} \dfrac{x^2 - 1}{x - 1}$

40. $\lim_{x \to 3} \dfrac{x^2 - 2x - 3}{x - 3}$

41. $\lim_{x \to 4} \dfrac{x^2 - 16}{4 - x}$

42. $\lim_{t \to 2} \dfrac{3t^2 - 7t + 2}{2 - t}$

43. $\lim_{x \to b} \dfrac{(x - b)^{50} - x + b}{x - b}$

44. $\lim_{x \to -b} \dfrac{(x + b)^7 + (x + b)^{10}}{4(x + b)}$

45. $\lim_{x \to -1} \dfrac{(2x - 1)^2 - 9}{x + 1}$

46. $\lim_{h \to 0} \dfrac{\frac{1}{5 + h} - \frac{1}{5}}{h}$

47. $\lim_{x \to 9} \dfrac{\sqrt{x} - 3}{x - 9}$

48. $\lim_{t \to 3} \left(\left(4t - \dfrac{2}{t - 3} \right)(6 + t - t^2) \right)$

49. $\lim_{x \to a} \dfrac{x - a}{\sqrt{x} - \sqrt{a}}$, $a > 0$

50. $\lim_{x \to a} \dfrac{x^2 - a^2}{\sqrt{x} - \sqrt{a}}$, $a > 0$

51. $\lim_{h \to 0} \dfrac{\sqrt{16 + h} - 4}{h}$

52. $\lim_{x \to a} \dfrac{x^3 - a^3}{x - a}$

T **53. Slope of a tangent line**

a. Sketch a graph of $y = 2^x$ and carefully draw three secant lines connecting the points $P(0, 1)$ and $Q(x, 2^x)$, for $x = -3, -2$, and -1.

b. Find the slope of the line that passes through $P(0, 1)$ and $Q(x, 2^x)$, for $x \neq 0$.

c. Complete the table and make a conjecture about the value of $\lim_{x \to 0^-} \dfrac{2^x - 1}{x}$.

x	-1	-0.1	-0.01	-0.001	-0.0001	-0.00001
$\dfrac{2^x - 1}{x}$						

T **54. Slope of a tangent line**

a. Sketch a graph of $y = 3^x$ and carefully draw four secant lines connecting the points $P(0, 1)$ and $Q(x, 3^x)$, for $x = -2, -1, 1$, and 2.

b. Find the slope of the line that passes through $P(0, 1)$ and $Q(x, 3^x)$, for $x \neq 0$.

c. Complete the table and make a conjecture about the value of $\lim_{x \to 0} \dfrac{3^x - 1}{x}$.

x	-0.1	-0.01	-0.001	-0.0001	0.0001	0.001	0.01	0.1
$\dfrac{3^x - 1}{x}$								

T **55. Applying the Squeeze Theorem**

a. Show that $-|x| \leq x \sin \dfrac{1}{x} \leq |x|$, for $x \neq 0$.

b. Illustrate the inequalities in part (a) with a graph.

c. Use the Squeeze Theorem to show that $\lim_{x \to 0} x \sin \dfrac{1}{x} = 0$.

T **56. A cosine limit by the Squeeze Theorem** It can be shown that $1 - \dfrac{x^2}{2} \leq \cos x \leq 1$, for x near 0.

a. Illustrate these inequalities with a graph.

b. Use these inequalities to evaluate $\lim_{x \to 0} \cos x$.

T **57. A sine limit by the Squeeze Theorem** It can be shown that $1 - \dfrac{x^2}{6} \leq \dfrac{\sin x}{x} \leq 1$, for x near 0.

a. Illustrate these inequalities with a graph.

b. Use these inequalities to evaluate $\lim_{x \to 0} \dfrac{\sin x}{x}$.

T **58. A logarithm limit by the Squeeze Theorem**

a. Draw a graph to verify that $-|x| \leq x^2 \ln x^2 \leq |x|$, for $-1 \leq x \leq 1$, where $x \neq 0$.

b. Use the Squeeze Theorem to evaluate $\lim_{x \to 0} x^2 \ln x^2$.

Further Explorations

59. Explain why or why not Determine whether the following statements are true and give an explanation or counterexample. Assume a and L are finite numbers.

a. If $\lim_{x \to a} f(x) = L$, then $f(a) = L$.

b. If $\lim_{x \to a^-} f(x) = L$, then $\lim_{x \to a^+} f(x) = L$.

c. If $\lim_{x \to a} f(x) = L$ and $\lim_{x \to a} g(x) = L$, then $f(a) = g(a)$.

d. The limit $\lim_{x \to a} \frac{f(x)}{g(x)}$ does not exist if $g(a) = 0$.

e. If $\lim_{x \to 1^+} \sqrt{f(x)} = \sqrt{\lim_{x \to 1^+} f(x)}$, it follows that $\lim_{x \to 1} \sqrt{f(x)} = \sqrt{\lim_{x \to 1} f(x)}$.

60–67. Evaluating limits *Evaluate the following limits, where c and k are constants.*

60. $\lim_{h \to 0} \frac{100}{(10h - 1)^{11} + 2}$

61. $\lim_{x \to 2} (5x - 6)^{3/2}$

62. $\lim_{x \to 3} \frac{\frac{1}{x^2 + 2x} - \frac{1}{15}}{x - 3}$

63. $\lim_{x \to 1} \frac{\sqrt{10x - 9} - 1}{x - 1}$

64. $\lim_{x \to 2} \left(\frac{1}{x - 2} - \frac{2}{x^2 - 2x} \right)$

65. $\lim_{h \to 0} \frac{(5 + h)^2 - 25}{h}$

66. $\lim_{x \to c} \frac{x^2 - 2cx + c^2}{x - c}$

67. $\lim_{w \to -k} \frac{w^2 + 5kw + 4k^2}{w^2 + kw}$, for $k \neq 0$

68. Finding a constant Suppose

$$f(x) = \begin{cases} 3x + b & \text{if } x \le 2 \\ x - 2 & \text{if } x > 2. \end{cases}$$

Determine a value of the constant b for which $\lim_{x \to 2} f(x)$ exists and state the value of the limit, if possible.

69. Finding a constant Suppose

$$g(x) = \begin{cases} x^2 - 5x & \text{if } x \le -1 \\ ax^3 - 7 & \text{if } x > -1. \end{cases}$$

Determine a value of the constant a for which $\lim_{x \to -1} g(x)$ exists and state the value of the limit, if possible.

70–76. Useful factorization formula *Calculate the following limits using the factorization formula*

$$x^n - a^n = (x - a)(x^{n-1} + x^{n-2}a + x^{n-3}a^2 + \cdots + xa^{n-2} + a^{n-1}),$$

where n is a positive integer and a is a real number.

70. $\lim_{x \to 2} \frac{x^5 - 32}{x - 2}$

71. $\lim_{x \to 1} \frac{x^6 - 1}{x - 1}$

72. $\lim_{x \to -1} \frac{x^7 + 1}{x + 1}$ (*Hint:* Use the formula for $x^7 - a^7$ with $a = -1$.)

73. $\lim_{x \to a} \frac{x^5 - a^5}{x - a}$

74. $\lim_{x \to a} \frac{x^n - a^n}{x - a}$, for any positive integer n

75. $\lim_{x \to 1} \frac{\sqrt[3]{x} - 1}{x - 1}$ (*Hint:* $x - 1 = (\sqrt[3]{x})^3 - (1)^3$.)

76. $\lim_{x \to 16} \frac{\sqrt[4]{x} - 2}{x - 16}$

77–80. Limits involving conjugates *Evaluate the following limits.*

77. $\lim_{x \to 1} \frac{x - 1}{\sqrt{x} - 1}$

78. $\lim_{x \to 1} \frac{x - 1}{\sqrt{4x + 5} - 3}$

79. $\lim_{x \to 4} \frac{3(x - 4)\sqrt{x + 5}}{3 - \sqrt{x + 5}}$

80. $\lim_{x \to 0} \frac{x}{\sqrt{cx + 1} - 1}$, where c is a nonzero constant

81. Creating functions satisfying given limit conditions Find functions f and g such that $\lim_{x \to 1} f(x) = 0$ and $\lim_{x \to 1} (f(x)\, g(x)) = 5$.

82. Creating functions satisfying given limit conditions Find a function f satisfying $\lim_{x \to 1} \left(\frac{f(x)}{x - 1} \right) = 2$.

83. Finding constants Find constants b and c in the polynomial $p(x) = x^2 + bx + c$ such that $\lim_{x \to 2} \frac{p(x)}{x - 2} = 6$. Are the constants unique?

Applications

84. A problem from relativity theory Suppose a spaceship of length L_0 travels at a high speed v relative to an observer. To the observer, the ship appears to have a smaller length given by the *Lorentz contraction formula*

$$L = L_0\sqrt{1 - \frac{v^2}{c^2}},$$

where c is the speed of light.

a. What is the observed length L of the ship if it is traveling at 50% of the speed of light?

b. What is the observed length L of the ship if it is traveling at 75% of the speed of light?

c. In parts (a) and (b), what happens to L as the speed of the ship increases?

d. Find $\lim_{v \to c^-} L_0\sqrt{1 - \frac{v^2}{c^2}}$ and explain the significance of this limit.

85. Limit of the radius of a cylinder A right circular cylinder with a height of 10 cm and a surface area of S cm^2 has a radius given by

$$r(S) = \frac{1}{2}\left(\sqrt{100 + \frac{2S}{\pi}} - 10 \right).$$

Find $\lim_{S \to 0^+} r(S)$ and interpret your result.

86. Torricelli's Law A cylindrical tank is filled with water to a depth of 9 meters. At $t = 0$, a drain in the bottom of the tank is opened and water flows out of the tank. The depth of water in the tank (measured from the bottom of the tank) t seconds after the drain is opened is approximated by $d(t) = (3 - 0.015t)^2$, for $0 \le t \le 200$. Evaluate and interpret $\lim_{t \to 200^-} d(t)$.

T **87. Electric field** The magnitude of the electric field at a point x meters from the midpoint of a 0.1-m line of charge is given by $E(x) = \frac{4.35}{x\sqrt{x^2 + 0.01}}$ (in units of newtons per coulomb, N/C). Evaluate $\lim_{x \to 10} E(x)$.

Additional Exercises

88–89. Limits of composite functions

88. If $\lim_{x \to 1} f(x) = 4$, find $\lim_{x \to -1} f(x^2)$.

89. Suppose $g(x) = f(1 - x)$, for all x, $\lim_{x \to 1^+} f(x) = 4$, and $\lim_{x \to 1^-} f(x) = 6$. Find $\lim_{x \to 0^+} g(x)$ and $\lim_{x \to 0^-} g(x)$.

90. Two trigonometric inequalities Consider the angle θ in standard position in a unit circle, where $0 \le \theta < \pi/2$ or $-\pi/2 < \theta < 0$ (use both figures).

a. Show that $|AC| = |\sin\theta|$, for $-\pi/2 < \theta < \pi/2$. (*Hint:* Consider the cases $0 \le \theta < \pi/2$ and $-\pi/2 < \theta < 0$ separately.)

b. Show that $|\sin\theta| < |\theta|$, for $-\pi/2 < \theta < \pi/2$. (*Hint:* The length of arc AB is θ, if $0 \le \theta < \pi/2$, and $-\theta$, if $-\pi/2 < \theta < 0$.)

c. Conclude that $-|\theta| \le \sin\theta \le |\theta|$, for $-\pi/2 < \theta < \pi/2$.

d. Show that $0 \le 1 - \cos\theta \le |\theta|$, for $-\pi/2 < \theta < \pi/2$.

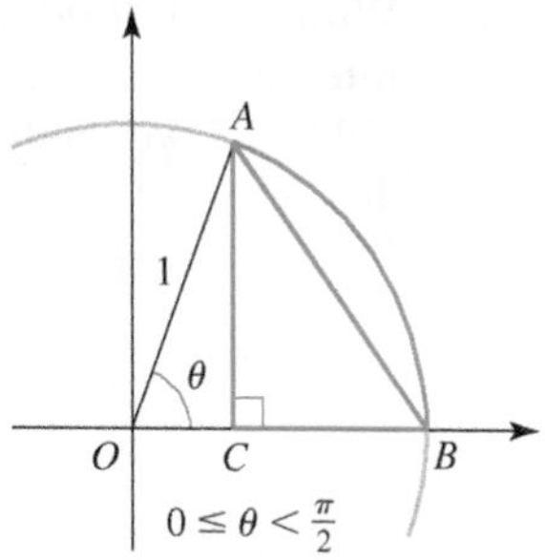

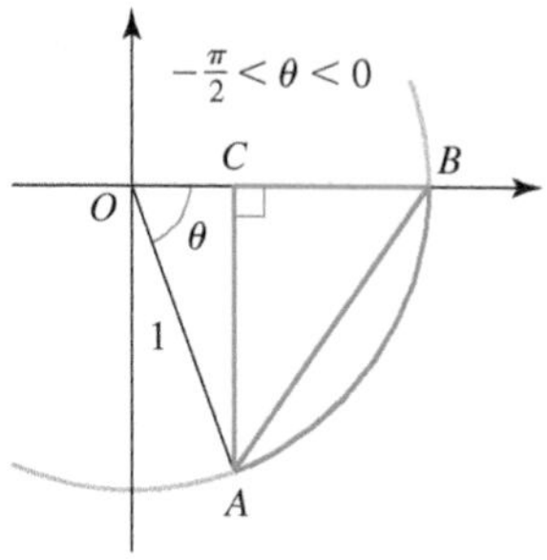

91. Theorem 2.4a Given the polynomial

$$p(x) = b_n x^n + b_{n-1}x^{n-1} + \cdots + b_1 x + b_0,$$

prove that $\lim_{x \to a} p(x) = p(a)$ for any value of a.

QUICK CHECK ANSWERS

1. 0, 2 **2.** 2 **3.** 3 **4.** 1 ◄

2.4 Infinite Limits

Two more limit scenarios are frequently encountered in calculus and are discussed in this and the following section. An *infinite limit* occurs when function values increase or decrease without bound near a point. The other type of limit, known as a *limit at infinity,* occurs when the independent variable x increases or decreases without bound. The ideas behind infinite limits and limits at infinity are quite different. Therefore, it is important to distinguish these limits and the methods used to calculate them.

An Overview

To illustrate the differences between infinite limits and limits at infinity, consider the values of $f(x) = 1/x^2$ in Table 2.6. As x approaches 0 from either side, $f(x)$ grows larger and larger. Because $f(x)$ does not approach a finite number as x approaches 0, $\lim_{x \to 0} f(x)$ does not exist. Nevertheless, we use limit notation and write $\lim_{x \to 0} f(x) = \infty$. The infinity symbol indicates that $f(x)$ grows arbitrarily large as x approaches 0. This is an example of an *infinite limit*; in general, the *dependent variable* becomes arbitrarily large in magnitude as the *independent variable* approaches a finite number.

Table 2.6

x	$f(x) = 1/x^2$
± 0.1	100
± 0.01	10,000
± 0.001	1,000,000
↓	↓
0	∞

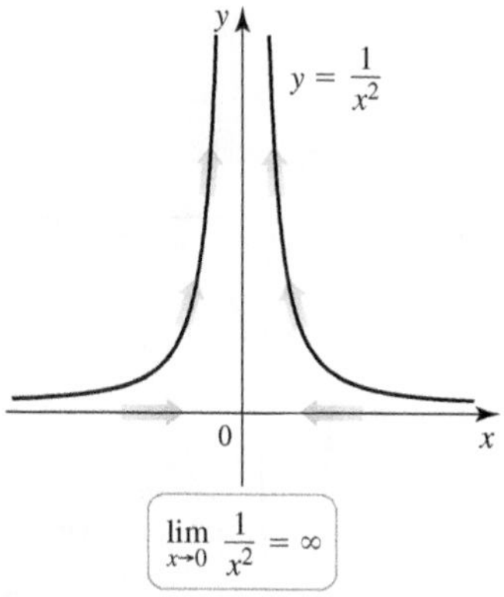

With *limits at infinity*, the opposite occurs: The *dependent variable* approaches a finite number as the *independent variable* becomes arbitrarily large in magnitude. In Table 2.7 we see that $f(x) = 1/x^2$ approaches 0 as x increases. In this case, we write $\lim_{x\to\infty} f(x) = 0$.

Table 2.7

x	$f(x) = 1/x^2$
10	0.01
100	0.0001
1000	0.000001
$\downarrow$	$\downarrow$
∞	0

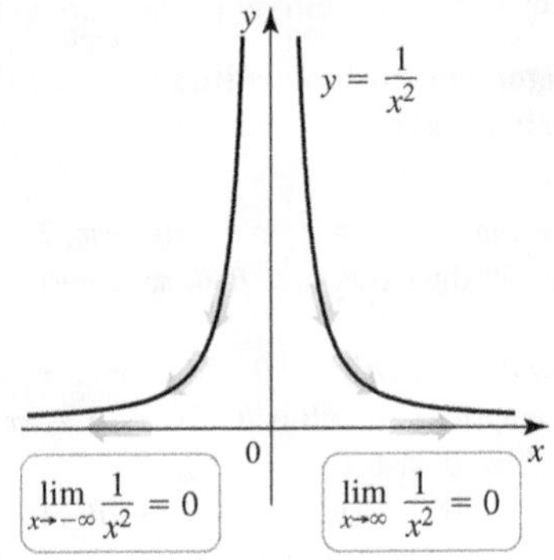

A general picture of these two limit scenarios—occurring with the same function—is shown in Figure 2.23.

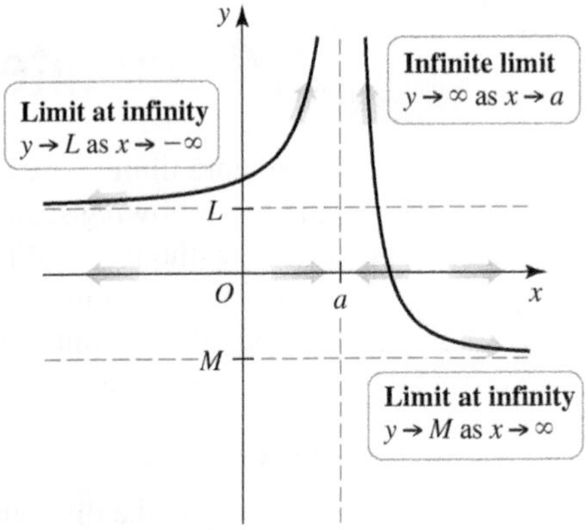

Figure 2.23

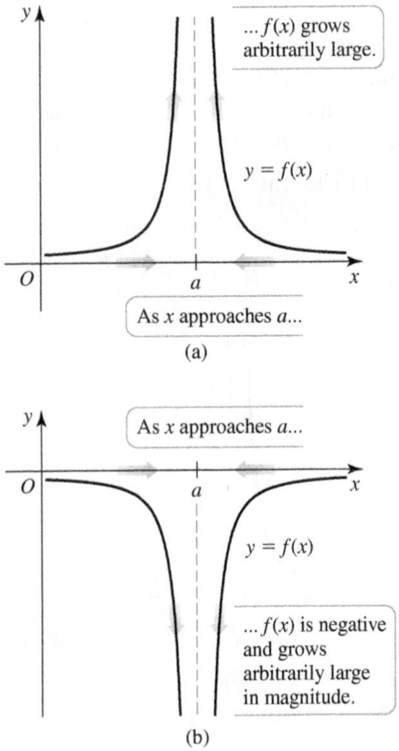

Figure 2.24

Infinite Limits

The following definition of infinite limits is informal, but it is adequate for most functions encountered in this book. A precise definition is given in Section 2.7.

> DEFINITION **Infinite Limits**
>
> Suppose f is defined for all x near a. If $f(x)$ grows arbitrarily large for all x sufficiently close (but not equal) to a (Figure 2.24a), we write
>
> $$\lim_{x\to a} f(x) = \infty$$
>
> and say the limit of $f(x)$ as x approaches a is infinity.
>
> If $f(x)$ is negative and grows arbitrarily large in magnitude for all x sufficiently close (but not equal) to a (Figure 2.24b), we write
>
> $$\lim_{x\to a} f(x) = -\infty$$
>
> and say the limit of $f(x)$ as x approaches a is negative infinity. *In both cases, the limit does not exist.*

EXAMPLE 1 **Infinite limits** Analyze $\lim_{x \to 1} \frac{x}{(x^2 - 1)^2}$ and $\lim_{x \to -1} \frac{x}{(x^2 - 1)^2}$ using the graph of the function.

SOLUTION The graph of $f(x) = \frac{x}{(x^2 - 1)^2}$ (Figure 2.25) shows that as x approaches 1 (from either side), the values of f grow arbitrarily large. Therefore, the limit does not exist and we write

$$\lim_{x \to 1} \frac{x}{(x^2 - 1)^2} = \infty.$$

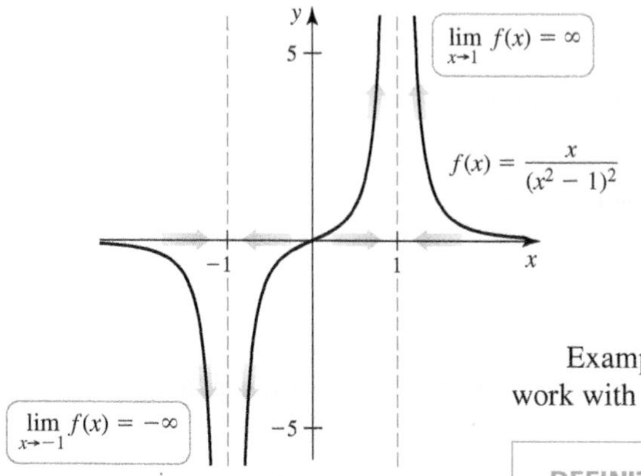

Figure 2.25

As x approaches -1, the values of f are negative and grow arbitrarily large in magnitude; therefore,

$$\lim_{x \to -1} \frac{x}{(x^2 - 1)^2} = -\infty.$$

Related Exercises 7–8 ◀

Example 1 illustrates *two-sided* infinite limits. As with finite limits, we also need to work with right-sided and left-sided infinite limits.

> **DEFINITION One-Sided Infinite Limits**
>
> Suppose f is defined for all x near a with $x > a$. If $f(x)$ becomes arbitrarily large for all x sufficiently close to a with $x > a$, we write $\lim_{x \to a^+} f(x) = \infty$ (Figure 2.26a).
>
> The one-sided infinite limits $\lim_{x \to a^+} f(x) = -\infty$ (Figure 2.26b), $\lim_{x \to a^-} f(x) = \infty$ (Figure 2.26c), and $\lim_{x \to a^-} f(x) = -\infty$ (Figure 2.26d) are defined analogously.

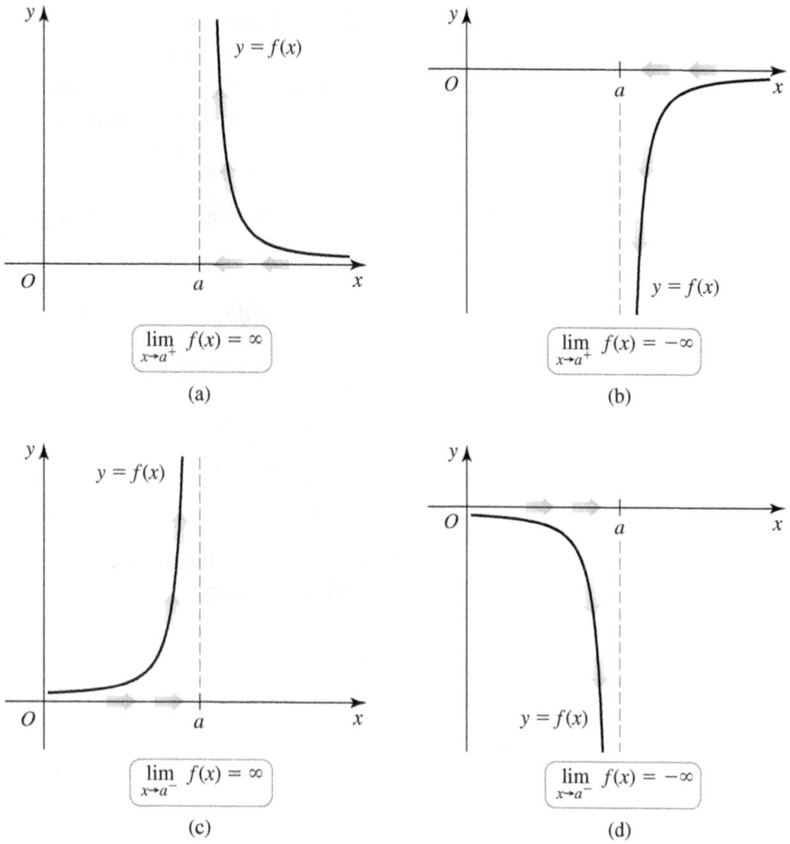

Figure 2.26

QUICK CHECK 1 Sketch the graph of a function and its vertical asymptote that satisfies the conditions $\lim_{x \to 2^+} f(x) = -\infty$ and $\lim_{x \to 2^-} f(x) = \infty$. ◂

In all the infinite limits illustrated in Figure 2.26, the line $x = a$ is called a *vertical asymptote*; it is a vertical line that is approached by the graph of f as x approaches a.

> **DEFINITION Vertical Asymptote**
>
> If $\lim_{x \to a} f(x) = \pm\infty$, $\lim_{x \to a^+} f(x) = \pm\infty$, or $\lim_{x \to a^-} f(x) = \pm\infty$, the line $x = a$ is called a **vertical asymptote** of f.

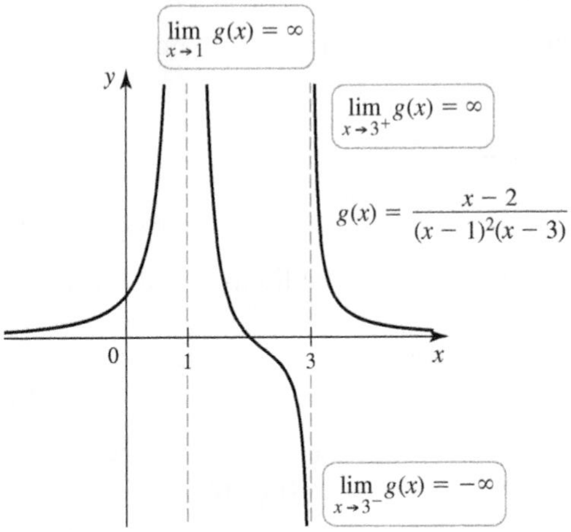

Figure 2.27

EXAMPLE 2 Determining limits graphically The vertical lines $x = 1$ and $x = 3$ are vertical asymptotes of the function $g(x) = \dfrac{x-2}{(x-1)^2(x-3)}$. Use Figure 2.27 to analyze the following limits.

a. $\lim_{x \to 1} g(x)$ **b.** $\lim_{x \to 3^-} g(x)$ **c.** $\lim_{x \to 3} g(x)$

SOLUTION

a. The values of g grow arbitrarily large as x approaches 1 from either side. Therefore, $\lim_{x \to 1} g(x) = \infty$.

b. The values of g are negative and grow arbitrarily large in magnitude as x approaches 3 from the left, so $\lim_{x \to 3^-} g(x) = -\infty$.

c. Note that $\lim_{x \to 3^+} g(x) = \infty$ and $\lim_{x \to 3^-} g(x) = -\infty$. Because g behaves differently as $x \to 3^-$ and as $x \to 3^+$, we do not write $\lim_{x \to 3} g(x) = \infty$. We simply say that the limit does not exist.

Related Exercises 9–16 ◂

Finding Infinite Limits Analytically

Many infinite limits are analyzed using a simple arithmetic property: The fraction a/b grows arbitrarily large in magnitude if b approaches 0 while a remains nonzero and relatively constant. For example, consider the fraction $(5 + x)/x$ for values of x approaching 0 from the right (Table 2.8).

Table 2.8

x	$\dfrac{5+x}{x}$
0.01	$\dfrac{5.01}{0.01} = 501$
0.001	$\dfrac{5.001}{0.001} = 5001$
0.0001	$\dfrac{5.0001}{0.0001} = 50{,}001$
↓	↓
0^+	∞

We see that $\dfrac{5+x}{x} \to \infty$ as $x \to 0^+$ because the numerator $5 + x$ approaches 5 while the denominator is positive and approaches 0. Therefore, we write $\lim_{x \to 0^+} \dfrac{5+x}{x} = \infty$. Similarly, $\lim_{x \to 0^-} \dfrac{5+x}{x} = -\infty$ because the numerator approaches 5 while the denominator approaches 0 through negative values.

EXAMPLE 3 Determining limits analytically Analyze the following limits.

a. $\lim_{x \to 3^+} \dfrac{2-5x}{x-3}$ **b.** $\lim_{x \to 3^-} \dfrac{2-5x}{x-3}$

SOLUTION

a. As $x \to 3^+$, the numerator $2 - 5x$ approaches $2 - 5(3) = -13$ while the denominator $x - 3$ is positive and approaches 0. Therefore,

$$\lim_{x \to 3^+} \frac{\overbrace{2-5x}^{\text{approaches } -13}}{\underbrace{x-3}_{\text{positive and approaches } 0}} = -\infty.$$

b. As $x \to 3^-$, $2 - 5x$ approaches $2 - 5(3) = -13$ while $x - 3$ is negative and approaches 0. Therefore,

$$\lim_{x \to 3^-} \frac{\overbrace{2 - 5x}^{\text{approaches } -13}}{\underbrace{x - 3}_{\text{negative and approaches } 0}} = \infty.$$

These limits imply that the given function has a vertical asymptote at $x = 3$; they also imply that the two-sided limit $\lim_{x \to 3} \frac{2x - 5}{x - 3}$ does not exist.

Related Exercises 17–28 ◀

QUICK CHECK 2 Analyze $\lim_{x \to 0^+} \frac{x - 5}{x}$ and $\lim_{x \to 0^-} \frac{x - 5}{x}$ by determining the sign of the numerator and denominator. ◀

EXAMPLE 4 Determining limits analytically Analyze $\lim_{x \to -4^+} \frac{-x^3 + 5x^2 - 6x}{-x^3 - 4x^2}$.

➤ We can assume that $x \neq 0$ because we are considering function values near $x = -4$.

SOLUTION First we factor and simplify, assuming $x \neq 0$:

$$\frac{-x^3 + 5x^2 - 6x}{-x^3 - 4x^2} = \frac{-x(x - 2)(x - 3)}{-x^2(x + 4)} = \frac{(x - 2)(x - 3)}{x(x + 4)}.$$

As $x \to -4^+$, we find that

$$\lim_{x \to -4^+} \frac{-x^3 + 5x^2 - 6x}{-x^3 - 4x^2} = \lim_{x \to -4^+} \frac{\overbrace{(x - 2)(x - 3)}^{\text{approaches } 42}}{\underbrace{x(x + 4)}_{\text{negative and approaches } 0}} = -\infty.$$

This limit implies that the given function has a vertical asymptote at $x = -4$.

Related Exercises 17–28 ◀

QUICK CHECK 3 Verify that $x(x + 4) \to 0$ through negative values as $x \to -4^+$. ◀

➤ Example 5 illustrates that $f(x)/g(x)$ might not grow arbitrarily large in magnitude if *both* $f(x)$ and $g(x)$ approach 0. Such limits are called *indeterminate forms*; they are examined in detail in Section 4.7.

EXAMPLE 5 Location of vertical asymptotes Let $f(x) = \frac{x^2 - 4x + 3}{x^2 - 1}$. Determine the following limits and find the vertical asymptotes of f. Verify your work with a graphing utility.

a. $\lim_{x \to 1} f(x)$ **b.** $\lim_{x \to -1^-} f(x)$ **c.** $\lim_{x \to -1^+} f(x)$

SOLUTION

a. Notice that as $x \to 1$, both the numerator and denominator of f approach 0, and the function is undefined at $x = 1$. To compute $\lim_{x \to 1} f(x)$, we first factor:

$$\begin{aligned}
\lim_{x \to 1} f(x) &= \lim_{x \to 1} \frac{x^2 - 4x + 3}{x^2 - 1} \\
&= \lim_{x \to 1} \frac{(x - 1)(x - 3)}{(x - 1)(x + 1)} && \text{Factor.} \\
&= \lim_{x \to 1} \frac{(x - 3)}{(x + 1)} && \text{Cancel like factors, } x \neq 1. \\
&= \frac{1 - 3}{1 + 1} = -1. && \text{Substitute } x = 1.
\end{aligned}$$

➤ It is permissible to cancel the factor $x - 1$ in $\lim_{x \to 1} \frac{(x - 1)(x - 3)}{(x - 1)(x + 1)}$ because x approaches 1 but is not equal to 1. Therefore, $x - 1 \neq 0$.

Therefore, $\lim_{x \to 1} f(x) = -1$ (even though $f(1)$ is undefined). The line $x = 1$ is *not* a vertical asymptote of f.

b. In part (a) we showed that

$$f(x) = \frac{x^2 - 4x + 3}{x^2 - 1} = \frac{x - 3}{x + 1}, \quad \text{provided } x \neq 1.$$

We use this fact again. As x approaches -1 from the left, the one-sided limit is

$$\lim_{x \to -1^-} f(x) = \lim_{x \to -1^-} \frac{\overbrace{x - 3}^{\text{approaches } -4}}{\underbrace{x + 1}_{\text{negative and approaches } 0}} = \infty.$$

c. As x approaches -1 from the right, the one-sided limit is

$$\lim_{x \to -1^+} f(x) = \lim_{x \to -1^+} \frac{\overbrace{x - 3}^{\text{approaches } -4}}{\underbrace{x + 1}_{\text{positive and approaches } 0}} = -\infty.$$

The infinite limits $\lim_{x \to -1^+} f(x) = -\infty$ and $\lim_{x \to -1^-} f(x) = \infty$ each imply that the line $x = -1$ is a vertical asymptote of f. The graph of f generated by a graphing utility *may* appear as shown in Figure 2.28a. If so, two corrections must be made. A hole should appear in the graph at $(1, -1)$ because $\lim_{x \to 1} f(x) = -1$, but $f(1)$ is undefined. It is also a good idea to replace the solid vertical line with a dashed line to emphasize that the vertical asymptote is not a part of the graph of f (Figure 2.28b).

➤ Graphing utilities vary in how they display vertical asymptotes. The errors shown in Figure 2.28a do not occur on all graphing utilities.

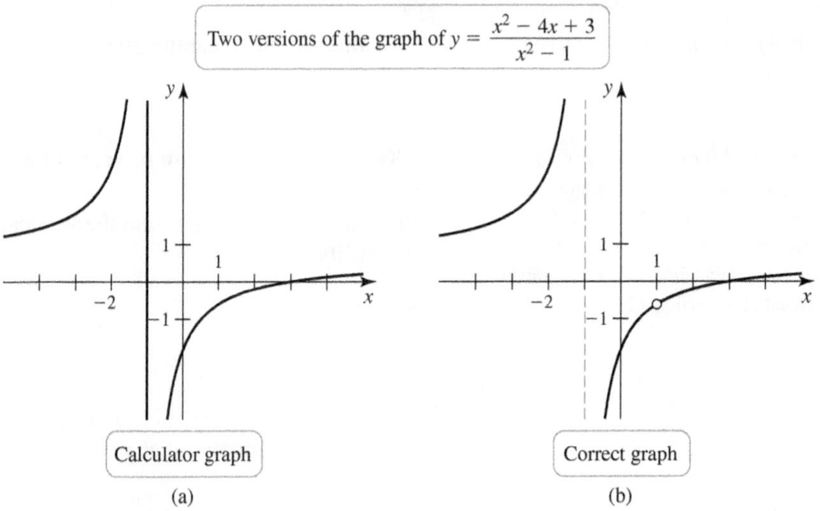

Figure 2.28

Related Exercises 29–34 ◄

QUICK CHECK 4 The line $x = 2$ is not a vertical asymptote of $y = \frac{(x - 1)(x - 2)}{x - 2}$. Why not? ◄

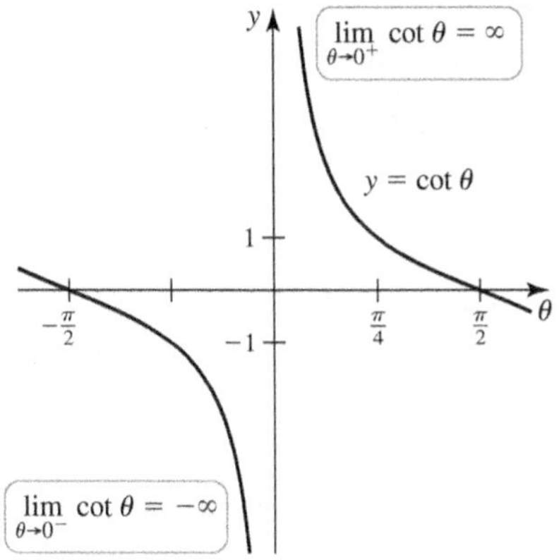

Figure 2.29

EXAMPLE 6 Limits of trigonometric functions Analyze the following limits.

a. $\lim_{\theta \to 0^+} \cot \theta$ **b.** $\lim_{\theta \to 0^-} \cot \theta$

SOLUTION

a. Recall that $\cot \theta = \cos \theta / \sin \theta$. Furthermore (Example 8, Section 2.3), $\lim_{\theta \to 0^+} \cos \theta = 1$ and $\sin \theta$ is positive and approaches 0 as $\theta \to 0^+$. Therefore, as $\theta \to 0^+$, $\cot \theta$ becomes arbitrarily large and positive, which means $\lim_{\theta \to 0^+} \cot \theta = \infty$. This limit is confirmed by the graph of $\cot \theta$ (Figure 2.29), which has a vertical asymptote at $\theta = 0$.

b. In this case, $\lim_{\theta \to 0^-} \cos \theta = 1$ and as $\theta \to 0^-$, $\sin \theta \to 0$ with $\sin \theta < 0$. Therefore, as $\theta \to 0^-$, $\cot \theta$ is negative and becomes arbitrarily large in magnitude. It follows that $\lim_{\theta \to 0^-} \cot \theta = -\infty$, as confirmed by the graph of $\cot \theta$.

Related Exercises 35–40 ◀

SECTION 2.4 EXERCISES

Review Questions

1. Use a graph to explain the meaning of $\lim_{x \to a^+} f(x) = -\infty$.

2. Use a graph to explain the meaning of $\lim_{x \to a} f(x) = \infty$.

3. What is a vertical asymptote?

4. Consider the function $F(x) = f(x)/g(x)$ with $g(a) = 0$. Does F necessarily have a vertical asymptote at $x = a$? Explain your reasoning.

5. Suppose $f(x) \to 100$ and $g(x) \to 0$, with $g(x) < 0$, as $x \to 2$. Determine $\lim_{x \to 2} \frac{f(x)}{g(x)}$.

6. Evaluate $\lim_{x \to 3^-} \frac{1}{x - 3}$ and $\lim_{x \to 3^+} \frac{1}{x - 3}$.

Basic Skills

T 7. **Analyzing infinite limits numerically** Compute the values of $f(x) = \frac{x + 1}{(x - 1)^2}$ in the following table and use them to determine $\lim_{x \to 1} f(x)$.

x	$\frac{x+1}{(x-1)^2}$	x	$\frac{x+1}{(x-1)^2}$
1.1		0.9	
1.01		0.99	
1.001		0.999	
1.0001		0.9999	

8. **Analyzing infinite limits graphically** Use the graph of $f(x) = \frac{x}{(x^2 - 2x - 3)^2}$ to determine $\lim_{x \to -1} f(x)$ and $\lim_{x \to 3} f(x)$.

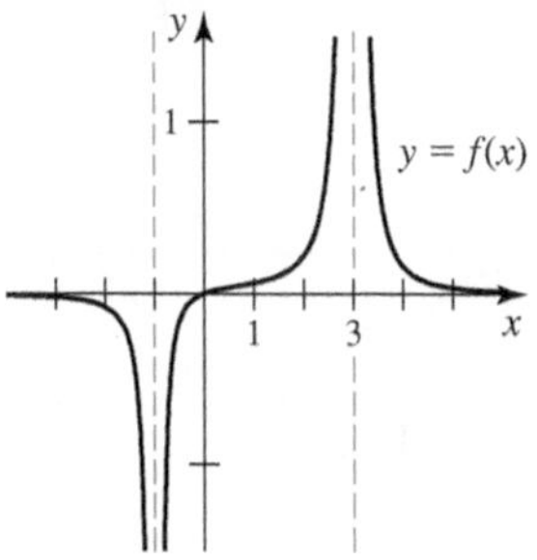

9. **Analyzing infinite limits graphically** The graph of f in the figure has vertical asymptotes at $x = 1$ and $x = 2$. Analyze the following limits.

a. $\lim_{x \to 1^-} f(x)$ **b.** $\lim_{x \to 1^+} f(x)$ **c.** $\lim_{x \to 1} f(x)$

d. $\lim_{x \to 2^-} f(x)$ **e.** $\lim_{x \to 2^+} f(x)$ **f.** $\lim_{x \to 2} f(x)$

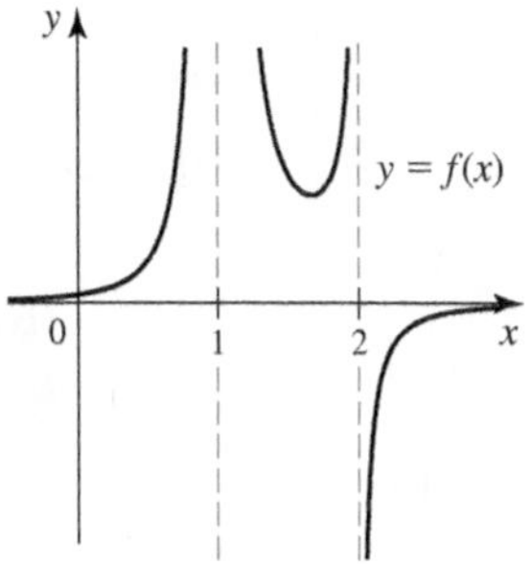

10. Analyzing infinite limits graphically The graph of g in the figure has vertical asymptotes at $x = 2$ and $x = 4$. Analyze the following limits.

a. $\lim_{x\to 2^-} g(x)$ **b.** $\lim_{x\to 2^+} g(x)$ **c.** $\lim_{x\to 2} g(x)$
d. $\lim_{x\to 4^-} g(x)$ **e.** $\lim_{x\to 4^+} g(x)$ **f.** $\lim_{x\to 4} g(x)$

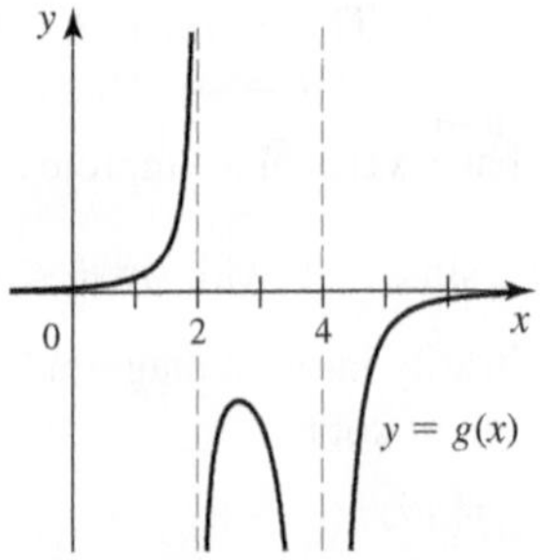

11. Analyzing infinite limits graphically The graph of h in the figure has vertical asymptotes at $x = -2$ and $x = 3$. Analyze the following limits.

a. $\lim_{x\to -2^-} h(x)$ **b.** $\lim_{x\to -2^+} h(x)$ **c.** $\lim_{x\to -2} h(x)$
d. $\lim_{x\to 3^-} h(x)$ **e.** $\lim_{x\to 3^+} h(x)$ **f.** $\lim_{x\to 3} h(x)$

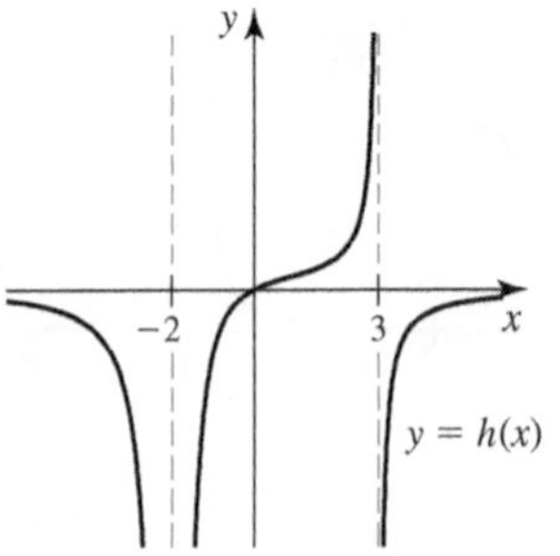

12. Analyzing infinite limits graphically The graph of p in the figure has vertical asymptotes at $x = -2$ and $x = 3$. Analyze the following limits.

a. $\lim_{x\to -2^-} p(x)$ **b.** $\lim_{x\to -2^+} p(x)$ **c.** $\lim_{x\to -2} p(x)$
d. $\lim_{x\to 3^-} p(x)$ **e.** $\lim_{x\to 3^+} p(x)$ **f.** $\lim_{x\to 3} p(x)$

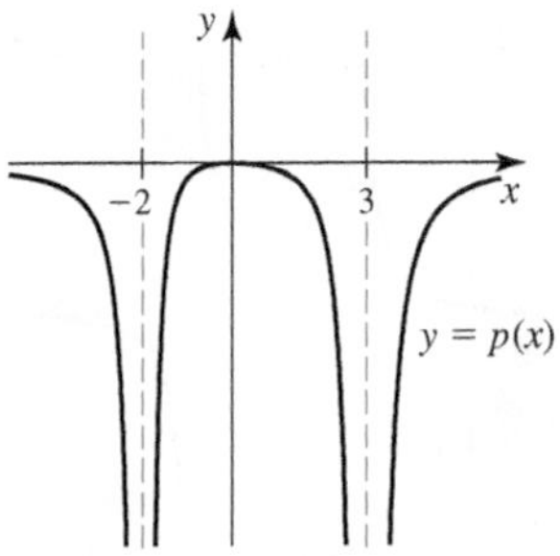

T **13. Analyzing infinite limits graphically** Graph the function $f(x) = \dfrac{1}{x^2 - x}$ using a graphing utility with the window $[-1, 2] \times [-10, 10]$. Use your graph to determine the following limits.

a. $\lim_{x\to 0^-} f(x)$ **b.** $\lim_{x\to 0^+} f(x)$ **c.** $\lim_{x\to 1^-} f(x)$ **d.** $\lim_{x\to 1^+} f(x)$

T **14. Analyzing infinite limits graphically** Graph the function $f(x) = \dfrac{e^{-x}}{x(x+2)^2}$ using a graphing utility. (Experiment with your choice of a graphing window.) Use your graph to determine the following limits.

a. $\lim_{x\to -2^+} f(x)$ **b.** $\lim_{x\to -2} f(x)$ **c.** $\lim_{x\to 0^-} f(x)$ **d.** $\lim_{x\to 0^+} f(x)$

15. Sketching graphs Sketch a possible graph of a function f, together with vertical asymptotes, satisfying all the following conditions on $[0, 4]$.

$f(1) = 0,$ $f(3)$ is undefined, $\lim_{x\to 3} f(x) = 1,$

$\lim_{x\to 0^+} f(x) = -\infty,$ $\lim_{x\to 2} f(x) = \infty,$ $\lim_{x\to 4^-} f(x) = \infty$

16. Sketching graphs Sketch a possible graph of a function g, together with vertical asymptotes, satisfying all the following conditions.

$g(2) = 1,$ $g(5) = -1,$ $\lim_{x\to 4} g(x) = -\infty,$

$\lim_{x\to 7^-} g(x) = \infty,$ $\lim_{x\to 7^+} g(x) = -\infty$

17–28. Determining limits analytically *Determine the following limits or state that they do not exist.*

17. a. $\lim_{x\to 2^+} \dfrac{1}{x-2}$ **b.** $\lim_{x\to 2^-} \dfrac{1}{x-2}$ **c.** $\lim_{x\to 2} \dfrac{1}{x-2}$

18. a. $\lim_{x\to 3^+} \dfrac{2}{(x-3)^3}$ **b.** $\lim_{x\to 3^-} \dfrac{2}{(x-3)^3}$ **c.** $\lim_{x\to 3} \dfrac{2}{(x-3)^3}$

19. a. $\lim_{x\to 4^+} \dfrac{x-5}{(x-4)^2}$ **b.** $\lim_{x\to 4^-} \dfrac{x-5}{(x-4)^2}$ **c.** $\lim_{x\to 4} \dfrac{x-5}{(x-4)^2}$

20. a. $\lim_{x\to 1^+} \dfrac{x-2}{(x-1)^3}$ **b.** $\lim_{x\to 1^-} \dfrac{x-2}{(x-1)^3}$ **c.** $\lim_{x\to 1} \dfrac{x-2}{(x-1)^3}$

21. a. $\lim_{x\to 3^+} \dfrac{(x-1)(x-2)}{(x-3)}$ **b.** $\lim_{x\to 3^-} \dfrac{(x-1)(x-2)}{(x-3)}$

c. $\lim_{x\to 3} \dfrac{(x-1)(x-2)}{(x-3)}$

22. a. $\lim_{x\to -2^+} \dfrac{(x-4)}{x(x+2)}$ **b.** $\lim_{x\to -2^-} \dfrac{(x-4)}{x(x+2)}$

c. $\lim_{x\to -2} \dfrac{(x-4)}{x(x+2)}$

23. a. $\lim_{x\to 2^+} \dfrac{x^2-4x+3}{(x-2)^2}$ **b.** $\lim_{x\to 2^-} \dfrac{x^2-4x+3}{(x-2)^2}$

c. $\lim_{x\to 2} \dfrac{x^2-4x+3}{(x-2)^2}$

24. a. $\lim_{x\to -2^+} \dfrac{x^3-5x^2+6x}{x^4-4x^2}$ **b.** $\lim_{x\to -2^-} \dfrac{x^3-5x^2+6x}{x^4-4x^2}$

c. $\lim_{x\to -2} \dfrac{x^3-5x^2+6x}{x^4-4x^2}$ **d.** $\lim_{x\to 2} \dfrac{x^3-5x^2+6x}{x^4-4x^2}$

25. $\lim_{x\to 0} \frac{x^3 - 5x^2}{x^2}$

26. $\lim_{t\to 5} \frac{4t^2 - 100}{t - 5}$

27. $\lim_{x\to 1^+} \frac{x^2 - 5x + 6}{x - 1}$

28. $\lim_{z\to 4} \frac{z - 5}{(z^2 - 10z + 24)^2}$

29. Location of vertical asymptotes Analyze the following limits and find the vertical asymptotes of $f(x) = \frac{x - 5}{x^2 - 25}$.

a. $\lim_{x\to 5} f(x)$ **b.** $\lim_{x\to -5^-} f(x)$ **c.** $\lim_{x\to -5^+} f(x)$

30. Location of vertical asymptotes Analyze the following limits and find the vertical asymptotes of $f(x) = \frac{x + 7}{x^4 - 49x^2}$.

a. $\lim_{x\to 7^-} f(x)$ **b.** $\lim_{x\to 7^+} f(x)$ **c.** $\lim_{x\to -7} f(x)$ **d.** $\lim_{x\to 0} f(x)$

31–34. Finding vertical asymptotes *Find all vertical asymptotes $x = a$ of the following functions. For each value of a, determine $\lim_{x\to a^+} f(x)$, $\lim_{x\to a^-} f(x)$, and $\lim_{x\to a} f(x)$.*

31. $f(x) = \frac{x^2 - 9x + 14}{x^2 - 5x + 6}$

32. $f(x) = \frac{\cos x}{x^2 + 2x}$

33. $f(x) = \frac{x + 1}{x^3 - 4x^2 + 4x}$

34. $f(x) = \frac{x^3 - 10x^2 + 16x}{x^2 - 8x}$

35–38. Trigonometric limits *Determine the following limits.*

35. $\lim_{\theta\to 0^+} \csc\theta$

36. $\lim_{x\to 0^-} \csc x$

37. $\lim_{x\to 0^+} (-10 \cot x)$

38. $\lim_{\theta\to \pi/2^+} \frac{1}{3}\tan\theta$

T **39. Analyzing infinite limits graphically** Graph the function $y = \tan x$ with the window $[-\pi, \pi] \times [-10, 10]$. Use the graph to analyze the following limits.

a. $\lim_{x\to \pi/2^+} \tan x$ **b.** $\lim_{x\to \pi/2^-} \tan x$

c. $\lim_{x\to -\pi/2^+} \tan x$ **d.** $\lim_{x\to -\pi/2^-} \tan x$

T **40. Analyzing infinite limits graphically** Graph the function $y = \sec x \tan x$ with the window $[-\pi, \pi] \times [-10, 10]$. Use the graph to analyze the following limits.

a. $\lim_{x\to \pi/2^+} \sec x \tan x$ **b.** $\lim_{x\to \pi/2^-} \sec x \tan x$

c. $\lim_{x\to -\pi/2^+} \sec x \tan x$ **d.** $\lim_{x\to -\pi/2^-} \sec x \tan x$

Further Explorations

41. Explain why or why not Determine whether the following statements are true and give an explanation or counterexample.

a. The line $x = 1$ is a vertical asymptote of the function $f(x) = \frac{x^2 - 7x + 6}{x^2 - 1}$.

b. The line $x = -1$ is a vertical asymptote of the function $f(x) = \frac{x^2 - 7x + 6}{x^2 - 1}$.

c. If g has a vertical asymptote at $x = 1$ and $\lim_{x\to 1^+} g(x) = \infty$, then $\lim_{x\to 1^-} g(x) = \infty$.

42. Finding a function with vertical asymptotes Find polynomials p and q such that $f = p/q$ is undefined at 1 and 2, but f has a vertical asymptote only at 2. Sketch a graph of your function.

43. Finding a function with infinite limits Give a formula for a function f that satisfies $\lim_{x\to 6^+} f(x) = \infty$ and $\lim_{x\to 6^-} f(x) = -\infty$.

44. Matching Match functions a–f with graphs A–F in the figure without using a graphing utility.

a. $f(x) = \frac{x}{x^2 + 1}$ **b.** $f(x) = \frac{x}{x^2 - 1}$

c. $f(x) = \frac{1}{x^2 - 1}$ **d.** $f(x) = \frac{x}{(x - 1)^2}$

e. $f(x) = \frac{1}{(x - 1)^2}$ **f.** $f(x) = \frac{x}{x + 1}$

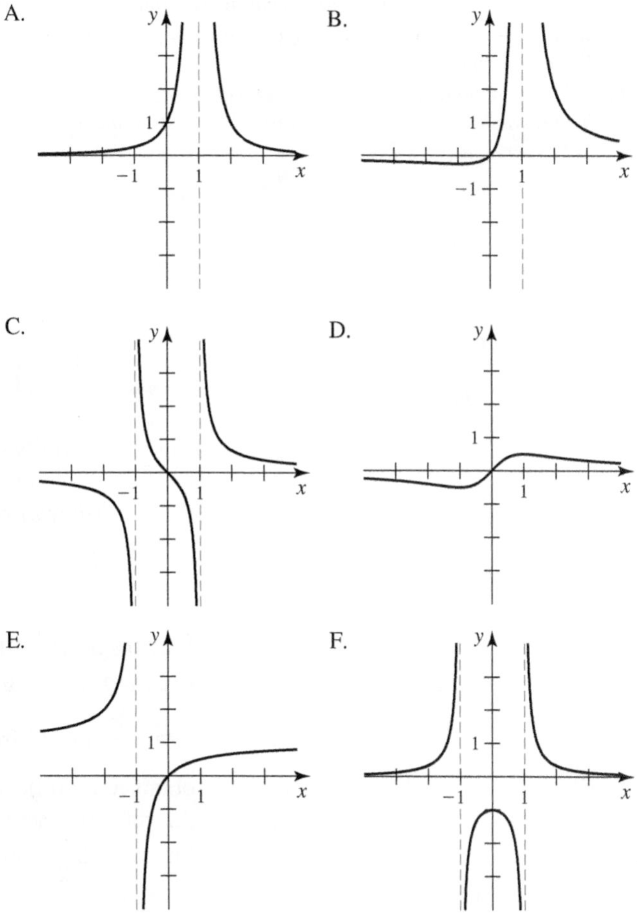

T **45–52. Asymptotes** *Use analytical methods and/or a graphing utility to identify the vertical asymptotes (if any) of the following functions.*

45. $f(x) = \frac{x^2 - 3x + 2}{x^{10} - x^9}$

46. $g(x) = 2 - \ln x^2$

47. $h(x) = \frac{e^x}{(x + 1)^3}$

48. $p(x) = \sec\left(\frac{\pi x}{2}\right)$, for $|x| < 2$

49. $g(\theta) = \tan \frac{\pi\theta}{10}$

50. $q(s) = \frac{\pi}{s - \sin s}$

51. $f(x) = \frac{1}{\sqrt{x} \sec x}$

52. $g(x) = e^{1/x}$

Additional Exercises

53. **Limits with a parameter** Let $f(x) = \frac{x^2 - 7x + 12}{x - a}$.

a. For what values of a, if any, does $\lim_{x \to a^+} f(x)$ equal a finite number?

b. For what values of a, if any, does $\lim_{x \to a^+} f(x) = \infty$?

c. For what values of a, if any, does $\lim_{x \to a^+} f(x) = -\infty$?

54–55. Steep secant lines

a. *Given the graph of f in the following figures, find the slope of the secant line that passes through $(0, 0)$ and $(h, f(h))$ in terms of h, for $h > 0$ and $h < 0$.*

b. *Analyze the limit of the slope of the secant line found in part (a) as $h \to 0^+$ and $h \to 0^-$. What does this tell you about the line tangent to the curve at $(0, 0)$?*

54. $f(x) = x^{1/3}$

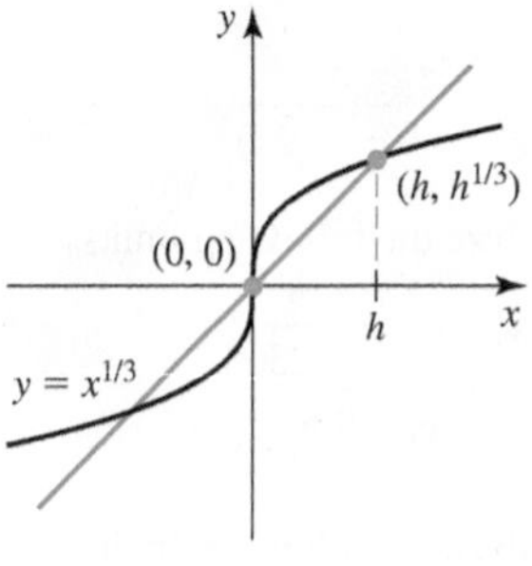

55. $f(x) = x^{2/3}$

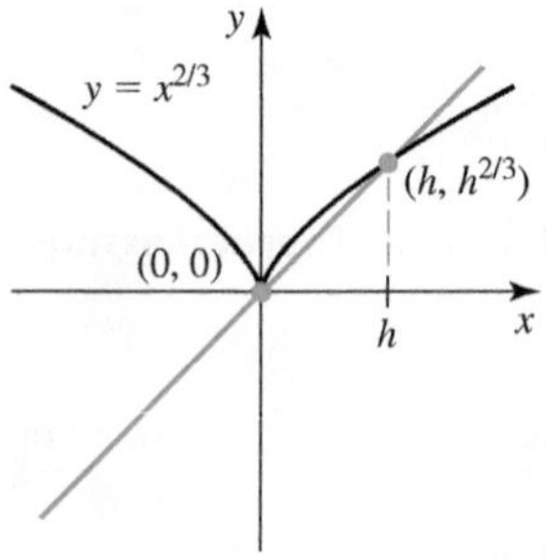

QUICK CHECK ANSWERS

1. Answers will vary, but all graphs should have a vertical asymptote at $x = 2$. **2.** $-\infty$; ∞ **3.** As $x \to -4^+$, $x < 0$ and $(x + 4) > 0$, so $x(x + 4) \to 0$ through negative values. **4.** $\lim_{x\to 2} \frac{(x - 1)(x - 2)}{x - 2} = \lim_{x\to 2} (x - 1) = 1$, which is not an infinite limit, so $x = 2$ is not a vertical asymptote. ◀

2.5 Limits at Infinity

Limits at infinity—as opposed to infinite limits—occur when the independent variable becomes large in magnitude. For this reason, limits at infinity determine what is called the *end behavior* of a function. An application of these limits is to determine whether a system (such as an ecosystem or a large oscillating structure) reaches a steady state as time increases.

Limits at Infinity and Horizontal Asymptotes

Figure 2.30 shows the graph of $y = \tan x$ (black curve) with vertical asymptotes at $x = \pm\frac{\pi}{2}$. Recall from Section 1.3 that on the interval $\left(-\frac{\pi}{2}, \frac{\pi}{2}\right)$, the graph of $\tan^{-1} x$ is obtained by reflecting the graph of $\tan x$ across the line $y = x$. Notice that when we do this reflection across the line $y = x$, the vertical asymptotes of $\tan x$ become the horizontal lines $y = \pm\frac{\pi}{2}$, which are associated with the graph of $y = \tan^{-1} x$ (blue curve). The

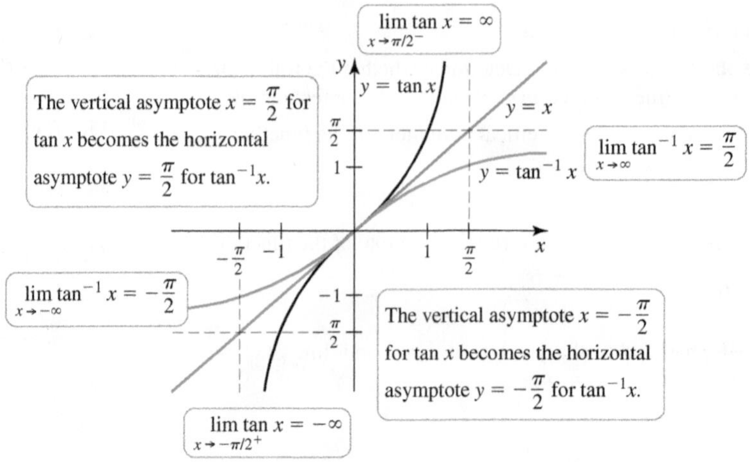

Figure 2.30

figure shows that as x becomes arbitrarily large (denoted $x \to \infty$), the graph of $\tan^{-1} x$ approaches the horizontal line $y = \frac{\pi}{2}$, and as x becomes arbitrarily large in magnitude and negative (denoted $x \to -\infty$), the graph of $\tan^{-1} x$ approaches the horizontal line $y = -\frac{\pi}{2}$. Observe that the limits for $\tan^{-1} x$ as $x \to \pm\infty$ correspond perfectly with the one-sided limits for $\tan x$ as $x \to \pm\frac{\pi}{2}$. We use limit notation to summarize the behavior of these two functions concisely:

$$\lim_{x \to \infty} \tan^{-1} x = \frac{\pi}{2} \quad \text{corresponds to} \quad \lim_{x \to \pi/2^-} \tan x = \infty \text{ and}$$

$$\lim_{x \to -\infty} \tan^{-1} x = -\frac{\pi}{2} \quad \text{corresponds to} \quad \lim_{x \to -\pi/2^+} \tan x = -\infty.$$

The one-sided limits for $\tan x$ are infinite limits from Section 2.4; they indicate vertical asymptotes. The limits we have written for $\tan^{-1} x$ are called *limits at infinity*, and the horizontal lines $y = \pm\frac{\pi}{2}$ approached by the graph of $\tan^{-1} x$ are *horizontal asymptotes*.

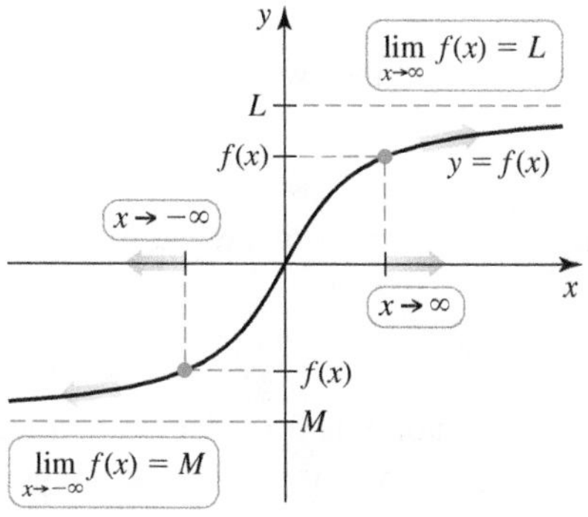

Figure 2.31

DEFINITION Limits at Infinity and Horizontal Asymptotes

If $f(x)$ becomes arbitrarily close to a finite number L for all sufficiently large and positive x, then we write

$$\lim_{x \to \infty} f(x) = L.$$

We say the limit of $f(x)$ as x approaches infinity is L. In this case, the line $y = L$ is a **horizontal asymptote** of f (Figure 2.31). The limit at negative infinity, $\lim_{x \to -\infty} f(x) = M$, is defined analogously. When this limit exists, $y = M$ is a horizontal asymptote.

QUICK CHECK 1 Evaluate $x/(x + 1)$ for $x = 10$, 100, and 1000. What is $\lim_{x \to \infty} \frac{x}{x + 1}$? ◀

➤ The limit laws of Theorem 2.3 and the Squeeze Theorem apply if $x \to a$ is replaced with $x \to \infty$ or $x \to -\infty$.

EXAMPLE 1 Limits at infinity Evaluate the following limits.

a. $\lim_{x \to -\infty} \left(2 + \frac{10}{x^2}\right)$ **b.** $\lim_{x \to \infty} \left(5 + \frac{\sin x}{\sqrt{x}}\right)$

SOLUTION

a. As x becomes large and negative, x^2 becomes large and positive; in turn, $10/x^2$ approaches 0. By the limit laws of Theorem 2.3,

$$\lim_{x \to -\infty} \left(2 + \frac{10}{x^2}\right) = \underbrace{\lim_{x \to -\infty} 2}_{\text{equals 2}} + \underbrace{\lim_{x \to -\infty} \left(\frac{10}{x^2}\right)}_{\text{equals 0}} = 2 + 0 = 2.$$

Therefore, the graph of $y = 2 + 10/x^2$ approaches the horizontal asymptote $y = 2$ as $x \to -\infty$ (Figure 2.32). Notice that $\lim_{x \to \infty} \left(2 + \frac{10}{x^2}\right)$ is also equal to 2, which implies that the graph has a single horizontal asymptote.

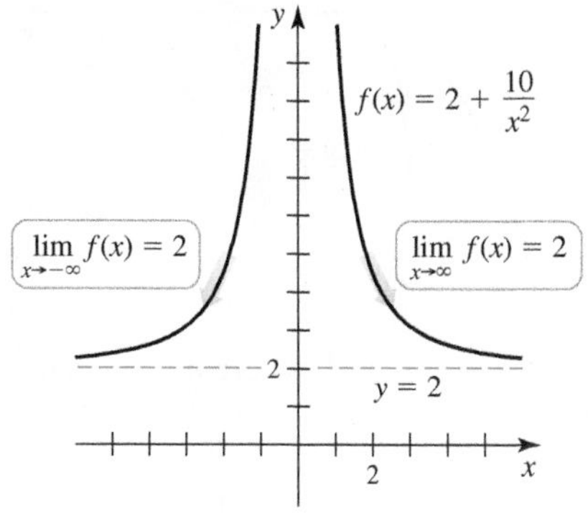

Figure 2.32

b. The numerator of $\sin x/\sqrt{x}$ is bounded between -1 and 1; therefore, for $x > 0$,

$$-\frac{1}{\sqrt{x}} \le \frac{\sin x}{\sqrt{x}} \le \frac{1}{\sqrt{x}}.$$

As $x \to \infty$, $\sqrt{x}$ becomes arbitrarily large, which means that

$$\lim_{x \to \infty} \frac{-1}{\sqrt{x}} = \lim_{x \to \infty} \frac{1}{\sqrt{x}} = 0.$$

It follows by the Squeeze Theorem (Theorem 2.5) that $\lim_{x \to \infty} \frac{\sin x}{\sqrt{x}} = 0$.

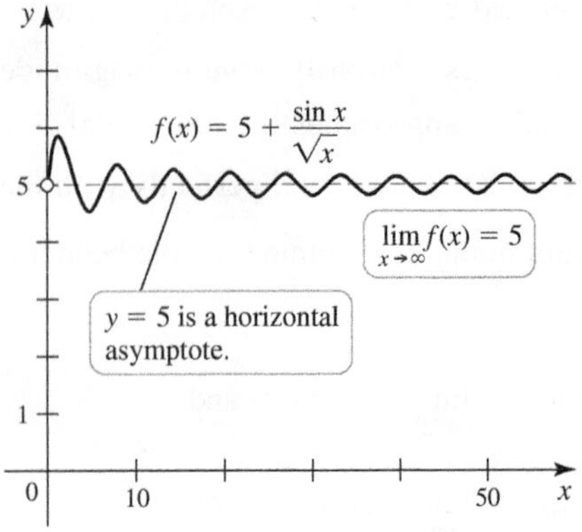

Figure 2.33

Using the limit laws of Theorem 2.3,

$$\lim_{x\to\infty}\left(5 + \frac{\sin x}{\sqrt{x}}\right) = \underbrace{\lim_{x\to\infty} 5}_{\text{equals } 5} + \underbrace{\lim_{x\to\infty}\frac{\sin x}{\sqrt{x}}}_{\text{equals } 0} = 5.$$

The graph of $y = 5 + \frac{\sin x}{\sqrt{x}}$ approaches the horizontal asymptote $y = 5$ as x becomes large (Figure 2.33). Note that the curve intersects its asymptote infinitely many times.

Related Exercises 9–14 ◀

Infinite Limits at Infinity

It is possible for a limit to be *both* an infinite limit and a limit at infinity. This type of limit occurs if $f(x)$ becomes arbitrarily large in magnitude as x becomes arbitrarily large in magnitude. Such a limit is called an *infinite limit at infinity* and is illustrated by the function $f(x) = x^3$ (Figure 2.34).

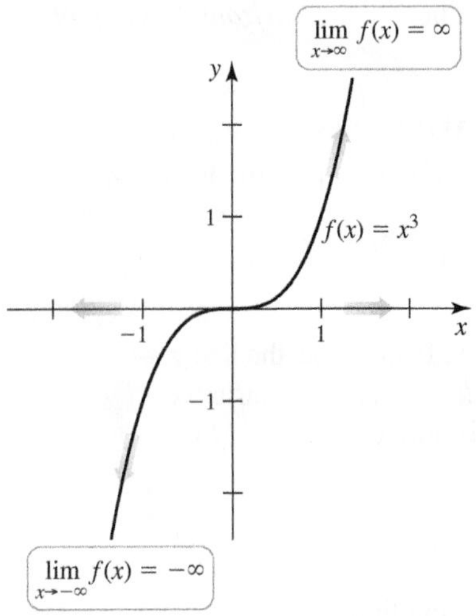

Figure 2.34

> **DEFINITION Infinite Limits at Infinity**
>
> If $f(x)$ becomes arbitrarily large as x becomes arbitrarily large, then we write
>
> $$\lim_{x\to\infty} f(x) = \infty.$$
>
> The limits $\lim_{x\to\infty} f(x) = -\infty$, $\lim_{x\to-\infty} f(x) = \infty$, and $\lim_{x\to-\infty} f(x) = -\infty$ are defined similarly.

Infinite limits at infinity tell us about the behavior of polynomials for large-magnitude values of x. First, consider power functions $f(x) = x^n$, where n is a positive integer. Figure 2.35 shows that when n is even, $\lim_{x\to\pm\infty} x^n = \infty$, and when n is odd, $\lim_{x\to\infty} x^n = \infty$ and $\lim_{x\to-\infty} x^n = -\infty$.

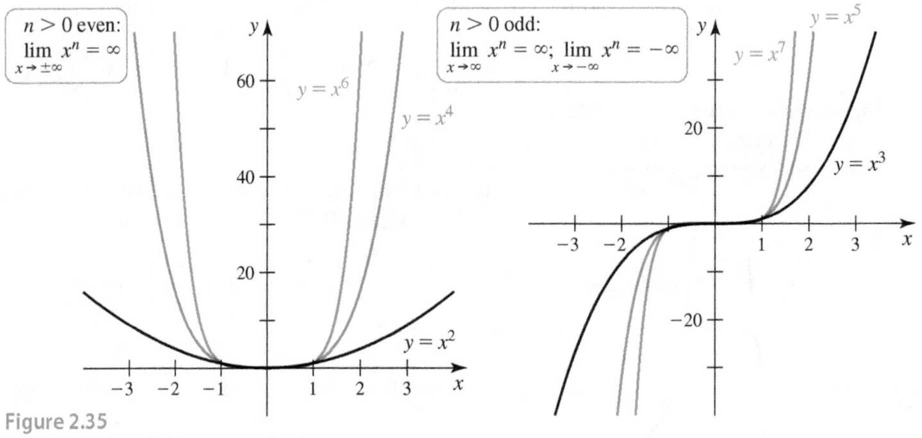

Figure 2.35

It follows that reciprocals of power functions $f(x) = 1/x^n = x^{-n}$, where n is a positive integer, behave as follows:

$$\lim_{x\to\infty}\frac{1}{x^n} = \lim_{x\to\infty} x^{-n} = 0 \quad\text{and}\quad \lim_{x\to-\infty}\frac{1}{x^n} = \lim_{x\to-\infty} x^{-n} = 0.$$

QUICK CHECK 2 Describe the behavior of $p(x) = -3x^3$ as $x \to \infty$ and as $x \to -\infty$. ◀

From here, it is a short step to finding the behavior of any polynomial as $x \to \pm\infty$. Let $p(x) = a_n x^n + a_{n-1}x^{n-1} + \cdots + a_2x^2 + a_1x + a_0$. We now write p in the equivalent form

$$p(x) = x^n\left(a_n + \underbrace{\frac{a_{n-1}}{x}}_{\to 0} + \underbrace{\frac{a_{n-2}}{x^2}}_{\to 0} + \cdots + \underbrace{\frac{a_0}{x^n}}_{\to 0}\right).$$

Notice that as x becomes large in magnitude, all the terms in p except the first term approach zero. Therefore, as $x \to \pm\infty$, we see that $p(x) \approx a_n x^n$. This means that as $x \to \pm\infty$, the behavior of p is determined by the term $a_n x^n$ with the highest power of x.

> **THEOREM 2.6 Limits at Infinity of Powers and Polynomials**
> Let n be a positive integer and let p be the polynomial
> $p(x) = a_n x^n + a_{n-1}x^{n-1} + \cdots + a_2x^2 + a_1x + a_0$, where $a_n \neq 0$.
>
> 1. $\lim_{x\to\pm\infty} x^n = \infty$ when n is even.
> 2. $\lim_{x\to\infty} x^n = \infty$ and $\lim_{x\to-\infty} x^n = -\infty$ when n is odd.
> 3. $\lim_{x\to\pm\infty} \frac{1}{x^n} = \lim_{x\to\pm\infty} x^{-n} = 0$.
> 4. $\lim_{x\to\pm\infty} p(x) = \lim_{x\to\pm\infty} a_n x^n = \pm\infty$, depending on the degree of the polynomial and the sign of the leading coefficient a_n.

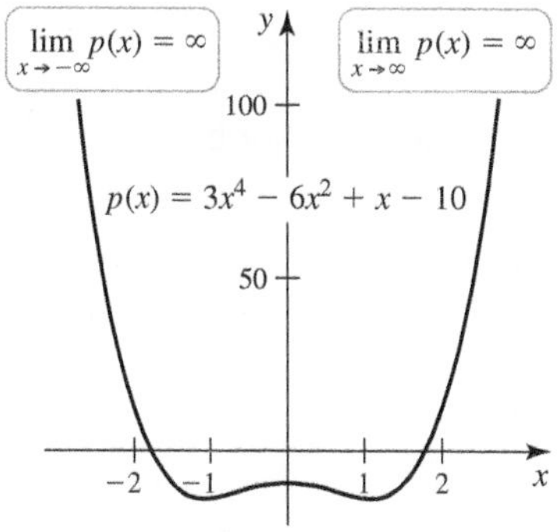

Figure 2.36

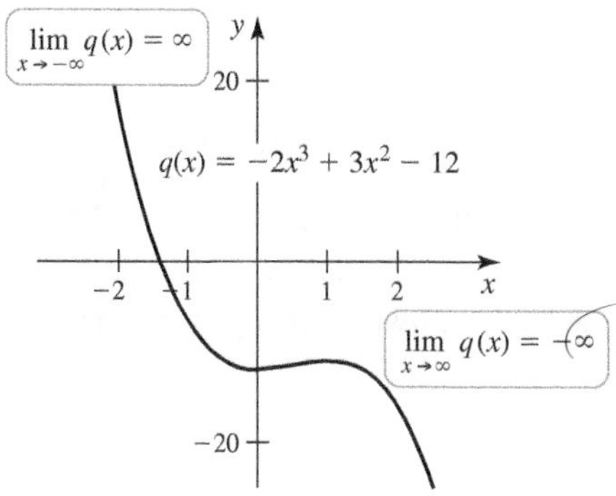

Figure 2.37

EXAMPLE 2 Limits at infinity Evaluate the limits as $x \to \pm\infty$ of the following functions.

a. $p(x) = 3x^4 - 6x^2 + x - 10$ **b.** $q(x) = -2x^3 + 3x^2 - 12$

SOLUTION

a. We use the fact that the limit is determined by the behavior of the leading term:

$$\lim_{x\to\infty}(3x^4 - 6x^2 + x - 10) = \lim_{x\to\infty} 3\underbrace{x^4}_{\to\infty} = \infty.$$

Similarly,

$$\lim_{x\to-\infty}(3x^4 - 6x^2 + x - 10) = \lim_{x\to-\infty} 3\underbrace{x^4}_{\to\infty} = \infty.$$

Figure 2.36 illustrates these limits.

b. Noting that the leading coefficient is negative, we have

$$\lim_{x\to\infty}(-2x^3 + 3x^2 - 12) = \lim_{x\to\infty}(-2\underbrace{x^3}_{\to\infty}) = -\infty$$

$$\lim_{x\to-\infty}(-2x^3 + 3x^2 - 12) = \lim_{x\to-\infty}(-2\underbrace{x^3}_{\to-\infty}) = \infty.$$

The graph of q (Figure 2.37) confirms these results.

Related Exercises 15–24 ◀

End Behavior

The behavior of polynomials as $x \to \pm\infty$ is an example of what is often called *end behavior*. Having treated polynomials, we now turn to the end behavior of rational, algebraic, and transcendental functions.

EXAMPLE 3 End behavior of rational functions Determine the end behavior for the following rational functions.

a. $f(x) = \dfrac{3x + 2}{x^2 - 1}$ **b.** $g(x) = \dfrac{40x^4 + 4x^2 - 1}{10x^4 + 8x^2 + 1}$ **c.** $h(x) = \dfrac{x^3 - 2x + 1}{2x + 4}$

SOLUTION

a. An effective approach for determining limits of rational functions at infinity is to divide both the numerator and denominator by x^n, where n is the degree of the

➤ Recall that the *degree* of a polynomial is the highest power of x that appears.

polynomial in the denominator. This strategy forces the terms corresponding to lower powers of x to approach 0 in the limit. In this case, we divide by x^2:

$$\lim_{x\to\infty}\frac{3x+2}{x^2-1}=\lim_{x\to\infty}\frac{\dfrac{3x+2}{x^2}}{\dfrac{x^2-1}{x^2}}=\lim_{x\to\infty}\frac{\overbrace{\dfrac{3}{x}+\dfrac{2}{x^2}}^{\text{approaches 0}}}{1-\underbrace{\dfrac{1}{x^2}}_{\text{approaches 0}}}=\frac{0}{1}=0.$$

A similar calculation gives $\lim_{x\to-\infty}\dfrac{3x+2}{x^2-1}=0$; therefore, the graph of f has the horizontal asymptote $y=0$. You should confirm that the zeros of the denominator are -1 and 1, which correspond to vertical asymptotes (Figure 2.38). In this example, the degree of the polynomial in the numerator is *less than* the degree of the polynomial in the denominator.

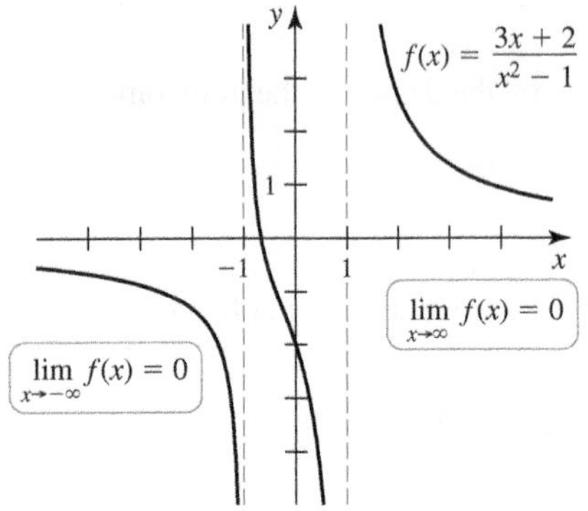

Figure 2.38

b. Again we divide both the numerator and denominator by the largest power appearing in the denominator, which is x^4:

$$\lim_{x\to\infty}\frac{40x^4+4x^2-1}{10x^4+8x^2+1}=\lim_{x\to\infty}\frac{\dfrac{40x^4}{x^4}+\dfrac{4x^2}{x^4}-\dfrac{1}{x^4}}{\dfrac{10x^4}{x^4}+\dfrac{8x^2}{x^4}+\dfrac{1}{x^4}}\qquad\text{Divide the numerator and denominator by } x^4.$$

$$=\lim_{x\to\infty}\frac{40+\overbrace{\dfrac{4}{x^2}}^{\text{approaches 0}}-\overbrace{\dfrac{1}{x^4}}^{\text{approaches 0}}}{10+\underbrace{\dfrac{8}{x^2}}_{\text{approaches 0}}+\underbrace{\dfrac{1}{x^4}}_{\text{approaches 0}}}\qquad\text{Simplify.}$$

$$=\frac{40+0+0}{10+0+0}=4.\qquad\text{Evaluate limits.}$$

Using the same steps (dividing each term by x^4), it can be shown that $\lim_{x\to-\infty}\dfrac{40x^4+4x^2-1}{10x^4+8x^2+1}=4$. This function has the horizontal asymptote $y=4$ (Figure 2.39). Notice that the degree of the polynomial in the numerator *equals* the degree of the polynomial in the denominator.

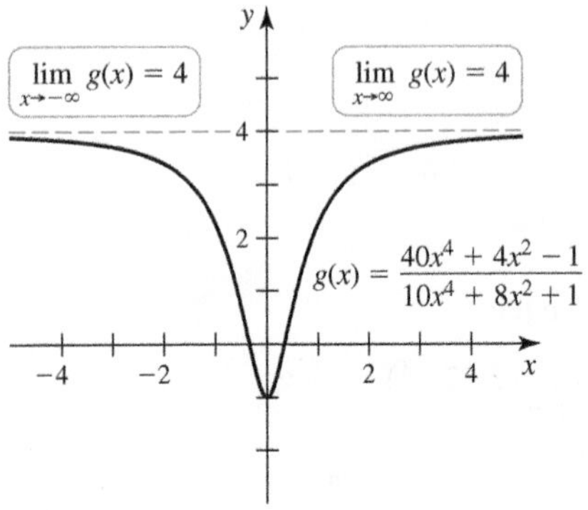

Figure 2.39

c. We divide the numerator and denominator by the largest power of x appearing in the denominator, which is x, and then take the limit:

$$\lim_{x\to\infty}\frac{x^3-2x+1}{2x+4}=\lim_{x\to\infty}\frac{\dfrac{x^3}{x}-\dfrac{2x}{x}+\dfrac{1}{x}}{\dfrac{2x}{x}+\dfrac{4}{x}}\qquad\text{Divide the numerator and denominator by } x.$$

$$=\lim_{x\to\infty}\frac{\overbrace{x^2}^{\text{arbitrarily large}}-\overbrace{2}^{\text{constant}}+\overbrace{\dfrac{1}{x}}^{\text{approaches 0}}}{\underbrace{2}_{\text{constant}}+\underbrace{\dfrac{4}{x}}_{\text{approaches 0}}}\qquad\text{Simplify.}$$

$$=\infty.\qquad\text{Take limits.}$$

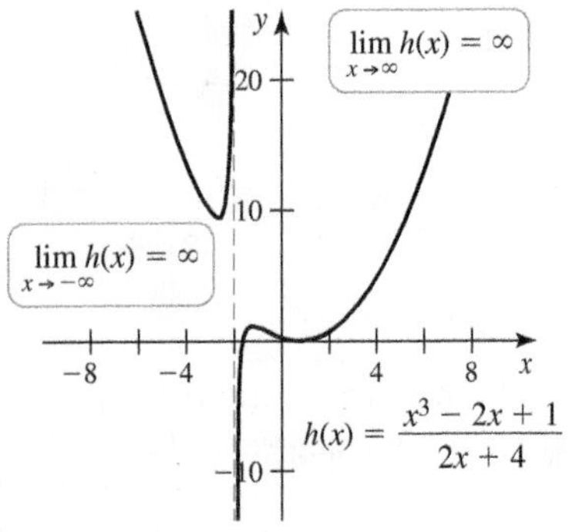

Figure 2.40

As $x\to\infty$, all the terms in this function either approach zero or are constant—except the x^2-term in the numerator, which becomes arbitrarily large. Therefore, the limit of the function does not exist. Using a similar analysis, we find that $\lim_{x\to-\infty}\dfrac{x^3-2x+1}{2x+4}=\infty$. These limits are not finite, so the graph of the function has no horizontal asymptote (Figure 2.40).

There is, however, a vertical asymptote due to the fact that $x = -2$ is a zero of the denominator. In this case, the degree of the polynomial in the numerator is *greater than* the degree of the polynomial in the denominator.

Related Exercises 25–34 ◀

A special case of end behavior arises with rational functions. As shown in the next example, if the graph of a function f approaches a line (with finite and nonzero slope) as $x \to \pm\infty$, then that line is a **slant asymptote**, or **oblique asymptote**, of f.

EXAMPLE 4 Slant asymptotes Determine the end behavior of the function $f(x) = \dfrac{2x^2 + 6x - 2}{x + 1}$.

SOLUTION We first divide the numerator and denominator by the largest power of x appearing in the denominator, which is x:

$$\lim_{x\to\infty} \frac{2x^2 + 6x - 2}{x + 1} = \lim_{x\to\infty} \frac{\dfrac{2x^2}{x} + \dfrac{6x}{x} - \dfrac{2}{x}}{\dfrac{x}{x} + \dfrac{1}{x}} \qquad \text{Divide the numerator and denominator by } x.$$

$$= \lim_{x\to\infty} \frac{\overbrace{2x}^{\text{arbitrarily large}} + \overbrace{6}^{\text{constant}} - \overbrace{\dfrac{2}{x}}^{\text{approaches } 0}}{\underbrace{1}_{\text{constant}} + \underbrace{\dfrac{1}{x}}_{\text{approaches } 0}} \qquad \text{Simplify.}$$

$$= \infty. \qquad \text{Take limits.}$$

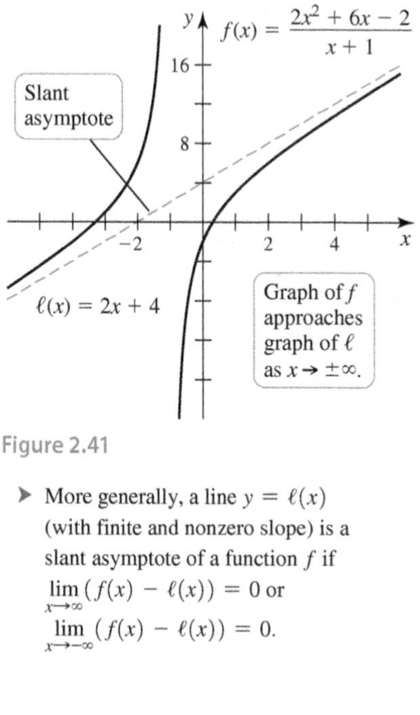

Figure 2.41

➤ More generally, a line $y = \ell(x)$ (with finite and nonzero slope) is a slant asymptote of a function f if $\lim_{x\to\infty} (f(x) - \ell(x)) = 0$ or $\lim_{x\to-\infty} (f(x) - \ell(x)) = 0$.

QUICK CHECK 3 Use Theorem 2.7 to find the vertical and horizontal asymptotes of $y = \dfrac{10x}{3x - 1}$. ◀

A similar analysis shows that $\lim_{x\to-\infty} \dfrac{2x^2 + 6x - 2}{x + 1} = -\infty$. Because these limits are not finite, f has no horizontal asymptote.

However, there is more to be learned about the end behavior of this function. Using long division, the function f is written

$$f(x) = \frac{2x^2 + 6x - 2}{x + 1} = \underbrace{2x + 4}_{\ell(x)} - \underbrace{\frac{6}{x + 1}}_{\substack{\text{approaches 0 as} \\ x \to \infty}}.$$

As $x \to \infty$, the term $6/(x + 1)$ approaches 0, and we see that the function f behaves like the linear function $\ell(x) = 2x + 4$. For this reason, the graphs of f and ℓ approach each other as $x \to \infty$ (Figure 2.41). A similar argument shows that the graphs of f and ℓ also approach each other as $x \to -\infty$. The line described by ℓ is a slant asymptote; it occurs with rational functions only when the degree of the polynomial in the numerator exceeds the degree of the polynomial in the denominator by exactly 1.

Related Exercises 35–40 ◀

The conclusions reached in Examples 3 and 4 can be generalized for all rational functions. These results are summarized in Theorem 2.7 (Exercise 80).

THEOREM 2.7 End Behavior and Asymptotes of Rational Functions

Suppose $f(x) = \dfrac{p(x)}{q(x)}$ is a rational function, where

$$p(x) = a_m x^m + a_{m-1}x^{m-1} + \cdots + a_2x^2 + a_1x + a_0 \quad \text{and}$$
$$q(x) = b_n x^n + b_{n-1}x^{n-1} + \cdots + b_2x^2 + b_1x + b_0,$$

with $a_m \neq 0$ and $b_n \neq 0$.

a. Degree of numerator less than degree of denominator If $m < n$, then $\lim_{x\to\pm\infty} f(x) = 0$ and $y = 0$ is a horizontal asymptote of f.

b. Degree of numerator equals degree of denominator If $m = n$, then $\lim_{x\to\pm\infty} f(x) = a_m/b_n$ and $y = a_m/b_n$ is a horizontal asymptote of f.

c. Degree of numerator greater than degree of denominator If $m > n$, then $\lim_{x\to\pm\infty} f(x) = \infty$ or $-\infty$ and f has no horizontal asymptote.

d. Slant asymptote If $m = n + 1$, then $\lim_{x\to\pm\infty} f(x) = \infty$ or $-\infty$, f has no horizontal asymptote, but f has a slant asymptote.

e. Vertical asymptotes Assuming that f is in reduced form (p and q share no common factors), vertical asymptotes occur at the zeros of q.

Although it isn't stated explicitly, Theorem 2.7 implies that a rational function can have at most one horizontal asymptote, and whenever there is a horizontal asymptote, $\lim_{x\to\infty} \frac{p(x)}{q(x)} = \lim_{x\to-\infty} \frac{p(x)}{q(x)}$. The same cannot be said of other functions, as the next examples show.

EXAMPLE 5 **End behavior of an algebraic function** Determine the end behavior of $f(x) = \frac{10x^3 - 3x^2 + 8}{\sqrt{25x^6 + x^4 + 2}}$.

SOLUTION The square root in the denominator forces us to revise the strategy used with rational functions. First, consider the limit as $x \to \infty$. The highest power of the polynomial in the denominator is 6. However, the polynomial is under a square root, so effectively, the term with the highest power in the denominator is $\sqrt{x^6} = x^3$. Dividing the numerator and denominator by x^3, for $x > 0$, the limit becomes

$$\lim_{x\to\infty} \frac{10x^3 - 3x^2 + 8}{\sqrt{25x^6 + x^4 + 2}} = \lim_{x\to\infty} \frac{\frac{10x^3}{x^3} - \frac{3x^2}{x^3} + \frac{8}{x^3}}{\sqrt{\frac{25x^6}{x^6} + \frac{x^4}{x^6} + \frac{2}{x^6}}} \quad \text{Divide by } \sqrt{x^6} = x^3.$$

$$= \lim_{x\to\infty} \frac{10 - \overbrace{\frac{3}{x}}^{\text{approaches 0}} + \overbrace{\frac{8}{x^3}}^{\text{approaches 0}}}{\sqrt{25 + \underbrace{\frac{1}{x^2}}_{\text{approaches 0}} + \underbrace{\frac{2}{x^6}}_{\text{approaches 0}}}} \quad \text{Simplify.}$$

$$= \frac{10}{\sqrt{25}} = 2. \quad \text{Evaluate limits.}$$

As $x \to -\infty$, x^3 is negative, so we divide the numerator and denominator by $\sqrt{x^6} = -x^3$ (which is positive):

$$\lim_{x\to-\infty} \frac{10x^3 - 3x^2 + 8}{\sqrt{25x^6 + x^4 + 2}} = \lim_{x\to-\infty} \frac{\frac{10x^3}{-x^3} - \frac{3x^2}{-x^3} + \frac{8}{-x^3}}{\sqrt{\frac{25x^6}{x^6} + \frac{x^4}{x^6} + \frac{2}{x^6}}} \quad \text{Divide by } \sqrt{x^6} = -x^3 > 0.$$

$$= \lim_{x\to-\infty} \frac{-10 + \overbrace{\frac{3}{x}}^{\text{approaches 0}} - \overbrace{\frac{8}{x^3}}^{\text{approaches 0}}}{\sqrt{25 + \underbrace{\frac{1}{x^2}}_{\text{approaches 0}} + \underbrace{\frac{2}{x^6}}_{\text{approaches 0}}}} \quad \text{Simplify.}$$

$$= -\frac{10}{\sqrt{25}} = -2. \quad \text{Evaluate limits.}$$

➤ Recall that

$$\sqrt{x^2} = |x| = \begin{cases} x & \text{if } x \ge 0 \\ -x & \text{if } x < 0. \end{cases}$$

Therefore,

$$\sqrt{x^6} = |x^3| = \begin{cases} x^3 & \text{if } x \ge 0 \\ -x^3 & \text{if } x < 0. \end{cases}$$

Because x is negative as $x \to -\infty$, we have $\sqrt{x^6} = -x^3$.

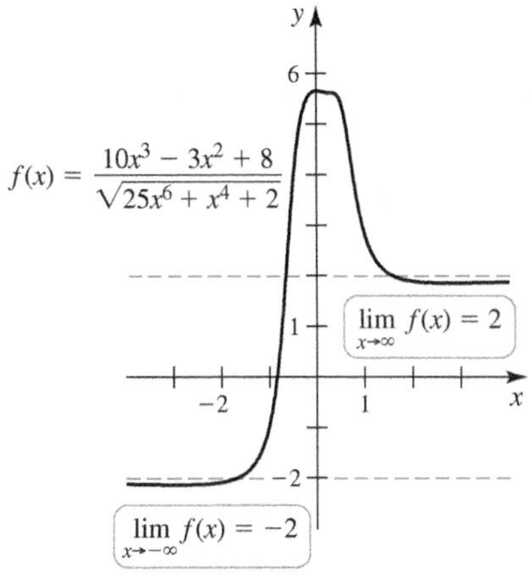

Figure 2.42

The limits reveal two asymptotes, $y = 2$ and $y = -2$. Observe that the graph crosses both horizontal asymptotes (Figure 2.42).

Related Exercises 41–44 ◀

EXAMPLE 6 **End behavior of transcendental functions** Determine the end behavior of the following transcendental functions.

a. $f(x) = e^x$ and $g(x) = e^{-x}$ **b.** $h(x) = \ln x$ **c.** $f(x) = \cos x$

SOLUTION

a. The graph of $f(x) = e^x$ (Figure 2.43) makes it clear that as $x \to \infty$, e^x increases without bound. All exponential functions b^x with $b > 1$ behave this way, because raising a number greater than 1 to ever-larger powers produces numbers that increase without bound. The figure also suggests that as $x \to -\infty$, the graph of e^x approaches the horizontal asymptote $y = 0$. This claim is confirmed analytically by recognizing that

$$\lim_{x\to-\infty} e^x = \lim_{x\to\infty} e^{-x} = \lim_{x\to\infty} \frac{1}{e^x} = 0.$$

Therefore, $\lim_{x\to\infty} e^x = \infty$ and $\lim_{x\to-\infty} e^x = 0$. Because $e^{-x} = 1/e^x$, it follows that $\lim_{x\to\infty} e^{-x} = 0$ and $\lim_{x\to-\infty} e^{-x} = \infty$.

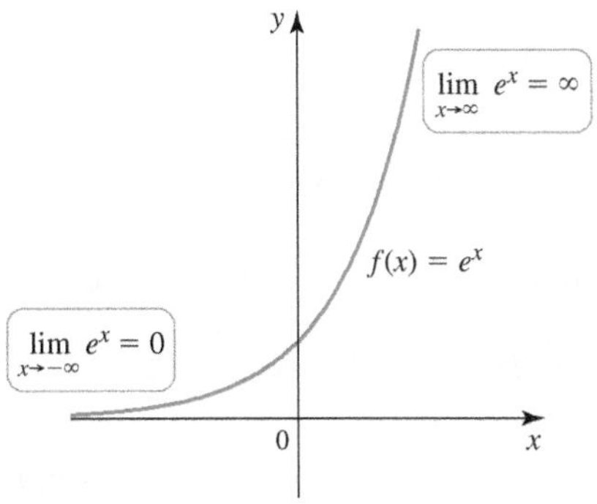

Figure 2.43

b. The domain of $\ln x$ is $\{x: x > 0\}$, so we evaluate $\lim_{x\to0^+} \ln x$ and $\lim_{x\to\infty} \ln x$ to determine end behavior. For the first limit, recall that $\ln x$ is the inverse of e^x (Figure 2.44), and the graph of $\ln x$ is a reflection of the graph of e^x across the line $y = x$. The horizontal asymptote $(y = 0)$ of e^x is also reflected across $y = x$, becoming a vertical asymptote $(x = 0)$ for $\ln x$. These observations imply that $\lim_{x\to0^+} \ln x = -\infty$.

It is not obvious whether the graph of $\ln x$ approaches a horizontal asymptote or whether the function grows without bound as $x \to \infty$. Furthermore, the numerical evidence (Table 2.9) is inconclusive because $\ln x$ increases very slowly. The inverse relation between e^x and $\ln x$ is again useful. The fact that the *domain* of e^x is $(-\infty, \infty)$ implies that the *range* of $\ln x$ is also $(-\infty, \infty)$. Therefore, the values of $\ln x$ lie in the interval $(-\infty, \infty)$, and it follows that $\lim_{x\to\infty} \ln x = \infty$.

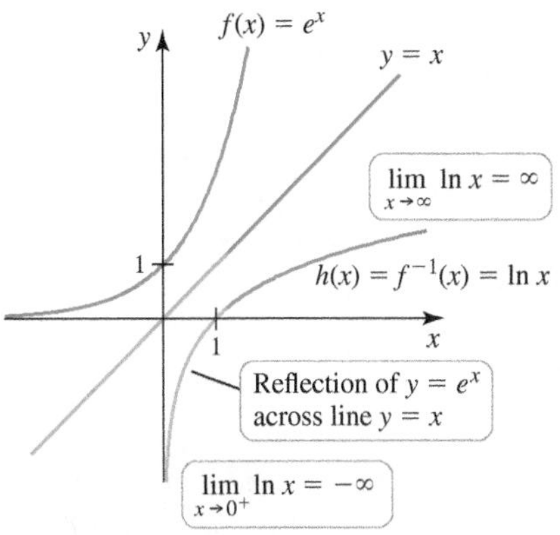

Figure 2.44

Table 2.9

x	$\ln x$
10	2.303
10^5	11.513
10^{10}	23.026
10^{50}	115.129
10^{99}	227.956
↓	↓
∞	???

c. The cosine function oscillates between -1 and 1 as $x \to \infty$ (Figure 2.45). Therefore, $\lim_{x\to\infty} \cos x$ does not exist. For the same reason, $\lim_{x\to-\infty} \cos x$ does not exist.

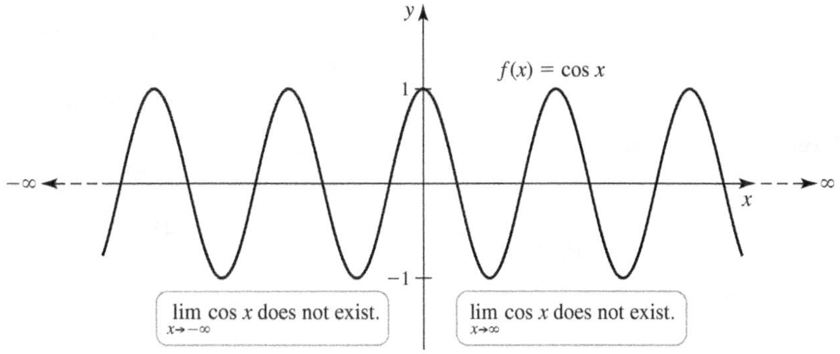

Figure 2.45

Related Exercises 45–50 ◀

The end behavior of exponential and logarithmic functions is important. We summarize these results in the following theorem.

THEOREM 2.8 End Behavior of e^x, e^{-x}, and $\ln x$
The end behavior for e^x and e^{-x} on $(-\infty, \infty)$ and $\ln x$ on $(0, \infty)$ is given by the following limits:

$$\lim_{x\to\infty} e^x = \infty \quad \text{and} \quad \lim_{x\to-\infty} e^x = 0,$$

$$\lim_{x\to\infty} e^{-x} = 0 \quad \text{and} \quad \lim_{x\to-\infty} e^{-x} = \infty,$$

$$\lim_{x\to 0^+} \ln x = -\infty \quad \text{and} \quad \lim_{x\to\infty} \ln x = \infty.$$

QUICK CHECK 4 How do the functions e^{10x} and e^{-10x} behave as $x \to \infty$ and as $x \to -\infty$? ◄

SECTION 2.5 EXERCISES

Review Questions

1. Explain the meaning of $\lim_{x\to-\infty} f(x) = 10$.
2. What is a horizontal asymptote?
3. Determine $\lim_{x\to\infty} \frac{f(x)}{g(x)}$ if $f(x) \to 100{,}000$ and $g(x) \to \infty$ as $x \to \infty$.
4. Describe the end behavior of $g(x) = e^{-2x}$.
5. Describe the end behavior of $f(x) = -2x^3$.
6. The text describes four cases that arise when examining the end behavior of a rational function $f(x) = p(x)/q(x)$. Describe the end behavior associated with each case.
7. Evaluate $\lim_{x\to\infty} e^x$, $\lim_{x\to-\infty} e^x$, and $\lim_{x\to\infty} e^{-x}$.
8. Use a sketch to find the end behavior of $f(x) = \ln x$.

Basic Skills

9–14. Limits at infinity *Evaluate the following limits.*

9. $\lim_{x\to\infty}\left(3 + \frac{10}{x^2}\right)$
10. $\lim_{x\to\infty}\left(5 + \frac{1}{x} + \frac{10}{x^2}\right)$
11. $\lim_{\theta\to\infty} \frac{\cos\theta}{\theta^2}$
12. $\lim_{x\to\infty} \frac{3 + 2x + 4x^2}{x^2}$
13. $\lim_{x\to\infty} \frac{\cos x^5}{\sqrt{x}}$
14. $\lim_{x\to-\infty}\left(5 + \frac{100}{x} + \frac{\sin^4 x^3}{x^2}\right)$

15–24. Infinite limits at infinity *Determine the following limits.*

15. $\lim_{x\to\infty} x^{12}$
16. $\lim_{x\to-\infty} 3x^{11}$
17. $\lim_{x\to\infty} x^{-6}$
18. $\lim_{x\to-\infty} x^{-11}$
19. $\lim_{x\to\infty} (3x^{12} - 9x^7)$
20. $\lim_{x\to-\infty} (3x^7 + x^2)$
21. $\lim_{x\to-\infty} (-3x^{16} + 2)$
22. $\lim_{x\to-\infty} 2x^{-8}$
23. $\lim_{x\to\infty} (-12x^{-5})$
24. $\lim_{x\to-\infty} (2x^{-8} + 4x^3)$

25–34. Rational functions *Determine $\lim_{x\to\infty} f(x)$ and $\lim_{x\to-\infty} f(x)$ for the following rational functions. Then give the horizontal asymptote of f (if any).*

25. $f(x) = \frac{4x}{20x + 1}$
26. $f(x) = \frac{3x^2 - 7}{x^2 + 5x}$
27. $f(x) = \frac{6x^2 - 9x + 8}{3x^2 + 2}$
28. $f(x) = \frac{4x^2 - 7}{8x^2 + 5x + 2}$
29. $f(x) = \frac{3x^3 - 7}{x^4 + 5x^2}$
30. $f(x) = \frac{x^4 + 7}{x^5 + x^2 - x}$
31. $f(x) = \frac{2x + 1}{3x^4 - 2}$
32. $f(x) = \frac{12x^8 - 3}{3x^8 - 2x^7}$
33. $f(x) = \frac{40x^5 + x^2}{16x^4 - 2x}$
34. $f(x) = \frac{-x^3 + 1}{2x + 8}$

T 35–40. Slant (oblique) asymptotes *Complete the following steps for the given functions.*

a. Use polynomial long division to find the slant asymptote of f.

b. Find the vertical asymptotes of f.

c. Graph f and all its asymptotes with a graphing utility. Then sketch a graph of the function by hand, correcting any errors appearing in the computer-generated graph.

35. $f(x) = \frac{x^2 - 3}{x + 6}$
36. $f(x) = \frac{x^2 - 1}{x + 2}$
37. $f(x) = \frac{x^2 - 2x + 5}{3x - 2}$
38. $f(x) = \frac{3x^2 - 2x + 7}{2x - 5}$
39. $f(x) = \frac{4x^3 + 4x^2 + 7x + 4}{1 + x^2}$
40. $f(x) = \frac{3x^2 - 2x + 5}{3x + 4}$

41–44. Algebraic functions *Determine $\lim_{x\to\infty} f(x)$ and $\lim_{x\to-\infty} f(x)$ for the following functions. Then give the horizontal asymptote(s) of f (if any).*

41. $f(x) = \frac{4x^3 + 1}{2x^3 + \sqrt{16x^6 + 1}}$
42. $f(x) = \frac{\sqrt{x^2 + 1}}{2x + 1}$
43. $f(x) = \frac{\sqrt[3]{x^6 + 8}}{4x^2 + \sqrt{3x^4 + 1}}$
44. $f(x) = 4x(3x - \sqrt{9x^2 + 1})$

45–50. Transcendental functions *Determine the end behavior of the following transcendental functions by analyzing appropriate limits. Then provide a simple sketch of the associated graph, showing asymptotes if they exist.*

45. $f(x) = -3e^{-x}$
46. $f(x) = 2^x$
47. $f(x) = 1 - \ln x$
48. $f(x) = |\ln x|$
49. $f(x) = \sin x$
50. $f(x) = \frac{50}{e^{2x}}$

Further Explorations

51. **Explain why or why not** Determine whether the following statements are true and give an explanation or counterexample.
    a. The graph of a function never crosses one of its horizontal asymptotes.
    b. A rational function f has both $\lim_{x\to\infty} f(x) = L$ (where L is finite) and $\lim_{x\to-\infty} f(x) = \infty$.
    c. The graph of a function can have at most two horizontal asymptotes.

52–61. Horizontal and vertical asymptotes

a. Analyze $\lim_{x\to\infty} f(x)$ and $\lim_{x\to-\infty} f(x)$, and then identify any horizontal asymptotes.

b. Find the vertical asymptotes. For each vertical asymptote $x = a$, analyze $\lim_{x\to a^-} f(x)$ and $\lim_{x\to a^+} f(x)$.

52. $f(x) = \dfrac{x^2 - 4x + 3}{x - 1}$

53. $f(x) = \dfrac{2x^3 + 10x^2 + 12x}{x^3 + 2x^2}$

54. $f(x) = \dfrac{\sqrt{16x^4 + 64x^2} + x^2}{2x^2 - 4}$

55. $f(x) = \dfrac{3x^4 + 3x^3 - 36x^2}{x^4 - 25x^2 + 144}$

56. $f(x) = 16x^2\left(4x^2 - \sqrt{16x^4 + 1}\right)$

57. $f(x) = \dfrac{x^2 - 9}{x(x - 3)}$

58. $f(x) = \dfrac{x - 1}{x^{2/3} - 1}$

59. $f(x) = \dfrac{\sqrt{x^2 + 2x + 6} - 3}{x - 1}$

60. $f(x) = \dfrac{|1 - x^2|}{x(x + 1)}$

61. $f(x) = \sqrt{|x|} - \sqrt{|x - 1|}$

62–65. End behavior for transcendental functions

62. The central branch of $f(x) = \tan x$ is shown in the figure.
    a. Analyze $\lim_{x\to\pi/2^-} \tan x$ and $\lim_{x\to-\pi/2^+} \tan x$. Are these infinite limits or limits at infinity?
    b. Sketch a graph of $g(x) = \tan^{-1}x$ by reflecting the graph of f over the line $y = x$ and use it to evaluate $\lim_{x\to\infty} \tan^{-1}x$ and $\lim_{x\to-\infty} \tan^{-1} x$.

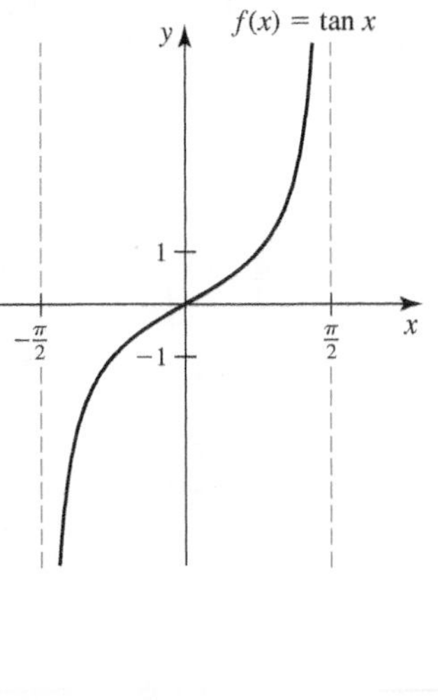

63. Consider the graph $y = \sec^{-1} x$ (see Section 1.4) and evaluate the following limits using the graph. Assume the domain is $\{x: |x| \geq 1\}$.
    a. $\lim_{x\to\infty} \sec^{-1} x$
    b. $\lim_{x\to-\infty} \sec^{-1} x$

64. The **hyperbolic cosine function**, denoted $\cosh x$, is used to model the shape of a hanging cable (a telephone wire, for example). It is defined as $\cosh x = \dfrac{e^x + e^{-x}}{2}$.
    a. Determine its end behavior by analyzing $\lim_{x\to\infty} \cosh x$ and $\lim_{x\to-\infty} \cosh x$.
    b. Evaluate cosh 0. Use symmetry and part (a) to sketch a plausible graph for $y = \cosh x$.

65. The **hyperbolic sine function** is defined as $\sinh x = \dfrac{e^x - e^{-x}}{2}$.
    a. Determine its end behavior by analyzing $\lim_{x\to\infty} \sinh x$ and $\lim_{x\to-\infty} \sinh x$.
    b. Evaluate sinh 0. Use symmetry and part (a) to sketch a plausible graph for $y = \sinh x$.

66–67. Sketching graphs *Sketch a possible graph of a function f that satisfies all the given conditions. Be sure to identify all vertical and horizontal asymptotes.*

66. $f(-1) = -2$, $f(1) = 2$, $f(0) = 0$, $\lim_{x\to\infty} f(x) = 1$, $\lim_{x\to-\infty} f(x) = -1$

67. $\lim_{x\to0^+} f(x) = \infty$, $\lim_{x\to0^-} f(x) = -\infty$, $\lim_{x\to\infty} f(x) = 1$, $\lim_{x\to-\infty} f(x) = -2$

68. **Asymptotes** Find the vertical and horizontal asymptotes of $f(x) = e^{1/x}$.

69. **Asymptotes** Find the vertical and horizontal asymptotes of $f(x) = \dfrac{\cos x + 2\sqrt{x}}{\sqrt{x}}$.

Applications

70–75. Steady states *If a function f represents a system that varies in time, the existence of $\lim_{t\to\infty} f(t)$ means that the system reaches a steady state (or equilibrium). For the following systems, determine whether a steady state exists and give the steady-state value.*

70. The population of a bacteria culture is given by $p(t) = \dfrac{2500}{t + 1}$.

71. The population of a culture of tumor cells is given by $p(t) = \dfrac{3500t}{t + 1}$.

72. The amount of drug (in milligrams) in the blood after an IV tube is inserted is $m(t) = 200(1 - 2^{-t})$.

73. The value of an investment in dollars is given by $v(t) = 1000e^{0.065t}$.

74. The population of a colony of squirrels is given by $p(t) = \dfrac{1500}{3 + 2e^{-0.1t}}$.

75. The amplitude of an oscillator is given by $a(t) = 2\left(\dfrac{t + \sin t}{t}\right)$.

76–79. Looking ahead to sequences *A sequence is an infinite, ordered list of numbers that is often defined by a function. For example, the sequence* $\{2, 4, 6, 8, \ldots\}$ *is specified by the function* $f(n) = 2n$, *where* $n = 1, 2, 3, \ldots$. *The limit of such a sequence is* $\lim_{n\to\infty} f(n)$, *provided the limit exists. All the limit laws for limits at infinity may be applied to limits of sequences. Find the limit of the following sequences or state that the limit does not exist.*

76. $\left\{4, 2, \frac{4}{3}, 1, \frac{4}{5}, \frac{2}{3}, \ldots\right\}$, which is defined by $f(n) = \frac{4}{n}$, for $n = 1, 2, 3, \ldots$

77. $\left\{0, \frac{1}{2}, \frac{2}{3}, \frac{3}{4}, \ldots\right\}$, which is defined by $f(n) = \frac{n-1}{n}$, for $n = 1, 2, 3, \ldots$

78. $\left\{\frac{1}{2}, \frac{4}{3}, \frac{9}{4}, \frac{16}{5}, \ldots\right\}$, which is defined by $f(n) = \frac{n^2}{n+1}$, for $n = 1, 2, 3, \ldots$

79. $\left\{2, \frac{3}{4}, \frac{4}{9}, \frac{5}{16}, \ldots\right\}$, which is defined by $f(n) = \frac{n+1}{n^2}$, for $n = 1, 2, 3, \ldots$

Additional Exercises

80. End behavior of a rational function Suppose $f(x) = \frac{p(x)}{q(x)}$ is a rational function, where
$p(x) = a_m x^m + a_{m-1}x^{m-1} + \cdots + a_2 x^2 + a_1 x + a_0$,
$q(x) = b_n x^n + b_{n-1}x^{n-1} + \cdots + b_2 x^2 + b_1 x + b_0$, $a_m \neq 0$, and $b_n \neq 0$.

a. Prove that if $m = n$, then $\lim_{x\to\pm\infty} f(x) = \frac{a_m}{b_n}$.

b. Prove that if $m < n$, then $\lim_{x\to\pm\infty} f(x) = 0$.

81. Horizontal and slant asymptotes

a. Is it possible for a rational function to have both slant and horizontal asymptotes? Explain.

b. Is it possible for an algebraic function to have two distinct slant asymptotes? Explain or give an example.

T **82. End behavior of exponentials** Use the following instructions to determine the end behavior of $f(x) = \frac{e^x + e^{2x}}{e^{2x} + e^{3x}}$.

a. Evaluate $\lim_{x\to\infty} f(x)$ by first dividing the numerator and denominator by e^{3x}.

b. Evaluate $\lim_{x\to-\infty} f(x)$ by first dividing the numerator and denominator by e^{2x}.

c. Give the horizontal asymptote(s).

d. Graph f to confirm your work in parts (a)–(c).

T **83–84. Limits of exponentials** *Evaluate* $\lim_{x\to\infty} f(x)$ *and* $\lim_{x\to-\infty} f(x)$. *Then state the horizontal asymptote(s) of f. Confirm your findings by plotting f.*

83. $f(x) = \frac{2e^x + 3e^{2x}}{e^{2x} + e^{3x}}$

84. $f(x) = \frac{3e^x + e^{-x}}{e^x + e^{-x}}$

T **85. Subtle asymptotes** Use analytical methods to identify all the asymptotes of $f(x) = \frac{\ln(9 - x^2)}{2e^x - e^{-x}}$. Then confirm your results by locating the asymptotes with a graphing utility.

QUICK CHECK ANSWERS

1. 10/11, 100/101, 1000/1001, 1 **2.** $p(x) \to -\infty$ as $x \to \infty$ and $p(x) \to \infty$ as $x \to -\infty$ **3.** Horizontal asymptote is $y = \frac{10}{3}$; vertical asymptote is $x = \frac{1}{3}$. **4.** $\lim_{x\to\infty} e^{10x} = \infty$, $\lim_{x\to-\infty} e^{10x} = 0$, $\lim_{x\to\infty} e^{-10x} = 0$, $\lim_{x\to-\infty} e^{-10x} = \infty$ ◀

2.6 Continuity

The graphs of many functions encountered in this text contain no holes, jumps, or breaks. For example, if $L = f(t)$ represents the length of a fish t years after it is hatched, then the length of the fish changes gradually as t increases. Consequently, the graph of $L = f(t)$ contains no breaks (Figure 2.46a). Some functions, however, do contain abrupt changes in their values. Consider a parking meter that accepts only quarters and each quarter buys 15 minutes of parking. Letting $c(t)$ be the cost (in dollars) of parking for t minutes, the graph of c has breaks at integer multiples of 15 minutes (Figure 2.46b).

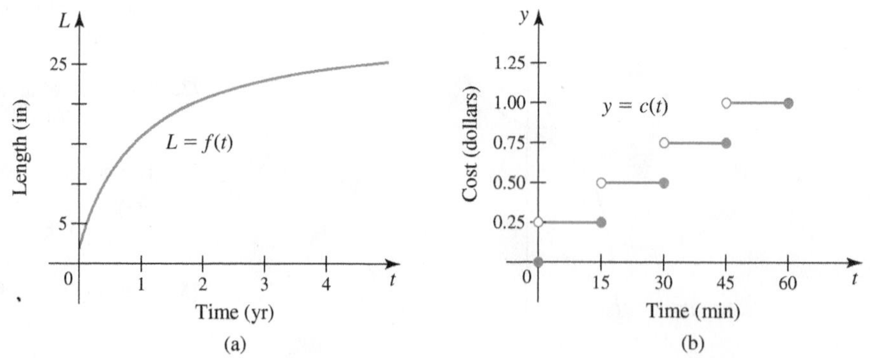

Figure 2.46

QUICK CHECK 1 For what values of t in $(0, 60)$ does the graph of $y = c(t)$ in Figure 2.46b have a discontinuity?◄

Informally, we say that a function f is *continuous* at a if the graph of f does not have a hole or break at a (that is, if the graph near a can be drawn without lifting the pencil). If a function is not continuous at a, then a is a *point of discontinuity*.

Continuity at a Point

This informal description of continuity is sufficient for determining the continuity of simple functions, but it is not precise enough to deal with more complicated functions such as

$$h(x) = \begin{cases} x \sin \dfrac{1}{x} & \text{if } x \neq 0 \\ 0 & \text{if } x = 0. \end{cases}$$

It is difficult to determine whether the graph of h has a break at 0 because it oscillates rapidly as x approaches 0 (Figure 2.47). We need a better definition.

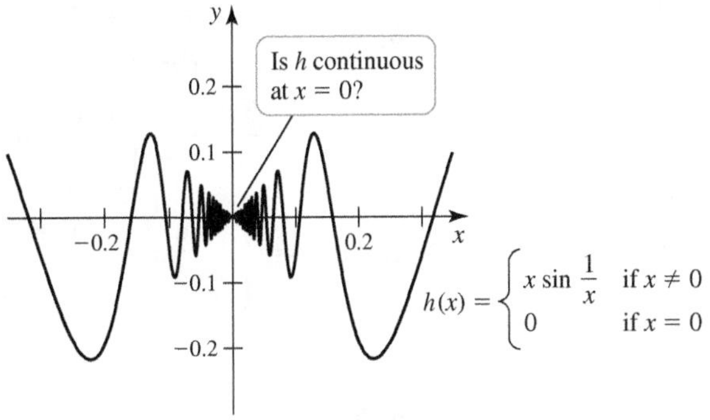

Figure 2.47

> **DEFINITION Continuity at a Point**
>
> A function f is **continuous** at a if $\lim_{x \to a} f(x) = f(a)$. If f is not continuous at a, then a is a **point of discontinuity**.

There is more to this definition than first appears. If $\lim_{x \to a} f(x) = f(a)$, then $f(a)$ and $\lim_{x \to a} f(x)$ must both exist, and they must be equal. The following checklist is helpful in determining whether a function is continuous at a.

> **Continuity Checklist**
>
> In order for f to be continuous at a, the following three conditions must hold.
>
> 1. $f(a)$ is defined (a is in the domain of f).
> 2. $\lim_{x \to a} f(x)$ exists.
> 3. $\lim_{x \to a} f(x) = f(a)$ (the value of f equals the limit of f at a).

If *any* item in the continuity checklist fails to hold, the function fails to be continuous at a. From this definition, we see that continuity has an important practical consequence:

If f is continuous at a, then $\lim_{x \to a} f(x) = f(a)$, and direct substitution may be used to evaluate $\lim_{x \to a} f(x)$.

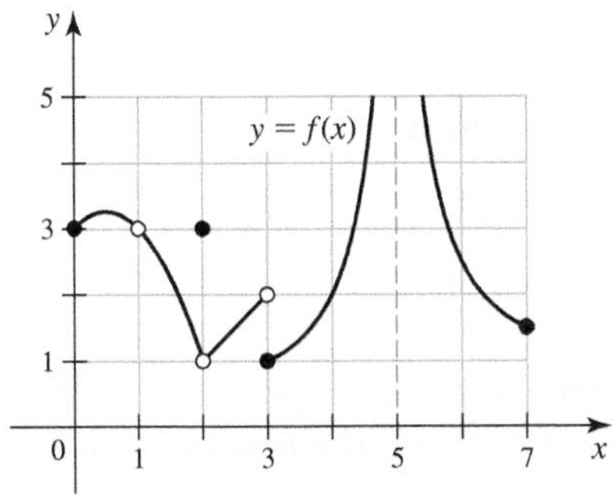

Figure 2.48

EXAMPLE 1 **Points of discontinuity** Use the graph of f in Figure 2.48 to identify values of x on the interval $(0, 7)$ at which f has a discontinuity.

➤ In Example 1, the discontinuities at $x = 1$ and $x = 2$ are called **removable discontinuities** because they can be removed by redefining the function at these points (in this case, $f(1) = 3$ and $f(2) = 1$). The discontinuity at $x = 3$ is called a **jump discontinuity**. The discontinuity at $x = 5$ is called an **infinite discontinuity**. These terms are discussed in Exercises 95–101.

SOLUTION The function f has discontinuities at $x = 1, 2, 3$, and 5 because the graph contains holes or breaks at these locations. The continuity checklist tells us why f is not continuous at these points.

- $f(1)$ is not defined.
- $f(2) = 3$ and $\lim_{x \to 2} f(x) = 1$. Therefore, $f(2)$ and $\lim_{x \to 2} f(x)$ exist but are not equal.
- $\lim_{x \to 3} f(x)$ does not exist because the left-sided limit $\lim_{x \to 3^-} f(x) = 2$ differs from the right-sided limit $\lim_{x \to 3^+} f(x) = 1$.
- Neither $\lim_{x \to 5} f(x)$ nor $f(5)$ exists.

Related Exercises 9–12 ◀

EXAMPLE 2 **Identifying discontinuities** Determine whether the following functions are continuous at a. Justify each answer using the continuity checklist.

a. $f(x) = \dfrac{3x^2 + 2x + 1}{x - 1}; \quad a = 1$

b. $g(x) = \dfrac{3x^2 + 2x + 1}{x - 1}; \quad a = 2$

c. $h(x) = \begin{cases} x \sin \dfrac{1}{x} & \text{if } x \neq 0 \\ 0 & \text{if } x = 0 \end{cases}; a = 0$

SOLUTION

a. The function f is not continuous at 1 because $f(1)$ is undefined.

b. Because g is a rational function and the denominator is nonzero at 2, it follows by Theorem 2.3 that $\lim_{x \to 2} g(x) = g(2) = 17$. Therefore, g is continuous at 2.

c. By definition, $h(0) = 0$. In Exercise 55 of Section 2.3, we used the Squeeze Theorem to show that $\lim_{x \to 0} x \sin \dfrac{1}{x} = 0$. Therefore, $\lim_{x \to 0} h(x) = h(0)$, which implies that h is continuous at 0.

Related Exercises 13–20 ◀

The following theorems make it easier to test various combinations of functions for continuity at a point.

THEOREM 2.9 **Continuity Rules**

If f and g are continuous at a, then the following functions are also continuous at a. Assume c is a constant and $n > 0$ is an integer.

a. $f + g$ **b.** $f - g$

c. cf **d.** fg

e. f/g, provided $g(a) \neq 0$ **f.** $(f(x))^n$

To prove the first result, note that if f and g are continuous at a, then $\lim_{x \to a} f(x) = f(a)$ and $\lim_{x \to a} g(x) = g(a)$. From the limit laws of Theorem 2.3, it follows that

$$\lim_{x \to a} (f(x) + g(x)) = f(a) + g(a).$$

Therefore, $f + g$ is continuous at a. Similar arguments lead to the continuity of differences, products, quotients, and powers of continuous functions. The next theorem is a direct consequence of Theorem 2.9.

THEOREM 2.10 Polynomial and Rational Functions

a. A polynomial function is continuous for all x.

b. A rational function (a function of the form $\frac{p}{q}$, where p and q are polynomials) is continuous for all x for which $q(x) \neq 0$.

EXAMPLE 3 Applying the continuity theorems For what values of x is the function $f(x) = \frac{x}{x^2 - 7x + 12}$ continuous?

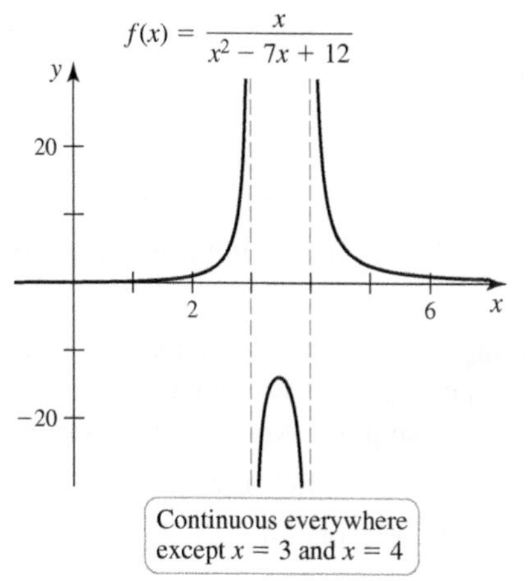

Figure 2.49

SOLUTION

a. Because f is rational, Theorem 2.10b implies it is continuous for all x at which the denominator is nonzero. The denominator factors as $(x - 3)(x - 4)$, so it is zero at $x = 3$ and $x = 4$. Therefore, f is continuous for all x except $x = 3$ and $x = 4$ (Figure 2.49). *Related Exercises 21–26* ◄

The following theorem allows us to determine when a composition of two functions is continuous at a point. Its proof is informative and is outlined in Exercise 102.

THEOREM 2.11 Continuity of Composite Functions at a Point
If g is continuous at a and f is continuous at $g(a)$, then the composite function $f \circ g$ is continuous at a.

QUICK CHECK 2 Evaluate $\lim_{x \to 4} \sqrt{x^2 + 9}$ and $\sqrt{\lim_{x \to 4} (x^2 + 9)}$. How do these results illustrate that the order of a function evaluation and a limit may be switched for continuous functions? ◄

Theorem 2.11 is useful because it allows us to conclude that the composition of two continuous functions is continuous at a point. For example, the composite function $\left(\frac{x}{x - 1}\right)^3$ is continuous for all $x \neq 1$. Furthermore, under the stated conditions on f and g, the limit of $f \circ g$ is evaluated by direct substitution; that is,

$$\lim_{x \to a} f(g(x)) = f(g(a)).$$

EXAMPLE 4 Limit of a composition Evaluate $\lim_{x \to 0} \left(\frac{x^4 - 2x + 2}{x^6 + 2x^4 + 1}\right)^{10}$.

SOLUTION The rational function $\frac{x^4 - 2x + 2}{x^6 + 2x^4 + 1}$ is continuous for all x because its denominator is always positive (Theorem 2.10b). Therefore, $\left(\frac{x^4 - 2x + 2}{x^6 + 2x^4 + 1}\right)^{10}$, which is the composition of the continuous function $f(x) = x^{10}$ and a continuous rational function, is continuous for all x by Theorem 2.11. By direct substitution,

$$\lim_{x \to 0} \left(\frac{x^4 - 2x + 2}{x^6 + 2x^4 + 1}\right)^{10} = \left(\frac{0^4 - 2 \cdot 0 + 2}{0^6 + 2 \cdot 0^4 + 1}\right)^{10} = 2^{10} = 1024.$$

Related Exercises 27–30 ◄

Closely related to Theorem 2.11 are two useful results dealing with limits of composite functions. We present these results—one a more general version of the other—in a single theorem.

THEOREM 2.12 Limits of Composite Functions

1. If g is continuous at a and f is continuous at $g(a)$, then
$$\lim_{x\to a} f(g(x)) = f\Big(\lim_{x\to a} g(x)\Big).$$

2. If $\lim_{x\to a} g(x) = L$ and f is continuous at L, then
$$\lim_{x\to a} f(g(x)) = f\Big(\lim_{x\to a} g(x)\Big).$$

Proof: The first statement follows directly from Theorem 2.11, which states that $\lim_{x\to a} f(g(x)) = f(g(a))$. If g is continuous at a, then $\lim_{x\to a} g(x) = g(a)$, and it follows that
$$\lim_{x\to a} f(g(x)) = f(\underbrace{g(a)}_{\lim_{x\to a} g(x)}) = f\Big(\lim_{x\to a} g(x)\Big).$$

The proof of the second statement relies on the formal definition of a limit, which is discussed in Section 2.7. ◀

Both statements of Theorem 2.12 justify interchanging the order of a limit and a function evaluation. By the second statement, the inner function of the composition needn't be continuous at the point of interest, but it must have a limit at that point. Note also that $\lim_{x\to a}$ can be replaced with $\lim_{x\to a^+}$ or $\lim_{x\to a^-}$ in Theorem 2.12, provided g is right- or left-continuous at a, respectively, in statement (1). In statement (2), $\lim_{x\to a}$ can be replaced with $\lim_{x\to\infty}$ or $\lim_{x\to-\infty}$.

EXAMPLE 5 Limits of a composite functions Evaluate the following limits.

a. $\lim_{x\to -1} \sqrt{2x^2 - 1}$ **b.** $\lim_{x\to 2} \cos\left(\dfrac{x^2-4}{x-2}\right)$

SOLUTION

a. We show later in this section that $\sqrt{x}$ is continuous for $x \geq 0$. The inner function of the composite function $\sqrt{2x^2-1}$ is $2x^2 - 1$; it is continuous and positive at -1. By the first statement of Theorem 2.12,
$$\lim_{x\to -1} \sqrt{2x^2-1} = \sqrt{\underbrace{\lim_{x\to -1}(2x^2-1)}_{1}} = \sqrt{1} = 1.$$

b. We show later in this section that $\cos x$ is continuous at all points of its domain. The inner function of the composite function $\cos\left(\dfrac{x^2-4}{x-2}\right)$ is $\dfrac{x^2-4}{x-2}$, which is not continuous at 2. However,
$$\lim_{x\to 2}\frac{x^2-4}{x-2} = \lim_{x\to 2}\frac{(x-2)(x+2)}{x-2} = \lim_{x\to 2}(x+2) = 4.$$

Therefore, by the second statement of Theorem 2.12,
$$\lim_{x\to 2}\cos\left(\frac{x^2-4}{x-2}\right) = \cos\Big(\underbrace{\lim_{x\to 2}\frac{x^2-4}{x-2}}_{4}\Big) = \cos 4 \approx -0.654.$$

Related Exercises 31–34 ◀

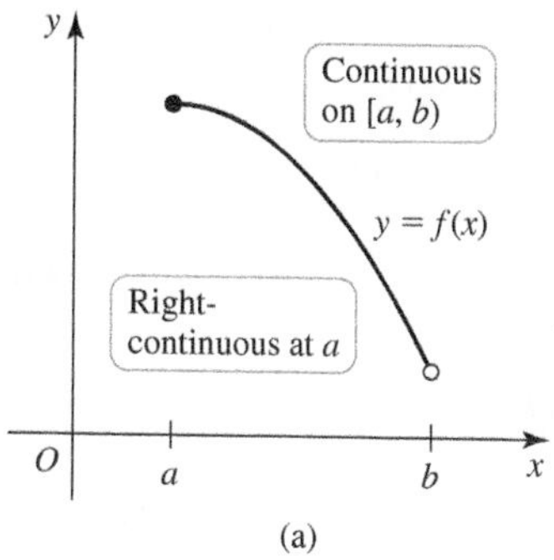

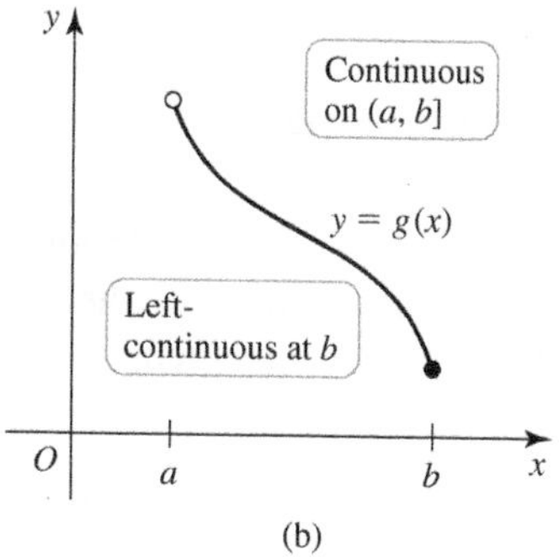

Figure 2.50

Continuity on an Interval

A function is *continuous on an interval* if it is continuous at every point in that interval. Consider the functions f and g whose graphs are shown in Figure 2.50. Both these functions are continuous for all x in (a, b), but what about the endpoints? To answer this question, we introduce the ideas of *left-continuity* and *right-continuity*.

> DEFINITION **Continuity at Endpoints**
>
> A function f is **continuous from the left** (or **left-continuous**) at a if $\lim_{x \to a^-} f(x) = f(a)$, and f is **continuous from the right** (or **right-continuous**) at a if $\lim_{x \to a^+} f(x) = f(a)$.

Combining the definitions of left-continuous and right-continuous with the definition of continuity at a point, we define what it means for a function to be continuous on an interval.

> DEFINITION **Continuity on an Interval**
>
> A function f is **continuous on an interval I** if it is continuous at all points of I. If I contains its endpoints, continuity on I means continuous from the right or left at the endpoints.

To illustrate these definitions, consider again the functions in Figure 2.50. In Figure 2.50a, f is continuous from the right at a because $\lim_{x \to a^+} f(x) = f(a)$, but it is not continuous from the left at b because $f(b)$ is not defined. Therefore, f is continuous on the interval $[a, b)$. The behavior of the function g in Figure 2.50b is the opposite: It is continuous from the left at b, but it is not continuous from the right at a. Therefore, g is continuous on $(a, b]$.

QUICK CHECK 3 Modify the graphs of the functions f and g in Figure 2.50 to obtain functions that are continuous on $[a, b]$. ◀

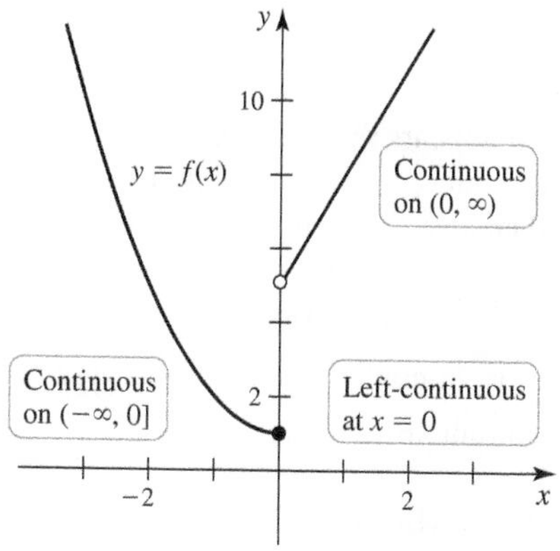

Figure 2.51

EXAMPLE 6 **Intervals of continuity** Determine the intervals of continuity for

$$f(x) = \begin{cases} x^2 + 1 & \text{if } x \le 0 \\ 3x + 5 & \text{if } x > 0. \end{cases}$$

SOLUTION This piecewise function consists of two polynomials that describe a parabola and a line (Figure 2.51). By Theorem 2.10, f is continuous for all $x \neq 0$. From its graph, it appears that f is left-continuous at 0. This observation is verified by noting that

$$\lim_{x \to 0^-} f(x) = \lim_{x \to 0^-} (x^2 + 1) = 1,$$

which means that $\lim_{x \to 0^-} f(x) = f(0)$. However, because

$$\lim_{x \to 0^+} f(x) = \lim_{x \to 0^+} (3x + 5) = 5 \neq f(0),$$

we see that f is not right-continuous at 0. Therefore, f is continuous on $(-\infty, 0]$ and on $(0, \infty)$.

Related Exercises 35–40 ◀

Functions Involving Roots

Recall that Limit Law 7 of Theorem 2.3 states

$$\lim_{x \to a} (f(x))^{n/m} = \left(\lim_{x \to a} f(x)\right)^{n/m},$$

provided $f(x) \geq 0$, for x near a, if m is even and n/m is reduced. Therefore, if m is odd and f is continuous at a, then $[f(x)]^{n/m}$ is continuous at a, because

$$\lim_{x \to a} (f(x))^{n/m} = \left(\lim_{x \to a} f(x)\right)^{n/m} = (f(a))^{n/m}.$$

When m is even, the continuity of $(f(x))^{n/m}$ must be handled more carefully because this function is defined only when $f(x) \geq 0$. Exercise 59 of Section 2.7 establishes an important fact:

> *If f is continuous at a and $f(a) > 0$, then $f(x) > 0$ for all values of x in the domain of f and in some interval containing a.*

Combining this fact with Theorem 2.11 (the continuity of composite functions), it follows that $(f(x))^{n/m}$ is continuous at a provided $f(a) > 0$. At points where $f(a) = 0$, the behavior of $(f(x))^{n/m}$ varies. Often we find that $(f(x))^{n/m}$ is left- or right-continuous at that point, or it may be continuous from both sides.

> **THEOREM 2.13 Continuity of Functions with Roots**
> Assume that m and n are positive integers with no common factors. If m is an odd integer, then $(f(x))^{n/m}$ is continuous at all points at which f is continuous.
> If m is even, then $(f(x))^{n/m}$ is continuous at all points a at which f is continuous and $f(a) > 0$.

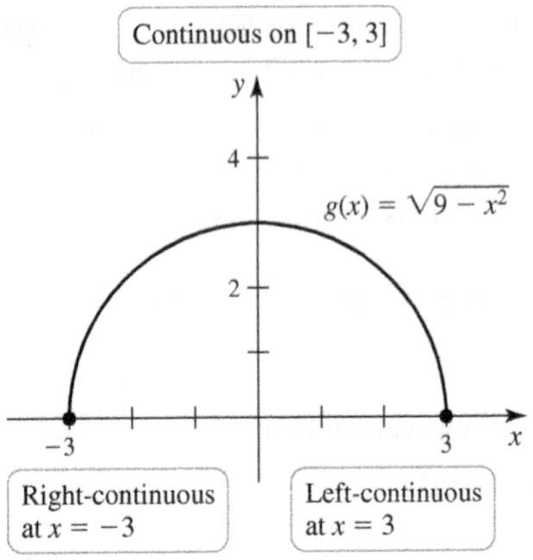

Figure 2.52

EXAMPLE 7 Continuity with roots For what values of x are the following functions continuous?

a. $g(x) = \sqrt{9 - x^2}$ **b.** $f(x) = (x^2 - 2x + 4)^{2/3}$

SOLUTION

a. The graph of g is the upper half of the circle $x^2 + y^2 = 9$ (which can be verified by solving $x^2 + y^2 = 9$ for y). From Figure 2.52, it appears that g is continuous on $[-3, 3]$. To verify this fact, note that g involves an even root ($m = 2, n = 1$ in Theorem 2.13). If $-3 < x < 3$, then $9 - x^2 > 0$ and by Theorem 2.13, g is continuous for all x on $(-3, 3)$.

At the right endpoint, $\lim_{x \to 3^-} \sqrt{9 - x^2} = 0 = g(3)$ by Limit Law 7, which implies that g is left-continuous at 3. Similarly, g is right-continuous at -3 because $\lim_{x \to -3^+} \sqrt{9 - x^2} = 0 = g(-3)$. Therefore, g is continuous on $[-3, 3]$.

b. The polynomial $x^2 - 2x + 4$ is continuous for all x by Theorem 2.10a. Because f involves an odd root ($m = 3, n = 2$ in Theorem 2.13), f is continuous for all x.

Related Exercises 41–50 ◀

QUICK CHECK 4 On what interval is $f(x) = x^{1/4}$ continuous? On what interval is $f(x) = x^{2/5}$ continuous? ◀

Continuity of Transcendental Functions

The understanding of continuity that we have developed with algebraic functions may now be applied to transcendental functions.

Trigonometric Functions In Example 8 of Section 2.3, we used the Squeeze Theorem to show that $\lim_{x \to 0} \sin x = 0$ and $\lim_{x \to 0} \cos x = 1$. Because $\sin 0 = 0$ and $\cos 0 = 1$, these limits imply that $\sin x$ and $\cos x$ are continuous at 0. The graph of $y = \sin x$ (Figure 2.53) suggests that $\lim_{x \to a} \sin x = \sin a$ for any value of a, which means that $\sin x$ is continuous on $(-\infty, \infty)$. The graph of $y = \cos x$ also indicates that $\cos x$ is continuous for all x. Exercise 105 outlines a proof of these results.

With these facts in hand, we appeal to Theorem 2.9e to discover that the remaining trigonometric functions are continuous on their domains. For example, because $\sec x = 1/\cos x$, the secant function is continuous for all x for which $\cos x \neq 0$ (for all x except odd multiples of $\pi/2$) (Figure 2.54). Likewise, the tangent, cotangent, and cosecant functions are continuous at all points of their domains.

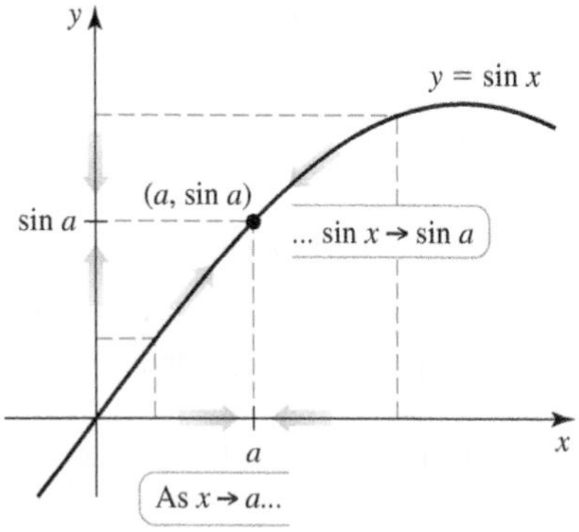

Figure 2.53

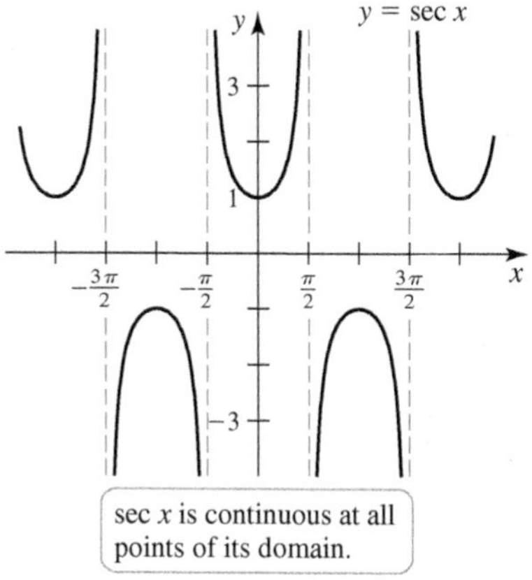

Figure 2.54

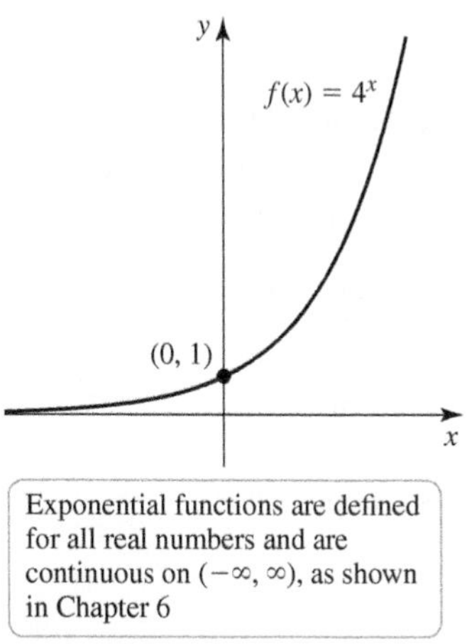

Figure 2.55

Exponential Functions The continuity of exponential functions of the form $f(x) = b^x$, with $0 < b < 1$ or $b > 1$, raises an important question. Consider the function $f(x) = 4^x$ (Figure 2.55). Evaluating f is routine if x is rational:

$$4^3 = 4 \cdot 4 \cdot 4 = 64; \quad 4^{-2} = \frac{1}{4^2} = \frac{1}{16}; \quad 4^{3/2} = \sqrt{4^3} = 8; \quad \text{and} \quad 4^{-1/3} = \frac{1}{\sqrt[3]{4}}.$$

But what is meant by 4^x when x is an irrational number, such as $\sqrt{2}$? In order for $f(x) = 4^x$ to be continuous for all real numbers, it must also be defined when x is an irrational number. Providing a working definition for an expression such as $4^{\sqrt{2}}$ requires mathematical results that don't appear until Chapter 6. Until then, we assume without proof that the domain of $f(x) = b^x$ is the set of all real numbers and that f is continuous at all points of its domain.

Inverse Functions Suppose a function f is continuous and one-to-one on an interval I. Reflecting the graph of f through the line $y = x$ generates the graph of f^{-1}. The reflection process introduces no discontinuities in the graph of f^{-1}, so it is plausible (and indeed true) that f^{-1} is continuous on the interval corresponding to I. We state this fact without a formal proof.

> THEOREM 2.14 **Continuity of Inverse Functions**
> If a function f is continuous on an interval I and has an inverse on I, then its inverse f^{-1} is also continuous (on the interval consisting of the points $f(x)$, where x is in I).

Because all the trigonometric functions are continuous on their domains, they are also continuous when their domains are restricted for the purpose of defining inverse functions. Therefore, by Theorem 2.14, the inverse trigonometric functions are continuous at all points of their domains.

Logarithmic functions of the form $f(x) = \log_b x$ are continuous at all points of their domains for the same reason: They are inverses of exponential functions, which are one-to-one and continuous. Collecting all these facts, we have the following theorem.

THEOREM 2.15 Continuity of Transcendental Functions
The following functions are continuous at all points of their domains.

Trigonometric		**Inverse Trigonometric**		**Exponential**	
$\sin x$	$\cos x$	$\sin^{-1} x$	$\cos^{-1} x$	b^x	e^x
$\tan x$	$\cot x$	$\tan^{-1} x$	$\cot^{-1} x$	**Logarithmic**	
$\sec x$	$\csc x$	$\sec^{-1} x$	$\csc^{-1} x$	$\log_b x$	$\ln x$

For each function listed in Theorem 2.15, we have $\lim_{x \to a} f(x) = f(a)$, provided a is in the domain of the function. This means that limits of these functions may be evaluated by direct substitution at points in the domain.

EXAMPLE 8 Limits involving transcendental functions Analyze the following limits after determining the continuity of the functions involved.

a. $\displaystyle\lim_{x \to 0} \frac{\cos^2 x - 1}{\cos x - 1}$ **b.** $\displaystyle\lim_{x \to 1} \left(\sqrt[4]{\ln x} + \tan^{-1} x\right)$

SOLUTION

a. Both $\cos^2 x - 1$ and $\cos x - 1$ are continuous for all x by Theorems 2.9 and 2.15. However, the ratio of these functions is continuous only when $\cos x - 1 \neq 0$, which occurs when x is not an integer multiple of 2π. Note that both the numerator and denominator of $\dfrac{\cos^2 x - 1}{\cos x - 1}$ approach 0 as $x \to 0$. To evaluate the limit, we factor and simplify:

$$\lim_{x \to 0} \frac{\cos^2 x - 1}{\cos x - 1} = \lim_{x \to 0} \frac{(\cos x - 1)(\cos x + 1)}{\cos x - 1} = \lim_{x \to 0} (\cos x + 1)$$

(where $\cos x - 1$ may be canceled because it is nonzero as x approaches 0). The limit on the right is now evaluated using direct substitution:

$$\lim_{x \to 0} (\cos x + 1) = \cos 0 + 1 = 2.$$

➤ Limits like the one in Example 8a are denoted 0/0 and are known as *indeterminate forms*, to be studied further in Section 4.7.

b. By Theorem 2.15, $\ln x$ is continuous on its domain $(0, \infty)$. However, $\ln x > 0$ only when $x > 1$, so Theorem 2.13 implies that $\sqrt[4]{\ln x}$ is continuous on $(1, \infty)$. At $x = 1$, $\sqrt[4]{\ln x}$ is right-continuous (Quick Check 5). The domain of $\tan^{-1} x$ is all real numbers, and it is continuous on $(-\infty, \infty)$. Therefore, $f(x) = \sqrt[4]{\ln x} + \tan^{-1} x$ is continuous on $[1, \infty)$. Because the domain of f does not include points with $x < 1$, $\lim_{x \to 1^-} \left(\sqrt[4]{\ln x} + \tan^{-1} x\right)$ does not exist, which implies that $\lim_{x \to 1} \left(\sqrt[4]{\ln x} + \tan^{-1} x\right)$ does not exist.

Related Exercises 51–56 ◀

QUICK CHECK 5 Show that $f(x) = \sqrt[4]{\ln x}$ is right-continuous at $x = 1$. ◀

We close this section with an important theorem that has both practical and theoretical uses.

The Intermediate Value Theorem

A common problem in mathematics is finding solutions to equations of the form $f(x) = L$. Before attempting to find values of x satisfying this equation, it is worthwhile to determine whether a solution exists.

The existence of solutions is often established using a result known as the *Intermediate Value Theorem*. Given a function f and a constant L, we assume L lies strictly between $f(a)$ and $f(b)$. The Intermediate Value Theorem says that if f is continuous on $[a, b]$, then the graph of f must cross the horizontal line $y = L$ at least once (Figure 2.56). Although this theorem is easily illustrated, its proof is beyond the scope of this text.

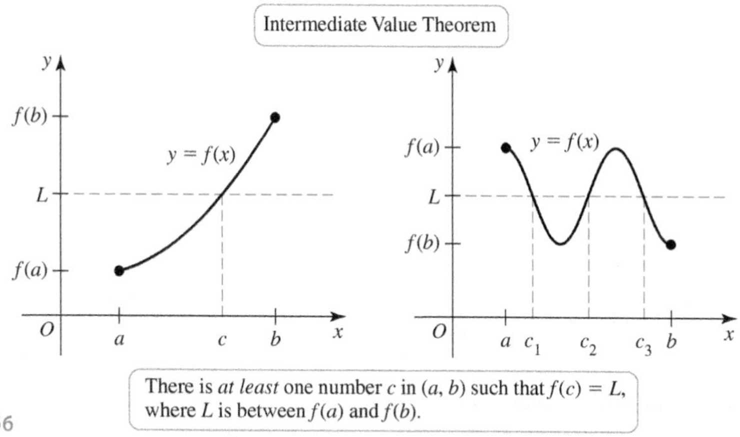

Figure 2.56

> **THEOREM 2.16 The Intermediate Value Theorem**
> Suppose f is continuous on the interval $[a, b]$ and L is a number strictly between $f(a)$ and $f(b)$. Then there exists at least one number c in (a, b) satisfying $f(c) = L$.

The importance of continuity in Theorem 2.16 is illustrated in Figure 2.57, where we see a function f that is not continuous on $[a, b]$. For the value of L shown in the figure, there is no value of c in (a, b) satisfying $f(c) = L$. The next example illustrates a practical application of the Intermediate Value Theorem.

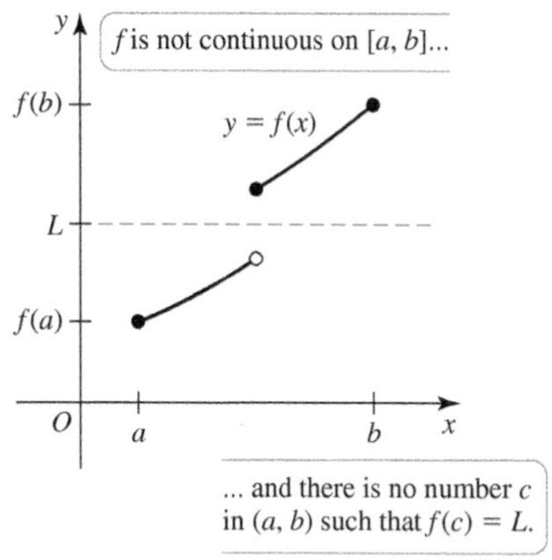

Figure 2.57

QUICK CHECK 6 Does the equation $f(x) = x^3 + x + 1 = 0$ have a solution on the interval $[-1, 1]$? Explain. ◄

EXAMPLE 9 Finding an interest rate Suppose you invest \$1000 in a special 5-year savings account with a fixed annual interest rate r, with monthly compounding. The amount of money A in the account after 5 years (60 months) is $A(r) = 1000\left(1 + \frac{r}{12}\right)^{60}$. Your goal is to have \$1400 in the account after 5 years.

a. Use the Intermediate Value Theorem to show there is a value of r in (0, 0.08)—that is, an interest rate between 0% and 8%—for which $A(r) = 1400$.

b. Use a graphing utility to illustrate your explanation in part (a) and then estimate the interest rate required to reach your goal.

SOLUTION

a. As a polynomial in r (of degree 60), $A(r) = 1000\left(1 + \frac{r}{12}\right)^{60}$ is continuous for all r. Evaluating $A(r)$ at the endpoints of the interval $[0, 0.08]$, we have $A(0) = 1000$ and $A(0.08) \approx 1489.85$. Therefore,

$$A(0) < 1400 < A(0.08),$$

and it follows, by the Intermediate Value Theorem, that there is a value of r in $(0, 0.08)$ for which $A(r) = 1400$.

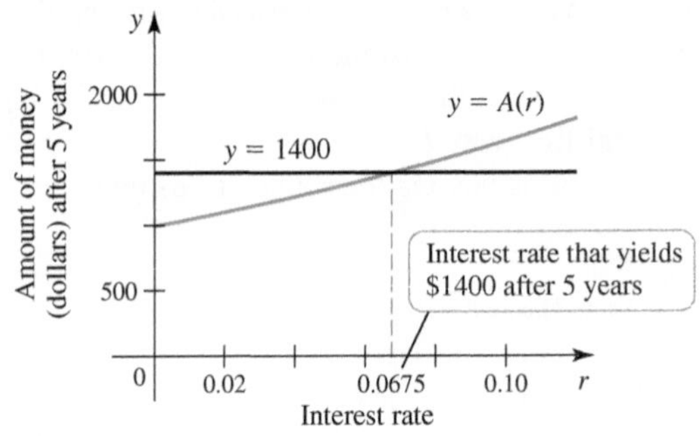

Figure 2.58

b. The graphs of $y = A(r)$ and the horizontal line $y = 1400$ are shown in Figure 2.58; it is evident that they intersect between $r = 0$ and $r = 0.08$. Solving $A(r) = 1400$ algebraically or using a root finder reveals that the curve and line intersect at $r \approx 0.0675$. Therefore, an interest rate of approximately 6.75% is required for the investment to be worth \$1400 after 5 years.

Related Exercises 57–64 ◀

SECTION 2.6 EXERCISES

Review Questions

1. Which of the following functions are continuous for all values in their domain? Justify your answers.
   a. $a(t) =$ altitude of a skydiver t seconds after jumping from a plane
   b. $n(t) =$ number of quarters needed to park legally in a metered parking space for t minutes
   c. $T(t) =$ temperature t minutes after midnight in Chicago on January 1
   d. $p(t) =$ number of points scored by a basketball player after t minutes of a basketball game

2. Give the three conditions that must be satisfied by a function to be continuous at a point.

3. What does it mean for a function to be continuous on an interval?

4. We informally describe a function f to be continuous at a if its graph contains no holes or breaks at a. Explain why this is not an adequate definition of continuity.

5. Complete the following sentences.
   a. A function is continuous from the left at a if ________.
   b. A function is continuous from the right at a if ________.

6. Describe the points (if any) at which a rational function fails to be continuous.

7. What is the domain of $f(x) = e^x/x$ and where is f continuous?

8. Explain the Intermediate Value Theorem using words and pictures.

Basic Skills

9–12. Discontinuities from a graph *Determine the points at which the following functions f have discontinuities. At each point of discontinuity, state the conditions in the continuity checklist that are violated.*

9.

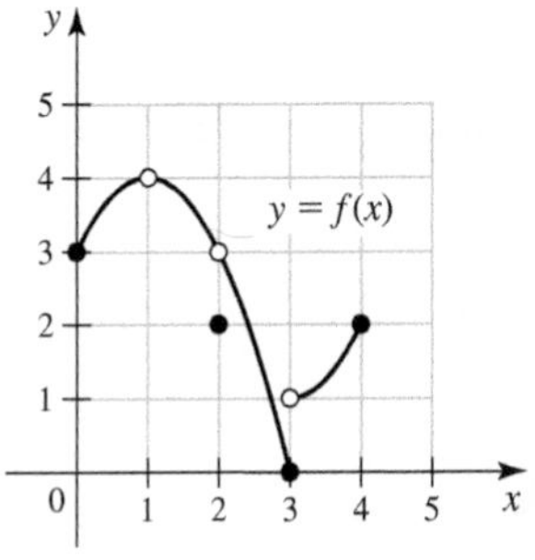

10.

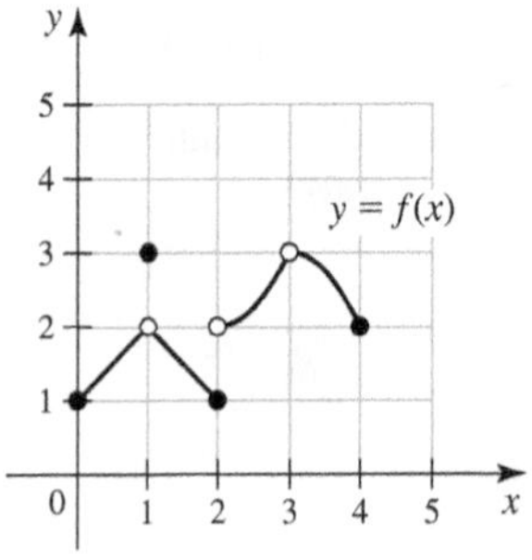

11.

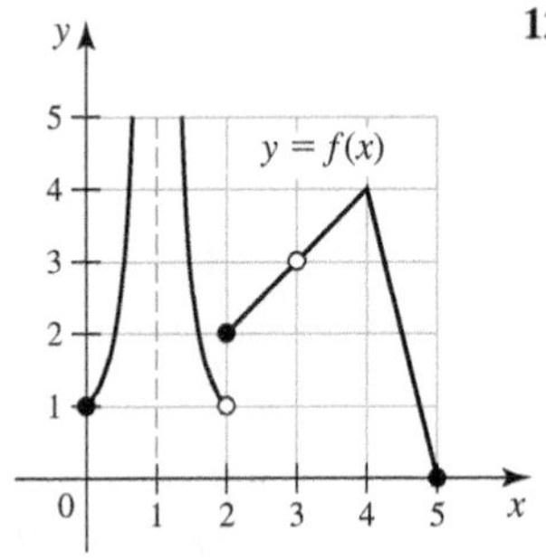

12.

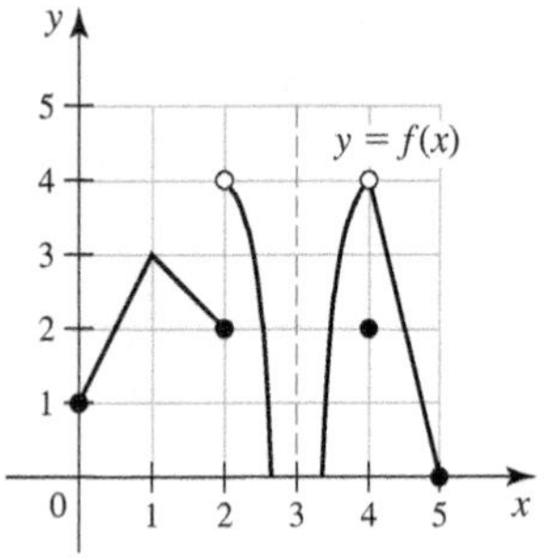

13–20. Continuity at a point *Determine whether the following functions are continuous at a. Use the continuity checklist to justify your answer.*

13. $f(x) = \dfrac{2x^2 + 3x + 1}{x^2 + 5x}$; $a = 5$

14. $f(x) = \dfrac{2x^2 + 3x + 1}{x^2 + 5x}$; $a = -5$

15. $f(x) = \sqrt{x - 2}$; $a = 1$

16. $g(x) = \dfrac{1}{x - 3}$; $a = 3$

17. $f(x) = \begin{cases} \dfrac{x^2 - 1}{x - 1} & \text{if } x \neq 1 \\ 3 & \text{if } x = 1 \end{cases}$; $a = 1$

18. $f(x) = \begin{cases} \dfrac{x^2 - 4x + 3}{x - 3} & \text{if } x \neq 3 \\ 2 & \text{if } x = 3 \end{cases}$; $a = 3$

19. $f(x) = \dfrac{5x - 2}{x^2 - 9x + 20}$; $a = 4$

20. $f(x) = \begin{cases} \dfrac{x^2 + x}{x + 1} & \text{if } x \neq -1 \\ 2 & \text{if } x = -1 \end{cases}$; $a = -1$

21–26. Continuity on intervals *Use Theorem 2.10 to determine the intervals on which the following functions are continuous.*

21. $p(x) = 4x^5 - 3x^2 + 1$

22. $g(x) = \dfrac{3x^2 - 6x + 7}{x^2 + x + 1}$

23. $f(x) = \frac{x^5 + 6x + 17}{x^2 - 9}$

24. $s(x) = \frac{x^2 - 4x + 3}{x^2 - 1}$

25. $f(x) = \frac{1}{x^2 - 4}$

26. $f(t) = \frac{t + 2}{t^2 - 4}$

27–30. Limits of compositions *Evaluate each limit and justify your answer.*

27. $\lim_{x \to 0} (x^8 - 3x^6 - 1)^{40}$

28. $\lim_{x \to 2} \left(\frac{3}{2x^5 - 4x^2 - 50} \right)^4$

29. $\lim_{x \to 1} \left(\frac{x + 5}{x + 2} \right)^4$

30. $\lim_{x \to \infty} \left(\frac{2x + 1}{x} \right)^3$

31–34. Limits of composite functions *Evaluate each limit and justify your answer.*

31. $\lim_{x \to 4} \sqrt{\frac{x^3 - 2x^2 - 8x}{x - 4}}$

32. $\lim_{t \to 4} \tan \frac{t - 4}{\sqrt{t} - 2}$

33. $\lim_{x \to 0} \ln \frac{2 \sin x}{x}$

34. $\lim_{x \to 0} \left(\frac{x}{\sqrt{16x + 1} - 1} \right)^{1/3}$

35–38. Intervals of continuity *Determine the intervals of continuity for the following functions.*

35. The graph of Exercise 9

36. The graph of Exercise 10

37. The graph of Exercise 11

38. The graph of Exercise 12

39. **Intervals of continuity** Let

$$f(x) = \begin{cases} 2x & \text{if } x < 1 \\ x^2 + 3x & \text{if } x \geq 1. \end{cases}$$

a. Use the continuity checklist to show that f is not continuous at 1.
b. Is f continuous from the left or right at 1?
c. State the interval(s) of continuity.

40. **Intervals of continuity** Let

$$f(x) = \begin{cases} x^3 + 4x + 1 & \text{if } x \leq 0 \\ 2x^3 & \text{if } x > 0. \end{cases}$$

a. Use the continuity checklist to show that f is not continuous at 0.
b. Is f continuous from the left or right at 0?
c. State the interval(s) of continuity.

41–46. Functions with roots *Determine the interval(s) on which the following functions are continuous. Be sure to consider right- and left-continuity at the endpoints.*

41. $f(x) = \sqrt{2x^2 - 16}$

42. $g(x) = \sqrt{x^4 - 1}$

43. $f(x) = \sqrt[3]{x^2 - 2x - 3}$

44. $f(t) = (t^2 - 1)^{3/2}$

45. $f(x) = (2x - 3)^{2/3}$

46. $f(z) = (z - 1)^{3/4}$

47–50. Limits with roots *Evaluate each limit and justify your answer.*

47. $\lim_{x \to 2} \sqrt{\frac{4x + 10}{2x - 2}}$

48. $\lim_{x \to -1} (x^2 - 4 + \sqrt[3]{x^2 - 9})$

49. $\lim_{x \to 3} \sqrt{x^2 + 7}$

50. $\lim_{t \to 2} \frac{t^2 + 5}{1 + \sqrt{t^2 + 5}}$

51–56. Continuity and limits with transcendental functions *Determine the interval(s) on which the following functions are continuous; then analyze the given limits.*

51. $f(x) = \csc x;\ \lim_{x \to \pi/4} f(x);\ \lim_{x \to 2\pi^-} f(x)$

52. $f(x) = e^{\sqrt{x}};\ \lim_{x \to 4} f(x);\ \lim_{x \to 0^+} f(x)$

53. $f(x) = \frac{1 + \sin x}{\cos x};\ \lim_{x \to \pi/2^-} f(x);\ \lim_{x \to 4\pi/3} f(x)$

54. $f(x) = \frac{\ln x}{\sin^{-1} x};\ \lim_{x \to 1^-} f(x)$

55. $f(x) = \frac{e^x}{1 - e^x};\ \lim_{x \to 0^-} f(x);\ \lim_{x \to 0^+} f(x)$

56. $f(x) = \frac{e^{2x} - 1}{e^x - 1};\ \lim_{x \to 0} f(x)$

T 57. **Intermediate Value Theorem and interest rates** Suppose \$5000 is invested in a savings account for 10 years (120 months), with an annual interest rate of r, compounded monthly. The amount of money in the account after 10 years is $A(r) = 5000(1 + r/12)^{120}$.

a. Use the Intermediate Value Theorem to show there is a value of r in $(0, 0.08)$—an interest rate between 0% and 8%—that allows you to reach your savings goal of \$7000 in 10 years.
b. Use a graph to illustrate your explanation in part (a); then approximate the interest rate required to reach your goal.

T 58. **Intermediate Value Theorem and mortgage payments** You are shopping for a \$150,000, 30-year (360-month) loan to buy a house. The monthly payment is

$$m(r) = \frac{150{,}000(r/12)}{1 - (1 + r/12)^{-360}},$$

where r is the annual interest rate. Suppose banks are currently offering interest rates between 6% and 8%.

a. Use the Intermediate Value Theorem to show there is a value of r in $(0.06, 0.08)$—an interest rate between 6% and 8%—that allows you to make monthly payments of \$1000 per month.
b. Use a graph to illustrate your explanation to part (a). Then determine the interest rate you need for monthly payments of \$1000.

T **59–64. Applying the Intermediate Value Theorem**

a. Use the Intermediate Value Theorem to show that the following equations have a solution on the given interval.
b. Use a graphing utility to find all the solutions to the equation on the given interval.
c. Illustrate your answers with an appropriate graph.

59. $2x^3 + x - 2 = 0;\ (-1, 1)$

60. $\sqrt{x^4 + 25x^3 + 10} = 5;\ (0, 1)$

61. $x^3 - 5x^2 + 2x = -1;\ (-1, 5)$

62. $-x^5 - 4x^2 + 2\sqrt{x} + 5 = 0;\ (0, 3)$

63. $x + e^x = 0;\ (-1, 0)$

64. $x \ln x - 1 = 0;\ (1, e)$

Further Explorations

65. **Explain why or why not** Determine whether the following statements are true and give an explanation or counterexample.
   a. If a function is left-continuous and right-continuous at a, then it is continuous at a.
   b. If a function is continuous at a, then it is left-continuous and right-continuous at a.
   c. If $a < b$ and $f(a) \le L \le f(b)$, then there is some value of c in (a, b) for which $f(c) = L$.
   d. Suppose f is continuous on $[a, b]$. Then there is a point c in (a, b) such that $f(c) = (f(a) + f(b))/2$.

66. **Continuity of the absolute value function** Prove that the absolute value function $|x|$ is continuous for all values of x. (*Hint:* Using the definition of the absolute value function, compute $\lim_{x \to 0^-} |x|$ and $\lim_{x \to 0^+} |x|$.)

67–70. Continuity of functions with absolute values *Use the continuity of the absolute value function (Exercise 66) to determine the interval(s) on which the following functions are continuous.*

67. $f(x) = |x^2 + 3x - 18|$

68. $g(x) = \left|\dfrac{x + 4}{x^2 - 4}\right|$

69. $h(x) = \left|\dfrac{1}{\sqrt{x} - 4}\right|$

70. $h(x) = |x^2 + 2x + 5| + \sqrt{x}$

71–80. Miscellaneous limits *Evaluate the following limits or state that they do not exist.*

71. $\displaystyle\lim_{x \to \pi} \frac{\cos^2 x + 3\cos x + 2}{\cos x + 1}$

72. $\displaystyle\lim_{x \to 3\pi/2} \frac{\sin^2 x + 6\sin x + 5}{\sin^2 x - 1}$

73. $\displaystyle\lim_{x \to \pi/2} \frac{\sin x - 1}{\sqrt{\sin x} - 1}$

74. $\displaystyle\lim_{\theta \to 0} \frac{\dfrac{1}{2 + \sin\theta} - \dfrac{1}{2}}{\sin\theta}$

75. $\displaystyle\lim_{x \to 0} \frac{\cos x - 1}{\sin^2 x}$

76. $\displaystyle\lim_{x \to 0^+} \frac{1 - \cos^2 x}{\sin x}$

77. $\displaystyle\lim_{x \to \infty} \frac{\tan^{-1} x}{x}$

78. $\displaystyle\lim_{t \to \infty} \frac{\cos t}{e^{3t}}$

79. $\displaystyle\lim_{x \to 1^-} \frac{x}{\ln x}$

80. $\displaystyle\lim_{x \to 0^+} \frac{x}{\ln x}$

81. **Pitfalls using technology** The graph of the *sawtooth function* $y = x - \lfloor x \rfloor$, where $\lfloor x \rfloor$ is the greatest integer function or floor function (Exercise 37, Section 2.2), was obtained using a graphing utility (see figure). Identify any inaccuracies appearing in the graph and then plot an accurate graph by hand.

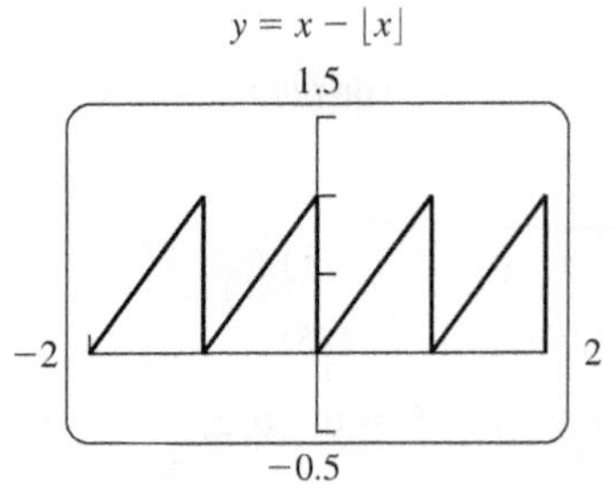

82. **Pitfalls using technology** Graph the function $f(x) = \dfrac{\sin x}{x}$ using a graphing window of $[-\pi, \pi] \times [0, 2]$.
   a. Sketch a copy of the graph obtained with your graphing device and describe any inaccuracies appearing in the graph.
   b. Sketch an accurate graph of the function. Is f continuous at 0?
   c. What is the value of $\displaystyle\lim_{x \to 0} \frac{\sin x}{x}$?

83. **Sketching functions**
   a. Sketch the graph of a function that is not continuous at 1, but is defined at 1.
   b. Sketch the graph of a function that is not continuous at 1, but has a limit at 1.

84. **An unknown constant** Determine the value of the constant a for which the function

$$f(x) = \begin{cases} \dfrac{x^2 + 3x + 2}{x + 1} & \text{if } x \neq -1 \\ a & \text{if } x = -1 \end{cases}$$

is continuous at -1.

85. **An unknown constant** Let

$$g(x) = \begin{cases} x^2 + x & \text{if } x < 1 \\ a & \text{if } x = 1 \\ 3x + 5 & \text{if } x > 1. \end{cases}$$

   a. Determine the value of a for which g is continuous from the left at 1.
   b. Determine the value of a for which g is continuous from the right at 1.
   c. Is there a value of a for which g is continuous at 1? Explain.

86. **Asymptotes of a function containing exponentials** Let $f(x) = \dfrac{2e^x + 5e^{3x}}{e^{2x} - e^{3x}}$. Analyze $\lim_{x \to 0^-} f(x)$, $\lim_{x \to 0^+} f(x)$, $\lim_{x \to -\infty} f(x)$, and $\lim_{x \to \infty} f(x)$. Then give the horizontal and vertical asymptotes of f. Plot f to verify your results.

87. **Asymptotes of a function containing exponentials** Let $f(x) = \dfrac{2e^x + 10e^{-x}}{e^x + e^{-x}}$. Analyze $\lim_{x \to 0} f(x)$, $\lim_{x \to -\infty} f(x)$, and $\lim_{x \to \infty} f(x)$. Then give the horizontal and vertical asymptotes of f. Plot f to verify your results.

88–89. Applying the Intermediate Value Theorem *Use the Intermediate Value Theorem to verify that the following equations have three solutions on the given interval. Use a graphing utility to find the approximate roots.*

88. $x^3 + 10x^2 - 100x + 50 = 0;\ (-20, 10)$

89. $70x^3 - 87x^2 + 32x - 3 = 0;\ (0, 1)$

Applications

90. Parking costs Determine the intervals of continuity for the parking cost function c introduced at the outset of this section (see figure). Consider $0 \le t \le 60$.

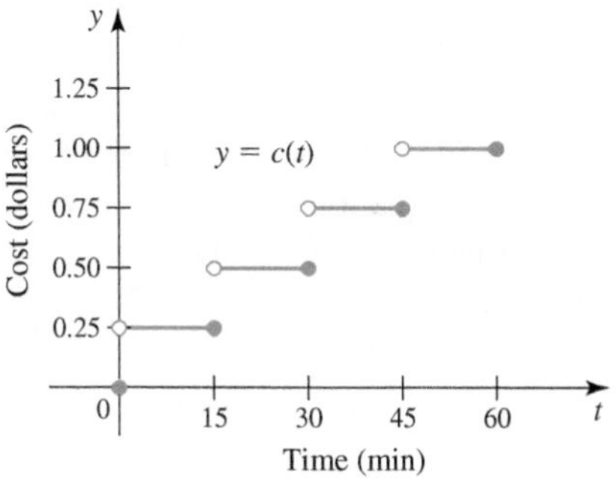

T 91. Investment problem Assume you invest \$250 at the end of each year for 10 years at an annual interest rate of r. The amount of money in your account after 10 years is $A = \dfrac{250((1+r)^{10} - 1)}{r}$. Assume your goal is to have \$3500 in your account after 10 years.

a. Use the Intermediate Value Theorem to show that there is an interest rate r in the interval $(0.01, 0.10)$—between 1% and 10%—that allows you to reach your financial goal.
b. Use a calculator to estimate the interest rate required to reach your financial goal.

92. Applying the Intermediate Value Theorem Suppose you park your car at a trailhead in a national park and begin a 2-hr hike to a lake at 7 A.M. on a Friday morning. On Sunday morning, you leave the lake at 7 A.M. and start the 2-hr hike back to your car. Assume the lake is 3 mi from your car. Let $f(t)$ be your distance from the car t hours after 7 A.M. on Friday morning and let $g(t)$ be your distance from the car t hours after 7 A.M. on Sunday morning.

a. Evaluate $f(0), f(2), g(0)$, and $g(2)$.
b. Let $h(t) = f(t) - g(t)$. Find $h(0)$ and $h(2)$.
c. Use the Intermediate Value Theorem to show that there is some point along the trail that you will pass at exactly the same time of morning on both days.

93. The monk and the mountain A monk set out from a monastery in the valley at dawn. He walked all day up a winding path, stopping for lunch and taking a nap along the way. At dusk, he arrived at a temple on the mountaintop. The next day the monk made the return walk to the valley, leaving the temple at dawn, walking the same path for the entire day, and arriving at the monastery in the evening. Must there be one point along the path that the monk occupied at the same time of day on both the ascent and descent? (*Hint:* The question can be answered without the Intermediate Value Theorem.) (*Source:* Arthur Koestler, *The Act of Creation.*)

Additional Exercises

94. Does continuity of $|f|$ imply continuity of f? Let

$$g(x) = \begin{cases} 1 & \text{if } x \ge 0 \\ -1 & \text{if } x < 0. \end{cases}$$

a. Write a formula for $|g(x)|$.
b. Is g continuous at $x = 0$? Explain.
c. Is $|g|$ continuous at $x = 0$? Explain.
d. For any function f, if $|f|$ is continuous at a, does it necessarily follow that f is continuous at a? Explain.

95–96. Classifying discontinuities *The discontinuities in graphs (a) and (b) are* **removable discontinuities** *because they disappear if we define or redefine f at a so that $f(a) = \lim_{x\to a} f(x)$. The function in graph (c) has a* **jump discontinuity** *because left and right limits exist at a but are unequal. The discontinuity in graph (d) is an* **infinite discontinuity** *because the function has a vertical asymptote at a.*

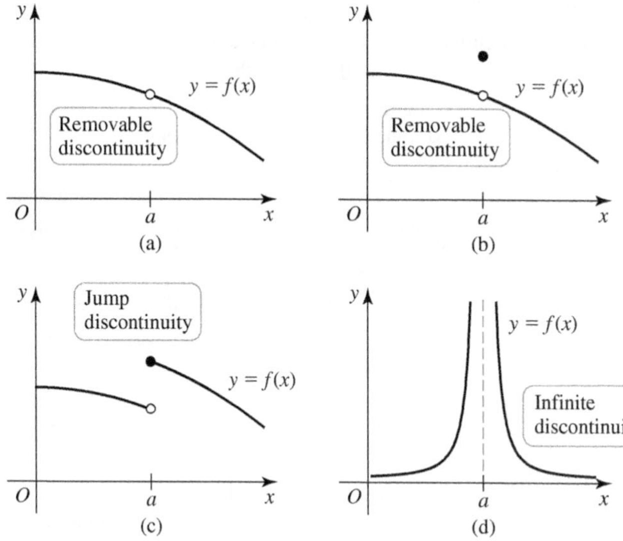

95. Is the discontinuity at a in graph (c) removable? Explain.

96. Is the discontinuity at a in graph (d) removable? Explain.

97–98. Removable discontinuities *Show that the following functions have a removable discontinuity at the given point. See Exercises 95–96.*

97. $f(x) = \dfrac{x^2 - 7x + 10}{x - 2}$; $x = 2$

98. $g(x) = \begin{cases} \dfrac{x^2 - 1}{1 - x} & \text{if } x \ne 1 \\ 3 & \text{if } x = 1 \end{cases}$; $x = 1$

99. Do removable discontinuities exist? See Exercises 95–96.

a. Does the function $f(x) = x \sin(1/x)$ have a removable discontinuity at $x = 0$?
b. Does the function $g(x) = \sin(1/x)$ have a removable discontinuity at $x = 0$?

T 100–101. Classifying discontinuities *Classify the discontinuities in the following functions at the given points. See Exercises 95–96.*

100. $f(x) = \dfrac{|x - 2|}{x - 2}$; $x = 2$

101. $h(x) = \dfrac{x^3 - 4x^2 + 4x}{x(x - 1)}$; $x = 0$ and $x = 1$

102. Continuity of composite functions Prove Theorem 2.11: If g is continuous at a and f is continuous at $g(a)$, then the composition $f \circ g$ is continuous at a. (*Hint:* Write the definition of continuity for f and g separately; then combine them to form the definition of continuity for $f \circ g$.)

103. Continuity of compositions

a. Find functions f and g such that each function is continuous at 0 but $f \circ g$ is not continuous at 0.
b. Explain why examples satisfying part (a) do not contradict Theorem 2.12.

104. Violation of the Intermediate Value Theorem? Let $f(x) = \frac{|x|}{x}$. Then $f(-2) = -1$ and $f(2) = 1$. Therefore, $f(-2) < 0 < f(2)$, but there is no value of c between -2 and 2 for which $f(c) = 0$. Does this fact violate the Intermediate Value Theorem? Explain.

105. Continuity of $\sin x$ and $\cos x$

a. Use the identity $\sin(a + h) = \sin a \cos h + \cos a \sin h$ with the fact that $\lim_{x \to 0} \sin x = 0$ to prove that $\lim_{x \to a} \sin x = \sin a$, thereby establishing that $\sin x$ is continuous for all x. (*Hint:* Let $h = x - a$ so that $x = a + h$ and note that $h \to 0$ as $x \to a$.)

b. Use the identity $\cos(a + h) = \cos a \cos h - \sin a \sin h$ with the fact that $\lim_{x \to 0} \cos x = 1$ to prove that $\lim_{x \to a} \cos x = \cos a$.

QUICK CHECK ANSWERS

1. $t = 15, 30, 45$ **2.** Both expressions have a value of 5, showing that $\lim_{x \to a} f(g(x)) = f(\lim_{x \to a} g(x))$. **3.** Fill in the endpoints. **4.** $[0, \infty); (-\infty, \infty)$ **5.** Note that $\lim_{x \to 1^+} \sqrt[4]{\ln x} = \sqrt[4]{\lim_{x \to 1^+} \ln x} = 0$ and $f(1) = \sqrt[4]{\ln 1} = 0$. Because the limit from the right and the value of the function at $x = 1$ are equal, the function is right-continuous at $x = 1$. **6.** The equation has a solution on the interval $[-1, 1]$ because f is continuous on $[-1, 1]$ and $f(-1) < 0 < f(1)$. ◄

2.7 Precise Definitions of Limits

The limit definitions already encountered in this chapter are adequate for most elementary limits. However, some of the terminology used, such as *sufficiently close* and *arbitrarily large*, needs clarification. The goal of this section is to give limits a solid mathematical foundation by transforming the previous limit definitions into precise mathematical statements.

Moving Toward a Precise Definition

Assume the function f is defined for all x near a, except possibly at a. Recall that $\lim_{x \to a} f(x) = L$ means that $f(x)$ is arbitrarily close to L for all x sufficiently close (but not equal) to a. This limit definition is made precise by observing that the distance between $f(x)$ and L is $|f(x) - L|$ and that the distance between x and a is $|x - a|$. Therefore, we write $\lim_{x \to a} f(x) = L$ if we can make $|f(x) - L|$ arbitrarily small for any x, distinct from a, with $|x - a|$ sufficiently small. For instance, if we want $|f(x) - L|$ to be less than 0.1, then we must find a number $\delta > 0$ such that

$$|f(x) - L| < 0.1 \quad \text{whenever} \quad |x - a| < \delta \quad \text{and} \quad x \neq a.$$

If, instead, we want $|f(x) - L|$ to be less than 0.001, then we must find *another* number $\delta > 0$ such that

$$|f(x) - L| < 0.001 \quad \text{whenever} \quad 0 < |x - a| < \delta.$$

For the limit to exist, it must be true that for *any* $\varepsilon > 0$, we can always find a $\delta > 0$ such that

$$|f(x) - L| < \varepsilon \quad \text{whenever} \quad 0 < |x - a| < \delta.$$

➤ The phrase *for all x near a* means for all x in an open interval containing a.

➤ The Greek letters δ (delta) and ε (epsilon) represent small positive numbers in the discussion of limits.

➤ The two conditions $|x - a| < \delta$ and $x \neq a$ are written concisely as $0 < |x - a| < \delta$.

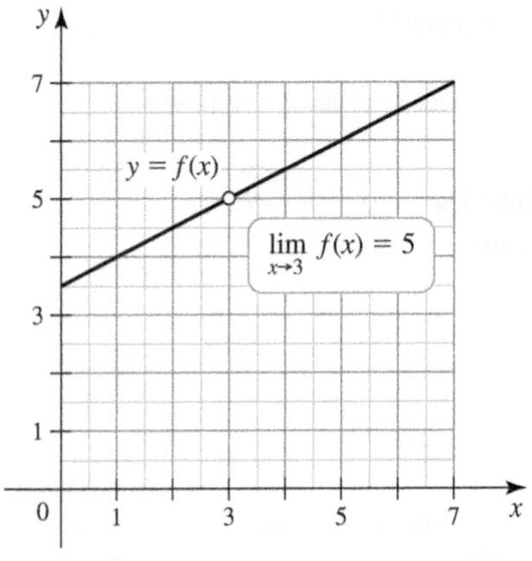

Figure 2.59

EXAMPLE 1 **Determining values of δ from a graph** Figure 2.59 shows the graph of a linear function f with $\lim_{x \to 3} f(x) = 5$. For each value of $\varepsilon > 0$, determine a value of $\delta > 0$ satisfying the statement

$$|f(x) - 5| < \varepsilon \quad \text{whenever} \quad 0 < |x - 3| < \delta.$$

a. $\varepsilon = 1$ **b.** $\varepsilon = \frac{1}{2}$

SOLUTION

a. With $\varepsilon = 1$, we want $f(x)$ to be less than 1 unit from 5, which means $f(x)$ is between 4 and 6. To determine a corresponding value of δ, draw the horizontal lines $y = 4$ and $y = 6$ (Figure 2.60a). Then sketch vertical lines passing through the points where the horizontal lines and the graph of f intersect (Figure 2.60b). We see that the vertical

➤ The founders of calculus, Isaac Newton (1642–1727) and Gottfried Leibniz (1646–1716), developed the core ideas of calculus without using a precise definition of a limit. It was not until the 19th century that a rigorous definition was introduced by Augustin-Louis Cauchy (1789–1857) and later refined by Karl Weierstrass (1815–1897).

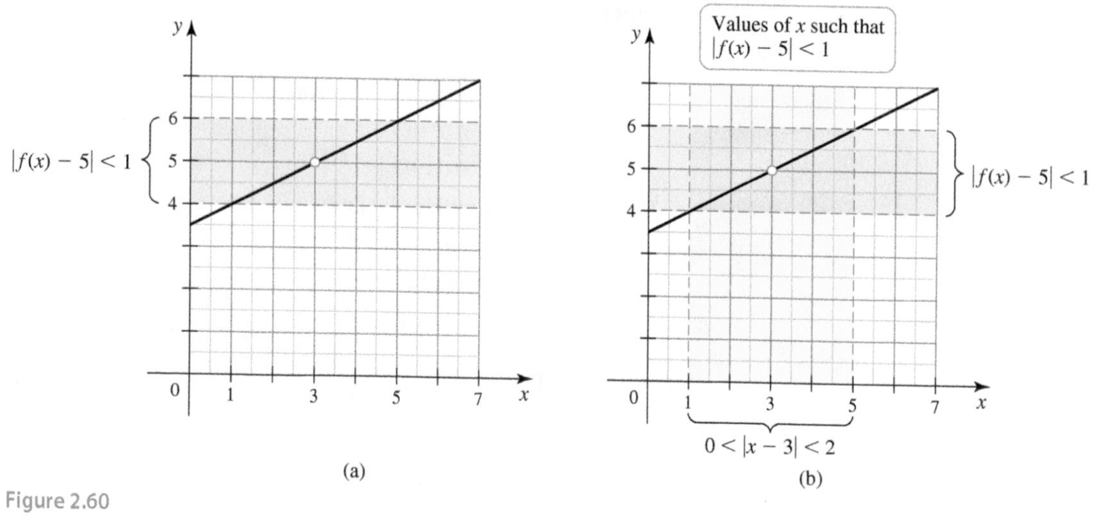

Figure 2.60

lines intersect the x-axis at $x = 1$ and $x = 5$. Note that $f(x)$ is less than 1 unit from 5 on the y-axis if x is within 2 units of 3 on the x-axis. So for $\varepsilon = 1$, we let $\delta = 2$ or any smaller positive value.

➤ Once an acceptable value of δ is found satisfying the statement

$$|f(x) - L| < \varepsilon \quad \text{whenever}$$
$$0 < |x - a| < \delta,$$

any smaller positive value of δ also works.

b. With $\varepsilon = \frac{1}{2}$, we want $f(x)$ to lie within a half-unit of 5, or equivalently, $f(x)$ must lie between 4.5 and 5.5. Proceeding as in part (a), we see that $f(x)$ is within a half-unit of 5 on the y-axis (Figure 2.61a) if x is less than 1 unit from 3 (Figure 2.61b). So for $\varepsilon = \frac{1}{2}$, we let $\delta = 1$ or any smaller positive number.

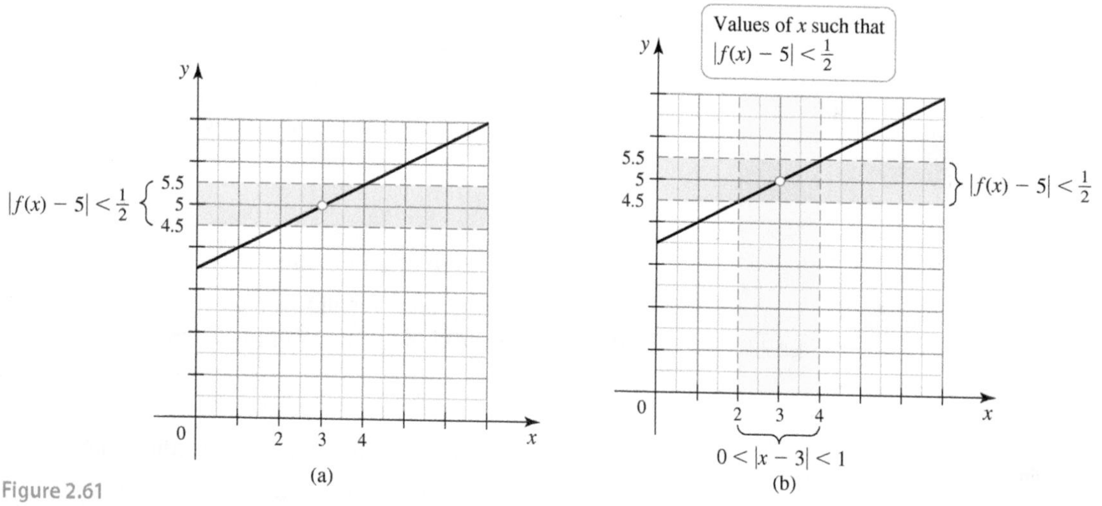

Figure 2.61

Related Exercises 9–12 ◀

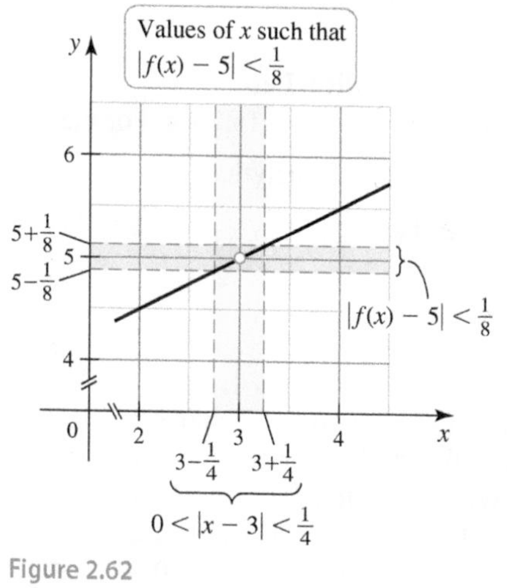

Figure 2.62

The idea of a limit, as illustrated in Example 1, may be described in terms of a contest between two people named Epp and Del. First, Epp picks a particular number $\varepsilon > 0$; then he challenges Del to find a corresponding value of $\delta > 0$ such that

$$|f(x) - 5| < \varepsilon \quad \text{whenever} \quad 0 < |x - 3| < \delta. \tag{1}$$

To illustrate, suppose Epp chooses $\varepsilon = 1$. From Example 1, we know that Del will satisfy (1) by choosing $0 < \delta \le 2$. If Epp chooses $\varepsilon = \frac{1}{2}$, then (by Example 1) Del responds by letting $0 < \delta \le 1$. If Epp lets $\varepsilon = \frac{1}{8}$, then Del chooses $0 < \delta \le \frac{1}{4}$ (Figure 2.62). In fact, there is a pattern: For *any* $\varepsilon > 0$ that Epp chooses, no matter how small, Del will satisfy (1) by choosing a positive value of δ satisfying $0 < \delta \le 2\varepsilon$. Del has discovered a mathematical relationship: If $0 < \delta \le 2\varepsilon$ and $0 < |x - 3| < \delta$, then $|f(x) - 5| < \varepsilon$, for *any* $\varepsilon > 0$. This conversation illustrates the general procedure for proving that $\lim_{x \to a} f(x) = L$.

QUICK CHECK 1 In Example 1, find a positive number δ satisfying the statement

$$|f(x) - 5| < \frac{1}{100} \quad \text{whenever} \quad 0 < |x - 3| < \delta.$$

A Precise Definition

Example 1 dealt with a linear function, but it points the way to a precise definition of a limit for any function. As shown in Figure 2.63, $\lim_{x \to a} f(x) = L$ means that for *any* positive number ε, there is another positive number δ such that

$$|f(x) - L| < \varepsilon \quad \text{whenever} \quad 0 < |x - a| < \delta.$$

In all limit proofs, the goal is to find a relationship between ε and δ that gives an admissible value of δ, in terms of ε only. This relationship must work for any positive value of ε.

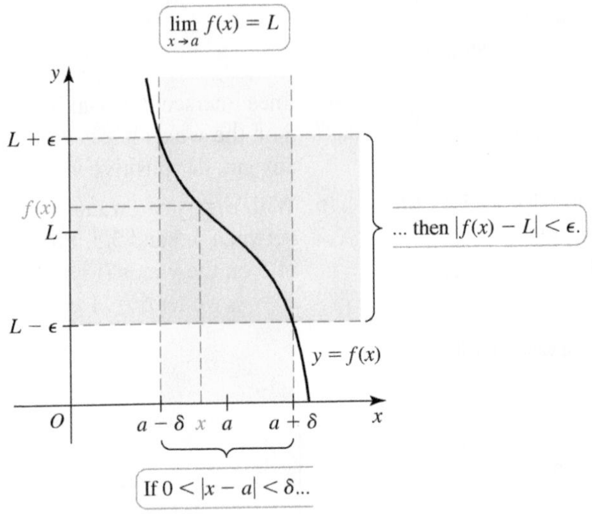

Figure 2.63

DEFINITION Limit of a Function

Assume that $f(x)$ exists for all x in some open interval containing a, except possibly at a. We say **the limit of $f(x)$ as x approaches a is L**, written

$$\lim_{x \to a} f(x) = L,$$

if for *any* number $\varepsilon > 0$ there is a corresponding number $\delta > 0$ such that

$$|f(x) - L| < \varepsilon \quad \text{whenever} \quad 0 < |x - a| < \delta.$$

➤ The value of δ in the precise definition of a limit depends only on ε.

➤ Definitions of the one-sided limits $\lim_{x \to a^+} f(x) = L$ and $\lim_{x \to a^-} f(x) = L$ are discussed in Exercises 39–43.

EXAMPLE 2 Finding δ for a given ε using a graphing utility Let $f(x) = x^3 - 6x^2 + 12x - 5$ and demonstrate that $\lim_{x \to 2} f(x) = 3$ as follows. For the given values of ε, use a graphing utility to find a value of $\delta > 0$ such that

$$|f(x) - 3| < \varepsilon \quad \text{whenever} \quad 0 < |x - 2| < \delta.$$

a. $\varepsilon = 1$ **b.** $\varepsilon = \frac{1}{2}$

SOLUTION

a. The condition $|f(x) - 3| < \varepsilon = 1$ implies that $f(x)$ lies between 2 and 4. Using a graphing utility, we graph f and the lines $y = 2$ and $y = 4$ (Figure 2.64). These lines intersect the graph of f at $x = 1$ and at $x = 3$. We now sketch the vertical lines $x = 1$ and $x = 3$ and observe that $f(x)$ is within 1 unit of 3 whenever x is within 1 unit of 2 on the x-axis (Figure 2.64). Therefore, with $\varepsilon = 1$, we can choose any δ with $0 < \delta \leq 1$.

b. The condition $|f(x) - 3| < \varepsilon = \frac{1}{2}$ implies that $f(x)$ lies between 2.5 and 3.5 on the y-axis. We now find that the lines $y = 2.5$ and $y = 3.5$ intersect the graph of f at $x \approx 1.21$ and $x \approx 2.79$ (Figure 2.65). Observe that if x is less than 0.79 unit from 2 on the x-axis, then $f(x)$ is less than a half unit from 3 on the y-axis. Therefore, with $\varepsilon = \frac{1}{2}$ we can choose any δ with $0 < \delta \le 0.79$.

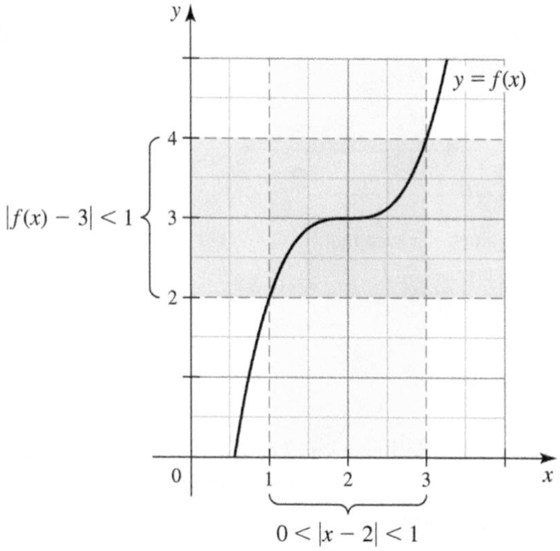

Figure 2.64

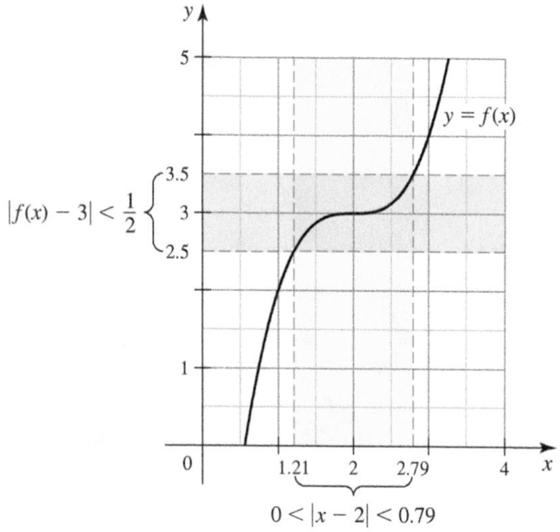

Figure 2.65

This procedure could be repeated for smaller and smaller values of $\varepsilon > 0$. For each value of ε, there exists a corresponding value of δ, proving that the limit exists.

Related Exercises 13–14 ◀

QUICK CHECK 2 For the function f given in Example 2, estimate a value of $\delta > 0$ satisfying $|f(x) - 3| < 0.25$ whenever $0 < |x - 2| < \delta$. ◀

The inequality $0 < |x - a| < \delta$ means that x lies between $a - \delta$ and $a + \delta$ with $x \neq a$. We say that the interval $(a - \delta, a + \delta)$ is **symmetric about a** because a is the midpoint of the interval. Symmetric intervals are convenient, but Example 3 demonstrates that we don't always get symmetric intervals without a bit of extra work.

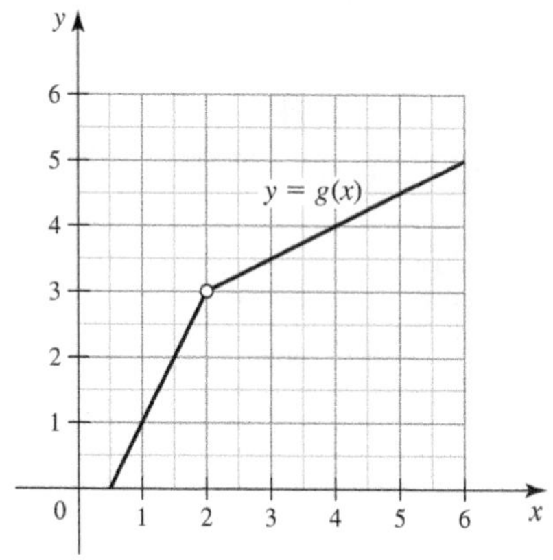

Figure 2.66

EXAMPLE 3 **Finding a symmetric interval** Figure 2.66 shows the graph of g with $\lim_{x \to 2} g(x) = 3$. For each value of ε, find the corresponding values of $\delta > 0$ that satisfy the condition

$$|g(x) - 3| < \varepsilon \quad \text{whenever} \quad 0 < |x - 2| < \delta.$$

a. $\varepsilon = 2$

b. $\varepsilon = 1$

c. For any given value of ε, make a conjecture about the corresponding values of δ that satisfy the limit condition.

SOLUTION

a. With $\varepsilon = 2$, we need a value of $\delta > 0$ such that $g(x)$ is within 2 units of 3, which means between 1 and 5, whenever x is less than δ units from 2. The horizontal lines $y = 1$ and $y = 5$ intersect the graph of g at $x = 1$ and $x = 6$. Therefore, $|g(x) - 3| < 2$ if x lies in the interval $(1, 6)$ with $x \neq 2$ (Figure 2.67a). However, we want x to lie in an interval that is *symmetric* about 2. We can guarantee that $|g(x) - 3| < 2$ only if x is less than 1 unit away from 2, on either side of 2 (Figure 2.67b). Therefore, with $\varepsilon = 2$, we take $\delta = 1$ or any smaller positive number.

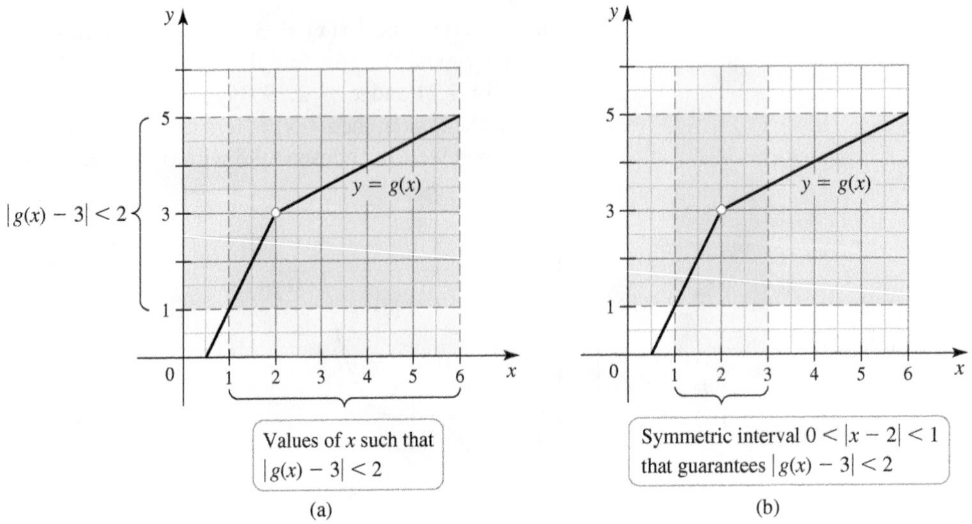

Figure 2.67

b. With $\varepsilon = 1$, $g(x)$ must lie between 2 and 4 (Figure 2.68a). This implies that x must be within a half unit to the left of 2 and within 2 units to the right of 2. Therefore, $|g(x) - 3| < 1$ provided x lies in the interval $(1.5, 4)$. To obtain a symmetric interval about 2, we take $\delta = \frac{1}{2}$ or any smaller positive number. Then we are guaranteed that $|g(x) - 3| < 1$ when $0 < |x - 2| < \frac{1}{2}$ (Figure 2.68b).

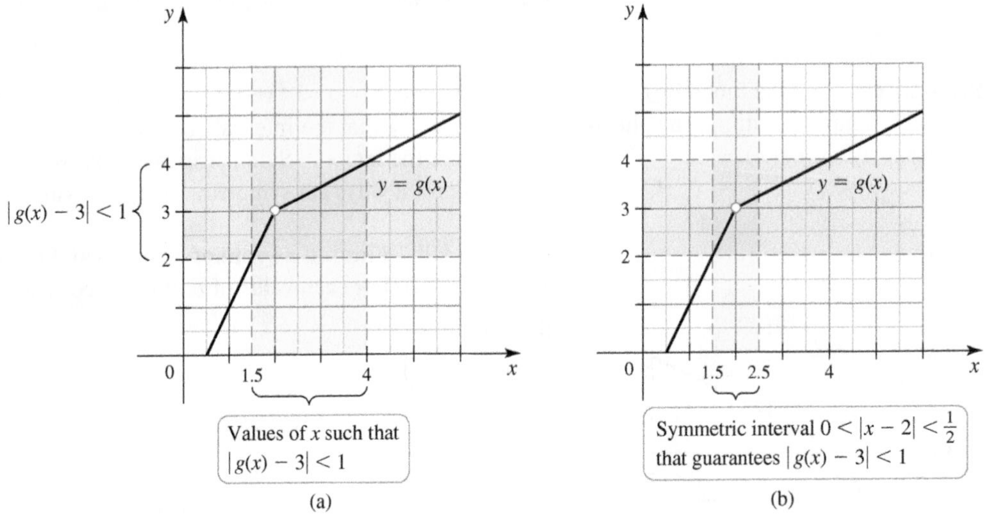

Figure 2.68

c. From parts (a) and (b), it appears that if we choose $\delta \le \varepsilon/2$, the limit condition is satisfied for any $\varepsilon > 0$.

Related Exercises 15–18 ◀

In Examples 2 and 3, we showed that a limit exists by discovering a relationship between ε and δ that satisfies the limit condition. We now generalize this procedure.

Limit Proofs

We use the following two-step process to prove that $\lim_{x \to a} f(x) = L$.

➤ The first step of the limit-proving process is the preliminary work of finding a candidate for δ. The second step verifies that the δ found in the first step actually works.

Steps for proving that $\lim_{x \to a} f(x) = L$

1. **Find δ.** Let ε be an arbitrary positive number. Use the inequality $|f(x) - L| < \varepsilon$ to find a condition of the form $|x - a| < \delta$, where δ depends only on the value of ε.
2. **Write a proof.** For any $\varepsilon > 0$, assume $0 < |x - a| < \delta$ and use the relationship between ε and δ found in Step 1 to prove that $|f(x) - L| < \varepsilon$.

EXAMPLE 4 Limit of a linear function Prove that $\lim_{x \to 4} (4x - 15) = 1$ using the precise definition of a limit.

SOLUTION

Step 1: *Find δ.* In this case, $a = 4$ and $L = 1$. Assuming $\varepsilon > 0$ is given, we use $|(4x - 15) - 1| < \varepsilon$ to find an inequality of the form $|x - 4| < \delta$. If $|(4x - 15) - 1| < \varepsilon$, then

$$|4x - 16| < \varepsilon$$

$$4|x - 4| < \varepsilon \quad \text{Factor } 4x - 16.$$

$$|x - 4| < \frac{\varepsilon}{4}. \quad \text{Divide by 4 and identify } \delta = \varepsilon/4.$$

We have shown that $|(4x - 15) - 1| < \varepsilon$ implies that $|x - 4| < \varepsilon/4$. Therefore, a plausible relationship between δ and ε is $\delta = \varepsilon/4$. We now write the actual proof.

Step 2: *Write a proof.* Let $\varepsilon > 0$ be given and assume $0 < |x - 4| < \delta$ where $\delta = \varepsilon/4$. The aim is to show that $|(4x - 15) - 1| < \varepsilon$ for all x such that $0 < |x - 4| < \delta$. We simplify $|(4x - 15) - 1|$ and isolate the $|x - 4|$ term:

$$\begin{aligned} |(4x - 15) - 1| &= |4x - 16| \\ &= 4\underbrace{|x - 4|}_{\text{less than } \delta = \varepsilon/4} \\ &< 4\left(\frac{\varepsilon}{4}\right) = \varepsilon. \end{aligned}$$

We have shown that for any $\varepsilon > 0$,

$$|f(x) - L| = |(4x - 15) - 1| < \varepsilon \quad \text{whenever} \quad 0 < |x - 4| < \delta,$$

provided $0 < \delta \le \varepsilon/4$. Therefore, $\lim_{x \to 4} (4x - 15) = 1$.

Related Exercises 19–24 ◀

Justifying Limit Laws

The precise definition of a limit is used to prove the limit laws in Theorem 2.3. Essential in several of these proofs is the **triangle inequality**, which states that

$$|x + y| \le |x| + |y|, \quad \text{for all real numbers } x \text{ and } y.$$

EXAMPLE 5 Proof of Limit Law 1 Prove that if $\lim_{x \to a} f(x)$ and $\lim_{x \to a} g(x)$ exist, then

$$\lim_{x \to a} (f(x) + g(x)) = \lim_{x \to a} f(x) + \lim_{x \to a} g(x).$$

➤ Because $\lim_{x \to a} f(x)$ exists, if there exists a $\delta > 0$ for any given $\varepsilon > 0$, then there also exists a $\delta > 0$ for any given $\frac{\varepsilon}{2}$.

SOLUTION Assume that $\varepsilon > 0$ is given. Let $\lim_{x \to a} f(x) = L$, which implies that there exists a $\delta_1 > 0$ such that

$$|f(x) - L| < \frac{\varepsilon}{2} \quad \text{whenever} \quad 0 < |x - a| < \delta_1.$$

Similarly, let $\lim_{x \to a} g(x) = M$, which implies there exists a $\delta_2 > 0$ such that

$$|g(x) - M| < \frac{\varepsilon}{2} \quad \text{whenever} \quad 0 < |x - a| < \delta_2.$$

➤ The minimum value of a and b is denoted $\min\{a, b\}$. If $x = \min\{a, b\}$, then x is the smaller of a and b. If $a = b$, then x equals the common value of a and b. In either case, $x \le a$ and $x \le b$.

Let $\delta = \min\{\delta_1, \delta_2\}$ and suppose $0 < |x - a| < \delta$. Because $\delta \le \delta_1$, it follows that $0 < |x - a| < \delta_1$ and $|f(x) - L| < \varepsilon/2$. Similarly, because $\delta \le \delta_2$, it follows that $0 < |x - a| < \delta_2$ and $|g(x) - M| < \varepsilon/2$. Therefore,

$$\begin{aligned} |(f(x) + g(x)) - (L + M)| &= |(f(x) - L) + (g(x) - M)| && \text{Rearrange terms.} \\ &\le |f(x) - L| + |g(x) - M| && \text{Triangle inequality} \\ &< \frac{\varepsilon}{2} + \frac{\varepsilon}{2} = \varepsilon. \end{aligned}$$

➤ Proofs of other limit laws are outlined in Exercises 25–26.

We have shown that given any $\varepsilon > 0$, if $0 < |x - a| < \delta$, then $|(f(x) + g(x)) - (L + M)| < \varepsilon$, which implies that $\lim_{x \to a} (f(x) + g(x)) = L + M = \lim_{x \to a} f(x) + \lim_{x \to a} g(x)$.

Related Exercises 25–28 ◀

Infinite Limits

➤ Notice that for infinite limits, N plays the role that ε plays for regular limits. It sets a tolerance or bound for the function values $f(x)$.

In Section 2.4, we stated that $\lim_{x \to a} f(x) = \infty$ if $f(x)$ grows *arbitrarily large* as x approaches a. More precisely, this means that for any positive number N (no matter how large), $f(x)$ is larger than N if x is sufficiently close to a but not equal to a.

DEFINITION Two-Sided Infinite Limit

The **infinite limit** $\lim_{x \to a} f(x) = \infty$ means that for any positive number N, there exists a corresponding $\delta > 0$ such that

$$f(x) > N \quad \text{whenever} \quad 0 < |x - a| < \delta.$$

As shown in Figure 2.69, to prove that $\lim_{x \to a} f(x) = \infty$, we let N represent *any* positive number. Then we find a value of $\delta > 0$, depending only on N, such that

$$f(x) > N \quad \text{whenever} \quad 0 < |x - a| < \delta.$$

This process is similar to the two-step process for finite limits.

➤ Precise definitions for $\lim_{x \to a} f(x) = -\infty$, $\lim_{x \to a^+} f(x) = -\infty$, $\lim_{x \to a^+} f(x) = \infty$, $\lim_{x \to a^-} f(x) = -\infty$, and $\lim_{x \to a^-} f(x) = \infty$ are given in Exercises 45–49.

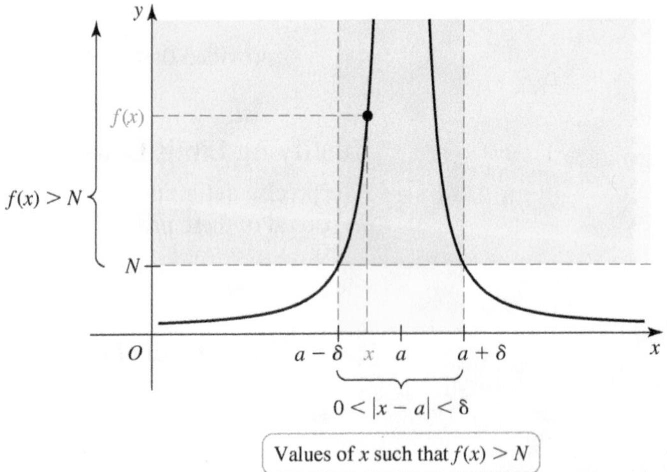

Figure 2.69

Steps for proving that $\lim_{x \to a} f(x) = \infty$

1. **Find δ.** Let N be an arbitrary positive number. Use the statement $f(x) > N$ to find an inequality of the form $|x - a| < \delta$, where δ depends only on N.
2. **Write a proof.** For any $N > 0$, assume $0 < |x - a| < \delta$ and use the relationship between N and δ found in Step 1 to prove that $f(x) > N$.

EXAMPLE 6 **An Infinite Limit Proof** Let $f(x) = \frac{1}{(x-2)^2}$. Prove that $\lim_{x \to 2} f(x) = \infty$.

SOLUTION

Step 1: Find $\delta > 0$. Assuming $N > 0$, we use the inequality $\frac{1}{(x-2)^2} > N$ to find δ, where δ depends only on N. Taking reciprocals of this inequality, it follows that

$$(x-2)^2 < \frac{1}{N}$$

$$|x-2| < \frac{1}{\sqrt{N}}. \quad \text{Take the square root of both sides.}$$

➤ Recall that $\sqrt{x^2} = |x|$.

The inequality $|x-2| < \frac{1}{\sqrt{N}}$ has the form $|x-2| < \delta$ if we let $\delta = \frac{1}{\sqrt{N}}$. We now write a proof based on this relationship between δ and N.

Step 2: Write a proof. Suppose $N > 0$ is given. Let $\delta = \frac{1}{\sqrt{N}}$ and assume $0 < |x-2| < \delta = \frac{1}{\sqrt{N}}$. Squaring both sides of the inequality $|x-2| < \frac{1}{\sqrt{N}}$ and taking reciprocals, we have

$$(x-2)^2 < \frac{1}{N} \quad \text{Square both sides.}$$

$$\frac{1}{(x-2)^2} > N. \quad \text{Take reciprocals of both sides.}$$

QUICK CHECK 3 In Example 6, if N is increased by a factor of 100, how must δ change? ◄

We see that for any positive N, if $0 < |x-2| < \delta = \frac{1}{\sqrt{N}}$, then $f(x) = \frac{1}{(x-2)^2} > N$. It follows that $\lim_{x \to 2} \frac{1}{(x-2)^2} = \infty$. Note that because $\delta = \frac{1}{\sqrt{N}}$, δ decreases as N increases.

Related Exercises 29–32 ◄

Limits at Infinity

Precise definitions can also be written for the limits at infinity $\lim_{x \to \infty} f(x) = L$ and $\lim_{x \to -\infty} f(x) = L$. For discussion and examples, see Exercises 50–51.

SECTION 2.7 EXERCISES

Review Questions

1. Suppose x lies in the interval $(1, 3)$ with $x \neq 2$. Find the smallest positive value of δ such that the inequality $0 < |x - 2| < \delta$ is true.

2. Suppose $f(x)$ lies in the interval $(2, 6)$. What is the smallest value of ε such that $|f(x) - 4| < \varepsilon$?

3. Which one of the following intervals is not symmetric about $x = 5$?

a. $(1, 9)$ **b.** $(4, 6)$ **c.** $(3, 8)$ **d.** $(4.5, 5.5)$

4. Does the set $\{x: 0 < |x - a| < \delta\}$ include the point $x = a$? Explain.

5. State the precise definition of $\lim_{x \to a} f(x) = L$.

6. Interpret $|f(x) - L| < \varepsilon$ in words.

7. Suppose $|f(x) - 5| < 0.1$ whenever $0 < x < 5$. Find all values of $\delta > 0$ such that $|f(x) - 5| < 0.1$ whenever $0 < |x - 2| < \delta$.

8. Give the definition of $\lim_{x \to a} f(x) = \infty$ and interpret it using pictures.

Basic Skills

9. Determining values of δ from a graph The function f in the figure satisfies $\lim_{x \to 2} f(x) = 5$. Determine the largest value of $\delta > 0$ satisfying each statement.

a. If $0 < |x - 2| < \delta$, then $|f(x) - 5| < 2$.
b. If $0 < |x - 2| < \delta$, then $|f(x) - 5| < 1$.

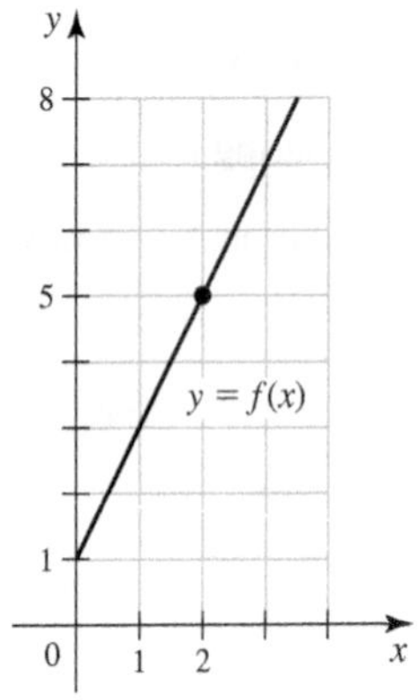

10. Determining values of δ from a graph The function f in the figure satisfies $\lim_{x \to 2} f(x) = 4$. Determine the largest value of $\delta > 0$ satisfying each statement.

a. If $0 < |x - 2| < \delta$, then $|f(x) - 4| < 1$.
b. If $0 < |x - 2| < \delta$, then $|f(x) - 4| < 1/2$.

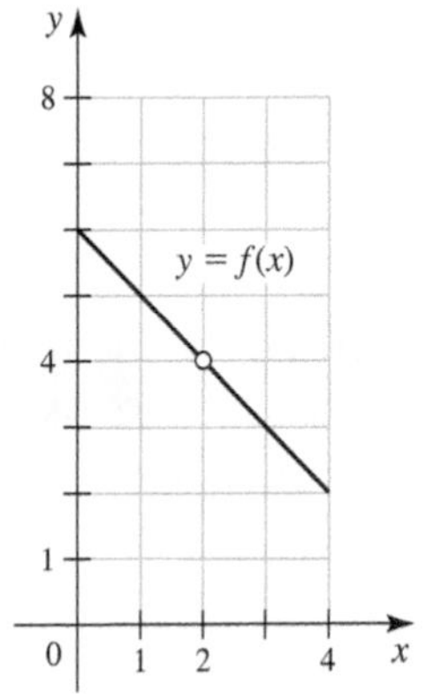

11. Determining values of δ from a graph The function f in the figure satisfies $\lim_{x \to 3} f(x) = 6$. Determine the largest value of $\delta > 0$ satisfying each statement.

a. If $0 < |x - 3| < \delta$, then $|f(x) - 6| < 3$.
b. If $0 < |x - 3| < \delta$, then $|f(x) - 6| < 1$.

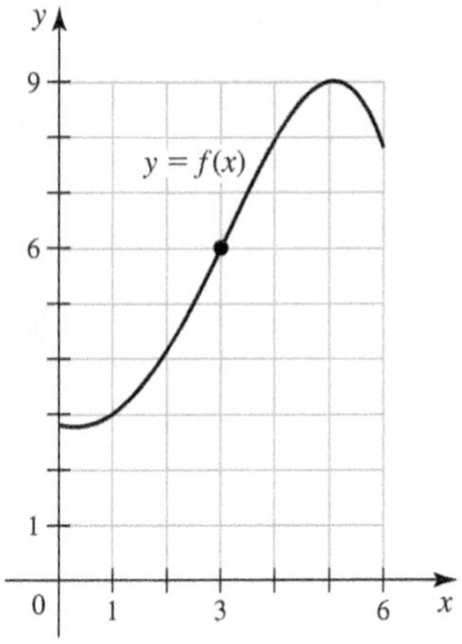

12. Determining values of δ from a graph The function f in the figure satisfies $\lim_{x \to 4} f(x) = 5$. Determine the largest value of $\delta > 0$ satisfying each statement.

a. If $0 < |x - 4| < \delta$, then $|f(x) - 5| < 1$.
b. If $0 < |x - 4| < \delta$, then $|f(x) - 5| < 0.5$.

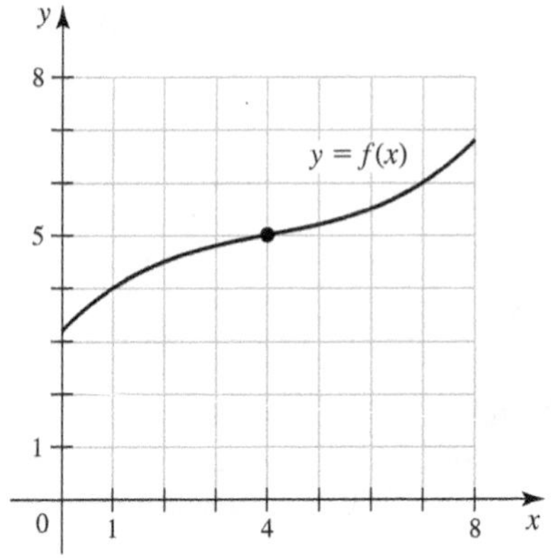

T 13. Finding δ for a given ε using a graph Let $f(x) = x^3 + 3$ and note that $\lim_{x \to 0} f(x) = 3$. For each value of ε, use a graphing utility to find all values of $\delta > 0$ such that $|f(x) - 3| < \varepsilon$ whenever $0 < |x - 0| < \delta$. Sketch graphs illustrating your work.

a. $\varepsilon = 1$ **b.** $\varepsilon = 0.5$

T 14. Finding δ for a given ε using a graph Let $g(x) = 2x^3 - 12x^2 + 26x + 4$ and note that $\lim_{x \to 2} g(x) = 24$. For each value of ε, use a graphing utility to find all values of $\delta > 0$ such that $|g(x) - 24| < \varepsilon$ whenever $0 < |x - 2| < \delta$. Sketch graphs illustrating your work.

a. $\varepsilon = 1$ **b.** $\varepsilon = 0.5$

15. Finding a symmetric interval The function f in the figure satisfies $\lim_{x \to 2} f(x) = 3$. For each value of ε, find all values of $\delta > 0$ such that

$$|f(x) - 3| < \varepsilon \quad \text{whenever} \quad 0 < |x - 2| < \delta. \qquad (2)$$

56–58. Proving that $\lim_{x \to a} f(x) \neq L$ *Use the following definition for the nonexistence of a limit. Assume f is defined for all values of x near a, except possibly at a. We write $\lim_{x \to a} f(x) \neq L$ if for some $\varepsilon > 0$, there is no value of $\delta > 0$ satisfying the condition*

$$|f(x) - L| < \varepsilon \quad \text{whenever} \quad 0 < |x - a| < \delta.$$

56. For the following function, note that $\lim_{x \to 2} f(x) \neq 3$. Find all values of $\varepsilon > 0$ for which the preceding condition for nonexistence is satisfied.

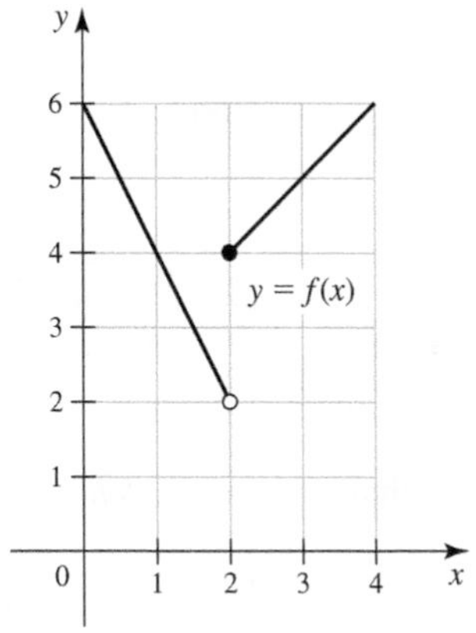

57. Prove that $\lim_{x \to 0} \frac{|x|}{x}$ does not exist.

58. Let

$$f(x) = \begin{cases} 0 & \text{if } x \text{ is rational} \\ 1 & \text{if } x \text{ is irrational.} \end{cases}$$

Prove that $\lim_{x \to a} f(x)$ does not exist for any value of a. (*Hint:* Assume $\lim_{x \to a} f(x) = L$ for some values of a and L and let $\varepsilon = \frac{1}{2}$.)

59. A continuity proof Suppose f is continuous at a and assume $f(a) > 0$. Show that there is a positive number $\delta > 0$ for which $f(x) > 0$ for all values of x in $(a - \delta, a + \delta)$. (In other words, f is positive for all values of x in the domain of f and in some interval containing a.)

QUICK CHECK ANSWERS

1. $\delta = \frac{1}{50}$ or smaller **2.** $\delta = 0.62$ or smaller **3.** δ must decrease by a factor of $\sqrt{100} = 10$ (at least). ◄

CHAPTER 2 REVIEW EXERCISES

1. Explain why or why not Determine whether the following statements are true and give an explanation or counterexample.

a. The rational function $\frac{x - 1}{x^2 - 1}$ has vertical asymptotes at $x = -1$ and $x = 1$.

b. Numerical or graphical methods always produce good estimates of $\lim_{x \to a} f(x)$.

c. The value of $\lim_{x \to a} f(x)$, if it exists, is found by calculating $f(a)$.

d. If $\lim_{x \to a} f(x) = \infty$ or $\lim_{x \to a} f(x) = -\infty$, then $\lim_{x \to a} f(x)$ does not exist.

e. If $\lim_{x \to a} f(x)$ does not exist, then either $\lim_{x \to a} f(x) = \infty$ or $\lim_{x \to a} f(x) = -\infty$.

f. The line $y = 2x + 1$ is a slant asymptote of the function $f(x) = \frac{2x^2 + x}{x - 3}$.

g. If a function is continuous on the intervals (a, b) and $[b, c)$, where $a < b < c$, then the function is also continuous on (a, c).

h. If $\lim_{x \to a} f(x)$ can be calculated by direct substitution, then f is continuous at $x = a$.

2. Estimating limits graphically Use the graph of f in the figure to find the following values, or state that they do not exist.

a. $f(-1)$ **b.** $\lim_{x \to -1^-} f(x)$ **c.** $\lim_{x \to -1^+} f(x)$ **d.** $\lim_{x \to -1} f(x)$

e. $f(1)$ **f.** $\lim_{x \to 1} f(x)$ **g.** $\lim_{x \to 2} f(x)$ **h.** $\lim_{x \to 3^-} f(x)$

i. $\lim_{x \to 3^+} f(x)$ **j.** $\lim_{x \to 3} f(x)$

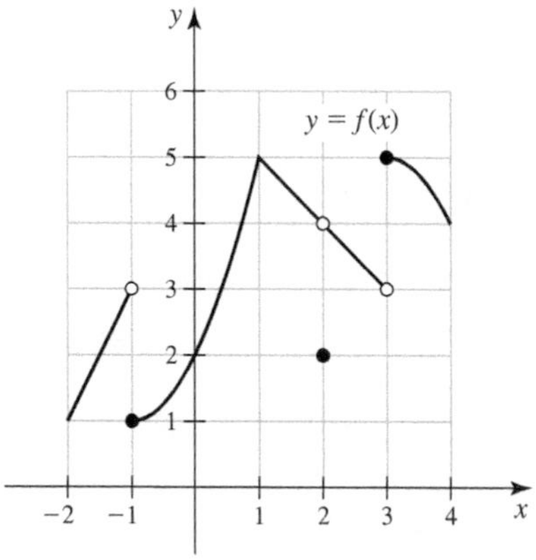

3. Points of discontinuity Use the graph of f in the figure to determine the values of x in the interval $(-3, 5)$ at which f fails to be continuous. Justify your answers using the continuity checklist.

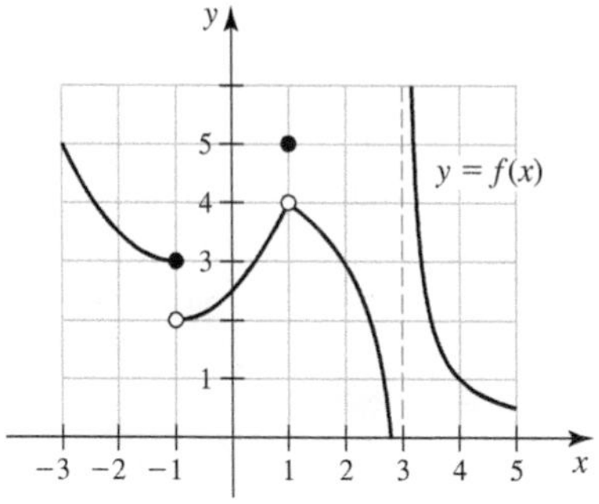

T 4. Computing a limit graphically and analytically

a. Graph $y = \dfrac{\sin 2\theta}{\sin \theta}$ with a graphing utility. Comment on any inaccuracies in the graph and then sketch an accurate graph of the function.

b. Estimate $\lim_{\theta \to 0} \dfrac{\sin 2\theta}{\sin \theta}$ using the graph in part (a).

c. Verify your answer to part (b) by finding the value of $\lim_{\theta \to 0} \dfrac{\sin 2\theta}{\sin \theta}$ analytically using the trigonometric identity $\sin 2\theta = 2 \sin \theta \cos \theta$.

T 5. Computing a limit numerically and analytically

a. Estimate $\lim_{x \to \pi/4} \dfrac{\cos 2x}{\cos x - \sin x}$ by making a table of values of $\dfrac{\cos 2x}{\cos x - \sin x}$ for values of x approaching $\pi/4$. Round your estimate to four digits.

b. Use analytic methods to find the value of $\lim_{x \to \pi/4} \dfrac{\cos 2x}{\cos x - \sin x}$.

6. Snowboard rental Suppose the rental cost for a snowboard is $25 for the first day (or any part of the first day) plus $15 for each additional day (or any part of a day).

a. Graph the function $c = f(t)$ that gives the cost of renting a snowboard for t days, for $0 \le t \le 5$.

b. Evaluate $\lim_{t \to 2.9} f(t)$.

c. Evaluate $\lim_{t \to 3^-} f(t)$ and $\lim_{t \to 3^+} f(t)$.

d. Interpret the meaning of the limits in part (c).

e. For what values of t is f continuous? Explain.

7. Sketching a graph Sketch the graph of a function f with all the following properties.

$$\lim_{x \to -2^-} f(x) = \infty \qquad \lim_{x \to -2^+} f(x) = -\infty \qquad \lim_{x \to 0} f(x) = \infty$$

$$\lim_{x \to 3^-} f(x) = 2 \qquad \lim_{x \to 3^+} f(x) = 4 \qquad f(3) = 1$$

8–21. Evaluating limits *Determine the following limits analytically.*

8. $\lim_{x \to 1000} 18\pi^2$

9. $\lim_{x \to 1} \sqrt{5x + 6}$

10. $\lim_{h \to 0} \dfrac{\sqrt{5x + 5h} - \sqrt{5x}}{h}$, where x is constant

11. $\lim_{x \to 1} \dfrac{x^3 - 7x^2 + 12x}{4 - x}$

12. $\lim_{x \to 4} \dfrac{x^3 - 7x^2 + 12x}{4 - x}$

13. $\lim_{x \to 1} \dfrac{1 - x^2}{x^2 - 8x + 7}$

14. $\lim_{x \to 3} \dfrac{\sqrt{3x + 16} - 5}{x - 3}$

15. $\lim_{x \to 3} \dfrac{1}{x - 3}\left(\dfrac{1}{\sqrt{x + 1}} - \dfrac{1}{2}\right)$

16. $\lim_{t \to 1/3} \dfrac{t - 1/3}{(3t - 1)^2}$

17. $\lim_{x \to 3} \dfrac{x^4 - 81}{x - 3}$

18. $\lim_{p \to 1} \dfrac{p^5 - 1}{p - 1}$

19. $\lim_{x \to 81} \dfrac{\sqrt[4]{x} - 3}{x - 81}$

20. $\lim_{\theta \to \pi/4} \dfrac{\sin^2 \theta - \cos^2 \theta}{\sin \theta - \cos \theta}$

21. $\lim_{x \to \pi/2} \dfrac{\dfrac{1}{\sqrt{\sin x}} - 1}{x + \pi/2}$

22. One-sided limits Analyze $\lim_{x \to 1^+} \sqrt{\dfrac{x - 1}{x - 3}}$ and $\lim_{x \to 1^-} \sqrt{\dfrac{x - 1}{x - 3}}$.

T 23. Applying the Squeeze Theorem

a. Use a graphing utility to illustrate the inequalities

$$\cos x \le \frac{\sin x}{x} \le \frac{1}{\cos x}$$

on $[-1, 1]$.

b. Use part (a) and the Squeeze Theorem to explain why $\lim_{x \to 0} \dfrac{\sin x}{x} = 1$.

24. Applying the Squeeze Theorem Assume the function g satisfies the inequality $1 \le g(x) \le \sin^2 x + 1$, for x near 0. Use the Squeeze Theorem to find $\lim_{x \to 0} g(x)$.

25–29. Finding infinite limits *Analyze the following limits.*

25. $\lim_{x \to 5} \dfrac{x - 7}{x(x - 5)^2}$

26. $\lim_{x \to -5^+} \dfrac{x - 5}{x + 5}$

27. $\lim_{x \to 3^-} \dfrac{x - 4}{x^2 - 3x}$

28. $\lim_{u \to 0^+} \dfrac{u - 1}{\sin u}$

29. $\lim_{x \to 0^-} \dfrac{2}{\tan x}$

T 30. Finding vertical asymptotes Let $f(x) = \dfrac{x^2 - 5x + 6}{x^2 - 2x}$.

a. Analyze $\lim_{x \to 0^-} f(x)$, $\lim_{x \to 0^+} f(x)$, $\lim_{x \to 2^-} f(x)$, and $\lim_{x \to 2^+} f(x)$.

b. Does the graph of f have any vertical asymptotes? Explain.

c. Graph f and then sketch the graph with paper and pencil, correcting any errors obtained with the graphing utility.

31–36. Limits at infinity *Evaluate the following limits or state that they do not exist.*

31. $\lim_{x \to \infty} \dfrac{2x - 3}{4x + 10}$

32. $\lim_{x \to \infty} \dfrac{x^4 - 1}{x^5 + 2}$

33. $\lim_{x \to -\infty} (-3x^3 + 5)$

34. $\lim_{z \to \infty} \left(e^{-2z} + \dfrac{2}{z}\right)$

35. $\lim_{x \to \infty} (3 \tan^{-1} x + 2)$

36. $\lim_{r \to \infty} \dfrac{1}{\ln r + 1}$

37–40. End behavior *Determine the end behavior of the following functions.*

37. $f(x) = \dfrac{4x^3 + 1}{1 - x^3}$

38. $f(x) = \dfrac{x + 1}{\sqrt{9x^2 + x}}$

39. $f(x) = 1 - e^{-2x}$

40. $f(x) = \dfrac{1}{\ln x^2}$

41–42. Vertical and horizontal asymptotes *Find all vertical and horizontal asymptotes of the following functions.*

41. $f(x) = \dfrac{1}{\tan^{-1} x}$

42. $f(x) = \dfrac{2x^2 + 6}{2x^2 + 3x - 2}$

43–46. Slant asymptotes

a. Analyze $\lim_{x\to\infty} f(x)$ and $\lim_{x\to-\infty} f(x)$ for each function.

b. Determine whether f has a slant asymptote. If so, write the equation of the slant asymptote.

43. $f(x) = \dfrac{3x^2 + 2x - 1}{4x + 1}$

44. $f(x) = \dfrac{9x^2 + 4}{(2x - 1)^2}$

45. $f(x) = \dfrac{1 + x - 2x^2 - x^3}{x^2 + 1}$

46. $f(x) = \dfrac{x(x + 2)^3}{3x^2 - 4x}$

47–50. Continuity at a point *Determine whether the following functions are continuous at a. Use the continuity checklist to justify your answers.*

47. $f(x) = \dfrac{1}{x - 5}$; $a = 5$

48. $g(x) = \begin{cases} \dfrac{x^2 - 16}{x - 4} & \text{if } x \neq 4 \\ 9 & \text{if } x = 4 \end{cases}$; $a = 4$

49. $h(x) = \sqrt{x^2 - 9}$; $a = 3$

50. $g(x) = \begin{cases} \dfrac{x^2 - 16}{x - 4} & \text{if } x \neq 4 \\ 8 & \text{if } x = 4 \end{cases}$; $a = 4$

51–54. Continuity on intervals *Find the intervals on which the following functions are continuous. Specify right- or left-continuity at the endpoints.*

51. $f(x) = \sqrt{x^2 - 5}$

52. $g(x) = e^{\sqrt{x-2}}$

53. $h(x) = \dfrac{2x}{x^3 - 25x}$

54. $g(x) = \cos e^x$

55. Determining unknown constants Let

$$g(x) = \begin{cases} 5x - 2 & \text{if } x < 1 \\ a & \text{if } x = 1 \\ ax^2 + bx & \text{if } x > 1. \end{cases}$$

Determine values of the constants a and b for which g is continuous at $x = 1$.

56. Left- and right-continuity

a. Is $h(x) = \sqrt{x^2 - 9}$ left-continuous at $x = 3$? Explain.

b. Is $h(x) = \sqrt{x^2 - 9}$ right-continuous at $x = 3$? Explain.

57. Sketching a graph Sketch the graph of a function that is continuous on $(0, 1]$ and continuous on $(1, 2)$ but is not continuous on $(0, 2)$.

T **58. Intermediate Value Theorem**

a. Use the Intermediate Value Theorem to show that the equation $x^5 + 7x + 5 = 0$ has a solution in the interval $(-1, 0)$.

b. Estimate a solution to $x^5 + 7x + 5 = 0$ in $(-1, 0)$ using a root finder.

T **59. Antibiotic dosing** The amount of an antibiotic (in mg) in the blood t hours after an intravenous line is opened is given by

$$m(t) = 100(e^{-0.1t} - e^{-0.3t}).$$

a. Use the Intermediate Value Theorem to show the amount of drug is 30 mg at some time in the interval $[0, 5]$ and again at some time in the interval $[5, 15]$.

b. Estimate the times at which $m = 30$ mg.

c. Is the amount of drug in the blood ever 50 mg?

60. Limit proof Give a formal proof that $\lim_{x\to1} (5x - 2) = 3$.

61. Limit proof Give a formal proof that $\lim_{x\to5} \dfrac{x^2 - 25}{x - 5} = 10$.

62. Limit proofs

a. Assume $|f(x)| \leq L$ for all x near a and $\lim_{x\to a} g(x) = 0$. Give a formal proof that $\lim_{x\to a} (f(x)g(x)) = 0$.

b. Find a function f for which $\lim_{x\to2} (f(x)(x - 2)) \neq 0$. Why doesn't this violate the result stated in (a)?

c. The Heaviside function is defined as

$$H(x) = \begin{cases} 0 & \text{if } x < 0 \\ 1 & \text{if } x \geq 0. \end{cases}$$

Explain why $\lim_{x\to0} [xH(x)] = 0$.

63. Infinite limit proof Give a formal proof that $\lim_{x\to2} \dfrac{1}{(x - 2)^4} = \infty$.

Chapter 2 Guided Projects

Applications of the material in this chapter and related topics can be found in the following Guided Projects. For additional information, see the Preface.

- Fixed-point iteration
- Local linearity

3

Derivatives

Chapter Preview Now that you are familiar with limits, the door to calculus stands open. The first task is to introduce the fundamental concept of the *derivative*. Suppose a function f represents a quantity of interest; for example, the variable cost of manufacturing an item, the population of a country, or the position of an orbiting satellite. The derivative of f is another function, denoted f', that gives the slope of the curve $y = f(x)$ as it changes with respect to x. Equivalently, the derivative of f gives the *instantaneous rate of change* of f with respect to the independent variable. We use limits not only to define the derivative but also to develop efficient rules for finding derivatives. The applications of the derivative—which we introduce along the way—are endless because almost everything around us is in a state of change, and derivatives describe change.

3.1 Introducing the Derivative

In this section, we return to the problem of finding the slope of a line tangent to a curve, introduced at the beginning of Chapter 2. This problem is important for several reasons.

- We identify the slope of the tangent line with the *instantaneous rate of change* of a function (Figure 3.1).
- The slopes of the tangent lines as they change along a curve are the values of a new function called the *derivative*.
- Looking farther ahead, if a curve represents the trajectory of a moving object, the tangent line at a point on the curve indicates the direction of motion at that point (Figure 3.2).

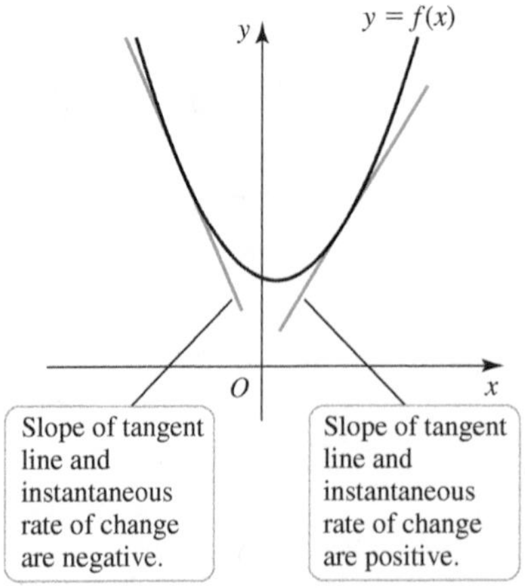

Figure 3.1

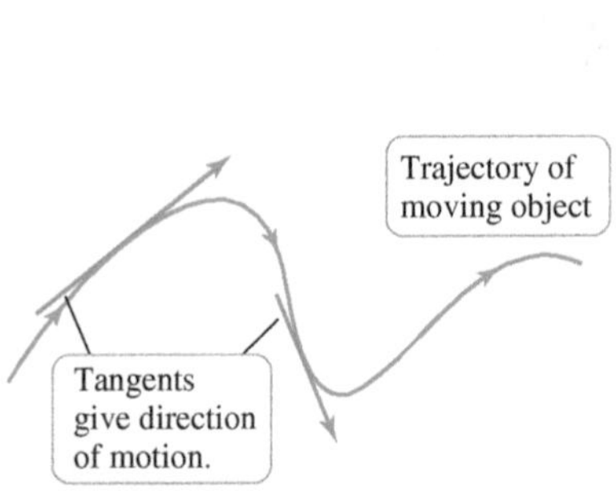

Figure 3.2

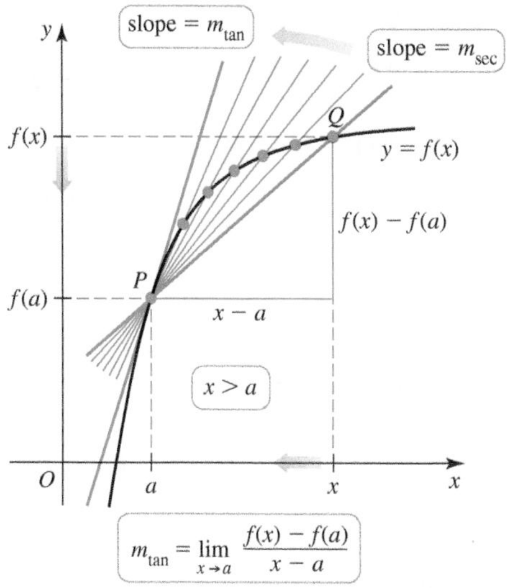

Figure 3.3

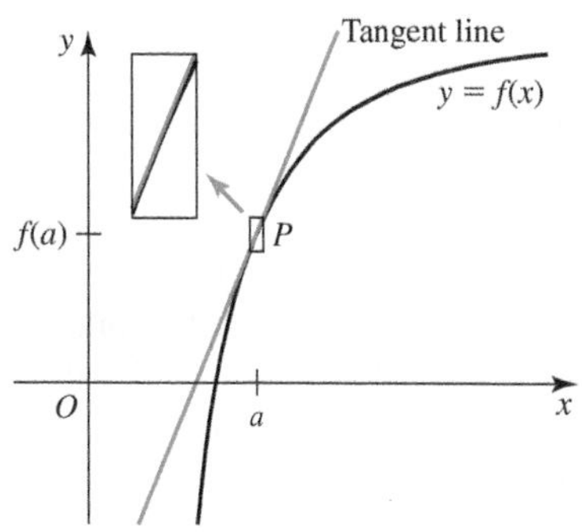

Figure 3.4

In Section 2.1, we gave an intuitive definition of a tangent line and used numerical evidence to estimate its slope. We now make these ideas precise.

Tangent Lines and Rates of Change

Consider the curve $y = f(x)$ and a secant line intersecting the curve at the points $P(a, f(a))$ and $Q(x, f(x))$ (Figure 3.3). The difference $f(x) - f(a)$ is the change in the value of f on the interval $[a, x]$, while $x - a$ is the change in x. As discussed in Chapters 1 and 2, the slope of the secant line $\overleftrightarrow{PQ}$ is

$$m_{\sec} = \frac{f(x) - f(a)}{x - a},$$

and it gives the *average rate of change* in f on the interval $[a, x]$.

Figure 3.3 also shows what happens as the variable point x approaches the fixed point a. If the curve is smooth at $P(a, f(a))$—it has no kinks or corners—the secant lines approach a *unique* line that intersects the curve at P; this line is the *tangent line* at P. As x approaches a, the slopes $m_{\sec}$ of the secant lines approach a unique number $m_{\tan}$ that we call the *slope of the tangent line*; that is,

$$m_{\tan} = \lim_{x \to a} \frac{f(x) - f(a)}{x - a}.$$

The slope of the tangent line at P is also called the *instantaneous rate of change* in f at a because it measures how quickly f changes at a.

The tangent line has another geometric interpretation. As discussed in Section 2.1, if the curve $y = f(x)$ is smooth at a point $P(a, f(a))$, then the curve looks more like a line as we zoom in on P. The line that is approached as we zoom in on P is the tangent line (Figure 3.4). A smooth curve has the property of *local linearity*, which means that if we look at a point on the curve locally (by zooming in), then the curve appears linear.

> The definition of $m_{\sec}$ involves a *difference quotient*, introduced in Section 1.1.

DEFINITION Rate of Change and the Slope of the Tangent Line

The **average rate of change** in f on the interval $[a, x]$ is the slope of the corresponding secant line:

$$m_{\sec} = \frac{f(x) - f(a)}{x - a}.$$

The **instantaneous rate of change** in f at a is

$$m_{\tan} = \lim_{x \to a} \frac{f(x) - f(a)}{x - a}, \qquad (1)$$

which is also the **slope of the tangent line** at $(a, f(a))$, provided this limit exists. The **tangent line** is the unique line through $(a, f(a))$ with slope $m_{\tan}$. Its equation is

$$y - f(a) = m_{\tan}(x - a).$$

QUICK CHECK 1 Sketch the graph of a function f near a point a. As in Figure 3.3, draw a secant line that passes through $(a, f(a))$ and a neighboring point $(x, f(x))$ with $x < a$. Use arrows to show how the secant lines approach the tangent line as x approaches a. ◄

> If x and y have physical units, then the average and instantaneous rates of change have units of (units of y)/(units of x). For example, if y has units of meters and x has units of seconds, the units of the rate of change are meters/second (m/s).

EXAMPLE 1 Equation of a tangent line Let $f(x) = -16x^2 + 96x$ (the position function examined in Section 2.1) and consider the point $P(1, 80)$ on the curve.

a. Find the slope of the line tangent to the graph of f at P.

b. Find an equation of the tangent line in part (a).

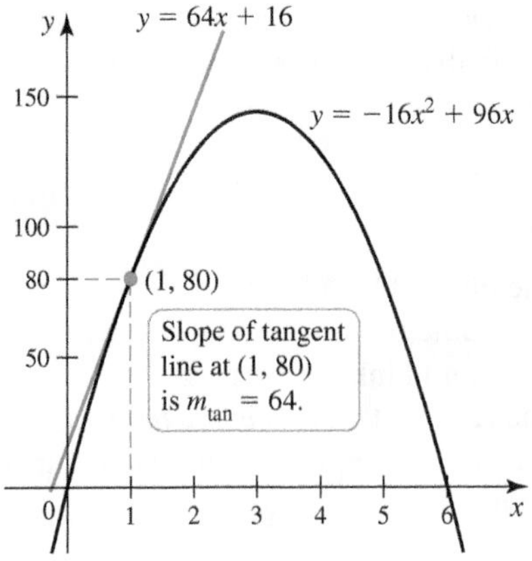

Figure 3.5

SOLUTION

a. We use the definition of the slope of the tangent line with $a = 1$:

$$m_{\tan} = \lim_{x\to 1} \frac{f(x) - f(1)}{x - 1} \quad \text{Definition of slope of tangent line}$$

$$= \lim_{x\to 1} \frac{(-16x^2 + 96x) - 80}{x - 1} \quad f(x) = -16x^2 + 96x; f(1) = 80$$

$$= \lim_{x\to 1} \frac{-16(x-5)(x-1)}{x - 1} \quad \text{Factor the numerator.}$$

$$= -16 \underbrace{\lim_{x\to 1}(x - 5)}_{-4} = 64. \quad \text{Cancel factors } (x \neq 1) \text{ and evaluate the limit.}$$

These calculations confirm the conjecture made in Section 2.1: The slope of the line tangent to the graph of $f(x) = -16x^2 + 96x$ at $(1, 80)$ is 64.

b. An equation of the line passing through $(1, 80)$ with slope $m_{\tan} = 64$ is $y - 80 = 64(x - 1)$ or $y = 64x + 16$. The graph of f and the tangent line at $(1, 80)$ are shown in Figure 3.5.

Related Exercises 9–14 ◀

QUICK CHECK 2 In Example 1, is the slope of the tangent line at $(2, 128)$ greater than or less than the slope at $(1, 80)$? ◀

An alternative formula for the slope of the tangent line is helpful for future work. Consider again the curve $y = f(x)$ and the secant line intersecting the curve at the points P and Q. We now let $(a, f(a))$ and $(a + h, f(a + h))$ be the coordinates of P and Q, respectively (Figure 3.6). The difference in the x-coordinates of P and Q is $(a + h) - a = h$. Note that Q is located to the right of P if $h > 0$ and to the left of P if $h < 0$.

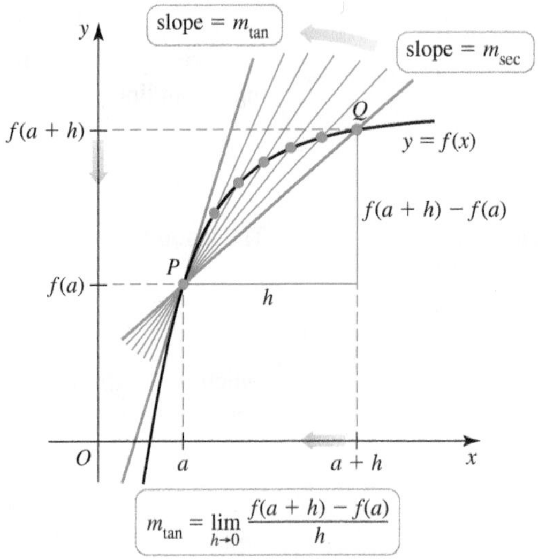

Figure 3.6

The slope of the secant line $\overleftrightarrow{PQ}$ using the new notation is $m_{\sec} = \dfrac{f(a + h) - f(a)}{h}$.

As h approaches 0, the variable point Q approaches P and the slopes of the secant lines approach the slope of the tangent line. Therefore, the slope of the tangent line at $(a, f(a))$, which is also the instantaneous rate of change of f at a, is

$$m_{\tan} = \lim_{h\to 0} \frac{f(a + h) - f(a)}{h}.$$

ALTERNATIVE DEFINITION Rate of Change and the Slope of the Tangent Line

The **average rate of change** in f on the interval $[a, a + h]$ is the slope of the corresponding secant line:

$$m_{\text{sec}} = \frac{f(a + h) - f(a)}{h}.$$

The **instantaneous rate of change** in f at a is

$$m_{\tan} = \lim_{h \to 0} \frac{f(a + h) - f(a)}{h}, \qquad (2)$$

which is also the **slope of the tangent line** at $(a, f(a))$, provided this limit exists.

EXAMPLE 2 Equation of a tangent line Find an equation of the line tangent to the graph of $f(x) = x^3 + 4x$ at $(1, 5)$.

➤ By the definition of the limit as $h \to 0$, notice that h approaches 0 but $h \neq 0$. Therefore, it is permissible to cancel h from the numerator and denominator of $\frac{h(h^2 + 3h + 7)}{h}$.

SOLUTION We let $a = 1$ in definition (2) and first find $f(1 + h)$. After expanding and collecting terms, we have

$$f(1 + h) = (1 + h)^3 + 4(1 + h) = h^3 + 3h^2 + 7h + 5.$$

Substituting $f(1 + h)$ and $f(1) = 5$, the slope of the tangent line is

$$\begin{aligned} m_{\tan} &= \lim_{h \to 0} \frac{f(1 + h) - f(1)}{h} && \text{Definition of } m_{\tan} \\ &= \lim_{h \to 0} \frac{(h^3 + 3h^2 + 7h + 5) - 5}{h} && \text{Substitute } f(1 + h) \text{ and } f(1) = 5. \\ &= \lim_{h \to 0} \frac{h(h^2 + 3h + 7)}{h} && \text{Simplify.} \\ &= \lim_{h \to 0} (h^2 + 3h + 7) && \text{Cancel } h, \text{ noting } h \neq 0. \\ &= 7. && \text{Evaluate the limit.} \end{aligned}$$

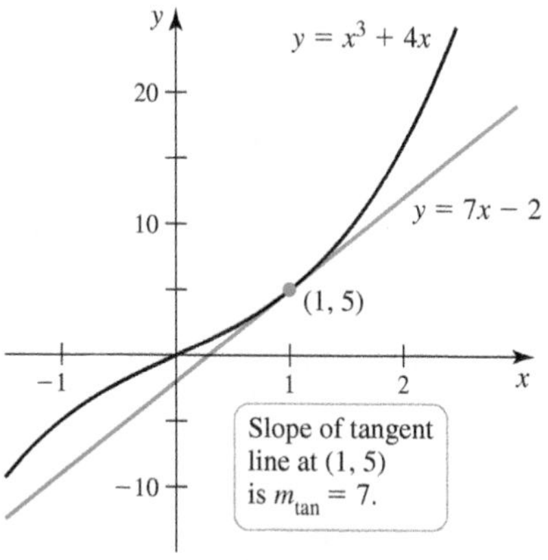

Figure 3.7

The tangent line has slope $m_{\tan} = 7$ and passes through the point $(1, 5)$ (Figure 3.7); its equation is $y - 5 = 7(x - 1)$ or $y = 7x - 2$. We could also say that the instantaneous rate of change of f at $x = 1$ is 7.

Related Exercises 15–26 ◄

QUICK CHECK 3 Set up the calculation in Example 2 using definition (1) for the slope of the tangent line rather than definition (2). Does the calculation appear more difficult using definition (1)? ◄

The Derivative Function

So far we have computed the slope of the tangent line at one fixed point on a curve. If this point is moved along the curve, the tangent line also moves, and, in general, its slope changes (Figure 3.8). For this reason, the slope of the tangent line for the function f is itself a function, called the *derivative* of f.

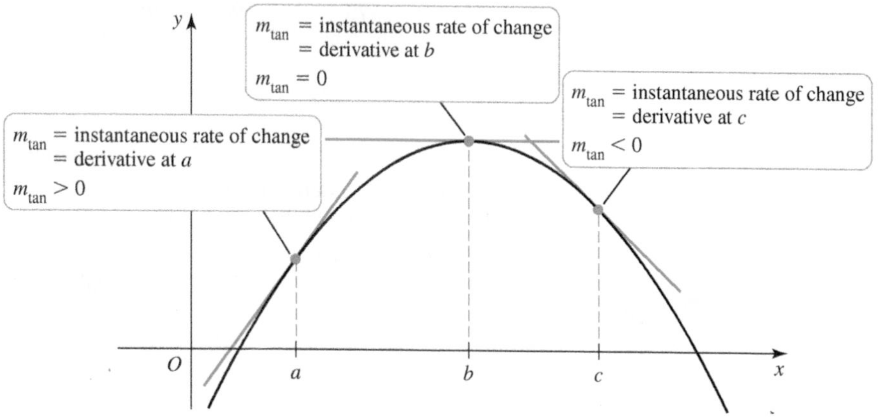

Figure 3.8

We let f' (read *f prime*) denote the derivative function for f, which means that $f'(a)$, when it exists, is the slope of the line tangent to the graph of f at $(a, f(a))$. Using definition (2) for the slope of the tangent line, we have

$$f'(a) = m_{\tan} = \lim_{h \to 0} \frac{f(a+h) - f(a)}{h}.$$

We now take an important step. The derivative is a special function, but it works just like any other function. For example, if the graph of f is smooth and 2 is in the domain of f, then $f'(2)$ is the slope of the line tangent to the graph of f at the point $(2, f(2))$. Similarly, if -2 is in the domain of f, then $f'(-2)$ is the slope of the tangent line at the point $(-2, f(-2))$. In fact, if x is *any* point in the domain of f, then $f'(x)$ is the slope of the tangent line at the point $(x, f(x))$. When we introduce a variable point x, the expression $f'(x)$ becomes the *derivative function.*

➤ To emphasize an important point, $f'(2)$ or $f'(-2)$ or $f'(a)$, for a real number a, are real numbers, whereas f' or $f'(x)$ refer to the derivative *function*.

➤ The process of finding f' is called *differentiation*, and to *differentiate* f means to find f'.

➤ Just as we have two definitions for the slope of the tangent line, we may also use the following definition for the derivative of f at a:

$$f'(a) = \lim_{x \to a} \frac{f(x) - f(a)}{x - a}.$$

DEFINITION The Derivative Function

The **derivative** of f is the function

$$f'(x) = \lim_{h \to 0} \frac{f(x+h) - f(x)}{h},$$

provided the limit exists and x is the domain of f. If $f'(x)$ exists, we say that f is **differentiable** at x. If f is differentiable at every point of an open interval I, we say that f is differentiable on I.

Notice that the definition of f' applies only at points in the domain of f. Therefore, the domain of f' is no larger than the domain of f. If the limit in the definition of f' fails to exist at some points, then the domain of f' is a subset of the domain of f. Let's use this definition to compute a derivative function.

EXAMPLE 3 Computing a derivative Consider once again the function $f(x) = -16x^2 + 96x$ of Example 1 and find its derivative.

SOLUTION

➤ Notice that this argument applies for $h > 0$ and for $h < 0$; that is, the limit as $h \to 0^+$ and the limit as $h \to 0^-$ are equal.

$$
\begin{aligned}
f'(x) &= \lim_{h \to 0} \frac{f(x+h) - f(x)}{h} && \text{Definition of } f'(x) \\
&= \lim_{h \to 0} \frac{\overbrace{-16(x+h)^2 + 96(x+h)}^{f(x+h)} - \overbrace{(-16x^2 + 96x)}^{f(x)}}{h} && \text{Substitute.} \\
&= \lim_{h \to 0} \frac{-16(x^2 + 2xh + h^2) + 96x + 96h + 16x^2 - 96x}{h} && \text{Expand the numerator.} \\
&= \lim_{h \to 0} \frac{h(-32x + 96 - 16h)}{h} && \text{Simplify and factor out } h. \\
&= \lim_{h \to 0} (-32x + 96 - 16h) = -32x + 96 && \text{Cancel } h \text{ and evaluate the limit.}
\end{aligned}
$$

The derivative is $f'(x) = -32x + 96$, which gives the slope of the tangent line (equivalently, the instantaneous rate of change) at *any* point on the curve. For example, at the point $(1, 80)$, the slope of the tangent line is $f'(1) = -32(1) + 96 = 64$, confirming the calculation in Example 1. The slope of the tangent line at $(3, 144)$ is $f'(3) = -32(3) + 96 = 0$, which means the tangent line is horizontal at that point (Figure 3.9).

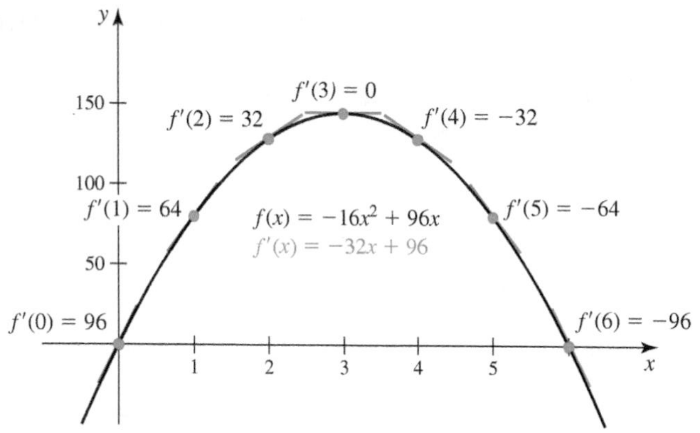

Figure 3.9

Related Exercises 27–40 ◀

QUICK CHECK 4 In Example 3, determine the slope of the tangent line at $x = 2$. ◀

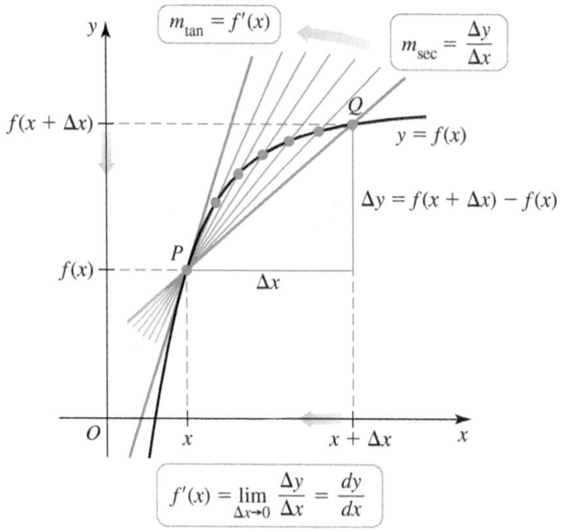

Figure 3.10

➤ The notation $\frac{dy}{dx}$ is read *the derivative of y with respect to x* or *dy dx*. It does not mean *dy* divided by *dx*, but it is a reminder of the limit of the quotient $\Delta y/\Delta x$.

➤ The derivative notation dy/dx was introduced by Gottfried Wilhelm von Leibniz (1646–1716), one of the coinventors of calculus. His notation is used today in its original form. The notation used by Sir Isaac Newton (1642–1727), the other coinventor of calculus, is used less frequently.

Derivative Notation

For historical and practical reasons, several notations for the derivative are used. To see the origin of one notation, recall that the slope of the secant line through two points $P(x, f(x))$ and $Q(x + h, f(x + h))$ on the curve $y = f(x)$ is $\frac{f(x + h) - f(x)}{h}$. The quantity h is the change in the x-coordinate in moving from P to Q. A standard notation for change is the symbol Δ (uppercase Greek letter delta). So we replace h with Δx to represent the change in x. Similarly, $f(x + h) - f(x) = f(x + \Delta x) - f(x)$ is the change in y, denoted Δy (Figure 3.10). Therefore, the slope of the secant line is

$$m_{\sec} = \frac{f(x + \Delta x) - f(x)}{\Delta x} = \frac{\Delta y}{\Delta x}.$$

By letting $\Delta x \to 0$, the slope of the tangent line at $(x, f(x))$ is

$$f'(x) = \lim_{\Delta x \to 0} \frac{f(x + \Delta x) - f(x)}{\Delta x} = \lim_{\Delta x \to 0} \frac{\Delta y}{\Delta x} = \frac{dy}{dx}.$$

The new notation for the derivative is $\frac{dy}{dx}$; it reminds us that $f'(x)$ is the limit of $\frac{\Delta y}{\Delta x}$ as $\Delta x \to 0$.

In addition to the notation $f'(x)$ and $\frac{dy}{dx}$, other common ways of writing the derivative include

$$\frac{df}{dx}, \quad \frac{d}{dx}(f(x)), \quad D_x(f(x)), \quad \text{and} \quad y'(x).$$

The following notations represents the derivative of f evaluated at a.

$$f'(a), \quad y'(a), \quad \left.\frac{df}{dx}\right|_{x=a}, \quad \text{and} \quad \left.\frac{dy}{dx}\right|_{x=a}$$

QUICK CHECK 5 What are some other ways to write $f'(3)$, where $y = f(x)$? ◀

EXAMPLE 4 A derivative calculation Let $y = f(x) = \sqrt{x}$.

a. Compute $\frac{dy}{dx}$.

b. Find an equation of the line tangent to the graph of f at $(4, 2)$.

➤ Example 4 gives the first of many derivative formulas to be presented in the text:

$$\frac{d}{dx}(\sqrt{x}) = \frac{1}{2\sqrt{x}}.$$

Remember this result. It will be used often.

SOLUTION

a.
$$\begin{aligned}
\frac{dy}{dx} &= \lim_{h\to 0} \frac{f(x+h) - f(x)}{h} && \text{Definition of } \frac{dy}{dx} = f'(x) \\
&= \lim_{h\to 0} \frac{\sqrt{x+h} - \sqrt{x}}{h} && \text{Substitute } f(x) = \sqrt{x}. \\
&= \lim_{h\to 0} \frac{(\sqrt{x+h} - \sqrt{x})}{h} \frac{(\sqrt{x+h} + \sqrt{x})}{(\sqrt{x+h} + \sqrt{x})} && \text{Multiply the numerator and denominator by } \sqrt{x+h} + \sqrt{x}. \\
&= \lim_{h\to 0} \frac{1}{\sqrt{x+h} + \sqrt{x}} = \frac{1}{2\sqrt{x}} && \text{Simplify and evaluate the limit.}
\end{aligned}$$

b. The slope of the tangent line at $(4, 2)$ is

$$\left.\frac{dy}{dx}\right|_{x=4} = \frac{1}{2\sqrt{4}} = \frac{1}{4}.$$

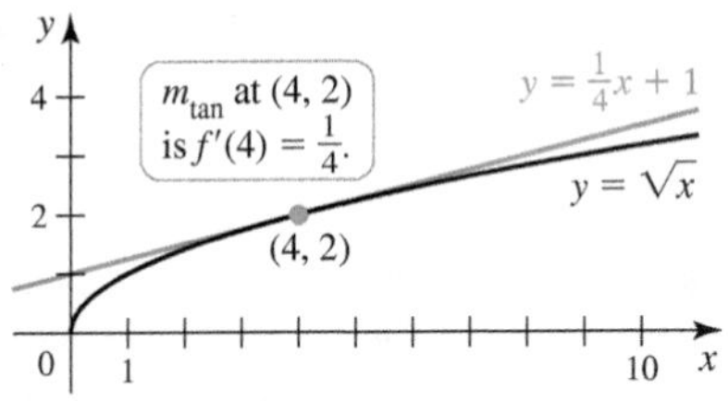

Figure 3.11

Therefore, an equation of the tangent line (Figure 3.11) is

$$y - 2 = \frac{1}{4}(x - 4) \quad \text{or} \quad y = \frac{1}{4}x + 1.$$

Related Exercises 41–42 ◀

QUICK CHECK 6 In Example 4, do the slopes of the tangent lines increase or decrease as x increases? Explain. ◀

If a function is given in terms of variables other than x and y, we make an adjustment to the derivative definition. For example, if $y = g(t)$, we replace f with g and x with t to obtain the *derivative of g with respect to t*:

$$g'(t) = \lim_{h\to 0} \frac{g(t+h) - g(t)}{h}.$$

Other notations for $g'(t)$ include $\frac{dg}{dt}$, $\frac{d}{dt}(g(t))$, $D_t(g(t))$, and $y'(t)$.

QUICK CHECK 7 Express the derivative of $p = q(r)$ in three ways. ◀

EXAMPLE 5 Another derivative calculation Let $g(t) = 1/t^2$ and compute $g'(t)$.

SOLUTION

$$\begin{aligned}
g'(t) &= \lim_{h\to 0} \frac{g(t+h) - g(t)}{h} && \text{Definition of } g' \\
&= \lim_{h\to 0} \frac{1}{h}\left(\frac{1}{(t+h)^2} - \frac{1}{t^2}\right) && \text{Substitute } g(t) = 1/t^2. \\
&= \lim_{h\to 0} \frac{1}{h}\left(\frac{t^2 - (t+h)^2}{t^2(t+h)^2}\right) && \text{Common denominator} \\
&= \lim_{h\to 0} \frac{1}{h}\left(\frac{-2ht - h^2}{t^2(t+h)^2}\right) && \text{Expand the numerator and simplify.} \\
&= \lim_{h\to 0} \left(\frac{-2t - h}{t^2(t+h)^2}\right) && h \neq 0; \text{ cancel } h. \\
&= -\frac{2}{t^3} && \text{Evaluate the limit.}
\end{aligned}$$

Related Exercises 43–46 ◀

SECTION 3.1 EXERCISES

Review Questions

1. Use definition (1) (p. 127) for the slope of a tangent line to explain how slopes of secant lines approach the slope of the tangent line at a point.
2. Explain why the slope of a secant line can be interpreted as an average rate of change.
3. Explain why the slope of the tangent line can be interpreted as an instantaneous rate of change.
4. For a given function f, what does f' represent?
5. Given a function f and a point a in its domain, what does $f'(a)$ represent?
6. Explain the relationships among the slope of a tangent line, the instantaneous rate of change, and the value of the derivative at a point.
7. Why is the notation $\frac{dy}{dx}$ used to represent the derivative?
8. Give three different notations for the derivative of f with respect to x.

Basic Skills

9–14. Equations of tangent lines by definition (1)

a. Use definition (1) (p. 127) to find the slope of the line tangent to the graph of f at P.
b. Determine an equation of the tangent line at P.
c. Plot the graph of f and the tangent line at P.

9. $f(x) = x^2 - 5;\ P(3, 4)$
10. $f(x) = -3x^2 - 5x + 1;\ P(1, -7)$
11. $f(x) = -5x + 1;\ P(1, -4)$
12. $f(x) = 5;\ P(1, 5)$
13. $f(x) = \frac{1}{x};\ P(-1, -1)$
14. $f(x) = \frac{4}{x^2};\ P(-1, 4)$

15–26. Equations of tangent lines by definition (2)

a. Use definition (2) (p. 129) to find the slope of the line tangent to the graph of f at P.
b. Determine an equation of the tangent line at P.

15. $f(x) = 2x + 1;\ P(0, 1)$
16. $f(x) = 3x^2 - 4x;\ P(1, -1)$
17. $f(x) = -7x;\ P(-1, 7)$
18. $f(x) = 8 - 2x^2;\ P(0, 8)$
19. $f(x) = x^2 - 4;\ P(2, 0)$
20. $f(x) = 1/x;\ P(1, 1)$
21. $f(x) = x^3;\ P(1, 1)$
22. $f(x) = \frac{1}{2x + 1};\ P(0, 1)$
23. $f(x) = \frac{1}{3 - 2x};\ P\left(-1, \frac{1}{5}\right)$
24. $f(x) = \sqrt{x - 1};\ P(2, 1)$
25. $f(x) = \sqrt{x + 3};\ P(1, 2)$
26. $f(x) = \frac{x}{x + 1};\ P(-2, 2)$

27–36. Derivatives and tangent lines

a. For the following functions and values of a, find $f'(a)$.
b. Determine an equation of the line tangent to the graph of f at the point $(a, f(a))$ for the given value of a.

27. $f(x) = 8x;\ a = -3$
28. $f(x) = x^2;\ a = 3$
29. $f(x) = 4x^2 + 2x;\ a = -2$
30. $f(x) = 2x^3;\ a = 10$
31. $f(x) = \frac{1}{\sqrt{x}};\ a = \frac{1}{4}$
32. $f(x) = \frac{1}{x^2};\ a = 1$
33. $f(x) = \sqrt{2x + 1};\ a = 4$
34. $f(x) = \sqrt{3x};\ a = 12$
35. $f(x) = \frac{1}{x + 5};\ a = 5$
36. $f(x) = \frac{1}{3x - 1};\ a = 2$

37–40. Lines tangent to parabolas

a. Find the derivative function f' for the following functions f.
b. Find an equation of the line tangent to the graph of f at $(a, f(a))$ for the given value of a.
c. Graph f and the tangent line.

37. $f(x) = 3x^2 + 2x - 10;\ a = 1$
38. $f(x) = 3x^2;\ a = 0$
39. $f(x) = 5x^2 - 6x + 1;\ a = 2$
40. $f(x) = 1 - x^2;\ a = -1$
41. **A derivative formula**
    a. Use the definition of the derivative to determine $\frac{d}{dx}(ax^2 + bx + c)$, where a, b, and c are constants.
    b. Let $f(x) = 4x^2 - 3x + 10$ and use part (a) to find $f'(x)$.
    c. Use part (b) to find $f'(1)$.
42. **A derivative formula**
    a. Use the definition of the derivative to determine $\frac{d}{dx}(\sqrt{ax + b})$, where a and b are constants.
    b. Let $f(x) = \sqrt{5x + 9}$ and use part (a) to find $f'(x)$.
    c. Use part (b) to find $f'(-1)$.

43–46. Derivative calculations *Evaluate the derivative of the following functions at the given point.*

43. $y = 1/(t + 1);\ t = 1$
44. $y = t - t^2;\ t = 2$
45. $c = 2\sqrt{s} - 1;\ s = 25$
46. $A = \pi r^2;\ r = 3$

Further Explorations

47. **Explain why or why not** Determine whether the following statements are true and give an explanation or counterexample.
    a. For linear functions, the slope of any secant line always equals the slope of any tangent line.
    b. The slope of the secant line passing through the points P and Q is less than the slope of the tangent line at P.
    c. Consider the graph of the parabola $f(x) = x^2$. For $x > 0$ and $h > 0$, the secant line through $(x, f(x))$ and $(x + h, f(x + h))$ always has a greater slope than the tangent line at $(x, f(x))$.
48. **Slope of a line** Consider the line $f(x) = mx + b$, where m and b are constants. Show that $f'(x) = m$ for all x. Interpret this result.

49–52. Calculating derivatives

a. For the following functions, find f' using the definition.
b. Determine an equation of the line tangent to the graph of f at $(a, f(a))$ for the given value of a.

49. $f(x) = \sqrt{3x + 1};\ a = 8$
50. $f(x) = \sqrt{x + 2};\ a = 7$
51. $f(x) = \frac{2}{3x + 1};\ a = -1$
52. $f(x) = \frac{1}{x};\ a = -5$

53–54. Analyzing slopes *Use the points A, B, C, D, and E in the following graphs to answer these questions.*

a. *At which points is the slope of the curve negative?*
b. *At which points is the slope of the curve positive?*
c. *Using A–E, list the slopes in decreasing order.*

53.

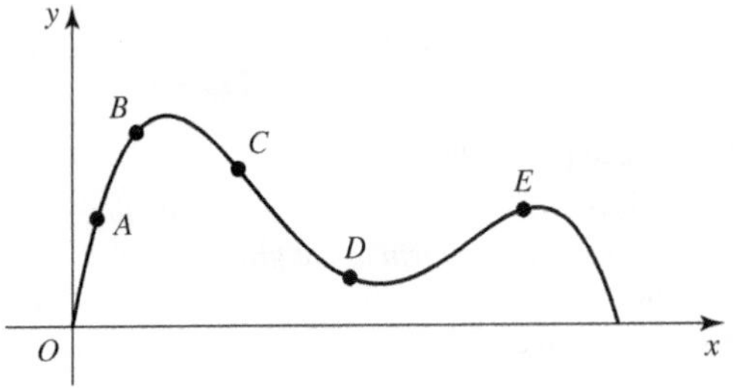

54.

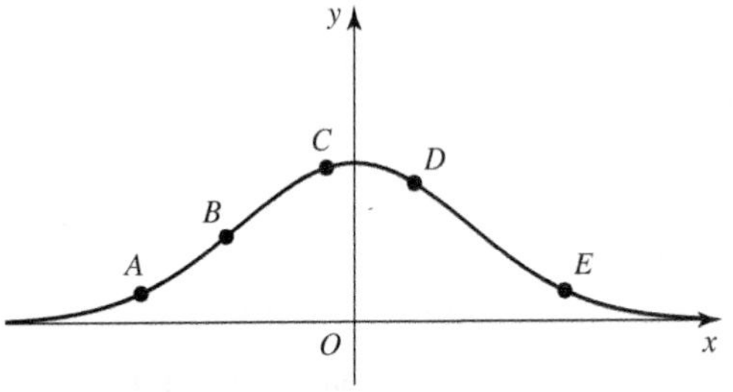

Applications

T **55. Power and energy** Energy is the capacity to do work, and power is the rate at which energy is used or consumed. Therefore, if $E(t)$ is the energy function for a system, then $P(t) = E'(t)$ is the power function. A unit of energy is the kilowatt-hour (1 kWh is the amount of energy needed to light ten 100-W lightbulbs for an hour); the corresponding units for power are kilowatts. The following figure shows the energy consumed by a small community over a 25-hour period.

a. Estimate the power at $t = 10$ and $t = 20$ hr. Be sure to include units in your calculation.
b. At what times on the interval $[0, 25]$ is the power zero?
c. At what times on the interval $[0, 25]$ is the power a maximum?

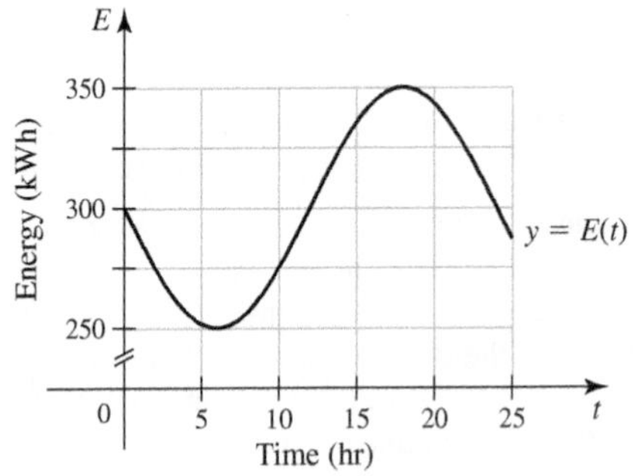

T **56. Population of Las Vegas** Let $p(t)$ represent the population of the Las Vegas metropolitan area t years after 1950, as shown in the table and figure.

a. Compute the average rate of growth of Las Vegas from 1970 to 1980.
b. Explain why the average rate of growth calculated in part (a) is a good estimate of the instantaneous rate of growth of Las Vegas in 1975.
c. Compute the average rate of growth of Las Vegas from 1990 to 2000. Is the average rate of growth an overestimate or underestimate of the instantaneous rate of growth of Las Vegas in 2000? Approximate the growth rate in 2000.

Year	1950	1960	1970	1980	1990	2000	2010
t	0	10	20	30	40	50	60
$p(t)$	59,900	139,126	304,744	528,000	852,737	1,563,282	1,951,269

(*Source:* U.S. Bureau of Census)

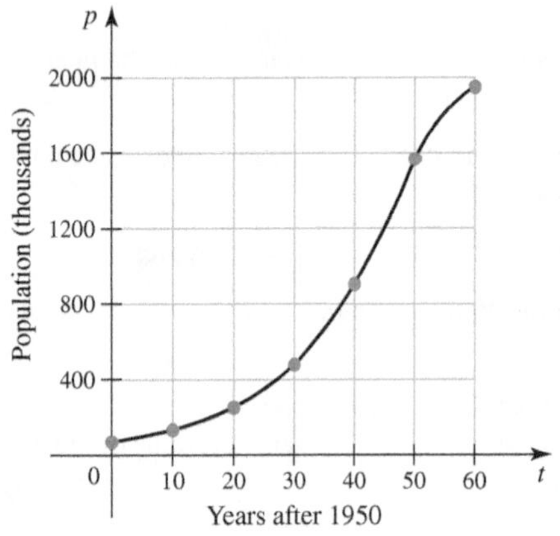

57–60. Find the function *The following limits represent the slope of a curve $y = f(x)$ at the point $(a, f(a))$. Determine a possible function f and number a; then calculate the limit.*

57. $\displaystyle\lim_{x \to 2} \frac{\frac{1}{x+1} - \frac{1}{3}}{x - 2}$

58. $\displaystyle\lim_{h \to 0} \frac{\sqrt{2 + h} - \sqrt{2}}{h}$

59. $\displaystyle\lim_{h \to 0} \frac{(2 + h)^4 - 16}{h}$

60. $\displaystyle\lim_{x \to 1} \frac{3x^2 + 4x - 7}{x - 1}$

61. Is it differentiable? Is $f(x) = \dfrac{x^2 - 5x + 6}{x - 2}$ differentiable at $x = 2$? Justify your answer.

62. Looking ahead: Derivative of x^n Use the definition $f'(x) = \displaystyle\lim_{h \to 0} \frac{f(x + h) - f(x)}{h}$ to find $f'(x)$ for the following functions.

a. $f(x) = x^2$
b. $f(x) = x^3$
c. $f(x) = x^4$
d. Based on your answers to parts (a)–(c), propose a formula for $f'(x)$ if $f(x) = x^n$, where n is a positive integer.

63. Determining the unknown constant Let

$$f(x) = \begin{cases} 2x^2 & \text{if } x \le 1 \\ ax - 2 & \text{if } x > 1. \end{cases}$$

Determine a value of a (if possible) for which f' is continuous at $x = 1$.

64–67. Approximating derivatives *Assuming the limit exists, the definition of the derivative $f'(a) = \displaystyle\lim_{h \to 0} \frac{f(a + h) - f(a)}{h}$ implies that if h is small, then an approximation to $f'(a)$ is given by*

$$f'(a) \approx \frac{f(a + h) - f(a)}{h}.$$

If $h > 0$, then this approximation is called a ***forward difference quotient****; if $h < 0$, it is a* ***backward difference quotient****. As shown in the following exercises, these formulas are used to approximate f' at a point when f is a complicated function or when f is represented by a set of data points.*

64. Let $f(x) = \sqrt{x}$.

a. Find the exact value of $f'(4)$.

b. Show that $f'(4) \approx \frac{f(4 + h) - f(4)}{h} = \frac{\sqrt{4 + h} - 2}{h}$.

c. Complete columns 2 and 5 of the following table and describe how $\frac{\sqrt{4 + h} - 2}{h}$ behaves as h approaches 0.

h	$\frac{\sqrt{4+h}-2}{h}$	Error	h	$\frac{\sqrt{4+h}-2}{h}$	Error
0.1			−0.1		
0.01			−0.01		
0.001			−0.001		
0.0001			−0.0001		

d. The accuracy of an approximation is measured by

$$\text{error} = |\text{exact value} - \text{approximate value}|.$$

Use the exact value of $f'(4)$ in part (a) to complete columns 3 and 6 in the table. Describe the behavior of the errors as h approaches 0.

65. Another way to approximate derivatives is to use the **centered difference quotient**:

$$f'(a) \approx \frac{f(a + h) - f(a - h)}{2h}.$$

Again, consider $f(x) = \sqrt{x}$.

a. Graph f near the point $(4, 2)$ and let $h = \frac{1}{2}$ in the centered difference quotient. Draw the line whose slope is computed by the centered difference quotient and explain why the centered difference quotient approximates $f'(4)$.

b. Use the centered difference quotient to approximate $f'(4)$ by completing the following table.

h	Approximation	Error
0.1		
0.01		
0.001		

c. Explain why it is not necessary to use negative values of h in the table in part (b).

d. Compare the accuracy of the derivative estimates in part (b) with those found in Exercise 64.

66. The following table gives the distance $f(t)$ fallen by a smoke jumper t seconds after she opens her chute.

a. Use the forward difference quotient with $h = 0.5$ to estimate the velocity of the smoke jumper at $t = 2$ seconds.

b. Repeat part (a) using the centered difference quotient.

t (seconds)	$f(t)$ (feet)
0	0
0.5	4
1.0	15
1.5	33
2.0	55
2.5	81
3.0	109
3.5	138
4.0	169

67. The *error function* (denoted erf (x)) is an important function in statistics because it is related to the normal distribution. Its graph is shown in the figure, and values at several points are shown in the table.

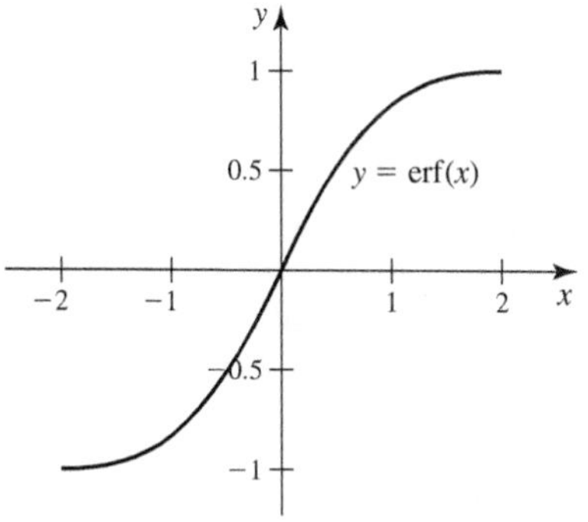

x	erf (x)	x	erf (x)
0.75	0.711156	1.05	0.862436
0.8	0.742101	1.1	0.880205
0.85	0.770668	1.15	0.896124
0.9	0.796908	1.2	0.910314
0.95	0.820891	1.25	0.922900
1.0	0.842701	1.3	0.934008

a. Use forward and centered difference quotients to find approximations to $\left.\frac{d}{dx}(\text{erf}(x))\right|_{x=1}$.

b. Given that $\left.\frac{d}{dx}(\text{erf}(x))\right|_{x=1} = \frac{2}{e\sqrt{\pi}}$, compute the error in the approximations in part (a).

QUICK CHECK ANSWERS

2. The slope is less at $x = 2$. **3.** Definition (1) requires factoring the numerator or long division to cancel $(x - 1)$. **4.** 32 **5.** $\left.\frac{df}{dx}\right|_{x=3}, \left.\frac{dy}{dx}\right|_{x=3}, y'(3)$

6. The slopes of the tangent lines decrease as x increases. The values of $f'(x) = \frac{1}{2\sqrt{x}}$ also decrease as x increases.

7. $\frac{dq}{dr}, \frac{dp}{dr}, D_r(q(r)), q'(r), p'(r)$ ◄

3.2 Working with Derivatives

Having defined the derivative, we now spend some time becoming acquainted with this new and important function. In this section, we explore how the graphs of a function and its derivative are related, and we explain the important relationship between continuity and differentiability.

Graphs of Derivatives

The function f' is called the derivative of f because it is *derived* from f. The following examples illustrate how to *derive* the graph of f' from the graph of f.

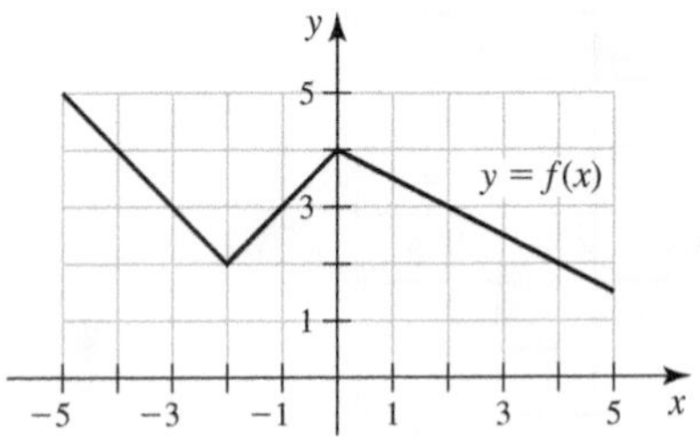

Figure 3.12

EXAMPLE 1 **Graph of the derivative** Sketch the graph of f' from the graph of f (Figure 3.12).

SOLUTION The graph of f consists of line segments, which are their own tangent lines. Therefore, the slope of the curve $y = f(x)$, for $x < -2$, is -1; that is, $f'(x) = -1$, for $x < -2$. Similarly, $f'(x) = 1$, for $-2 < x < 0$, and $f'(x) = -\frac{1}{2}$, for $x > 0$. Figure 3.13 shows the graph of f in black and the graph of f' in red.

➤ In terms of limits at $x = -2$, we can write $\lim_{h \to 0^-} \frac{f(-2 + h) - f(-2)}{h} = -1$ and $\lim_{h \to 0^+} \frac{f(-2 + h) - f(-2)}{h} = 1$. Because the one-sided limits are not equal, $f'(-2)$ does not exist. The analogous one-sided limits at $x = 0$ are also unequal.

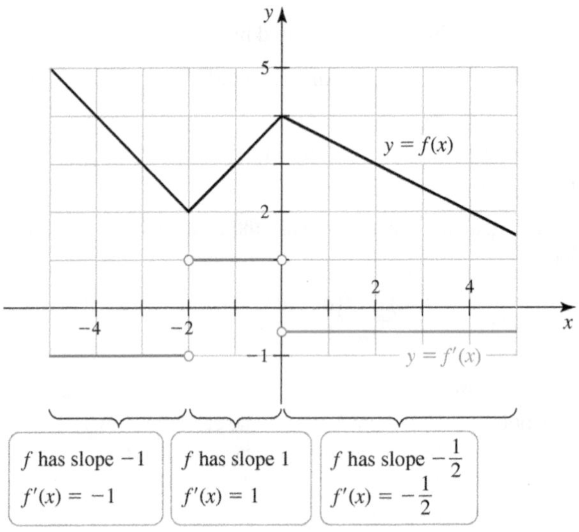

Figure 3.13

QUICK CHECK 1 In Example 1, why is f' not continuous at $x = -2$ and at $x = 0$? ◄

Notice that the slopes of the tangent lines change abruptly at $x = -2$ and $x = 0$. As a result, $f'(-2)$ and $f'(0)$ are undefined and the graph of the derivative has a discontinuity at these points. *Related Exercises 5–12* ◄

EXAMPLE 2 **Graph of the derivative** Sketch the graph of g' using the graph of g (Figure 3.14).

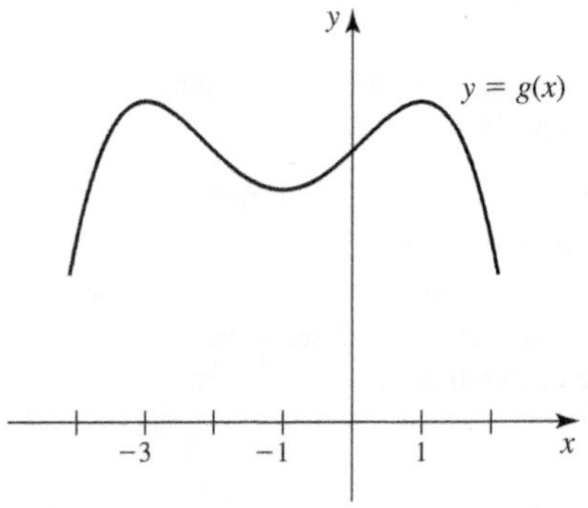

Figure 3.14

SOLUTION Without an equation for g, the best we can do is to find the general shape of the graph of g'. Here are the key observations.

1. Note that the lines tangent to the graph of g at $x = -3, -1$, and 1 have a slope of 0. Therefore,

$$g'(-3) = g'(-1) = g'(1) = 0,$$

which means the graph of g' has x-intercepts at these points (Figure 3.15a).

2. For $x < -3$, the slopes of the tangent lines are positive and decrease to 0 as x approaches -3 from the left. Therefore, $g'(x)$ is positive for $x < -3$ and decreases to 0 as x approaches -3.
3. For $-3 < x < -1$, $g'(x)$ is negative; it initially decreases as x increases and then increases to 0 at $x = -1$. For $-1 < x < 1$, $g'(x)$ is positive; it initially increases as x increases and then returns to 0 at $x = 1$.
4. Finally, $g'(x)$ is negative and decreasing for $x > 1$. Because the slope of g changes gradually, the graph of g' is continuous with no jumps or breaks (Figure 3.15b).

QUICK CHECK 2 Is it true that if $f(x) > 0$ at a point, then $f'(x) > 0$ at that point? Is it true that if $f'(x) > 0$ at a point, then $f(x) > 0$ at that point? Explain. ◄

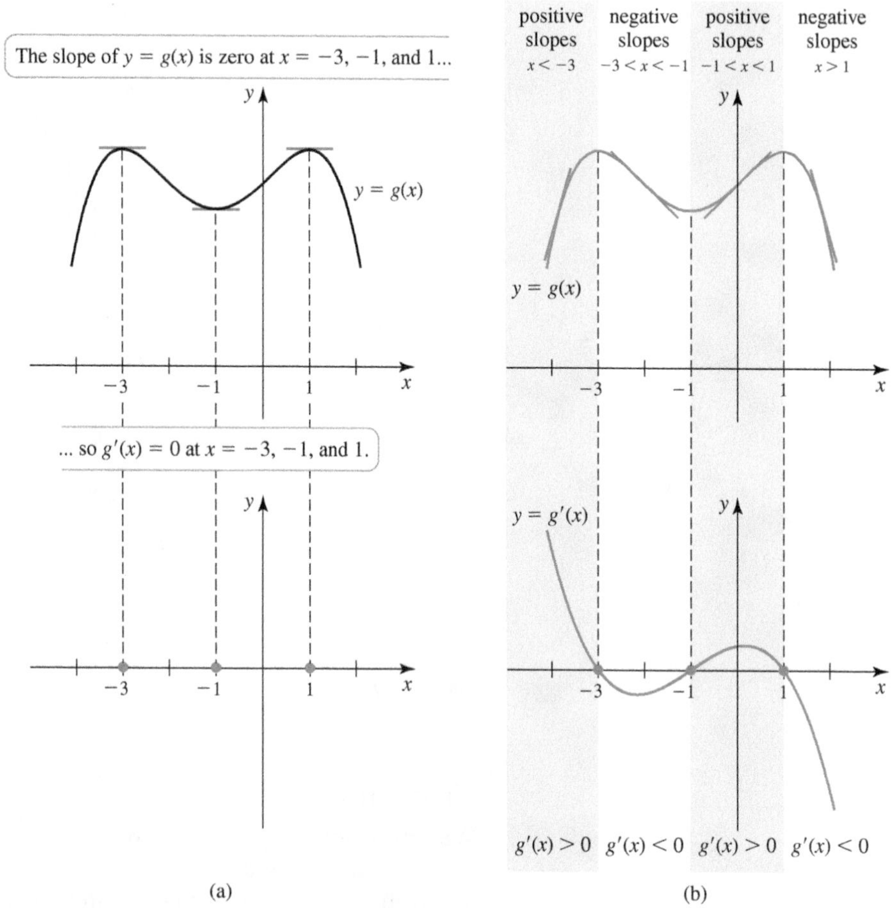

Figure 3.15

Related Exercises 5–12 ◄

EXAMPLE 3 **Graphing the derivative with asymptotes** The graph of the function f is shown in Figure 3.16. Sketch a graph of its derivative.

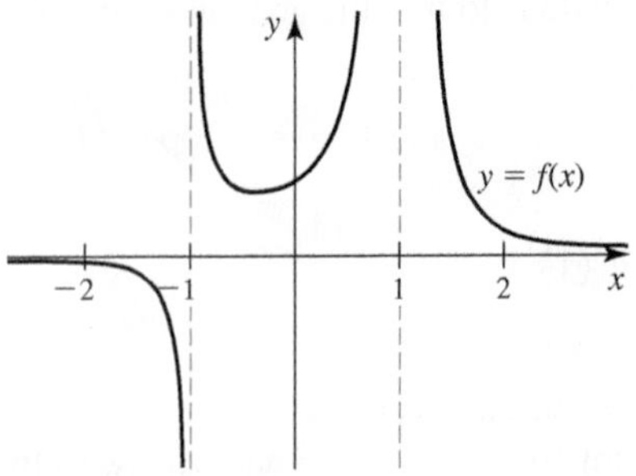

Figure 3.16

➤ Although it is the case in Example 3, a function and its derivative do not always share the same vertical asymptotes.

SOLUTION Identifying intervals on which the slopes of tangent lines are zero, positive, and negative, we make the following observations:

- A horizontal tangent line occurs at approximately $\left(-\frac{1}{3}, f\left(-\frac{1}{3}\right)\right)$. Therefore, $f'\left(-\frac{1}{3}\right) = 0$.
- On the interval $(-\infty, -1)$, slopes of tangent lines are negative and increase in magnitude without bound as we approach -1 from the left.
- On the interval $\left(-1, -\frac{1}{3}\right)$, slopes of tangent lines are negative and increase to zero at $-\frac{1}{3}$.
- On the interval $\left(-\frac{1}{3}, 1\right)$, slopes of tangent lines are positive and increase without bound as we approach 1 from the left.
- On the interval $(1, \infty)$, slopes of tangent lines are negative and increase to zero.

Assembling all this information, we obtain a graph of f' shown in Figure 3.17. Notice that f and f' have the same vertical asymptotes. However, as we pass through -1, the sign of f changes, but the sign of f' does not change. As we pass through 1, the sign of f does not change, but the sign of f' does change.

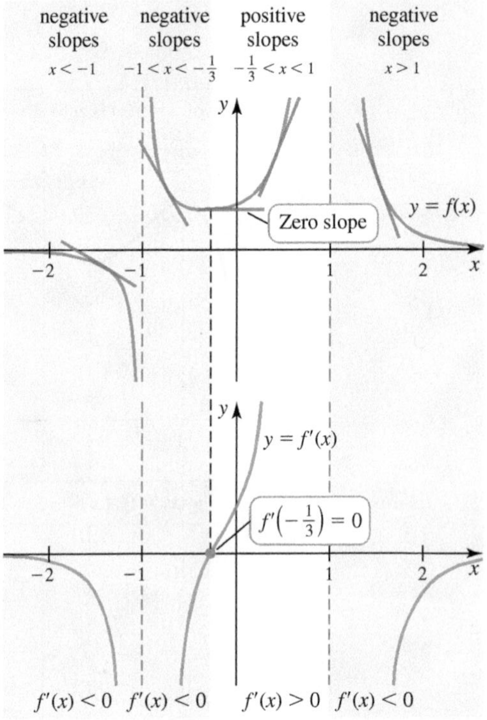

Figure 3.17

Related Exercises 13–14 ◀

Continuity

We now return to the discussion of continuity (Section 2.6) and investigate the relationship between continuity and differentiability. Specifically, we show that if a function is differentiable at a point, then it is also continuous at that point.

> **THEOREM 3.1 Differentiable Implies Continuous**
> If f is differentiable at a, then f is continuous at a.

Proof: Because f is differentiable at a point a, we know that

$$f'(a) = \lim_{x \to a} \frac{f(x) - f(a)}{x - a}$$

exists. To show that f is continuous at a, we must show that $\lim_{x \to a} f(x) = f(a)$. The key is the identity

➤ Expression (1) is an identity because it holds for all $x \neq a$, which can be seen by canceling $x - a$ and simplifying.

$$f(x) = \frac{f(x) - f(a)}{x - a}(x - a) + f(a), \quad \text{for } x \neq a. \tag{1}$$

Taking the limit as x approaches a on both sides of (1) and simplifying, we have

$$\begin{aligned}
\lim_{x \to a} f(x) &= \lim_{x \to a}\left(\frac{f(x) - f(a)}{x - a}(x - a) + f(a)\right) && \text{Use identity.}\\
&= \underbrace{\lim_{x \to a}\left(\frac{f(x) - f(a)}{x - a}\right)}_{f'(a)} \underbrace{\lim_{x \to a}(x - a)}_{0} + \underbrace{\lim_{x \to a} f(a)}_{f(a)} && \text{Theorem 2.3}\\
&= f'(a) \cdot 0 + f(a) && \text{Evaluate limits.}\\
&= f(a). && \text{Simplify.}
\end{aligned}$$

Therefore, $\lim_{x \to a} f(x) = f(a)$, which means that f is continuous at a. ◄

QUICK CHECK 3 Verify that the right-hand side of (1) equals $f(x)$ if $x \neq a$. ◄

Theorem 3.1 tells us that if f is differentiable at a point, then it is necessarily continuous at that point. Therefore, if f is *not* continuous at a point, then f is *not* differentiable there (Figure 3.18). So Theorem 3.1 can be stated in another way.

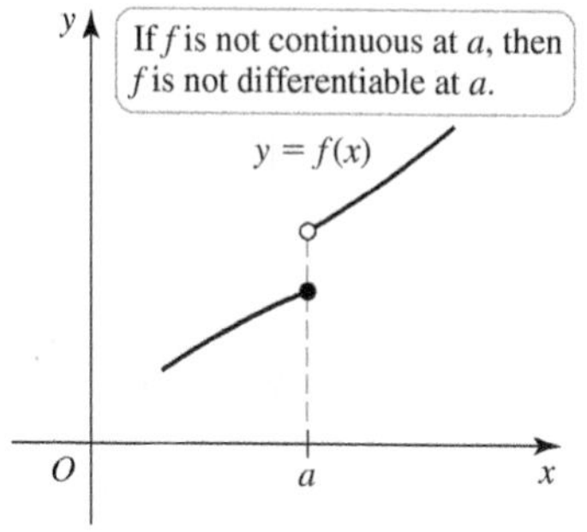

Figure 3.18

➤ The alternative version of Theorem 3.1 is called the *contrapositive* of the first statement of Theorem 3.1. A statement and its contrapositive are two equivalent ways of expressing the same statement. For example, the statement

If I live in Denver, then I live in Colorado is logically equivalent to its contrapositive:

If I do not live in Colorado, then I do not live in Denver.

➤ To avoid confusion about continuity and differentiability, it helps to think about the function $f(x) = |x|$: It is continuous everywhere but not differentiable at 0.

THEOREM 3.1 (ALTERNATIVE VERSION) Not Continuous Implies Not Differentiable
If f is not continuous at a, then f is not differentiable at a.

It is tempting to read more into Theorem 3.1 than what it actually states. If f is continuous at a point, f is *not* necessarily differentiable at that point. For example, consider the continuous function in Figure 3.19 and note the **corner point** at a. Ignoring the portion of the graph for $x > a$, we might be tempted to conclude that ℓ_1 is the line tangent to the curve at a. Ignoring the part of the graph for $x < a$, we might incorrectly conclude that ℓ_2 is the line tangent to the curve at a. The slopes of ℓ_1 and ℓ_2 are not equal. Because of the abrupt change in the slope of the curve at a, f is not differentiable at a: The limit that defines f' does not exist at a.

➤ Continuity requires that $\lim_{x \to a} (f(x) - f(a)) = 0.$ Differentiability requires more: $\lim_{x \to a} \frac{f(x) - f(a)}{x - a}$ must exist.

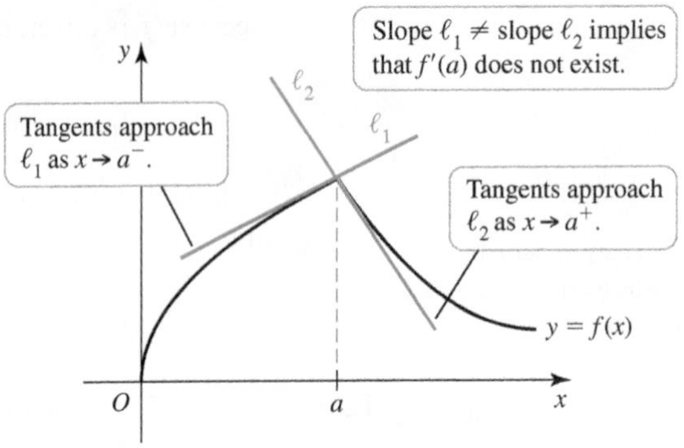

Figure 3.19

➤ See Exercises 33–36 for a formal definition of a vertical tangent line.

Another common situation occurs when the graph of a function f has a vertical tangent line at a. In this case, $f'(a)$ is undefined because the slope of a vertical line is undefined. A vertical tangent line may occur at a sharp point on the curve called a **cusp** (for example, the function $f(x) = \sqrt{|x|}$ in Figure 3.20a). In other cases, a vertical tangent line may occur without a cusp (for example, the function $f(x) = \sqrt[3]{x}$ in Figure 3.20b).

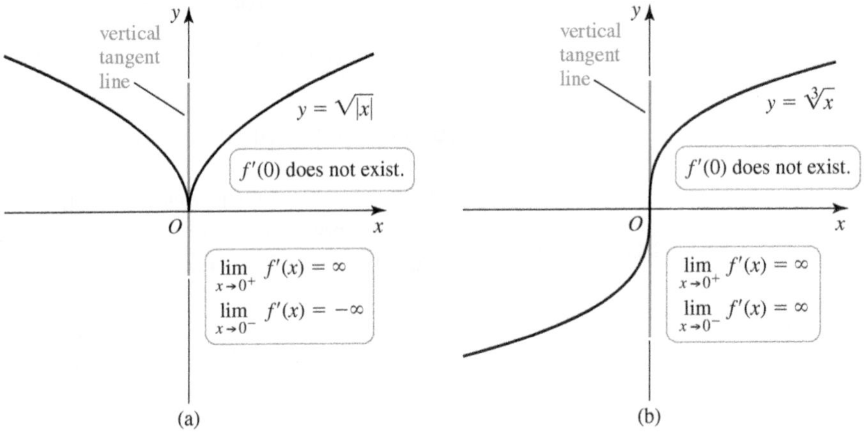

Figure 3.20

When Is a Function Not Differentiable at a Point?

A function f is *not* differentiable at a if at least one of the following conditions holds:

a. f is not continuous at a (Figure 3.18).

b. f has a corner at a (Figure 3.19).

c. f has a vertical tangent at a (Figure 3.20).

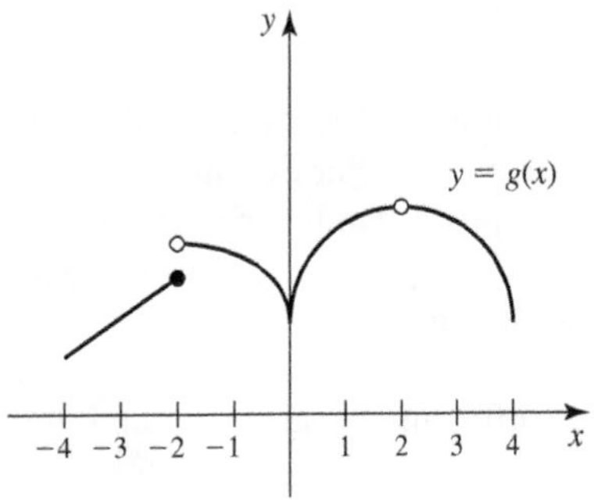

Figure 3.21

EXAMPLE 4 **Continuous and differentiable** Consider the graph of g in Figure 3.21.

a. Find the values of x in the interval $(-4, 4)$ at which g is not continuous.

b. Find the values of x in the interval $(-4, 4)$ at which g is not differentiable.

c. Sketch a graph of the derivative of g.

SOLUTION

a. The function g fails to be continuous at -2 (where the one-sided limits are not equal) and at 2 (where g is not defined).

b. Because it is not continuous at ± 2, g is not differentiable at those points. Furthermore, g is not differentiable at 0, because the graph has a cusp at that point.

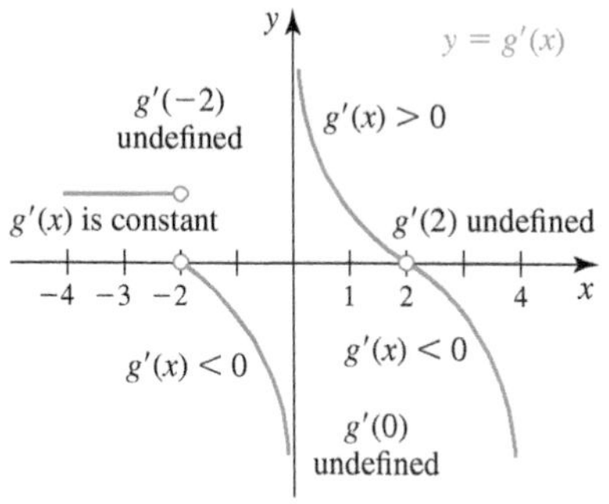

Figure 3.22

c. A sketch of the derivative (Figure 3.22) has the following features:

- $g'(x) > 0$, for $-4 < x < -2$ and $0 < x < 2$
- $g'(x) < 0$, for $-2 < x < 0$ and $2 < x < 4$
- $g'(x)$ approaches $-\infty$ as $x \to 0^-$ and as $x \to 4^-$, and $g'(x)$ approaches ∞ as $x \to 0^+$
- $g'(x)$ approaches 0 as $x \to 2$ from either side, although $g'(2)$ does not exist.

Related Exercises 15–16 ◀

SECTION 3.2 EXERCISES

Review Questions

1. Explain why $f'(x)$ could be positive or negative at a point where $f(x) > 0$.

2. Explain why $f(x)$ could be positive or negative at a point where $f'(x) < 0$.

3. If f is differentiable at a, must f be continuous at a?

4. If f is continuous at a, must f be differentiable at a?

Basic Skills

5–6. Derivatives from graphs *Use the graph of f to sketch a graph of f'.*

5.

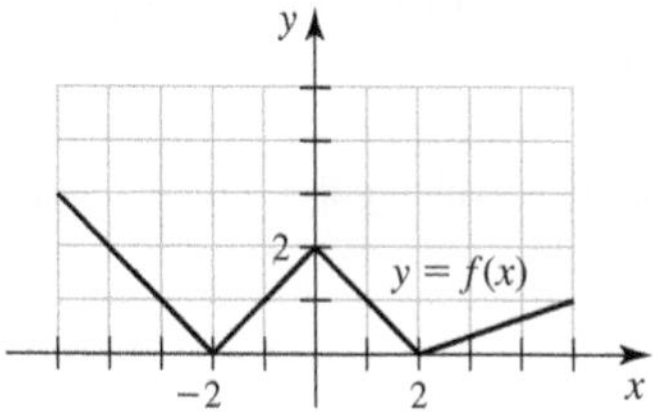

6.

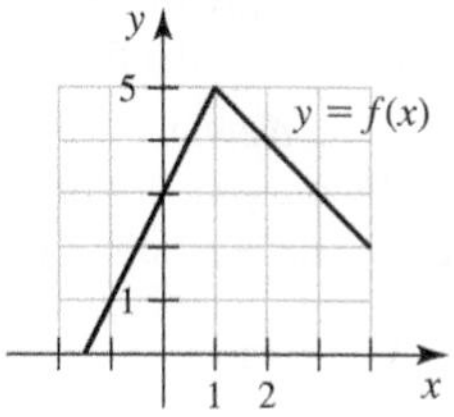

7. Matching functions with derivatives Match graphs a–d of functions with graphs A–C of their derivatives.

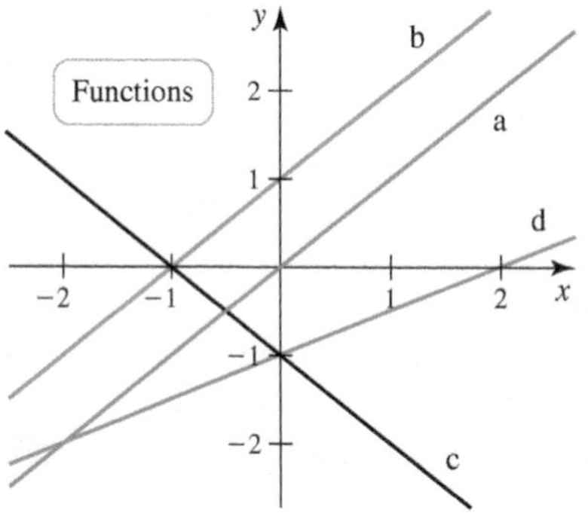

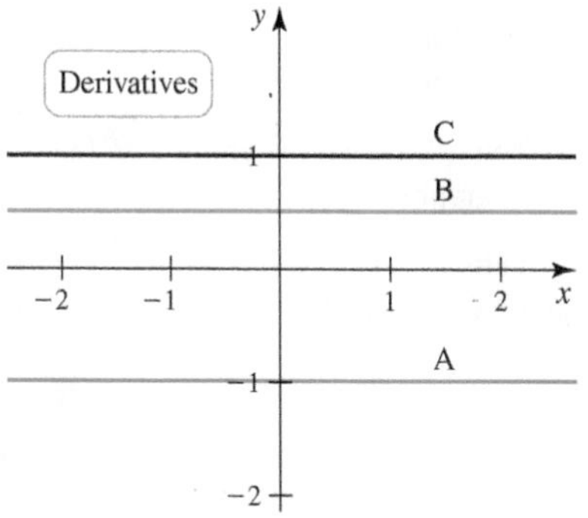

8. Matching derivatives with functions Match graphs a–d of derivative functions with possible graphs A–D of the corresponding functions.

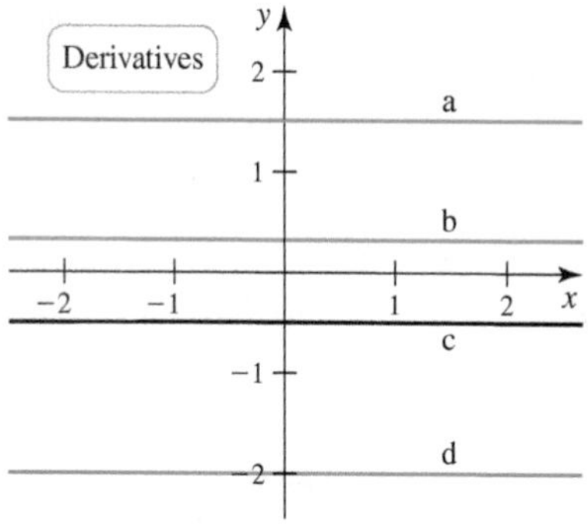

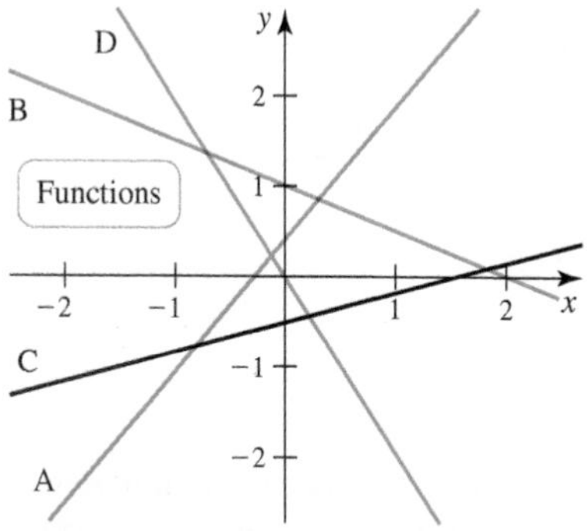

9. Matching functions with derivatives Match the functions a–d in the first set of figures with the derivative functions A–D in the next set of figures

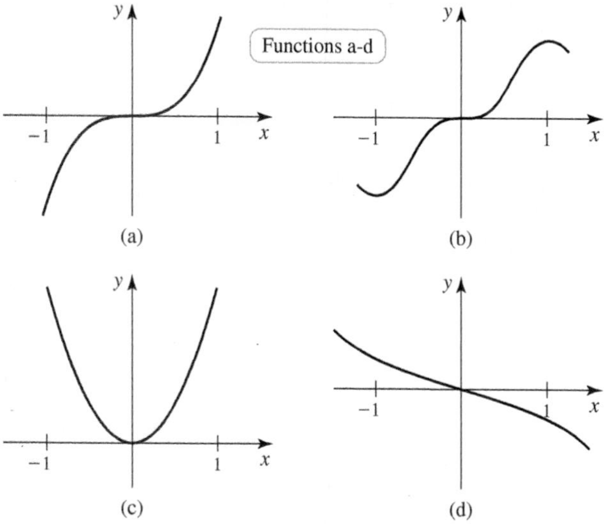

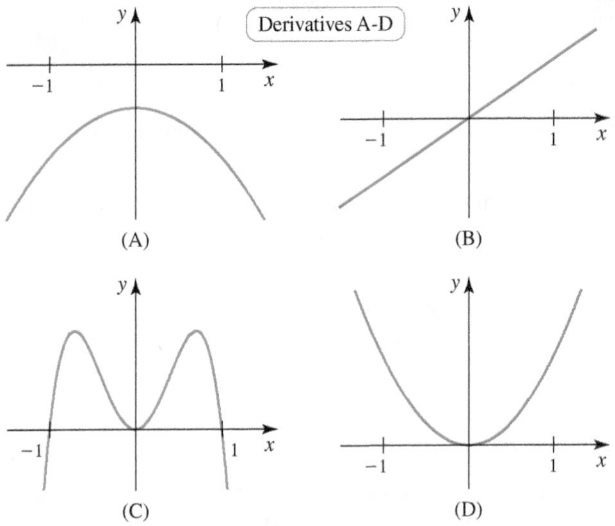

10–12. Sketching derivatives *Reproduce the graph of f and then plot a graph of f′ on the same set of axes.*

10.

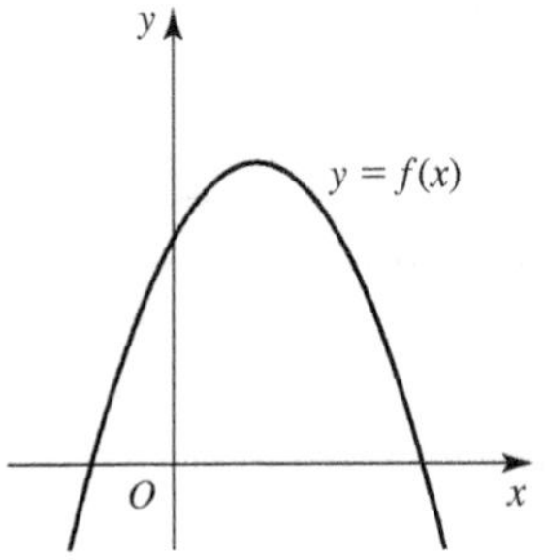

11.

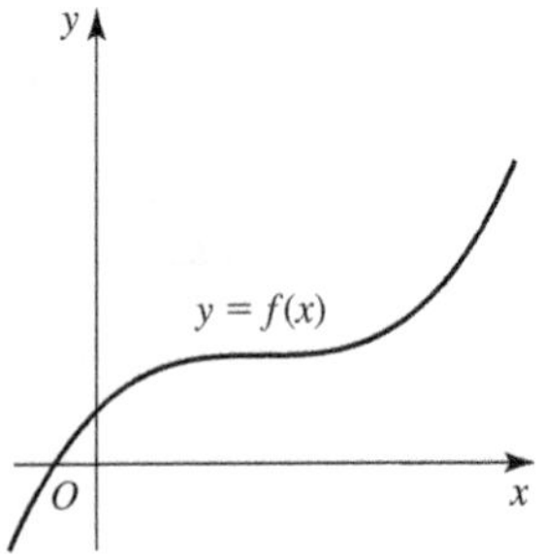

12.

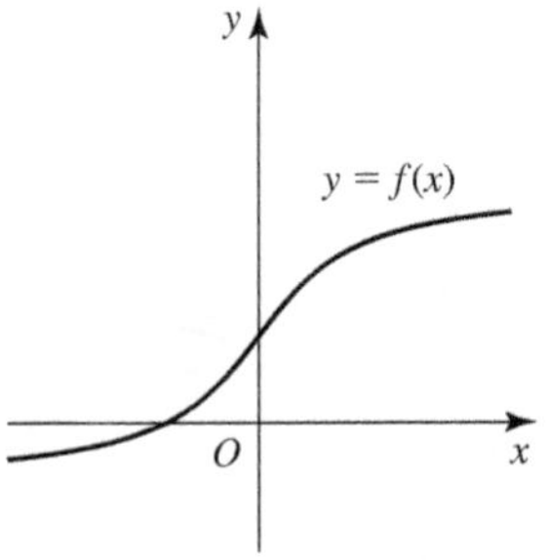

13–14. Graphing the derivative with asymptotes *Sketch a graph of the derivative of the functions f shown in the figures.*

13.

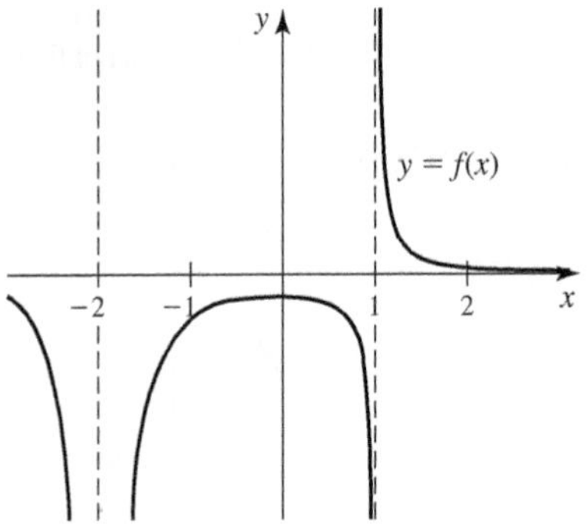

14.

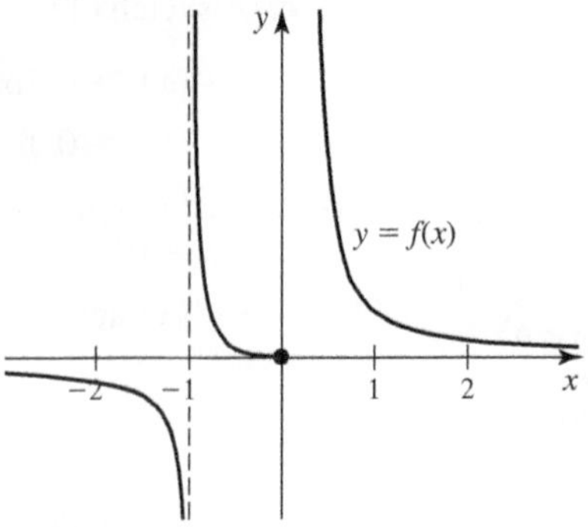

15. Where is the function continuous? Differentiable? Use the graph of f in the figure to do the following.

a. Find the values of x in $(0, 3)$ at which f is not continuous.
b. Find the values of x in $(0, 3)$ at which f is not differentiable.
c. Sketch a graph of f'.

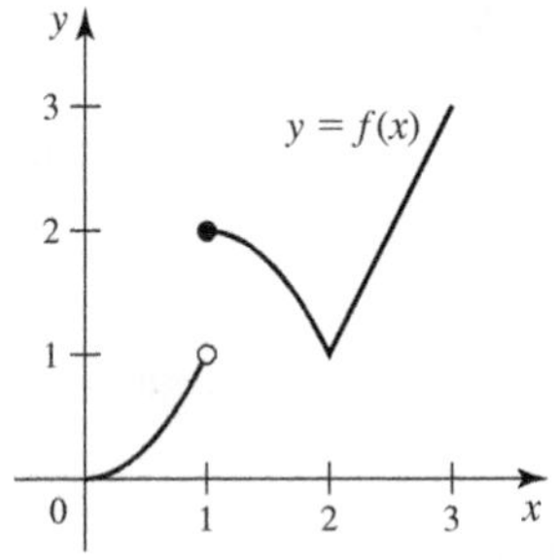

16. Where is the function continuous? Differentiable? Use the graph of g in the figure to do the following.

a. Find the values of x in $(0, 4)$ at which g is not continuous.
b. Find the values of x in $(0, 4)$ at which g is not differentiable.
c. Sketch a graph of g'.

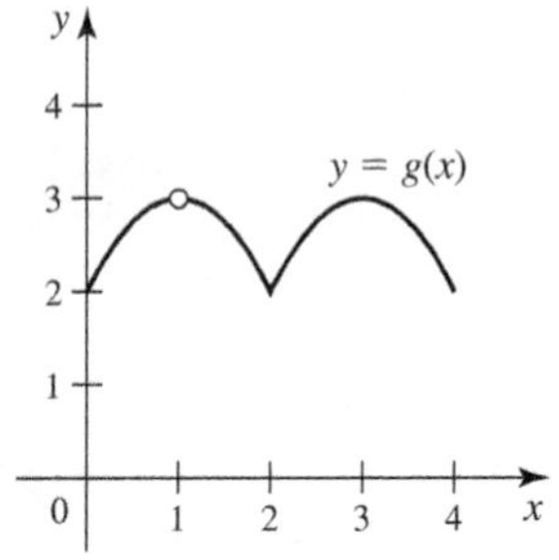

Further Explorations

17. Explain why or why not Determine whether the following statements are true and give an explanation or counterexample.

a. If the function f is differentiable for all values of x, then f is continuous for all values of x.
b. The function $f(x) = |x + 1|$ is continuous for all x, but not differentiable for all x.
c. It is possible for the domain of f to be (a, b) and the domain of f' to be $[a, b]$.

18. Finding f from f' Sketch the graph of $f'(x) = 2$. Then sketch three possible graphs of f.

19. Finding f from f' Sketch the graph of $f'(x) = x$. Then sketch a possible graph of f. Is more than one graph possible?

20. Finding f from f' Create the graph of a continuous function f such that

$$f'(x) = \begin{cases} 1 & \text{if } x < 0 \\ 0 & \text{if } 0 < x < 1 \\ -1 & \text{if } x > 1. \end{cases}$$

Is more than one graph possible?

21–24. Normal lines *A line perpendicular to another line or to a tangent line is called a* ***normal line****. Find an equation of the line perpendicular to the line that is tangent to the following curves at the given point P.*

21. $y = 3x - 4;\ P(1, -1)$

22. $y = \sqrt{x};\ P(4, 2)$

23. $y = \dfrac{2}{x};\ P(1, 2)$

24. $y = x^2 - 3x;\ P(3, 0)$

25–28. Aiming a tangent line *Given the function f and the point Q, find all points P on the graph of f such that the line tangent to f at P passes though Q. Check your work by graphing f and the tangent lines.*

25. $f(x) = x^2 + 1;\ Q(3, 6)$

26. $f(x) = -x^2 + 4x - 3;\ Q(0, 6)$

27. $f(x) = \dfrac{1}{x};\ Q(-2, 4)$

T **28.** $f(x) = e^{-x};\ Q(1, -4)$

Applications

29. Voltage on a capacitor A capacitor is a device in an electrical circuit that stores charge. In one particular circuit, the charge on the capacitor Q varies in time as shown in the figure.

a. At what time is the rate of change of the charge Q' the greatest?
b. Is Q' positive or negative for $t \geq 0$?
c. Is Q' an increasing or decreasing function of time (or neither)?
d. Sketch the graph of Q'. You do not need a scale on the vertical axis.

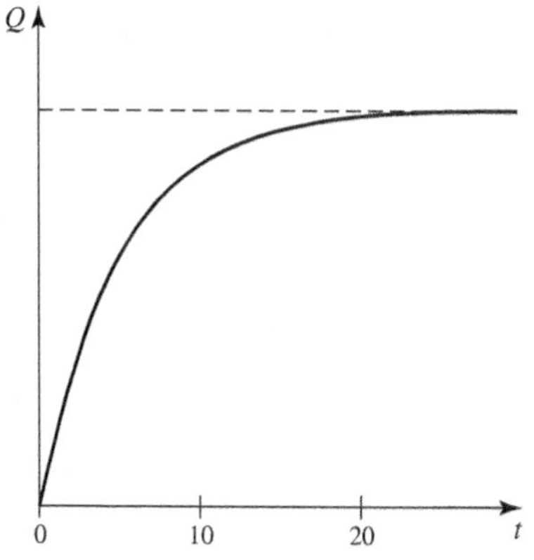

30. Logistic growth A common model for population growth uses the logistic (or sigmoid) curve. Consider the logistic curve in the figure, where $P(t)$ is the population at time $t \geq 0$.

a. At approximately what time is the rate of growth P' the greatest?
b. Is P' positive or negative for $t \geq 0$?
c. Is P' an increasing or decreasing function of time (or neither)?
d. Sketch the graph of P'. You do not need a scale on the vertical axis.

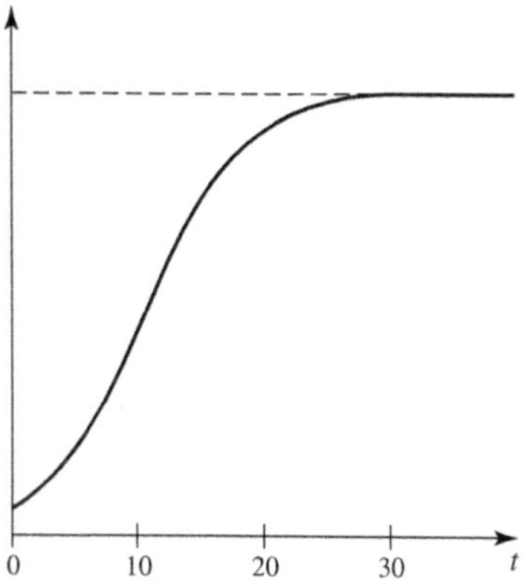

Additional Exercises

31–32. One-sided derivatives *The* ***right-sided*** *and* ***left-sided derivatives*** *of a function at a point a are given by*

$$f_+'(a) = \lim_{h \to 0^+} \frac{f(a + h) - f(a)}{h} \quad \text{and} \quad f_-'(a) = \lim_{h \to 0^-} \frac{f(a + h) - f(a)}{h},$$

respectively, provided these limits exist. The derivative $f'(a)$ exists if and only if $f_+'(a) = f_-'(a)$.

a. Sketch the following functions.
b. Compute $f_+'(a)$ and $f_-'(a)$ at the given point a.
c. Is f continuous at a? Is f differentiable at a?

31. $f(x) = |x - 2|;\ a = 2$

32. $f(x) = \begin{cases} 4 - x^2 & \text{if } x \leq 1 \\ 2x + 1 & \text{if } x > 1 \end{cases};\ a = 1$

33–36. Vertical tangent lines *If a function f is continuous at a and $\lim_{x \to a} |f'(x)| = \infty$, then the curve $y = f(x)$ has a vertical tangent line at a and the equation of the tangent line is $x = a$. If a is an endpoint of a domain, then the appropriate one-sided derivative (Exercises 31–32) is used. Use this information to answer the following questions.*

T **33.** Graph the following functions and determine the location of the vertical tangent lines.

a. $f(x) = (x - 2)^{1/3}$ **b.** $f(x) = (x + 1)^{2/3}$
c. $f(x) = \sqrt{|x - 4|}$ **d.** $f(x) = x^{5/3} - 2x^{1/3}$

34. The preceding definition of a vertical tangent line includes four cases: $\lim_{x \to a^+} f'(x) = \pm\infty$ combined with $\lim_{x \to a^-} f'(x) = \pm\infty$ (for example, one case is $\lim_{x \to a^+} f'(x) = -\infty$ and $\lim_{x \to a^-} f'(x) = \infty$). Sketch a continuous function that has a vertical tangent line at a in each of the four cases.

35. Verify that $f(x) = x^{1/3}$ has a vertical tangent line at $x = 0$.

T **36.** Graph the following curves and determine the location of any vertical tangent lines.

a. $x^2 + y^2 = 9$ **b.** $x^2 + y^2 + 2x = 0$

37. Continuity is necessary for differentiability

a. Graph the function $f(x) = \begin{cases} x & \text{for } x \leq 0 \\ x + 1 & \text{for } x > 0. \end{cases}$
b. For $x < 0$, what is $f'(x)$?
c. For $x > 0$, what is $f'(x)$?
d. Graph f' on its domain.
e. Is f differentiable at 0? Explain.

QUICK CHECK ANSWERS

1. The slopes of the tangent lines change abruptly at $x = -2$ and 0. **2.** No; no ◀

3.3 Rules of Differentiation

If you always had to use limits to evaluate derivatives, as we did in Section 3.1, calculus would be a tedious affair. The goal of this chapter is to establish rules and formulas for quickly evaluating derivatives—not just for individual functions but for entire families of functions. By the end of the chapter, you will have learned many derivative rules and formulas, all of which are listed in the endpapers of the book.

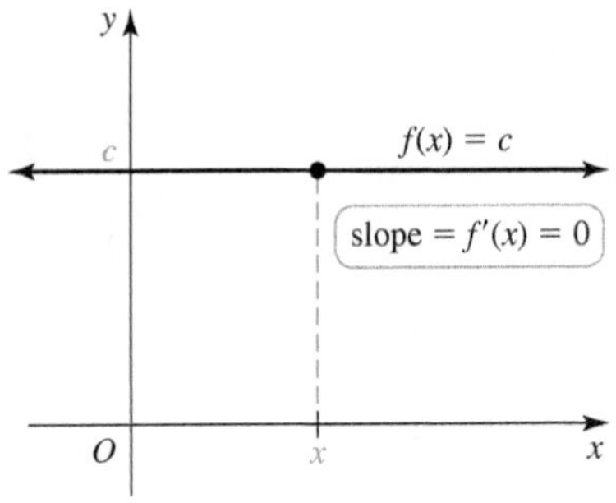

Figure 3.23

The Constant and Power Rules for Derivatives

The graph of the **constant function** $f(x) = c$ is a horizontal line with a slope of 0 at every point (Figure 3.23). It follows that $f'(x) = 0$ or, equivalently, $\frac{d}{dx}(c) = 0$ (Exercise 74). This observation leads to the *Constant Rule* for derivatives.

➤ We expect the derivative of a constant function to be 0 at every point because the values of a constant function do not change. This means the instantaneous rate of change is 0 at every point.

THEOREM 3.2 Constant Rule

If c is a real number, then $\frac{d}{dx}(c) = 0$.

QUICK CHECK 1 Find the values of $\frac{d}{dx}(5)$ and $\frac{d}{dx}(\pi)$. ◄

Next, consider power functions of the form $f(x) = x^n$, where n is a nonnegative integer. If you completed Exercise 62 in Section 3.1, you used the limit definition of the derivative to discover that

$$\frac{d}{dx}(x^2) = 2x, \quad \frac{d}{dx}(x^3) = 3x^2, \quad \text{and} \quad \frac{d}{dx}(x^4) = 4x^3.$$

In each case, the derivative of x^n could be evaluated by placing the exponent n in front of x as a coefficient and decreasing the exponent by 1. Based on these observations, we state and prove the following theorem.

➤ You will see several versions of the Power Rule as we progress. It is extended in exactly the same form given in Theorem 3.3—first to negative integer powers, then to rational powers, and finally to real powers.

THEOREM 3.3 Power Rule

If n is a nonnegative integer, then $\frac{d}{dx}(x^n) = nx^{n-1}$.

Proof: We let $f(x) = x^n$ and use the definition of the derivative in the form

$$f'(a) = \lim_{x \to a} \frac{f(x) - f(a)}{x - a}.$$

With $n = 1$ and $f(x) = x$, we have

$$f'(a) = \lim_{x \to a} \frac{f(x) - f(a)}{x - a} = \lim_{x \to a} \frac{x - a}{x - a} = 1,$$

as given by the Power Rule.

With $n \geq 2$ and $f(x) = x^n$, note that $f(x) - f(a) = x^n - a^n$. A factoring formula gives

$$x^n - a^n = (x - a)(x^{n-1} + x^{n-2}a + \cdots + xa^{n-2} + a^{n-1}).$$

➤ Note that this factoring formula agrees with familiar factoring formulas for differences of perfect squares and cubes:

$$x^2 - a^2 = (x - a)(x + a)$$
$$x^3 - a^3 = (x - a)(x^2 + ax + a^2).$$

Therefore,

$$\begin{aligned} f'(a) &= \lim_{x\to a} \frac{x^n - a^n}{x - a} && \text{Definition of } f'(a) \\ &= \lim_{x\to a} \frac{(x-a)(x^{n-1} + x^{n-2}a + \cdots + xa^{n-2} + a^{n-1})}{x-a} && \text{Factor } x^n - a^n. \\ &= \lim_{x\to a} (x^{n-1} + x^{n-2}a + \cdots + xa^{n-2} + a^{n-1}) && \text{Cancel common factors.} \\ &= \underbrace{a^{n-1} + a^{n-2}\cdot a + \cdots + a\cdot a^{n-2} + a^{n-1}}_{n \text{ terms}} = na^{n-1}. && \text{Evaluate the limit.} \end{aligned}$$

Replacing a with the variable x in $f'(a) = na^{n-1}$, we obtain the result given in the Power Rule for $n \geq 2$. Finally, note that the Constant Rule is consistent with the Power Rule with $n = 0$. ◄

EXAMPLE 1 Derivatives of power and constant functions Evaluate the following derivatives.

a. $\frac{d}{dx}(x^9)$ **b.** $\frac{d}{dx}(x)$ **c.** $\frac{d}{dx}(2^8)$

SOLUTION

a. $\frac{d}{dx}(x^9) = 9x^{9-1} = 9x^8$ Power Rule

b. $\frac{d}{dx}(x) = \frac{d}{dx}(x^1) = 1x^0 = 1$ Power Rule

c. You might be tempted to use the Power Rule here, but $2^8 = 256$ is a constant. So by the Constant Rule, $\frac{d}{dx}(2^8) = 0$.

Related Exercises 7–12 ◄

QUICK CHECK 2 Use the graph of $y = x$ to give a geometric explanation of why $\frac{d}{dx}(x) = 1$. ◄

Constant Multiple Rule

Consider the problem of finding the derivative of a constant c multiplied by a function f (assuming that f' exists). We apply the definition of the derivative in the form

$$f'(x) = \lim_{h\to 0} \frac{f(x+h) - f(x)}{h}$$

to the function cf:

$$\begin{aligned} \frac{d}{dx}(cf(x)) &= \lim_{h\to 0} \frac{cf(x+h) - cf(x)}{h} && \text{Definition of the derivative of } cf \\ &= \lim_{h\to 0} \frac{c(f(x+h) - f(x))}{h} && \text{Factor out } c. \\ &= c \lim_{h\to 0} \frac{f(x+h) - f(x)}{h} && \text{Theorem 2.3} \\ &= cf'(x). && \text{Definition of } f'(x) \end{aligned}$$

This calculation leads to the *Constant Multiple Rule* for derivatives.

➤ Theorem 3.4 says that the derivative of a constant multiplied by a function is the constant multiplied by the derivative of the function.

THEOREM 3.4 Constant Multiple Rule
If f is differentiable at x and c is a constant, then

$$\frac{d}{dx}(cf(x)) = cf'(x).$$

EXAMPLE 2 **Derivatives of constant multiples of functions** Evaluate the following derivatives.

a. $\frac{d}{dx}\left(-\frac{7x^{11}}{8}\right)$ **b.** $\frac{d}{dt}\left(\frac{3}{8}\sqrt{t}\right)$

SOLUTION

a.
$$\begin{aligned}\frac{d}{dx}\left(-\frac{7x^{11}}{8}\right) &= -\frac{7}{8}\cdot\frac{d}{dx}(x^{11}) && \text{Constant Multiple Rule}\\ &= -\frac{7}{8}\cdot 11x^{10} && \text{Power Rule}\\ &= -\frac{77}{8}x^{10} && \text{Simplify.}\end{aligned}$$

➤ In Example 4 of Section 3.1, we proved that $\frac{d}{dt}(\sqrt{t}) = \frac{1}{2\sqrt{t}}$.

b.
$$\begin{aligned}\frac{d}{dt}\left(\frac{3}{8}\sqrt{t}\right) &= \frac{3}{8}\cdot\frac{d}{dt}(\sqrt{t}) && \text{Constant Multiple Rule}\\ &= \frac{3}{8}\cdot\frac{1}{2\sqrt{t}} && \text{Replace } \frac{d}{dt}(\sqrt{t}) \text{ with } \frac{1}{2\sqrt{t}}.\\ &= \frac{3}{16\sqrt{t}}\end{aligned}$$

Related Exercises 13–18 ◀

Sum Rule

Many functions are sums of simpler functions. Therefore, it is useful to establish a rule for calculating the derivative of the sum of two or more functions.

➤ In words, Theorem 3.5 states that the derivative of a sum is the sum of the derivatives.

THEOREM 3.5 **Sum Rule**
If f and g are differentiable at x, then

$$\frac{d}{dx}(f(x) + g(x)) = f'(x) + g'(x).$$

Proof: Let $F = f + g$, where f and g are differentiable at x, and use the definition of the derivative:

$$\begin{aligned}\frac{d}{dx}(f(x) + g(x)) &= F'(x)\\ &= \lim_{h\to 0}\frac{F(x+h) - F(x)}{h} && \text{Definition of derivative}\\ &= \lim_{h\to 0}\frac{(f(x+h) + g(x+h)) - (f(x) + g(x))}{h} && \text{Replace } F \text{ with } f+g.\\ &= \lim_{h\to 0}\left[\frac{f(x+h) - f(x)}{h} + \frac{g(x+h) - g(x)}{h}\right] && \text{Regroup.}\\ &= \lim_{h\to 0}\frac{f(x+h) - f(x)}{h} + \lim_{h\to 0}\frac{g(x+h) - g(x)}{h} && \text{Theorem 2.3}\\ &= f'(x) + g'(x). && \text{Definition of } f' \text{ and } g'\end{aligned}$$ ◀

QUICK CHECK 3 If $f(x) = x^2$ and $g(x) = 2x$, what is the derivative of $f(x) + g(x)$? ◀

The Sum Rule can be extended to three or more differentiable functions, $f_1, f_2, \ldots, f_n$, to obtain the **Generalized Sum Rule**:

$$\frac{d}{dx}(f_1(x) + f_2(x) + \cdots + f_n(x)) = f_1'(x) + f_2'(x) + \cdots + f_n'(x).$$

The difference of two functions $f - g$ can be rewritten as the sum $f + (-g)$. By combining the Sum Rule with the Constant Multiple Rule, the **Difference Rule** is established:

$$\frac{d}{dx}(f(x) - g(x)) = f'(x) - g'(x).$$

Let's put the Sum and Difference Rules to work on one of the more common problems: differentiating polynomials.

EXAMPLE 3 Derivative of a polynomial Determine $\frac{d}{dw}(2w^3 + 9w^2 - 6w + 4)$.

SOLUTION

$$\frac{d}{dw}(2w^3 + 9w^2 - 6w + 4)$$

$$= \frac{d}{dw}(2w^3) + \frac{d}{dw}(9w^2) - \frac{d}{dw}(6w) + \frac{d}{dw}(4) \quad \text{Generalized Sum Rule and Difference Rule}$$

$$= 2\frac{d}{dw}(w^3) + 9\frac{d}{dw}(w^2) - 6\frac{d}{dw}(w) + \frac{d}{dw}(4) \quad \text{Constant Multiple Rule}$$

$$= 2 \cdot 3w^2 + 9 \cdot 2w - 6 \cdot 1 + 0 \quad \text{Power Rule and Constant Rule}$$

$$= 6w^2 + 18w - 6 \quad \text{Simplify.}$$

Related Exercises 19–34 ◀

The technique used to differentiate the polynomial in Example 3 may be used for *any* polynomial. Much of the remainder of this chapter is devoted to discovering differentiation rules for the families of functions introduced in Chapter 1: rational, exponential, logarithmic, algebraic, and trigonometric functions.

The Derivative of the Natural Exponential Function

The exponential function $f(x) = b^x$ was introduced in Chapter 1. Let's begin by looking at the graphs of two members of this family, $y = 2^x$ and $y = 3^x$ (Figure 3.24). The slope of the line tangent to the graph of $f(x) = b^x$ at $x = 0$ is given by

$$f'(0) = \lim_{h \to 0} \frac{f(0 + h) - f(0)}{h} = \lim_{h \to 0} \frac{b^h - b^0}{h} = \lim_{h \to 0} \frac{b^h - 1}{h}.$$

We investigate this limit numerically for $b = 2$ and $b = 3$. Table 3.1 shows values of $\frac{2^h - 1}{h}$ and $\frac{3^h - 1}{h}$ (which are slopes of secant lines) for values of h approaching 0 from the right.

➤ The limit $\lim_{h \to 0} \frac{2^h - 1}{h}$ was explored in Example 7 of Section 2.3.

Table 3.1

h	$\frac{2^h - 1}{h}$	$\frac{3^h - 1}{h}$
1.0	1.000000	2.000000
0.1	0.717735	1.161232
0.01	0.695555	1.104669
0.001	0.693387	1.099216
0.0001	0.693171	1.098673
0.00001	0.693150	1.098618

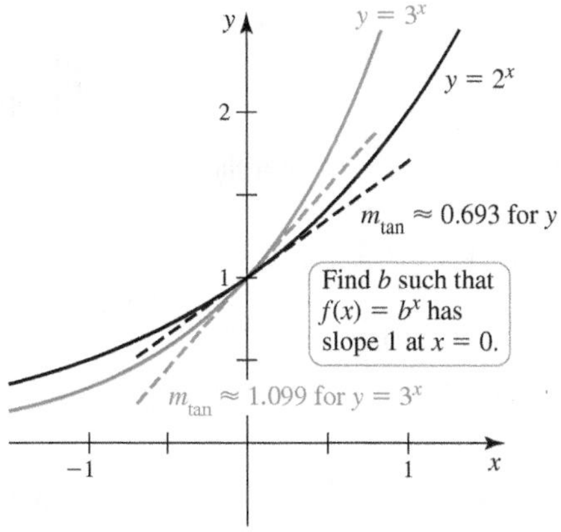

Figure 3.24

Exercise 64 gives similar approximations for the limit as h approaches 0 from the left. These numerical values suggest that

$$\lim_{h\to 0} \frac{2^h - 1}{h} \approx 0.693 \quad \text{Less than 1}$$

$$\lim_{h\to 0} \frac{3^h - 1}{h} \approx 1.099. \quad \text{Greater than 1}$$

These two facts, together with the graphs in Figure 3.24, suggest that there is a number b with $2 < b < 3$ such that the graph of $y = b^x$ has a tangent line with slope 1 at $x = 0$. This number b has the property that

$$\lim_{h\to 0} \frac{b^h - 1}{h} = 1.$$

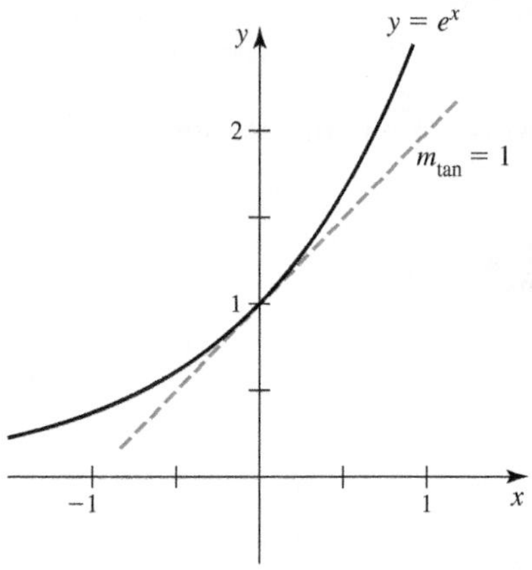

Figure 3.25

It can be shown that, indeed, such a number b exists. In fact, it is the number $e = 2.718281828459\ldots$ that was introduced in Chapter 1. Therefore, the exponential function whose tangent line has slope 1 at $x = 0$ is the *natural exponential function* $f(x) = e^x$ (Figure 3.25).

➤ The constant e was identified and named by the Swiss mathematician Leonhard Euler (1707–1783) (pronounced "oiler").

DEFINITION The Number *e*

The number $e = 2.718281828459\ldots$ satisfies

$$\lim_{h\to 0} \frac{e^h - 1}{h} = 1.$$

It is the base of the natural exponential function $f(x) = e^x$.

With the preceding facts in mind, the derivative of $f(x) = e^x$ is computed as follows:

$$\begin{aligned}
\frac{d}{dx}(e^x) &= \lim_{h\to 0} \frac{e^{x+h} - e^x}{h} && \text{Definition of the derivative}\\
&= \lim_{h\to 0} \frac{e^x \cdot e^h - e^x}{h} && \text{Property of exponents}\\
&= \lim_{h\to 0} \frac{e^x(e^h - 1)}{h} && \text{Factor out } e^x.\\
&= e^x \cdot \underbrace{\lim_{h\to 0} \frac{e^h - 1}{h}}_{1} && e^x \text{ is constant as } h \to 0\text{; definition of } e.\\
&= e^x \cdot 1 = e^x.
\end{aligned}$$

We have proved a remarkable fact: The derivative of the exponential function is itself; it is the only function (other than constant multiples of e^x and $f(x) = 0$) with this property.

➤ The Power Rule *cannot* be applied to exponential functions; that is, $\frac{d}{dx}(e^x) \neq xe^{x-1}$. Also note that $\frac{d}{dx}(e^{10}) \neq e^{10}$. Instead, $\frac{d}{dx}(e^c) = 0$, for any real number c, because e^c is a constant.

THEOREM 3.6 The Derivative of e^x

The function $f(x) = e^x$ is differentiable for all real numbers x, and

$$\frac{d}{dx}(e^x) = e^x.$$

QUICK CHECK 4 Find the derivative of $f(x) = 4e^x - 3x^2$. ◄

Slopes of Tangent Lines

The derivative rules presented in this section allow us to determine slopes of tangent lines and rates of change for many functions.

EXAMPLE 4 Finding tangent lines

a. Write an equation of the line tangent to the graph of $f(x) = 2x - \frac{e^x}{2}$ at the point $(0, -\frac{1}{2})$.

b. Find the point(s) on the graph of f at which the tangent line is horizontal.

SOLUTION

a. To find the slope of the tangent line at $(0, -\frac{1}{2})$, we first calculate $f'(x)$:

$$\begin{aligned} f'(x) &= \frac{d}{dx}\left(2x - \frac{e^x}{2}\right) \\ &= \frac{d}{dx}(2x) - \frac{d}{dx}\left(\frac{1}{2}e^x\right) && \text{Difference Rule} \\ &= 2\underbrace{\frac{d}{dx}(x)}_{1} - \frac{1}{2}\cdot\underbrace{\frac{d}{dx}(e^x)}_{e^x} && \text{Constant Multiple Rule} \\ &= 2 - \frac{1}{2}e^x. && \text{Evaluate derivatives.} \end{aligned}$$

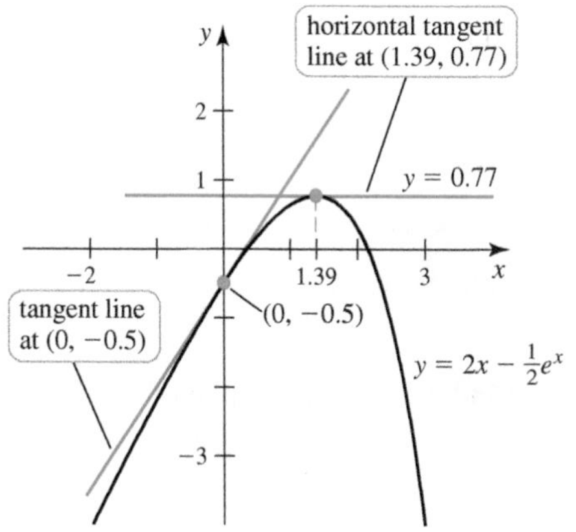

Figure 3.26

It follows that the slope of the tangent line at $(0, -\frac{1}{2})$ is

$$f'(0) = 2 - \frac{1}{2}e^0 = \frac{3}{2}.$$

Figure 3.26 shows the tangent line passing through $(0, -\frac{1}{2})$; it has the equation

$$y - \left(-\frac{1}{2}\right) = \frac{3}{2}(x - 0) \quad \text{or} \quad y = \frac{3}{2}x - \frac{1}{2}.$$

➤ Observe that the function has a maximum value of approximately 0.77 at the point where the tangent line has a slope of 0. We explore the importance of horizontal tangent lines in Chapter 4.

b. Because the slope of a horizontal tangent line is 0, our goal is to solve $f'(x) = 2 - \frac{1}{2}e^x = 0$. Multiplying both sides of this equation by 2 and rearranging gives the equation $e^x = 4$. Taking the natural logarithm of both sides, we find that $x = \ln 4$. Therefore, $f'(x) = 0$ at $x = \ln 4 \approx 1.39$, and f has a horizontal tangent at $(\ln 4, f(\ln 4)) \approx (1.39, 0.77)$ (Figure 3.26).

Related Exercises 35–43 ◄

EXAMPLE 5 Slope of a tangent line Let $f(x) = 2x^3 - 15x^2 + 24x$. For what values of x does the line tangent to the graph of f have a slope of 6?

SOLUTION The tangent line has a slope of 6 when

$$f'(x) = 6x^2 - 30x + 24 = 6.$$

Subtracting 6 from both sides of the equation and factoring, we have

$$6(x^2 - 5x + 3) = 0.$$

Using the quadratic formula, the roots are

$$x = \frac{5 - \sqrt{13}}{2} \approx 0.697 \quad \text{and} \quad x = \frac{5 + \sqrt{13}}{2} \approx 4.303.$$

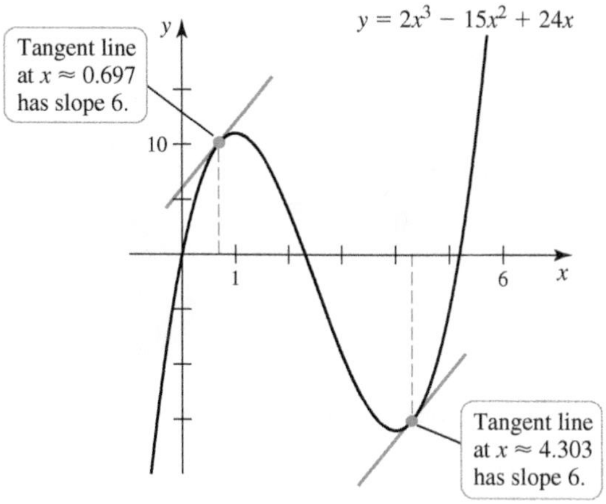

Figure 3.27

Therefore, the slope of the curve at these points is 6 (Figure 3.27).

Related Exercises 35–43 ◄

QUICK CHECK 5 Determine the point(s) at which $f(x) = x^3 - 12x$ has a horizontal tangent line. ◄

Higher-Order Derivatives

➤ The prime notation, f', f'', and f''', is typically used only for the first, second, and third derivatives.

Because the derivative of a function f is a function in its own right, we can take the derivative of f'. The result is the *second derivative of f*, denoted f'' (read *f double prime*). The derivative of the second derivative is the *third derivative of f*, denoted f''' or (read *f triple prime*). In general, derivatives of order $n \geq 2$ are called *higher-order derivatives*.

DEFINITION Higher-Order Derivatives

Assuming $y = f(x)$ can be differentiated as often as necessary, the **second derivative** of f is

$$f''(x) = \frac{d}{dx}(f'(x)).$$

For integers $n \geq 2$, the ***n*th derivative** of f is

$$f^{(n)}(x) = \frac{d}{dx}(f^{(n-1)}(x)).$$

➤ Parentheses are placed around n to distinguish a derivative from a power. Therefore, $f^{(n)}$ is the nth derivative of f and f^n is the function f raised to the nth power.

➤ The notation $\frac{d^2f}{dx^2}$ comes from $\frac{d}{dx}\left(\frac{df}{dx}\right)$ and is read *d 2 f dx squared.*

Other common notations for the second derivative of $y = f(x)$ include $\frac{d^2y}{dx^2}$ and $\frac{d^2f}{dx^2}$; the notations $\frac{d^ny}{dx^n}$, $\frac{d^nf}{dx^n}$, and $y^{(n)}$ are used for the nth derivative of f.

EXAMPLE 6 Finding higher-order derivatives Find the third derivative of the following functions.

a. $f(x) = 3x^3 - 5x + 12$ **b.** $y = 3t + 2e^t$

SOLUTION

a.

$$f'(x) = 9x^2 - 5$$

$$f''(x) = \frac{d}{dx}(9x^2 - 5) = 18x$$

$$f'''(x) = 18$$

➤ In Example 6a, note that $f^{(4)}(x) = 0$, which means that all successive derivatives are also 0. In general, the nth derivative of an nth-degree polynomial is a constant, which implies that derivatives of order $k > n$ are 0.

b. Here we use an alternative notation for higher-order derivatives:

$$\frac{dy}{dt} = \frac{d}{dt}(3t + 2e^t) = 3 + 2e^t$$

$$\frac{d^2y}{dt^2} = \frac{d}{dt}(3 + 2e^t) = 2e^t$$

$$\frac{d^3y}{dt^3} = \frac{d}{dt}(2e^t) = 2e^t.$$

In this case, $\frac{d^ny}{dt^n} = 2e^t$, for $n \geq 2$.

Related Exercises 44–48 ◀

QUICK CHECK 6 With $f(x) = x^5$, find $f^{(5)}(x)$ and $f^{(6)}(x)$. With $g(x) = e^x$, find $g^{(100)}(x)$. ◀

SECTION 3.3 EXERCISES

Review Questions

Assume the derivatives of f and g exist in Exercises 1–6.

1. If the limit definition of a derivative can be used to find f', then what is the purpose of using other rules to find f'?
2. In this section, we showed that the rule $\frac{d}{dx}(x^n) = nx^{n-1}$ is valid for what values of n?
3. Give a nonzero function that is its own derivative.
4. How do you find the derivative of the sum of two functions $f + g$?
5. How do you find the derivative of a constant multiplied by a function?
6. How do you find the fifth derivative of a function?

Basic Skills

7–12. Derivatives of power and constant functions *Find the derivative of the following functions.*

7. $y = x^5$ **8.** $f(t) = t^{11}$ **9.** $f(x) = 5$

10. $g(x) = e^3$ **11.** $h(t) = t$ **12.** $f(v) = v^{100}$

13–18. Derivatives of constant multiples of functions *Find the derivative of the following functions. See Example 4 of Section 3.1 for the derivative of* $\sqrt{x}$.

13. $f(x) = 5x^3$ **14.** $g(w) = \frac{5}{6}w^{12}$ **15.** $p(x) = 8x$

16. $g(t) = 6\sqrt{t}$ **17.** $g(t) = 100t^2$ **18.** $f(s) = \dfrac{\sqrt{s}}{4}$

19–24. Derivatives of the sum of functions *Find the derivative of the following functions.*

19. $f(x) = 3x^4 + 7x$ **20.** $g(x) = 6x^5 - x$

21. $f(x) = 10x^4 - 32x + e^2$ **22.** $f(t) = 6\sqrt{t} - 4t^3 + 9$

23. $g(w) = 2w^3 + 3w^2 + 10w$ **24.** $s(t) = 4\sqrt{t} - \frac{1}{4}t^4 + t + 1$

25–28. Derivatives of products *Find the derivative of the following functions by first expanding the expression. Simplify your answers.*

25. $f(x) = (2x + 1)(3x^2 + 2)$

26. $g(r) = (5r^3 + 3r + 1)(r^2 + 3)$

27. $h(x) = (x^2 + 1)^2$

28. $h(x) = \sqrt{x}(\sqrt{x} - 1)$

29–34. Derivatives of quotients *Find the derivative of the following functions by first simplifying the expression.*

29. $f(w) = \dfrac{w^3 - w}{w}$ **30.** $y = \dfrac{12s^3 - 8s^2 + 12s}{4s}$

31. $g(x) = \dfrac{x^2 - 1}{x - 1}$ **32.** $h(x) = \dfrac{x^3 - 6x^2 + 8x}{x^2 - 2x}$

33. $y = \dfrac{x - a}{\sqrt{x} - \sqrt{a}}$; a is a positive constant.

34. $y = \dfrac{x^2 - 2ax + a^2}{x - a}$; a is a constant.

T 35–38. Equations of tangent lines

a. Find an equation of the line tangent to the given curve at a.
b. Use a graphing utility to graph the curve and the tangent line on the same set of axes.

35. $y = -3x^2 + 2;\ a = 1$

36. $y = x^3 - 4x^2 + 2x - 1;\ a = 2$

37. $y = e^x;\ a = \ln 3$

38. $y = \dfrac{e^x}{4} - x;\ a = 0$

39. Finding slope locations Let $f(x) = x^2 - 6x + 5$.

a. Find the values of x for which the slope of the curve $y = f(x)$ is 0.
b. Find the values of x for which the slope of the curve $y = f(x)$ is 2.

40. Finding slope locations Let $f(t) = t^3 - 27t + 5$.

a. Find the values of t for which the slope of the curve $y = f(t)$ is 0.
b. Find the values of t for which the slope of the curve $y = f(t)$ is 21.

41. Finding slope locations Let $f(x) = 2x^3 - 3x^2 - 12x + 4$.

a. Find all points on the graph of f at which the tangent line is horizontal.
b. Find all points on the graph of f at which the tangent line has slope 60.

42. Finding slope locations Let $f(x) = 2e^x - 6x$.

a. Find all points on the graph of f at which the tangent line is horizontal.
b. Find all points on the graph of f at which the tangent line has slope 12.

43. Finding slope locations Let $f(x) = 4\sqrt{x} - x$.

a. Find all points on the graph of f at which the tangent line is horizontal.
b. Find all points on the graph of f at which the tangent line has slope $-\frac{1}{2}$.

44–48. Higher-order derivatives *Find* $f'(x)$, $f''(x)$, *and* $f'''(x)$ *for the following functions.*

44. $f(x) = 3x^3 + 5x^2 + 6x$ **45.** $f(x) = 5x^4 + 10x^3 + 3x + 6$

46. $f(x) = 3x^2 + 5e^x$ **47.** $f(x) = \dfrac{x^2 - 7x - 8}{x + 1}$

48. $f(x) = 10e^x$

Further Explorations

49. Explain why or why not Determine whether the following statements are true and give an explanation or counterexample.

a. $\dfrac{d}{dx}(10^5) = 5 \cdot 10^4$.
b. The slope of a line tangent to $f(x) = e^x$ is never 0.
c. $\dfrac{d}{dx}(e^3) = e^3$.
d. $\dfrac{d}{dx}(e^x) = xe^{x-1}$.
e. $\dfrac{d^n}{dx^n}(5x^3 + 2x + 5) = 0$, for any integer $n \geq 3$.

50. Tangent lines Suppose $f(3) = 1$ and $f'(3) = 4$. Let $g(x) = x^2 + f(x)$ and $h(x) = 3f(x)$.

a. Find an equation of the line tangent to $y = g(x)$ at $x = 3$.
b. Find an equation of the line tangent to $y = h(x)$ at $x = 3$.

51. Derivatives from tangent lines Suppose the line tangent to the graph of f at $x = 2$ is $y = 4x + 1$ and suppose the line tangent to the graph of g at $x = 2$ has slope 3 and passes through $(0, -2)$. Find an equation of the line tangent to the following curves at $x = 2$.

a. $y = f(x) + g(x)$
b. $y = f(x) - 2g(x)$
c. $y = 4f(x)$

52. Tangent line Find the equation of the line tangent to the curve $y = x + \sqrt{x}$ that has slope 2.

53. Tangent line given Determine the constants b and c such that the line tangent to $f(x) = x^2 + bx + c$ at $x = 1$ is $y = 4x + 2$.

54–57. Derivatives from a graph *Let $F = f + g$ and $G = 3f - g$, where the graphs of f and g are shown in the figure. Find the following derivatives.*

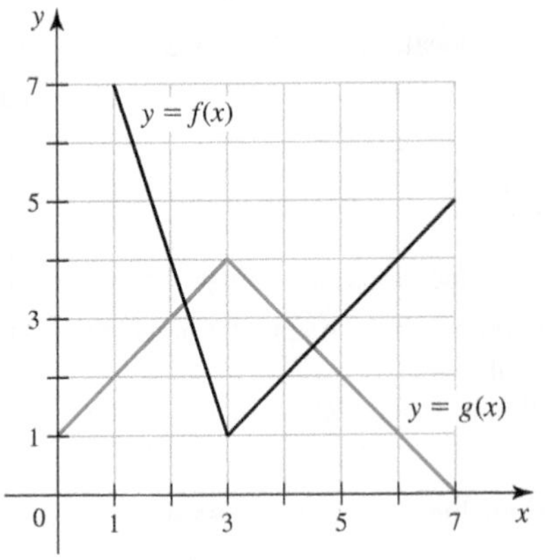

54. $F'(2)$ **55.** $G'(2)$ **56.** $F'(5)$ **57.** $G'(5)$

58–60. Derivatives from a table *Use the table to find the following derivatives.*

x	1	2	3	4	5
$f'(x)$	3	5	2	1	4
$g'(x)$	2	4	3	1	5

58. $\left.\frac{d}{dx}(f(x) + g(x))\right|_{x=1}$ **59.** $\left.\frac{d}{dx}(1.5f(x))\right|_{x=2}$

60. $\left.\frac{d}{dx}(2x - 3g(x))\right|_{x=4}$

61–63. Derivatives from limits *The following limits represent $f'(a)$ for some function f and some real number a.*

a. Find a possible function f and number a.
b. Evaluate the limit by computing $f'(a)$.

61. $\lim_{h\to 0} \frac{\sqrt{9+h} - \sqrt{9}}{h}$

62. $\lim_{h\to 0} \frac{(1+h)^8 + (1+h)^3 - 2}{h}$

63. $\lim_{x\to 1} \frac{x^{100} - 1}{x - 1}$

T 64. Important limits Complete the following table and give approximations for $\lim_{h\to 0^-} \frac{2^h - 1}{h}$ and $\lim_{h\to 0^-} \frac{3^h - 1}{h}$.

h	$\frac{2^h - 1}{h}$	$\frac{3^h - 1}{h}$
−1.0		
−0.1		
−0.01		
−0.001		
−0.0001		
−0.00001		

T 65–68. Calculator limits *Use a calculator to approximate the following limits.*

65. $\lim_{x\to 0} \frac{e^{3x} - 1}{x}$ **66.** $\lim_{n\to\infty} \left(1 + \frac{1}{n}\right)^n$

67. $\lim_{x\to 0^+} x^x$ **68.** $\lim_{x\to 0^+} \left(\frac{1}{x}\right)^x$

69. Calculating limits exactly The limit $\lim_{x\to 0} \frac{e^x - 1}{x}$ is the derivative of a function f at a point a. Find one possible f and a, and evaluate the limit.

Applications

T 70. Projectile trajectory The position of a small rocket that is launched vertically upward is given by $s(t) = -5t^2 + 40t + 100$, for $0 \le t \le 10$, where t is measured in seconds and s is measured in meters above the ground.

a. Find the rate of change in the position (instantaneous velocity) of the rocket, for $0 \le t \le 10$.
b. At what time is the instantaneous velocity zero?
c. At what time does the instantaneous velocity have the greatest magnitude, for $0 \le t \le 10$?
d. Graph the position and instantaneous velocity, for $0 \le t \le 10$.

71. Height estimate The distance an object falls (when released from rest, under the influence of Earth's gravity, and with no air resistance) is given by $d(t) = 16t^2$, where d is measured in feet and t is measured in seconds. A rock climber sits on a ledge on a vertical wall and carefully observes the time it takes a small stone to fall from the ledge to the ground.

a. Compute $d'(t)$. What units are associated with the derivative and what does it measure? Interpret the derivative.
b. If it takes 6 s for a stone to fall to the ground, how high is the ledge? How fast is the stone moving when it strikes the ground (in mi/hr)?

72. Cell growth When observations begin at $t = 0$, a cell culture has 1200 cells and continues to grow according to the function $p(t) = 1200\,e^t$, where p is the number of cells and t is measured in days.

a. Compute $p'(t)$. What units are associated with the derivative and what does it measure?
b. On the interval $[0, 4]$, when is the growth rate $p'(t)$ the least? When is it the greatest?

73. City urbanization City planners model the size of their city using the function $A(t) = -\frac{1}{50}t^2 + 2t + 20$, for $0 \le t \le 50$, where A is measured in square miles and t is the number of years after 2010.

a. Compute $A'(t)$. What units are associated with this derivative and what does the derivative measure?
b. How fast will the city be growing when it reaches a size of 38 mi^2?
c. Suppose that the population density of the city remains constant from year to year at 1000 people/mi^2. Determine the growth rate of the population in 2030.

Additional Exercises

74. Constant Rule proof For the constant function $f(x) = c$, use the definition of the derivative to show that $f'(x) = 0$.

75. Alternative proof of the Power Rule The Binomial Theorem states that for any positive integer n,

$$(a + b)^n = a^n + na^{n-1}b + \frac{n(n-1)}{2 \cdot 1} a^{n-2}b^2 + \frac{n(n-1)(n-2)}{3 \cdot 2 \cdot 1} a^{n-3}b^3 + \cdots + nab^{n-1} + b^n.$$

Use this formula and the definition

$f'(x) = \lim_{h \to 0} \frac{f(x+h) - f(x)}{h}$ to show that $\frac{d}{dx}(x^n) = nx^{n-1}$, for any positive integer n.

76. Looking ahead: Power Rule for negative integers Suppose n is a negative integer and $f(x) = x^n$. Use the following steps to prove that $f'(a) = na^{n-1}$, which means the Power Rule for positive integers extends to all integers. This result is proved in Section 3.4 by a different method.

a. Assume that $m = -n$, so that $m > 0$. Use the definition $f'(a) = \lim_{x \to a} \frac{x^n - a^n}{x - a} = \lim_{x \to a} \frac{x^{-m} - a^{-m}}{x - a}$. Simplify using the factoring rule (which is valid for $n > 0$) $x^n - a^n = (x - a)(x^{n-1} + x^{n-2}a + \cdots + xa^{n-2} + a^{n-1})$ until it is possible to take the limit.

b. Use this result to find $\frac{d}{dx}(x^{-7})$ and $\frac{d}{dx}\left(\frac{1}{x^{10}}\right)$.

77. Extending the Power Rule to $n = \frac{1}{2}, \frac{3}{2}$, and $\frac{5}{2}$ With Theorem 3.3 and Exercise 76, we have shown that the Power Rule, $\frac{d}{dx}(x^n) = nx^{n-1}$, applies to any integer n. Later in the chapter, we extend this rule so that it applies to any rational number n.

a. Explain why the Power Rule is consistent with the formula $\frac{d}{dx}(\sqrt{x}) = \frac{1}{2\sqrt{x}}$.

b. Prove that the Power Rule holds for $n = \frac{3}{2}$. (*Hint:* Use the definition of the derivative: $\frac{d}{dx}(x^{3/2}) = \lim_{h \to 0} \frac{(x+h)^{3/2} - x^{3/2}}{h}$.)

c. Prove that the Power Rule holds for $n = \frac{5}{2}$.

d. Propose a formula for $\frac{d}{dx}(x^{n/2})$, for any positive integer n.

78. Computing the derivative of $f(x) = e^{-x}$

a. Use the definition of the derivative to show that $\frac{d}{dx}(e^{-x}) = e^{-x} \cdot \lim_{h \to 0} \frac{e^{-h} - 1}{h}$.

b. Show that the limit in part (a) is equal to -1. (*Hint:* Use the facts that $\lim_{h \to 0} \frac{e^h - 1}{h} = 1$ and e^x is continuous for all x.)

c. Use parts (a) and (b) to find the derivative of $f(x) = e^{-x}$.

79. Computing the derivative of $f(x) = e^{2x}$

a. Use the definition of the derivative to show that $\frac{d}{dx}(e^{2x}) = e^{2x} \cdot \lim_{h \to 0} \frac{e^{2h} - 1}{h}$.

b. Show that the limit in part (a) is equal to 2. (*Hint:* Factor $e^{2h} - 1$.)

c. Use parts (a) and (b) to find the derivative of $f(x) = e^{2x}$.

80. Computing the derivative of $f(x) = x^2e^x$

a. Use the definition of the derivative to show that $\frac{d}{dx}(x^2e^x) = e^x \cdot \lim_{h \to 0} \frac{(x^2 + 2xh + h^2)e^h - x^2}{h}$.

b. Manipulate the limit in part (a) to arrive at $f'(x) = e^x(x^2 + 2x)$. (*Hint:* Use the fact that $\lim_{h \to 0} \frac{e^h - 1}{h} = 1$.)

QUICK CHECK ANSWERS

1. $\frac{d}{dx}(5) = 0$ and $\frac{d}{dx}(\pi) = 0$ because 5 and π are constants. **2.** The slope of the curve $y = x$ is 1 at any point; therefore, $\frac{d}{dx}(x) = 1$. **3.** $2x + 2$ **4.** $f'(x) = 4e^x - 6x$ **5.** $x = 2$ and $x = -2$ **6.** $f^{(5)}(x) = 120, f^{(6)}(x) = 0$, $g^{(100)}(x) = e^x$ ◄

3.4 The Product and Quotient Rules

The derivative of a sum of functions is the sum of the derivatives. So you might assume that the derivative of a product of functions is the product of the derivatives. Consider, however, the functions $f(x) = x^3$ and $g(x) = x^4$. In this case, $\frac{d}{dx}(f(x)g(x)) = \frac{d}{dx}(x^7) = 7x^6$, but $f'(x)g'(x) = 3x^2 \cdot 4x^3 = 12x^5$. Therefore, $\frac{d}{dx}(f \cdot g) \neq f' \cdot g'$. Similarly, the derivative of a quotient is *not* the quotient of the derivatives. The purpose of this section is to develop rules for differentiating products and quotients of functions.

Product Rule

Here is an anecdote that suggests the formula for the Product Rule. Imagine running along a road at a constant speed. Your speed is determined by two factors: the length of your stride and the number of strides you take each second. Therefore,

$$\text{running speed} = \text{stride length} \cdot \text{stride rate}.$$

For example, if your stride length is 3 ft per stride and you take 2 strides/s, then your speed is 6 ft/s.

Now suppose your stride length increases by 0.5 ft, from 3 to 3.5 ft. Then the change in speed is calculated as follows:

$$\begin{aligned}\textit{change} \text{ in speed} &= \text{change in stride length} \cdot \text{stride rate}\\ &= 0.5 \cdot 2 = 1 \text{ ft/s}.\end{aligned}$$

Alternatively, suppose your stride length remains constant but your stride rate increases by 0.25 strides/s, from 2 to 2.25 strides/s. Then

$$\begin{aligned}\textit{change} \text{ in speed} &= \text{stride length} \cdot \text{change in stride rate}\\ &= 3 \cdot 0.25 = 0.75 \text{ ft/s}.\end{aligned}$$

If both your stride rate and stride length change simultaneously, we expect two contributions to the change in your running speed:

$$\begin{aligned}\textit{change} \text{ in speed} &= (\text{change in stride length} \cdot \text{stride rate})\\ &\quad + (\text{stride length} \cdot \text{change in stride rate})\\ &= 1 \text{ ft/s} + 0.75 \text{ ft/s} = 1.75 \text{ ft/s}.\end{aligned}$$

This argument correctly suggests that the derivative (or rate of change) of a product of two functions has *two components*, as shown by the following rule.

➤ In words, Theorem 3.7 states that the derivative of the product of two functions equals the derivative of the first function multiplied by the second function plus the first function multiplied by the derivative of the second function.

THEOREM 3.7 Product Rule

If f and g are differentiable at x, then

$$\frac{d}{dx}(f(x)g(x)) = f'(x)g(x) + f(x)g'(x).$$

Proof: We apply the definition of the derivative to the function fg:

$$\frac{d}{dx}(f(x)g(x)) = \lim_{h\to 0} \frac{f(x+h)g(x+h) - f(x)g(x)}{h}.$$

A useful tactic is to add $-f(x)g(x+h) + f(x)g(x+h)$ (which equals 0) to the numerator, so that

$$\frac{d}{dx}(f(x)g(x)) = \lim_{h\to 0} \frac{f(x+h)g(x+h) - f(x)g(x+h) + f(x)g(x+h) - f(x)g(x)}{h}.$$

The fraction is now split and the numerators are factored:

$$\begin{aligned}&\frac{d}{dx}(f(x)g(x))\\ &= \lim_{h\to 0} \frac{f(x+h)g(x+h) - f(x)g(x+h)}{h} + \lim_{h\to 0} \frac{f(x)g(x+h) - f(x)g(x)}{h}\\ &= \lim_{h\to 0}\Bigg(\underbrace{\frac{f(x+h) - f(x)}{h}}_{\substack{\text{approaches } f'(x) \text{ as}\\ h\to 0}} \cdot \underbrace{g(x+h)}_{\substack{\text{approaches}\\ g(x)\\ \text{as } h\to 0}}\Bigg) + \lim_{h\to 0}\Bigg(\underbrace{f(x)}_{\substack{\text{equals}\\ f(x) \text{ as}\\ h\to 0}} \cdot \underbrace{\frac{g(x+h) - g(x)}{h}}_{\substack{\text{approaches } g'(x)\\ \text{as } h\to 0}}\Bigg)\\ &= f'(x) \cdot g(x) + f(x) \cdot g'(x).\end{aligned}$$

➤ As $h \to 0$, $f(x)$ does not change in value because it is independent of h.

The continuity of g is used to conclude that $\lim_{h\to 0} g(x+h) = g(x)$. ◄

EXAMPLE 1 **Using the Product Rule** Find and simplify the following derivatives.

a. $\frac{d}{dv}(v^2(2\sqrt{v} + 1))$ **b.** $\frac{d}{dx}(x^2 e^x)$

➤ In Example 4 of Section 3.1, we proved that $\frac{d}{dv}(\sqrt{v}) = \frac{1}{2\sqrt{v}}$.

SOLUTION

a.
$$\frac{d}{dv}(v^2(2\sqrt{v} + 1)) = \left(\frac{d}{dv}(v^2)\right)(2\sqrt{v} + 1) + v^2\left(\frac{d}{dv}(2\sqrt{v} + 1)\right) \quad \text{Product Rule}$$
$$= 2v(2\sqrt{v} + 1) + v^2\left(2 \cdot \frac{1}{2\sqrt{v}}\right) \quad \text{Evaluate the derivatives.}$$
$$= 4v^{3/2} + 2v + v^{3/2} = 5v^{3/2} + 2v \quad \text{Simplify.}$$

b.
$$\frac{d}{dx}(x^2 e^x) = \underbrace{2x}_{\frac{d}{dx}(x^2)} \cdot e^x + x^2 \cdot \underbrace{e^x}_{\frac{d}{dx}(e^x)} = xe^x\,(2 + x)$$

Related Exercises 7–18 ◀

QUICK CHECK 1 Find the derivative of $f(x) = x^5$. Then find the same derivative using the Product Rule with $f(x) = x^2 x^3$. ◀

Quotient Rule

Consider the quotient $q(x) = \frac{f(x)}{g(x)}$ and note that $f(x) = g(x)q(x)$. By the Product Rule, we have

$$f'(x) = g'(x)q(x) + g(x)q'(x).$$

Solving for $q'(x)$, we find that

$$q'(x) = \frac{f'(x) - g'(x)q(x)}{g(x)}.$$

Substituting $q(x) = \frac{f(x)}{g(x)}$ produces a rule for finding $q'(x)$:

$$q'(x) = \frac{f'(x) - g'(x)\frac{f(x)}{g(x)}}{g(x)} \quad \text{Replace } q(x) \text{ with } \frac{f(x)}{g(x)}.$$
$$= \frac{g(x)\left(f'(x) - g'(x)\frac{f(x)}{g(x)}\right)}{g(x) \cdot g(x)} \quad \text{Multiply numerator and denominator by } g(x).$$
$$= \frac{g(x)f'(x) - f(x)g'(x)}{(g(x))^2}. \quad \text{Simplify.}$$

➤ In words, Theorem 3.8 states that the derivative of the quotient of two functions equals the denominator multiplied by the derivative of the numerator minus the numerator multiplied by the derivative of the denominator, all divided by the denominator squared. An easy way to remember the Quotient Rule is with

$$\frac{LoD(Hi) - HiD(Lo)}{(Lo)^2}.$$

This calculation produces the correct result for the derivative of a quotient. However, there is one subtle point: How do we know that the derivative of f/g exists in the first place? A complete proof of the Quotient Rule is outlined in Exercise 86.

> **THEOREM 3.8** **Quotient Rule**
> If f and g are differentiable at x and $g(x) \neq 0$, then the derivative of f/g at x exists and
> $$\frac{d}{dx}\left(\frac{f(x)}{g(x)}\right) = \frac{g(x)f'(x) - f(x)g'(x)}{(g(x))^2}.$$

EXAMPLE 2 **Using the Quotient Rule** Find and simplify the following derivatives.

a. $\frac{d}{dx}\left(\frac{x^2 + 3x + 4}{x^2 - 1}\right)$ **b.** $\frac{d}{dx}(e^{-x})$

SOLUTION

a.
$$\frac{d}{dx}\left(\frac{x^2+3x+4}{x^2-1}\right) = \frac{\overbrace{(x^2-1)(2x+3)}^{(x^2-1)\cdot\text{the derivative of }(x^2+3x+4)} - \overbrace{(x^2+3x+4)2x}^{(x^2+3x+4)\cdot\text{the derivative of }(x^2-1)}}{\underbrace{(x^2-1)^2}_{\text{the denominator }(x^2-1)\text{ squared}}} \qquad \text{Quotient Rule}$$

$$= \frac{2x^3-2x+3x^2-3-2x^3-6x^2-8x}{(x^2-1)^2} \qquad \text{Expand.}$$

$$= \frac{-3x^2-10x-3}{(x^2-1)^2} \qquad \text{Simplify.}$$

➤ The Product and Quotient Rules are used on a regular basis throughout this text. It is a good idea to memorize these rules (along with the other derivative rules and formulas presented in this chapter) so that you can evaluate derivatives quickly.

b. We rewrite e^{-x} as $\frac{1}{e^x}$ and use the Quotient Rule:

$$\frac{d}{dx}\left(\frac{1}{e^x}\right) = \frac{e^x \cdot 0 - 1 \cdot e^x}{(e^x)^2} = -\frac{1}{e^x} = -e^{-x}.$$

Related Exercises 19–32 ◄

QUICK CHECK 2 Find the derivative of $f(x) = x^5$. Then find the same derivative using the Quotient Rule with $f(x) = x^8/x^3$. ◄

EXAMPLE 3 Finding tangent lines Find an equation of the line tangent to the graph of $f(x) = \frac{x^2+1}{x^2-4}$ at the point $(3, 2)$. Plot the curve and tangent line.

SOLUTION To find the slope of the tangent line, we compute f' using the Quotient Rule:

$$f'(x) = \frac{(x^2-4)\,2x - (x^2+1)\,2x}{(x^2-4)^2} \qquad \text{Quotient Rule}$$

$$= \frac{2x^3-8x-2x^3-2x}{(x^2-4)^2} = -\frac{10x}{(x^2-4)^2}. \qquad \text{Simplify.}$$

The slope of the tangent line at $(3, 2)$ is

$$m_{\tan} = f'(3) = -\frac{10(3)}{(3^2-4)^2} = -\frac{6}{5}.$$

Therefore, an equation of the tangent line is

$$y - 2 = -\frac{6}{5}(x-3), \quad \text{or} \quad y = -\frac{6}{5}x + \frac{28}{5}.$$

The graphs of f and the tangent line are shown in Figure 3.28.

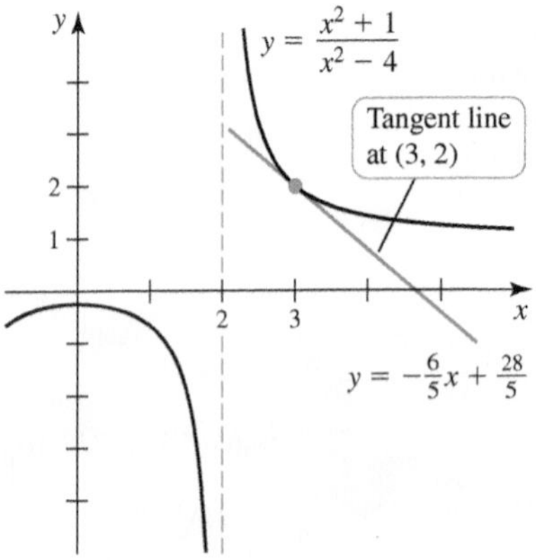

Figure 3.28

Related Exercises 33–36 ◄

Extending the Power Rule to Negative Integers

The Power Rule in Section 3.3 says that $\frac{d}{dx}(x^n) = nx^{n-1}$, for nonnegative integers n. Using the Quotient Rule, we show that the Power Rule also holds if n is a negative integer. Assume n is a negative integer and let $m = -n$, so that $m > 0$. Then

$$\frac{d}{dx}(x^n) = \frac{d}{dx}\left(\frac{1}{x^m}\right) \qquad x^n = \frac{1}{x^{-n}} = \frac{1}{x^m}$$

$$= \frac{x^m \overbrace{\left(\frac{d}{dx}(1)\right)}^{\text{derivative of a constant is 0}} - 1\overbrace{\left(\frac{d}{dx}x^m\right)}^{\text{equals } mx^{m-1}}}{(x^m)^2} \qquad \text{Quotient Rule}$$

$$= -\frac{mx^{m-1}}{x^{2m}} \qquad \text{Simplify.}$$

$$= -mx^{-m-1} \qquad \frac{x^{m-1}}{x^{2m}} = x^{m-1-2m}$$

$$= nx^{n-1}. \qquad \text{Replace } -m \text{ with } n.$$

This calculation leads to the first extension of the Power Rule; the rule now applies to all integers.

> **THEOREM 3.9 Extended Power Rule**
> If n is any integer, then
> $$\frac{d}{dx}(x^n) = nx^{n-1}.$$

QUICK CHECK 3 Find the derivative of $f(x) = 1/x^5$ in two different ways: using the Extended Power Rule and using the Quotient Rule. ◄

EXAMPLE 4 Using the Extended Power Rule Find the following derivatives.

a. $\frac{d}{dx}\left(\frac{9}{x^5}\right)$ **b.** $\frac{d}{dt}\left(\frac{3t^{16} - 4}{t^6}\right)$

SOLUTION

a. $\frac{d}{dx}\left(\frac{9}{x^5}\right) = \frac{d}{dx}(9x^{-5}) = 9(-5x^{-6}) = -45x^{-6} = -\frac{45}{x^6}$

b. The derivative of $\frac{3t^{16} - 4}{t^6}$ can be evaluated by the Quotient Rule, but an alternative method is to rewrite the expression using negative powers:

$$\frac{3t^{16} - 4}{t^6} = \frac{3t^{16}}{t^6} - \frac{4}{t^6} = 3t^{10} - 4t^{-6}.$$

We now differentiate using the Extended Power Rule:

$$\frac{d}{dt}\left(\frac{3t^{16} - 4}{t^6}\right) = \frac{d}{dt}(3t^{10} - 4t^{-6}) = 30t^9 + 24t^{-7}.$$

Related Exercises 37–42 ◄

The Derivative of e^{kx}

Consider the composite function $y = e^{2x}$, for which we presently have no differentiation rule. We rewrite the function and apply the Product Rule:

$$\frac{d}{dx}(e^{2x}) = \frac{d}{dx}(e^x \cdot e^x) \qquad e^{2x} = e^x \cdot e^x$$

$$= \frac{d}{dx}(e^x) \cdot e^x + e^x \cdot \frac{d}{dx}(e^x) \qquad \text{Product Rule}$$

$$= e^x \cdot e^x + e^x \cdot e^x = 2e^{2x}. \qquad \text{Evaluate derivatives.}$$

In a similar fashion, $y = e^{3x}$ is differentiated by writing it as the product $y = e^x \cdot e^{2x}$. You should verify that $\frac{d}{dx}(e^{3x}) = 3e^{3x}$. Extending this strategy, it can be shown that $\frac{d}{dx}(e^{kx}) = ke^{kx}$, for positive integers k (Exercise 88 illustrates a proof by induction). The Quotient Rule is used to show that the rule holds for negative integers k (Exercise 89). Finally, we prove in Section 3.7 (Exercise 94) that the rule holds for all real numbers k.

> **THEOREM 3.10 The derivative of e^{kx}**
> For real numbers k,
> $$\frac{d}{dx}(e^{kx}) = ke^{kx}.$$

EXAMPLE 5 Exponential derivatives Compute dy/dx for the following functions.

a. $y = xe^{5x}$ **b.** $y = 1000e^{0.07x}$

SOLUTION

a. We use the Product Rule and the fact that $\frac{d}{dx}(e^{kx}) = ke^{kx}$:

$$\frac{dy}{dx} = \underbrace{1}_{\frac{d}{dx}(x) = 1} \cdot e^{5x} + x \cdot \underbrace{5e^{5x}}_{\frac{d}{dx}(e^{5x}) = 5e^{5x}} = (1 + 5x)e^{5x}.$$

b. Here we use the Constant Multiple Rule:

$$\frac{dy}{dx} = 1000 \cdot \frac{d}{dx}(e^{0.07x}) = 1000 \cdot 0.07e^{0.07x} = 70e^{0.07x}.$$

Related Exercises 43–50 ◀

QUICK CHECK 4 Find the derivative of $f(x) = 4e^{0.5x}$. ◀

Rates of Change

Remember that the derivative has multiple uses and interpretations. The following example illustrates the derivative as a rate of change of a population. Specifically, the derivative tells us when the population is growing most rapidly and how the population behaves in the long run.

EXAMPLE 6 Population growth rates The population of a culture of cells increases and approaches a constant level (often called a *steady state* or a *carrying capacity*). The population is modeled by the function $p(t) = \frac{400}{1 + 3e^{-0.5t}}$, where $t \geq 0$ is measured in hours (Figure 3.29).

a. Compute and graph the instantaneous growth rate of the population, for any $t \geq 0$.

b. At approximately what time is the instantaneous growth rate the greatest?

c. What is the steady-state population?

SOLUTION

a. The instantaneous growth rate is given by the derivative of the population function:

$$p'(t) = \frac{d}{dt}\left(\frac{400}{1 + 3e^{-0.5t}}\right)$$

$$= \frac{(1 + 3e^{-0.5t}) \cdot \overbrace{\frac{d}{dt}(400)}^{\text{equals } 0} - 400\frac{d}{dt}(1 + 3e^{-0.5t})}{(1 + 3e^{-0.5t})^2} \quad \text{Quotient Rule}$$

$$= \frac{-400(-1.5e^{-0.5t})}{(1 + 3e^{-0.5t})^2} = \frac{600e^{-0.5t}}{(1 + 3e^{-0.5t})^2}. \quad \text{Simplify.}$$

➤ Methods for determining exactly when the growth rate is a maximum are discussed in Chapter 4.

The growth rate has units of cells per hour; its graph is shown in Figure 3.29.

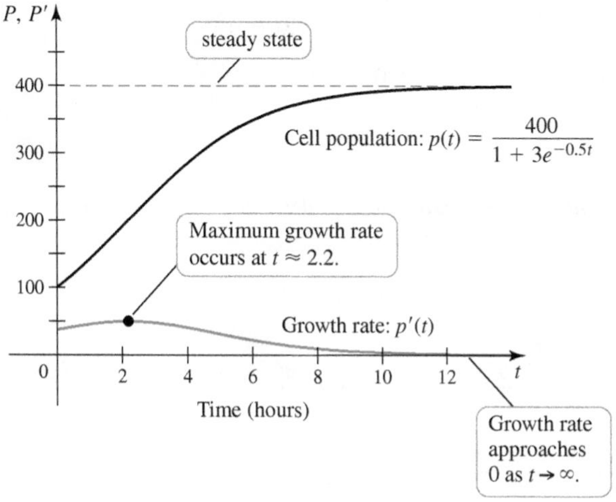

Figure 3.29

b. The growth rate $p'(t)$ has a maximum at the point at which the population curve is steepest. Using a graphing utility, this point corresponds to $t \approx 2.2$ hr and the growth rate has a value of $p'(2.2) \approx 50$ cells/hr.

c. To determine whether the population approaches a fixed value after a long period of time (the steady-state population), we must investigate the limit of the population function as $t \to \infty$. In this case, the steady-state population exists and is

$$\lim_{t\to\infty} p(t) = \lim_{t\to\infty} \frac{400}{1 + \underbrace{3e^{-0.5t}}_{\text{approaches } 0}} = 400,$$

which is confirmed by the population curve in Figure 3.29. Notice that as the population approaches its steady state, the growth rate p' approaches zero. *Related Exercises 51–56* ◀

Combining Derivative Rules

Some situations call for the use of multiple differentiation rules. This section concludes with one such example.

EXAMPLE 7 **Combining derivative rules** Find the derivative of

$$y = \frac{4xe^x}{x^2 + 1}.$$

SOLUTION In this case, we have the quotient of two functions, with a product $(4x\,e^x)$ in the numerator.

$$\frac{dy}{dx} = \frac{(x^2 + 1) \cdot \frac{d}{dx}(4xe^x) - (4xe^x) \cdot \frac{d}{dx}(x^2 + 1)}{(x^2 + 1)^2} \quad \text{Quotient Rule}$$

$$= \frac{(x^2 + 1)(4e^x + 4xe^x) - (4xe^x)(2x)}{(x^2 + 1)^2} \quad \tfrac{d}{dx}(4xe^x) = 4e^x + 4xe^x \text{ by the Product Rule}$$

$$= \frac{4e^x(x^3 - x^2 + x + 1)}{(x^2 + 1)^2} \quad \text{Simplify.}$$

Related Exercises 57–60 ◀

SECTION 3.4 EXERCISES

Review Questions

1. How do you find the derivative of the product of two functions that are differentiable at a point?
2. How do you find the derivative of the quotient of two functions that are differentiable at a point?
3. State the Extended Power Rule for differentiating x^n. For what values of n does the rule apply?
4. Show two ways to differentiate $f(x) = 1/x^{10}$.
5. What is the derivative of $y = e^{kx}$? For what values of k does this rule apply?
6. Show two ways to differentiate $f(x) = (x - 3)(x^2 + 4)$.

Basic Skills

7–14. Derivatives of products *Find the derivative of the following functions.*

7. $f(x) = 3x^4(2x^2 - 1)$
8. $g(x) = 6x - 2xe^x$
9. $f(t) = t^5e^t$
10. $g(w) = e^w(5w^2 + 3w + 1)$
11. $h(x) = (x - 1)(x^3 + x^2 + x + 1)$
12. $f(x) = \left(1 + \frac{1}{x^2}\right)(x^2 + 1)$
13. $g(w) = e^w(w^3 - 1)$
14. $s(t) = 4e^t\sqrt{t}$

15–18. Derivatives by two different methods

a. *Use the Product Rule to find the derivative of the given function. Simplify your result.*
b. *Find the derivative by expanding the product first. Verify that your answer agrees with part (a).*

15. $f(x) = (x - 1)(3x + 4)$
16. $y = (t^2 + 7t)(3t - 4)$
17. $g(y) = (3y^4 - y^2)(y^2 - 4)$
18. $h(z) = (z^3 + 4z^2 + z)(z - 1)$

19–28. Derivatives of quotients *Find the derivative of the following functions.*

19. $f(x) = \dfrac{x}{x + 1}$
20. $f(x) = \dfrac{x^3 - 4x^2 + x}{x - 2}$
21. $f(x) = \dfrac{e^x}{e^x + 1}$
22. $f(x) = \dfrac{2e^x - 1}{2e^x + 1}$
23. $f(x) = xe^{-x}$
24. $f(x) = e^{-x}\sqrt{x}$
25. $y = (3t - 1)(2t - 2)^{-1}$
26. $h(w) = \dfrac{w^2 - 1}{w^2 + 1}$
27. $g(x) = \dfrac{e^x}{x^2 - 1}$
28. $y = (2\sqrt{x} - 1)(4x + 1)^{-1}$

29–32. Derivatives by two different methods

a. *Use the Quotient Rule to find the derivative of the given function. Simplify your result.*
b. *Find the derivative by first simplifying the function. Verify that your answer agrees with part (a).*

29. $f(w) = \dfrac{w^3 - w}{w}$
30. $y = \dfrac{4s^3 - 8s^2 + 4s}{4s}$
31. $y = \dfrac{x^2 - a^2}{x - a}$, where a is a constant.
32. $y = \dfrac{x^2 - 2ax + a^2}{x - a}$, where a is a constant.

T 33–36. Equations of tangent lines

a. *Find an equation of the line tangent to the given curve at a.*
b. *Use a graphing utility to graph the curve and the tangent line on the same set of axes.*

33. $y = \dfrac{x + 5}{x - 1}$; $a = 3$
34. $y = \dfrac{2x^2}{3x - 1}$; $a = 1$
35. $y = 1 + 2x + xe^x$; $a = 0$
36. $y = \dfrac{e^x}{x}$; $a = 1$

37–42. Extended Power Rule *Find the derivative of the following functions.*

37. $f(x) = 3x^{-9}$
38. $y = \dfrac{4}{p^3}$
39. $g(t) = 3t^2 + \dfrac{6}{t^7}$
40. $y = \dfrac{w^4 + 5w^2 + w}{w^2}$
41. $g(t) = \dfrac{t^3 + 3t^2 + t}{t^3}$
42. $p(x) = \dfrac{4x^3 + 3x + 1}{2x^5}$

43–50. Derivatives with exponentials *Compute the derivative of the following functions.*

43. $f(x) = xe^{7x}$
44. $g(t) = 2te^{t/2}$
45. $f(x) = 15e^{3x}$
46. $y = 3x^2 - 2x + e^{-2x}$
47. $g(x) = \dfrac{x}{e^{3x}}$
48. $f(x) = (1 - 2x)e^{-x}$
49. $y = \dfrac{2e^x + 3e^{-x}}{3}$
50. $A = 2500e^{0.075t}$

T 51–52. Population growth *Consider the following population functions.*

a. *Find the instantaneous growth rate of the population, for $t \geq 0$.*
b. *What is the instantaneous growth rate at $t = 5$?*
c. *Estimate the time when the instantaneous growth rate is the greatest.*
d. *Evaluate and interpret $\lim_{t\to\infty} p'(t)$.*
e. *Use a graphing utility to graph the population and its growth rate.*

51. $p(t) = \dfrac{200t}{t + 2}$
52. $p(t) = \dfrac{800}{1 + 7e^{-0.2t}}$

53. **Antibiotic decay** The half-life of an antibiotic in the bloodstream is 10 hours. If an initial dose of 20 milligrams is administered, the quantity left after t hours is modeled by $Q(t) = 20e^{-0.0693t}$, for $t \geq 0$.
    a. Find the instantaneous rate of change of the amount of antibiotic in the bloodstream, for $t \geq 0$.

b. How fast is the amount of antibiotic changing at $t = 0$? At $t = 2$?

c. Evaluate and interpret $\lim_{t\to\infty} Q(t)$ and $\lim_{t\to\infty} Q'(t)$.

T **54. Bank account** A \$200 investment in a savings account grows according to $A(t) = 200e^{0.0398t}$, for $t \geq 0$, where t is measured in years.

a. Find the balance of the account after 10 years.

b. How fast is the account growing (in dollars/year) at $t = 10$?

c. Use your answers to parts (a) and (b) to write the equation of the line tangent to the curve $A = 200e^{0.0398t}$ at the point $(10, A(10))$.

55. Finding slope locations Let $f(x) = xe^{2x}$.

a. Find the values of x for which the slope of the curve $y = f(x)$ is 0.

b. Explain the meaning of your answer to part (a) in terms of the graph of f.

56. Finding slope locations Let $f(t) = 100e^{-0.05t}$.

a. Find the values of t for which the slope of the curve $y = f(t)$ is -5.

b. Does the graph of f have a horizontal tangent line?

57–60. Combining rules *Compute the derivative of the following functions.*

57. $g(x) = \dfrac{(x+1)e^x}{x-2}$

58. $h(x) = \dfrac{(x-1)(2x^2-1)}{x^3-1}$

59. $h(x) = \dfrac{xe^x}{x+1}$

60. $h(x) = \dfrac{x+1}{x^2e^x}$

Further Explorations

61. Explain why or why not Determine whether the following statements are true and give an explanation or counterexample.

a. $\dfrac{d}{dx}(e^5) = 5e^4$.

b. The Quotient Rule must be used to evaluate $\dfrac{d}{dx}\left(\dfrac{x^2+3x+2}{x}\right)$.

c. $\dfrac{d}{dx}\left(\dfrac{1}{x^5}\right) = \dfrac{1}{5x^4}$.

d. $\dfrac{d^n}{dx^n}(e^{3x}) = 3^n e^{3x}$, for any integer $n \geq 1$.

62–63. Higher-order derivatives *Find $f'(x)$, $f''(x)$, and $f'''(x)$.*

62. $f(x) = \dfrac{1}{x}$

63. $f(x) = x^2e^{3x}$

64–65. First and second derivatives *Find $f'(x)$ and $f''(x)$.*

64. $f(x) = \dfrac{x}{x+2}$

65. $f(x) = \dfrac{x^2-7x}{x+1}$

66–71. Choose your method *Use any method to evaluate the derivative of the following functions.*

66. $f(x) = \dfrac{4-x^2}{x-2}$

67. $f(x) = 4x^2 - \dfrac{2x}{5x+1}$

68. $f(z) = z^2(e^{3z}+4) - \dfrac{2z}{z^2+1}$

69. $h(r) = \dfrac{2 - r - \sqrt{r}}{r+1}$

70. $y = \dfrac{x-a}{\sqrt{x}-\sqrt{a}}$, where a is a positive constant.

71. $h(x) = (5x^7 + 5x)(6x^3 + 3x^2 + 3)$

72. Tangent lines Suppose $f(2) = 2$ and $f'(2) = 3$. Let $g(x) = x^2 \cdot f(x)$ and $h(x) = \dfrac{f(x)}{x-3}$.

a. Find an equation of the line tangent to $y = g(x)$ at $x = 2$.

b. Find an equation of the line tangent to $y = h(x)$ at $x = 2$.

T **73. The Witch of Agnesi** The graph of $y = \dfrac{a^3}{x^2+a^2}$, where a is a constant, is called the *witch of Agnesi* (named after the 18th-century Italian mathematician Maria Agnesi).

a. Let $a = 3$ and find an equation of the line tangent to $y = \dfrac{27}{x^2+9}$ at $x = 2$.

b. Plot the function and the tangent line found in part (a).

74–79. Derivatives from a table *Use the following table to find the given derivatives.*

x	1	2	3	4
$f(x)$	5	4	3	2
$f'(x)$	3	5	2	1
$g(x)$	4	2	5	3
$g'(x)$	2	4	3	1

74. $\left.\dfrac{d}{dx}(f(x)g(x))\right|_{x=1}$

75. $\left.\dfrac{d}{dx}\left(\dfrac{f(x)}{g(x)}\right)\right|_{x=2}$

76. $\left.\dfrac{d}{dx}(xf(x))\right|_{x=3}$

77. $\left.\dfrac{d}{dx}\left(\dfrac{f(x)}{x+2}\right)\right|_{x=4}$

78. $\left.\dfrac{d}{dx}\left(\dfrac{xf(x)}{g(x)}\right)\right|_{x=4}$

79. $\left.\dfrac{d}{dx}\left(\dfrac{f(x)g(x)}{x}\right)\right|_{x=4}$

80. Derivatives from tangent lines Suppose the line tangent to the graph of f at $x = 2$ is $y = 4x + 1$ and suppose $y = 3x - 2$ is the line tangent to the graph of g at $x = 2$. Find an equation of the line tangent to the following curves at $x = 2$.

a. $y = f(x)g(x)$

b. $y = \dfrac{f(x)}{g(x)}$

Applications

81. Electrostatic force The magnitude of the electrostatic force between two point charges Q and q of the same sign is given by $F(x) = \dfrac{kQq}{x^2}$, where x is the distance (measured in meters) between the charges and $k = 9 \times 10^9$ N-m^2/C^2 is a physical constant (C stands for coulomb, the unit of charge; N stands for newton, the unit of force).

a. Find the instantaneous rate of change of the force with respect to the distance between the charges.

b. For two identical charges with $Q = q = 1$ C, what is the instantaneous rate of change of the force at a separation of $x = 0.001$ m?

c. Does the magnitude of the instantaneous rate of change of the force increase or decrease with the separation? Explain.

82. Gravitational force The magnitude of the gravitational force between two objects of mass M and m is given by $F(x) = -\dfrac{GMm}{x^2}$, where x is the distance between the centers of mass of the objects and $G = 6.7 \times 10^{-11}$ N-m^2/kg^2 is the gravitational constant (N stands for newton, the unit of force; the negative sign indicates an attractive force).

a. Find the instantaneous rate of change of the force with respect to the distance between the objects.

b. For two identical objects of mass $M = m = 0.1$ kg, what is the instantaneous rate of change of the force at a separation of $x = 0.01$ m?

c. Does the instantaneous rate of change of the force increase or decrease with the separation? Explain.

Additional Exercises

83. Special Product Rule In general, the derivative of a product is not the product of the derivatives. Find nonconstant functions f and g such that the derivative of fg equals $f'g'$.

84. Special Quotient Rule In general, the derivative of a quotient is not the quotient of the derivatives. Find nonconstant functions f and g such that the derivative of f/g equals f'/g'.

85. Means and tangents Suppose f is differentiable on an interval containing a and b, and let $P(a, f(a))$ and $Q(b, f(b))$ be distinct points on the graph of f. Let c be the x-coordinate of the point at which the lines tangent to the curve at P and Q intersect, assuming that the tangent lines are not parallel (see figure).

a. If $f(x) = x^2$, show that $c = (a + b)/2$, the arithmetic mean of a and b, for real numbers a and b.

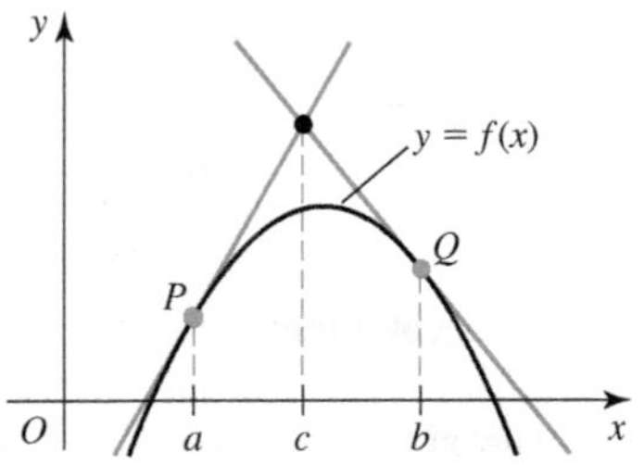

b. If $f(x) = \sqrt{x}$, show that $c = \sqrt{ab}$, the geometric mean of a and b, for $a > 0$ and $b > 0$.

c. If $f(x) = 1/x$, show that $c = 2ab/(a + b)$, the harmonic mean of a and b, for $a > 0$ and $b > 0$.

d. Find an expression for c in terms of a and b for any (differentiable) function f whenever c exists.

86. Proof of the Quotient Rule Let $F = f/g$ be the quotient of two functions that are differentiable at x.

a. Use the definition of F' to show that
$$\frac{d}{dx}\left(\frac{f(x)}{g(x)}\right) = \lim_{h \to 0} \frac{f(x + h)g(x) - f(x)g(x + h)}{hg(x + h)g(x)}.$$

b. Now add $-f(x)g(x) + f(x)g(x)$ (which equals 0) to the numerator in the preceding limit to obtain
$$\lim_{h \to 0} \frac{f(x + h)g(x) - f(x)g(x) + f(x)g(x) - f(x)g(x + h)}{hg(x + h)g(x)}.$$
Use this limit to obtain the Quotient Rule.

c. Explain why $F' = (f/g)'$ exists, whenever $g(x) \neq 0$.

87. Product Rule for the second derivative Assuming the first and second derivatives of f and g exist at x, find a formula for $\dfrac{d^2}{dx^2}(f(x)g(x))$.

88. Proof by induction: derivative of e^{kx} for positive integers k Proof by induction is a method in which one begins by showing that a statement, which involves positive integers, is true for a particular value (usually $k = 1$). In the second step, the statement is assumed to be true for $k = n$, and the statement is proved for $k = n + 1$, which concludes the proof.

a. Show that $\dfrac{d}{dx}(e^{kx}) = ke^{kx}$, for $k = 1$.

b. Assume the rule is true for $k = n$ (that is, assume $\dfrac{d}{dx}(e^{nx}) = ne^{nx}$), and show this assumption implies that the rule is true for $k = n + 1$. (*Hint:* Write $e^{(n+1)x}$ as the product of two functions and use the Product Rule.)

89. Derivative of e^{kx} for negative integers k Use the Quotient Rule and Exercise 88 to show that $\dfrac{d}{dx}(e^{kx}) = ke^{kx}$, for negative integers k.

90. Quotient Rule for the second derivative Assuming the first and second derivatives of f and g exist at x, find a formula for $\dfrac{d^2}{dx^2}\left(\dfrac{f(x)}{g(x)}\right)$.

91. Product Rule for three functions Assume that f, g, and h are differentiable at x.

a. Use the Product Rule (twice) to find a formula for $\dfrac{d}{dx}(f(x)g(x)h(x))$.

b. Use the formula in (a) to find $\dfrac{d}{dx}(e^{2x}(x - 1)(x + 3))$.

92. One of the Leibniz Rules One of several Leibniz Rules in calculus deals with higher-order derivatives of products. Let $(fg)^{(n)}$ denote the nth derivative of the product fg, for $n \geq 1$.

a. Prove that $(fg)^{(2)} = f''g + 2f'g' + fg''$.

b. Prove that, in general,
$$(fg)^{(n)} = \sum_{k=0}^{n} \binom{n}{k} f^{(k)} g^{(n-k)},$$
where $\dbinom{n}{k} = \dfrac{n!}{k!(n - k)!}$ are the binomial coefficients.

c. Compare the result of (b) to the expansion of $(a + b)^n$.

QUICK CHECK ANSWERS

1. $f'(x) = 5x^4$ by either method **2.** $f'(x) = 5x^4$ by either method **3.** $f'(x) = -5x^{-6}$ by either method **4.** $f'(x) = 2e^{0.5x}$ ◄

3.5 Derivatives of Trigonometric Functions

➤ Results stated in this section assume that angles are measured in *radians*.

From variations in market trends and ocean temperatures to daily fluctuations in tides and hormone levels, change is often cyclical or periodic. Trigonometric functions are well suited for describing such cyclical behavior. In this section, we investigate the derivatives of trigonometric functions and their many uses.

Two Special Limits

Our principal goal is to determine derivative formulas for $\sin x$ and $\cos x$. To do this, we use two special limits.

Table 3.2

x	$\dfrac{\sin x}{x}$
± 0.1	0.9983341665
± 0.01	0.9999833334
± 0.001	0.9999998333

THEOREM 3.11 Trigonometric Limits

$$\lim_{x\to 0} \frac{\sin x}{x} = 1 \qquad \lim_{x\to 0} \frac{\cos x - 1}{x} = 0$$

Note that these limits cannot be evaluated by direct substitution because in both cases, the numerator and denominator approach zero as $x \to 0$. We first examine numerical and graphical evidence supporting Theorem 3.11, and then we offer an analytic proof.

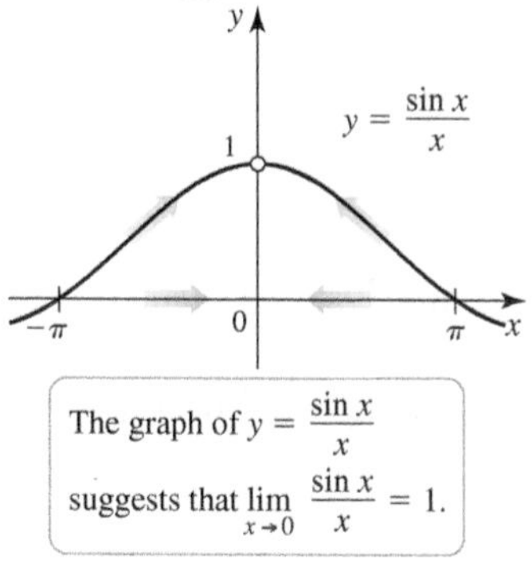

Figure 3.30

The values of $\frac{\sin x}{x}$, rounded to 10 digits, appear in Table 3.2. As x approaches zero from both sides, it appears that $\frac{\sin x}{x}$ approaches 1. Figure 3.30 shows a graph of $y = \frac{\sin x}{x}$, with a hole at $x = 0$, where the function is undefined. The graphical evidence also strongly suggests (but does not prove) that $\lim_{x\to 0} \frac{\sin x}{x} = 1$. Similar evidence indicates that $\frac{\cos x - 1}{x}$ approaches 0 as x approaches 0.

Using a geometric argument and the methods of Chapter 2, we now prove that $\lim_{x\to 0} \frac{\sin x}{x} = 1$. The proof that $\lim_{x\to 0} \frac{\cos x - 1}{x} = 0$ is found in Exercise 73.

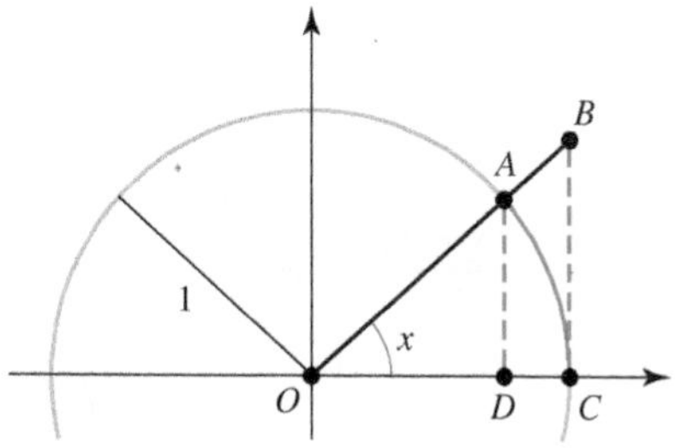

Figure 3.31

Proof: Consider Figure 3.31, in which $\triangle OAD$, $\triangle OBC$, and the sector OAC of the unit circle (with central angle x) are shown. Observe that with $0 < x < \pi/2$,

$$\text{area of } \triangle OAD < \text{area of sector } OAC < \text{area of } \triangle OBC. \qquad (1)$$

Because the circle in Figure 3.31 is a *unit* circle, $OA = OC = 1$. It follows that $\sin x = \frac{AD}{OA} = AD$, $\cos x = \frac{OD}{OA} = OD$, and $\tan x = \frac{BC}{OC} = BC$. From these observations, we conclude that

- the area of $\triangle OAD = \frac{1}{2}(OD)(AD) = \frac{1}{2}\cos x \sin x$,
- the area of sector $OAC = \frac{1}{2} \cdot 1^2 \cdot x = \frac{x}{2}$, and
- the area of $\triangle OBC = \frac{1}{2}(OC)(BC) = \frac{1}{2}\tan x$.

➤ Area of a sector of a circle of radius r formed by a central angle θ:

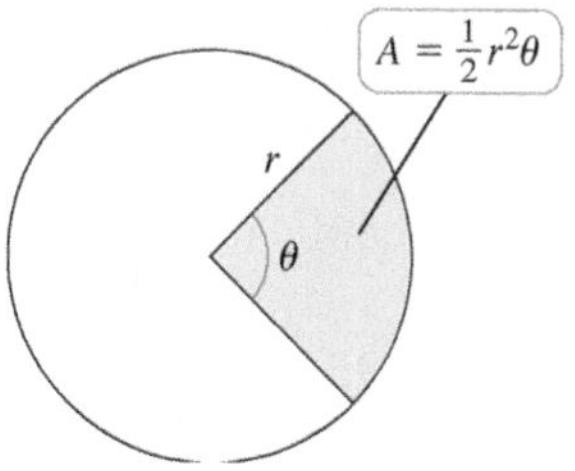

Substituting these results into (1), we have

$$\frac{1}{2}\cos x \sin x < \frac{x}{2} < \frac{1}{2}\tan x.$$

Replacing $\tan x$ with $\dfrac{\sin x}{\cos x}$ and multiplying the inequalities by $\dfrac{2}{\sin x}$ (which is positive) leads to the inequalities

$$\cos x < \frac{x}{\sin x} < \frac{1}{\cos x}.$$

When we take reciprocals and reverse the inequalities, we have

$$\cos x < \frac{\sin x}{x} < \frac{1}{\cos x}, \qquad (2)$$

for $0 < x < \pi/2$.

A similar argument shows that the inequalities in (2) also hold for $-\pi/2 < x < 0$. Taking the limit as $x \to 0$ in (2), we find that

$$\underbrace{\lim_{x\to 0} \cos x}_{1} < \lim_{x\to 0} \frac{\sin x}{x} < \underbrace{\lim_{x\to 0} \frac{1}{\cos x}}_{1}.$$

➤ $\lim_{x\to 0} \frac{\sin x}{x} = 1$ implies that if $|x|$ is small, then $\sin x \approx x$.

The Squeeze Theorem (Theorem 2.5) now implies that $\lim_{x\to 0} \dfrac{\sin x}{x} = 1$. ◄

EXAMPLE 1 **Calculating trigonometric limits** Evaluate the following limits.

a. $\lim_{x\to 0} \dfrac{\sin 4x}{x}$ **b.** $\lim_{x\to 0} \dfrac{\sin 3x}{\sin 5x}$

SOLUTION

a. To use the fact that $\lim_{x\to 0} \dfrac{\sin x}{x} = 1$, the argument of the sine function in the numerator must be the same as the denominator. Multiplying and dividing $\dfrac{\sin 4x}{x}$ by 4, we evaluate the limit as follows:

$$\begin{aligned}
\lim_{x\to 0} \frac{\sin 4x}{x} &= \lim_{x\to 0} \frac{4 \sin 4x}{4x} && \text{Multiply and divide by 4.}\\
&= 4\underbrace{\lim_{t\to 0} \frac{\sin t}{t}}_{1} && \text{Factor out 4 and let } t = 4x;\ t \to 0 \text{ as } x \to 0.\\
&= 4(1) = 4. && \text{Theorem 3.11}
\end{aligned}$$

b. The first step is to divide the numerator and denominator of $\dfrac{\sin 3x}{\sin 5x}$ by x:

$$\frac{\sin 3x}{\sin 5x} = \frac{(\sin 3x)/x}{(\sin 5x)/x}.$$

As in part (a), we now divide and multiply $\dfrac{\sin 3x}{x}$ by 3 and divide and multiply $\dfrac{\sin 5x}{x}$ by 5. In the numerator, we let $t = 3x$, and in the denominator, we let $u = 5x$. In each case, $t \to 0$ and $u \to 0$ as $x \to 0$. Therefore,

$$\lim_{x\to 0} \frac{\sin 3x}{\sin 5x} = \lim_{x\to 0} \frac{\frac{3\sin 3x}{3x}}{\frac{5\sin 5x}{5x}} \qquad \text{Multiply and divide by 3 and 5.}$$

$$= \frac{3}{5}\frac{\lim_{t\to 0}(\sin t)/t}{\lim_{u\to 0}(\sin u)/u} \qquad \text{Let } t = 3x \text{ in numerator and } u = 5x \text{ in denominator.}$$

$$= \frac{3}{5}\cdot\frac{1}{1} = \frac{3}{5}. \qquad \text{Both limits equal 1.}$$

Related Exercises 7–16 ◀

QUICK CHECK 1 Evaluate $\lim_{x\to 0} \frac{\tan 2x}{x}$. ◀

We now use the important limits of Theorem 3.11 to establish the derivatives of $\sin x$ and $\cos x$.

Derivatives of Sine and Cosine Functions

We start with the definition of the derivative,

$$f'(x) = \lim_{h\to 0} \frac{f(x+h) - f(x)}{h},$$

with $f(x) = \sin x$, and then appeal to the sine addition identity

$$\sin(x+h) = \sin x \cos h + \cos x \sin h.$$

The derivative is

$$f'(x) = \lim_{h\to 0} \frac{\sin(x+h) - \sin x}{h} \qquad \text{Definition of derivative}$$

$$= \lim_{h\to 0} \frac{\sin x \cos h + \cos x \sin h - \sin x}{h} \qquad \text{Sine addition identity}$$

$$= \lim_{h\to 0} \frac{\sin x(\cos h - 1) + \cos x \sin h}{h} \qquad \text{Factor } \sin x.$$

$$= \lim_{h\to 0} \frac{\sin x(\cos h - 1)}{h} + \lim_{h\to 0} \frac{\cos x \sin h}{h} \qquad \text{Theorem 2.3}$$

$$= \sin x \underbrace{\left(\lim_{h\to 0} \frac{\cos h - 1}{h}\right)}_{0} + \cos x \underbrace{\left(\lim_{h\to 0} \frac{\sin h}{h}\right)}_{1} \qquad \text{Both } \sin x \text{ and } \cos x \text{ are independent of } h.$$

$$= (\sin x)(0) + \cos x(1) \qquad \text{Theorem 3.11}$$

$$= \cos x. \qquad \text{Simplify.}$$

We have proved the important result that $\frac{d}{dx}(\sin x) = \cos x$.

The fact that $\frac{d}{dx}(\cos x) = -\sin x$ is proved in a similar way using a cosine addition identity (Exercise 75).

> **THEOREM 3.12 Derivatives of Sine and Cosine**
>
> $$\frac{d}{dx}(\sin x) = \cos x \qquad \frac{d}{dx}(\cos x) = -\sin x$$

From a geometric point of view, these derivative formulas make sense. Because $f(x) = \sin x$ is a periodic function, we expect its derivative to be periodic. Observe that the horizontal tangent lines on the graph of $f(x) = \sin x$ (Figure 3.32a) occur at the zeros of $f'(x) = \cos x$. Similarly, the horizontal tangent lines on the graph of $f(x) = \cos x$ occur at the zeros of $f'(x) = -\sin x$ (Figure 3.32b).

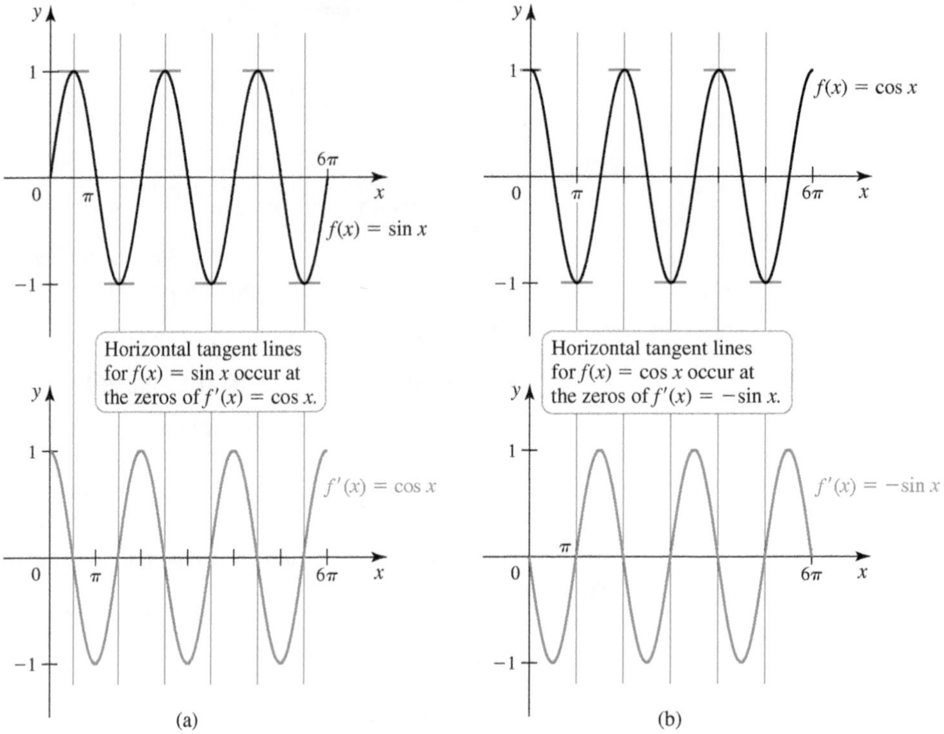

Figure 3.32

QUICK CHECK 2 At what points on the interval $[0, 2\pi]$ does the graph of $f(x) = \sin x$ have tangent lines with positive slopes? At what points on the interval $[0, 2\pi]$ is $\cos x > 0$? Explain the connection. ◄

EXAMPLE 2 Derivatives involving trigonometric functions Calculate dy/dx for the following functions.

a. $y = e^{2x} \cos x$ **b.** $y = \sin x - x \cos x$ **c.** $y = \dfrac{1 + \sin x}{1 - \sin x}$

SOLUTION

a. $$\frac{dy}{dx} = \frac{d}{dx}(e^{2x}\cos x) = \underbrace{2e^{2x}\cos x}_{\text{derivative of } e^{2x} \cdot \cos x} + \underbrace{e^{2x}(-\sin x)}_{e^{2x} \cdot \text{derivative of } \cos x} \quad \text{Product Rule}$$

$$= e^{2x}(2\cos x - \sin x) \quad \text{Simplify.}$$

b. $$\frac{dy}{dx} = \frac{d}{dx}(\sin x) - \frac{d}{dx}(x \cos x) \quad \text{Difference Rule}$$

$$= \cos x - (\underbrace{(1)\cos x}_{\text{derivative of } x \cdot \cos x} + \underbrace{x(-\sin x)}_{x \cdot \text{derivative of } \cos x}) \quad \text{Product Rule}$$

$$= x \sin x \quad \text{Simplify.}$$

c. $$\frac{dy}{dx} = \frac{(1 - \sin x)\overbrace{(\cos x)}^{\text{derivative of } 1 + \sin x} - (1 + \sin x)\overbrace{(-\cos x)}^{\text{derivative of } 1 - \sin x}}{(1 - \sin x)^2} \quad \text{Quotient Rule}$$

$$= \frac{\cos x - \cos x \sin x + \cos x + \sin x \cos x}{(1 - \sin x)^2} \quad \text{Expand.}$$

$$= \frac{2\cos x}{(1 - \sin x)^2} \quad \text{Simplify.}$$

Related Exercises 17–28 ◀

Derivatives of Other Trigonometric Functions

The derivatives of $\tan x$, $\cot x$, $\sec x$, and $\csc x$ are obtained using the derivatives of $\sin x$ and $\cos x$ together with the Quotient Rule and trigonometric identities.

➤ Recall that $\tan x = \frac{\sin x}{\cos x}$, $\cot x = \frac{\cos x}{\sin x}$, $\sec x = \frac{1}{\cos x}$, and $\csc x = \frac{1}{\sin x}$.

EXAMPLE 3 **Derivative of the tangent function** Calculate $\frac{d}{dx}(\tan x)$.

SOLUTION Using the identity $\tan x = \frac{\sin x}{\cos x}$ and the Quotient Rule, we have

$$\frac{d}{dx}(\tan x) = \frac{d}{dx}\left(\frac{\sin x}{\cos x}\right)$$

$$= \frac{\overbrace{\cos x}^{\text{derivative of } \sin x}\cos x - \sin x\overbrace{(-\sin x)}^{\text{derivative of } \cos x}}{\cos^2 x} \quad \text{Quotient Rule}$$

$$= \frac{\cos^2 x + \sin^2 x}{\cos^2 x} \quad \text{Simplify numerator.}$$

$$= \frac{1}{\cos^2 x} = \sec^2 x. \quad \cos^2 x + \sin^2 x = 1$$

Therefore, $\frac{d}{dx}(\tan x) = \sec^2 x$.

Related Exercises 29–31 ◀

➤ One way to remember Theorem 3.13 is to learn the derivatives of the sine, tangent, and secant functions. Then replace each function with its corresponding **cofunction** and put a negative sign on the right-hand side of the new derivative formula.

$$\frac{d}{dx}(\sin x) = \cos x \quad \leftrightarrow \quad \frac{d}{dx}(\cos x) = -\sin x$$

$$\frac{d}{dx}(\tan x) = \sec^2 x \quad \leftrightarrow \quad \frac{d}{dx}(\cot x) = -\csc^2 x$$

$$\frac{d}{dx}(\sec x) = \sec x \tan x \quad \leftrightarrow \quad \frac{d}{dx}(\csc x) = -\csc x \cot x$$

The derivatives of $\cot x$, $\sec x$, and $\csc x$ are given in Theorem 3.13 (Exercises 29–31).

THEOREM 3.13 **Derivatives of the Trigonometric Functions**

$$\frac{d}{dx}(\sin x) = \cos x \qquad \frac{d}{dx}(\cos x) = -\sin x$$

$$\frac{d}{dx}(\tan x) = \sec^2 x \qquad \frac{d}{dx}(\cot x) = -\csc^2 x$$

$$\frac{d}{dx}(\sec x) = \sec x \tan x \qquad \frac{d}{dx}(\csc x) = -\csc x \cot x$$

QUICK CHECK 3 The formulas for $\frac{d}{dx}(\cot x)$, $\frac{d}{dx}(\sec x)$, and $\frac{d}{dx}(\csc x)$ can be determined using the Quotient Rule. Why? ◀

EXAMPLE 4 Derivatives involving sec x and csc x Find the derivative of $y = \sec x \csc x$.

SOLUTION

$$\begin{aligned}
\frac{dy}{dx} &= \frac{d}{dx}(\sec x \cdot \csc x) \\
&= \underbrace{\sec x \tan x}_{\text{derivative of } \sec x} \csc x + \sec x \underbrace{(-\csc x \cot x)}_{\text{derivative of } \csc x} && \text{Product Rule} \\
&= \underbrace{\frac{1}{\cos x}}_{\sec x} \cdot \underbrace{\frac{\sin x}{\cos x}}_{\tan x} \cdot \underbrace{\frac{1}{\sin x}}_{\csc x} - \underbrace{\frac{1}{\cos x}}_{\sec x} \cdot \underbrace{\frac{1}{\sin x}}_{\csc x} \cdot \underbrace{\frac{\cos x}{\sin x}}_{\cot x} && \text{Write functions in terms of } \sin x \text{ and } \cos x. \\
&= \frac{1}{\cos^2 x} - \frac{1}{\sin^2 x} && \text{Cancel and simplify.} \\
&= \sec^2 x - \csc^2 x && \text{Definition of } \sec x \text{ and } \csc x
\end{aligned}$$

Related Exercises 32–40 ◀

QUICK CHECK 4 Why is the derivative of $\sec x \csc x$ equal to the derivative of $\frac{1}{\cos x \sin x}$? ◀

Higher-Order Trigonometric Derivatives

Higher-order derivatives of the sine and cosine functions are important in many applications, particularly in problems that involve oscillations, vibrations, or waves. A few higher-order derivatives of $y = \sin x$ reveal a pattern.

$$\frac{dy}{dx} = \cos x \qquad \frac{d^2y}{dx^2} = \frac{d}{dx}(\cos x) = -\sin x$$

$$\frac{d^3y}{dx^3} = \frac{d}{dx}(-\sin x) = -\cos x \qquad \frac{d^4y}{dx^4} = \frac{d}{dx}(-\cos x) = \sin x$$

We see that the higher-order derivatives of $\sin x$ cycle back periodically to $\pm \sin x$. In general, it can be shown that $\frac{d^{2n}y}{dx^{2n}} = (-1)^n \sin x$, with a similar result for $\cos x$ (Exercise 80). This cyclic behavior in the derivatives of $\sin x$ and $\cos x$ does not occur with the other trigonometric functions.

QUICK CHECK 5 Find $\frac{d^2y}{dx^2}$ and $\frac{d^4y}{dx^4}$ when $y = \cos x$. Find $\frac{d^{40}y}{dx^{40}}$ and $\frac{d^{42}y}{dx^{42}}$ when $y = \sin x$. ◀

EXAMPLE 5 Second-order derivatives Find the second derivative of $y = \csc x$.

SOLUTION By Theorem 3.13, $\frac{dy}{dx} = -\csc x \cot x$.

Applying the Product Rule gives the second derivative:

$$\begin{aligned}
\frac{d^2y}{dx^2} &= \frac{d}{dx}(-\csc x \cot x) \\
&= \left(\frac{d}{dx}(-\csc x)\right)\cot x - \csc x \frac{d}{dx}(\cot x) && \text{Product Rule} \\
&= (\csc x \cot x)\cot x - \csc x\,(-\csc^2 x) && \text{Calculate derivatives.} \\
&= \csc x\,(\cot^2 x + \csc^2 x). && \text{Factor.}
\end{aligned}$$

Related Exercises 41–48 ◀

SECTION 3.5 EXERCISES

Review Questions

1. Why is it not possible to evaluate $\lim_{x\to 0} \frac{\sin x}{x}$ by direct substitution?

2. How is $\lim_{x\to 0} \frac{\sin x}{x}$ used in this section?

3. Explain why the Quotient Rule is used to determine the derivative of $\tan x$ and $\cot x$.

4. How can you use the derivatives $\frac{d}{dx}(\sin x) = \cos x$, $\frac{d}{dx}(\tan x) = \sec^2 x$, and $\frac{d}{dx}(\sec x) = \sec x \tan x$ to remember the derivatives of $\cos x$, $\cot x$, and $\csc x$?

5. Let $f(x) = \sin x$. What is the value of $f'(\pi)$?

6. Where does the graph of $\sin x$ have a horizontal tangent line? Where does $\cos x$ have a value of zero? Explain the connection between these two observations.

Basic Skills

7–16. Trigonometric limits *Use Theorem 3.11 to evaluate the following limits.*

7. $\lim_{x\to 0} \frac{\sin 3x}{x}$

8. $\lim_{x\to 0} \frac{\sin 5x}{3x}$

9. $\lim_{x\to 0} \frac{\sin 7x}{\sin 3x}$

10. $\lim_{x\to 0} \frac{\sin 3x}{\tan 4x}$

11. $\lim_{x\to 0} \frac{\tan 5x}{x}$

12. $\lim_{\theta\to 0} \frac{\cos^2 \theta - 1}{\theta}$

13. $\lim_{x\to 0} \frac{\tan 7x}{\sin x}$

14. $\lim_{\theta\to 0} \frac{\sec \theta - 1}{\theta}$

15. $\lim_{x\to 2} \frac{\sin (x - 2)}{x^2 - 4}$

16. $\lim_{x\to -3} \frac{\sin (x + 3)}{x^2 + 8x + 15}$

17–28. Calculating derivatives *Find dy/dx for the following functions.*

17. $y = \sin x + \cos x$

18. $y = 5x^2 + \cos x$

19. $y = e^{-x} \sin x$

20. $y = \sin x + 4e^{0.5x}$

21. $y = x \sin x$

22. $y = e^{6x} \sin x$

23. $y = \frac{\cos x}{\sin x + 1}$

24. $y = \frac{1 - \sin x}{1 + \sin x}$

25. $y = \sin x \cos x$

26. $y = \frac{(x^2 - 1) \sin x}{\sin x + 1}$

27. $y = \cos^2 x$

28. $y = \frac{x \sin x}{1 + \cos x}$

29–31. Derivatives of other trigonometric functions *Verify the following derivative formulas using the Quotient Rule.*

29. $\frac{d}{dx}(\cot x) = -\csc^2 x$

30. $\frac{d}{dx}(\sec x) = \sec x \tan x$

31. $\frac{d}{dx}(\csc x) = -\csc x \cot x$

32–40. Derivatives involving other trigonometric functions *Find the derivative of the following functions.*

32. $y = \tan x + \cot x$

33. $y = \sec x + \csc x$

34. $y = \sec x \tan x$

35. $y = e^{5x} \csc x$

36. $y = \frac{\tan w}{1 + \tan w}$

37. $y = \frac{\cot x}{1 + \csc x}$

38. $y = \frac{\tan t}{1 + \sec t}$

39. $y = \frac{1}{\sec z \csc z}$

40. $y = \csc^2 \theta - 1$

41–48. Second-order derivatives *Find y'' for the following functions.*

41. $y = x \sin x$

42. $y = \cos x$

43. $y = e^x \sin x$

44. $y = \frac{1}{2} e^x \cos x$

45. $y = \cot x$

46. $y = \tan x$

47. $y = \sec x \csc x$

48. $y = \cos \theta \sin \theta$

Further Explorations

49. **Explain why or why not** Determine whether the following statements are true and give an explanation or counterexample.

 a. $\frac{d}{dx}(\sin^2 x) = \cos^2 x$.

 b. $\frac{d^2}{dx^2}(\sin x) = \sin x$.

 c. $\frac{d^4}{dx^4}(\cos x) = \cos x$.

 d. The function $\sec x$ is not differentiable at $x = \pi/2$.

50–55. Trigonometric limits *Evaluate the following limits or state that they do not exist.*

50. $\lim_{x\to 0} \frac{\sin ax}{bx}$, where a and b are constants with $b \neq 0$

51. $\lim_{x\to 0} \frac{\sin ax}{\sin bx}$, where a and b are constants with $b \neq 0$

52. $\lim_{x\to \pi/2} \frac{\cos x}{x - (\pi/2)}$

53. $\lim_{x\to 0} \frac{3 \sec^5 x}{x^2 + 4}$

54. $\lim_{x\to \infty} \frac{\cos x}{x}$

55. $\lim_{x\to \pi/4} 3 \csc 2x \cot 2x$

56–61. Calculating derivatives *Find dy/dx for the following functions.*

56. $y = \frac{\sin x}{1 + \cos x}$

57. $y = x \cos x \sin x$

58. $y = \frac{1}{2 + \sin x}$

59. $y = \frac{\sin x}{\sin x - \cos x}$

60. $y = \frac{x \cos x}{1 + x^3}$

61. $y = \frac{1 - \cos x}{1 + \cos x}$

62–65. Equations of tangent lines

a. Find an equation of the line tangent to the following curves at the given value of x.

b. Use a graphing utility to plot the curve and the tangent line.

62. $y = 4 \sin x \cos x;\ x = \frac{\pi}{3}$

63. $y = 1 + 2 \sin x;\ x = \frac{\pi}{6}$

64. $y = \csc x;\ x = \frac{\pi}{4}$

65. $y = \frac{\cos x}{1 - \cos x};\ x = \frac{\pi}{3}$

66. Locations of tangent lines

a. For what values of x does $g(x) = x - \sin x$ have a horizontal tangent line?

b. For what values of x does $g(x) = x - \sin x$ have a slope of 1?

67. Locations of horizontal tangent lines For what values of x does $f(x) = x - 2 \cos x$ have a horizontal tangent line?

68. Matching Match the graphs of the functions in a–d with the graphs of their derivatives in A–D.

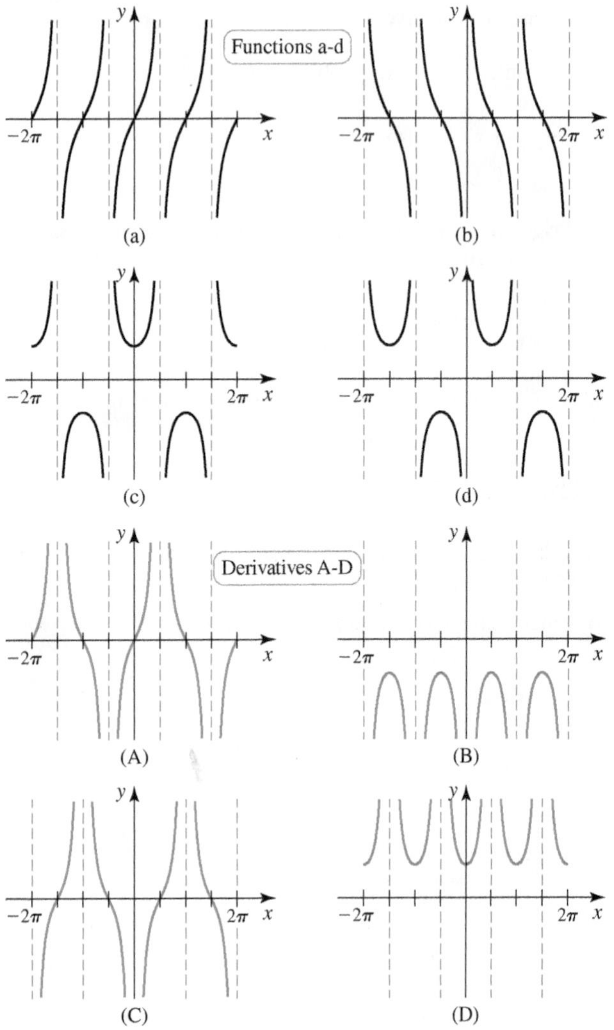

Applications

69. Velocity of an oscillator An object oscillates along a vertical line, and its position in centimeters is given by $y(t) = 30(\sin t - 1)$, where $t \geq 0$ is measured in seconds and y is positive in the upward direction.

a. Graph the position function, for $0 \leq t \leq 10$.

b. Find the velocity of the oscillator, $v(t) = y'(t)$.

c. Graph the velocity function, for $0 \leq t \leq 10$.

d. At what times and positions is the velocity zero?

e. At what times and positions is the velocity a maximum?

f. The acceleration of the oscillator is $a(t) = v'(t)$. Find and graph the acceleration function.

70. Damped sine wave The graph of $f(t) = e^{-kt} \sin t$ with $k > 0$ is called a *damped* sine wave; it is used in a variety of applications, such as modeling the vibrations of a shock absorber.

a. Use a graphing utility to graph f for $k = 1, \frac{1}{2}$, and $\frac{1}{10}$ to understand why these curves are called damped sine waves. What effect does k have on the behavior of the graph?

b. Compute $f'(t)$ for $k = 1$ and use it to determine where the graph of f has a horizontal tangent.

c. Evaluate $\lim_{t \to \infty} e^{-t} \sin t$ by using the Squeeze Theorem. What does the result say about the oscillations of a damped sine wave?

71. A differential equation A differential equation is an equation involving an unknown function and its derivatives. Consider the differential equation $y''(t) + y(t) = 0$ (see Chapter 8).

a. Show that $y = A \sin t$ satisfies the equation for any constant A.

b. Show that $y = B \cos t$ satisfies the equation for any constant B.

c. Show that $y = A \sin t + B \cos t$ satisfies the equation for any constants A and B.

Additional Exercises

72. Using identities Use the identity $\sin 2x = 2 \sin x \cos x$ to find $\frac{d}{dx}(\sin 2x)$. Then use the identity $\cos 2x = \cos^2 x - \sin^2 x$ to express the derivative of $\sin 2x$ in terms of $\cos 2x$.

73. Proof of $\lim_{x \to 0} \frac{\cos x - 1}{x} = 0$ Use the trigonometric identity $\cos^2 x + \sin^2 x = 1$ to prove that $\lim_{x \to 0} \frac{\cos x - 1}{x} = 0$. (*Hint:* Begin by multiplying the numerator and denominator by $\cos x + 1$.)

74. Another method for proving $\lim_{x \to 0} \frac{\cos x - 1}{x} = 0$ Use the half-angle formula $\sin^2 x = \frac{1 - \cos 2x}{2}$ to prove that $\lim_{x \to 0} \frac{\cos x - 1}{x} = 0$.

75. Proof of $\frac{d}{dx}(\cos x) = -\sin x$ Use the definition of the derivative and the trigonometric identity

$$\cos(x + h) = \cos x \cos h - \sin x \sin h$$

to prove that $\frac{d}{dx}(\cos x) = -\sin x$.

76. Continuity of a piecewise function Let

$$f(x) = \begin{cases} \dfrac{3 \sin x}{x} & \text{if } x \neq 0 \\ a & \text{if } x = 0. \end{cases}$$

For what values of a is f continuous?

77. Continuity of a piecewise function Let

$$g(x) = \begin{cases} \dfrac{1 - \cos x}{2x} & \text{if } x \neq 0 \\ a & \text{if } x = 0. \end{cases}$$

For what values of a is g continuous?

T **78. Computing limits with angles in degrees** Suppose your graphing calculator has two functions, one called $\sin x$, which calculates the sine of x when x is in radians, and the other called $s(x)$, which calculates the sine of x when x is in degrees.

a. Explain why $s(x) = \sin\left(\dfrac{\pi}{180}x\right)$.

b. Evaluate $\lim_{x \to 0} \dfrac{s(x)}{x}$. Verify your answer by estimating the limit on your calculator.

79. Derivatives of $\sin^n x$ Calculate the following derivatives using the Product Rule.

a. $\dfrac{d}{dx}(\sin^2 x)$ **b.** $\dfrac{d}{dx}(\sin^3 x)$ **c.** $\dfrac{d}{dx}(\sin^4 x)$

d. Based on your answers to parts (a)–(c), make a conjecture about $\dfrac{d}{dx}(\sin^n x)$, where n is a positive integer. Then prove the result by induction.

80. Higher-order derivatives of $\sin x$ and $\cos x$ Prove that $\dfrac{d^{2n}}{dx^{2n}}(\sin x) = (-1)^n \sin x$ and $\dfrac{d^{2n}}{dx^{2n}}(\cos x) = (-1)^n \cos x$.

81–84. Identifying derivatives from limits *The following limits equal the derivative of a function f at a point a.*

a. *Find one possible f and a.*

b. *Evaluate the limit.*

81. $\lim_{h \to 0} \dfrac{\sin\left(\frac{\pi}{6} + h\right) - \frac{1}{2}}{h}$ **82.** $\lim_{h \to 0} \dfrac{\cos\left(\frac{\pi}{6} + h\right) - \frac{\sqrt{3}}{2}}{h}$

83. $\lim_{x \to \pi/4} \dfrac{\cot x - 1}{x - \frac{\pi}{4}}$ **84.** $\lim_{h \to 0} \dfrac{\tan\left(\frac{5\pi}{6} + h\right) + \frac{1}{\sqrt{3}}}{h}$

T **85–86. Difference quotients** *Suppose that f is differentiable for all x and consider the function*

$$D(x) = \frac{f(x + 0.01) - f(x)}{0.01}.$$

For the following functions, graph D on the given interval, and explain why the graph appears as it does. What is the relationship between the functions f and D?

85. $f(x) = \sin x$ on $[-\pi, \pi]$

86. $f(x) = \dfrac{x^3}{3} + 1$ on $[-2, 2]$

QUICK CHECK ANSWERS

1. 2 **2.** $0 < x < \frac{\pi}{2}$ and $\frac{3\pi}{2} < x < 2\pi$. The value of $\cos x$ is the slope of the line tangent to the curve $y = \sin x$. **3.** The Quotient Rule is used because each function is a quotient when written in terms of the sine and cosine functions. **4.** $\dfrac{1}{\cos x \sin x} = \dfrac{1}{\cos x} \cdot \dfrac{1}{\sin x} = \sec x \csc x$ **5.** $\dfrac{d^2 y}{dx^2} = -\cos x$, $\dfrac{d^4 y}{dx^4} = \cos x$, $\dfrac{d^{40}}{dx^{40}}(\sin x) = \sin x$, $\dfrac{d^{42}}{dx^{42}}(\sin x) = -\sin x$ ◀

3.6 Derivatives as Rates of Change

The theme of this section is the *derivative as a rate of change*. Observing the world around us, we see that almost everything is in a state of change: The size of the Internet is increasing; your blood pressure fluctuates; as supply increases, prices decrease; and the universe is expanding. This section explores a few of the many applications of this idea and demonstrates why calculus is called the mathematics of change.

One-Dimensional Motion

➤ When describing the motion of objects, it is customary to use t as the independent variable to represent time. Generally, motion is assumed to begin at $t = 0$.

Describing the motion of objects such as projectiles and planets was one of the challenges that led to the development of calculus in the 17th century. We begin by considering the motion of an object confined to one dimension; that is, the object moves along a line. This motion could be horizontal (for example, a car moving along a straight highway), or it could be vertical (such as a projectile launched vertically into the air).

Position and Velocity Suppose an object moves along a straight line and its location at time t is given by the **position function** $s = f(t)$. All positions are measured relative to a reference point $s = 0$. The **displacement** of the object between $t = a$ and $t = a + \Delta t$ is $\Delta s = f(a + \Delta t) - f(a)$, where the elapsed time is Δt units (Figure 3.33).

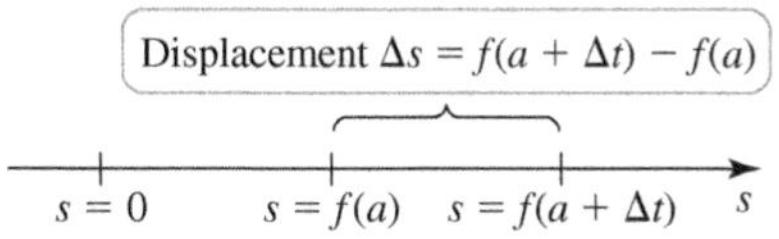

Figure 3.33

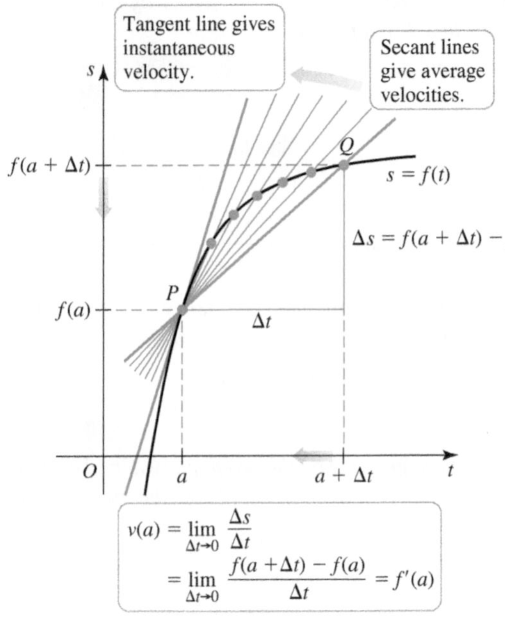

Figure 3.34

Recall from Section 2.1 that the *average velocity* of the object over the interval $[a, a + \Delta t]$ is the displacement Δs of the object divided by the elapsed time Δt:

$$v_{av} = \frac{\Delta s}{\Delta t} = \frac{f(a + \Delta t) - f(a)}{\Delta t}.$$

The average velocity is the slope of the secant line passing through the points $P(a, f(a))$ and $Q(a + \Delta t, f(a + \Delta t))$ (Figure 3.34).

As Δt approaches 0, the average velocity is calculated over smaller and smaller time intervals, and the limiting value of these average velocities, when it exists, is the *instantaneous velocity* at a. This is the same argument used to arrive at the derivative. The conclusion is that the instantaneous velocity at time a, denoted $v(a)$, is the derivative of the position function evaluated at a:

$$v(a) = \lim_{\Delta t \to 0} \frac{f(a + \Delta t) - f(a)}{\Delta t} = f'(a).$$

Equivalently, the instantaneous velocity at a is the rate of change in the position function at a; it also equals the slope of the line tangent to the curve $s = f(t)$ at $P(a, f(a))$.

➤ Using the various derivative notations, the velocity is also written $v(t) = s'(t) = ds/dt$. If *average* or *instantaneous* is not specified, *velocity* is understood to mean instantaneous velocity.

DEFINITION Average and Instantaneous Velocity

Let $s = f(t)$ be the position function of an object moving along a line. The **average velocity** of the object over the time interval $[a, a + \Delta t]$ is the slope of the secant line between $(a, f(a))$ and $(a + \Delta t, f(a + \Delta t))$:

$$v_{av} = \frac{f(a + \Delta t) - f(a)}{\Delta t}.$$

The **instantaneous velocity** at a is the slope of the line tangent to the position curve, which is the derivative of the position function:

$$v(a) = \lim_{\Delta t \to 0} \frac{f(a + \Delta t) - f(a)}{\Delta t} = f'(a).$$

QUICK CHECK 1 Does the speedometer in your car measure average or instantaneous velocity? ◄

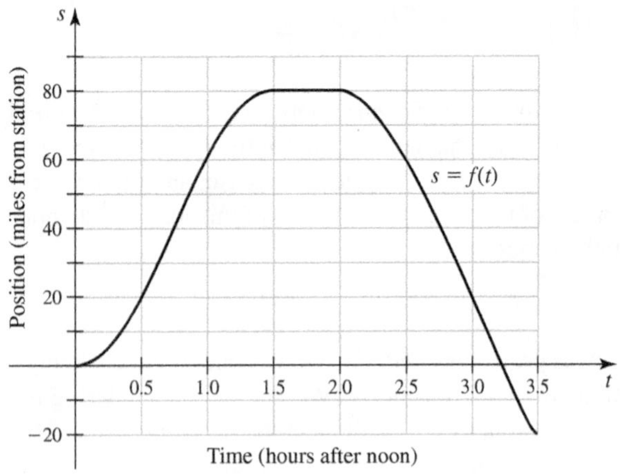

Figure 3.35

EXAMPLE 1 Position and velocity of a patrol car Assume a police station is located along a straight east-west freeway. At noon ($t = 0$), a patrol car leaves the station heading east. The position function of the car $s = f(t)$ gives the location of the car in miles east ($s > 0$) or west ($s < 0$) of the station t hours after noon (Figure 3.35).

a. Describe the location of the patrol car during the first 3.5 hr of the trip.

b. Calculate the displacement and average velocity of the car between 2:00 P.M. and 3:30 P.M. ($2 \le t \le 3.5$).

c. At what time(s) is the instantaneous velocity greatest *as the car travels east*?

SOLUTION

a. The graph of the position function indicates the car travels 80 miles east between $t = 0$ (noon) and $t = 1.5$ (1:30 P.M.). The car is at rest and its position does not change from $t = 1.5$ to $t = 2$ (that is, from 1:30 P.M. to 2:00 P.M.). Starting at $t = 2$, the car's distance from the station decreases, which means the car travels west, eventually ending up 20 miles west of the station at $t = 3.5$ (3:30 P.M.) (Figure 3.36).

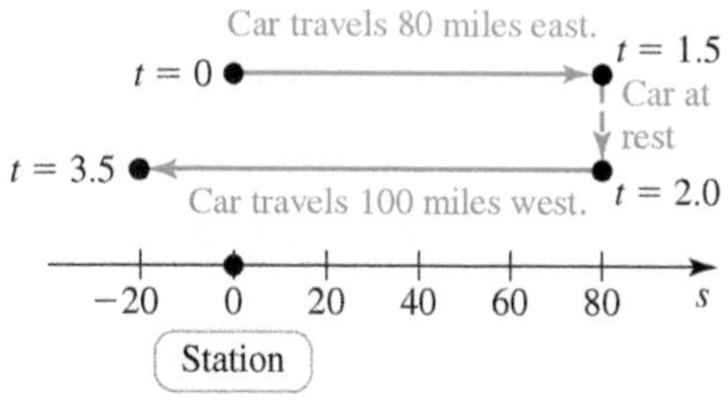

Figure 3.36

b. The position of the car at 3:30 P.M. is $f(3.5) = -20$ (Figure 3.35; the negative sign indicates the car is 20 miles *west* of the station), and the position of the car at 2:00 P.M. is $f(2) = 80$. Therefore, the displacement is

$$\Delta s = f(3.5) - f(2) = -20 \text{ mi} - 80 \text{ mi} = -100 \text{ mi}$$

during an elapsed time of $\Delta t = 3.5 - 2 = 1.5$ hr (the *negative* displacement indicates that the car moved 100 miles *west*). The average velocity is

$$v_{\text{av}} = \frac{\Delta s}{\Delta t} = \frac{-100 \text{ mi}}{1.5 \text{ hr}} \approx -66.7 \text{ mi/hr}.$$

c. The greatest eastward instantaneous velocity corresponds to points at which the graph of the position function has the greatest positive slope. The greatest slope occurs between $t = 0.5$ and $t = 1$. During this time interval, the car also has a nearly constant velocity because the curve is approximately linear. We conclude that the eastward velocity is largest from 12:30 P.M. to 1:00 P.M. *Related Exercises 9–10* ◄

Speed and Acceleration When only the magnitude of the velocity is of interest, we use *speed*, which is the absolute value of the velocity:

$$\text{speed} = |v|.$$

For example, a car with an instantaneous velocity of -30 mi/hr has a speed of 30 mi/hr.

A more complete description of an object moving along a line includes its *acceleration*, which is the rate of change of the velocity; that is, acceleration is the derivative of the velocity function with respect to time t. If the acceleration is positive, the object's velocity increases; if it is negative, the object's velocity decreases. Because velocity is the derivative of the position function, acceleration is the second derivative of the position. Therefore,

$$a = \frac{dv}{dt} = \frac{d^2s}{dt^2}.$$

➤ Newton's First Law of Motion says that in the absence of external forces, a moving object has no acceleration, which means the magnitude and direction of the velocity are constant.

DEFINITION Velocity, Speed, and Acceleration

Suppose an object moves along a line with position $s = f(t)$. Then

the **velocity** at time t is $$v = \frac{ds}{dt} = f'(t),$$

the **speed** at time t is $$|v| = |f'(t)|, \text{ and}$$

the **acceleration** at time t is $$a = \frac{dv}{dt} = \frac{d^2s}{dt^2} = f''(t).$$

QUICK CHECK 2 For an object moving along a line, is it possible for its velocity to increase while its speed decreases? Is it possible for its velocity to decrease while its speed increases? Give an example to support your answers. ◀

➤ The units of derivatives are consistent with the notation. If s is measured in meters and t is measured in seconds, the units of the velocity $\frac{ds}{dt}$ are m/s. The units of the acceleration $\frac{d^2s}{dt^2}$ are m/s^2.

EXAMPLE 2 Velocity and acceleration Suppose the position (in feet) of an object moving horizontally at time t (in seconds) is $s = t^2 - 5t$, for $0 \le t \le 5$ (Figure 3.37). Assume that positive values of s correspond to positions to the right of $s = 0$.

a. Graph the velocity function on the interval $0 \le t \le 5$ and determine when the object is stationary, moving to the left, and moving to the right.

b. Graph the acceleration function on the interval $0 \le t \le 5$.

c. Describe the motion of the object.

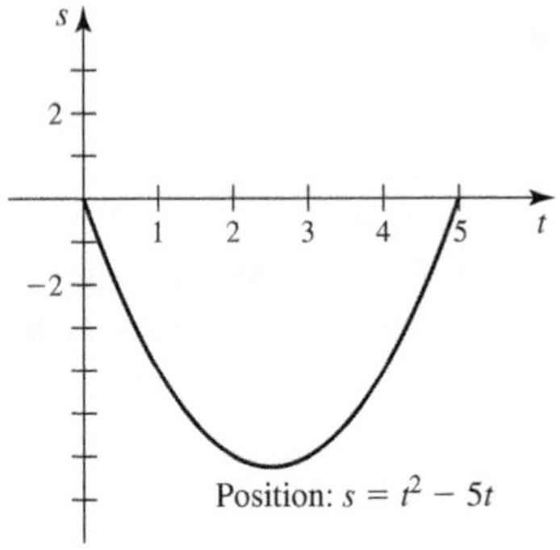

Figure 3.37

SOLUTION

a. The velocity is $v = s'(t) = 2t - 5$. The object is stationary when $v = 2t - 5 = 0$, or at $t = 2.5$. Solving $v = 2t - 5 > 0$, the velocity is positive (motion to the right) for $\frac{5}{2} < t \le 5$. Similarly, the velocity is negative (motion to the left) for $0 \le t < \frac{5}{2}$. Though the velocity of the object is increasing at all times, its speed is decreasing for $0 \le t < \frac{5}{2}$, and then increasing for $\frac{5}{2} < t \le 5$. The graph of the velocity function (Figure 3.38) confirms these observations.

b. The acceleration is the derivative of the velocity or $a = v'(t) = s''(t) = 2$. This means that the acceleration is 2 ft/s^2, for $0 \le t \le 5$ (Figure 3.39).

c. Starting at an initial position of $s(0) = 0$, the object moves in the negative direction (to the left) with decreasing speed until it comes to rest momentarily at $s\left(\frac{5}{2}\right) = -\frac{25}{4}$. The object then moves in the positive direction (to the right) with increasing speed, reaching its initial position at $t = 5$. During this time interval, the acceleration is constant.

➤ Figure 3.37 gives the graph of the position function, not the path of the object. The motion is along a horizontal line.

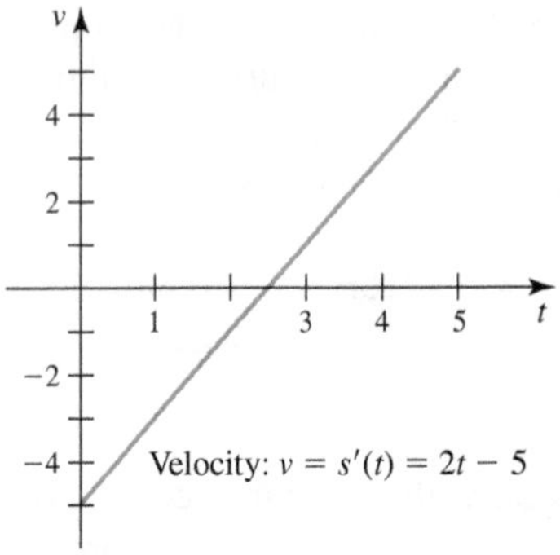

Figure 3.38

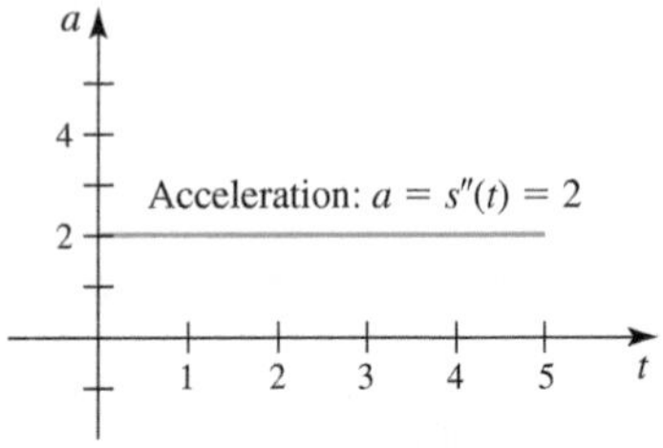

Figure 3.39

Related Exercises 11–16 ◀

QUICK CHECK 3 Describe the velocity of an object that has a positive constant acceleration. Could an object have a positive acceleration and a decreasing speed? ◀

➤ The acceleration due to Earth's gravitational field is denoted g. In metric units, $g \approx 9.8\ m/s^2$ on the surface of Earth; in the U.S. Customary System (USCS), $g \approx 32\ ft/s^2$.

Free Fall We now consider a problem in which an object moves vertically in Earth's gravitational field, assuming that no other forces (such as air resistance) are at work.

EXAMPLE 3 Motion in a gravitational field Suppose a stone is thrown vertically upward with an initial velocity of 64 ft/s from a bridge 96 ft above a river. By Newton's laws of motion, the position of the stone (measured as the height above the river) after t seconds is

$$s(t) = -16t^2 + 64t + 96,$$

where $s = 0$ is the level of the river (Figure 3.40a).

➤ The position function in Example 3 is derived in Section 6.1. Once again we mention that the graph of the position function is not the path of the stone.

a. Find the velocity and acceleration functions.

b. What is the highest point above the river reached by the stone?

c. With what velocity will the stone strike the river?

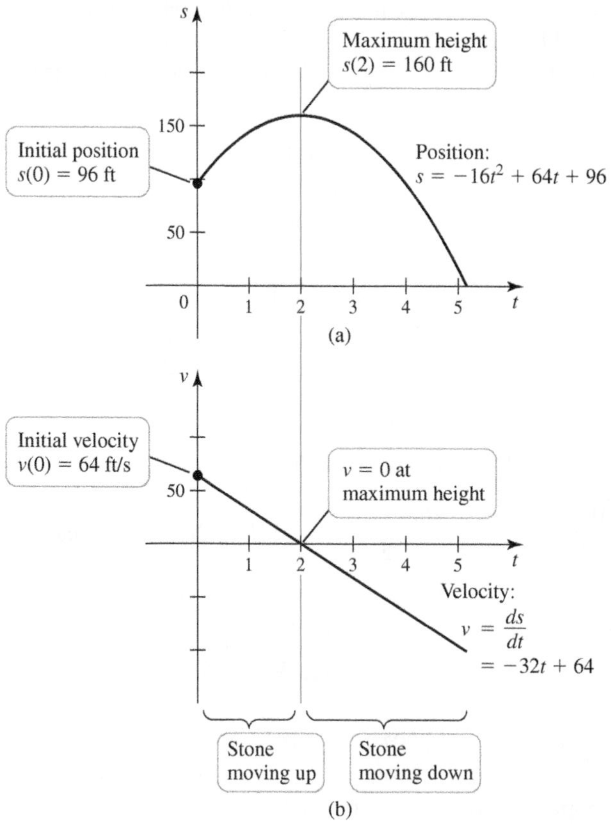

Figure 3.40

SOLUTION

a. The velocity of the stone is the derivative of the position function, and its acceleration is the derivative of the velocity function. Therefore,

$$v = \frac{ds}{dt} = -32t + 64 \quad \text{and} \quad a = \frac{dv}{dt} = -32.$$

b. When the stone reaches its high point, its velocity is zero (Figure 3.40b). Solving $v(t) = -32t + 64 = 0$ yields $t = 2$; therefore, the stone reaches its maximum height 2 seconds after it is thrown. Its height (in feet) at that instant is

$$s(2) = -16(2)^2 + 64(2) + 96 = 160.$$

c. To determine the velocity at which the stone strikes the river, we first determine *when* it reaches the river. The stone strikes the river when $s(t) = -16t^2 + 64t + 96 = 0$. Dividing both sides of the equation by -16, we obtain $t^2 - 4t - 6 = 0$. Using the quadratic formula, the solutions are $t \approx 5.16$ or $t \approx -1.16$. Because the stone is thrown at $t = 0$, only positive values of t are of interest; therefore, the relevant root is $t \approx 5.16$. The velocity of the stone (in ft/s) when it strikes the river is approximately

$$v(5.16) = -32(5.16) + 64 = -101.12.$$

Related Exercises 17–18 ◀

QUICK CHECK 4 In Example 3, does the rock have a greater speed at $t = 1$ or $t = 3$? ◀

Growth Models

Much of the change in the world around us can be classified as *growth*: Populations, prices, and computer networks all tend to increase in size. Modeling growth is important because it often leads to an understanding of underlying processes and allows for predictions.

We let $p = f(t)$ be the measure of a quantity of interest (for example, the population of a species or the consumer price index), where $t \geq 0$ represents time. The average growth rate of p between time $t = a$ and a later time $t = a + \Delta t$ is the change Δp divided by elapsed time Δt. Therefore, the **average growth rate** of p on the interval $[a, a + \Delta t]$ is

$$\frac{\Delta p}{\Delta t} = \frac{f(a + \Delta t) - f(a)}{\Delta t}.$$

If we now let $\Delta t \to 0$, then $\frac{\Delta p}{\Delta t}$ approaches the derivative $\frac{dp}{dt}$, which is the **instantaneous growth rate** (or simply **growth rate**) of p with respect to time:

$$\frac{dp}{dt} = \lim_{\Delta t \to 0} \frac{\Delta p}{\Delta t}.$$

Once again, we see the derivative appearing as an instantaneous rate of change. In the next example, a growth function and its derivative are approximated using real data.

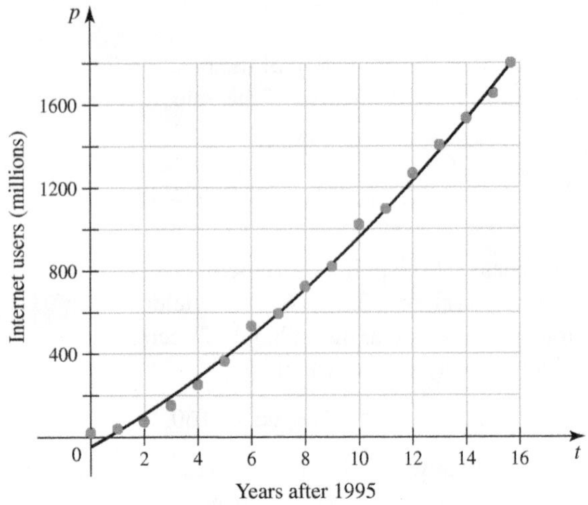

Figure 3.41

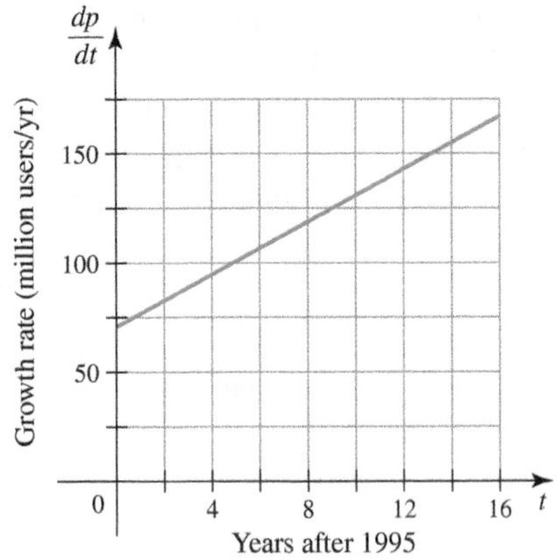

Figure 3.42

EXAMPLE 4 **Internet growth** The number of worldwide Internet users between 1995 and 2011 is shown in Figure 3.41. A reasonable fit to the data is given by the function $p(t) = 3.0t^2 + 70.8t - 45.8$, where t measures years after 1995.

a. Use the function p to approximate the average growth rate of Internet users from 2000 ($t = 5$) to 2005 ($t = 10$).

b. What was the instantaneous growth rate of the Internet in 2006?

c. Use a graphing utility to plot the growth rate dp/dt. What does the graph tell you about the growth rate between 1995 and 2011?

d. Assuming that the growth function can be extended beyond 2011, what is the predicted number of Internet users in 2015 ($t = 20$)?

SOLUTION

a. The average growth rate over the interval $[5, 10]$ is

$$\frac{\Delta p}{\Delta t} = \frac{p(10) - p(5)}{10 - 5} \approx \frac{962 - 383}{5} \approx 116 \text{ million users/year.}$$

b. The growth rate at time t is $p'(t) = 6.0t + 70.8$. In 2006 ($t = 11$), the growth rate was $p'(11) \approx 137$ million users/year.

c. The graph of p', for $0 \le t \le 16$, is shown in Figure 3.42. We see that the growth rate is positive and increasing, for $t \ge 0$.

d. A projection of the number of Internet users in 2015 is $p(20) \approx 2570$ million users, or about 2.6 billion users. This figure represents roughly one-third of the world's population, assuming a projected population of 7.2 billion people in 2015.

Related Exercises 19–20 ◀

QUICK CHECK 5 Using the growth function in Example 4, compare the growth rates in 1996 and 2010. ◀

Economics and Business

Our final examples illustrate how derivatives arise in economics and business. As you will see, the mathematics of derivatives is the same as it is in other applications. However, the vocabulary and interpretation are quite different.

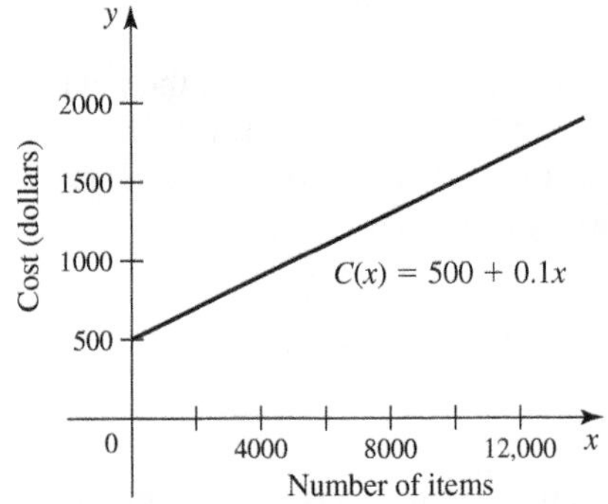

Figure 3.43

➤ Although x is a whole number of units, we treat it as a continuous variable, which is reasonable if x is large.

Average and Marginal Cost Imagine a company that manufactures large quantities of a product such as mousetraps, DVD players, or snowboards. Associated with the manufacturing process is a *cost function* $C(x)$ that gives the cost of manufacturing the first x items of the product. A simple cost function might have the form $y = C(x) = 500 + 0.1x$, as shown in Figure 3.43. It includes a **fixed cost** of \$500 (setup costs and overhead) that is independent of the number of items produced. It also includes a **unit cost**, or **variable cost**, of \$0.10 per item produced. For example, the cost of producing the first 1000 items is $C(1000) = \$600$.

If the company produces x items at a cost of $C(x)$, then the *average cost* is $\frac{C(x)}{x}$ per item. For the cost function $C(x) = 500 + 0.1x$, the average cost is

$$\frac{C(x)}{x} = \frac{500 + 0.1x}{x} = \frac{500}{x} + 0.1.$$

For example, the average cost of manufacturing the first 1000 items is

$$\frac{C(1000)}{1000} = \frac{\$600}{1000} = \$0.60/\text{unit}.$$

Plotting $C(x)/x$, we see that the average cost decreases as the number of items produced increases (Figure 3.44).

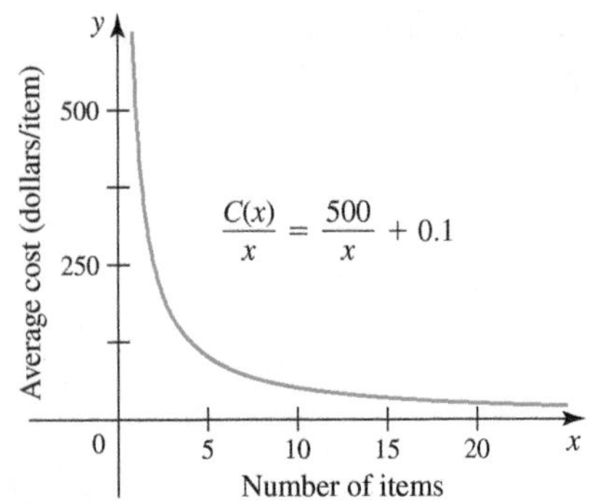

Figure 3.44

The average cost gives the cost of items already produced. But what about the cost of producing additional items? Having produced x items, the cost of producing another Δx items is $C(x + \Delta x) - C(x)$. Therefore, the average cost per item of producing those Δx additional items is

$$\frac{C(x + \Delta x) - C(x)}{\Delta x} = \frac{\Delta C}{\Delta x}.$$

➤ The average describes the past; the marginal describes the future.
—Old saying

If we let $\Delta x \rightarrow 0$, we see that

$$\lim_{\Delta x \rightarrow 0} \frac{\Delta C}{\Delta x} = C'(x),$$

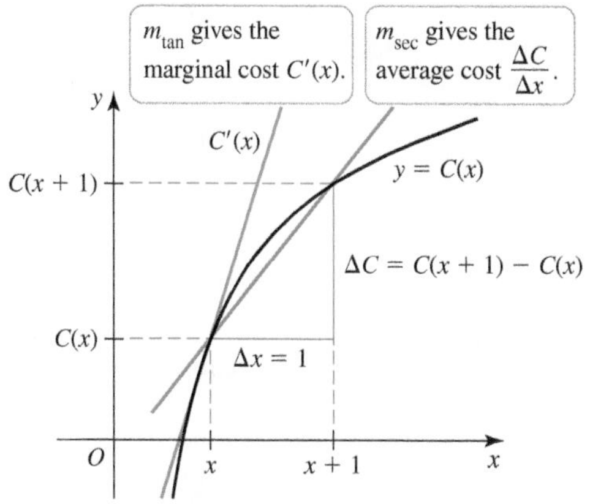

Figure 3.45

which is called the *marginal cost*. In reality, we cannot let $\Delta x \rightarrow 0$ because Δx represents whole numbers of items.

Here is a useful interpretation of the marginal cost. Suppose $\Delta x = 1$. Then $\Delta C = C(x + 1) - C(x)$ is the cost to produce *one* additional item. In this case, we write

$$\frac{\Delta C}{\Delta x} = \frac{C(x + 1) - C(x)}{1}.$$

If the *slope* of the cost curve does not vary significantly near the point x, then—as shown in Figure 3.45—we have

$$\frac{\Delta C}{\Delta x} \approx \lim_{\Delta x \rightarrow 0} \frac{\Delta C}{\Delta x} = C'(x).$$

➤ The approximation $\Delta C/\Delta x \approx C'(x)$ says that the slope of the secant line between $(x, C(x))$ and $(x + 1, C(x + 1))$ is approximately equal to the slope of the tangent line at $(x, C(x))$. This approximation is good if the cost curve is nearly linear over a 1-unit interval.

Therefore, the cost of producing one additional item, having already produced x items, is approximated by the marginal cost $C'(x)$. In the preceding example, we have $C'(x) = 0.1$; so if $x = 1000$ items have been produced, then the cost of producing the 1001st item is approximately $C'(1000) = \$0.10$. With this simple linear cost function, the marginal cost tells us what we already know: The cost of producing one additional item is the variable cost of \$0.10. With more realistic cost functions, the marginal cost may be variable.

DEFINITION Average and Marginal Cost

The **cost function** $C(x)$ gives the cost to produce the first x items in a manufacturing process. The **average cost** to produce x items is $\overline{C}(x) = C(x)/x$. The **marginal cost** $C'(x)$ is the approximate cost to produce one additional item after producing x items.

EXAMPLE 5 Average and marginal costs Suppose the cost of producing x items is given by the function (Figure 3.46)

$$C(x) = -0.02x^2 + 50x + 100, \quad \text{for} \quad 0 \leq x \leq 1000.$$

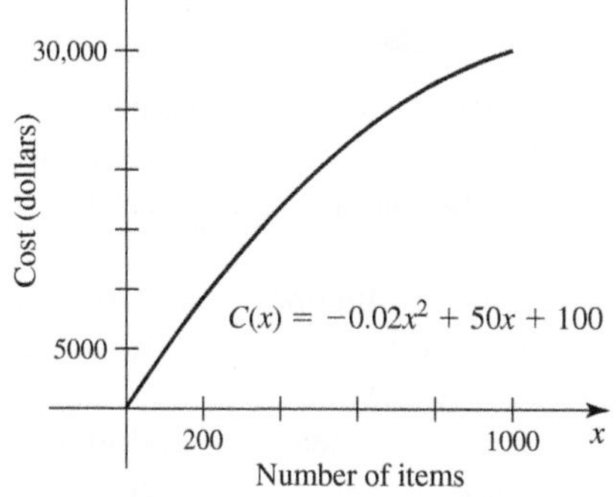

Figure 3.46

a. Determine the average and marginal cost functions.

b. Determine the average and marginal cost for the first 100 tems and interpret these values.

c. Determine the average and marginal cost for the first 900 items and interpret these values.

SOLUTION

a. The average cost is

$$\overline{C}(x) = \frac{C(x)}{x} = \frac{-0.02x^2 + 50x + 100}{x} = -0.02x + 50 + \frac{100}{x}$$

and the marginal cost is

$$\frac{dC}{dx} = -0.04x + 50.$$

The average cost decreases as the number of items produced increases (Figure 3.47a). The marginal cost decreases linearly with a slope of -0.04 (Figure 3.47b).

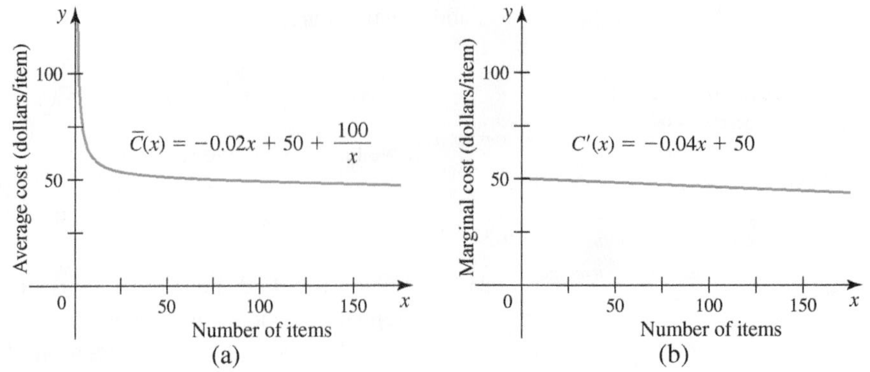

Figure 3.47

b. To produce $x = 100$ items, the average cost is

$$\bar{C}(100) = \frac{C(100)}{100} = \frac{-0.02(100)^2 + 50(100) + 100}{100} = \$49/\text{item}$$

and the marginal cost is

$$C'(100) = -0.04(100) + 50 = \$46/\text{item}.$$

These results mean that the average cost of producing the first 100 items is \$49 per item, but the cost of producing one additional item (the 101st item) is approximately \$46. Therefore, producing one more item is less expensive than the average cost of producing the first 100 items.

c. To produce $x = 900$ items, the average cost is

$$\bar{C}(900) = \frac{C(900)}{900} = \frac{-0.02(900)^2 + 50(900) + 100}{900} \approx \$32/\text{item}$$

and the marginal cost is

$$C'(900) = -0.04(900) + 50 = \$14/\text{item}.$$

The comparison with part (b) is revealing. The average cost of producing 900 items has dropped to \$32 per item. More striking is that the marginal cost (the cost of producing the 901st item) has dropped to \$14. *Related Exercises 21–24* ◀

QUICK CHECK 6 In Example 5, what happens to the average cost as the number of items produced increases from $x = 1$ to $x = 100$? ◀

Elasticity in Economics Economists apply the term *elasticity* to prices, income, capital, labor, and other variables in systems with input and output. Elasticity describes how changes in the input to a system are related to changes in the output. Because elasticity involves change, it also involves derivatives.

A general rule is that as the price p of an item increases, the number of sales of that item decreases. This relationship is expressed in a demand function. For example, suppose sales at a gas station have the linear demand function $D(p) = 1200 - 200p$ (Figure 3.48), where $D(p)$ is the number of gallons sold per day at a price p (measured in dollars). According to this function, if gas sells at \$3.60/gal, then the owner can expect to sell $D(3.6) = 480$ gallons. If the price is increased, sales decrease.

Suppose the price of a gallon of gasoline increases from \$3.60 to \$3.96 per gallon; call this change $\Delta p = \$0.36$. The resulting change in the number of gallons sold is $\Delta D = D(3.96) - D(3.60) = -72$. (The change is a decrease, so it is negative.) Comparisons of the variables are more meaningful if we work with percentages. Increasing the price from \$3.60 to \$3.96 per gallon is a percentage change of $\frac{\Delta p}{p} = \frac{\$0.36}{\$3.60} = 10\%$. Similarly, the corresponding percentage change in the gallons sold is $\frac{\Delta D}{D} = \frac{-72}{480} = -15\%$.

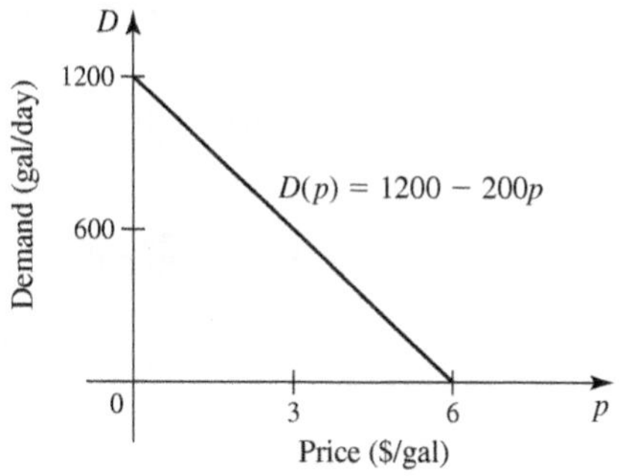

Figure 3.48

The *price elasticity of the demand* (or simply, *elasticity*) is the ratio of the percentage change in demand to the percentage change in price; that is, $E = \frac{\Delta D/D}{\Delta p/p}$. In the case of the gas demand function, the elasticity of this particular price change is $\frac{-15\%}{10\%} = -1.5$.

The elasticity is more useful when it is expressed as a function of the price. To do this, we consider small changes in p and assume the corresponding changes in D are also small. Using the definition of the derivative, the elasticity *function* is

$$E(p) = \lim_{\Delta p \to 0} \frac{\Delta D/D}{\Delta p/p} = \lim_{\Delta p \to 0} \frac{\Delta D}{\Delta p}\left(\frac{p}{D}\right) = \frac{dD}{dp}\frac{p}{D}.$$

Applying this definition to the gas demand function, we find that

$$\begin{aligned} E(p) &= \frac{dD}{dp}\frac{p}{D} \\ &= \frac{d}{dp}\underbrace{(1200 - 200p)}_{D}\frac{p}{\underbrace{1200 - 200p}_{D}} && \text{Substitute } D = 1200 - 200p. \\ &= -200\left(\frac{p}{1200 - 200p}\right) && \text{Differentiate.} \\ &= \frac{p}{p-6}. && \text{Simplify.} \end{aligned}$$

Given a particular price, the elasticity is interpreted as the percentage change in the demand that results for every 1% change in the price. For example, in the gas demand case, with $p = \$3.60$, the elasticity is $E(3.6) = -1.5$; therefore, a 2% increase in the price results in a change of $-1.5 \cdot 2\% = -3\%$ (a decrease) in the number of gallons sold.

➤ Some books define the elasticity as $E(p) = -\frac{dD}{dp}\frac{p}{D}$ to make $E(p)$ positive.

DEFINITION Elasticity

If the demand for a product varies with the price according the function $D = f(p)$, then the **price elasticity of the demand** is $E(p) = \frac{dD}{dp}\frac{p}{D}$.

EXAMPLE 6 **Elasticity in pork prices** The demand for processed pork in Canada is described by the function $D(p) = 286 - 20p$. (*Source: Microeconomics*, J. Perloff, Addison Wesley, 2012)

a. Compute and graph the price elasticity of the demand.

b. When $-\infty < E < -1$, the demand is said to be **elastic**. When $-1 < E < 0$, the demand is said to be **inelastic**. Interpret these terms.

c. For what prices is the demand for pork elastic? Inelastic?

SOLUTION

a. Substituting the demand function into the definition of elasticity, we find that

$$\begin{aligned} E(p) &= \frac{dD}{dp}\frac{p}{D} \\ &= \frac{d}{dp}\underbrace{(286 - 20p)}_{D}\frac{p}{\underbrace{286 - 20p}_{D}} && \text{Substitute } D = 286 - 20p. \\ &= -20\left(\frac{p}{286 - 20p}\right) && \text{Differentiate.} \\ &= -\frac{10p}{143 - 10p}. && \text{Simplify.} \end{aligned}$$

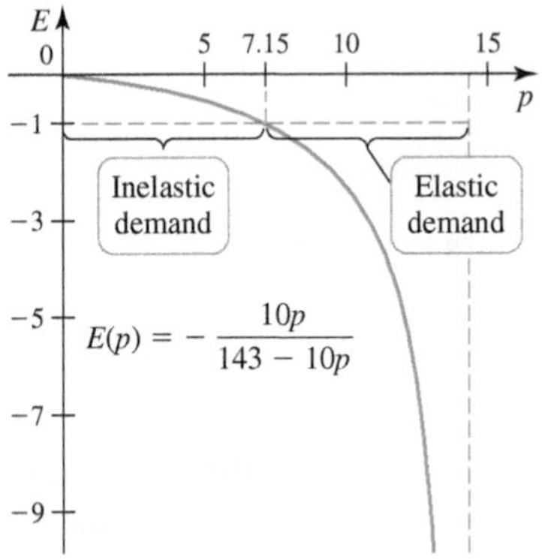

Figure 3.49

Notice that the elasticity is undefined at $p = 14.3$, which is the price at which the demand reaches zero. (According to the model, no pork can be sold at prices above \$14.30.) Therefore, the domain of the elasticity function is $[0, 14.3)$, and on the interval $(0, 14.3)$, the elasticity is negative (Figure 3.49).

b. For prices with an elasticity in the interval $-\infty < E(p) < -1$, a $P\%$ increase in the price results in *more* than a $P\%$ decrease in the demand; this is the case of elastic (sensitive) demand. If a price has an elasticity in the interval $-1 < E(p) < 0$, a $P\%$ increase in the price results in *less* than a $P\%$ decrease in the demand; this is the case of inelastic (insensitive) demand.

➤ When $E(p) = 0$, the demand for a good is said to be *perfectly inelastic*. In Example 6, this case occurs when $p = 0$.

c. Solving $E(p) = -\frac{10p}{143 - 10p} = -1$, we find that $E(p) < -1$, for $p > 7.15$. For prices in this interval, the demand is elastic (Figure 3.49). For prices with $0 < p < 7.15$, the demand is inelastic.

Related Exercises 25–28 ◀

SECTION 3.6 EXERCISES

Review Questions

1. Explain the difference between the average rate of change and the instantaneous rate of change of a function f.

2. Complete the following statement. If $\frac{dy}{dx}$ is large, then small changes in x result in relatively ________ changes in the value of y.

3. Complete the following statement: If $\frac{dy}{dx}$ is small, then small changes in x result in relatively ________ changes in the value of y.

4. What is the difference between the *velocity* and *speed* of an object moving in a straight line?

5. Define the acceleration of an object moving in a straight line.

6. An object moving along a line has a constant negative acceleration. Describe the velocity of the object.

7. Suppose the average cost of producing 200 gas stoves is \$70 per stove and the marginal cost at $x = 200$ is \$65 per stove. Interpret these costs.

8. Explain why a decreasing demand function has a negative elasticity function.

Basic Skills

9. **Highway travel** A state patrol station is located on a straight north-south freeway. A patrol car leaves the station at 9:00 A.M. heading north with position function $s = f(t)$ that gives its location in miles t hours after 9:00 A.M. (see figure). Assume s is positive when the car is north of the patrol station.

   a. Determine the average velocity of the car during the first 45 minutes of the trip.

   b. Find the average velocity of the car over the interval $[0.25, 0.75]$. Is the average velocity a good estimate of the velocity at 9:30 A.M.?

c. Find the average velocity of the car over the interval $[1.75, 2.25]$. Estimate the velocity of the car at 11:00 A.M. and determine the direction in which the patrol car is moving.
d. Describe the motion of the patrol car relative to the patrol station between 9:00 A.M. and noon.

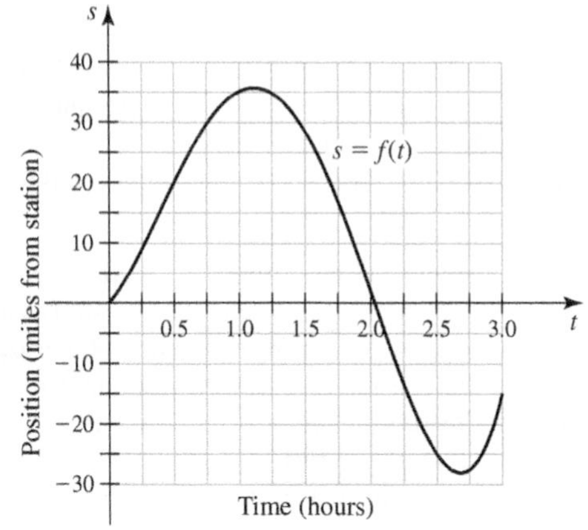

10. **Airline travel** The following figure shows the position function of an airliner on an out-and-back trip from Seattle to Minneapolis, where $s = f(t)$ is the number of ground miles from Seattle t hours after take-off at 6:00 A.M. The plane returns to Seattle 8.5 hours later at 2:30 P.M.
   a. Calculate the average velocity of the airliner during the first 1.5 hours of the trip $(0 \le t \le 1.5)$.
   b. Calculate the average velocity of the airliner between 1:30 P.M. and 2:30 P.M. $(7.5 \le t \le 8.5)$.
   c. At what time(s) is the velocity 0? Give a plausible explanation.
   d. Determine the velocity of the airliner at noon $(t = 6)$ and explain why the velocity is negative.

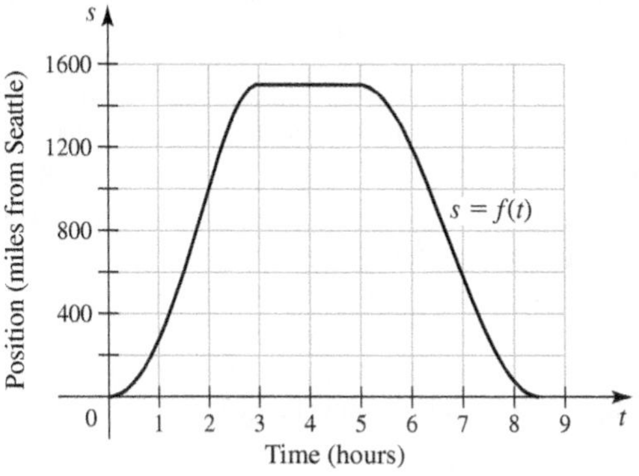

11–16. Position, velocity, and acceleration *Suppose the position of an object moving horizontally after t seconds is given by the following functions $s = f(t)$, where s is measured in feet, with $s > 0$ corresponding to positions right of the origin.*

a. Graph the position function.
b. Find and graph the velocity function. When is the object stationary, moving to the right, and moving to the left?
c. Determine the velocity and acceleration of the object at $t = 1$.
d. Determine the acceleration of the object when its velocity is zero.
e. On what intervals is the speed increasing?

11. $f(t) = t^2 - 4t;\ 0 \le t \le 5$
12. $f(t) = -t^2 + 4t - 3;\ 0 \le t \le 5$
13. $f(t) = 2t^2 - 9t + 12;\ 0 \le t \le 3$
14. $f(t) = 18t - 3t^2;\ 0 \le t \le 8$
15. $f(t) = 2t^3 - 21t^2 + 60t;\ 0 \le t \le 6$
16. $f(t) = -6t^3 + 36t^2 - 54t;\ 0 \le t \le 4$

17. **A stone thrown vertically** Suppose a stone is thrown vertically upward from the edge of a cliff with an initial velocity of 64 ft/s from a height of 32 ft above the ground. The height s (in ft) of the stone above the ground t seconds after it is thrown is $s = -16t^2 + 64t + 32$.
   a. Determine the velocity v of the stone after t seconds.
   b. When does the stone reach its highest point?
   c. What is the height of the stone at the highest point?
   d. When does the stone strike the ground?
   e. With what velocity does the stone strike the ground?
   f. On what intervals is the speed increasing?

18. **A stone thrown vertically on Mars** Suppose a stone is thrown vertically upward from the edge of a cliff on Mars (where the acceleration due to gravity is only about 12 ft/s^2) with an initial velocity of 64 ft/s from a height of 192 ft above the ground. The height s of the stone above the ground after t seconds is given by $s = -6t^2 + 64t + 192$.
   a. Determine the velocity v of the stone after t seconds.
   b. When does the stone reach its highest point?
   c. What is the height of the stone at the highest point?
   d. When does the stone strike the ground?
   e. With what velocity does the stone strike the ground?

T 19. **Population growth in Georgia** The population of the state of Georgia (in thousands) from 1995 $(t = 0)$ to 2005 $(t = 10)$ is modeled by the polynomial $p(t) = -0.27t^2 + 101t + 7055$.
   a. Determine the average growth rate from 1995 to 2005.
   b. What was the growth rate for Georgia in 1997 $(t = 2)$ and 2005 $(t = 10)$?
   c. Use a graphing utility to graph p', for $0 \le t \le 10$. What does this graph tell you about population growth in Georgia during the period of time from 1995 to 2005?

T 20. **Consumer price index** The U.S. consumer price index (CPI) measures the cost of living based on a value of 100 in the years 1982–1984. The CPI for the years 1995–2012 (see figure) is modeled by the function $c(t) = 151e^{0.026t}$, where t represents years after 1995.
   a. Was the average growth rate of the CPI greater between the years 1995 and 2000 or between 2005 and 2010?
   b. Was the growth rate of the CPI greater in 2000 $(t = 5)$ or 2005 $(t = 10)$?
   c. Use a graphing utility to graph the growth rate, for $0 \le t \le 15$. What does the graph tell you about growth in the cost of living during this time period?

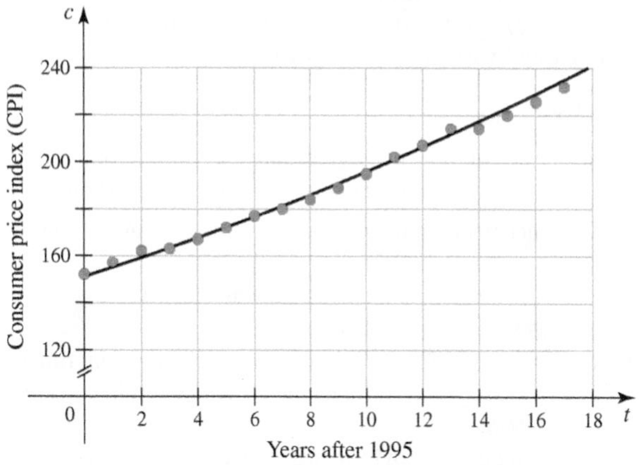

21–24. Average and marginal cost *Consider the following cost functions.*

a. Find the average cost and marginal cost functions.
b. Determine the average and marginal cost when $x = a$.
c. Interpret the values obtained in part (b).

21. $C(x) = 1000 + 0.1x,\ 0 \le x \le 5000,\ a = 2000$

22. $C(x) = 500 + 0.02x,\ 0 \le x \le 2000,\ a = 1000$

23. $C(x) = -0.01x^2 + 40x + 100,\ 0 \le x \le 1500,\ a = 1000$

24. $C(x) = -0.04x^2 + 100x + 800,\ 0 \le x \le 1000,\ a = 500$

25. Demand and elasticity Based on sales data over the past year, the owner of a DVD store devises the demand function $D(p) = 40 - 2p$, where $D(p)$ is the number of DVDs that can be sold in one day at a price of p dollars.

- **a.** According to the model, how many DVDs can be sold in a day at price of $10?
- **b.** According to the model, what is the maximum price that can charged (above which no DVDs can be sold)?
- **c.** Find the elasticity function for this demand function.
- **d.** For what prices is the demand elastic? Inelastic?
- **e.** If the price of DVDs is raised from $10.00 to $10.25, what is the exact percentage decrease in demand (using the demand function)?
- **f.** If the price of DVDs is raised from $10.00 to $10.25, what is the approximate percentage decrease in demand (using the elasticity function)?

26. Demand and elasticity The economic advisor of a large tire store proposes the demand function $D(p) = \dfrac{1800}{p - 40}$, where $D(p)$ is the number of tires of one brand and size that can be sold in one day at a price p.

- **a.** Recalling that the demand must be positive, what is the domain of this function?
- **b.** According to the model, how many tires can be sold in a day at a price of $60 per tire?
- **c.** Find the elasticity function on the domain of the demand function.
- **d.** For what prices is the demand elastic? Inelastic?
- **e.** If the price of tires is raised from $60 to $62, what is the approximate percentage decrease in demand (using the elasticity function)?

27. Exponential demand function Compute the elasticity for the exponential demand function $D(p) = ae^{-bp}$, where a and b are positive real numbers. For what prices is the demand elastic? Inelastic?

28. Power demand function Show that the demand function $D(p) = a/p^b$, where a and b are positive real numbers, has a constant elasticity for all positive prices.

Further Explorations

29. Explain why or why not Determine whether the following statements are true and give an explanation or counterexample.

- **a.** If the acceleration of an object remains constant, then its velocity is constant.
- **b.** If the acceleration of an object moving along a line is always 0, then its velocity is constant.
- **c.** It is impossible for the instantaneous velocity at all times $a \le t \le b$ to equal the average velocity over the interval $a \le t \le b$.
- **d.** A moving object can have negative acceleration and increasing speed.

30. A feather dropped on the moon On the moon, a feather will fall to the ground at the same rate as a heavy stone. Suppose a feather is dropped from a height of 40 m above the surface of the moon. Then its height s (in meters) above the ground after t seconds is $s = 40 - 0.8t^2$. Determine the velocity and acceleration of the feather the moment it strikes the surface of the moon.

31. Comparing velocities A stone is thrown vertically into the air at an initial velocity of 96 ft/s. On Mars, the height s (in feet) of the stone above the ground after t seconds is $s = 96t - 6t^2$ and on Earth it is $s = 96t - 16t^2$. How much higher will the stone travel on Mars than on Earth?

32. Comparing velocities Two stones are thrown vertically upward with matching initial velocities of 48 ft/s at time $t = 0$. One stone is thrown from the edge of a bridge that is 32 ft above the ground and the other stone is thrown from ground level. The height of the stone thrown from the bridge after t seconds is $f(t) = -16t^2 + 48t + 32$, and the height of the stone thrown from the ground after t seconds is $g(t) = -16t^2 + 48t$.

- **a.** Show that the stones reach their high points at the same time.
- **b.** How much higher does the stone thrown from the bridge go than the stone thrown from the ground?
- **c.** When do the stones strike the ground and with what velocities?

33. Matching heights A stone is thrown from the edge of a bridge that is 48 ft above the ground with an initial velocity of 32 ft/s. The height of this stone above the ground t seconds after it is thrown is $f(t) = -16t^2 + 32t + 48$. If a second stone is thrown from the ground, then its height above the ground after t seconds is given by $g(t) = -16t^2 + v_0 t$, where v_0 is the initial velocity of the second stone. Determine the value of v_0 such that both stones reach the same high point.

34. Velocity of a car The graph shows the position $s = f(t)$ of a car t hours after 5:00 P.M. relative to its starting point $s = 0$, where s is measured in miles.

- **a.** Describe the velocity of the car. Specifically, when is it speeding up and when is it slowing down?
- **b.** At approximately what time is the car traveling the fastest? The slowest?
- **c.** What is the approximate maximum velocity of the car? The approximate minimum velocity?

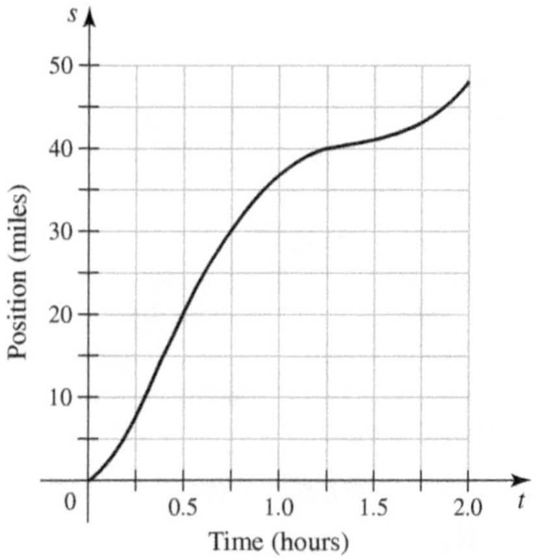

35. Velocity from position The graph of $s = f(t)$ represents the position of an object moving along a line at time $t \geq 0$.

a. Assume the velocity of the object is 0 when $t = 0$. For what other values of t is the velocity of the object zero?
b. When is the object moving in the positive direction and when is it moving in the negative direction?
c. Sketch a graph of the velocity function.
d. On what intervals is the speed increasing?

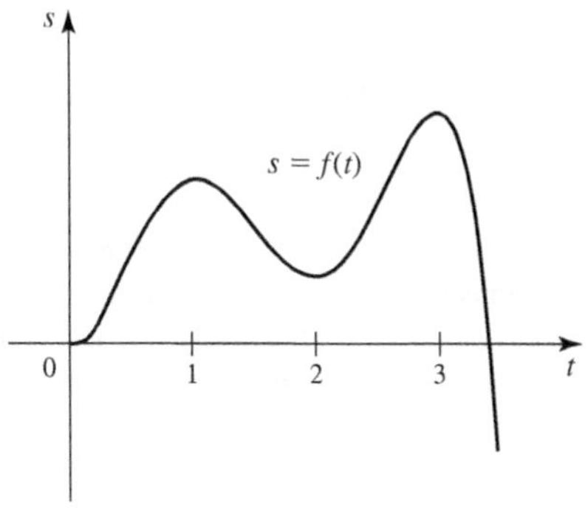

36. Fish length Assume the length L (in cm) of a particular species of fish after t years is modeled by the following graph.

a. What does dL/dt represent and what happens to this derivative as t increases?
b. What does the derivative tell you about how this species of fish grows?
c. Sketch a graph of L' and L''.

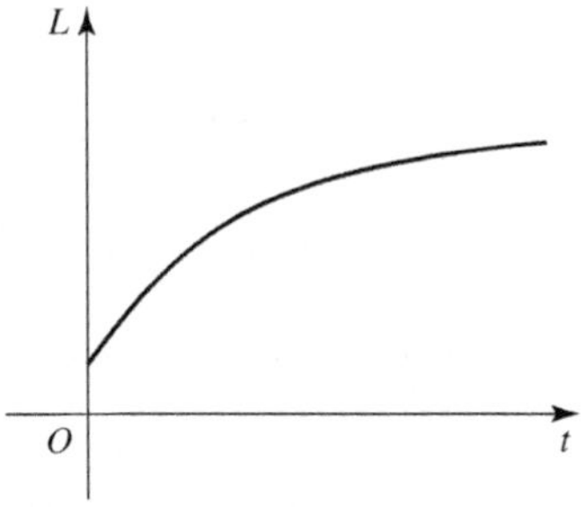

37–40. Average and marginal profit *Let $C(x)$ represent the cost of producing x items and $p(x)$ be the sale price per item if x items are sold. The profit $P(x)$ of selling x items is $P(x) = x\,p(x) - C(x)$ (revenue minus costs). The* ***average profit per item*** *when x items are sold is $P(x)/x$ and the* ***marginal profit*** *is dP/dx. The marginal profit approximates the profit obtained by selling one more item given that x items have already been sold. Consider the following cost functions C and price functions p.*

a. *Find the profit function P.*
b. *Find the average profit function and marginal profit function.*
c. *Find the average profit and marginal profit if $x = a$ units are sold.*
d. *Interpret the meaning of the values obtained in part (c).*

37. $C(x) = -0.02x^2 + 50x + 100,\ p(x) = 100,\ a = 500$

38. $C(x) = -0.02x^2 + 50x + 100,\ p(x) = 100 - 0.1x,\ a = 500$

39. $C(x) = -0.04x^2 + 100x + 800,\ p(x) = 200,\ a = 1000$

40. $C(x) = -0.04x^2 + 100x + 800,\ p(x) = 200 - 0.1x,$ $a = 1000$

Applications

41. Population growth of the United States Suppose $p(t)$ represents the population of the United States (in millions) t years after the year 1900. The graph of the growth rate p' is shown in the figure.

a. Approximately when (in what year) was the U.S. population growing most slowly between 1900 to 1990? Estimate the growth rate in that year.
b. Approximately when (in what year) was the U.S. population growing most rapidly between 1900 and 1990? Estimate the growth rate in that year.
c. In what years, if any, was p decreasing?
d. In what years was the population growth rate increasing?

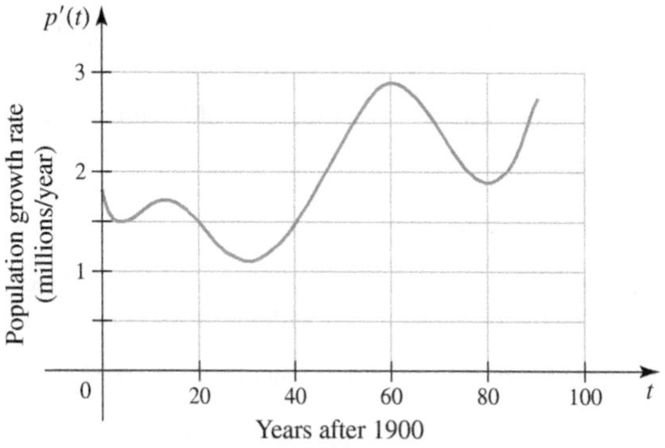

T **42. Average and marginal production** Economists use *production functions* to describe how the output of a system varies with respect to another variable such as labor or capital. For example, the production function $P(L) = 200L + 10L^2 - L^3$ gives the output of a system as a function of the number of laborers L. The *average product* $A(L)$ is the average output per laborer when L laborers are working; that is $A(L) = P(L)/L$. The *marginal product* $M(L)$ is the approximate change in output when one additional laborer is added to L laborers; that is, $M(L) = \frac{dP}{dL}$.

a. For the given production function, compute and graph P, A, and M.
b. Suppose the peak of the average product curve occurs at $L = L_0$, so that $A'(L_0) = 0$. Show that for a general production function, $M(L_0) = A(L_0)$.

T **43. Velocity of a marble** The position (in meters) of a marble rolling up a long incline is given by $s = \frac{100t}{t+1}$, where t is measured in seconds and $s = 0$ is the starting point.

a. Graph the position function.
b. Find the velocity function for the marble.
c. Graph the velocity function and give a description of the motion of the marble.
d. At what time is the marble 80 m from its starting point?
e. At what time is the velocity 50 m/s?

T **44. Tree growth** Let b represent the base diameter of a conifer tree and let h represent the height of the tree, where b is measured in centimeters and h is measured in meters. Assume the height is related to the base diameter by the function $h = 5.67 + 0.70b + 0.0067b^2$.

a. Graph the height function.
b. Plot and interpret the meaning of $\frac{dh}{db}$.

45. A different interpretation of marginal cost Suppose a large company makes 25,000 gadgets per year in batches of x items at a time. After analyzing setup costs to produce each batch and taking into account storage costs, it has been determined that the total cost $C(x)$ of producing 25,000 gadgets in batches of x items at a time is given by

$$C(x) = 1{,}250{,}000 + \frac{125{,}000{,}000}{x} + 1.5x.$$

a. Determine the marginal cost and average cost functions. Graph and interpret these functions.
b. Determine the average cost and marginal cost when $x = 5000$.
c. The meaning of average cost and marginal cost here is different from earlier examples and exercises. Interpret the meaning of your answer in part (b).

46. Diminishing returns A cost function of the form $C(x) = \frac{1}{2}x^2$ reflects *diminishing returns to scale*. Find and graph the cost, average cost, and marginal cost functions. Interpret the graphs and explain the idea of diminishing returns.

47. Revenue function A store manager estimates that the demand for an energy drink decreases with increasing price according to the function $d(p) = \frac{100}{p^2 + 1}$, which means that at price p (in dollars), $d(p)$ units can be sold. The revenue generated at price p is $R(p) = p \cdot d(p)$ (price multiplied by number of units).

a. Find and graph the revenue function.
b. Find and graph the marginal revenue $R'(p)$.
c. From the graphs of R and R', estimate the price that should be charged to maximize the revenue.

48. Fuel economy Suppose you own a fuel-efficient hybrid automobile with a monitor on the dashboard that displays the mileage and gas consumption. The number of miles you can drive with g gallons of gas remaining in the tank on a particular stretch of highway is given by $m(g) = 50g - 25.8g^2 + 12.5g^3 - 1.6g^4$, for $0 \le g \le 4$.

a. Graph and interpret the mileage function.
b. Graph and interpret the gas mileage $m(g)/g$.
c. Graph and interpret dm/dg.

49. Spring oscillations A spring hangs from the ceiling at equilibrium with a mass attached to its end. Suppose you pull downward on the mass and release it 10 inches below its equilibrium position with an upward push. The distance x (in inches) of the mass from its equilibrium position after t seconds is given by the function $x(t) = 10 \sin t - 10 \cos t$, where x is positive when the mass is above the equilibrium position.

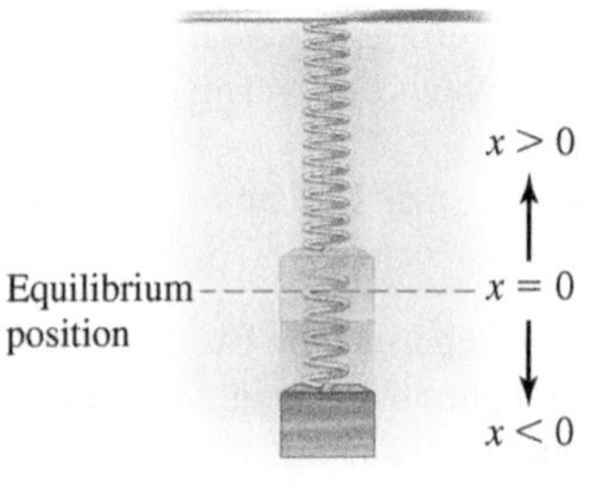

a. Graph and interpret this function.
b. Find $\frac{dx}{dt}$ and interpret the meaning of this derivative.
c. At what times is the velocity of the mass zero?
d. The function given here is a model for the motion of an object on a spring. In what ways is this model unrealistic?

50. Pressure and altitude Earth's atmospheric pressure decreases with altitude from a sea level pressure of 1000 millibars (a unit of pressure used by meteorologists). Letting z be the height above Earth's surface (sea level) in km, the atmospheric pressure is modeled by $p(z) = 1000e^{-z/10}$.

a. Compute the pressure at the summit of Mt. Everest which has an elevation of roughly 10 km. Compare the pressure on Mt. Everest to the pressure at sea level.
b. Compute the average change in pressure in the first 5 km above Earth's surface.
c. Compute the rate of change of the pressure at an elevation of 5 km.
d. Does $p'(z)$ increase or decrease with z? Explain.
e. What is the meaning of $\lim_{z \to \infty} p(z) = 0$?

51. A race Jean and Juan run a one-lap race on a circular track. Their angular positions on the track during the race are given by the functions $\theta(t)$ and $\varphi(t)$, respectively, where $0 \le t \le 4$ and t is measured in minutes (see figure). These angles are measured in radians, where $\theta = \varphi = 0$ represent the starting position and $\theta = \varphi = 2\pi$ represent the finish position. The angular velocities of the runners are $\theta'(t)$ and $\varphi'(t)$.

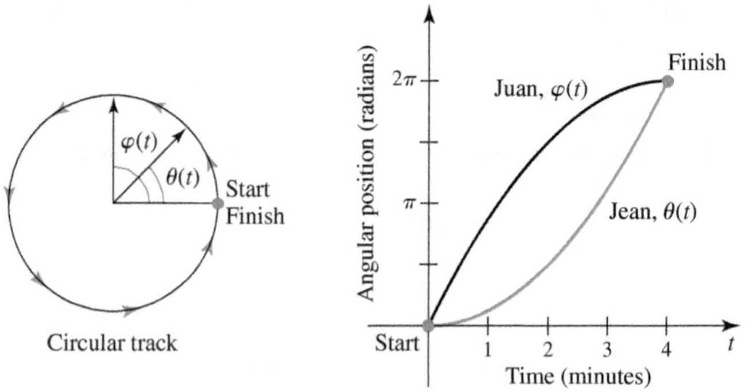

a. Compare in words the angular velocity of the two runners and the progress of the race.
b. Which runner has the greater average angular velocity?
c. Who wins the race?
d. Jean's position is given by $\theta(t) = \pi t^2/8$. What is her angular velocity at $t = 2$ and at what time is her angular velocity the greatest?
e. Juan's position is given by $\varphi(t) = \pi t(8 - t)/8$. What is his angular velocity at $t = 2$ and at what time is his angular velocity the greatest?

52. Power and energy Power and energy are often used interchangeably, but they are quite different. **Energy** is what makes matter move or heat up. It is measured in units of **joules** or **Calories**, where 1 Cal = 4184 J. One hour of walking consumes roughly 10^6 J, or 240 Cal. On the other hand, **power** is the rate at which energy is used, which is measured in **watts**, where 1 W = 1 J/s. Other useful units of power are **kilowatts** (1 kW = 10^3 W) and **megawatts** (1 MW = 10^6 W). If energy is used at a rate of 1 kW for one hour, the total amount of energy used is 1 **kilowatt-hour** (1 kWh = 3.6×10^6 J). Suppose the cumulative energy used in a large building over a 24-hr period is given by $E(t) = 100t + 4t^2 - \frac{t^3}{9}$ kWh, where $t = 0$ corresponds to midnight.

a. Graph the energy function.
b. The power is the rate of energy consumption; that is, $P(t) = E'(t)$. Find the power over the interval $0 \le t \le 24$.
c. Graph the power function and interpret the graph. What are the units of power in this case?

T **53. Flow from a tank** A cylindrical tank is full at time $t = 0$ when a valve in the bottom of the tank is opened. By Torricelli's Law, the volume of water in the tank after t hours is $V = 100(200 - t)^2$, measured in cubic meters.

a. Graph the volume function. What is the volume of water in the tank before the valve is opened?
b. How long does it take the tank to empty?
c. Find the rate at which water flows from the tank and plot the flow rate function.
d. At what time is the magnitude of the flow rate a minimum? A maximum?

T **54. Cell population** The population of a culture of cells after t days is approximated by the function $P(t) = \frac{1600}{1 + 7e^{-0.02t}}$, for $t \geq 0$.

a. Graph the population function.
b. What is the average growth rate during the first 10 days?
c. Looking at the graph, when does the growth rate appear to be a maximum?
d. Differentiate the population function to determine the growth rate function $P'(t)$.
e. Graph the growth rate. When is it a maximum and what is the population at the time that the growth rate is a maximum?

T **55. Bungee jumper** A woman attached to a bungee cord jumps from a bridge that is 30 m above a river. Her height in meters above the river t seconds after the jump is $y(t) = 15(1 + e^{-t}\cos t)$, for $t \geq 0$.

a. Determine her velocity at $t = 1$ and $t = 3$.
b. Use a graphing utility to determine when she is moving downward and when she is moving upward during the first 10 s.
c. Use a graphing utility to estimate the maximum upward velocity.

T **56. Spring runoff** The flow of a small stream is monitored for 90 days between May 1 and August 1. The total water that flows past a gauging station is given by

$$V(t) = \begin{cases} \frac{4}{5}t^2 & \text{if } 0 \leq t < 45 \\ -\frac{4}{5}(t^2 - 180t + 4050) & \text{if } 45 \leq t < 90, \end{cases}$$

where V is measured in cubic feet and t is measured in days, with $t = 0$ corresponding to May 1.

a. Graph the volume function.
b. Find the flow rate function $V'(t)$ and graph it. What are the units of the flow rate?
c. Describe the flow of the stream over the 3-month period. Specifically, when is the flow rate a maximum?

57. Temperature distribution A thin copper rod, 4 meters in length, is heated at its midpoint, and the ends are held at a constant temperature of 0°. When the temperature reaches equilibrium, the temperature profile is given by $T(x) = 40x(4 - x)$, where $0 \leq x \leq 4$ is the position along the rod. The **heat flux** at a point on the rod equals $-kT'(x)$, where $k > 0$ is a constant. If the heat flux is positive at a point, heat moves in the positive x-direction at that point, and if the heat flux is negative, heat moves in the negative x-direction.

a. With $k = 1$, what is the heat flux at $x = 1$? At $x = 3$?
b. For what values of x is the heat flux negative? Positive?
c. Explain the statement that heat flows out of the rod at its ends.

QUICK CHECK ANSWERS

1. Instantaneous velocity **2.** Yes; yes **3.** If an object has positive acceleration, then its velocity is increasing. If the velocity is negative but increasing, then the acceleration is positive and the speed is decreasing. For example, the velocity may increase from -2 m/s to -1 m/s to 0 m/s. **4.** $v(1) = 32$ ft/s and $v(3) = -32$ ft/s, so the speed is 32 ft/s at both times. **5.** The growth rate in 1996 ($t = 1$) is approximately 77 million users/year. It is less than half of the growth rate in 2010 ($t = 15$), which is approximately 161 million users/year. **6.** As x increases from 1 to 100, the average cost decreases from \$150/item to \$49/item. ◀

3.7 The Chain Rule

The differentiation rules presented so far allow us to find derivatives of many functions. However, these rules are inadequate for finding the derivatives of most *composite functions*. Here is a typical situation. If $f(x) = x^3$ and $g(x) = 5x + 4$, then their composition is $f(g(x)) = (5x + 4)^3$. One way to find the derivative is by expanding $(5x + 4)^3$ and differentiating the resulting polynomial. Unfortunately, this strategy becomes prohibitive for functions such as $(5x + 4)^{100}$. We need a better approach.

QUICK CHECK 1 Explain why it is not practical to calculate $\frac{d}{dx}(5x + 4)^{100}$ by first expanding $(5x + 4)^{100}$. ◀

Chain Rule Formulas

An efficient method for differentiating composite functions, called the *Chain Rule*, is motivated by the following example. Suppose Yancey, Uri, and Xan pick apples. Let y, u, and x represent the number of apples picked in some period of time by Yancey, Uri, and Xan, respectively. Yancey picks apples three times faster than Uri, which means the rate at which Yancey picks apples with respect to Uri is $\frac{dy}{du} = 3$. Uri picks apples twice as fast

➤ Expressions such as dy/dx should not be treated as fractions. Nevertheless, you can check symbolically that you have written the Chain Rule correctly by noting that du appears in the "numerator" and "denominator." If it were "canceled," the Chain Rule would have dy/dx on both sides.

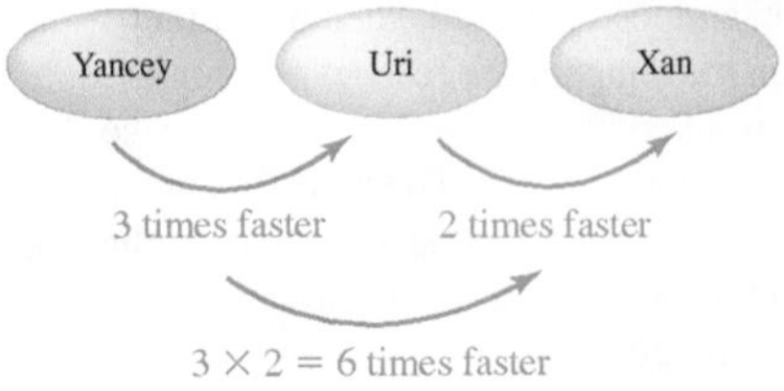

Figure 3.50

as Xan, so $\frac{du}{dx} = 2$. Therefore, Yancey picks apples at a rate that is $3 \cdot 2 = 6$ times greater than Xan's rate, which means that $\frac{dy}{dx} = 6$ (Figure 3.50). Observe that

$$\frac{dy}{dx} = \frac{dy}{du} \cdot \frac{du}{dx} = 3 \cdot 2 = 6.$$

The equation $\frac{dy}{dx} = \frac{dy}{du} \cdot \frac{du}{dx}$ is one form of the Chain Rule. It is referred to as Version 1 of the Chain Rule in this text.

Alternatively, the Chain Rule may be expressed in terms of composite functions. Let $y = f(u)$ and $u = g(x)$, which means y is related to x through the composite function $y = f(u) = f(g(x))$. The derivative $\frac{dy}{dx}$ is now expressed as the product

$$\underbrace{\frac{d}{dx}\big(f(g(x))\big)}_{\frac{dy}{dx}} = \underbrace{f'(u)}_{\frac{dy}{du}} \cdot \underbrace{g'(x)}_{\frac{du}{dx}}.$$

Replacing u with $g(x)$ results in

$$\frac{d}{dx}\big(f(g(x))\big) = f'(g(x)) \cdot g'(x),$$

which we refer to as Version 2 of the Chain Rule.

➤ The two versions of the Chain Rule differ only in notation. Mathematically, they are identical. Version 2 of the Chain Rule states that the derivative of $y = f(g(x))$ is the derivative of f evaluated at $g(x)$ multiplied by the derivative of g evaluated at x.

THEOREM 3.14 The Chain Rule

Suppose $y = f(u)$ is differentiable at $u = g(x)$ and $u = g(x)$ is differentiable at x. The composite function $y = f(g(x))$ is differentiable at x, and its derivative can be expressed in two equivalent ways.

Version 1 $\frac{dy}{dx} = \frac{dy}{du} \cdot \frac{du}{dx}$

Version 2 $\frac{d}{dx}\big(f(g(x))\big) = f'(g(x)) \cdot g'(x)$

➤ There may be several ways to choose an inner function $u = g(x)$ and an outer function $y = f(u)$. Nevertheless, we often refer to *the* inner and *the* outer function for the most obvious choices.

A proof of the Chain Rule is given at the end of this section. For now, it's important to learn how to use it. With the composite function $f(g(x))$, we refer to g as the *inner function* and f as the *outer function* of the composition. The key to using the Chain Rule is identifying the inner and outer functions. The following four steps outline the differentiation process, although you will soon find that the procedure can be streamlined.

PROCEDURE Using the Chain Rule

Assume the differentiable function $y = f(g(x))$ is given.

1. Identify an outer function f and an inner function g, and let $u = g(x)$.
2. Replace $g(x)$ with u to express y in terms of u:

$$y = f(\underbrace{g(x)}_{u}) \Rightarrow y = f(u).$$

3. Calculate the product $\frac{dy}{du} \cdot \frac{du}{dx}$.
4. Replace u with $g(x)$ in $\frac{dy}{du}$ to obtain $\frac{dy}{dx}$.

QUICK CHECK 2 Identify an inner function (call it g) of $y = (5x + 4)^3$. Let $u = g(x)$ and express the outer function f in terms of u. ◀

EXAMPLE 1 **Version 1 of the Chain Rule** For each of the following composite functions, find the inner function $u = g(x)$ and the outer function $y = f(u)$. Use Version 1 of the Chain Rule to find $\frac{dy}{dx}$.

a. $y = (5x + 4)^3$ **b.** $y = \sin^3 x$ **c.** $y = \sin x^3$

SOLUTION

a. The inner function of $y = (5x + 4)^3$ is $u = 5x + 4$, and the outer function is $y = u^3$. By Version 1 of the Chain Rule, we have

$$\begin{aligned}\frac{dy}{dx} &= \frac{dy}{du}\cdot\frac{du}{dx} && \text{Version 1}\\ &= 3u^2\cdot 5 && y = u^3 \Rightarrow \frac{dy}{du} = 3u^2\\ & && u = 5x + 4 \Rightarrow \frac{du}{dx} = 5\\ &= 3(5x + 4)^2\cdot 5 && \text{Replace } u \text{ with } 5x + 4.\\ &= 15(5x + 4)^2.\end{aligned}$$

b. Replacing the shorthand form $y = \sin^3 x$ with $y = (\sin x)^3$, we identify the inner function as $u = \sin x$. Letting $y = u^3$, we have

$$\frac{dy}{dx} = \frac{dy}{du}\cdot\frac{du}{dx} = 3u^2\cdot\cos x = \underbrace{3\sin^2 x}_{3u^2}\cos x.$$

➤ When using trigonometric functions, expressions such as $\sin^n(x)$ always mean $(\sin x)^n$, except when $n = -1$. In Example 1, $\sin^3 x = (\sin x)^3$.

c. Although $y = \sin x^3$ appears to be similar to the function $y = \sin^3 x$ in part (b), the inner function in this case is $u = x^3$ and the outer function is $y = \sin u$. Therefore,

$$\frac{dy}{dx} = \frac{dy}{du}\cdot\frac{du}{dx} = (\cos u)\cdot 3x^2 = 3x^2\cos x^3.$$

Related Exercises 7–18 ◀

QUICK CHECK 3 In Example 1a, we showed that $\frac{d}{dx}((5x + 4)^3) = 15(5x + 4)^2$. Verify this result by expanding $(5x + 4)^3$ and differentiating. ◀

Version 2 of the Chain Rule, $\frac{d}{dx}\big(f(g(x))\big) = f'(g(x))\cdot g'(x)$, is equivalent to Version 1; it just uses different derivative notation. With Version 2, we identify an outer function $y = f(u)$ and an inner function $u = g(x)$. Then $\frac{d}{dx}\big(f(g(x))\big)$ is the product of $f'(u)$ evaluated at $u = g(x)$ and $g'(x)$.

EXAMPLE 2 **Version 2 of the Chain Rule** Use Version 2 of the Chain Rule to calculate the derivatives of the following functions.

a. $(6x^3 + 3x + 1)^{10}$ **b.** $\sqrt{5x^2 + 1}$ **c.** $\left(\frac{5t^2}{3t^2 + 2}\right)^3$

SOLUTION

a. The inner function of $(6x^3 + 3x + 1)^{10}$ is $g(x) = 6x^3 + 3x + 1$, and the outer function is $f(u) = u^{10}$. The derivative of the outer function is $f'(u) = 10u^9$, which, when evaluated at $g(x)$, is $10(6x^3 + 3x + 1)^9$. The derivative of the inner function is $g'(x) = 18x^2 + 3$. Multiplying the derivatives of the outer and inner functions, we have

$$\begin{aligned}\frac{d}{dx}((6x^3 + 3x + 1)^{10}) &= \underbrace{10(6x^3 + 3x + 1)^9}_{f'(u)\text{ evaluated at } g(x)}\cdot\underbrace{(18x^2 + 3)}_{g'(x)}\\ &= 30(6x^2 + 1)(6x^3 + 3x + 1)^9. && \text{Factor and simplify.}\end{aligned}$$

b. The inner function of $\sqrt{5x^2+1}$ is $g(x) = 5x^2 + 1$, and the outer function is $f(u) = \sqrt{u}$. The derivatives of these functions are $f'(u) = \dfrac{1}{2\sqrt{u}}$ and $g'(x) = 10x$. Therefore,

$$\frac{d}{dx}\sqrt{5x^2+1} = \underbrace{\frac{1}{2\sqrt{5x^2+1}}}_{f'(u)\text{ evaluated at }g(x)} \cdot \underbrace{10x}_{g'(x)} = \frac{5x}{\sqrt{5x^2+1}}.$$

c. The inner function of $\left(\dfrac{5t^2}{3t^2+2}\right)^3$ is $g(t) = \dfrac{5t^2}{3t^2+2}$. The outer function is $f(u) = u^3$, whose derivative is $f'(u) = 3u^2$. The derivative of the inner function requires the Quotient Rule. Applying the Chain Rule, we have

$$\frac{d}{dt}\left(\frac{5t^2}{3t^2+2}\right)^3 = \underbrace{3\left(\frac{5t^2}{3t^2+2}\right)^2}_{f'(u)\text{ evaluated at }g(t)} \cdot \underbrace{\frac{(3t^2+2)10t - 5t^2(6t)}{(3t^2+2)^2}}_{g'(t)\text{ by the Quotient Rule}} = \frac{1500t^5}{(3t^2+2)^4}.$$

Related Exercises 19–36 ◀

The Chain Rule is also used to calculate the derivative of a composite function for a specific value of the variable. If $h(x) = f(g(x))$ and a is a real number, then $h'(a) = f'(g(a))g'(a)$, provided the necessary derivatives exist. Therefore, $h'(a)$ is the derivative of f evaluated at $g(a)$ multiplied by the derivative of g evaluated at a.

Table 3.3

x	$f'(x)$	$g(x)$	$g'(x)$
1	5	2	3
2	7	1	4

EXAMPLE 3 Calculating derivatives at a point Let $h(x) = f(g(x))$. Use the values in Table 3.3 to calculate $h'(1)$ and $h'(2)$.

SOLUTION We use $h'(a) = f'(g(a))g'(a)$ with $a = 1$:

$$h'(1) = f'(g(1))g'(1) = f'(2)g'(1) = 7 \cdot 3 = 21.$$

With $a = 2$, we have

$$h'(2) = f'(g(2))g'(2) = f'(1)g'(2) = 5 \cdot 4 = 20.$$

Related Exercises 37–38 ◀

EXAMPLE 4 Applying the Chain Rule A trail runner programs her GPS unit to record her altitude a (in feet) every 10 minutes during a training run in the mountains; the resulting data are shown in Table 3.4. Meanwhile, at a nearby weather station, a weather probe records the atmospheric pressure p (in hectopascals, or hPa) at various altitudes, shown in Table 3.5.

Table 3.4

t (minutes)	0	10	20	30	40	50	60	70	80
$a(t)$ (altitude)	10,000	10,220	10,510	10,980	11,660	12,330	12,710	13,330	13,440

Table 3.5

a (altitude)	5485	7795	10,260	11,330	12,330	13,330	14,330	15,830	16,230
$p(a)$ (pressure)	1000	925	840	821	793	765	738	700	690

Use the Chain Rule to estimate the rate of change in pressure per unit time experienced by the trail runner when she is 50 minutes into her run.

SOLUTION We seek the rate of change in the pressure $\frac{dp}{dt}$, which is given by the Chain Rule:

$$\frac{dp}{dt} = \frac{dp}{da}\frac{da}{dt}.$$

➤ The difference quotient $\frac{p(a+h) - p(a)}{h}$ is a *forward difference quotient* when $h > 0$ (see Exercises 64–67 in Section 3.1).

The runner is at an altitude of 12,330 feet 50 minutes into her run, so we must compute dp/da when $a = 12{,}330$ and da/dt when $t = 50$. These derivatives can be approximated using the following forward difference quotients.

$$\left.\frac{dp}{da}\right|_{a=12{,}330} \approx \frac{p(12{,}330 + 1000) - p(12{,}330)}{1000} = \frac{765 - 793}{1000} = -0.028\frac{\text{hPa}}{\text{ft}}$$

$$\left.\frac{da}{dt}\right|_{t=50} \approx \frac{a(50 + 10) - a(50)}{10} = \frac{12{,}710 - 12{,}330}{10} = 38.0\frac{\text{ft}}{\text{min}}$$

We now compute the rate of change of the pressure with respect to time:

$$\begin{aligned}\frac{dp}{dt} &= \frac{dp}{da}\frac{da}{dt}\\ &\approx -0.028\frac{\text{hPa}}{\text{ft}} \cdot 38.0\frac{\text{ft}}{\text{min}} = -1.06\frac{\text{hPa}}{\text{min}}.\end{aligned}$$

As expected, dp/dt is negative because the pressure decreases with increasing altitude (Table 3.5) as the runner ascends the trail. Note also that the units are consistent.

Related Exercises 39–40 ◀

Chain Rule for Powers

The Chain Rule leads to a general derivative rule for powers of differentiable functions. In fact, we have already used it in several examples. Consider the function $f(x) = (g(x))^n$, where n is an integer. Letting $f(u) = u^n$ be the outer function and $u = g(x)$ be the inner function, we obtain the Chain Rule for powers of functions.

➤ In Section 3.9, Theorem 3.15 is generalized to all real numbers n.

THEOREM 3.15 Chain Rule for Powers
If g is differentiable for all x in its domain and n is an integer, then

$$\frac{d}{dx}\left((g(x))^n\right) = n(g(x))^{n-1}g'(x).$$

EXAMPLE 5 Chain Rule for powers Find $\frac{d}{dx}(\tan x + 10)^{21}$.

SOLUTION With $g(x) = \tan x + 10$, the Chain Rule gives

$$\begin{aligned}\frac{d}{dx}(\tan x + 10)^{21} &= 21(\tan x + 10)^{20}\frac{d}{dx}(\tan x + 10)\\ &= 21(\tan x + 10)^{20}\sec^2 x.\end{aligned}$$

Related Exercises 41–44 ◀

The Composition of Three or More Functions

We can differentiate the composition of three or more functions by applying the Chain Rule repeatedly, as shown in the following example.

➤ Before dismissing the function in Example 6 as merely a tool to teach the Chain Rule, consider the graph of a related function, $y = \sin(e^{1.3 \cos x}) + 1$ (Figure 3.51). This periodic function has two peaks per cycle and could be used as a simple model of traffic flow (two rush hours followed by light traffic in the middle of the night), tides (high tide, medium tide, high tide, low tide, ...), or the presence of certain allergens in the air (peaks in the spring and fall).

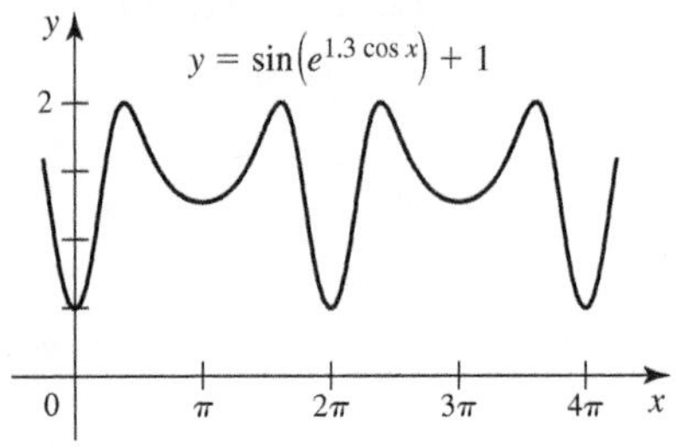

Figure 3.51

EXAMPLE 6 Composition of three functions Calculate the derivative of $\sin(e^{\cos x})$.

SOLUTION The inner function of $\sin(e^{\cos x})$ is $e^{\cos x}$. Because $e^{\cos x}$ is also a composition of two functions, the Chain Rule is used again to calculate $\frac{d}{dx}(e^{\cos x})$, where $\cos x$ is the inner function:

$$\begin{aligned}
\frac{d}{dx}(\underbrace{\sin}_{\text{outer}}(\underbrace{e^{\cos x}}_{\text{inner}})) &= \cos(e^{\cos x})\frac{d}{dx}(e^{\cos x}) && \text{Chain Rule}\\
&= \cos(e^{\cos x})\underbrace{e^{\cos x}\cdot\frac{d}{dx}(\cos x)}_{\frac{d}{dx}(e^{\cos x})} && \text{Chain Rule}\\
&= \cos(e^{\cos x})\cdot e^{\cos x}(-\sin x) && \text{Differentiate } \cos x.\\
&= -\sin x \cdot e^{\cos x}\cdot\cos(e^{\cos x}). && \text{Simplify.}
\end{aligned}$$

Related Exercises 45–56 ◄

QUICK CHECK 4 Let $y = \tan^{10}(x^5)$. Find f, g, and h such that $y = f(u)$, where $u = g(v)$ and $v = h(x)$. ◄

The Chain Rule is often used together with other derivative rules. Example 7 illustrates how several differentiation rules are combined.

EXAMPLE 7 Combining rules Find $\frac{d}{dx}(x^2\sqrt{x^2+1})$.

SOLUTION The given function is the product of x^2 and $\sqrt{x^2+1}$, and $\sqrt{x^2+1}$ is a composite function. We apply the Product Rule and then the Chain Rule:

$$\begin{aligned}
\frac{d}{dx}(x^2\sqrt{x^2+1}) &= \underbrace{\frac{d}{dx}(x^2)}_{2x}\cdot\sqrt{x^2+1} + x^2\cdot\underbrace{\frac{d}{dx}(\sqrt{x^2+1})}_{\text{Use Chain Rule}} && \text{Product Rule}\\
&= 2x\sqrt{x^2+1} + x^2\cdot\frac{1}{2\sqrt{x^2+1}}\cdot 2x && \text{Chain Rule}\\
&= 2x\sqrt{x^2+1} + \frac{x^3}{\sqrt{x^2+1}} && \text{Simplify.}\\
&= \frac{3x^3+2x}{\sqrt{x^2+1}}. && \text{Simplify.}
\end{aligned}$$

Related Exercises 57–68 ◄

Proof of the Chain Rule

Suppose f is differentiable at $u = g(a)$, g is differentiable at a, and $h(x) = f(g(x))$. By the definition of the derivative of h,

$$h'(a) = \lim_{x\to a}\frac{h(x)-h(a)}{x-a} = \lim_{x\to a}\frac{f(g(x))-f(g(a))}{x-a}. \qquad (1)$$

We assume that $g(a) \neq g(x)$ for values of x near a but not equal to a. This assumption holds for most, but not all, functions encountered in this text. For a proof of the Chain Rule without this assumption, see Exercise 103.

We multiply the right side of equation (1) by $\frac{g(x) - g(a)}{g(x) - g(a)}$, which equals 1, and let $v = g(x)$ and $u = g(a)$. The result is

$$h'(a) = \lim_{x \to a} \frac{f(g(x)) - f(g(a))}{g(x) - g(a)} \cdot \frac{g(x) - g(a)}{x - a}$$

$$= \lim_{x \to a} \frac{f(v) - f(u)}{v - u} \cdot \frac{g(x) - g(a)}{x - a}.$$

By assumption, g is differentiable at a; therefore, it is continuous at a. This means that $\lim_{x \to a} g(x) = g(a)$, so $v \to u$ as $x \to a$. Consequently,

$$h'(a) = \underbrace{\lim_{v \to u} \frac{f(v) - f(u)}{v - u}}_{f'(u)} \cdot \underbrace{\lim_{x \to a} \frac{g(x) - g(a)}{x - a}}_{g'(a)} = f'(u)g'(a).$$

Because f and g are differentiable at u and a, respectively, the two limits in this expression exist; therefore, $h'(a)$ exists. Noting that $u = g(a)$, we have $h'(a) = f'(g(a))g'(a)$. Replacing a with the variable x gives the Chain Rule: $h'(x) = f'(g(x))g'(x)$. ◄

SECTION 3.7 EXERCISES

Review Questions

1. Two equivalent forms of the Chain Rule for calculating the derivative of $y = f(g(x))$ are presented in this section. State both forms.

2. Let $h(x) = f(g(x))$, where f and g are differentiable on their domains. If $g(1) = 3$ and $g'(1) = 5$, what else do you need to know to calculate $h'(1)$?

3. Fill in the blanks. The derivative of $f(g(x))$ equals f' evaluated at ________ multiplied by g' evaluated at ________.

4. Identify the inner and outer functions in the composition $\cos^4 x$.

5. Identify the inner and outer functions in the composition $(x^2 + 10)^{-5}$.

6. Express $Q(x) = \cos^4(x^2 + 1)$ as the composition of three functions; that is, identify f, g, and h so that $Q(x) = f(g(h(x)))$.

Basic Skills

7–18. Version 1 of the Chain Rule *Use Version 1 of the Chain Rule to calculate* $\frac{dy}{dx}$.

7. $y = (3x + 7)^{10}$ **8.** $y = (5x^2 + 11x)^{20}$ **9.** $y = \sin^5 x$

10. $y = \cos x^5$ **11.** $y = e^{5x-7}$ **12.** $y = \sqrt{7x - 1}$

13. $y = \sqrt{x^2 + 1}$ **14.** $y = e^{\sqrt{x}}$ **15.** $y = \tan 5x^2$

16. $y = \sin \frac{x}{4}$ **17.** $y = \sec e^x$ **18.** $y = e^{-x^2}$

19–34. Version 2 of the Chain Rule *Use Version 2 of the Chain Rule to calculate the derivatives of the following functions.*

19. $y = (3x^2 + 7x)^{10}$ **20.** $y = (x^2 + 2x + 7)^8$

21. $y = \sqrt{10x + 1}$ **22.** $y = \sqrt{x^2 + 9}$

23. $y = 5(7x^3 + 1)^{-3}$ **24.** $y = \cos 5t$

25. $y = \sec(3x + 1)$ **26.** $y = \csc e^x$

27. $y = \tan e^x$ **28.** $y = e^{\tan t}$

29. $y = \sin(4x^3 + 3x + 1)$ **30.** $y = \csc(t^2 + t)$

31. $y = \sin(2\sqrt{x})$ **32.** $y = \cos^4 \theta + \sin^4 \theta$

33. $y = (\sec x + \tan x)^5$ **34.** $y = \sin(4 \cos z)$

35–36. Similar-looking composite functions *Two composite functions are given that look similar, but in fact are quite different. Identify the inner function $u = g(x)$ and the outer function $y = f(u)$; then evaluate $\frac{dy}{dx}$ using the Chain Rule.*

35. a. $y = \cos^3 x$
b. $y = \cos x^3$

36. a. $y = (e^x)^3$
b. $y = e^{(x^3)}$

37. Chain Rule using a table Let $h(x) = f(g(x))$ and $p(x) = g(f(x))$. Use the table to compute the following derivatives.

a. $h'(3)$ **b.** $h'(2)$ **c.** $p'(4)$
d. $p'(2)$ **e.** $h'(5)$

x	1	2	3	4	5
$f(x)$	0	3	5	1	0
$f'(x)$	5	2	−5	−8	−10
$g(x)$	4	5	1	3	2
$g'(x)$	2	10	20	15	20

38. Chain Rule using a table Let $h(x) = f(g(x))$ and $k(x) = g(g(x))$. Use the table to compute the following derivatives.

a. $h'(1)$ **b.** $h'(2)$ **c.** $h'(3)$ **d.** $k'(3)$
e. $k'(1)$ **f.** $k'(5)$

x	1	2	3	4	5
$f'(x)$	−6	−3	8	7	2
$g(x)$	4	1	5	2	3
$g'(x)$	9	7	3	−1	−5

39. Applying the Chain Rule Use the data in Tables 3.4 and 3.5 of Example 4 to estimate the rate of change in pressure with respect to time experienced by the runner when she is at an altitude of 13,330 ft. Make use of a forward difference quotient when estimating the required derivatives.

40. Changing temperature The *lapse rate* is the rate at which the temperature in Earth's atmosphere decreases with altitude. For example, a lapse rate of 6.5° Celsius/km means the temperature *decreases* at a rate of 6.5°C per kilometer of altitude. The lapse rate varies with location and with other variables such as humidity. However, at a given time and location, the lapse rate is often nearly constant in the first 10 kilometers of the atmosphere. A radiosonde (weather balloon) is released from Earth's surface, and its altitude (measured in km above sea level) at various times (measured in hours) is given in the table below.

Time (hr)	0	0.5	1	1.5	2	2.5
Altitude (km)	0.5	1.2	1.7	2.1	2.5	2.9

a. Assuming a lapse rate of 6.5° C/km, what is the approximate rate of change of the temperature with respect to time as the balloon rises 1.5 hours into the flight? Specify the units of your result, and use a forward difference quotient when estimating the required derivative.
b. How does an increase in lapse rate change your answer in part (a)?
c. Is it necessary to know the actual temperature to carry out the calculation in part (a)? Explain.

41–44. Chain Rule for powers *Use the Chain Rule to find the derivative of the following functions.*

41. $y = (2x^6 - 3x^3 + 3)^{25}$
42. $y = (\cos x + 2\sin x)^8$
43. $y = (1 + 2\tan x)^{15}$
44. $y = (1 - e^x)^4$

45–56. Repeated use of the Chain Rule *Calculate the derivative of the following functions.*

45. $y = \sqrt{1 + \cot^2 x}$
46. $y = \sqrt{(3x - 4)^2 + 3x}$
47. $y = \sin(\sin(e^x))$
48. $y = \sin^2(e^{3x+1})$
49. $y = \sin^5(\cos 3x)$
50. $y = \cos^4(7x^3)$
51. $y = \tan(e^{\sqrt{3x}})$
52. $y = (1 - e^{-0.05x})^{-1}$
53. $y = \sqrt{x + \sqrt{x}}$
54. $y = \sqrt{x + \sqrt{x + \sqrt{x}}}$
55. $y = f(g(x^2))$, where f and g are differentiable for all real numbers
56. $y = (f(g(x^m)))^n$, where f and g are differentiable for all real numbers, and m and n are integers

57–68. Combining rules *Use the Chain Rule combined with other differentiation rules to find the derivative of the following functions.*

57. $y = \left(\frac{x}{x+1}\right)^5$
58. $y = \left(\frac{e^x}{x+1}\right)^8$
59. $y = e^{x^2+1}\sin x^3$
60. $y = \tan(x e^x)$
61. $y = \theta^2 \sec 5\theta$
62. $y = \left(\frac{3x}{4x+2}\right)^5$
63. $y = ((x + 2)(x^2 + 1))^4$
64. $y = e^{2x}(2x - 7)^5$
65. $y = \sqrt{x^4 + \cos 2x}$
66. $y = \frac{te^t}{t+1}$
67. $y = (p + \pi)^2 \sin p^2$
68. $y = (z + 4)^3 \tan z$

Further Explorations

69. Explain why or why not Determine whether the following statements are true and give an explanation or counterexample.

a. The function $x \sin x$ can be differentiated without using the Chain Rule.
b. The function $e^{\sqrt{x+1}}$ should be differentiated using the Chain Rule.
c. The derivative of a product is *not* the product of the derivatives, but the derivative of a composition is a product of derivatives.
d. $\frac{d}{dx}P(Q(x)) = P'(x)Q'(x)$.

70–73. Second derivatives *Find* $\frac{d^2y}{dx^2}$ *for the following functions.*

70. $y = x\cos x^2$
71. $y = \sin x^2$
72. $y = \sqrt{x^2 + 2}$
73. $y = e^{-2x^2}$

74. Derivatives by different methods

a. Calculate $\frac{d}{dx}(x^2 + x)^2$ using the Chain Rule. Simplify your answer.
b. Expand $(x^2 + x)^2$ first and then calculate the derivative. Verify that your answer agrees with part (a).

75–76. Square root derivatives *Find the derivative of the following functions.*

75. $y = \sqrt{f(x)}$, where f is differentiable and nonnegative at x
76. $y = \sqrt{f(x)g(x)}$, where f and g are differentiable and nonnegative at x

T **77. Tangent lines** Determine an equation of the line tangent to the graph of $y = \frac{(x^2 - 1)^2}{x^3 - 6x - 1}$ at the point $(3, 8)$. Graph the function and the tangent line.

T **78. Tangent lines** Determine equations of the lines tangent to the graph of $y = x\sqrt{5 - x^2}$ at the points $(1, 2)$ and $(-2, -2)$. Graph the function and the tangent lines.

79. Tangent lines Assume f and g are differentiable on their domains with $h(x) = f(g(x))$. Suppose the equation of the line tangent to the graph of g at the point $(4, 7)$ is $y = 3x - 5$ and the equation of the line tangent to the graph of f at $(7, 9)$ is $y = -2x + 23$.

a. Calculate $h(4)$ and $h'(4)$.
b. Determine an equation of the line tangent to the graph of h at the point on the graph where $x = 4$.

80. Tangent lines Assume f is a differentiable function whose graph passes through the point $(1, 4)$. Suppose $g(x) = f(x^2)$ and the line tangent to the graph of f at $(1, 4)$ is $y = 3x + 1$. Determine each of the following.

a. $g(1)$ b. $g'(x)$ c. $g'(1)$
d. An equation of the line tangent to the graph of g when $x = 1$

81. Tangent lines Find the equation of the line tangent to $y = e^{2x}$ at $x = \frac{1}{2}\ln 3$. Graph the function and the tangent line.

82. Composition containing sin *x* Suppose f is differentiable on $[-2, 2]$ with $f'(0) = 3$ and $f'(1) = 5$. Let $g(x) = f(\sin x)$. Evaluate the following expressions.

a. $g'(0)$ b. $g'\left(\frac{\pi}{2}\right)$ c. $g'(\pi)$

83. Composition containing sin *x* Suppose f is differentiable for all real numbers with $f(0) = -3$, $f(1) = 3$, $f'(0) = 3$, and $f'(1) = 5$. Let $g(x) = \sin(\pi f(x))$. Evaluate the following expressions.

a. $g'(0)$ b. $g'(1)$

Applications

84–86. Vibrations of a spring *Suppose an object of mass m is attached to the end of a spring hanging from the ceiling. The mass is at its equilibrium position $y = 0$ when the mass hangs at rest. Suppose you push the mass to a position y_0 units above its equilibrium position and release it. As the mass oscillates up and down (neglecting any friction in the system), the position y of the mass after t seconds is*

$$y = y_0 \cos\left(t\sqrt{\frac{k}{m}}\right), \qquad (2)$$

where $k > 0$ is a constant measuring the stiffness of the spring (the larger the value of k, the stiffer the spring) and y is positive in the upward direction.

84. Use equation (2) to answer the following questions.

a. Find $\frac{dy}{dt}$, the velocity of the mass. Assume k and m are constant.
b. How would the velocity be affected if the experiment were repeated with four times the mass on the end of the spring?
c. How would the velocity be affected if the experiment were repeated with a spring having four times the stiffness (k is increased by a factor of 4)?
d. Assume that y has units of meters, t has units of seconds, m has units of kg, and k has units of kg/s^2. Show that the units of the velocity in part (a) are consistent.

85. Use equation (2) to answer the following questions.

a. Find the second derivative $\frac{d^2y}{dt^2}$.
b. Verify that $\frac{d^2y}{dt^2} = -\frac{k}{m}y$.

86. Use equation (2) to answer the following questions.

a. The *period* T is the time required by the mass to complete one oscillation. Show that $T = 2\pi\sqrt{\frac{m}{k}}$.
b. Assume k is constant and calculate $\frac{dT}{dm}$.
c. Give a physical explanation of why $\frac{dT}{dm}$ is positive.

T **87. A damped oscillator** The displacement of a mass on a spring suspended from the ceiling is given by $y = 10e^{-t/2}\cos\frac{\pi t}{8}$.

a. Graph the displacement function.
b. Compute and graph the velocity of the mass, $v(t) = y'(t)$.
c. Verify that the velocity is zero when the mass reaches the high and low points of its oscillation.

88. Oscillator equation A mechanical oscillator (such as a mass on a spring or a pendulum) subject to frictional forces satisfies the equation (called a differential equation)

$$y''(t) + 2y'(t) + 5y(t) = 0,$$

where y is the displacement of the oscillator from its equilibrium position. Verify by substitution that the function $y(t) = e^{-t}(\sin 2t - 2\cos 2t)$ satisfies this equation.

T **89. Hours of daylight** The number of hours of daylight at any point on Earth fluctuates throughout the year. In the northern hemisphere, the shortest day is on the winter solstice and the longest day is on the summer solstice. At 40° north latitude, the length of a day is approximated by

$$D(t) = 12 - 3\cos\left(\frac{2\pi(t + 10)}{365}\right),$$

where D is measured in hours and $0 \le t \le 365$ is measured in days, with $t = 0$ corresponding to January 1.

a. Approximately how much daylight is there on March 1 ($t = 59$)?
b. Find the rate at which the daylight function changes.
c. Find the rate at which the daylight function changes on March 1. Convert your answer to units of min/day and explain what this result means.
d. Graph the function $y = D'(t)$ using a graphing utility.
e. At what times of year is the length of day changing most rapidly? Least rapidly?

T **90. A mixing tank** A 500-liter (L) tank is filled with pure water. At time $t = 0$, a salt solution begins flowing into the tank at a rate of 5 L/min. At the same time, the (fully mixed) solution flows out of the tank at a rate of 5.5 L/min. The mass of salt in grams in the tank at any time $t \ge 0$ is given by

$$M(t) = 250(1000 - t)(1 - 10^{-30}(1000 - t)^{10})$$

and the volume of solution in the tank (in liters) is given by $V(t) = 500 - 0.5t$.

a. Graph the mass function and verify that $M(0) = 0$.
b. Graph the volume function and verify that the tank is empty when $t = 1000$ min.
c. The concentration of the salt solution in the tank (in g/L) is given by $C(t) = M(t)/V(t)$. Graph the concentration function and comment on its properties. Specifically, what are $C(0)$ and $\lim_{t\to 1000^-} C(t)$?
d. Find the rate of change of the mass $M'(t)$, for $0 \le t \le 1000$.
e. Find the rate of change of the concentration $C'(t)$, for $0 \le t \le 1000$.
f. For what times is the concentration of the solution increasing? Decreasing?

T 91. Power and energy The total energy in megawatt-hr (MWh) used by a town is given by

$$E(t) = 400t + \frac{2400}{\pi} \sin \frac{\pi t}{12},$$

where $t \geq 0$ is measured in hours, with $t = 0$ corresponding to noon.

a. Find the power, or rate of energy consumption, $P(t) = E'(t)$ in units of megawatts (MW).
b. At what time of day is the rate of energy consumption a maximum? What is the power at that time of day?
c. At what time of day is the rate of energy consumption a minimum? What is the power at that time of day?
d. Sketch a graph of the power function reflecting the times at which energy use is a minimum or maximum.

Additional Exercises

92. Deriving trigonometric identities

a. Differentiate both sides of the identity $\cos 2t = \cos^2 t - \sin^2 t$ to prove that $\sin 2t = 2 \sin t \cos t$.
b. Verify that you obtain the same identity for $\sin 2t$ as in part (a) if you differentiate the identity $\cos 2t = 2\cos^2 t - 1$.
c. Differentiate both sides of the identity $\sin 2t = 2 \sin t \cos t$ to prove that $\cos 2t = \cos^2 t - \sin^2 t$.

93. Proof of $\cos^2 x + \sin^2 x = 1$ Let $f(x) = \cos^2 x + \sin^2 x$.

a. Use the Chain Rule to show that $f'(x) = 0$.
b. Assume that if $f' = 0$, then f is a constant function. Calculate $f(0)$ and use it with part (a) to explain why $\cos^2 x + \sin^2 x = 1$.

94. Using the Chain Rule to prove that $\frac{d}{dx}(e^{kx}) = ke^{kx}$

a. Identify the inner function g and the outer function f for the composition $f(g(x)) = e^{kx}$, where k is a real number.
b. Use the Chain Rule to show that $\frac{d}{dx}(e^{kx}) = ke^{kx}$.

95. Deriving the Quotient Rule using the Product Rule and Chain Rule Suppose you forgot the Quotient Rule for calculating $\frac{d}{dx}\left(\frac{f(x)}{g(x)}\right)$. Use the Chain Rule and Product Rule with the identity $\frac{f(x)}{g(x)} = f(x)(g(x))^{-1}$ to derive the Quotient Rule.

96. The Chain Rule for second derivatives

a. Derive a formula for the second derivative, $\frac{d^2}{dx^2}(f(g(x)))$.
b. Use the formula in part (a) to calculate $\frac{d^2}{dx^2}(\sin(3x^4 + 5x^2 + 2))$.

T 97–100. Calculating limits *The following limits are the derivatives of a composite function h at a point a.*

a. Find a possible function h and number a.
b. Use the Chain Rule to find each limit. Verify your answer using a calculator.

97. $\lim_{x \to 2} \frac{(x^2 - 3)^5 - 1}{x - 2}$

98. $\lim_{x \to 0} \frac{\sqrt{4 + \sin x} - 2}{x}$

99. $\lim_{h \to 0} \frac{\sin(\pi/2 + h)^2 - \sin(\pi^2/4)}{h}$

100. $\lim_{h \to 0} \frac{\frac{1}{3((1 + h)^5 + 7)^{10}} - \frac{1}{3(8)^{10}}}{h}$

101. Limit of a difference quotient Assuming that f is differentiable for all x, simplify $\lim_{x \to 5} \frac{f(x^2) - f(25)}{x - 5}$.

102. Derivatives of even and odd functions Recall that f is even if $f(-x) = f(x)$, for all x in the domain of f, and f is odd if $f(-x) = -f(x)$, for all x in the domain of f.

a. If f is a differentiable, even function on its domain, determine whether f' is even, odd, or neither.
b. If f is a differentiable, odd function on its domain, determine whether f' is even, odd, or neither.

103. A general proof of the Chain Rule Let f and g be differentiable functions with $h(x) = f(g(x))$. For a given constant a, let $u = g(a)$ and $v = g(x)$, and define

$$H(v) = \begin{cases} \frac{f(v) - f(u)}{v - u} - f'(u) & \text{if } v \neq u \\ 0 & \text{if } v = u. \end{cases}$$

a. Show that $\lim_{v \to u} H(v) = 0$.
b. For any value of u show that $f(v) - f(u) = (H(v) + f'(u))(v - u)$.
c. Show that

$$h'(a) = \lim_{x \to a}\left((H(g(x)) + f'(g(a))) \cdot \frac{g(x) - g(a)}{x - a}\right).$$

d. Show that $h'(a) = f'(g(a))g'(a)$.

QUICK CHECK ANSWERS

1. The expansion of $(5x + 4)^{100}$ contains 101 terms. It would take too much time to calculate the expansion and the derivative. **2.** The inner function is $u = 5x + 4$, and the outer function is $y = u^3$. **4.** $f(u) = u^{10}$; $u = g(v) = \tan v$; $v = h(x) = x^5$ ◄

3.8 Implicit Differentiation

This chapter has been devoted to calculating derivatives of functions of the form $y = f(x)$, where y is defined *explicitly* as a function of x. However, relations between variables are often expressed *implicitly*. For example, the equation of the unit circle $x^2 + y^2 = 1$ does not specify y directly, but rather defines y implicitly. This equation does not represent a single function because its graph fails the vertical line test (Figure 3.52a). If, however, the equation $x^2 + y^2 = 1$ is solved for y, then *two* functions emerge: $y = -\sqrt{1 - x^2}$ and $y = \sqrt{1 - x^2}$ (Figure 3.52b). Having identified two explicit functions that describe the circle, their derivatives are found using the Chain Rule.

$$\text{If } y = \sqrt{1 - x^2}, \text{ then } \frac{dy}{dx} = -\frac{x}{\sqrt{1 - x^2}}. \quad (1)$$

$$\text{If } y = -\sqrt{1 - x^2}, \text{ then } \frac{dy}{dx} = \frac{x}{\sqrt{1 - x^2}}. \quad (2)$$

We use equation (1) to find the slope of the curve at any point on the upper half of the unit circle and equation (2) to find the slope of the curve at any point on the lower half of the circle.

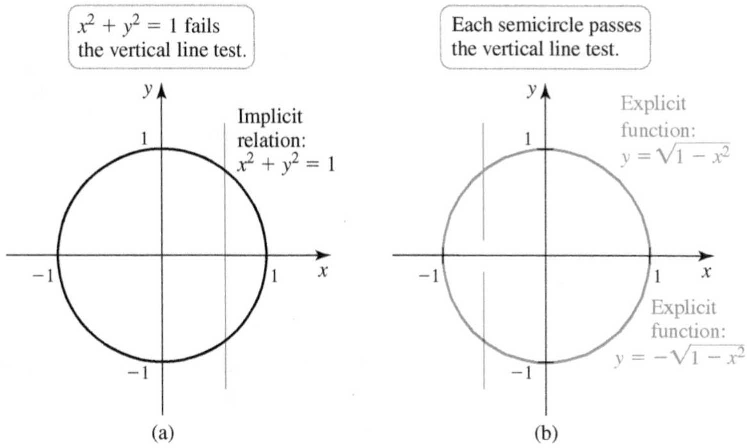

Figure 3.52

QUICK CHECK 1 The equation $x - y^2 = 0$ implicitly defines what two functions? ◄

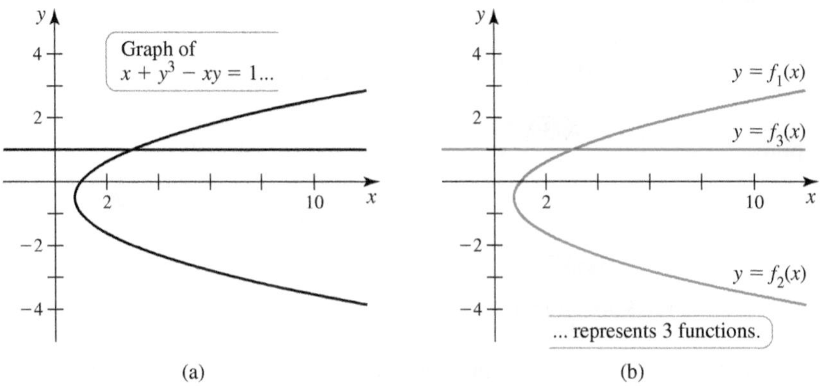

Figure 3.53

While it is straightforward to solve some implicit equations for y (such as $x^2 + y^2 = 1$ or $x - y^2 = 0$), it is difficult or impossible to solve other equations for y. For example, the graph of $x + y^3 - xy = 1$ (Figure 3.53a) represents three functions: the upper half of a parabola $y = f_1(x)$, the lower half of a parabola $y = f_2(x)$, and the horizontal line $y = f_3(x)$ (Figure 3.53b). Solving for y to obtain these three functions is challenging (Exercise 61), and even after solving for y, derivatives for each of the three functions must be calculated separately. The goal of this section is to find a *single* expression for the derivative *directly* from an equation without first solving for y. This technique, called **implicit differentiation**, is demonstrated through examples.

EXAMPLE 1 Implicit differentiation

a. Calculate $\frac{dy}{dx}$ directly from the equation for the unit circle $x^2 + y^2 = 1$.

b. Find the slope of the unit circle at $\left(\frac{1}{2}, \frac{\sqrt{3}}{2}\right)$ and $\left(\frac{1}{2}, -\frac{\sqrt{3}}{2}\right)$.

SOLUTION

a. To indicate the choice of x as the independent variable, it is helpful to replace the variable y with $y(x)$:

$$x^2 + (y(x))^2 = 1. \quad \text{Replace } y \text{ with } y(x).$$

We now take the derivative of each term in the equation *with respect to x*:

$$\underbrace{\frac{d}{dx}(x^2)}_{2x} + \underbrace{\frac{d}{dx}(y(x))^2}_{\text{Use the Chain Rule}} = \underbrace{\frac{d}{dx}(1)}_{0}.$$

By the Chain Rule, $\frac{d}{dx}(y(x))^2 = 2y(x)y'(x)$, or $\frac{d}{dx}(y^2) = 2y\frac{dy}{dx}$. Substituting this result, we have

$$2x + 2y\frac{dy}{dx} = 0.$$

The last step is to solve for $\frac{dy}{dx}$:

$$2y\frac{dy}{dx} = -2x \quad \text{Subtract } 2x \text{ from both sides.}$$

$$\frac{dy}{dx} = -\frac{x}{y}. \quad \text{Divide by } 2y \text{ and simplify.}$$

This result holds provided $y \neq 0$. At the points $(1, 0)$ and $(-1, 0)$, the circle has vertical tangent lines.

b. Notice that the derivative $\frac{dy}{dx} = -\frac{x}{y}$ depends on *both* x and y. Therefore, to find the slope of the circle at $\left(\frac{1}{2}, \frac{\sqrt{3}}{2}\right)$, we substitute both $x = 1/2$ and $y = \sqrt{3}/2$ into the derivative formula. The result is

$$\left.\frac{dy}{dx}\right|_{\left(\frac{1}{2}, \frac{\sqrt{3}}{2}\right)} = -\frac{1/2}{\sqrt{3}/2} = -\frac{1}{\sqrt{3}}.$$

The slope of the curve at $\left(\frac{1}{2}, -\frac{\sqrt{3}}{2}\right)$ is

$$\left.\frac{dy}{dx}\right|_{\left(\frac{1}{2}, -\frac{\sqrt{3}}{2}\right)} = -\frac{1/2}{-\sqrt{3}/2} = \frac{1}{\sqrt{3}}.$$

The curve and tangent lines are shown in Figure 3.54. *Related Exercises 5–12* ◀

➤ Implicit differentiation usually produces an expression for dy/dx in terms of both x and y. The notation $\left.\frac{dy}{dx}\right|_{(a, b)}$ tells us to replace x with a and y with b in the expression for dy/dx.

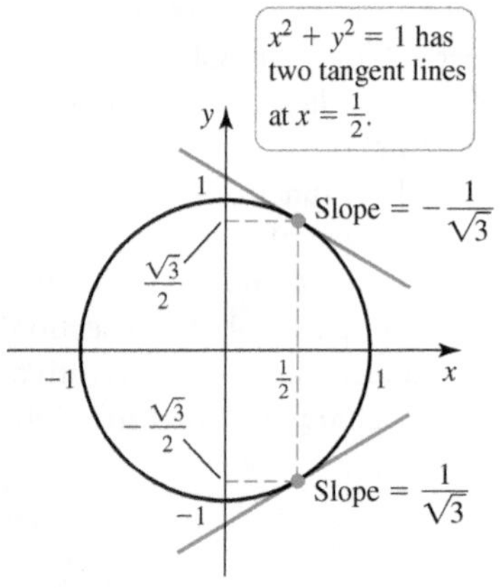

Figure 3.54

Example 1 illustrates the technique of implicit differentiation. It is done without solving for y, and it produces $\frac{dy}{dx}$ in terms of both x and y. The derivative obtained in Example 1 is consistent with the derivatives calculated explicitly in equations (1) and (2). For the upper half of the circle, substituting $y = \sqrt{1 - x^2}$ into the implicit derivative $\frac{dy}{dx} = -\frac{x}{y}$ gives

$$\frac{dy}{dx} = -\frac{x}{y} = -\frac{x}{\sqrt{1 - x^2}},$$

which agrees with equation (1). For the lower half of the circle, substituting $y = -\sqrt{1 - x^2}$ into $\frac{dy}{dx} = -\frac{x}{y}$ gives

$$\frac{dy}{dx} = -\frac{x}{y} = \frac{x}{\sqrt{1 - x^2}},$$

which is consistent with equation (2). Therefore, implicit differentiation gives a single unified derivative $\frac{dy}{dx} = -\frac{x}{y}$.

EXAMPLE 2 Implicit differentiation Find $y'(x)$ when $\sin xy = x^2 + y$.

SOLUTION It is impossible to solve this equation for y in terms of x, so we differentiate implicitly. Differentiating both sides of the equation with respect to x, using the Chain Rule and the Product Rule on the left side, gives

$$(\cos xy)(y + xy') = 2x + y'.$$

We now solve for y':

$$xy'\cos xy - y' = 2x - y\cos xy \quad \text{Rearrange terms.}$$

$$y'(x\cos xy - 1) = 2x - y\cos xy \quad \text{Factor on left side.}$$

$$y' = \frac{2x - y\cos xy}{x\cos xy - 1}. \quad \text{Solve for } y'.$$

Notice that the final result gives y' in terms of both x and y. *Related Exercises 13–24* ◀

QUICK CHECK 2 Use implicit differentiation to find $\frac{dy}{dx}$ for $x - y^2 = 3$. ◀

Slopes of Tangent Lines

Derivatives obtained by implicit differentiation typically depend on x and y. Therefore, the slope of a curve at a particular point (a, b) requires both the x- and y-coordinates of the point. These coordinates are also needed to find an equation of the tangent line at that point.

QUICK CHECK 3 If a function is defined explicitly in the form $y = f(x)$, which coordinates are needed to find the slope of a tangent line—the x-coordinate, the y-coordinate, or both? ◀

➤ Because y is a function of x, we have

$$\frac{d}{dx}(x) = 1 \quad \text{and}$$

$$\frac{d}{dx}(y) = y'.$$

To differentiate y^3 with respect to x, we need the Chain Rule.

EXAMPLE 3 Finding tangent lines with implicit functions Find an equation of the line tangent to the curve $x^2 + xy - y^3 = 7$ at $(3, 2)$.

SOLUTION We calculate the derivative of each term of the equation $x^2 + xy - y^3 = 7$ with respect to x:

$$\frac{d}{dx}(x^2) + \frac{d}{dx}(xy) - \frac{d}{dx}(y^3) = \frac{d}{dx}(7) \quad \text{Differentiate each term.}$$

$$2x + \underbrace{y + xy'}_{\text{Product Rule}} - \underbrace{3y^2y'}_{\text{Chain Rule}} = 0 \quad \text{Calculate the derivatives.}$$

$$3y^2y' - xy' = 2x + y \quad \text{Group the terms containing } y'.$$

$$y' = \frac{2x + y}{3y^2 - x}. \quad \text{Factor and solve for } y'.$$

To find the slope of the tangent line at $(3, 2)$, we substitute $x = 3$ and $y = 2$ into the derivative formula:

$$\left.\frac{dy}{dx}\right|_{(3,2)} = \left.\frac{2x + y}{3y^2 - x}\right|_{(3,2)} = \frac{8}{9}.$$

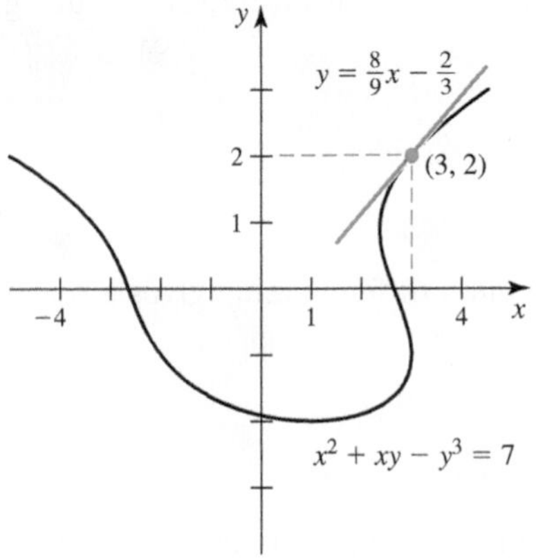

Figure 3.55

An equation of the line passing through $(3, 2)$ with slope $\frac{8}{9}$ is

$$y - 2 = \frac{8}{9}(x - 3) \quad \text{or} \quad y = \frac{8}{9}x - \frac{2}{3}.$$

Figure 3.55 shows the graphs of the curve $x^2 + xy - y^3 = 7$ and the tangent line.

Related Exercises 25–30 ◂

Higher-Order Derivatives of Implicit Functions

In previous sections of this chapter, we found higher-order derivatives $\frac{d^n y}{dx^n}$ by first calculating $\frac{dy}{dx}, \frac{d^2y}{dx^2}, \ldots,$ and $\frac{d^{n-1}y}{dx^{n-1}}$. The same approach is used with implicit differentiation.

EXAMPLE 4 **A second derivative** Find $\frac{d^2y}{dx^2}$ if $x^2 + y^2 = 1$.

SOLUTION The first derivative $\frac{dy}{dx} = -\frac{x}{y}$ was computed in Example 1.

We now calculate the derivative of each side of this equation and simplify the right side:

$$\frac{d}{dx}\left(\frac{dy}{dx}\right) = \frac{d}{dx}\left(-\frac{x}{y}\right) \qquad \text{Take derivatives with respect to } x.$$

$$\frac{d^2y}{dx^2} = -\frac{y \cdot 1 - x\frac{dy}{dx}}{y^2} \qquad \text{Quotient Rule}$$

$$= -\frac{y - x\left(-\frac{x}{y}\right)}{y^2} \qquad \text{Substitute for } \frac{dy}{dx}.$$

$$= -\frac{x^2 + y^2}{y^3} \qquad \text{Simplify.}$$

$$= -\frac{1}{y^3}. \qquad x^2 + y^2 = 1$$

Related Exercises 31–36 ◂

The Power Rule for Rational Exponents

The Extended Power Rule (Section 3.4) states that $\frac{d}{dx}(x^n) = nx^{n-1}$, if n is an integer. Using implicit differentiation, this rule can be further extended to rational values of n such as $\frac{1}{2}$ or $-\frac{5}{3}$. Assume p and q are integers with $q \neq 0$ and let $y = x^{p/q}$, where $x \geq 0$ when q is even. By raising each side of $y = x^{p/q}$ to the power q, we obtain $y^q = x^p$. Assuming that y is a differentiable function of x on its domain, both sides of $y^q = x^p$ are differentiated with respect to x:

$$qy^{q-1}\frac{dy}{dx} = px^{p-1}.$$

We now divide both sides by qy^{q-1} and simplify to obtain

$$\frac{dy}{dx} = \frac{p}{q}\cdot\frac{x^{p-1}}{y^{q-1}} = \frac{p}{q}\cdot\frac{x^{p-1}}{(x^{p/q})^{q-1}} \qquad \text{Substitute } x^{p/q} \text{ for } y.$$

$$= \frac{p}{q}\cdot\frac{x^{p-1}}{x^{p-p/q}} \qquad \text{Multiply exponents in the denominator.}$$

$$= \frac{p}{q}\cdot x^{p/q-1}. \qquad \text{Simplify by combining exponents.}$$

If we let $n = \frac{p}{q}$, then $\frac{d}{dx}(x^n) = nx^{n-1}$. So the Power Rule for rational exponents is the same as the Power Rule for integer exponents.

➤ The assumption that $y = x^{p/q}$ is differentiable on its domain is proved in Section 3.9, where the Power Rule is proved for all real powers; that is, we prove that $\frac{d}{dx}(x^n) = nx^{n-1}$ holds for any real number n.

> **THEOREM 3.16 Power Rule for Rational Exponents**
> Assume p and q are integers with $q \neq 0$. Then
> $$\frac{d}{dx}(x^{p/q}) = \frac{p}{q}x^{p/q-1},$$
> provided $x > 0$ when q is even.

QUICK CHECK 4 Verify the derivative formula $\frac{d}{dx}(\sqrt{x}) = \frac{1}{2\sqrt{x}}$ (first encountered in Example 4 of Section 3.1) by using Theorem 3.16. ◀

EXAMPLE 5 Rational exponent Calculate $\frac{dy}{dx}$ for the following functions.

a. $y = \frac{1}{\sqrt{x}}$ **b.** $y = (x^6 + 3x)^{2/3}$

SOLUTION

a. $\frac{dy}{dx} = \frac{d}{dx}(x^{-1/2}) = -\frac{1}{2}x^{-3/2} = -\frac{1}{2x^{3/2}}$

b. We apply the Chain Rule, where the outer function is $u^{2/3}$ and the inner function is $x^6 + 3x$:

$$\frac{dy}{dx} = \frac{d}{dx}((x^6 + 3x)^{2/3}) = \underbrace{\frac{2}{3}(x^6 + 3x)^{-1/3}}_{\text{derivative of outer function}}\underbrace{(6x^5 + 3)}_{\text{derivative of inner function}}$$
$$= \frac{2(2x^5 + 1)}{(x^6 + 3x)^{1/3}}.$$

Related Exercises 37–44 ◀

EXAMPLE 6 Implicit differentiation with rational exponents Find the slope of the curve $2(x + y)^{1/3} = y$ at the point $(4, 4)$.

SOLUTION We begin by differentiating both sides of the given equation:

$$\frac{2}{3}(x + y)^{-2/3}\left(1 + \frac{dy}{dx}\right) = \frac{dy}{dx} \quad \text{Implicit differentiation, Chain Rule, Theorem 3.16}$$
$$\frac{2}{3}(x + y)^{-2/3} = \frac{dy}{dx} - \frac{2}{3}(x + y)^{-2/3}\frac{dy}{dx} \quad \text{Expand and collect like terms.}$$
$$\frac{2}{3}(x + y)^{-2/3} = \frac{dy}{dx}\left(1 - \frac{2}{3}(x + y)^{-2/3}\right). \quad \text{Factor out } \frac{dy}{dx}.$$

Solving for dy/dx, we find that

$$\frac{dy}{dx} = \frac{\frac{2}{3}(x + y)^{-2/3}}{1 - \frac{2}{3}(x + y)^{-2/3}} \quad \text{Divide by } 1 - \frac{2}{3}(x + y)^{-2/3}.$$
$$\frac{dy}{dx} = \frac{2}{3(x + y)^{2/3} - 2}. \quad \text{Multiply by } 3(x + y)^{2/3} \text{ and simplify.}$$

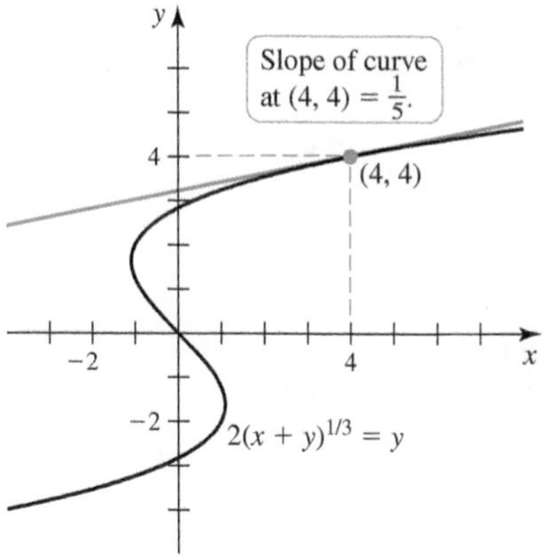

Figure 3.56

Note that the point $(4, 4)$ *does* lie on the curve (Figure 3.56). The slope of the curve at $(4, 4)$ is found by substituting $x = 4$ and $y = 4$ into the formula for $\frac{dy}{dx}$:

$$\left.\frac{dy}{dx}\right|_{(4,4)} = \frac{2}{3(8)^{2/3} - 2} = \frac{1}{5}.$$

Related Exercises 45–50 ◀

SECTION 3.8 EXERCISES

Review Questions

1. For some equations, such as $x^2 + y^2 = 1$ or $x - y^2 = 0$, it is possible to solve for y and then calculate $\frac{dy}{dx}$. Even in these cases, explain why implicit differentiation is usually a more efficient method for calculating the derivative.

2. Explain the differences between computing the derivatives of functions that are defined implicitly and explicitly.

3. Why are both the x-coordinate and the y-coordinate generally needed to find the slope of the tangent line at a point for an implicitly defined function?

4. In this section, for what values of n did we prove that $\frac{d}{dx}(x^n) = nx^{n-1}$?

Basic Skills

5–12. Implicit differentiation *Carry out the following steps.*

a. Use implicit differentiation to find $\frac{dy}{dx}$.

b. Find the slope of the curve at the given point.

5. $x^4 + y^4 = 2;\ (1, -1)$

6. $x = e^y;\ (2, \ln 2)$

7. $y^2 = 4x;\ (1, 2)$

8. $y^2 + 3x = 8;\ (1, \sqrt{5})$

9. $\sin y = 5x^4 - 5;\ (1, \pi)$

10. $\sqrt{x} - 2\sqrt{y} = 0;\ (4, 1)$

11. $\cos y = x;\ \left(0, \frac{\pi}{2}\right)$

12. $\tan xy = x + y;\ (0, 0)$

13–24. Implicit differentiation *Use implicit differentiation to find* $\frac{dy}{dx}$.

13. $\sin xy = x + y$

14. $e^{xy} = 2y$

15. $x + y = \cos y$

16. $x + 2y = \sqrt{y}$

17. $\cos y^2 + x = e^y$

18. $y = \frac{x + 1}{y - 1}$

19. $x^3 = \frac{x + y}{x - y}$

20. $(xy + 1)^3 = x - y^2 + 8$

21. $6x^3 + 7y^3 = 13xy$

22. $\sin x \cos y = \sin x + \cos y$

23. $\sqrt{x^4 + y^2} = 5x + 2y^3$

24. $\sqrt{x + y^2} = \sin y$

25–30. Tangent lines *Carry out the following steps.*

a. Verify that the given point lies on the curve.

b. Determine an equation of the line tangent to the curve at the given point.

25. $x^2 + xy + y^2 = 7;\ (2, 1)$

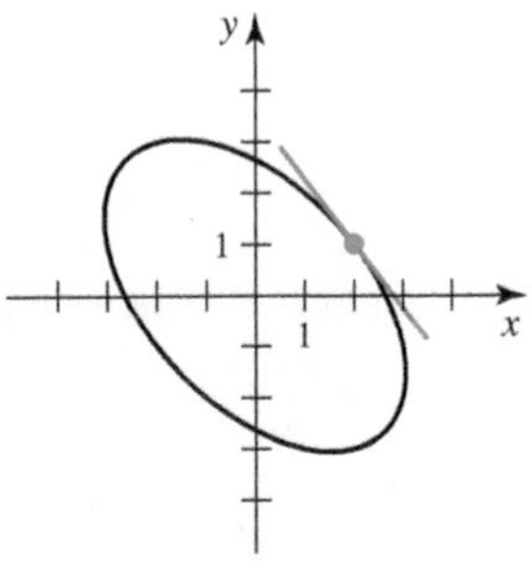

26. $x^4 - x^2y + y^4 = 1;\ (-1, 1)$

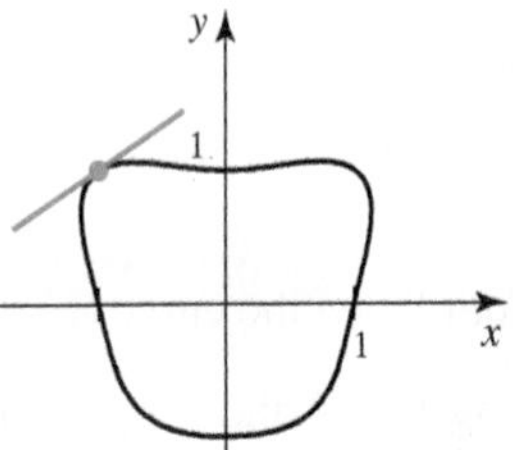

27. $\sin y + 5x = y^2;\ \left(\frac{\pi^2}{5}, \pi\right)$

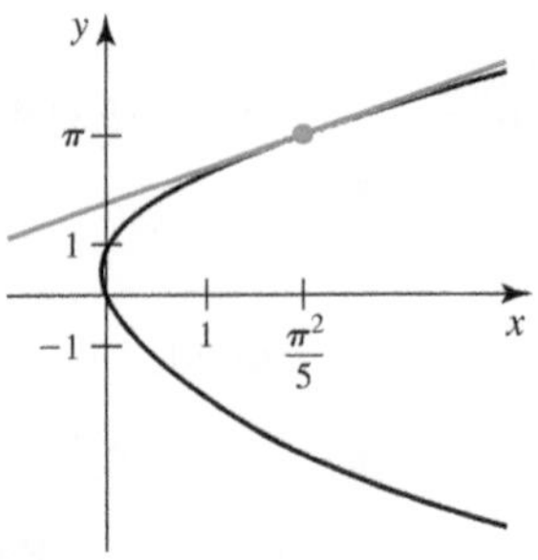

28. $x^3 + y^3 = 2xy;\ (1, 1)$

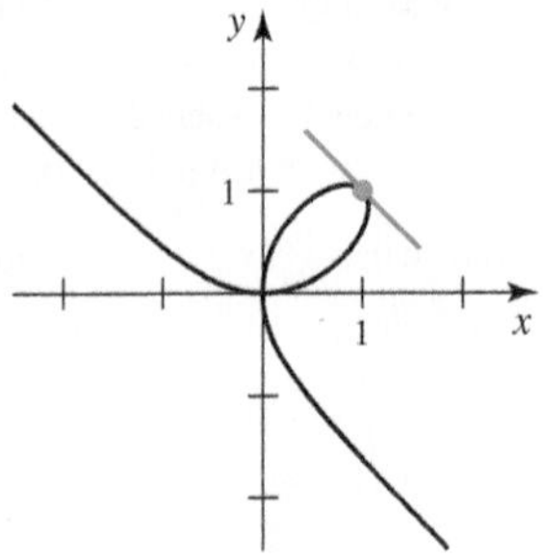

29. $\cos(x - y) + \sin y = \sqrt{2};\ \left(\frac{\pi}{2}, \frac{\pi}{4}\right)$

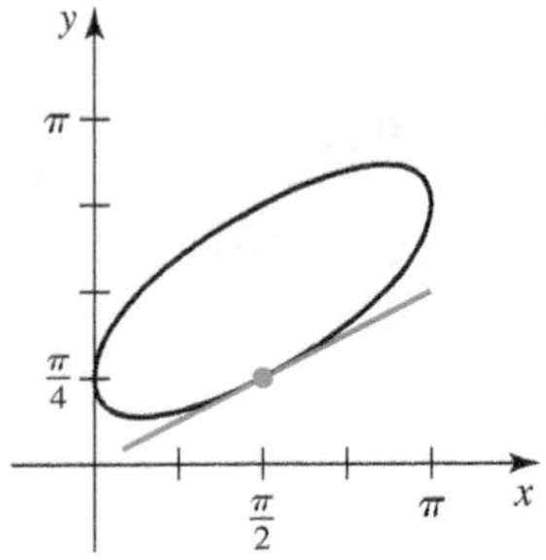

30. $(x^2 + y^2)^2 = \frac{25}{4}xy^2;\ (1, 2)$

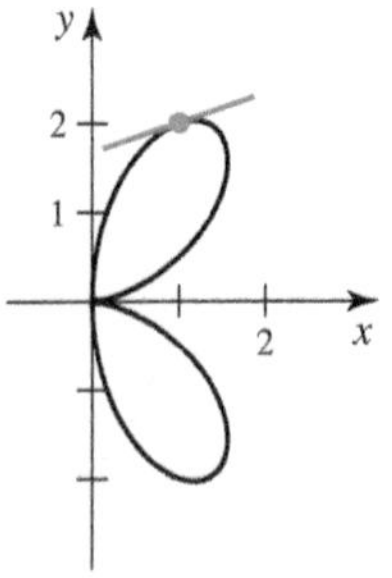

31–36. Second derivatives *Find* $\frac{d^2y}{dx^2}$.

31. $x + y^2 = 1$

32. $2x^2 + y^2 = 4$

33. $x + y = \sin y$

34. $x^4 + y^4 = 64$

35. $e^{2y} + x = y$

36. $\sin x + x^2y = 10$

37–44. Derivatives of functions with rational exponents *Find* $\frac{dy}{dx}$.

37. $y = x^{5/4}$

38. $y = \sqrt[3]{x^2 - x + 1}$

39. $y = (5x + 1)^{2/3}$

40. $y = e^x\sqrt{x^3}$

41. $y = \sqrt[4]{\frac{2x}{4x - 3}}$

42. $y = x(x + 1)^{1/3}$

43. $y = \sqrt[3]{(1 + x^{1/3})^2}$

44. $y = \frac{x}{\sqrt[5]{x} + x}$

45–50. Implicit differentiation with rational exponents *Determine the slope of the following curves at the given point.*

45. $\sqrt[3]{x} + \sqrt[3]{y^4} = 2;\ (1, 1)$

46. $x^{2/3} + y^{2/3} = 2;\ (1, 1)$

47. $x\sqrt[3]{y} + y = 10;\ (1, 8)$

48. $(x + y)^{2/3} = y;\ (4, 4)$

49. $xy + x^{3/2}y^{-1/2} = 2;\ (1, 1)$

50. $xy^{5/2} + x^{3/2}y = 12;\ (4, 1)$

Further Explorations

51. Explain why or why not Determine whether the following statements are true and give an explanation or counterexample.

a. For any equation containing the variables x and y, the derivative dy/dx can be found by first using algebra to rewrite the equation in the form $y = f(x)$.

b. For the equation of a circle of radius r, $x^2 + y^2 = r^2$, we have $\frac{dy}{dx} = -\frac{x}{y}$, for $y \neq 0$ and any real number $r > 0$.

c. If $x = 1$, then by implicit differentiation, $1 = 0$.

d. If $xy = 1$, then $y' = 1/x$.

T 52–54. Multiple tangent lines *Complete the following steps.*

a. Find equations of all lines tangent to the curve at the given value of x.

b. Graph the tangent lines on the given graph.

52. $x + y^3 - y = 1$; $x = 1$

53. $x + y^2 - y = 1$; $x = 1$

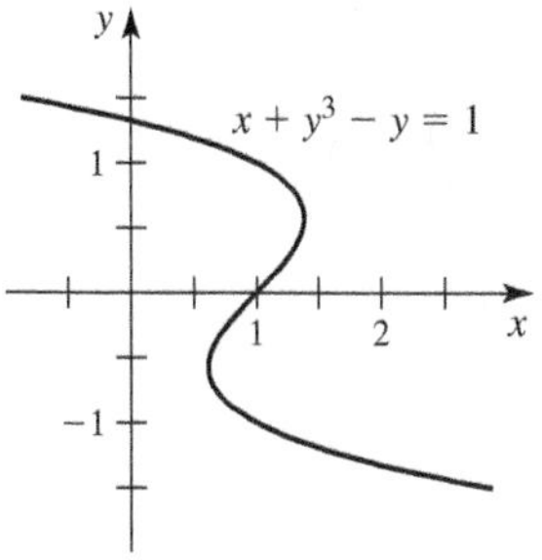

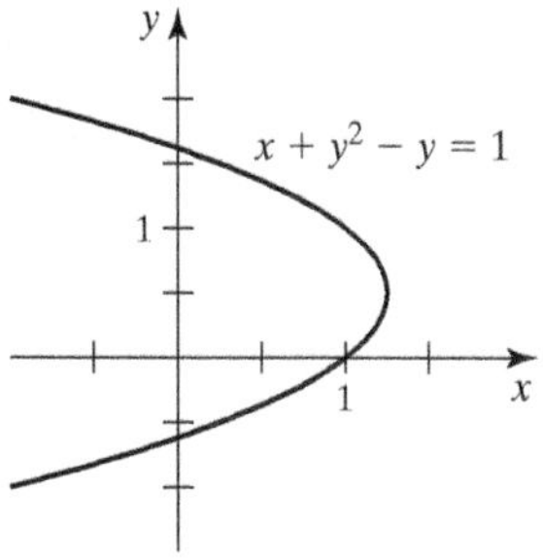

54. $4x^3 = y^2(4 - x)$; $x = 2$ (cissoid of Diocles)

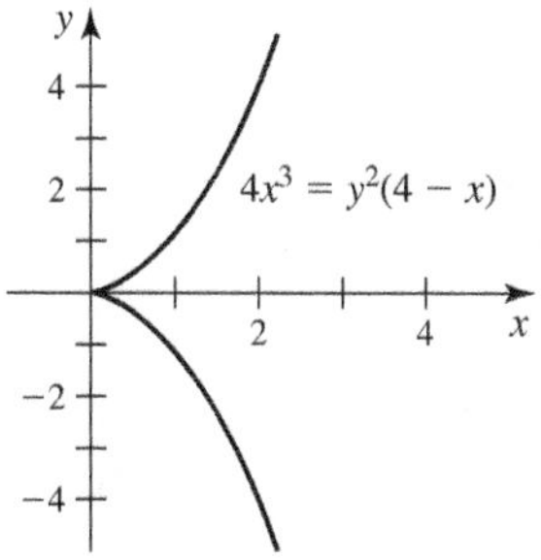

55. Witch of Agnesi Let $y(x^2 + 4) = 8$ (see figure).

a. Use implicit differentiation to find $\frac{dy}{dx}$.

b. Find equations of all lines tangent to the curve $y(x^2 + 4) = 8$ when $y = 1$.

c. Solve the equation $y(x^2 + 4) = 8$ for y to find an explicit expression for y and then calculate $\frac{dy}{dx}$.

d. Verify that the results of parts (a) and (c) are consistent.

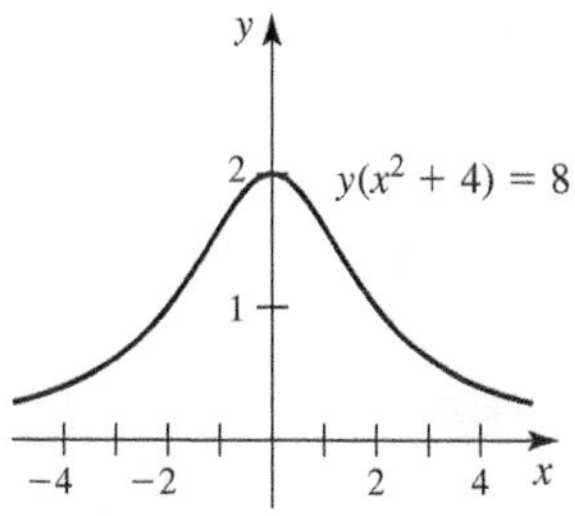

56. Vertical tangent lines

a. Determine the points at which the curve $x + y^3 - y = 1$ has a vertical tangent line (see Exercise 52).

b. Does the curve have any horizontal tangent lines? Explain.

57. Vertical tangent lines

a. Determine the points where the curve $x + y^2 - y = 1$ has a vertical tangent line (see Exercise 53).

b. Does the curve have any horizontal tangent lines? Explain.

T 58–59. Tangent lines for ellipses *Find the equations of the vertical and horizontal tangent lines of the following ellipses.*

58. $x^2 + 4y^2 + 2xy = 12$

59. $9x^2 + y^2 - 36x + 6y + 36 = 0$

60–64. Identifying functions from an equation *The following equations implicitly define one or more functions.*

a. Find $\frac{dy}{dx}$ using implicit differentiation.

b. Solve the given equation for y to identify the implicitly defined functions $y = f_1(x)$, $y = f_2(x)$, ...

c. Use the functions found in part (b) to graph the given equation.

60. $y^3 = ax^2$ (Neile's semicubical parabola)

61. $x + y^3 - xy = 1$ (*Hint:* Rewrite as $y^3 - 1 = xy - x$ and then factor both sides.)

62. $y^2 = \frac{x^2(4 - x)}{4 + x}$ (right strophoid)

63. $x^4 = 2(x^2 - y^2)$ (eight curve)

64. $y^2(x + 2) = x^2(6 - x)$ (trisectrix)

T 65–70. Normal lines *A* **normal line** *at a point P on a curve passes through P and is perpendicular to the line tangent to the curve at P (see figure). Use the following equations and graphs to determine an equation of the normal line at the given point. Illustrate your work by graphing the curve with the normal line.*

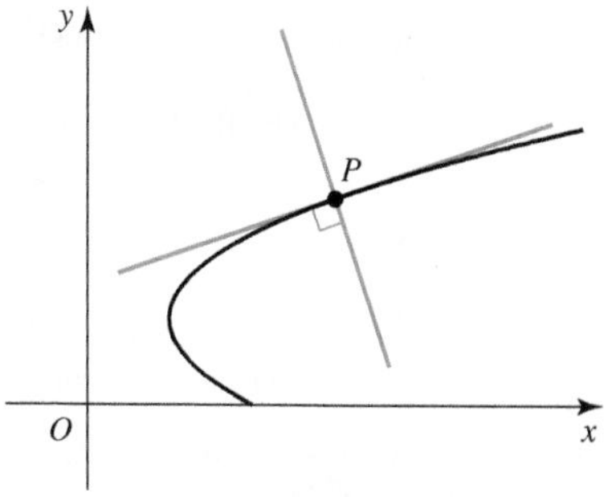

65. Exercise 25 **66.** Exercise 26 **67.** Exercise 27

68. Exercise 28 **69.** Exercise 29 **70.** Exercise 30

T 71–74. Visualizing tangent and normal lines

a. Determine an equation of the tangent line and normal line at the given point (x_0, y_0) on the following curves. (See instructions for Exercises 65–70.)

b. Graph the tangent and normal lines on the given graph.

71. $3x^3 + 7y^3 = 10y$; $(x_0, y_0) = (1, 1)$

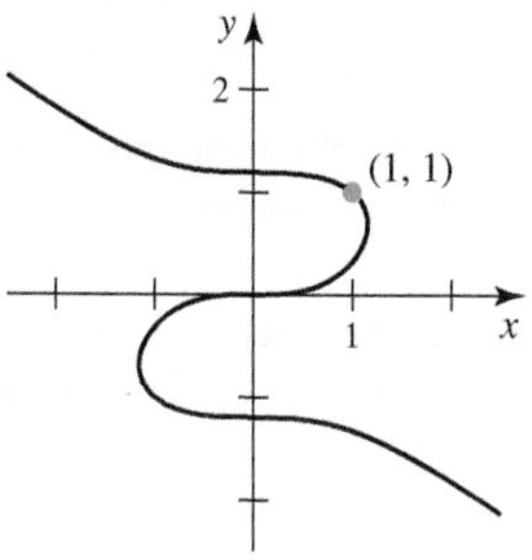

72. $x^4 = 2x^2 + 2y^2$;
$(x_0, y_0) = (2, 2)$
(kampyle of Eudoxus)

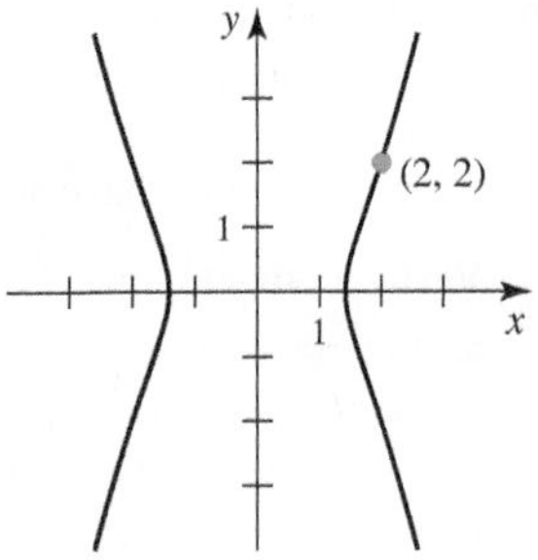

73. $(x^2 + y^2 - 2x)^2 = 2(x^2 + y^2)$;
$(x_0, y_0) = (2, 2)$
(limaçon of Pascal)

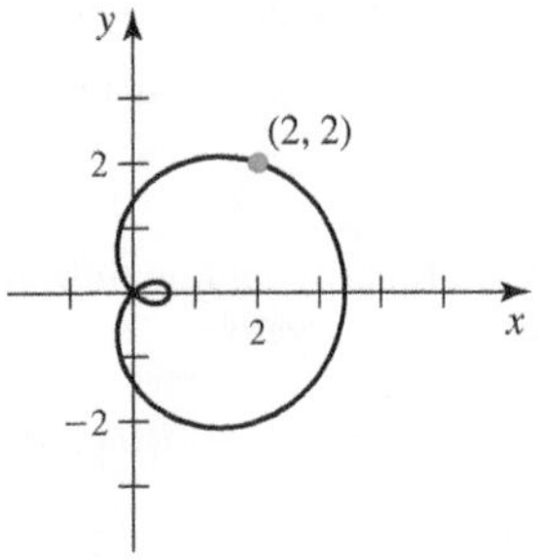

74. $(x^2 + y^2)^2 = \frac{25}{3}(x^2 - y^2)$;
$(x_0, y_0) = (2, -1)$
(lemniscate of Bernoulli)

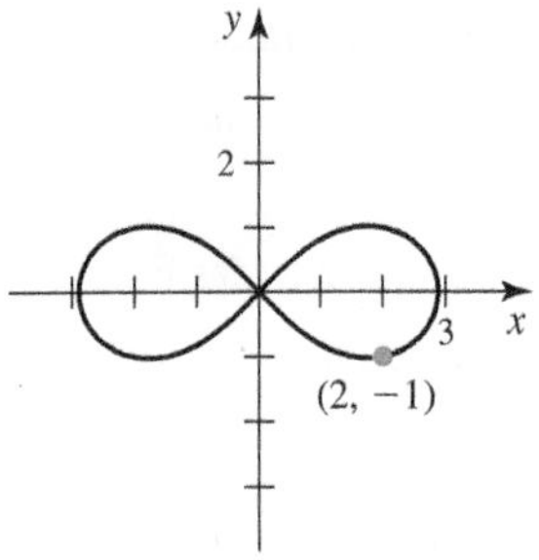

Applications

75. Cobb-Douglas production function The output of an economic system Q, subject to two inputs, such as labor L and capital K, is often modeled by the Cobb-Douglas production function $Q = cL^aK^b$. When $a + b = 1$, the case is called *constant returns to scale*. Suppose $Q = 1280$, $a = \frac{1}{3}$, $b = \frac{2}{3}$, and $c = 40$.

a. Find the rate of change of capital with respect to labor, dK/dL.
b. Evaluate the derivative in part (a) with $L = 8$ and $K = 64$.

76. Surface area of a cone The lateral surface area of a cone of radius r and height h (the surface area excluding the base) is $A = \pi r\sqrt{r^2 + h^2}$.

a. Find dr/dh for a cone with a lateral surface area of $A = 1500\pi$.
b. Evaluate this derivative when $r = 30$ and $h = 40$.

77. Volume of a spherical cap Imagine slicing through a sphere with a plane (sheet of paper). The smaller piece produced is called a spherical cap. Its volume is $V = \pi h^2(3r - h)/3$, where r is the radius of the sphere and h is the thickness of the cap.

a. Find dr/dh for a sphere with a volume of $5\pi/3$.
b. Evaluate this derivative when $r = 2$ and $h = 1$.

78. Volume of a torus The volume of a torus (doughnut or bagel) with an inner radius of a and an outer radius of b is $V = \pi^2(b + a)(b - a)^2/4$.

a. Find db/da for a torus with a volume of $64\pi^2$.
b. Evaluate this derivative when $a = 6$ and $b = 10$.

Additional Exercises

79–81. Orthogonal trajectories *Two curves are* **orthogonal** *to each other if their tangent lines are perpendicular at each point of intersection (recall that two lines are perpendicular to each other if their slopes are negative reciprocals). A family of curves forms* **orthogonal trajectories** *with another family of curves if each curve in one family is orthogonal to each curve in the other family. For example, the parabolas $y = cx^2$ form orthogonal trajectories with the family of ellipses $x^2 + 2y^2 = k$, where c and k are constants (see figure).*

Find dy/dx for each equation of the following pairs. Use the derivatives to explain why the families of curves form orthogonal trajectories.

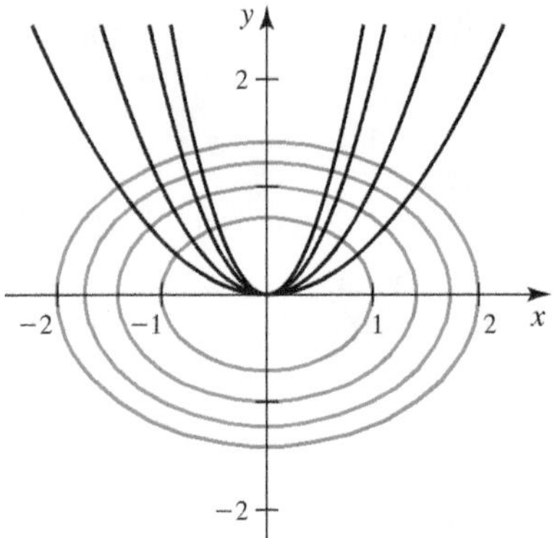

79. $y = mx$; $x^2 + y^2 = a^2$, where m and a are constants

80. $y = cx^2$; $x^2 + 2y^2 = k$, where c and k are constants

81. $xy = a$; $x^2 - y^2 = b$, where a and b are constants

82. Finding slope Find the slope of the curve $5\sqrt{x} - 10\sqrt{y} = \sin x$ at the point $(4\pi, \pi)$.

83. A challenging derivative Find $\frac{dy}{dx}$, where $(x^2 + y^2)(x^2 + y^2 + x) = 8xy^2$.

84. A challenging derivative Find $\frac{dy}{dx}$, where $\sqrt{3x^7 + y^2} = \sin^2 y + 100xy$.

85. A challenging second derivative Find $\frac{d^2y}{dx^2}$, where $\sqrt{y} + xy = 1$.

T **86–89. Work carefully** *Proceed with caution when using implicit differentiation to find points at which a curve has a specified slope. For the following curves, find the points on the curve (if they exist) at which the tangent line is horizontal or vertical. Once you have found possible points, make sure they actually lie on the curve. Confirm your results with a graph.*

86. $y^2 - 3xy = 2$

87. $x^2(3y^2 - 2y^3) = 4$

88. $x^2(y - 2) - e^y = 0$

89. $x(1 - y^2) + y^3 = 0$

QUICK CHECK ANSWERS

1. $y = \sqrt{x}$ and $y = -\sqrt{x}$ **2.** $\frac{dy}{dx} = \frac{1}{2y}$

3. Only the x-coordinate is needed.

4. $\frac{d}{dx}(\sqrt{x}) = \frac{d}{dx}(x^{1/2}) = \frac{1}{2}x^{-1/2} = \frac{1}{2\sqrt{x}}$ ◀

3.9 Derivatives of Logarithmic and Exponential Functions

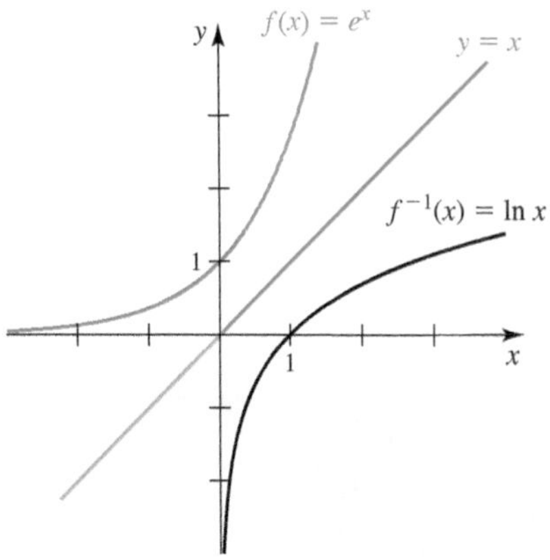

Figure 3.57

We return now to the major theme of this chapter: developing rules of differentiation for the standard families of functions. First, we discover how to differentiate the natural logarithmic function. From there, we treat general exponential and logarithmic functions.

The Derivative of $y = \ln x$

Recall from Section 1.3 that the natural exponential function $f(x) = e^x$ is a one-to-one function on the interval $(-\infty, \infty)$. Therefore, it has an inverse, which is the natural logarithmic function $f^{-1}(x) = \ln x$. The domain of f^{-1} is the range of f, which is $(0, \infty)$. The graphs of f and f^{-1} are symmetric about the line $y = x$ (Figure 3.57). This inverse relationship has several important consequences, summarized as follows.

➤ A careful development of property (3) is given in Section 6.8.

Inverse Properties for e^x and $\ln x$

1. $e^{\ln x} = x$, for $x > 0$, and $\ln(e^x) = x$, for all x.
2. $y = \ln x$ if and only if $x = e^y$.
3. For real numbers x and $b > 0$, $b^x = e^{\ln b^x} = e^{x \ln b}$.

QUICK CHECK 1 Simplify $e^{2 \ln x}$. Express 5^x using the base e. ◄

➤ Figure 3.57 also provides evidence that $\ln x$ is differentiable for $x > 0$: Its graph is smooth with no jumps or cusps.

With these preliminary observations, we now determine the derivative of $\ln x$. A theorem we prove in Section 3.10 says that because e^x is differentiable on its domain, its inverse $\ln x$ is also differentiable on its domain.

To find the derivative of $y = \ln x$, we begin with inverse property (2) and write $x = e^y$, where $x > 0$. The key step is to compute dy/dx with implicit differentiation. Using the Chain Rule to differentiate both sides of $x = e^y$ with respect to x, we have

$$x = e^y \qquad y = \ln x \text{ if and only if } x = e^y$$

$$1 = e^y \cdot \frac{dy}{dx} \qquad \text{Differentiate both sides with respect to } x.$$

$$\frac{dy}{dx} = \frac{1}{e^y} = \frac{1}{x}. \qquad \text{Solve for } dy/dx \text{ and use } x = e^y.$$

Therefore,

$$\frac{d}{dx}(\ln x) = \frac{1}{x}.$$

Because the domain of the natural logarithm is $(0, \infty)$, this rule is limited to positive values of x (Figure 3.58a).

An important extension is obtained by considering the function $\ln |x|$, which is defined for all $x \neq 0$. By the definition of the absolute value,

➤ Recall that

$$|x| = \begin{cases} x & \text{if } x \geq 0 \\ -x & \text{if } x < 0. \end{cases}$$

$$\ln |x| = \begin{cases} \ln x & \text{if } x > 0 \\ \ln(-x) & \text{if } x < 0. \end{cases}$$

For $x > 0$, it follows immediately that

$$\frac{d}{dx}(\ln |x|) = \frac{d}{dx}(\ln x) = \frac{1}{x}.$$

When $x < 0$, a similar calculation using the Chain Rule reveals that

$$\frac{d}{dx}(\ln|x|) = \frac{d}{dx}(\ln(-x)) = \frac{1}{(-x)}(-1) = \frac{1}{x}.$$

Therefore, we have the result that the derivative of $\ln|x|$ is $\frac{1}{x}$, for $x \neq 0$ (Figure 3.58b).

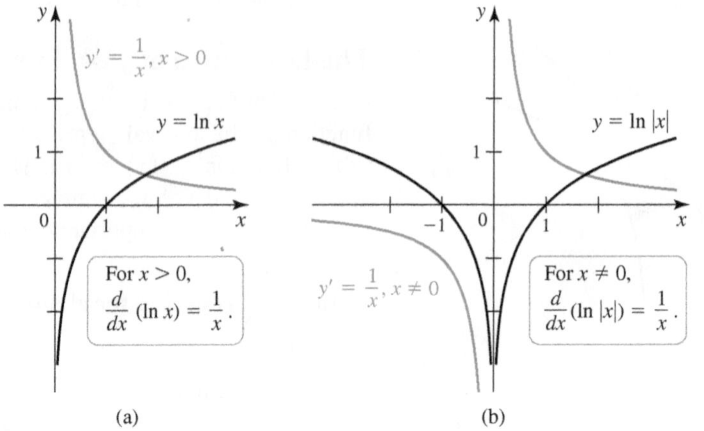

Figure 3.58

Taking these results one step further and using the Chain Rule to differentiate $\ln|u(x)|$, we obtain the following theorem.

> **THEOREM 3.17 Derivative of ln x**
>
> $$\frac{d}{dx}(\ln x) = \frac{1}{x}, \text{ for } x > 0 \qquad \frac{d}{dx}(\ln|x|) = \frac{1}{x}, \text{ for } x \neq 0$$
>
> If u is differentiable at x and $u(x) \neq 0$, then
>
> $$\frac{d}{dx}(\ln|u(x)|) = \frac{u'(x)}{u(x)}.$$

EXAMPLE 1 Derivatives involving ln x Find $\frac{dy}{dx}$ for the following functions.

a. $y = \ln 4x$ **b.** $y = x \ln x$ **c.** $y = \ln|\sec x|$ **d.** $y = \frac{\ln x^2}{x^2}$

SOLUTION

a. Using the Chain Rule,

$$\frac{dy}{dx} = \frac{d}{dx}(\ln 4x) = \frac{1}{4x}\cdot 4 = \frac{1}{x}.$$

An alternative method uses a property of logarithms before differentiating:

$$\frac{d}{dx}(\ln 4x) = \frac{d}{dx}(\ln 4 + \ln x) \qquad \ln xy = \ln x + \ln y$$

$$= 0 + \frac{1}{x} = \frac{1}{x}. \qquad \ln 4 \text{ is a constant.}$$

➤ Because $\ln x$ and $\ln 4x$ differ by an additive constant ($\ln 4x = \ln x + \ln 4$), the derivatives of $\ln x$ and $\ln 4x$ are equal.

b. By the Product Rule,

$$\frac{dy}{dx} = \frac{d}{dx}(x \ln x) = 1 \cdot \ln x + x \cdot \frac{1}{x} = \ln x + 1.$$

c. Using the Chain Rule and the second part of Theorem 3.17,

$$\frac{dy}{dx} = \frac{1}{\sec x}\left(\frac{d}{dx}(\sec x)\right) = \frac{1}{\sec x}(\sec x \tan x) = \tan x.$$

d. The Quotient Rule and Chain Rule give

$$\frac{dy}{dx} = \frac{x^2\left(\frac{1}{x^2}\cdot 2x\right) - (\ln x^2)\,2x}{(x^2)^2} = \frac{2x - 2x\ln x^2}{x^4} = \frac{2(1 - \ln x^2)}{x^3}.$$

Related Exercises 9–22 ◀

QUICK CHECK 2 Find $\frac{d}{dx}(\ln x^p)$, where $x > 0$ and p is a rational number, in two ways: (1) using the Chain Rule and (2) by first using a property of logarithms. ◀

The Derivative of b^x

A rule similar to $\frac{d}{dx}(e^x) = e^x$ exists for computing the derivative of b^x, where $b > 0$. Because $b^x = e^{x \ln b}$ by inverse property (3), its derivative is

$$\frac{d}{dx}(b^x) = \frac{d}{dx}(e^{x\ln b}) = \underbrace{e^{x\ln b}}_{b^x}\cdot \ln b. \quad \text{Chain Rule with } \frac{d}{dx}(x\ln b) = \ln b$$

Noting that $e^{x\ln b} = b^x$ results in the following theorem.

➤ Check that when $b = e$, Theorem 3.18 becomes

$$\frac{d}{dx}(e^x) = e^x.$$

THEOREM 3.18 Derivative of b^x
If $b > 0$ and $b \neq 1$, then for all x,

$$\frac{d}{dx}(b^x) = b^x \ln b.$$

Notice that when $b > 1$, $\ln b > 0$ and the graph of $y = b^x$ has tangent lines with positive slopes for all x. When $0 < b < 1$, $\ln b < 0$ and the graph of $y = b^x$ has tangent lines with negative slopes for all x. In either case, the tangent line at $(0, 1)$ has slope $\ln b$ (Figure 3.59).

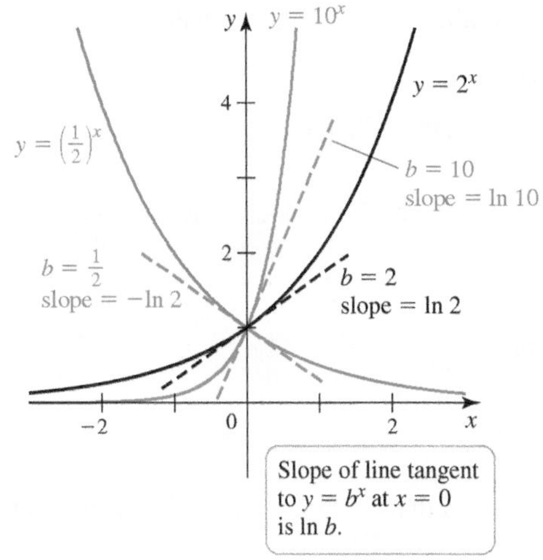

Figure 3.59

EXAMPLE 2 Derivatives with b^x Find the derivative of the following functions.

a. $f(x) = 3^x$ **b.** $g(t) = 108 \cdot 2^{t/12}$

SOLUTION

a. Using Theorem 3.18, $f'(x) = 3^x \ln 3$.

b.

$$g'(t) = 108\frac{d}{dt}(2^{t/12}) \quad \text{Constant Multiple Rule}$$

$$= 108 \cdot \ln 2 \cdot 2^{t/12}\underbrace{\frac{d}{dt}\left(\frac{t}{12}\right)}_{1/12} \quad \text{Chain Rule}$$

$$= 9\ln 2 \cdot 2^{t/12} \quad \text{Simplify.}$$

Related Exercises 23–30 ◀

Table 3.6

Mother's Age	Incidence of Down Syndrome	Decimal Equivalent
30	1 in 900	0.00111
35	1 in 400	0.00250
36	1 in 300	0.00333
37	1 in 230	0.00435
38	1 in 180	0.00556
39	1 in 135	0.00741
40	1 in 105	0.00952
42	1 in 60	0.01667
44	1 in 35	0.02875
46	1 in 20	0.05000
48	1 in 16	0.06250
49	1 in 12	0.08333

(*Source:* E.G. Hook and A. Lindsjo, *The American Journal of Human Genetics,* 30, Jan 1978)

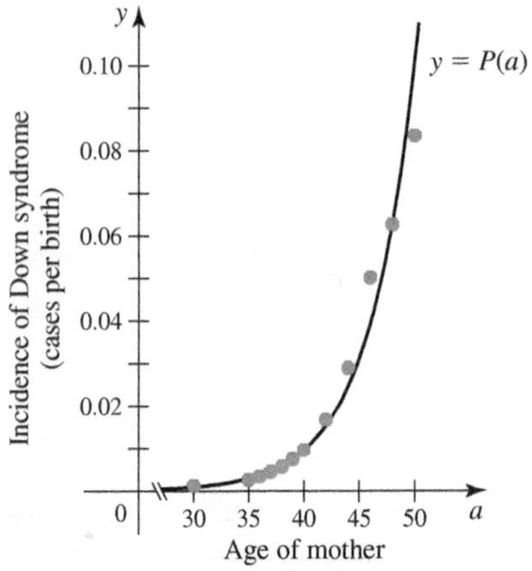

Figure 3.60

➤ The model in Example 3 was created using a method called *exponential regression.* The parameters A and B are chosen so that the function $P(a) = A\,B^a$ fits the data as closely as possible.

EXAMPLE 3 **An exponential model** Table 3.6 and Figure 3.60 show how the incidence of Down syndrome in newborn infants increases with the age of the mother. The data can be modeled with the exponential function $P(a) = \frac{1}{1{,}613{,}000}1.2733^a$, where a is the age of the mother (in years) and $P(a)$ is the incidence (number of Down syndrome children per total births).

a. According to the model, at what age is the incidence of Down syndrome equal to 0.01 (that is, 1 in 100)?

b. Compute $P'(a)$.

c. Find $P'(35)$ and $P'(46)$, and interpret each.

SOLUTION

a. We let $P(a) = 0.01$ and solve for a:

$$0.01 = \frac{1}{1{,}613{,}000}1.2733^a$$

$$\ln 16{,}130 = \ln(1.2733^a) \qquad \text{Multiply both sides by 1,613,000 and take logarithms of both sides.}$$

$$\ln 16{,}130 = a \ln 1.2733 \qquad \text{Property of logarithms}$$

$$a = \frac{\ln 16{,}130}{\ln 1.2733} \approx 40 \text{ (years old).} \qquad \text{Solve for } a.$$

b. $$P'(a) = \frac{1}{1{,}613{,}000}\frac{d}{da}(1.2733^a)$$
$$= \frac{1}{1{,}613{,}000}1.2733^a \ln 1.2733$$
$$\approx \frac{1}{6{,}676{,}000}1.2733^a$$

c. The derivative measures the rate of change of the incidence with respect to age. For a 35-year-old woman,

$$P'(35) = \frac{1}{6{,}676{,}000}1.2733^{35} \approx 0.0007,$$

which means the incidence increases at a rate of about 0.0007/year. By age 46, the rate of change is

$$P'(46) = \frac{1}{6{,}676{,}000}1.2733^{46} \approx 0.01,$$

which is a significant increase over the rate of change of the incidence at age 35.

Related Exercises 31–33 ◀

QUICK CHECK 3 Suppose $A = 500(1.045)^t$. Compute $\frac{dA}{dt}$. ◀

The General Power Rule

As it stands now, the Power Rule for derivatives says that $\frac{d}{dx}(x^p) = px^{p-1}$, for rational powers p. The rule is now extended to all real powers.

THEOREM 3.19 General Power Rule
For real numbers p and for $x > 0$,

$$\frac{d}{dx}(x^p) = px^{p-1}.$$

Furthermore, if u is a positive differentiable function on its domain, then

$$\frac{d}{dx}(u(x)^p) = p(u(x))^{p-1} \cdot u'(x).$$

Proof: For $x > 0$ and real numbers p, we have $x^p = e^{p \ln x}$ by inverse property (3). Therefore, the derivative of x^p is computed as follows:

$$\begin{aligned}
\frac{d}{dx}(x^p) &= \frac{d}{dx}(e^{p \ln x}) && \text{Inverse property (3)}\\
&= e^{p \ln x} \cdot \frac{p}{x} && \text{Chain Rule, } \frac{d}{dx}(p \ln x) = \frac{p}{x}\\
&= x^p \cdot \frac{p}{x} && e^{p \ln x} = x^p\\
&= px^{p-1}. && \text{Simplify.}
\end{aligned}$$

We see that $\frac{d}{dx}(x^p) = px^{p-1}$ for all real powers p. The second part of the General Power Rule follows from the Chain Rule. ◄

EXAMPLE 4 Computing derivatives Find the derivative of the following functions.

a. $y = x^\pi$ **b.** $y = \pi^x$ **c.** $y = (x^2 + 4)^e$

➤ Recall that power functions have the variable in the base, while exponential functions have the variable in the exponent.

SOLUTION

a. With $y = x^\pi$, we have a power function with an irrational exponent; by the General Power Rule,

$$\frac{dy}{dx} = \pi x^{\pi - 1}, \text{ for } x > 0.$$

b. Here we have an exponential function with base $b = \pi$. By Theorem 3.18,

$$\frac{dy}{dx} = \pi^x \ln \pi.$$

c. The Chain Rule and General Power Rule are required:

$$\frac{dy}{dx} = e(x^2 + 4)^{e-1} \cdot 2x = 2ex\,(x^2 + 4)^{e-1}.$$

Because $x^2 + 4 > 0$, for all x, the result is valid for all x.

Related Exercises 34–44 ◄

Functions of the form $f(x) = (g(x))^{h(x)}$, where both g and h are nonconstant functions, are neither exponential functions nor power functions (they are sometimes called *tower functions*). To compute their derivatives, we use the identity $b^x = e^{x \ln b}$ to rewrite f with base e:

$$f(x) = (g(x))^{h(x)} = e^{h(x) \ln g(x)}.$$

This function carries the restriction $g(x) > 0$. The derivative of f is then computed using the methods developed in this section. A specific case is illustrated in the following example.

EXAMPLE 5 **General exponential functions** Let $f(x) = x^{\sin x}$, for $x \geq 0$.

a. Find $f'(x)$. **b.** Evaluate $f'\left(\frac{\pi}{2}\right)$.

SOLUTION

a. The key step is to use $b^x = e^{x \ln b}$ to write f in the form

$$f(x) = x^{\sin x} = e^{(\sin x) \ln x}.$$

We now differentiate:

$$f'(x) = e^{(\sin x) \ln x} \frac{d}{dx}((\sin x) \ln x) \qquad \text{Chain Rule}$$

$$= \underbrace{e^{(\sin x) \ln x}}_{x^{\sin x}} \left((\cos x) \ln x + \frac{\sin x}{x} \right) \qquad \text{Product Rule}$$

$$= x^{\sin x} \left((\cos x) \ln x + \frac{\sin x}{x} \right).$$

b. Letting $x = \frac{\pi}{2}$, we find that

$$f'\left(\frac{\pi}{2}\right) = \left(\frac{\pi}{2}\right)^{\sin(\pi/2)} \left(\underbrace{\left(\cos \frac{\pi}{2}\right)}_{0} \ln \frac{\pi}{2} + \underbrace{\frac{\sin(\pi/2)}{\pi/2}}_{2/\pi} \right) \qquad \text{Substitute } x = \frac{\pi}{2}.$$

$$= \frac{\pi}{2}\left(0 + \frac{2}{\pi}\right) = 1.$$

Related Exercises 45–50 ◀

EXAMPLE 6 **Finding a horizontal tangent line** Determine whether the graph of $f(x) = x^x$, for $x > 0$, has any horizontal tangent lines.

SOLUTION A horizontal tangent occurs when $f'(x) = 0$. To find the derivative, we first write $f(x) = x^x = e^{x \ln x}$:

$$\frac{d}{dx}(x^x) = \frac{d}{dx}(e^{x \ln x})$$

$$= \underbrace{e^{x \ln x}}_{x^x} \left(1 \cdot \ln x + x \cdot \frac{1}{x}\right) \qquad \text{Chain Rule; Product Rule}$$

$$= x^x (\ln x + 1). \qquad \text{Simplify; } e^{x \ln x} = x^x.$$

The equation $f'(x) = 0$ implies that $x^x = 0$ or $\ln x + 1 = 0$. The first equation has no solution because $x^x = e^{x \ln x} > 0$, for all $x > 0$. We solve the second equation, $\ln x + 1 = 0$, as follows:

$$\ln x = -1$$

$$e^{\ln x} = e^{-1} \qquad \text{Exponentiate both sides.}$$

$$x = \frac{1}{e}. \qquad e^{\ln x} = x$$

Therefore, the graph of $f(x) = x^x$ (Figure 3.61) has a single horizontal tangent at $(e^{-1}, f(e^{-1})) \approx (0.368, 0.692)$.

Related Exercises 51–54 ◀

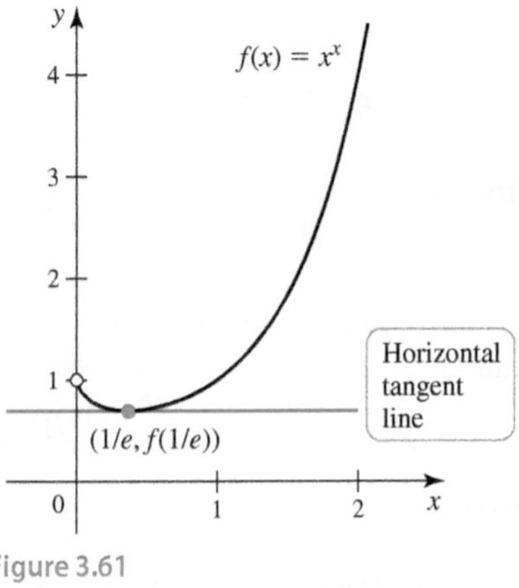

Figure 3.61

Derivatives of General Logarithmic Functions

The general exponential function $f(x) = b^x$ is one-to-one when $b > 0$ with $b \neq 1$. The inverse function $f^{-1}(x) = \log_b x$ is the logarithmic function with base b. The technique used to differentiate the natural logarithm applies to the general logarithmic function. We begin with the inverse relationship

$$y = \log_b x \Leftrightarrow x = b^y, \text{ where } x > 0.$$

Differentiating both sides of $x = b^y$ with respect to x, we obtain

$$1 = b^y \ln b \cdot \frac{dy}{dx} \quad \text{Implicit differentiation}$$

$$\frac{dy}{dx} = \frac{1}{b^y \ln b} \quad \text{Solve for } \frac{dy}{dx}.$$

$$\frac{dy}{dx} = \frac{1}{x \ln b}. \quad b^y = x.$$

➤ An alternative proof of Theorem 3.20 uses the change-of-base formula $\log_b x = \dfrac{\ln x}{\ln b}$ (Section 1.3). Differentiating both sides of this equation gives the same result.

A similar argument applied to $y = \log_b |x|$ with $x < 0$ leads to the following theorem.

THEOREM 3.20 Derivative of $\log_b x$
If $b > 0$ and $b \neq 1$, then

$$\frac{d}{dx}(\log_b x) = \frac{1}{x \ln b}, \text{ for } x > 0 \quad \text{and} \quad \frac{d}{dx}(\log_b |x|) = \frac{1}{x \ln b}, \text{ for } x \neq 0.$$

QUICK CHECK 4 Compute dy/dx for $y = \log_3 x$. ◄

EXAMPLE 7 Derivatives with general logarithms Compute the derivative of the following functions.

a. $f(x) = \log_5 (2x + 1)$ **b.** $T(n) = n \log_2 n$

SOLUTION

a. We use Theorem 3.20 with the Chain Rule assuming $2x + 1 > 0$:

$$f'(x) = \frac{1}{(2x + 1) \ln 5} \cdot 2 = \frac{2}{\ln 5} \cdot \frac{1}{2x + 1}. \quad \text{Chain Rule}$$

b.

$$T'(n) = \log_2 n + n \cdot \frac{1}{n \ln 2} = \log_2 n + \frac{1}{\ln 2} \quad \text{Product Rule}$$

We can change bases and write the result in base e:

$$T'(n) = \frac{\ln n}{\ln 2} + \frac{1}{\ln 2} = \frac{\ln n + 1}{\ln 2}.$$

➤ The function in Example 7b is used in computer science as an estimate of the computing time needed to carry out a *sorting algorithm* on a list of n items.

Related Exercises 55–60 ◄

QUICK CHECK 5 Show that the derivative computed in Example 7b can be expressed in base 2 as $T'(n) = \log_2 (en)$. ◄

Logarithmic Differentiation

Products, quotients, and powers of functions are usually differentiated using the derivative rules of the same name (perhaps combined with the Chain Rule). There are times, however, when the direct computation of a derivative is very tedious. Consider the function

$$f(x) = \frac{(x^3 - 1)^4 \sqrt{3x - 1}}{x^2 + 4}.$$

We would need the Quotient, Product, and Chain Rules just to compute $f'(x)$, and simplifying the result would require additional work. The properties of logarithms reviewed in Section 1.3 are useful for differentiating such functions.

➤ The properties of logarithms needed for logarithmic differentiation (where $x > 0$ and $y > 0$):

1. $\ln xy = \ln x + \ln y$
2. $\ln (x/y) = \ln x - \ln y$
3. $\ln x^y = y \ln x$

All three properties are used in Example 8.

EXAMPLE 8 Logarithmic differentiation Let $f(x) = \dfrac{(x^3 - 1)^4\sqrt{3x - 1}}{x^2 + 4}$ and compute $f'(x)$.

SOLUTION We begin by taking the natural logarithm of both sides and simplifying the result:

$$\begin{aligned}\ln(f(x)) &= \ln\left(\frac{(x^3-1)^4\sqrt{3x-1}}{x^2+4}\right)\\ &= \ln(x^3-1)^4 + \ln\sqrt{3x-1} - \ln(x^2+4) \qquad \log xy = \log x + \log y\\ &= 4\ln(x^3-1) + \tfrac{1}{2}\ln(3x-1) - \ln(x^2+4). \qquad \log x^y = y\log x\end{aligned}$$

➤ In the event that $f \le 0$ for some values of x, $\ln f(x)$ is not defined. In that case, we generally find the derivative of $|y| = |f(x)|$.

We now differentiate both sides using the Chain Rule; specifically, the derivative of the left side is $\dfrac{d}{dx}(\ln f(x)) = \dfrac{f'(x)}{f(x)}$. Therefore,

$$\frac{f'(x)}{f(x)} = 4\cdot\frac{1}{x^3-1}\cdot 3x^2 + \frac{1}{2}\cdot\frac{1}{3x-1}\cdot 3 - \frac{1}{x^2+4}\cdot 2x.$$

Solving for $f'(x)$, we have

$$f'(x) = f(x)\left(\frac{12x^2}{x^3-1} + \frac{3}{2(3x-1)} - \frac{2x}{x^2+4}\right).$$

Finally, we replace $f(x)$ with the original function:

$$f'(x) = \frac{(x^3-1)^4\sqrt{3x-1}}{x^2+4}\left(\frac{12x^2}{x^3-1} + \frac{3}{2(3x-1)} - \frac{2x}{x^2+4}\right).$$

Related Exercises 61–68 ◀

Logarithmic differentiation also provides an alternative method for finding derivatives of functions of the form $g(x)^{h(x)}$. The derivative of $f(x) = x^x$ (Example 6) is computed as follows, assuming $x > 0$:

$$\begin{aligned}f(x) &= x^x\\ \ln(f(x)) &= \ln(x^x) = x\ln x &&\text{Take logarithms of both sides; use properties.}\\ \frac{1}{f(x)}f'(x) &= 1\cdot\ln x + x\cdot\frac{1}{x} &&\text{Differentiate both sides.}\\ f'(x) &= f(x)(\ln x + 1) &&\text{Solve for } f'(x) \text{ and simplify.}\\ f'(x) &= x^x(\ln x + 1). &&\text{Replace } f(x) \text{ with } x^x.\end{aligned}$$

This result agrees with Example 6. The decision about which method to use is largely one of preference.

SECTION 3.9 EXERCISES

Review Questions

1. Use $x = e^y$ to explain why $\dfrac{d}{dx}(\ln x) = \dfrac{1}{x}$, for $x > 0$.

2. Sketch the graph of $f(x) = \ln|x|$ and explain how the graph shows that $f'(x) = \dfrac{1}{x}$.

3. Show that $\dfrac{d}{dx}(\ln kx) = \dfrac{d}{dx}(\ln x)$, where $x > 0$ and k is a positive real number.

4. State the derivative rule for the exponential function $f(x) = b^x$. How does it differ from the derivative formula for e^x?

5. State the derivative rule for the logarithmic function $f(x) = \log_b x$. How does it differ from the derivative formula for $\ln x$?

6. Explain why $b^x = e^{x\ln b}$.

7. Express the function $f(x) = g(x)^{h(x)}$ in terms of the natural logarithmic and natural exponential functions (base e).

8. Explain the general procedure of logarithmic differentiation.

Basic Skills

9–22. Derivatives involving $\ln x$ *Find the following derivatives.*

9. $\frac{d}{dx}(\ln 7x)$ **10.** $\frac{d}{dx}(x^2 \ln x)$ **11.** $\frac{d}{dx}(\ln x^2)$

12. $\frac{d}{dx}(\ln 2x^8)$ **13.** $\frac{d}{dx}(\ln |\sin x|)$ **14.** $\frac{d}{dx}\left(\frac{\ln x^2}{x}\right)$

15. $\frac{d}{dx}\left(\ln\left(\frac{x+1}{x-1}\right)\right)$ **16.** $\frac{d}{dx}(e^x \ln x)$ **17.** $\frac{d}{dx}((x^2+1)\ln x)$

18. $\frac{d}{dx}(\ln |x^2-1|)$ **19.** $\frac{d}{dx}(\ln(\ln x))$ **20.** $\frac{d}{dx}(\ln(\cos^2 x))$

21. $\frac{d}{dx}\left(\frac{\ln x}{\ln x + 1}\right)$ **22.** $\frac{d}{dx}(\ln(e^x + e^{-x}))$

23–30. Derivatives of b^x *Find the derivatives of the following functions.*

23. $y = 8^x$ **24.** $y = 5^{3t}$ **25.** $y = 5 \cdot 4^x$

26. $y = 4^{-x}\sin x$ **27.** $y = x^3 \cdot 3^x$ **28.** $P = \frac{40}{1 + 2^{-t}}$

29. $A = 250(1.045)^{4t}$ **30.** $y = \ln 10^x$

31. Exponential model The following table shows the *time of useful consciousness* at various altitudes in the situation where a pressurized airplane suddenly loses pressure. The change in pressure drastically reduces available oxygen, and hypoxia sets in. The upper value of each time interval is roughly modeled by $T = 10 \cdot 2^{-0.274a}$, where T measures time in minutes and a is the altitude over 22,000 in thousands of feet ($a = 0$ corresponds to 22,000 ft).

Altitude (in ft)	Time of Useful Consciousness
22,000	5 to 10 min
25,000	3 to 5 min
28,000	2.5 to 3 min
30,000	1 to 2 min
35,000	30 to 60 s
40,000	15 to 20 s
45,000	9 to 15 s

a. A Learjet flying at 38,000 ft ($a = 16$) suddenly loses pressure when the seal on a window fails. According to this model, how long do the pilot and passengers have to deploy oxygen masks before they become incapacitated?

b. What is the average rate of change of T with respect to a over the interval from 24,000 to 30,000 ft (include units)?

c. Find the instantaneous rate of change dT/da, compute it at 30,000 ft, and interpret its meaning.

32. Magnitude of an earthquake The energy (in joules) released by an earthquake of magnitude M is given by the equation $E = 25{,}000 \cdot 10^{1.5M}$. (This equation can be solved for M to define the magnitude of a given earthquake; it is a refinement of the original Richter scale created by Charles Richter in 1935.)

a. Compute the energy released by earthquakes of magnitude 1, 2, 3, 4, and 5. Plot the points on a graph and join them with a smooth curve.

b. Compute dE/dM and evaluate it for $M = 3$. What does this derivative mean? (M has no units, so the units of the derivative are J per change in magnitude.)

33. Diagnostic scanning Iodine-123 is a radioactive isotope used in medicine to test the function of the thyroid gland. If a 350-microcurie (μCi) dose of iodine-123 is administered to a patient, the quantity Q left in the body after t hours is approximately $Q = 350(\frac{1}{2})^{t/13.1}$.

a. How long does it take for the level of iodine-123 to drop to 10 μCi?

b. Find the rate of change of the quantity of iodine-123 at 12 hr, 1 day, and 2 days. What do your answers say about the rate at which iodine decreases as time increases?

34–44. General Power Rule *Use the General Power Rule where appropriate to find the derivative of the following functions.*

34. $f(x) = x^e$ **35.** $f(x) = 2^x$ **36.** $f(x) = 2x^{\sqrt{2}}$

37. $g(y) = e^y \cdot y^e$ **38.** $s(t) = \cos 2^t$

39. $r = e^{2\theta}$ **40.** $y = \ln(x^3 + 1)^\pi$

41. $f(x) = (2x - 3)x^{3/2}$ **42.** $y = \tan(x^{0.74})$

43. $f(x) = \frac{2^x}{2^x + 1}$ **44.** $f(x) = (2^x + 1)^\pi$

45–50. Derivatives of General Exponential Function (or g^h) *Find the derivative of each function and evaluate the derivative at the given value of a.*

45. $f(x) = x^{\cos x}$; $a = \pi/2$

46. $g(x) = x^{\ln x}$; $a = e$

47. $h(x) = x^{\sqrt{x}}$; $a = 4$

48. $f(x) = (x^2 + 1)^x$; $a = 1$

49. $f(x) = (\sin x)^{\ln x}$; $a = \pi/2$

50. $f(x) = (\tan x)^{x-1}$; $a = \pi/4$

51–54. Tangent lines and general exponential functions

51. Find an equation of the line tangent to $y = x^{\sin x}$ at the point $x = 1$.

52. Determine whether the graph of $y = x^{\sqrt{x}}$ has any horizontal tangent lines.

53. The graph of $y = (x^2)^x$ has two horizontal tangent lines. Find equations for both of them.

54. The graph of $y = x^{\ln x}$ has one horizontal tangent line. Find an equation for it.

55–60. Derivatives of logarithmic functions *Calculate the derivative of the following functions.*

55. $y = 4\log_3(x^2 - 1)$

56. $y = \log_{10} x$

57. $y = \cos x \ln(\cos^2 x)$

58. $y = \log_8 |\tan x|$

59. $y = \frac{1}{\log_4 x}$

60. $y = \log_2(\log_2 x)$

61–68. Logarithmic differentiation *Use logarithmic differentiation to evaluate $f'(x)$.*

61. $f(x) = \dfrac{(x+1)^{10}}{(2x-4)^8}$

62. $f(x) = x^2 \cos x$

63. $f(x) = x^{\ln x}$

64. $f(x) = \dfrac{\tan^{10} x}{(5x+3)^6}$

65. $f(x) = \dfrac{(x+1)^{3/2}(x-4)^{5/2}}{(5x+3)^{2/3}}$

66. $f(x) = \dfrac{x^8 \cos^3 x}{\sqrt{x-1}}$

67. $f(x) = (\sin x)^{\tan x}$

68. $f(x) = \left(1 + \dfrac{1}{x}\right)^{2x}$

Further Explorations

69. Explain why or why not Determine whether the following statements are true and give an explanation or counterexample.

a. The derivative of $\log_2 9 = 1/(9 \ln 2)$.

b. $\ln(x+1) + \ln(x-1) = \ln(x^2-1)$, for all x.

c. The exponential function 2^{x+1} can be written in base e as $e^{2\ln(x+1)}$.

d. $\dfrac{d}{dx}(\sqrt{2}^x) = x\sqrt{2}^{x-1}$.

e. $\dfrac{d}{dx}(x^{\sqrt{2}}) = \sqrt{2}\, x^{\sqrt{2}-1}$.

70–73. Higher-order derivatives *Find the following higher-order derivatives.*

70. $\left.\dfrac{d^3}{dx^3}(x^{4.2})\right|_{x=1}$

71. $\dfrac{d^2}{dx^2}(\log_{10} x)$

72. $\dfrac{d^n}{dx^n}(2^x)$

73. $\dfrac{d^3}{dx^3}(x^2 \ln x)$

74–76. Derivatives by different methods *Calculate the derivative of the following functions (i) using the fact that $b^x = e^{x \ln b}$ and (ii) by using logarithmic differentiation. Verify that both answers are the same.*

74. $y = (x^2+1)^x$

75. $y = 3^x$

76. $y = g(x)^{h(x)}$

77–82. Derivatives of logarithmic functions *Use the properties of logarithms to simplify the following functions before computing $f'(x)$.*

77. $f(x) = \ln(3x+1)^4$

78. $f(x) = \ln \dfrac{2x}{(x^2+1)^3}$

79. $f(x) = \ln \sqrt{10x}$

80. $f(x) = \log_2 \dfrac{8}{\sqrt{x+1}}$

81. $f(x) = \ln \dfrac{(2x-1)(x+2)^3}{(1-4x)^2}$

82. $f(x) = \ln(\sec^4 x \tan^2 x)$

T **83. Tangent lines** Find the equation of the line tangent to $y = 2^{\sin x}$ at $x = \pi/2$. Graph the function and the tangent line.

T **84. Horizontal tangents** The graph of $y = \cos x \cdot \ln \cos^2 x$ has seven horizontal tangent lines on the interval $[0, 2\pi]$. Find the approximate x-coordinates of all points at which these tangent lines occur.

85–92. General logarithmic and exponential derivatives *Compute the following derivatives. Use logarithmic differentiation where appropriate.*

85. $\dfrac{d}{dx}(x^{10x})$

86. $\dfrac{d}{dx}(2x)^{2x}$

87. $\dfrac{d}{dx}(x^{\cos x})$

88. $\dfrac{d}{dx}(x^{\pi} + \pi^x)$

89. $\dfrac{d}{dx}\left(1 + \dfrac{1}{x}\right)^x$

90. $\dfrac{d}{dx}(1+x^2)^{\sin x}$

91. $\dfrac{d}{dx}(x^{(x^{10})})$

92. $\dfrac{d}{dx}(\ln x)^{x^2}$

Applications

93–96. Logistic growth *Scientists often use the logistic growth function $P(t) = \dfrac{P_0 K}{P_0 + (K - P_0)e^{-r_0 t}}$ to model population growth, where P_0 is the initial population at time $t = 0$, K is the* **carrying capacity**, *and r_0 is the base growth rate. The carrying capacity is a theoretical upper bound on the total population that the surrounding environment can support. The figure shows the sigmoid (S-shaped) curve associated with a typical logistic model.*

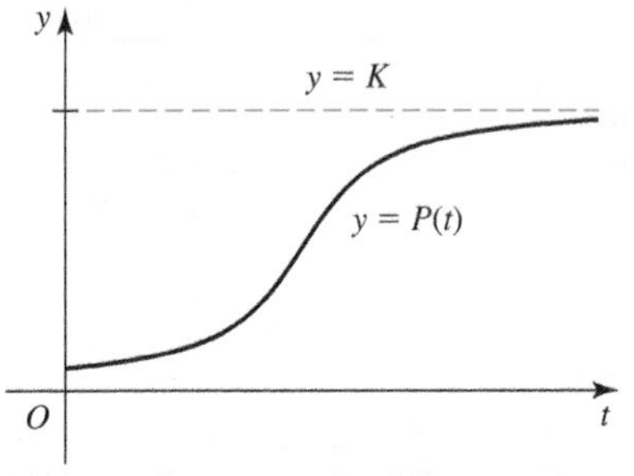

T **93. Gone fishing** When a reservoir is created by a new dam, 50 fish are introduced into the reservoir, which has an estimated carrying capacity of 8000 fish. A logistic model of the fish population is $P(t) = \dfrac{400{,}000}{50 + 7950e^{-0.5t}}$, where t is measured in years.

a. Graph P using a graphing utility. Experiment with different windows until you produce an S-shaped curve characteristic of the logistic model. What window works well for this function?

b. How long does it take the population to reach 5000 fish? How long does it take the population to reach 90% of the carrying capacity?

c. How fast (in fish per year) is the population growing at $t = 0$? At $t = 5$?

d. Graph P' and use the graph to estimate the year in which the population is growing fastest.

T **94. World population (part 1)** The population of the world reached 6 billion in 1999 ($t = 0$). Assume Earth's carrying capacity is 15 billion and the base growth rate is $r_0 = 0.025$ per year.

a. Write a logistic growth function for the world's population (in billions) and graph your equation on the interval $0 \le t \le 200$ using a graphing utility.

b. What will the population be in the year 2020? When will it reach 12 billion?

95. World population (part 2) The *relative growth rate r* of a function f measures the rate of change of the function compared to its value at a particular point. It is computed as $r(t) = f'(t)/f(t)$.

a. Confirm that the relative growth rate in 1999 ($t = 0$) for the logistic model in Exercise 94 is $r(0) = P'(0)/P(0) = 0.015$. This means the world's population was growing at 1.5% per year in 1999.

b. Compute the relative growth rate of the world's population in 2010 and 2020. What appears to be happening to the relative growth rate as time increases?

c. Evaluate $\lim_{t\to\infty} r(t) = \lim_{t\to\infty} \frac{P'(t)}{P(t)}$, where $P(t)$ is the logistic growth function from Exercise 94. What does your answer say about populations that follow a logistic growth pattern?

T **96. Population crash** The logistic model can be used for situations in which the initial population P_0 is above the carrying capacity K. For example, consider a deer population of 1500 on an island where a fire has reduced the carrying capacity to 1000 deer.

a. Assuming a base growth rate of $r_0 = 0.1$ and an initial population of $P(0) = 1500$, write a logistic growth function for the deer population and graph it. Based on the graph, what happens to the deer population in the long run?

b. How fast (in deer per year) is the population declining immediately after the fire at $t = 0$?

c. How long does it take the deer population to decline to 1200 deer?

97. Savings plan Beginning at age 30, a self-employed plumber saves \$250 per month in a retirement account until he reaches age 65. The account offers 6% interest, compounded monthly. The balance in the account after t years is given by $A(t) = 50{,}000(1.005^{12t} - 1)$.

a. Compute the balance in the account after 5, 15, 25, and 35 years. What is the average rate of change in the value of the account over the intervals $[5, 15]$, $[15, 25]$, and $[25, 35]$?

b. Suppose the plumber started saving at age 25 instead of age 30. Find the balance at age 65 (after 40 years of investing).

c. Use the derivative dA/dt to explain the surprising result in part (b) and to explain this advice: Start saving for retirement as early as possible.

Additional Exercises

T **98. Tangency question** It is easily verified that the graphs of $y = x^2$ and $y = e^x$ have no points of intersection (for $x > 0$), and the graphs of $y = x^3$ and $y = e^x$ have two points of intersection. It follows that for some real number $2 < p < 3$, the graphs of $y = x^p$ and $y = e^x$ have exactly one point of intersection (for $x > 0$). Using analytical and/or graphical methods, determine p and the coordinates of the single point of intersection.

T **99. Tangency question** It is easily verified that the graphs of $y = 1.1^x$ and $y = x$ have two points of intersection, and the graphs of $y = 2^x$ and $y = x$ have no points of intersection. It follows that for some real number $1 < p < 2$, the graphs of $y = p^x$ and $y = x$ have exactly one point of intersection. Using analytical and/or graphical methods, determine p and the coordinates of the single point of intersection.

T **100. Triple intersection** Graph the functions $f(x) = x^3$, $g(x) = 3^x$, and $h(x) = x^x$ and find their common intersection point (exactly).

101–104. Calculating limits exactly *Use the definition of the derivative to evaluate the following limits.*

101. $\lim_{x\to e} \frac{\ln x - 1}{x - e}$

102. $\lim_{h\to 0} \frac{\ln(e^8 + h) - 8}{h}$

103. $\lim_{h\to 0} \frac{(3 + h)^{3+h} - 27}{h}$

104. $\lim_{x\to 2} \frac{5^x - 25}{x - 2}$

105. Derivative of $u(x)^{v(x)}$ Use logarithmic differentiation to prove that

$$\frac{d}{dx}\left(u(x)^{v(x)}\right) = u(x)^{v(x)}\left(\frac{dv}{dx}\ln u(x) + \frac{v(x)}{u(x)}\frac{du}{dx}\right).$$

106. Tangent lines and exponentials. Assume b is given with $b > 0$ and $b \neq 1$. Find the y-coordinate of the point on the curve $y = b^x$ at which the tangent line passes through the origin. (*Source: The College Mathematics Journal*, 28, Mar 1997)

QUICK CHECK ANSWERS

1. x^2 (for $x > 0$); $e^{x \ln 5}$ **2.** Either way, $\frac{d}{dx}(\ln x^p) = \frac{p}{x}$.
3. $\frac{dA}{dt} = 500(1.045)^t \cdot \ln 1.045 \approx 22(1.045)^t$ **4.** $\frac{dy}{dx} = \frac{1}{x \ln 3}$
5. $T'(n) = \log_2 n + \frac{1}{\ln 2} = \log_2 n + \frac{1}{\frac{\log_2 2}{\log_2 e}} = \log_2 n + \log_2 e = \log_2 (en)$ ◄

3.10 Derivatives of Inverse Trigonometric Functions

The inverse trigonometric functions, introduced in Section 1.4, are major players in calculus. In this section, we develop the derivatives of the six inverse trigonometric functions and begin an exploration of their many applications. The method for differentiating the inverses of more general functions is also presented.

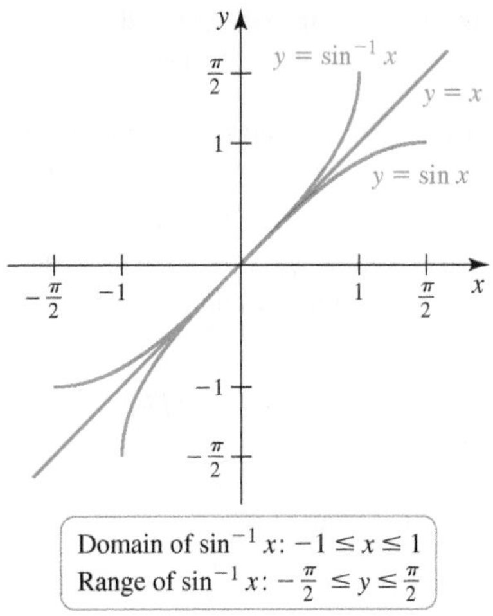

Figure 3.62

Inverse Sine and Its Derivative

Recall from Section 1.4 that $y = \sin^{-1} x$ is the value of y such that $x = \sin y$, where $-\pi/2 \le y \le \pi/2$. The domain of $\sin^{-1} x$ is $\{x: -1 \le x \le 1\}$ (Figure 3.62). The derivative of $y = \sin^{-1} x$ follows by differentiating both sides of $x = \sin y$ with respect to x, simplifying, and solving for dy/dx:

$$x = \sin y \qquad y = \sin^{-1} x \Leftrightarrow x = \sin y$$

$$\frac{d}{dx}(x) = \frac{d}{dx}(\sin y) \qquad \text{Differentiate with respect to } x.$$

$$1 = (\cos y)\frac{dy}{dx} \qquad \text{Chain Rule on the right side}$$

$$\frac{dy}{dx} = \frac{1}{\cos y}. \qquad \text{Solve for } \frac{dy}{dx}.$$

The identity $\sin^2 y + \cos^2 y = 1$ is used to express this derivative in terms of x. Solving for $\cos y$ yields

$$\cos y = \pm\sqrt{1 - \underbrace{\sin^2 y}_{x^2}} \qquad x = \sin y \Rightarrow x^2 = \sin^2 y$$

$$= \pm\sqrt{1 - x^2}.$$

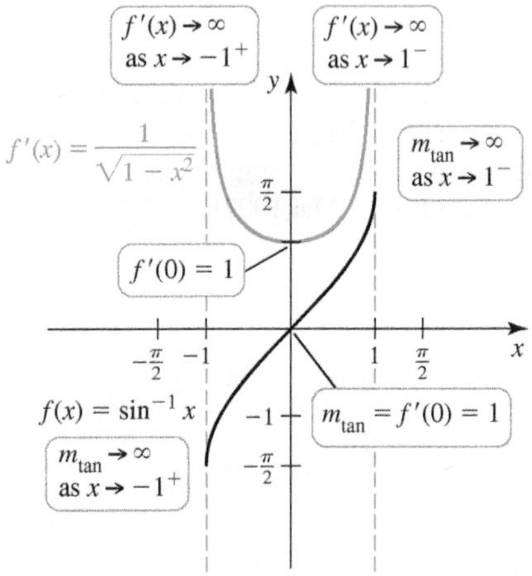

Figure 3.63

Because y is restricted to the interval $-\pi/2 \le y \le \pi/2$, we have $\cos y \ge 0$. Therefore, we choose the positive branch of the square root, and it follows that

$$\frac{dy}{dx} = \frac{d}{dx}(\sin^{-1} x) = \frac{1}{\sqrt{1 - x^2}}.$$

This result is consistent with the graph of $f(x) = \sin^{-1} x$ (Figure 3.63).

THEOREM 3.21 Derivative of Inverse Sine

$$\frac{d}{dx}(\sin^{-1} x) = \frac{1}{\sqrt{1 - x^2}}, \text{ for } -1 < x < 1$$

QUICK CHECK 1 Is $f(x) = \sin^{-1} x$ an even or odd function? Is $f'(x)$ an even or odd function? ◄

EXAMPLE 1 Derivatives involving the inverse sine Compute the following derivatives.

a. $\frac{d}{dx}(\sin^{-1}(x^2 - 1))$ **b.** $\frac{d}{dx}(\cos(\sin^{-1} x))$

SOLUTION We apply the Chain Rule for both derivatives.

a. $$\frac{d}{dx}(\sin^{-1} \underbrace{(x^2 - 1)}_{u}) = \underbrace{\frac{1}{\sqrt{1 - (x^2 - 1)^2}}}_{\substack{\text{derivative of } \sin^{-1} u \\ \text{evaluated at } u = x^2 - 1}} \cdot \underbrace{2x}_{u'(x)} = \frac{2x}{\sqrt{2x^2 - x^4}}$$

b. $$\frac{d}{dx}(\underbrace{\cos(\sin^{-1} x)}_{u}) = \underbrace{-\sin(\sin^{-1} x)}_{\substack{\text{derivative of the}\\ \text{outer function } \cos u\\ \text{evaluated at } u = \sin^{-1} x}} \cdot \underbrace{\frac{1}{\sqrt{1-x^2}}}_{\substack{\text{derivative of the}\\ \text{inner function } \sin^{-1} x}} = -\frac{x}{\sqrt{1-x^2}}$$

This result is valid for $-1 < x < 1$, where $\sin(\sin^{-1} x) = x$. *Related Exercises 7–12* ◀

➤ The result in Example 1b can also be obtained by noting that $\cos(\sin^{-1} x) = \sqrt{1 - x^2}$ and differentiating this expression (Exercise 75).

Derivatives of Inverse Tangent and Secant

The derivatives of the inverse tangent and inverse secant are derived using a method similar to that used for the inverse sine. Once these three derivative results are known, the derivatives of the inverse cosine, cotangent, and cosecant follow immediately.

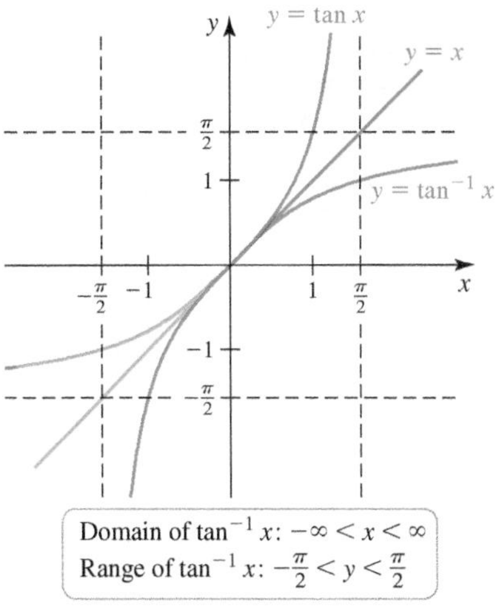

Figure 3.64

Inverse Tangent Recall from Section 1.4 that $y = \tan^{-1} x$ is the value of y such that $x = \tan y$, where $-\pi/2 < y < \pi/2$. The domain of $y = \tan^{-1} x$ is $\{x: -\infty < x < \infty\}$ (Figure 3.64). To find $\frac{dy}{dx}$, we differentiate both sides of $x = \tan y$ with respect to x and simplify:

$$x = \tan y \qquad y = \tan^{-1} x \Leftrightarrow x = \tan y$$

$$\frac{d}{dx}(x) = \frac{d}{dx}(\tan y) \qquad \text{Differentiate with respect to } x.$$

$$1 = \sec^2 y \cdot \frac{dy}{dx} \qquad \text{Chain Rule}$$

$$\frac{dy}{dx} = \frac{1}{\sec^2 y}. \qquad \text{Solve for } \frac{dy}{dx}.$$

To express this derivative in terms of x, we combine the trigonometric identity $\sec^2 y = 1 + \tan^2 y$ with $x = \tan y$ to obtain $\sec^2 y = 1 + x^2$. Substituting this result into the expression for dy/dx, it follows that

$$\frac{dy}{dx} = \frac{d}{dx}(\tan^{-1} x) = \frac{1}{1 + x^2}.$$

The graphs of the inverse tangent and its derivative (Figure 3.65) are informative. Letting $f(x) = \tan^{-1} x$ and $f'(x) = \frac{1}{1+x^2}$, we see that $f'(0) = 1$, which is the maximum value of the derivative; that is, $\tan^{-1} x$ has its maximum slope at $x = 0$. As $x \to \infty, f'(x)$ approaches zero; likewise, as $x \to -\infty, f'(x)$ approaches zero.

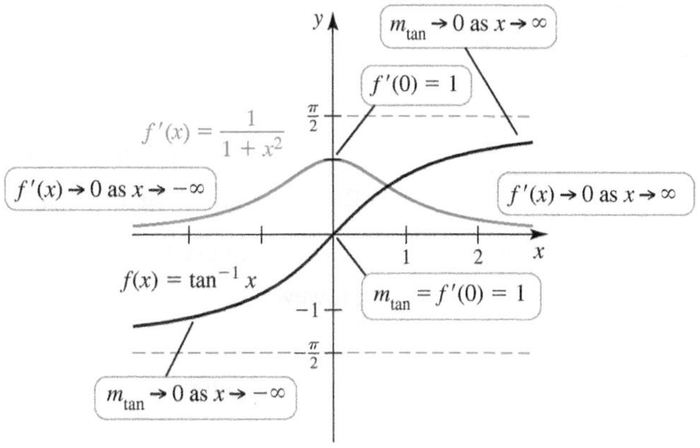

Figure 3.65

QUICK CHECK 2 How do the slopes of the lines tangent to the graph of $y = \tan^{-1} x$ behave as $x \to \infty$? ◀

Inverse Secant Recall from Section 1.4 that $y = \sec^{-1} x$ is the value of y such that $x = \sec y$, where $0 \le y \le \pi$, with $y \ne \pi/2$. The domain of $y = \sec^{-1} x$ is $\{x: |x| \ge 1\}$ (Figure 3.66).

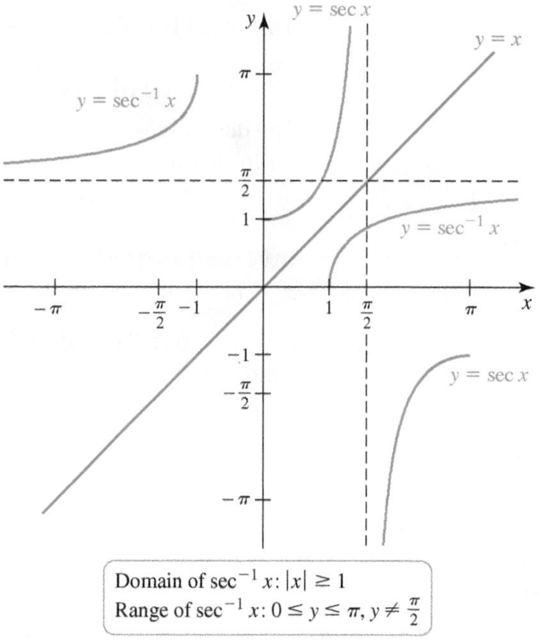

Figure 3.66

The derivative of the inverse secant presents a new twist. Let $y = \sec^{-1} x$, or $x = \sec y$, and then differentiate both sides of $x = \sec y$ with respect to x:

$$1 = \sec y \tan y \frac{dy}{dx}.$$

Solving for $\frac{dy}{dx}$ produces

$$\frac{dy}{dx} = \frac{d}{dx}(\sec^{-1} x) = \frac{1}{\sec y \tan y}.$$

The final step is to express $\sec y \tan y$ in terms of x by using the identity $\sec^2 y = 1 + \tan^2 y$. Solving this equation for $\tan y$, we have

$$\tan y = \pm\sqrt{\underbrace{\sec^2 y}_{x^2} - 1} = \pm\sqrt{x^2 - 1}.$$

Two cases must be examined to resolve the sign on the square root:

- By the definition of $y = \sec^{-1} x$, if $x \ge 1$, then $0 \le y < \pi/2$ and $\tan y > 0$. In this case, we choose the positive branch and take $\tan y = \sqrt{x^2 - 1}$.
- However, if $x \le -1$, then $\pi/2 < y \le \pi$ and $\tan y < 0$. Now we choose the negative branch.

This argument accounts for the $\tan y$ factor in the derivative. For the $\sec y$ factor, we have $\sec y = x$. Therefore, the derivative of the inverse secant is

$$\frac{d}{dx}(\sec^{-1} x) = \begin{cases} \dfrac{1}{x\sqrt{x^2 - 1}} & \text{if } x > 1 \\ -\dfrac{1}{x\sqrt{x^2 - 1}} & \text{if } x < -1, \end{cases}$$

which is an awkward result. The absolute value helps here: Recall that $|x| = x$, if $x > 0$, and $|x| = -x$, if $x < 0$. It follows that

$$\frac{d}{dx}(\sec^{-1} x) = \frac{1}{|x|\sqrt{x^2 - 1}}, \text{ for } |x| > 1.$$

We see that the slope of the inverse secant function is always positive, which is consistent with this derivative result (Figure 3.66).

Derivatives of Other Inverse Trigonometric Functions The hard work is complete. The derivative of the inverse cosine results from the identity

> This identity was proved in Example 5 of Section 1.4.

$$\cos^{-1} x + \sin^{-1} x = \frac{\pi}{2}.$$

Differentiating both sides of this equation with respect to x, we find that

$$\frac{d}{dx}(\cos^{-1} x) + \underbrace{\frac{d}{dx}(\sin^{-1} x)}_{1/\sqrt{1-x^2}} = \underbrace{\frac{d}{dx}\left(\frac{\pi}{2}\right)}_{0}.$$

Solving for $\frac{d}{dx}(\cos^{-1} x)$, the required derivative is

$$\frac{d}{dx}(\cos^{-1} x) = -\frac{1}{\sqrt{1 - x^2}}.$$

In a similar manner, the analogous identities

$$\cot^{-1} x + \tan^{-1} x = \frac{\pi}{2} \quad \text{and} \quad \csc^{-1} x + \sec^{-1} x = \frac{\pi}{2}$$

are used to show that the derivatives of $\cot^{-1} x$ and $\csc^{-1} x$ are the negative of the derivatives of $\tan^{-1} x$ and $\sec^{-1} x$, respectively (Exercise 73).

QUICK CHECK 3 Summarize how the derivatives of inverse trigonometric functions are related to the derivatives of the corresponding inverse cofunctions (for example, inverse tangent and inverse cotangent). ◄

THEOREM 3.22 Derivatives of Inverse Trigonometric Functions

$$\frac{d}{dx}(\sin^{-1} x) = \frac{1}{\sqrt{1 - x^2}} \qquad \frac{d}{dx}(\cos^{-1} x) = -\frac{1}{\sqrt{1 - x^2}}, \text{ for } -1 < x < 1$$

$$\frac{d}{dx}(\tan^{-1} x) = \frac{1}{1 + x^2} \qquad \frac{d}{dx}(\cot^{-1} x) = -\frac{1}{1 + x^2}, \text{ for } -\infty < x < \infty$$

$$\frac{d}{dx}(\sec^{-1} x) = \frac{1}{|x|\sqrt{x^2 - 1}} \qquad \frac{d}{dx}(\csc^{-1} x) = -\frac{1}{|x|\sqrt{x^2 - 1}}, \text{ for } |x| > 1$$

EXAMPLE 2 Derivatives of inverse trigonometric functions

a. Evaluate $f'(2\sqrt{3})$, where $f(x) = x \tan^{-1}(x/2)$.

b. Find an equation of the line tangent to the graph of $g(x) = \sec^{-1} 2x$ at the point $(1, \pi/3)$.

SOLUTION

a. $$f'(x) = 1 \cdot \tan^{-1}\frac{x}{2} + x\underbrace{\frac{1}{1 + (x/2)^2}\cdot\frac{1}{2}}_{\frac{d}{dx}(\tan^{-1}(x/2))} \quad \text{Product Rule and Chain Rule}$$

$$= \tan^{-1}\frac{x}{2} + \frac{2x}{4 + x^2} \quad \text{Simplify.}$$

We evaluate f' at $x = 2\sqrt{3}$ and note that $\tan^{-1}\sqrt{3} = \pi/3$:

$$f'(2\sqrt{3}) = \tan^{-1}\sqrt{3} + \frac{2(2\sqrt{3})}{4 + (2\sqrt{3})^2} = \frac{\pi}{3} + \frac{\sqrt{3}}{4}.$$

b. The slope of the tangent line at $(1, \pi/3)$ is $g'(1)$. Using the Chain Rule, we have

$$g'(x) = \frac{d}{dx}(\sec^{-1} 2x) = \frac{2}{|2x|\sqrt{4x^2 - 1}} = \frac{1}{|x|\sqrt{4x^2 - 1}}.$$

It follows that $g'(1) = 1/\sqrt{3}$. An equation of the tangent line is

$$y - \frac{\pi}{3} = \frac{1}{\sqrt{3}}(x - 1) \quad \text{or} \quad y = \frac{1}{\sqrt{3}}x + \frac{\pi}{3} - \frac{1}{\sqrt{3}}.$$

Related Exercises 13–34 ◄

Figure 3.67

EXAMPLE 3 Shadows in a ballpark As the sun descends behind the 150-ft grandstand of a baseball stadium, the shadow of the stadium moves across the field (Figure 3.67). Let ℓ be the line segment between the edge of the shadow and the sun, and let θ be the angle of elevation of the sun—the angle between ℓ and the horizontal. The length of the shadow s is the distance between the edge of the shadow and the base of the grandstand.

a. Express θ as a function of the shadow length s.

b. Compute $d\theta/ds$ when $s = 200$ ft and explain what this rate of change measures.

SOLUTION

a. The tangent of θ is

$$\tan\theta = \frac{150}{s},$$

where $s > 0$. Taking the inverse tangent of both sides of this equation, we find that

$$\theta = \tan^{-1}\frac{150}{s}.$$

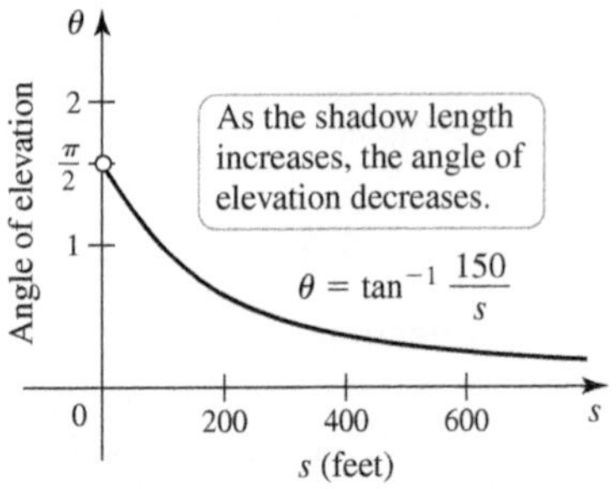

Figure 3.68

As shown in Figure 3.68, as the shadow length approaches zero, the sun's angle of elevation θ approaches $\pi/2$ ($\theta = \pi/2$ means the sun is overhead). As the shadow length increases, θ decreases and approaches zero.

b. Using the Chain Rule, we have

$$\begin{aligned}\frac{d\theta}{ds} &= \frac{1}{1 + (150/s)^2}\frac{d}{ds}\left(\frac{150}{s}\right) && \text{Chain Rule; } \frac{d}{du}(\tan^{-1}u) = \frac{1}{1+u^2}\\ &= \frac{1}{1 + (150/s)^2}\left(-\frac{150}{s^2}\right) && \text{Evaluate the derivative.}\\ &= -\frac{150}{s^2 + 22{,}500}. && \text{Simplify.}\end{aligned}$$

Notice that $d\theta/ds$ is negative for all values of s, which means longer shadows are associated with smaller angles of elevation (Figure 3.68). At $s = 200$ ft, we have

$$\left.\frac{d\theta}{ds}\right|_{s=200} = -\frac{150}{200^2 + 150^2} = -0.0024\,\frac{\text{rad}}{\text{ft}}.$$

When the length of the shadow is $s = 200$ ft, the angle of elevation is changing at a rate of -0.0024 rad/ft, or $-0.138°$/ft.

Related Exercises 35–36 ◄

QUICK CHECK 4 Example 3 makes the claim that $d\theta/ds = -0.0024$ rad/ft is equivalent to $-0.138°$/ft. Verify this claim. ◄

Derivatives of Inverse Functions in General

We found the derivatives of the inverse trigonometric functions using implicit differentiation. However, this approach does not always work. For example, suppose we know only f and its derivative f' and want to evaluate the derivative of f^{-1}. The key to finding the derivative of the inverse function lies in the symmetry of the graphs of f and f^{-1}.

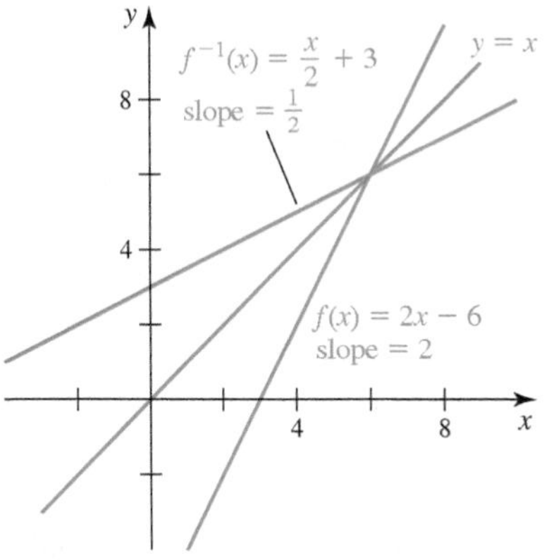

Figure 3.69

EXAMPLE 4 Linear functions, inverses, and derivatives Consider the general linear function $y = f(x) = mx + b$, where $m \neq 0$ and b are constants.

a. Write the inverse of f in the form $y = f^{-1}(x)$.

b. Find the derivative of the inverse $\frac{d}{dx}(f^{-1}(x))$.

c. Consider the specific case $f(x) = 2x - 6$. Graph f and f^{-1}, and find the slope of each line.

SOLUTION

a. Solving $y = mx + b$ for x, we find that $mx = y - b$, or

$$x = \frac{y}{m} - \frac{b}{m}.$$

Writing this function in the form $y = f^{-1}(x)$ (by reversing the roles of x and y), we have

$$y = f^{-1}(x) = \frac{x}{m} - \frac{b}{m},$$

which describes a line with slope $1/m$.

b. The derivative of f^{-1} is

$$(f^{-1})'(x) = \frac{1}{m} = \frac{1}{f'(x)}.$$

Notice that $f'(x) = m$, so the derivative of f^{-1} is the reciprocal of f'.

c. In the case that $f(x) = 2x - 6$, we have $f^{-1}(x) = x/2 + 3$. The graphs of these two lines are symmetric about the line $y = x$ (Figure 3.69). Furthermore, the slope of the line $y = f(x)$ is 2 and the slope of $y = f^{-1}(x)$ is $\frac{1}{2}$; that is, the slopes (and, therefore, the derivatives) are reciprocals of each other.

Related Exercises 37–39 ◀

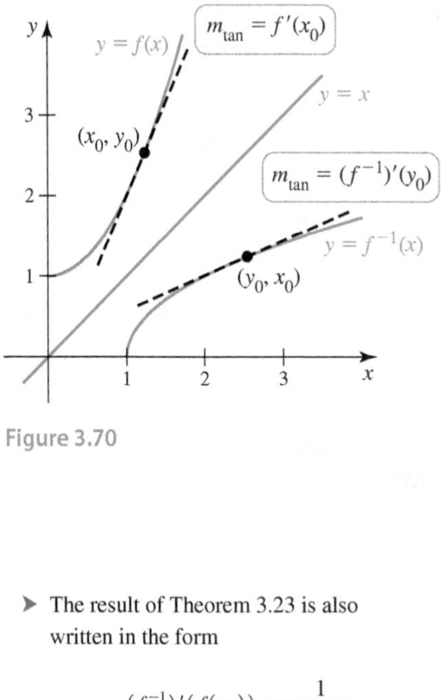

Figure 3.70

The reciprocal property obeyed by f' and $(f^{-1})'$ in Example 4 holds for all functions with inverses. Figure 3.70 shows the graphs of a typical one-to-one function and its inverse. It also shows a pair of symmetric points—(x_0, y_0) on the graph of f and (y_0, x_0) on the graph of f^{-1}—along with the tangent lines at these points. Notice that as the lines tangent to the graph of f get steeper (as x increases), the corresponding lines tangent to the graph of f^{-1} get less steep. The next theorem makes this relationship precise.

➤ The result of Theorem 3.23 is also written in the form

$$(f^{-1})'(f(x_0)) = \frac{1}{f'(x_0)}$$

or

$$(f^{-1})'(y_0) = \frac{1}{f'(f^{-1}(y_0))}.$$

THEOREM 3.23 Derivative of the Inverse Function
Let f be differentiable and have an inverse on an interval I. If x_0 is a point of I at which $f'(x_0) \neq 0$, then f^{-1} is differentiable at $y_0 = f(x_0)$ and

$$(f^{-1})'(y_0) = \frac{1}{f'(x_0)}, \text{ where } y_0 = f(x_0).$$

To understand this theorem, suppose that (x_0, y_0) is a point on the graph of f, which means that (y_0, x_0) is the corresponding point on the graph of f^{-1}. Then the slope of the line tangent to the graph of f^{-1} at the point (y_0, x_0) is the reciprocal of the slope of the line tangent to the graph of f at the point (x_0, y_0). Importantly, the theorem says that we can evaluate the derivative of the inverse function without finding the inverse function itself.

Proof: Before doing a short calculation, we note two facts:

- At a point x_0 where f is differentiable, $y_0 = f(x_0)$ and $x_0 = f^{-1}(y_0)$.
- As a differentiable function, f is continuous at x_0 (Theorem 3.1), which implies that f^{-1} is continuous at y_0 (Theorem 2.14). Therefore, as $y \to y_0$, $x \to x_0$.

Using the definition of the derivative, we have

$$(f^{-1})'(y_0) = \lim_{y \to y_0} \frac{f^{-1}(y) - f^{-1}(y_0)}{y - y_0} \qquad \text{Definition of derivative of } f^{-1}$$

$$= \lim_{x \to x_0} \frac{x - x_0}{f(x) - f(x_0)} \qquad y = f(x) \text{ and } x = f^{-1}(y);\ x \to x_0 \text{ as } y \to y_0$$

$$= \lim_{x \to x_0} \frac{1}{\dfrac{f(x) - f(x_0)}{x - x_0}} \qquad \frac{a}{b} = \frac{1}{b/a}$$

$$= \frac{1}{f'(x_0)}. \qquad \text{Definition of derivative of } f$$

We have shown that $(f^{-1})'(y_0)$ exists (f^{-1} is differentiable at y_0) and that it equals the reciprocal of $f'(x_0)$. ◄

QUICK CHECK 5 Sketch the graphs of $y = \sin x$ and $y = \sin^{-1} x$. Then verify that Theorem 3.23 holds at the point $(0, 0)$. ◄

EXAMPLE 5 Derivative of an inverse function The function $f(x) = \sqrt{x} + x^2 + 1$ is one-to-one, for $x \geq 0$, and has an inverse on that interval. Find the slope of the curve $y = f^{-1}(x)$ at the point $(3, 1)$.

SOLUTION The point $(1, 3)$ is on the graph of f; therefore, $(3, 1)$ is on the graph of f^{-1}. In this case, the slope of the curve $y = f^{-1}(x)$ at the point $(3, 1)$ is the reciprocal of the slope of the curve $y = f(x)$ at $(1, 3)$ (Figure 3.71). Note that $f'(x) = \dfrac{1}{2\sqrt{x}} + 2x$, which means that $f'(1) = \dfrac{1}{2} + 2 = \dfrac{5}{2}$. Therefore,

$$(f^{-1})'(3) = \frac{1}{f'(1)} = \frac{1}{5/2} = \frac{2}{5}.$$

Observe that it is not necessary to find a formula for f^{-1} to evaluate its derivative at a point.

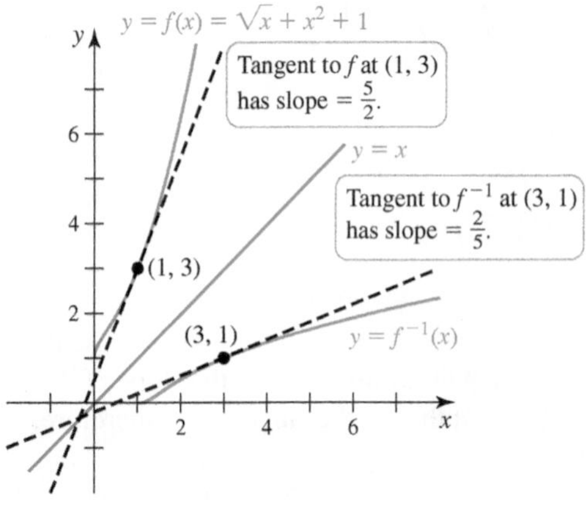

Figure 3.71

Related Exercises 40–50 ◄

EXAMPLE 6 Derivatives of an inverse function Use the values of a one-to-one differentiable function f in Table 3.7 to compute the indicated derivatives or state that the derivative cannot be determined.

Table 3.7

x	-1	0	1	2	3
$f(x)$	2	3	5	6	7
$f'(x)$	$1/2$	2	$3/2$	1	$2/3$

a. $(f^{-1})'(5)$ **b.** $(f^{-1})'(2)$ **c.** $(f^{-1})'(1)$

SOLUTION We use the realtionship $(f^{-1})'(y_0) = \dfrac{1}{f'(x_0)}$, where $y_0 = f(x_0)$.

a. In this case, $y_0 = f(x_0) = 5$. Using Table 3.7, we see that $x_0 = 1$ and $f'(1) = \dfrac{3}{2}$. Therefore, $(f^{-1})'(5) = \dfrac{1}{f'(1)} = \dfrac{2}{3}$.

b. In this case, $y_0 = f(x_0) = 2$, which implies that $x_0 = -1$ and $f'(-1) = \frac{1}{2}$. Therefore, $(f^{-1})'(2) = \frac{1}{f'(-1)} = 2$.

c. With $y_0 = f(x_0) = 1$, Table 3.7 does not supply a value of x_0. Therefore, neither $f'(x_0)$ nor $(f^{-1})'(1)$ can be determined.

Related Exercises 51–52 ◄

SECTION 3.10 EXERCISES

Review Questions

1. State the derivative formulas for $\sin^{-1} x$, $\tan^{-1} x$, and $\sec^{-1} x$.

2. What is the slope of the line tangent to the graph of $y = \sin^{-1} x$ at $x = 0$?

3. What is the slope of the line tangent to the graph of $y = \tan^{-1} x$ at $x = -2$?

4. How are the derivatives of $\sin^{-1} x$ and $\cos^{-1} x$ related?

5. Suppose f is a one-to-one function with $f(2) = 8$ and $f'(2) = 4$. What is the value of $(f^{-1})'(8)$?

6. Explain how to find $(f^{-1})'(y_0)$, given that $y_0 = f(x_0)$.

Basic Skills

7–12. Derivatives of inverse sine *Evaluate the derivatives of the following functions.*

7. $f(x) = \sin^{-1} 2x$
8. $f(x) = x \sin^{-1} x$
9. $f(w) = \cos(\sin^{-1} 2w)$
10. $f(x) = \sin^{-1}(\ln x)$
11. $f(x) = \sin^{-1}(e^{-2x})$
12. $f(x) = \sin^{-1}(e^{\sin x})$

13–30. Derivatives *Evaluate the derivatives of the following functions.*

13. $f(x) = \tan^{-1} 10x$
14. $f(x) = x \cot^{-1}(x/3)$
15. $f(y) = \tan^{-1}(2y^2 - 4)$
16. $g(z) = \tan^{-1}(1/z)$
17. $f(z) = \cot^{-1}\sqrt{z}$
18. $f(x) = \sec^{-1}\sqrt{x}$
19. $f(x) = \cos^{-1}(1/x)$
20. $f(t) = (\cos^{-1} t)^2$
21. $f(u) = \csc^{-1}(2u + 1)$
22. $f(t) = \ln(\tan^{-1} t)$
23. $f(y) = \cot^{-1}(1/(y^2 + 1))$
24. $f(w) = \sin(\sec^{-1} 2w)$
25. $f(x) = \sec^{-1}(\ln x)$
26. $f(x) = \tan^{-1}(e^{4x})$
27. $f(x) = \csc^{-1}(\tan e^x)$
28. $f(x) = \sin(\tan^{-1}(\ln x))$
29. $f(s) = \cot^{-1}(e^s)$
30. $f(x) = 1/\tan^{-1}(x^2 + 4)$

31–34. Tangent lines *Find an equation of the line tangent to the graph of f at the given point.*

31. $f(x) = \tan^{-1} 2x$; $(1/2, \pi/4)$
32. $f(x) = \sin^{-1}(x/4)$; $(2, \pi/6)$
33. $f(x) = \cos^{-1} x^2$; $(1/\sqrt{2}, \pi/3)$
34. $f(x) = \sec^{-1}(e^x)$; $(\ln 2, \pi/3)$

T **35. Angular size** A boat sails directly toward a 150-meter skyscraper that stands on the edge of a harbor. The angular size θ of the building is the angle formed by lines from the top and bottom of the building to the observer (see figure).
a. What is the rate of change of the angular size $d\theta/dx$ when the boat is $x = 500$ m from the building?
b. Graph $d\theta/dx$ as a function of x and determine the point at which the angular size changes most rapidly.

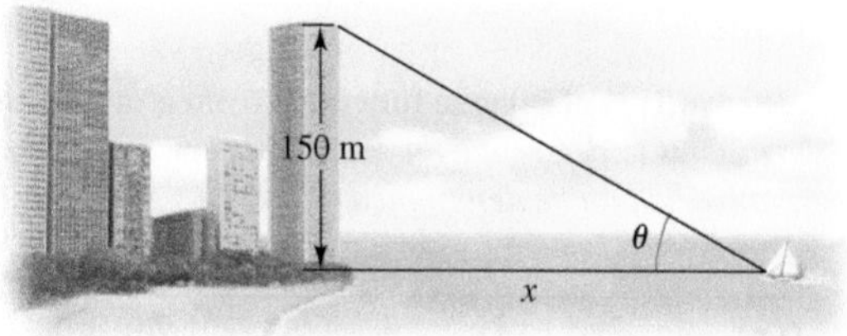

T **36. Angle of elevation** A small plane, moving at 70 m/s, flies horizontally on a line 400 meters directly above an observer. Let θ be the angle of elevation of the plane (see figure).
a. What is the rate of change of the angle of elevation $d\theta/dx$ when the plane is $x = 500$ m past the observer?
b. Graph $d\theta/dx$ as a function of x and determine the point at which θ changes most rapidly.

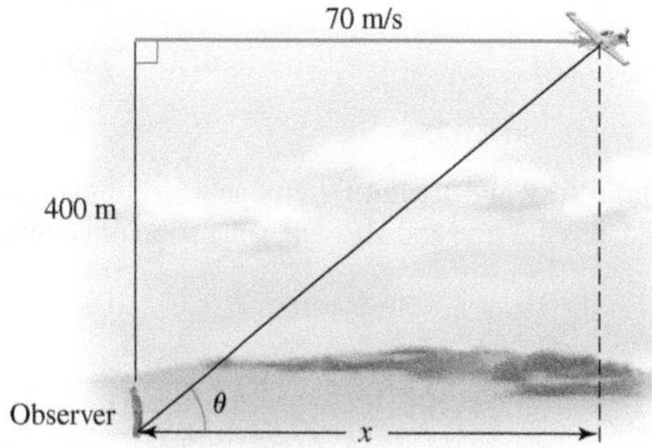

37–42. Derivatives of inverse functions at a point *Find the derivative of the inverse of the following functions at the specified point on the graph of the inverse function. You do not need to find f^{-1}.*

37. $f(x) = 3x + 4$; $(16, 4)$
38. $f(x) = \frac{1}{2}x + 8$; $(10, 4)$
39. $f(x) = -5x + 4$; $(-1, 1)$
40. $f(x) = x^2 + 1$, for $x \geq 0$; $(5, 2)$

41. $f(x) = \tan x;\ (1, \pi/4)$

42. $f(x) = x^2 - 2x - 3$, for $x \le 1$; $(12, -3)$

43–46. Slopes of tangent lines *Given the function f, find the slope of the line tangent to the graph of f^{-1} at the specified point on the graph of f^{-1}.*

43. $f(x) = \sqrt{x};\ (2, 4)$

44. $f(x) = x^3;\ (8, 2)$

45. $f(x) = (x + 2)^2;\ (36, 4)$

46. $f(x) = -x^2 + 8;\ (7, 1)$

47–50. Derivatives and inverse functions

47. Find $(f^{-1})'(3)$ if $f(x) = x^3 + x + 1$.

48. Find the slope of the curve $y = f^{-1}(x)$ at $(4, 7)$ if the slope of the curve $y = f(x)$ at $(7, 4)$ is $\frac{2}{3}$.

49. Suppose the slope of the curve $y = f^{-1}(x)$ at $(4, 7)$ is $\frac{4}{5}$. Find $f'(7)$.

50. Suppose the slope of the curve $y = f(x)$ at $(4, 7)$ is $\frac{1}{5}$. Find $(f^{-1})'(7)$.

51–52. Derivatives of inverse functions from a table *Use the following tables to determine the indicated derivatives or state that the derivative cannot be determined.*

51.

x	-2	-1	0	1	2
$f(x)$	2	3	4	6	7
$f'(x)$	1	1/2	2	3/2	1

a. $(f^{-1})'(4)$ **b.** $(f^{-1})'(6)$ **c.** $(f^{-1})'(1)$ **d.** $f'(1)$

52.

x	-4	-2	0	2	4
$f(x)$	0	1	2	3	4
$f'(x)$	5	4	3	2	1

a. $f'(f(0))$ **b.** $(f^{-1})'(0)$

c. $(f^{-1})'(1)$ **d.** $(f^{-1})'(f(4))$

Further Explorations

53. Explain why or why not Determine whether the following statements are true and give an explanation or counterexample.

a. $\frac{d}{dx}(\sin^{-1} x + \cos^{-1} x) = 0.$

b. $\frac{d}{dx}(\tan^{-1} x) = \sec^2 x.$

c. The lines tangent to the graph of $y = \sin^{-1} x$ on the interval $[-1, 1]$ have a minimum slope of 1.

d. The lines tangent to the graph of $y = \sin x$ on the interval $[-\pi/2, \pi/2]$ have a maximum slope of 1.

e. If $f(x) = 1/x$, then $(f^{-1})'(x) = -1/x^2$.

T 54–57. Graphing f and f'

a. Graph f with a graphing utility.

b. Compute and graph f'.

c. Verify that the zeros of f' correspond to points at which f has a horizontal tangent line.

54. $f(x) = (x - 1)\sin^{-1} x$ on $[-1, 1]$

55. $f(x) = (x^2 - 1)\sin^{-1} x$ on $[-1, 1]$

56. $f(x) = (\sec^{-1} x)/x$ on $[1, \infty)$

57. $f(x) = e^{-x}\tan^{-1} x$ on $[0, \infty)$

T 58. Graphing with inverse trigonometric functions

a. Graph the function $f(x) = \dfrac{\tan^{-1} x}{x^2 + 1}$.

b. Compute and graph f' and determine (perhaps approximately) the points at which $f'(x) = 0$.

c. Verify that the zeros of f' correspond to points at which f has a horizontal tangent line.

59–66. Derivatives of inverse functions *Consider the following functions (on the given interval, if specified). Find the inverse function, express it as a function of x, and find the derivative of the inverse function.*

59. $f(x) = 3x - 4$

60. $f(x) = |x + 2|$, for $x \le -2$

61. $f(x) = x^2 - 4$, for $x > 0$

62. $f(x) = \dfrac{x}{x + 5}$

63. $f(x) = \sqrt{x + 2}$, for $x \ge -2$

64. $f(x) = x^{2/3}$, for $x > 0$

65. $f(x) = x^{-1/2}$, for $x > 0$

66. $f(x) = x^3 + 3$

Applications

T 67. Towing a boat A boat is towed toward a dock by a cable attached to a winch that stands 10 feet above the water level (see figure). Let θ be the angle of elevation of the winch and let ℓ be the length of the cable as the boat is towed toward the dock.

a. Show that the rate of change of θ with respect to ℓ is

$$\frac{d\theta}{d\ell} = \frac{-10}{\ell\sqrt{\ell^2 - 100}}.$$

b. Compute $\frac{d\theta}{d\ell}$ when $\ell = 50$, 20, and 11 ft.

c. Find $\lim_{\ell \to 10^+} \frac{d\theta}{d\ell}$ and explain what happens as the last foot of cable is reeled in (note that the boat is at the dock when $\ell = 10$).

d. It is evident from the figure that θ increases as the boat is towed to the dock. Why, then, is $d\theta/d\ell$ negative?

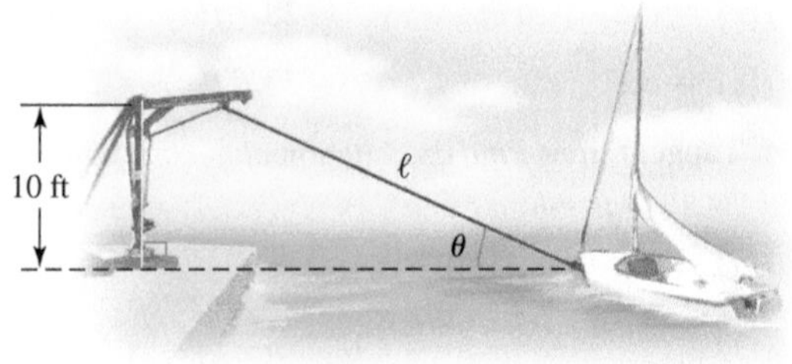

68. Tracking a dive A biologist standing at the bottom of an 80-foot vertical cliff watches a peregrine falcon dive from the top of the cliff at a 45° angle from the horizontal (see figure).

a. Express the angle of elevation θ from the biologist to the falcon as a function of the height h of the bird above the ground. (*Hint:* The vertical distance between the top of the cliff and the falcon is $80 - h$.)

b. What is the rate of change of θ with respect to the bird's height when it is 60 feet above the ground?

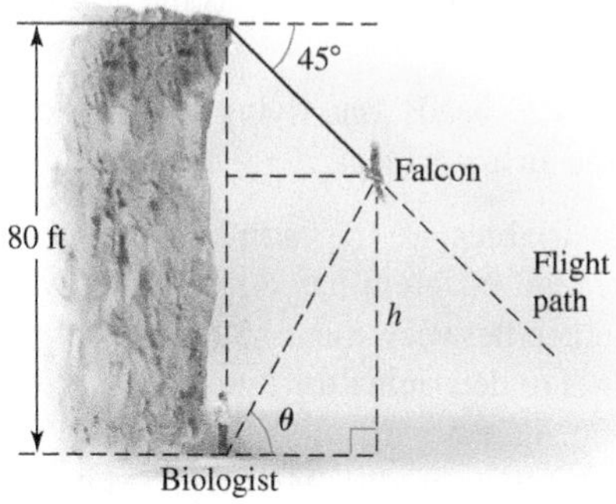

69. Angle to a particle, part I A particle travels clockwise on a circular path of diameter D, monitored by a sensor on the circle at point P; the other endpoint of the diameter on which the sensor lies is Q (see figure). Let θ be the angle between the diameter PQ and the line from the sensor to the particle. Let c be the length of the chord from the particle's position to Q.

a. Calculate $d\theta/dc$.

b. Evaluate $\left.\dfrac{d\theta}{dc}\right|_{c=0}$.

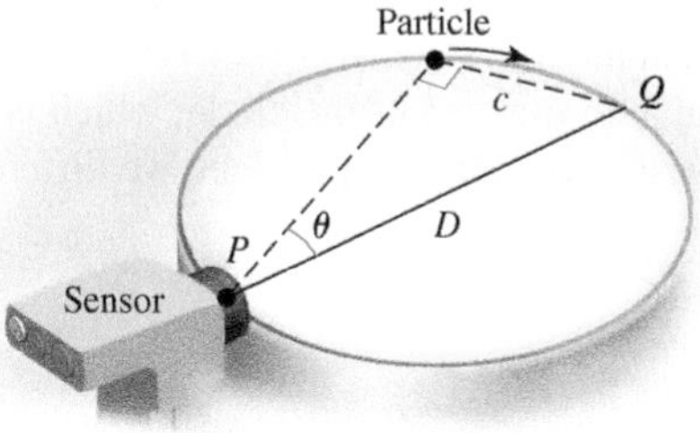

70. Angle to a particle, part II The figure in Exercise 69 shows the particle traveling away from the sensor, which may have influenced your solution (we expect you used the inverse sine function). Suppose instead that the particle approaches the sensor (see figure). How would this change the solution? Explain the differences in the two answers.

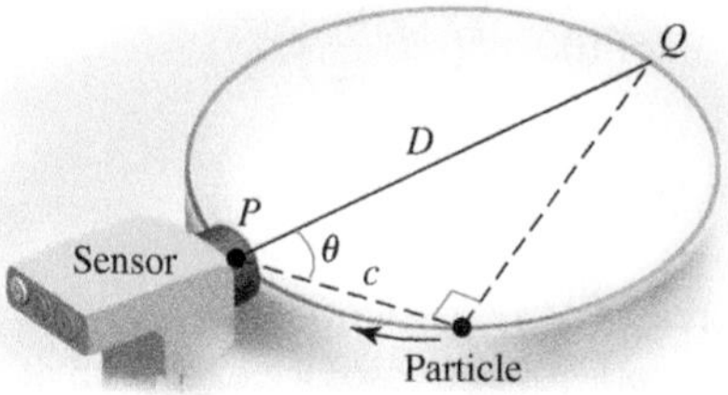

Additional Exercises

71. Derivative of the inverse sine Find the derivative of the inverse sine function using Theorem 3.23.

72. Derivative of the inverse cosine Find the derivative of the inverse cosine function in the following two ways.

a. Using Theorem 3.23

b. Using the identity $\sin^{-1} x + \cos^{-1} x = \pi/2$

73. Derivative of $\cot^{-1} x$ and $\csc^{-1} x$ Use a trigonometric identity to show that the derivatives of the inverse cotangent and inverse cosecant differ from the derivatives of the inverse tangent and inverse secant, respectively, by a multiplicative factor of -1.

74. Tangents and inverses Suppose $y = L(x) = ax + b$ (with $a \neq 0$) is the equation of the line tangent to the graph of a one-to-one function f at (x_0, y_0). Also, suppose that $y = M(x) = cx + d$ is the equation of the line tangent to the graph of f^{-1} at (y_0, x_0).

a. Express a and b in terms of x_0 and y_0.

b. Express c in terms of a, and d in terms of a, x_0, and y_0.

c. Prove that $L^{-1}(x) = M(x)$.

75–78. Identity proofs *Prove the following identities and give the values of x for which they are true.*

75. $\cos(\sin^{-1} x) = \sqrt{1 - x^2}$

76. $\cos(2\sin^{-1} x) = 1 - 2x^2$

77. $\tan(2\tan^{-1} x) = \dfrac{2x}{1 - x^2}$

78. $\sin(2\sin^{-1} x) = 2x\sqrt{1 - x^2}$

79. An inverse tangent identity

a. Use derivatives to show that $\tan^{-1}\dfrac{2}{n^2}$ and $\tan^{-1}(n + 1) - \tan^{-1}(n - 1)$ differ by a constant.

b. Prove that $\tan^{-1}\dfrac{2}{n^2} = \tan^{-1}(n + 1) - \tan^{-1}(n - 1)$.

(*Source: The College Mathematics Journal*, 32, 4, Sep 2001)

QUICK CHECK ANSWERS

1. $f(x) = \sin^{-1} x$ is odd and $f'(x) = 1/\sqrt{1 - x^2}$ is even. **2.** The slopes of the tangent lines approach 0. **3.** One is the negative of the other. **4.** Recall that $1° = \pi/180$ rad. So 0.0024 rad/ft is equivalent to 0.138°/ft. **5.** Both curves have a slope of 1 at $(0, 0)$. ◄

3.11 Related Rates

We now return to the theme of derivatives as rates of change in problems in which the variables change with respect to *time*. The essential feature of these problems is that two or more variables, which are related in a known way, are themselves changing in time. Here are two examples illustrating this type of problem.

- An oil rig springs a leak and the oil spreads in a (roughly) circular patch around the rig. If the radius of the oil patch increases at a known rate, how fast is the area of the patch changing (Example 1)?
- Two airliners approach an airport with known speeds, one flying west and one flying north. How fast is the distance between the airliners changing (Example 2)?

In the first problem, the two related variables are the radius and the area of the oil patch. Both are changing in time. The second problem has three related variables: the positions of the two airliners and the distance between them. Again, the three variables change in time. The goal in both problems is to determine the rate of change of one of the variables at a specific moment of time—hence the name *related rates*.

We present a progression of examples in this section. After the first example, a general procedure is given for solving related-rate problems.

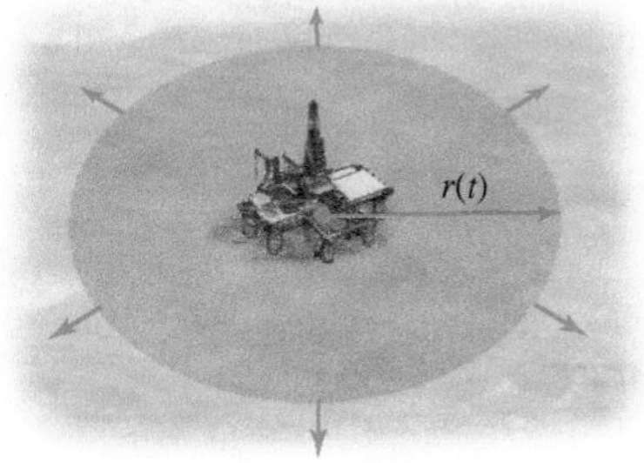

Figure 3.72

EXAMPLE 1 Spreading oil An oil rig springs a leak in calm seas, and the oil spreads in a circular patch around the rig. If the radius of the oil patch increases at a rate of 30 m/hr, how fast is the area of the patch increasing when the patch has a radius of 100 meters (Figure 3.72)?

SOLUTION Two variables change simultaneously: the radius of the circle and its area. The key relationship between the radius and area is $A = \pi r^2$. It helps to rewrite the basic relationship showing explicitly which quantities vary in time. In this case, we rewrite A and r as $A(t)$ and $r(t)$ to emphasize that they change with respect to t (time). The general expression relating the radius and area at any time t is $A(t) = \pi r(t)^2$.

The goal is to find the rate of change of the area of the circle, which is $A'(t)$, given that $r'(t) = 30$ m/hr. To introduce derivatives into the problem, we differentiate the area relation $A(t) = \pi r(t)^2$ with respect to t:

$$\begin{aligned} A'(t) &= \frac{d}{dt}(\pi r(t)^2) \\ &= \pi \frac{d}{dt}(r(t)^2) \\ &= \pi\,(2r(t))\,r'(t) && \text{Chain Rule} \\ &= 2\pi r(t)\,r'(t). && \text{Simplify.} \end{aligned}$$

Substituting the given values $r(t) = 100$ m and $r'(t) = 30$ m/hr, we have (including units)

$$\begin{aligned} A'(t) &= 2\pi r(t)\,r'(t) \\ &= 2\pi(100\text{ m})\left(30\frac{\text{m}}{\text{hr}}\right) \\ &= 6000\pi\frac{\text{m}^2}{\text{hr}}. \end{aligned}$$

➤ It is important to remember that substitution of specific values of the variables occurs *after* differentiating.

We see that the area of the oil spill increases at a rate of $6000\pi \approx 18{,}850\text{ m}^2/\text{hr}$. Including units is a simple way to check your work. In this case, we expect an answer with units of area per unit time, so m^2/hr makes sense.

Notice that the rate of change of the area depends on the radius of the spill. As the radius increases, the rate of change of the area also increases.

Related Exercises 5–19 ◀

QUICK CHECK 1 In Example 1, what is the rate of change of the area when the radius is 200 m? 300 m? ◀

Using Example 1 as a template, we offer a set of guidelines for solving related-rate problems. There are always variations that arise for individual problems, but here is a general procedure.

PROCEDURE Steps for Related-Rate Problems

1. Read the problem carefully, making a sketch to organize the given information. Identify the rates that are given and the rate that is to be determined.
2. Write one or more equations that express the basic relationships among the variables.
3. Introduce rates of change by differentiating the appropriate equation(s) with respect to time t.
4. Substitute known values and solve for the desired quantity.
5. Check that units are consistent and the answer is reasonable. (For example, does it have the correct sign?)

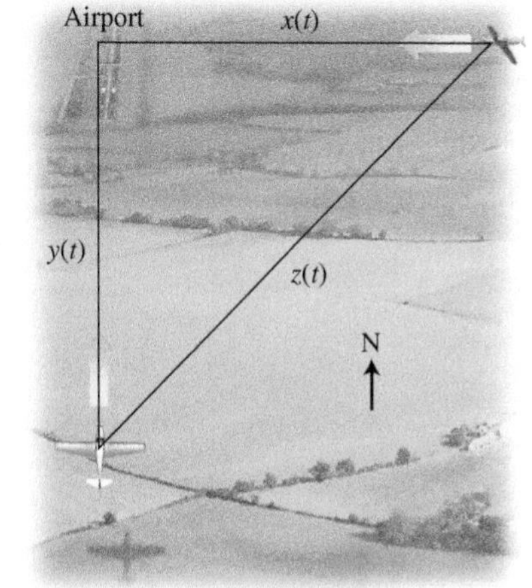

Figure 3.73

EXAMPLE 2 Converging airplanes Two small planes approach an airport, one flying due west at 120 mi/hr and the other flying due north at 150 mi/hr. Assuming they fly at the same constant elevation, how fast is the distance between the planes changing when the westbound plane is 180 miles from the airport and the northbound plane is 225 miles from the airport?

SOLUTION A sketch such as Figure 3.73 helps us visualize the problem and organize the information. Let $x(t)$ and $y(t)$ denote the distance from the airport to the westbound and northbound planes, respectively. The paths of the two planes form the legs of a right triangle, and the distance between them, denoted $z(t)$, is the hypotenuse. By the Pythagorean theorem, $z^2 = x^2 + y^2$.

Our aim is to find dz/dt, the rate of change of the distance between the planes. We first differentiate both sides of $z^2 = x^2 + y^2$ with respect to t:

$$\frac{d}{dt}(z^2) = \frac{d}{dt}(x^2 + y^2) \Rightarrow 2z\frac{dz}{dt} = 2x\frac{dx}{dt} + 2y\frac{dy}{dt}.$$

Notice that the Chain Rule is needed because x, y, and z are functions of t. Solving for dz/dt results in

$$\frac{dz}{dt} = \frac{2x\frac{dx}{dt} + 2y\frac{dy}{dt}}{2z} = \frac{x\frac{dx}{dt} + y\frac{dy}{dt}}{z}.$$

This equation relates the unknown rate dz/dt to the known quantities x, y, z, dx/dt, and dy/dt. For the westbound plane, $dx/dt = -120$ mi/hr (negative because the distance is decreasing), and for the northbound plane, $dy/dt = -150$ mi/hr. At the moment of interest, when $x = 180$ mi and $y = 225$ mi, the distance between the planes is

$$z = \sqrt{x^2 + y^2} = \sqrt{180^2 + 225^2} \approx 288 \text{ mi}.$$

Substituting these values gives

$$\frac{dz}{dt} = \frac{x\frac{dx}{dt} + y\frac{dy}{dt}}{z} \approx \frac{(180\text{ mi})(-120\text{ mi/hr}) + (225\text{ mi})(-150\text{ mi/hr})}{288\text{ mi}}$$
$$\approx -192 \text{ mi/hr}.$$

Notice that $dz/dt < 0$, which means the distance between the planes is *decreasing* at a rate of about 192 mi/hr.

Related Exercises 20–26 ◀

QUICK CHECK 2 Assuming the same plane speeds as in Example 2, how fast is the distance between the planes changing if $x = 60$ mi and $y = 75$ mi? ◀

➤ In Example 1, we replaced A and r with $A(t)$ and $r(t)$, respectively, to remind us of the independent variable. After some practice, this replacement is not necessary.

➤ One could solve the equation $z^2 = x^2 + y^2$ for z, with the result

$$z = \sqrt{x^2 + y^2},$$

and then differentiate. However, it is easier to differentiate implicitly as shown in the example.

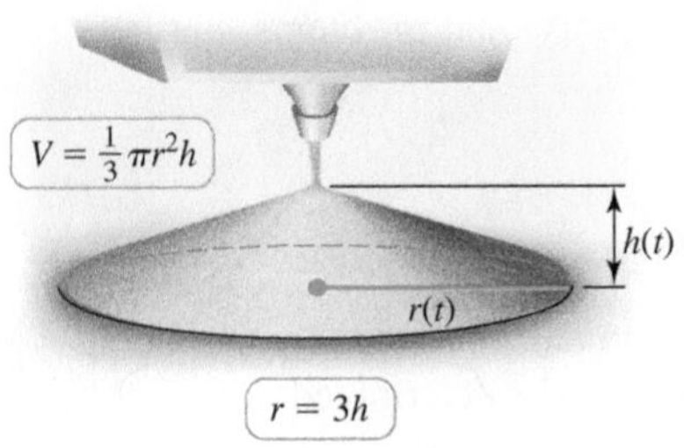

Figure 3.74

EXAMPLE 3 **Sandpile** Sand falls from an overhead bin, accumulating in a conical pile with a radius that is always three times its height. If the sand falls from the bin at a rate of 120 ft^3/min, how fast is the height of the sandpile changing when the pile is 10 ft high?

SOLUTION A sketch of the problem (Figure 3.74) shows the three relevant variables: the volume V, the radius r, and the height h of the sandpile. The aim is to find the rate of change of the height dh/dt at the instant that $h = 10$ ft, given that $dV/dt = 120\ \text{ft}^3/\text{min}$. The basic relationship among the variables is the formula for the volume of a cone, $V = \frac{1}{3}\pi r^2 h$. We now use the given fact that the radius is always three times the height. Substituting $r = 3h$ into the volume relationship gives V in terms of h:

$$V = \frac{1}{3}\pi r^2 h = \frac{1}{3}\pi(3h)^2 h = 3\pi h^3.$$

Rates of change are introduced by differentiating both sides of $V = 3\pi h^3$ with respect to t. Using the Chain Rule, we have

$$\frac{dV}{dt} = 9\pi h^2 \frac{dh}{dt}.$$

Now we find dh/dt at the instant that $h = 10$ ft, given that $dV/dt = 120\ \text{ft}^3/\text{min}$. Solving for dh/dt and substituting these values, we have

$$\frac{dh}{dt} = \frac{dV/dt}{9\pi h^2} \qquad \text{Solve for } \frac{dh}{dt}.$$

$$= \frac{120\ \text{ft}^3/\text{min}}{9\pi(10\ \text{ft})^2} \approx 0.042\ \frac{\text{ft}}{\text{min}}. \qquad \text{Substitute for } \frac{dV}{dt} \text{ and } h.$$

At the instant that the sandpile is 10 ft high, the height is changing at a rate of 0.042 ft/min. Notice how the units work out consistently.

Related Exercises 27–33 ◀

QUICK CHECK 3 In Example 3, what is the rate of change of the height when $h = 2$ ft? Does the rate of change of the height increase or decrease with increasing height? ◀

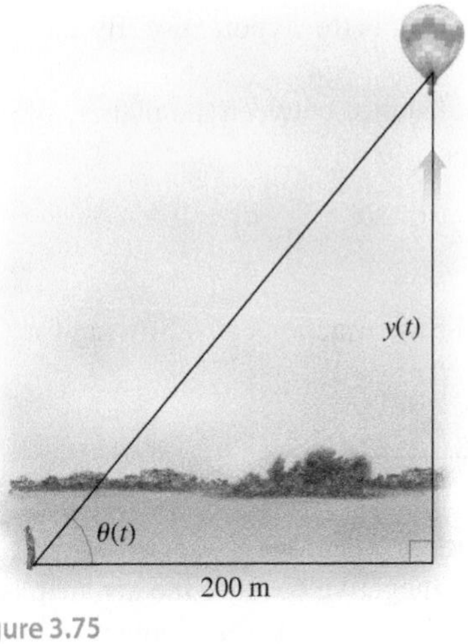

Figure 3.75

EXAMPLE 4 **Observing a launch** An observer stands 200 meters from the launch site of a hot-air balloon. The balloon rises vertically at a constant rate of 4 m/s. How fast is the angle of elevation of the balloon increasing 30 seconds after the launch? (The angle of elevation is the angle between the ground and the observer's line of sight to the balloon.)

SOLUTION Figure 3.75 shows the geometry of the launch. As the balloon rises, its distance from the ground y and its angle of elevation θ change simultaneously. An equation expressing the relationship between these variables is $\tan\theta = y/200$. To find $d\theta/dt$, we differentiate both sides of this relationship using the Chain Rule:

$$\sec^2\theta \frac{d\theta}{dt} = \frac{1}{200}\frac{dy}{dt}.$$

Next we solve for $\frac{d\theta}{dt}$:

$$\frac{d\theta}{dt} = \frac{dy/dt}{200\sec^2\theta} = \frac{(dy/dt)\cdot\cos^2\theta}{200}.$$

➤ The solution to Example 4 is reported in units of rad/s. Where did radians come from? Because a radian has no physical dimension (it is the ratio of an arc length and a radius), no unit appears. We write rad/s for clarity because $d\theta/dt$ is the rate of change of an angle.

The rate of change of the angle of elevation depends on the angle of elevation and the speed of the balloon. Thirty seconds after the launch, the balloon has risen $y = (4\ \text{m/s})(30\ \text{s}) = 120$ m. To complete the problem, we need the value of $\cos\theta$. Note that when $y = 120$ m, the distance between the observer and the balloon is

$$d = \sqrt{120^2 + 200^2} \approx 233.24\ \text{m}.$$

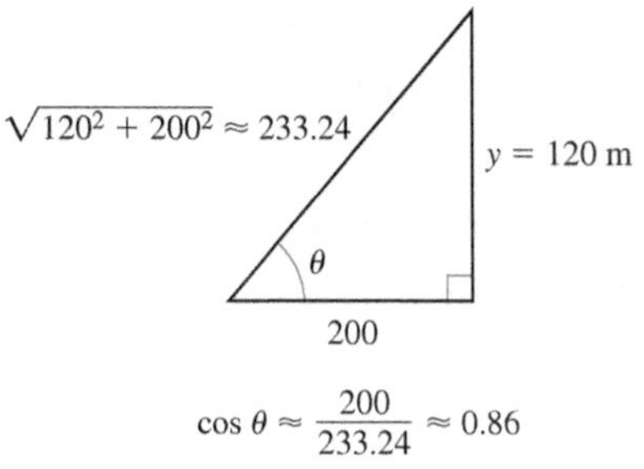

Figure 3.76

Therefore, $\cos\theta \approx 200/233.24 \approx 0.86$ (Figure 3.76), and the rate of change of the angle of elevation is

$$\frac{d\theta}{dt} = \frac{(dy/dt)\cdot\cos^2\theta}{200} \approx \frac{(4\text{ m/s})(0.86^2)}{200\text{ m}} = 0.015\text{ rad/s}.$$

At this instant, the balloon is rising at an angular rate of 0.015 rad/s, or slightly less than 1°/s, as seen by the observer.

Related Exercises 34–39 ◀

➤ Recall that to convert radians to degrees, we use

$$\text{degrees} = \frac{180}{\pi}\cdot\text{radians}.$$

QUICK CHECK 4 In Example 4, notice that as the balloon rises (as θ increases), the rate of change of the angle of elevation decreases to zero. When does the maximum value of $\theta'(t)$ occur, and what is it? ◀

SECTION 3.11 EXERCISES

Review Questions

1. Give an example in which one dimension of a geometric figure changes and produces a corresponding change in the area or volume of the figure.

2. Explain how implicit differentiation can simplify the work in a related-rates problem.

3. If two opposite sides of a rectangle increase in length, how must the other two opposite sides change if the area of the rectangle is to remain constant?

4. Explain why the term *related rates* describes the problems of this section.

Basic Skills

5. **Expanding square** The sides of a square increase in length at a rate of 2 m/s.
   a. At what rate is the area of the square changing when the sides are 10 m long?
   b. At what rate is the area of the square changing when the sides are 20 m long?
   c. Draw a graph that shows how the rate of change of the area varies with the side length.

6. **Shrinking square** The sides of a square decrease in length at a rate of 1 m/s.
   a. At what rate is the area of the square changing when the sides are 5 m long?
   b. At what rate are the lengths of the diagonals of the square changing?

7. **Expanding isosceles triangle** The legs of an isosceles right triangle increase in length at a rate of 2 m/s.
   a. At what rate is the area of the triangle changing when the legs are 2 m long?
   b. At what rate is the area of the triangle changing when the hypotenuse is 1 m long?
   c. At what rate is the length of the hypotenuse changing?

8. **Shrinking isosceles triangle** The hypotenuse of an isosceles right triangle decreases in length at a rate of 4 m/s.
   a. At what rate is the area of the triangle changing when the legs are 5 m long?
   b. At what rate are the lengths of the legs of the triangle changing?
   c. At what rate is the area of the triangle changing when the area is 4 m^2?

9. **Expanding circle** The area of a circle increases at a rate of 1 cm^2/s.
   a. How fast is the radius changing when the radius is 2 cm?
   b. How fast is the radius changing when the circumference is 2 cm?

10. **Expanding cube** The edges of a cube increase at a rate of 2 cm/s. How fast is the volume changing when the length of each edge is 50 cm?

11. **Shrinking circle** A circle has an initial radius of 50 ft when the radius begins decreasing at a rate of 2 ft/min. What is the rate of change of the area at the instant the radius is 10 ft?

12. **Shrinking cube** The volume of a cube decreases at a rate of 0.5 ft^3/min. What is the rate of change of the side length when the side lengths are 12 ft?

13. **Balloons** A spherical balloon is inflated and its volume increases at a rate of 15 in^3/min. What is the rate of change of its radius when the radius is 10 in?

14. **Piston compression** A piston is seated at the top of a cylindrical chamber with radius 5 cm when it starts moving into the chamber at a constant speed of 3 cm/s (see figure). What is the rate of change of the volume of the cylinder when the piston is 2 cm from the base of the chamber?

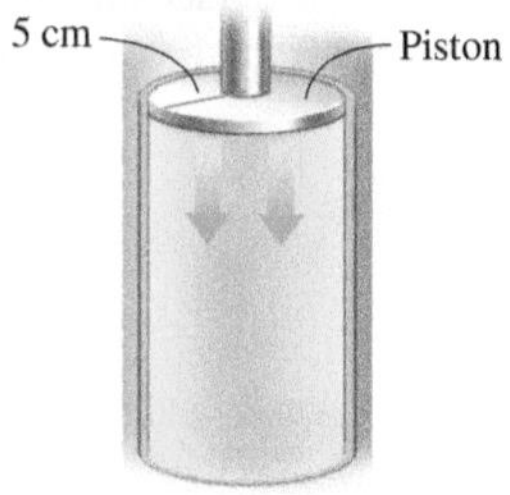

15. **Melting snowball** A spherical snowball melts at a rate proportional to its surface area. Show that the rate of change of the radius is constant. (*Hint:* Surface area $= 4\pi r^2$.)

16. Bug on a parabola A bug is moving along the right side of the parabola $y = x^2$ at a rate such that its distance from the origin is increasing at 1 cm/min. At what rates are the x- and y-coordinates of the bug increasing when the bug is at the point $(2, 4)$?

17. Another bug on a parabola A bug is moving along the parabola $y = x^2$. At what point on the parabola are the x- and y-coordinates changing at the same rate? (*Source: Calculus*, Tom M. Apostol, Vol. 1, John Wiley & Sons, New York, 1967.)

18. Expanding rectangle A rectangle initially has dimensions 2 cm by 4 cm. All sides begin increasing in length at a rate of 1 cm/s. At what rate is the area of the rectangle increasing after 20 s?

19. Filling a pool A swimming pool is 50 m long and 20 m wide. Its depth decreases linearly along the length from 3 m to 1 m (see figure). It is initially empty and is filled at a rate of 1 m^3/min. How fast is the water level rising 250 min after the filling begins? How long will it take to fill the pool?

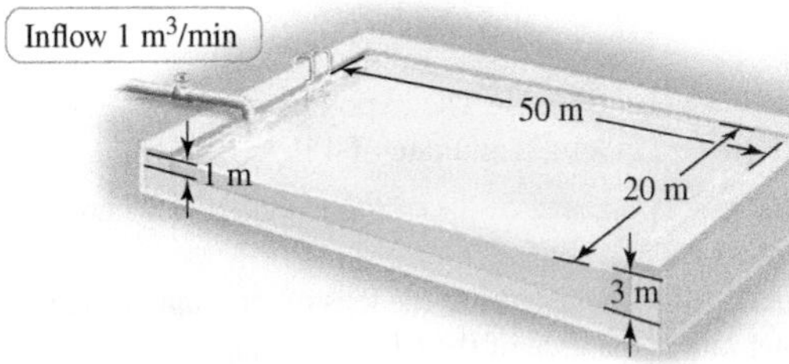

20. Altitude of a jet A jet ascends at a 10° angle from the horizontal with an airspeed of 550 mi/hr (its speed along its line of flight is 550 mi/hr). How fast is the altitude of the jet increasing? If the sun is directly overhead, how fast is the shadow of the jet moving on the ground?

21. Rate of dive of a submarine A surface ship is moving (horizontally) in a straight line at 10 km/hr. At the same time, an enemy submarine maintains a position directly below the ship while diving at an angle that is 20° below the horizontal. How fast is the submarine's altitude decreasing?

22. Divergent paths Two boats leave a port at the same time; one travels west at 20 mi/hr and the other travels south at 15 mi/hr. At what rate is the distance between them changing 30 minutes after they leave the port?

23. Ladder against the wall A 13-foot ladder is leaning against a vertical wall (see figure) when Jack begins pulling the foot of the ladder away from the wall at a rate of 0.5 ft/s. How fast is the top of the ladder sliding down the wall when the foot of the ladder is 5 ft from the wall?

24. Ladder against the wall again A 12-foot ladder is leaning against a vertical wall when Jack begins pulling the foot of the ladder away from the wall at a rate of 0.2 ft/s. What is the configuration of the ladder at the instant that the vertical speed of the top of the ladder equals the horizontal speed of the foot of the ladder?

25. Moving shadow A 5-foot-tall woman walks at 8 ft/s toward a streetlight that is 20 ft above the ground. What is the rate of change of the length of her shadow when she is 15 ft from the streetlight? At what rate is the tip of her shadow moving?

26. Baseball runners Runners stand at first and second base in a baseball game. At the moment a ball is hit, the runner at first base runs to second base at 18 ft/s; simultaneously, the runner on second runs to third base at 20 ft/s. How fast is the distance between the runners changing 1 second after the ball is hit (see figure)? (*Hint:* The distance between consecutive bases is 90 ft and the bases lie at the corners of a square.)

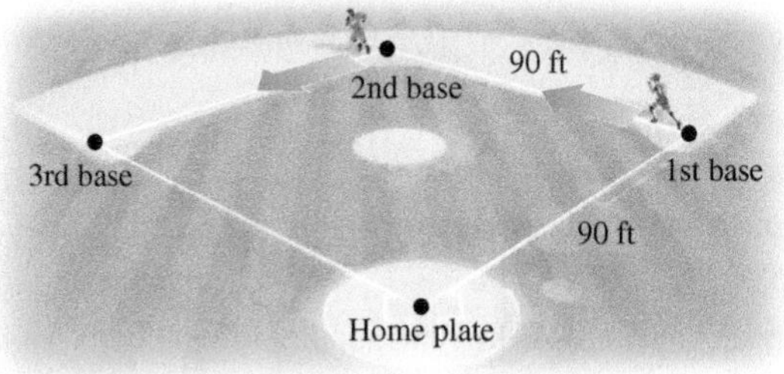

27. Growing sandpile Sand falls from an overhead bin and accumulates in a conical pile with a radius that is always three times its height. Suppose the height of the pile increases at a rate of 2 cm/s when the pile is 12 cm high. At what rate is the sand leaving the bin at that instant?

28. Draining a water heater A water heater that has the shape of a right cylindrical tank with a radius of 1 ft and a height of 4 ft is being drained. How fast is water draining out of the tank (in ft^3/min) if the water level is dropping at 6 in/min?

29. Draining a tank An inverted conical water tank with a height of 12 ft and a radius of 6 ft is drained through a hole in the vertex at a rate of 2 ft^3/s (see figure). What is the rate of change of the water depth when the water depth is 3 ft? (*Hint:* Use similar triangles.)

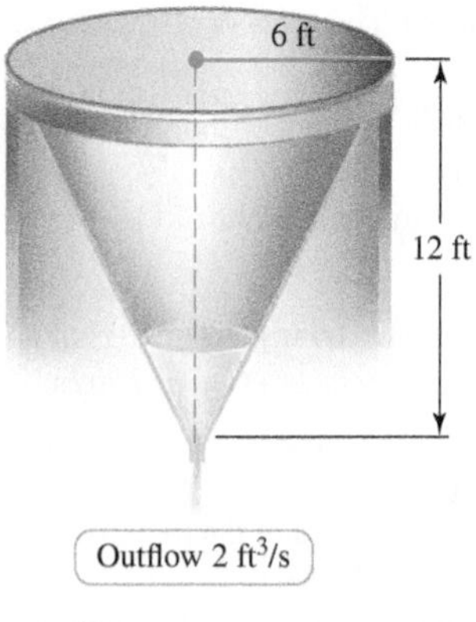

30. Drinking a soda At what rate is soda being sucked out of a cylindrical glass that is 6 in tall and has a radius of 2 in? The depth of the soda decreases at a constant rate of 0.25 in/s.

31. **Draining a cone** Water is drained out of an inverted cone having the same dimensions as the cone depicted in Exercise 29. If the water level drops at 1 ft/min, at what rate is water (in ft^3/min) draining from the tank when the water depth is 6 ft?

32. **Filling a hemispherical tank** A hemispherical tank with a radius of 10 m is filled from an inflow pipe at a rate of 3 m^3/min (see figure). How fast is the water level rising when the water level is 5 m from the bottom of the tank? (*Hint:* The volume of a cap of thickness h sliced from a sphere of radius r is $\pi h^2(3r - h)/3$.)

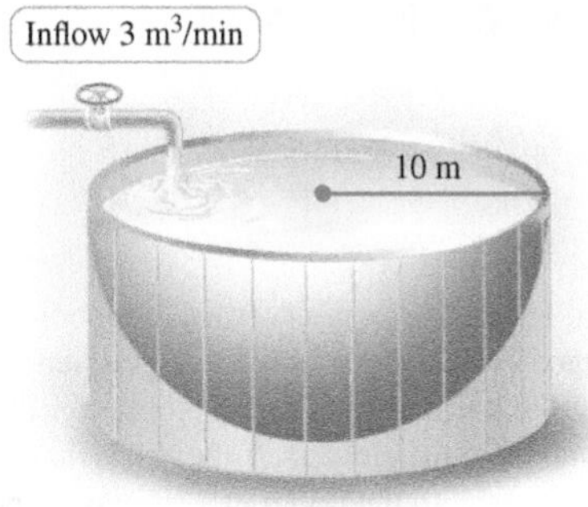

33. **Surface area of hemispherical tank** For the situation described in Exercise 32, what is the rate of change of the area of the exposed surface of the water when the water is 5 m deep?

34. **Observing a launch** An observer stands 300 ft from the launch site of a hot-air balloon. The balloon is launched vertically and maintains a constant upward velocity of 20 ft/s. What is the rate of change of the angle of elevation of the balloon when it is 400 ft from the ground? The angle of elevation is the angle θ between the observer's line of sight to the balloon and the ground.

35. **Another balloon story** A hot-air balloon is 150 ft above the ground when a motorcycle (traveling in a straight line on a horizontal road) passes directly beneath it going 40 mi/hr (58.67 ft/s). If the balloon rises vertically at a rate of 10 ft/s, what is the rate of change of the distance between the motorcycle and the balloon 10 seconds later?

36. **Fishing story** An angler hooks a trout and begins turning her circular reel at 1.5 rev/s. If the radius of the reel (and the fishing line on it) is 2 in, how fast is she reeling in her fishing line?

37. **Another fishing story** An angler hooks a trout and reels in his line at 4 in/s. Assume the tip of the fishing rod is 12 ft above the water and directly above the angler, and the fish is pulled horizontally directly toward the angler (see figure). Find the horizontal speed of the fish when it is 20 ft from the angler.

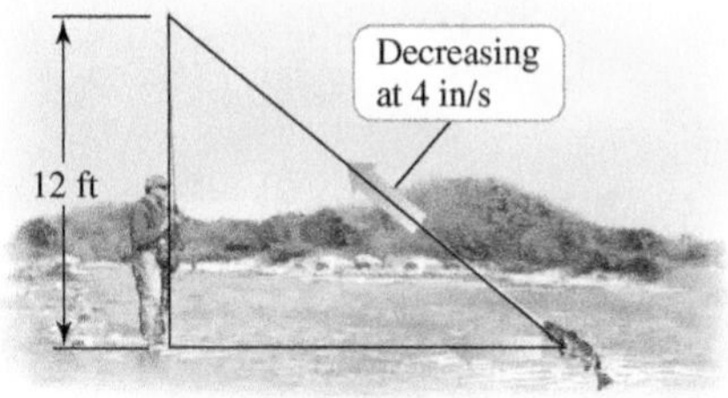

38. **Flying a kite** Once Kate's kite reaches a height of 50 ft (above her hands), it rises no higher but drifts due east in a wind blowing 5 ft/s. How fast is the string running through Kate's hands at the moment that she has released 120 ft of string?

39. **Rope on a boat** A rope passing through a capstan on a dock is attached to a boat offshore. The rope is pulled in at a constant rate of 3 ft/s, and the capstan is 5 ft vertically above the water. How fast is the boat traveling when it is 10 ft from the dock?

Further Explorations

40. **Parabolic motion** An arrow is shot into the air and moves along the parabolic path $y = x(50 - x)$ (see figure). The horizontal component of velocity is always 30 ft/s. What is the vertical component of velocity when (i) $x = 10$ and (ii) $x = 40$?

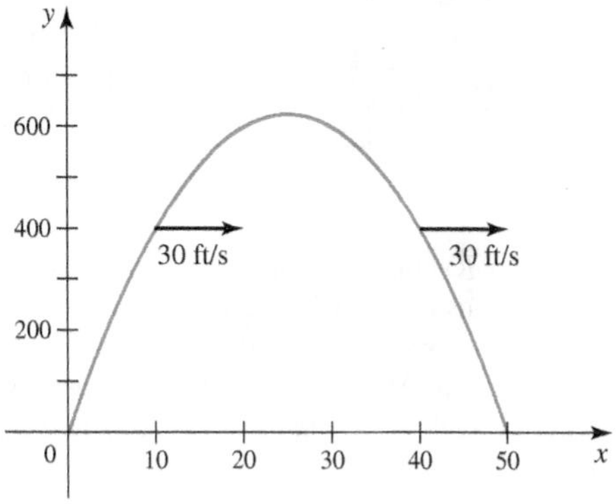

41. **Time-lagged flights** An airliner passes over an airport at noon traveling 500 mi/hr due west. At 1:00 P.M., another airliner passes over the same airport at the same elevation traveling due north at 550 mi/hr. Assuming both airliners maintain their (equal) elevations, how fast is the distance between them changing at 2:30 P.M.?

42. **Disappearing triangle** An equilateral triangle initially has sides of length 20 ft when each vertex moves toward the midpoint of the opposite side at a rate of 1.5 ft/min. Assuming the triangle remains equilateral, what is the rate of change of the area of the triangle at the instant the triangle disappears?

43. **Clock hands** The hands of the clock in the tower of the Houses of Parliament in London are approximately 3 m and 2.5 m in length. How fast is the distance between the tips of the hands changing at 9:00? (*Hint:* Use the Law of Cosines.)

44. **Filling two pools** Two cylindrical swimming pools are being filled simultaneously at the same rate (in m^3/min; see figure). The smaller pool has a radius of 5 m, and the water level rises at a rate of 0.5 m/min. The larger pool has a radius of 8 m. How fast is the water level rising in the larger pool?

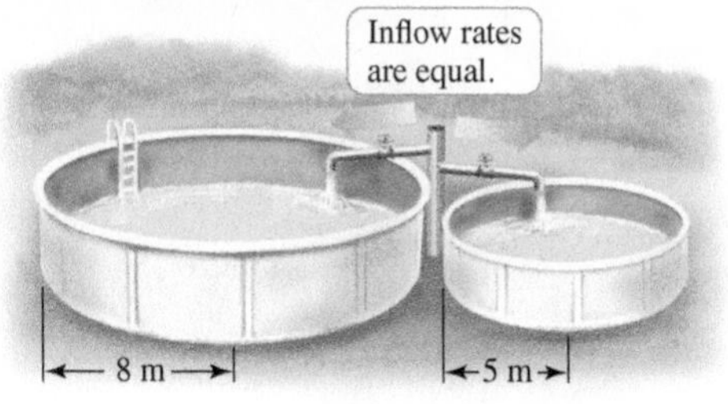

45. Filming a race A camera is set up at the starting line of a drag race 50 ft from a dragster at the starting line (camera 1 in the figure). Two seconds after the start of the race, the dragster has traveled 100 ft and the camera is turning at 0.75 rad/s while filming the dragster.

a. What is the speed of the dragster at this point?

b. A second camera (camera 2 in the figure) filming the dragster is located on the starting line 100 ft away from the dragster at the start of the race. How fast is this camera turning 2 seconds after the start of the race?

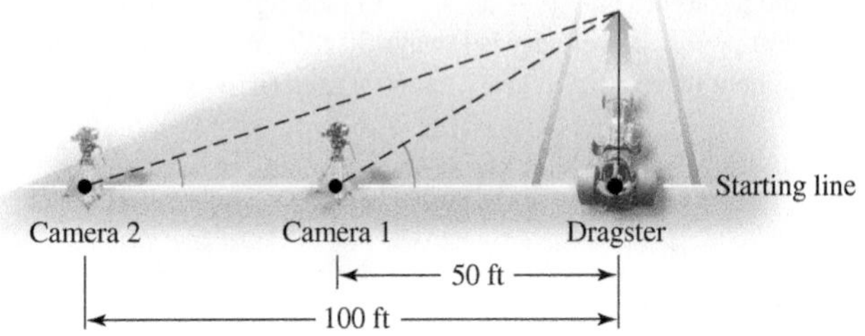

46. Two tanks A conical tank with an upper radius of 4 m and a height of 5 m drains into a cylindrical tank with a radius of 4 m and a height of 5 m (see figure). If the water level in the conical tank drops at a rate of 0.5 m/min, at what rate does the water level in the cylindrical tank rise when the water level in the conical tank is 3 m? 1 m?

47. Oblique tracking A port and a radar station are 2 mi apart on a straight shore running east and west (see figure). A ship leaves the port at noon traveling northeast at a rate of 15 mi/hr. If the ship maintains its speed and course, what is the rate of change of the tracking angle θ between the shore and the line between the radar station and the ship at 12:30 P.M.? (*Hint:* Use the Law of Sines.)

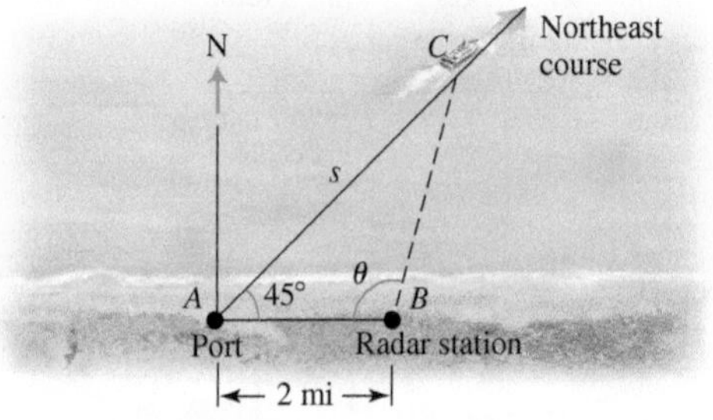

48. Oblique tracking A ship leaves port traveling southwest at a rate of 12 mi/hr. At noon, the ship reaches its closest approach to a radar station, which is on the shore 1.5 mi from the port. If the ship maintains its speed and course, what is the rate of change of the tracking angle θ between the radar station and the ship at 1:30 P.M. (see figure)? (*Hint:* Use the Law of Sines.)

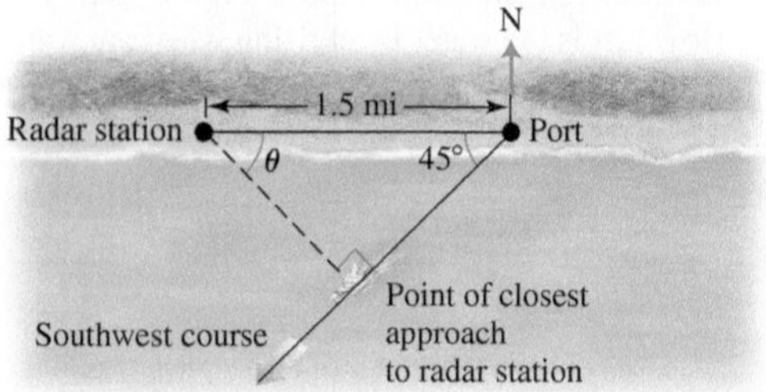

49. Watching an elevator An observer is 20 m above the ground floor of a large hotel atrium looking at a glass-enclosed elevator shaft that is 20 m horizontally from the observer (see figure). The angle of elevation of the elevator is the angle that the observer's line of sight makes with the horizontal (it may be positive or negative). Assuming that the elevator rises at a rate of 5 m/s, what is the rate of change of the angle of elevation when the elevator is 10 m above the ground? When the elevator is 40 m above the ground?

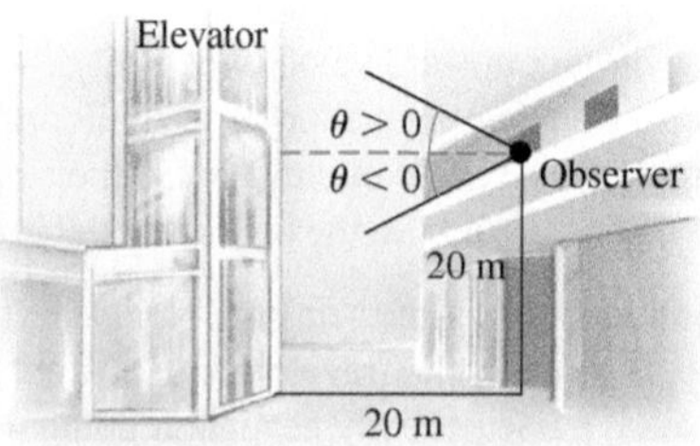

50. A lighthouse problem A lighthouse stands 500 m off a straight shore and the focused beam of its light revolves four times each minute. As shown in the figure, P is the point on shore closest to the lighthouse and Q is a point on the shore 200 m from P. What is the speed of the beam along the shore when it strikes the point Q? Describe how the speed of the beam along the shore varies with the distance between P and Q. Neglect the height of the lighthouse.

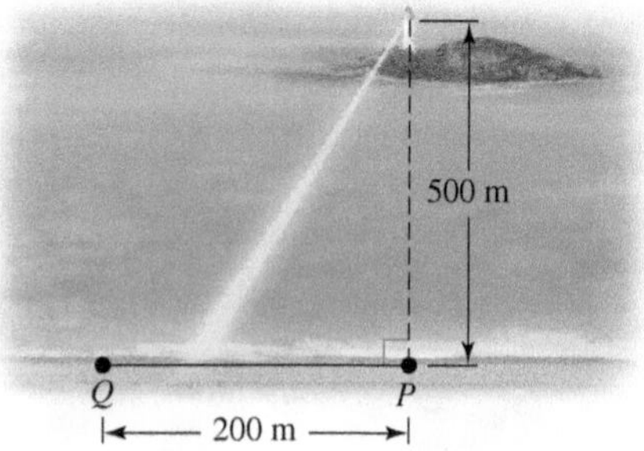

51. Navigation A boat leaves a port traveling due east at 12 mi/hr. At the same time, another boat leaves the same port traveling northeast at 15 mi/hr. The angle θ of the line between the boats is measured relative to due north (see figure). What is the rate of change of this angle 30 min after the boats leave the port? 2 hr after the boats leave the port?

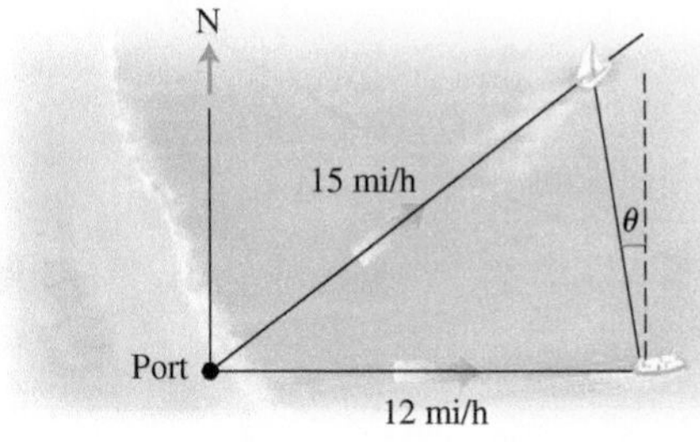

52. Watching a Ferris wheel An observer stands 20 m from the bottom of a 10-m-tall Ferris wheel on a line that is perpendicular to the face of the Ferris wheel. The wheel revolves at a rate of π rad/min, and the observer's line of sight with a specific seat on the wheel makes an angle θ with the ground (see figure). Forty seconds after that seat leaves the lowest point on the wheel, what is the rate of change of θ? Assume the observer's eyes are level with the bottom of the wheel.

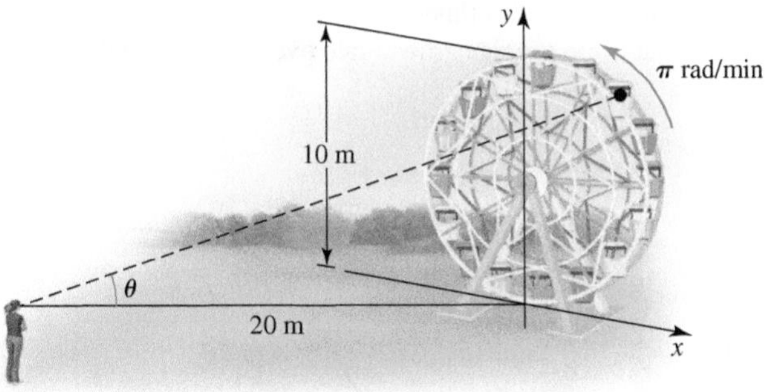

53. Viewing angle The bottom of a large theater screen is 3 ft above your eye level and the top of the screen is 10 ft above your eye level. Assume you walk away from the screen (perpendicular to the screen) at a rate of 3 ft/s while looking at the screen. What is the rate of change of the viewing angle θ when you are 30 ft from the wall on which the screen hangs, assuming the floor is horizontal (see figure)?

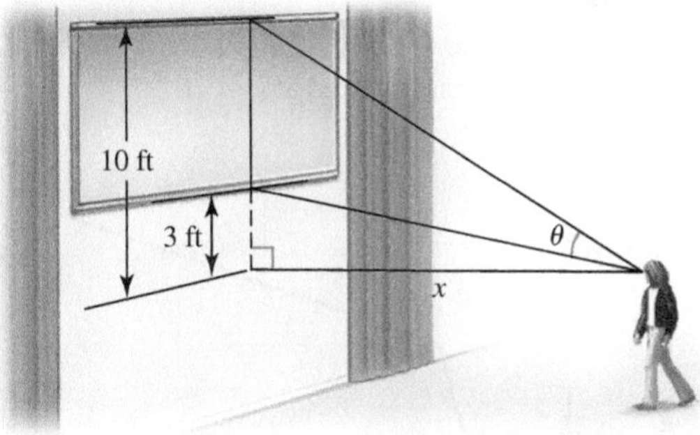

54. Searchlight—wide beam A revolving searchlight, which is 100 m from the nearest point on a straight highway, casts a horizontal beam along a highway (see figure). The beam leaves the spotlight at an angle of $\pi/16$ rad and revolves at a rate of $\pi/6$ rad/s. Let w be the width of the beam as it sweeps along the highway and θ be the angle that the center of the beam makes with the perpendicular to the highway. What is the rate of change of w when $\theta = \pi/3$? Neglect the height of the searchlight.

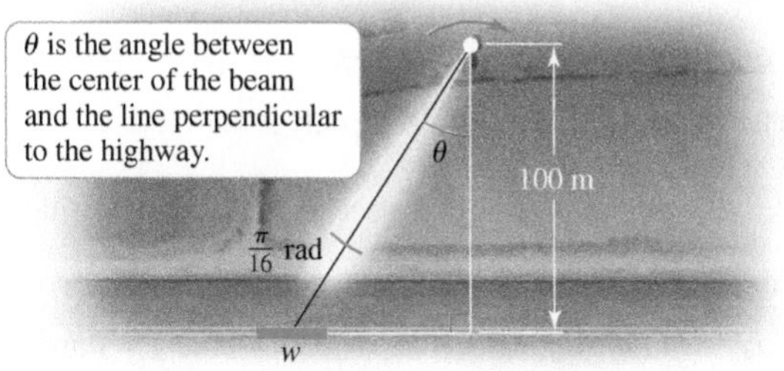

55. Draining a trough A trough in the shape of a half cylinder has length 5 m and radius 1 m. The trough is full of water when a valve is opened, and water flows out of the bottom of the trough at a rate of 1.5 m^3/hr (see figure). (*Hint:* The area of a sector of a circle of a radius r subtended by an angle θ is $r^2\theta/2$.)

a. How fast is the water level changing when the water level is 0.5 m from the bottom of the trough?

b. What is the rate of change of the surface area of the water when the water is 0.5 m deep?

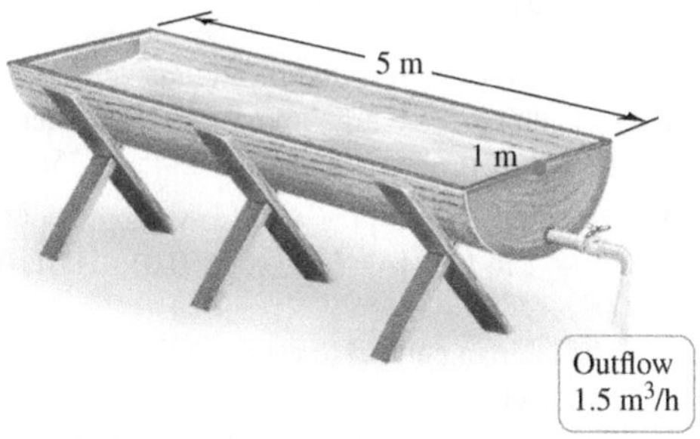

56. Divergent paths Two boats leave a port at the same time, one traveling west at 20 mi/hr and the other traveling southwest at 15 mi/hr. At what rate is the distance between them changing 30 min after they leave the port?

QUICK CHECK ANSWERS

1. $12{,}000\pi$ m^2/hr, $18{,}000\pi$ m^2/hr **2.** -192 mi/hr **3.** 1.1 ft/min; decreases with height **4.** $t = 0, \theta = 0, \theta'(0) = 0.02$ rad/s ◄

CHAPTER 3 REVIEW EXERCISES

1. Explain why or why not Determine whether the following statements are true and give an explanation or counterexample.

a. The function $f(x) = |2x + 1|$ is continuous for all x; therefore, it is differentiable for all x.

b. If $\frac{d}{dx}(f(x)) = \frac{d}{dx}(g(x))$, then $f = g$.

c. For any function f, $\frac{d}{dx}|f(x)| = |f'(x)|$.

d. The value of $f'(a)$ fails to exist only if the curve $y = f(x)$ has a vertical tangent line at $x = a$.

e. An object can have negative acceleration and increasing speed.

T 2–5. Slopes and tangent lines from the definition

a. Use either definition of the derivative to determine the slope of the curve $y = f(x)$ at the given point P.

b. Find an equation of the line tangent to the curve $y = f(x)$ at P; then graph the curve and the tangent line.

2. $f(x) = 4x^2 - 7x + 5;\ P(2, 7)$

3. $f(x) = 5x^3 + x;\ P(1, 6)$

4. $f(x) = \dfrac{x + 3}{2x + 1};\ P(0, 3)$

5. $f(x) = \dfrac{1}{2\sqrt{3x + 1}};\ P\left(0, \dfrac{1}{2}\right)$

T 6. Calculating average and instantaneous velocities Suppose the height s of an object (in m) above the ground after t seconds is approximated by the function $s = -4.9t^2 + 25t + 1$.

a. Make a table showing the average velocities of the object from time $t = 1$ to $t = 1 + h$, for $h = 0.01, 0.001, 0.0001$, and 0.00001.

b. Use the table in part (a) to estimate the instantaneous velocity of the object at $t = 1$.

c. Use limits to verify your estimate in part (b).

7. Population of the United States The population of the United States (in millions) by decade is given in the table, where t is the number of years after 1900. These data are plotted and fitted with a smooth curve $y = p(t)$ in the figure.

a. Compute the average rate of population growth from 1950 to 1960.

b. Explain why the average rate of growth from 1950 to 1960 is a good approximation to the (instantaneous) rate of growth in 1955.

c. Estimate the instantaneous rate of growth in 1985.

Year	1900	1910	1920	1930	1940	1950
t	0	10	20	30	40	50
$p(t)$	76.21	92.23	106.02	123.2	132.16	152.32

Year	1960	1970	1980	1990	2000	2010
t	60	70	80	90	100	110
$p(t)$	179.32	203.30	226.54	248.71	281.42	308.94

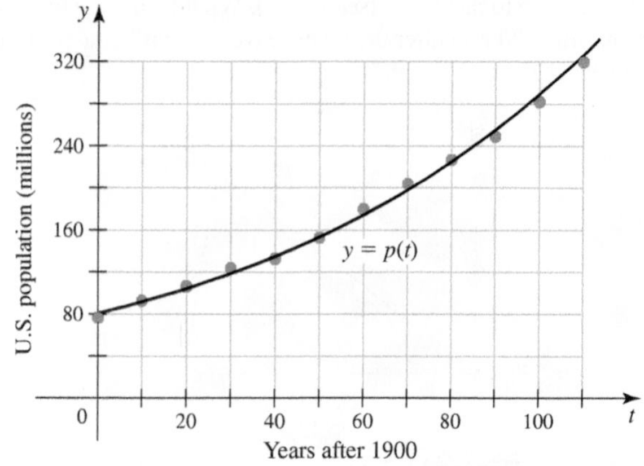

8. Growth rate of bacteria Suppose the following graph represents the number of bacteria in a culture t hours after the start of an experiment.

a. At approximately what time is the instantaneous growth rate the greatest, for $0 \le t \le 36$? Estimate the growth rate at this time.

b. At approximately what time in the interval $0 \le t \le 36$ is the instantaneous growth rate the least? Estimate the instantaneous growth rate at this time.

c. What is the average growth rate over the interval $0 \le t \le 36$?

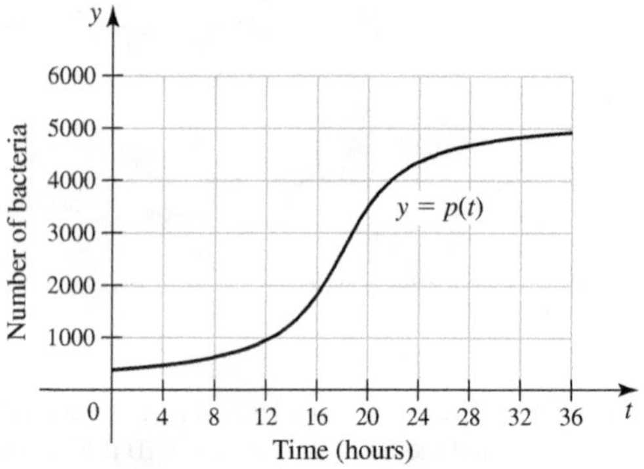

9. Velocity of a skydiver Assume the graph represents the distance (in m) fallen by a skydiver t seconds after jumping out of a plane.

a. Estimate the velocity of the skydiver at $t = 15$.

b. Estimate the velocity of the skydiver at $t = 70$.

c. Estimate the average velocity of the skydiver between $t = 20$ and $t = 90$.

d. Sketch a graph of the velocity function, for $0 \le t \le 120$.

e. What significant event occurred at $t = 30$?

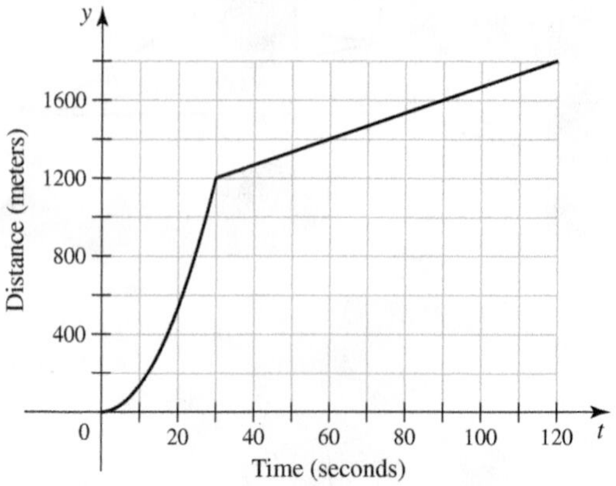

10–11. Using the definition of the derivative *Use the definition of the derivative to do the following.*

10. Verify that $f'(x) = 4x - 3$, where $f(x) = 2x^2 - 3x + 1$.

11. Verify that $g'(x) = \dfrac{1}{\sqrt{2x - 3}}$, where $g(x) = \sqrt{2x - 3}$.

12. Sketching a derivative graph Sketch a graph of f' for the function f shown in the figure.

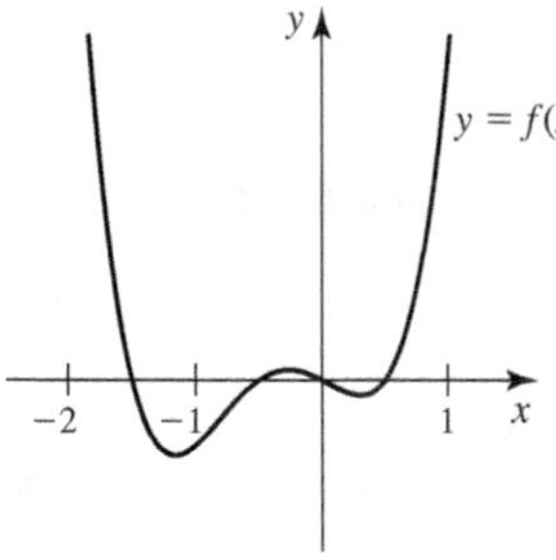

13. Sketching a derivative graph Sketch a graph of g' for the function g shown in the figure.

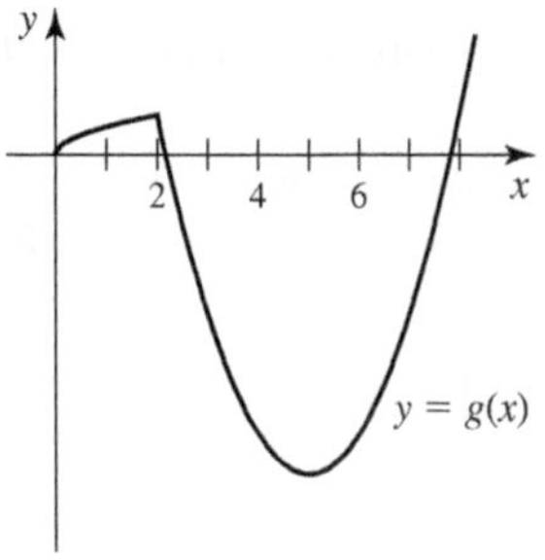

14. Matching functions and derivatives Match the functions in a–d with the derivatives in A–D.

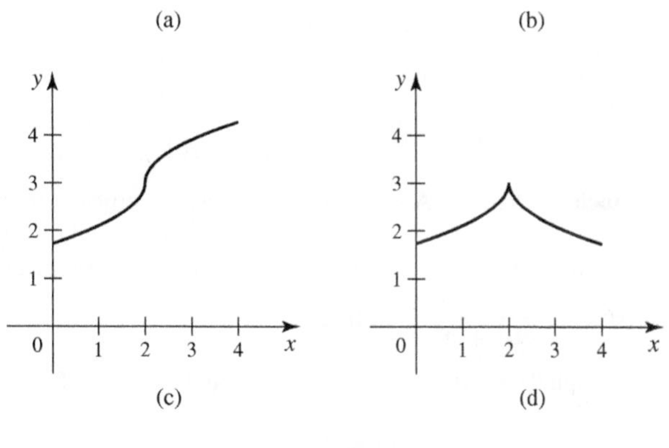

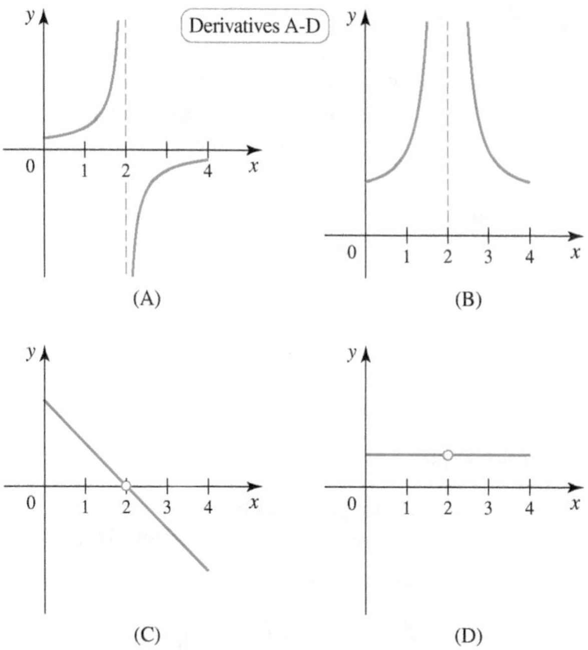

15–36. Evaluating derivatives *Evaluate and simplify the following derivatives.*

15. $\dfrac{d}{dx}\left(\dfrac{2}{3}x^3 + \pi x^2 + 7x + 1\right)$

16. $\dfrac{d}{dx}(2x\sqrt{x^2 - 2x + 2})$

17. $\dfrac{d}{dt}(5t^2 \sin t)$

18. $\dfrac{d}{dx}(5x + \sin^3 x + \sin x^3)$

19. $\dfrac{d}{d\theta}(4 \tan (\theta^2 + 3\theta + 2))$

20. $\dfrac{d}{dx}(\csc^5 3x)$

21. $\dfrac{d}{du}\left(\dfrac{4u^2 + u}{8u + 1}\right)$

22. $\dfrac{d}{dt}\left(\dfrac{3t^2 - 1}{3t^2 + 1}\right)^{-3}$

23. $\dfrac{d}{d\theta}(\tan (\sin \theta))$

24. $\dfrac{d}{dv}\left(\dfrac{v}{3v^2 + 2v + 1}\right)^{1/3}$

25. $\dfrac{d}{dx}(2x(\sin x)\sqrt{3x - 1})$

26. $\dfrac{d}{dx}(xe^{-10x})$

27. $\dfrac{d}{dx}(x \ln^2 x)$

28. $\dfrac{d}{dw}(e^{-w} \ln w)$

29. $\dfrac{d}{dx}(2^{x^2-x})$

30. $\dfrac{d}{dx}(\log_3 (x + 8))$

31. $\dfrac{d}{dx}\left(\sin^{-1}\dfrac{1}{x}\right)$

32. $\dfrac{d}{dx}(x^{\sin x})$

33. $f'(1)$ when $f(x) = x^{1/x}$

34. $f'(1)$ when $f(x) = \tan^{-1}(4x^2)$

35. $\dfrac{d}{dx}(x \sec^{-1} x)\Big|_{x=\frac{2}{\sqrt{3}}}$

36. $\dfrac{d}{dx}(\tan^{-1} e^{-x})\Big|_{x=0}$

37–39. Implicit differentiation *Calculate $y'(x)$ for the following relations.*

37. $y = \dfrac{e^y}{1 + \sin x}$

38. $\sin x \cos (y - 1) = \dfrac{1}{2}$

39. $y\sqrt{x^2 + y^2} = 15$

40. Quadratic functions

a. Show that if $(a, f(a))$ is any point on the graph of $f(x) = x^2$, then the slope of the tangent line at that point is $m = 2a$.

b. Show that if $(a, f(a))$ is any point on the graph of $f(x) = bx^2 + cx + d$, then the slope of the tangent line at that point is $m = 2ab + c$.

41–44. Tangent lines *Find an equation of the line tangent to the following curves at the given point.*

41. $y = 3x^3 + \sin x$; $(0, 0)$

42. $y = \dfrac{4x}{x^2 + 3}$; $(3, 1)$

43. $y + \sqrt{xy} = 6$; $(1, 4)$

44. $x^2y + y^3 = 75$; $(4, 3)$

45. Horizontal/vertical tangent lines For what value(s) of x is the line tangent to the curve $y = x\sqrt{6 - x}$ horizontal? Vertical?

46. A parabola property Let $f(x) = x^2$.

a. Show that $\dfrac{f(x) - f(y)}{x - y} = f'\left(\dfrac{x + y}{2}\right)$, for all $x \neq y$.

b. Is this property true for $f(x) = ax^2$, where a is a nonzero real number?

c. Give a geometrical interpretation of this property.

d. Is this property true for $f(x) = ax^3$?

47–48. Higher-order derivatives *Find y', y'', and y''' for the following functions.*

47. $y = \sin\sqrt{x}$ **48.** $y = (x - 3)\sqrt{x + 2}$

49–52. Derivative formulas *Evaluate the following derivatives. Express your answers in terms of f, g, f', and g'.*

49. $\dfrac{d}{dx}(x^2 f(x))$ **50.** $\dfrac{d}{dx}\sqrt{\dfrac{f(x)}{g(x)}}$

51. $\dfrac{d}{dx}\left(\dfrac{xf(x)}{g(x)}\right)$ **52.** $\dfrac{d}{dx}f(\sqrt{g(x)}),\ g(x) \geq 0$

53. Finding derivatives from a table Find the values of the following derivatives using the table.

x	1	3	5	7	9
$f(x)$	3	1	9	7	5
$f'(x)$	7	9	5	1	3
$g(x)$	9	7	5	3	1
$g'(x)$	5	9	3	1	7

a. $\dfrac{d}{dx}(f(x) + 2g(x))\Big|_{x=3}$ **b.** $\dfrac{d}{dx}\left(\dfrac{xf(x)}{g(x)}\right)\Big|_{x=1}$

c. $\dfrac{d}{dx}f(g(x^2))\Big|_{x=3}$ **d.** $\dfrac{d}{dx}(f(x)^3)\Big|_{x=5}$ **e.** $(g^{-1})'(7)$

54–55. Limits *The following limits represent the derivative of a function f at a point a. Find a possible f and a, and then evaluate the limit.*

54. $\displaystyle\lim_{h\to 0}\frac{\sin^2\left(\frac{\pi}{4} + h\right) - \frac{1}{2}}{h}$ **55.** $\displaystyle\lim_{x\to 5}\frac{\tan(\pi\sqrt{3x - 11})}{x - 5}$

56–57. Derivative of the inverse at a point *Consider the following functions. In each case, without finding the inverse, evaluate the derivative of the inverse at the given point.*

56. $f(x) = 1/(x + 1)$ at $f(0)$

57. $y = \sqrt{x^3 + x - 1}$ at $y = 3$

58–59. Derivative of the inverse *Find the derivative of the inverse of the following functions. Express the result with x as the independent variable.*

58. $f(x) = 12x - 16$ **59.** $f(x) = x^{-1/3}$

T **60. A function and its inverse function** The function $f(x) = \dfrac{x}{x + 1}$ is one-to-one for $x > -1$ and has an inverse on that interval.

a. Graph f, for $x > -1$.

b. Find the inverse function f^{-1} corresponding to the function graphed in part (a). Graph f^{-1} on the same set of axes as in part (a).

c. Evaluate the derivative of f^{-1} at the point $\left(\frac{1}{2}, 1\right)$.

d. Sketch the tangent lines on the graphs of f and f^{-1} at $\left(1, \frac{1}{2}\right)$ and $\left(\frac{1}{2}, 1\right)$, respectively.

61. Derivative of the inverse in two ways Let $f(x) = \sin x$, $f^{-1}(x) = \sin^{-1} x$, and $(x_0, y_0) = (\pi/4, 1/\sqrt{2})$.

a. Evaluate $(f^{-1})'(1/\sqrt{2})$ using Theorem 3.23.

b. Evaluate $(f^{-1})'(1/\sqrt{2})$ directly by differentiating f^{-1}. Check for agreement with part (a).

62–63. Derivatives from a graph *If possible, evaluate the following derivatives using the graphs of f and f'.*

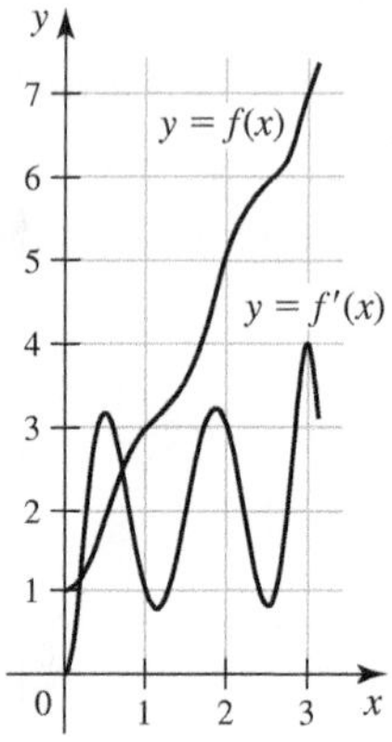

62. a. $\dfrac{d}{dx}(xf(x))\Big|_{x=2}$ **b.** $\dfrac{d}{dx}(f(x^2))\Big|_{x=1}$ **c.** $\dfrac{d}{dx}(f(f(x)))\Big|_{x=1}$

63. a. $(f^{-1})'(7)$ **b.** $(f^{-1})'(3)$ **c.** $(f^{-1})'(f(2))$

T **64. Velocity of a probe** A small probe is launched vertically from the ground. After it reaches its high point, a parachute deploys and the probe descends to Earth. The height of the probe above the ground is $s(t) = \dfrac{300t - 50t^2}{t^3 + 2}$, for $0 \leq t \leq 6$.

a. Graph the height function and describe the motion of the probe.

b. Find the velocity of the probe.

c. Graph the velocity function and determine the approximate time at which the velocity is a maximum.

65. Marginal and average cost Suppose the cost of producing x lawn mowers is $C(x) = -0.02x^2 + 400x + 5000$.

a. Determine the average and marginal costs for $x = 3000$ lawn mowers.

b. Interpret the meaning of your results in part (a).

66. Marginal and average cost Suppose a company produces fly rods. Assume $C(x) = -0.0001x^3 + 0.05x^2 + 60x + 800$ represents the cost of making x fly rods.

a. Determine the average and marginal costs for $x = 400$ fly rods.

b. Interpret the meaning of your results in part (a).

T **67. Population growth** Suppose $p(t) = -1.7t^3 + 72t^2 + 7200t + 80{,}000$ is the population of a city t years after 1950.

a. Determine the average rate of growth of the city from 1950 to 2000.

b. What was the rate of growth of the city in 1990?

T **68. Position of a piston** The distance between the head of a piston and the end of a cylindrical chamber is given by $x(t) = \dfrac{8t}{t + 1}$ cm, for $t \geq 0$ (measured in seconds). The radius of the cylinder is 4 cm.

a. Find the volume of the chamber, for $t \geq 0$.

b. Find the rate of change of the volume $V'(t)$, for $t \geq 0$.

c. Graph the derivative of the volume function. On what intervals is the volume increasing? Decreasing?

69. Boat rates Two boats leave a dock at the same time. One boat travels south at 30 mi/hr and the other travels east at 40 mi/hr. After half an hour, how fast is the distance between the boats increasing?

70. Rate of inflation of a balloon A spherical balloon is inflated at a rate of 10 cm^3/min. At what rate is the diameter of the balloon increasing when the balloon has a diameter of 5 cm?

71. Rate of descent of a hot-air balloon A rope is attached to the bottom of a hot-air balloon that is floating above a flat field. If the angle of the rope to the ground remains 65° and the rope is pulled in at 5 ft/s, how quickly is the elevation of the balloon changing?

72. Filling a tank Water flows into a conical tank at a rate of 2 ft^3/min. If the radius of the top of the tank is 4 ft and the height is 6 ft, determine how quickly the water level is rising when the water is 2 ft deep in the tank.

73. Angle of elevation A jet flies horizontally 500 ft directly above a spectator at an air show at 450 mi/hr. How quickly is the angle of elevation (between the ground and the line from the spectator to the jet) changing 2 seconds later?

74. Viewing angle A man whose eye level is 6 ft above the ground walks toward a billboard at a rate of 2 ft/s. The bottom of the billboard is 10 ft above the ground, and it is 15 ft high. The man's viewing angle is the angle formed by the lines between the man's eyes and the top and bottom of the billboard. At what rate is the viewing angle changing when the man is 30 ft from the billboard?

Chapter 3 Guided Projects

Applications of the material in this chapter and related topics can be found in the following Guided Projects. For additional information, see the Preface.

- Numerical differentiation
- Enzyme kinetics
- Elasticity in economics
- Pharmacokinetics—drug metabolism

4

Applications of the Derivative

Chapter Preview Much of the previous chapter was devoted to the basic mechanics of derivatives: evaluating them and interpreting them as rates of change. We now apply derivatives to a variety of mathematical questions, many of which concern the properties of functions and their graphs. One outcome of this work is a set of analytical curve-sketching methods that produce accurate graphs of functions. Equally important, derivatives allow us to formulate and solve a wealth of practical problems. For example, an asteroid passes perilously close to Earth: At what point along their trajectories is the distance separating them smallest, and what is the minimum distance? An economist has a mathematical model that relates the demand for a product to its price: What price maximizes the revenue? In this chapter, we develop the tools needed to answer such questions. In addition, we begin an ongoing discussion about approximating functions, we present an important result called the Mean Value Theorem, and we work with a powerful method that enables us to evaluate a new kind of limit. The chapter concludes with two important topics: a numerical approach to approximating roots of functions, called Newton's method, and a preview of integral calculus, which is the subject of Chapter 5.

4.1 Maxima and Minima

With a working understanding of derivatives, we now undertake one of the fundamental tasks of calculus: analyzing the behavior and producing accurate graphs of functions. An important question associated with any function concerns its maximum and minimum values: On a given interval (perhaps the entire domain), where does the function assume its largest and smallest values? Questions about maximum and minimum values take on added significance when a function represents a practical quantity, such as the profits of a company, the surface area of a container, or the speed of a space vehicle.

Absolute Maxima and Minima

Imagine taking a long hike through varying terrain from west to east. Your elevation changes as you walk over hills, through valleys, and across plains, and you reach several high and low points along the journey. Analogously, when we examine a function f over an interval on the x-axis, its values increase and decrease, reaching high points and low points (Figure 4.1). You can view our study of functions in this chapter as an exploratory hike along the x-axis.

> DEFINITION **Absolute Maximum and Minimum**
>
> Let f be defined on a set D containing c. If $f(c) \geq f(x)$ for every x in D, then $f(c)$ is an **absolute maximum** value of f on D. If $f(c) \leq f(x)$ for every x in D, then $f(c)$ is an **absolute minimum** value of f on D. An **absolute extreme value** is either an absolute maximum or an absolute minimum value.

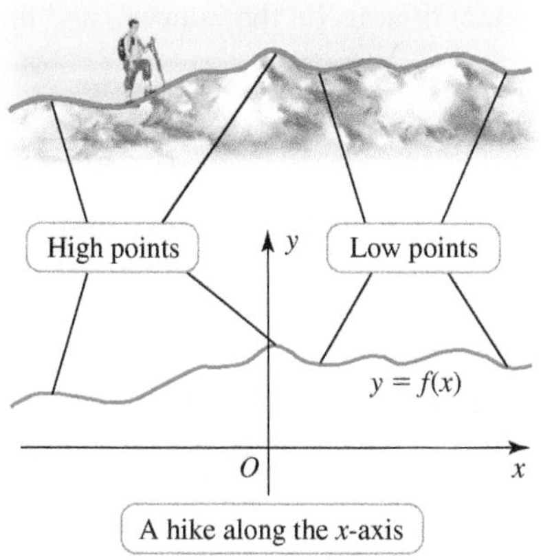

Figure 4.1

➤ Absolute maximum and minimum values are also called *global* maximum and minimum values. The plural of maximum is maxima; the plural of minimum is minima.

The existence and location of absolute extreme values depend on both the function and the interval of interest. Figure 4.2 shows various cases for the function $f(x) = x^2$. Notice that if the interval of interest is not closed, a function might not attain absolute extreme values (Figure 4.2a, c, and d).

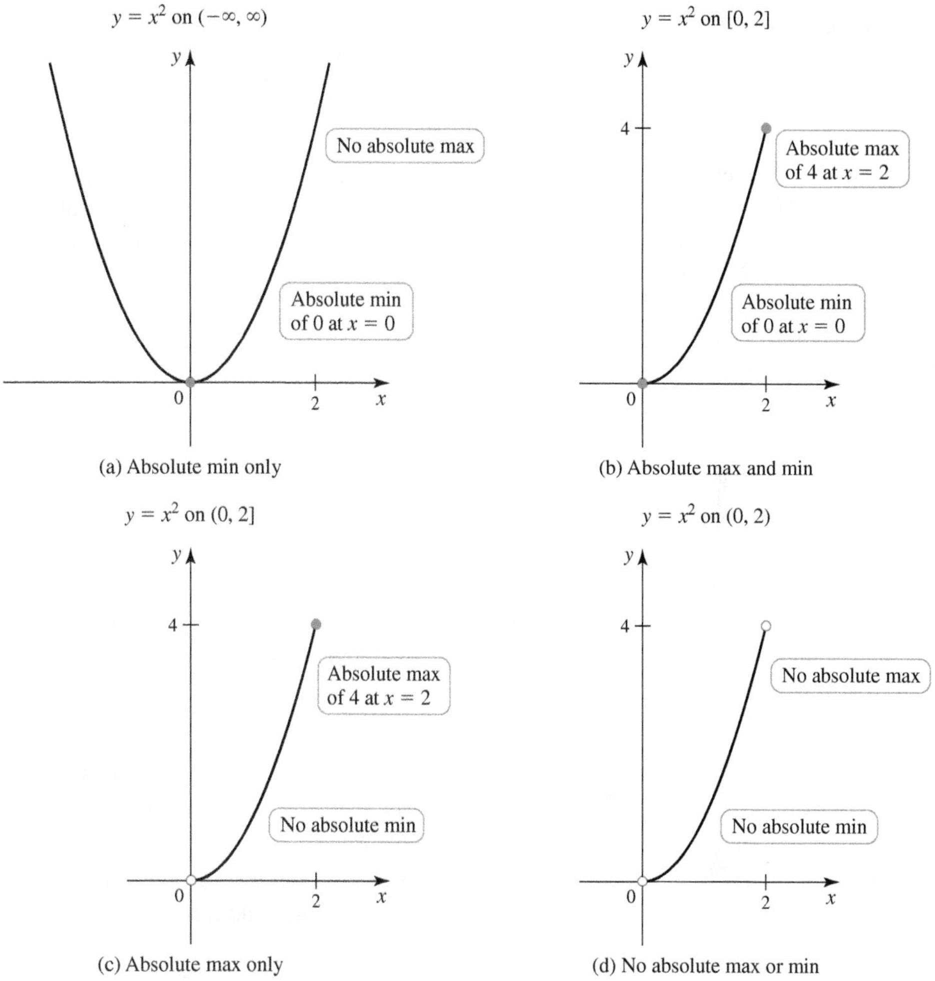

Figure 4.2

However, defining a function on a closed interval is not enough to guarantee the existence of absolute extreme values. Both functions in Figure 4.3 are defined at every point of a closed interval, but neither function attains an absolute maximum—the discontinuity in each function prevents it from happening.

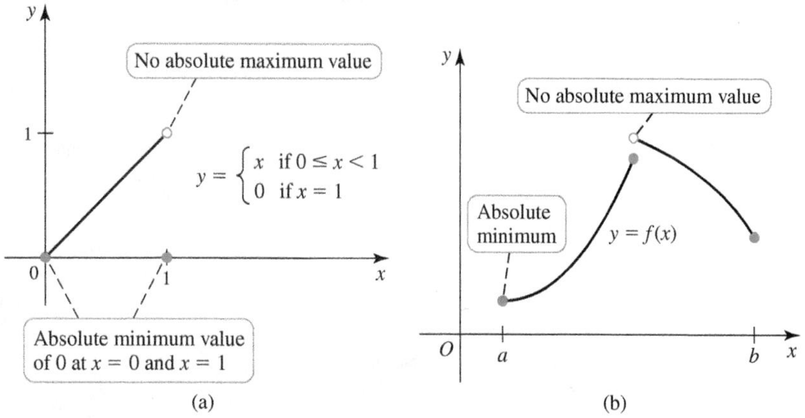

Figure 4.3

It turns out that *two* conditions ensure the existence of absolute maximum and minimum values on an interval: The function must be continuous on the interval, and the interval must be closed and bounded.

➤ The proof of the Extreme Value Theorem relies on properties of the real numbers, found in advanced books.

> **THEOREM 4.1 Extreme Value Theorem**
> A function that is continuous on a closed interval $[a, b]$ has an absolute maximum value and an absolute minimum value on that interval.

QUICK CHECK 1 Sketch the graph of a function that is continuous on an interval but does not have an absolute minimum value. Sketch the graph of a function that is defined on a closed interval but does not have an absolute minimum value. ◀

EXAMPLE 1 Locating absolute maximum and minimum values For the functions in Figure 4.4, identify the location of the absolute maximum value and the absolute minimum value on the interval $[a, b]$. Do the functions meet the conditions of the Extreme Value Theorem?

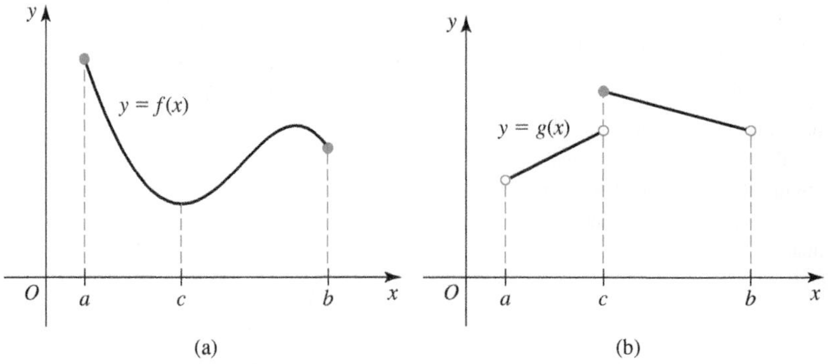

Figure 4.4

SOLUTION

a. The function f is continuous on the closed interval $[a, b]$, so the Extreme Value Theorem guarantees an absolute maximum (which occurs at a) and an absolute minimum (which occurs at c).

b. The function g does not satisfy the conditions of the Extreme Value Theorem because it is not continuous, and it is defined only on the open interval (a, b). It does not have an absolute minimum value. It does, however, have an absolute maximum at c. Therefore, a function may violate the conditions of the Extreme Value Theorem and still have an absolute maximum or minimum (or both).

Related Exercises 11–14 ◀

Local Maxima and Minima

Figure 4.5 shows a function defined on the interval $[a, b]$. It has an absolute minimum at the endpoint a and an absolute maximum at the interior point e. In addition, the function

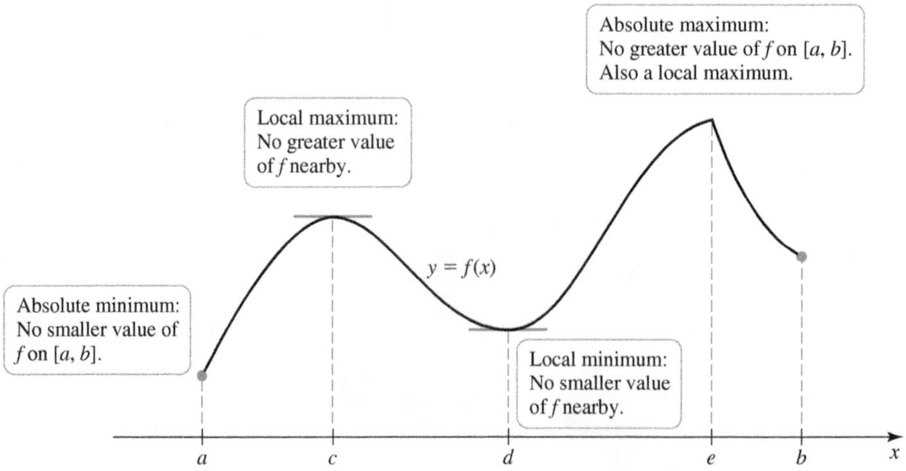

Figure 4.5

has special behavior at c, where its value is greatest *among values at nearby points*, and at d, where its value is least *among values at nearby points.* A point at which a function takes on the maximum or minimum value among values at nearby points is important.

➤ Local maximum and minimum values are also called *relative maximum* and *minimum values*. *Local extrema* (plural) and *local extremum* (singular) refer to either local maxima or local minima.

> **DEFINITION Local Maximum and Minimum Values**
>
> Suppose c is an interior point of some interval I on which f is defined. If $f(c) \geq f(x)$ for all x in I, then $f(c)$ is a **local maximum** value of f. If $f(c) \leq f(x)$ for all x in I, then $f(c)$ is a **local minimum** value of f.

In this book, we adopt the convention that local maximum values and local minimum values occur only at interior points of the interval(s) of interest. For example, in Figure 4.5, the minimum value that occurs at the endpoint a is not a local minimum. However, it is the absolute minimum of the function on $[a, b]$.

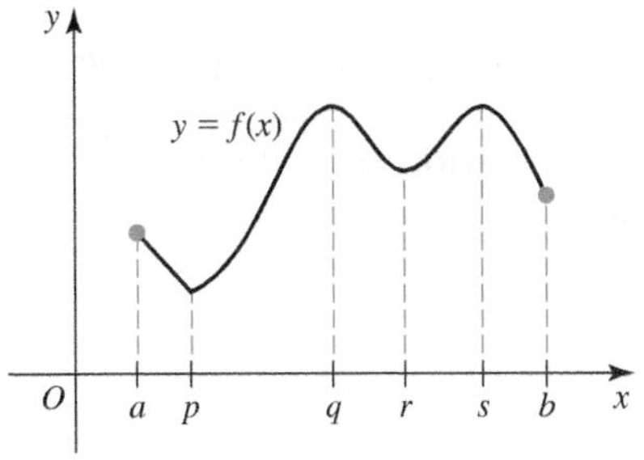

Figure 4.6

EXAMPLE 2 Locating various maxima and minima Figure 4.6 shows the graph of a function defined on $[a, b]$. Identify the location of the various maxima and minima using the terms *absolute* and *local.*

SOLUTION The function f is continuous on a closed interval; by Theorem 4.1, it has absolute maximum and minimum values on $[a, b]$. The function has a local minimum value and its absolute minimum value at p. It has another local minimum value at r. The absolute maximum value of f occurs at both q and s (which also correspond to local maximum values).

Related Exercises 15–22 ◀

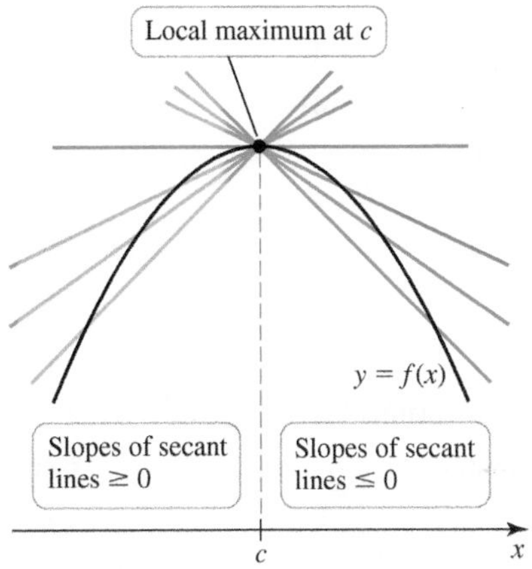

Figure 4.7

Critical Points Another look at Figure 4.6 shows that local maxima and minima occur at points in the open interval (a, b) where the derivative is zero $(x = q, r, \text{ and } s)$ and at points where the derivative fails to exist $(x = p)$. We now make this observation precise.

Figure 4.7 illustrates a function that is differentiable at c with a local maximum at c. For x near c with $x < c$, the secant lines through $(x, f(x))$ and $(c, f(c))$ have nonnegative slopes. For x near c with $x > c$, the secant lines through $(x, f(x))$ and $(c, f(c))$ have nonpositive slopes. As $x \to c$, the slopes of these secant lines approach the slope of the tangent line at $(c, f(c))$. These observations imply that the slope of the tangent line must be both nonnegative and nonpositive, which happens only if $f'(c) = 0$. Similar reasoning leads to the same conclusion for a function with a local minimum at c: $f'(c)$ must be zero. This argument is an outline of the proof (Exercise 83) of the following theorem.

> **THEOREM 4.2 Local Extreme Value Theorem**
>
> If f has a local maximum or minimum value at c and $f'(c)$ exists, then $f'(c) = 0$.

➤ Theorem 4.2, often attributed to Fermat, is one of the clearest examples in mathematics of a necessary, but not sufficient, condition. A local maximum (or minimum) at c necessarily implies a critical point at c, but a critical point at c is not sufficient to imply a local maximum (or minimum) there.

Local extrema can also occur at points c where $f'(c)$ does not exist. Figure 4.8 shows two such cases, one in which c is a point of discontinuity and one in which f has a corner point at c. Because local extrema may occur at points c where $f'(c) = 0$ *and* where $f'(c)$ does not exist, we make the following definition.

> **DEFINITION Critical Point**
>
> An interior point c of the domain of f at which $f'(c) = 0$ or $f'(c)$ fails to exist is called a **critical point** of f.

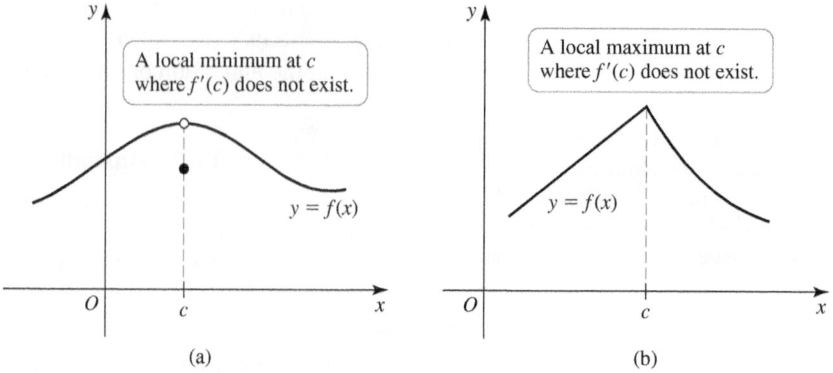

Figure 4.8

Note that the converse of Theorem 4.2 is not necessarily true. It is possible that $f'(c) = 0$ at a point without a local maximum or local minimum value occurring there (Figure 4.9a). It is also possible that $f'(c)$ fails to exist, with no local extreme value occurring at c (Figure 4.9b). Therefore, critical points are *candidates* for the location of local extreme values, but you must determine whether they actually correspond to local maxima or minima. This procedure is discussed in Section 4.2.

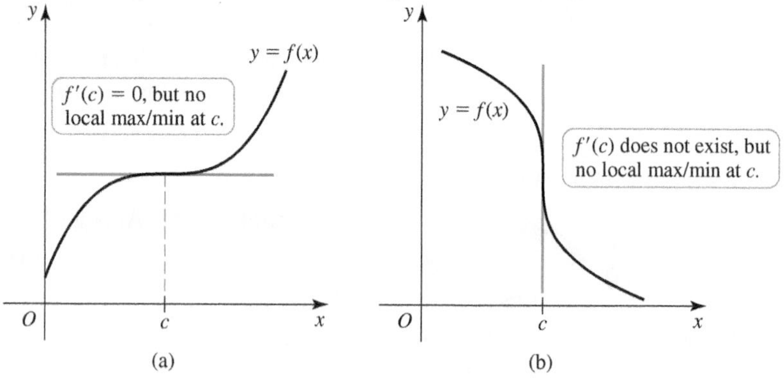

Figure 4.9

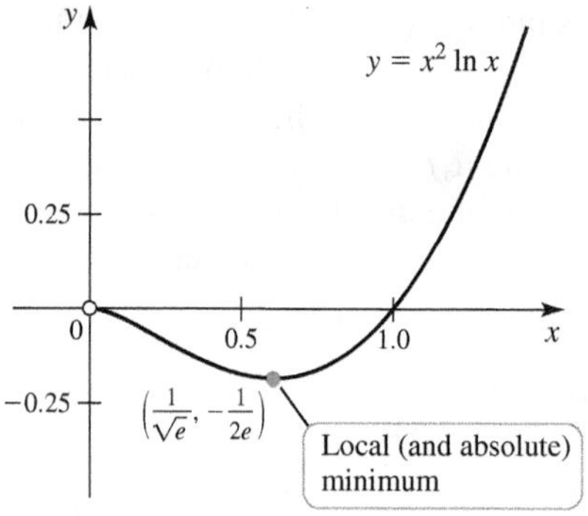

Figure 4.10

EXAMPLE 3 **Locating critical points** Find the critical points of $f(x) = x^2 \ln x$.

SOLUTION Note that f is differentiable on its domain, which is $(0, \infty)$. By the Product Rule,

$$f'(x) = 2x \cdot \ln x + x^2 \cdot \frac{1}{x} = x(2 \ln x + 1).$$

Setting $f'(x) = 0$ gives $x(2 \ln x + 1) = 0$, which has the solution $x = e^{-1/2} = 1/\sqrt{e}$. Because $x = 0$ is not in the domain of f, it is not a critical point. Therefore, the only critical point is $x = 1/\sqrt{e} \approx 0.61$. A graph of f (Figure 4.10) reveals that a local (and, indeed, absolute) minimum value occurs at $1/\sqrt{e}$, where the value of the function is $-1/(2e)$.

Related Exercises 23–36 ◄

QUICK CHECK 2 Consider the function $f(x) = x^3$. Where is the critical point of f? Does f have a local maximum or minimum at the critical point? ◄

Locating Absolute Maxima and Minima

Theorem 4.1 guarantees the existence of absolute extreme values of a continuous function on a closed interval $[a, b]$, but it doesn't say where these values are located. Two observations lead to a procedure for locating absolute extreme values.

- An absolute extreme value in the interior of an interval is also a local extreme value, and we know that local extreme values occur at the critical points of f.
- Absolute extreme values may also occur at the endpoints of the interval of interest.

These two facts suggest the following procedure for locating the absolute extreme values of a function continuous on a closed interval.

> **PROCEDURE Locating Absolute Extreme Values on a Closed Interval**
>
> Assume the function f is continuous on the closed interval $[a, b]$.
>
> 1. Locate the critical points c in (a, b), where $f'(c) = 0$ or $f'(c)$ does not exist. These points are candidates for absolute maxima and minima.
> 2. Evaluate f at the critical points and at the endpoints of $[a, b]$.
> 3. Choose the largest and smallest values of f from Step 2 for the absolute maximum and minimum values, respectively.

Note that the preceding procedure box does not address the case in which f is continuous on an open interval. If the interval of interest is an open interval, then absolute extreme values—if they exist—occur at interior points.

EXAMPLE 4 Absolute extreme values Find the absolute maximum and minimum values of the following functions.

a. $f(x) = x^4 - 2x^3$ on the interval $[-2, 2]$

b. $g(x) = x^{2/3}(2 - x)$ on the interval $[-1, 2]$

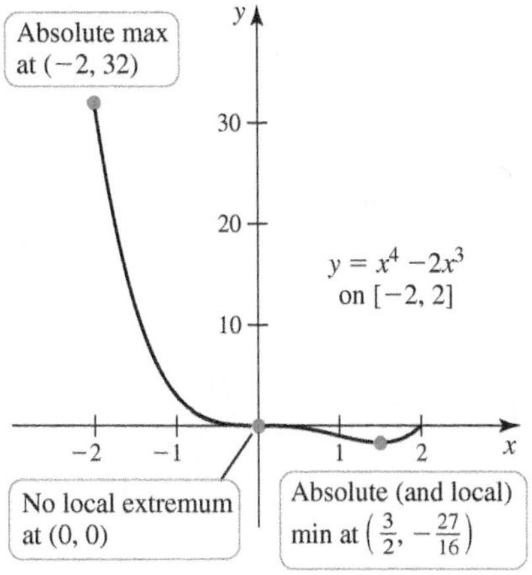

Figure 4.11

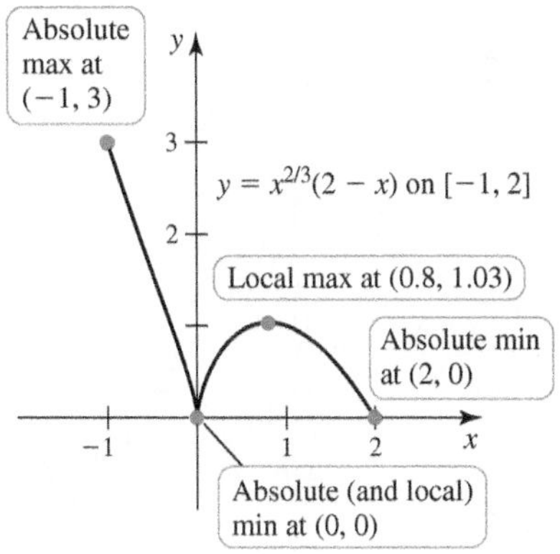

Figure 4.12

SOLUTION

a. Because f is a polynomial, its derivative exists everywhere. So if f has critical points, they are points at which $f'(x) = 0$. Computing f' and setting it equal to zero, we have

$$f'(x) = 4x^3 - 6x^2 = 2x^2(2x - 3) = 0.$$

Solving this equation gives the critical points $x = 0$ and $x = \frac{3}{2}$, both of which lie in the interval $[-2, 2]$; these points and the endpoints are *candidates* for the location of absolute extrema. Evaluating f at each of these points, we have

$$f(-2) = 32, \quad f(0) = 0, \quad f(\tfrac{3}{2}) = -\tfrac{27}{16}, \quad \text{and} \quad f(2) = 0.$$

The largest of these function values is $f(-2) = 32$, which is the absolute maximum of f on $[-2, 2]$. The smallest of these values is $f(\frac{3}{2}) = -\frac{27}{16}$, which is the absolute minimum of f on $[-2, 2]$. The graph of f (Figure 4.11) shows that the critical point $x = 0$ corresponds to neither a local maximum nor a local minimum.

b. Differentiating $g(x) = x^{2/3}(2 - x) = 2x^{2/3} - x^{5/3}$, we have

$$g'(x) = \frac{4}{3}x^{-1/3} - \frac{5}{3}x^{2/3} = \frac{4 - 5x}{3x^{1/3}}.$$

Because $g'(0)$ is undefined and 0 is in the domain of g, $x = 0$ is a critical point. In addition, $g'(x) = 0$ when $4 - 5x = 0$, so $x = \frac{4}{5}$ is also a critical point. These two critical points and the endpoints are *candidates* for the location of absolute extrema. The next step is to evaluate g at the critical points and endpoints:

$$g(-1) = 3, \quad g(0) = 0, \quad g(\tfrac{4}{5}) \approx 1.03, \quad \text{and} \quad g(2) = 0.$$

The largest of these function values is $g(-1) = 3$, which is the absolute maximum value of g on $[-1, 2]$. The least of these values is 0, which occurs twice. Therefore, g has its absolute minimum value on $[-1, 2]$ at the critical point $x = 0$ and the endpoint $x = 2$ (Figure 4.12). *Related Exercises 37–50* ◀

We now apply these ideas to a practical situation.

EXAMPLE 5 Trajectory high point A stone is launched vertically upward from a bridge 80 ft above the ground at a speed of 64 ft/s. Its height above the ground t seconds after the launch is given by

$$f(t) = -16t^2 + 64t + 80, \quad \text{for } 0 \le t \le 5.$$

When does the stone reach its maximum height?

➤ The derivation of the position function for an object moving in a gravitational field is given in Section 6.1.

SOLUTION We must evaluate the height function at the critical points and at the endpoints. The critical points satisfy the equation

$$f'(t) = -32t + 64 = -32(t - 2) = 0,$$

so the only critical point is $t = 2$. We now evaluate f at the endpoints and at the critical point:

$$f(0) = 80, \quad f(2) = 144, \quad \text{and} \quad f(5) = 0.$$

On the interval $[0, 5]$, the absolute maximum occurs at $t = 2$, at which time the stone reaches a height of 144 ft. Because $f'(t)$ is the velocity of the stone, the maximum height occurs at the instant the velocity is zero.

Related Exercises 51–54 ◀

SECTION 4.1 EXERCISES

Review Questions

1. What does it mean for a function to have an absolute extreme value at a point c of an interval $[a, b]$?
2. What are local maximum and minimum values of a function?
3. What conditions must be met to ensure that a function has an absolute maximum value and an absolute minimum value on an interval?
4. Sketch the graph of a function that is continuous on an open interval (a, b) but has neither an absolute maximum nor an absolute minimum value on (a, b).
5. Sketch the graph of a function that has an absolute maximum, a local minimum, but no absolute minimum on $[0, 3]$.
6. What is a critical point of a function?
7. Sketch the graph of a function f that has a local maximum value at a point c where $f'(c) = 0$.
8. Sketch the graph of a function f that has a local minimum value at a point c where $f'(c)$ is undefined.
9. How do you determine the absolute maximum and minimum values of a continuous function on a closed interval?
10. Explain how a function can have an absolute minimum value at an endpoint of an interval.

Basic Skills

11–14. Absolute maximum/minimum values *Use the following graphs to identify the points (if any) on the interval $[a, b]$ at which the function has an absolute maximum value or an absolute minimum value.*

11.

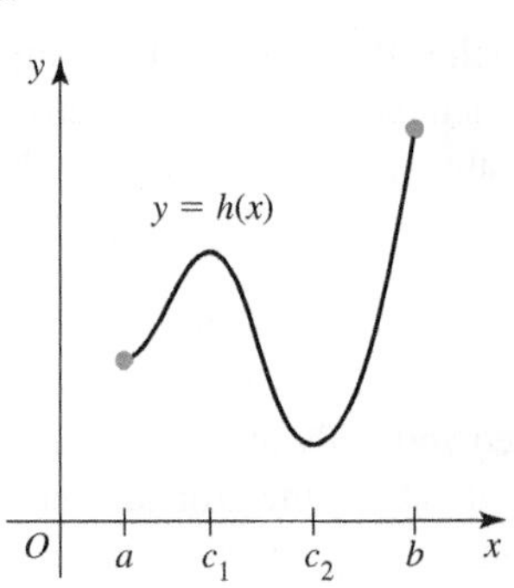

12.

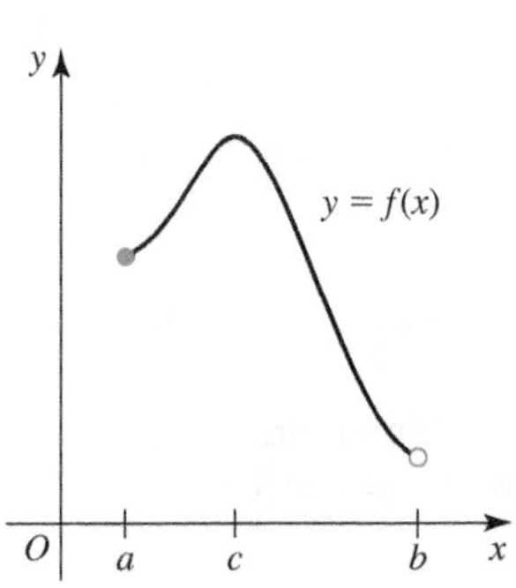

13.

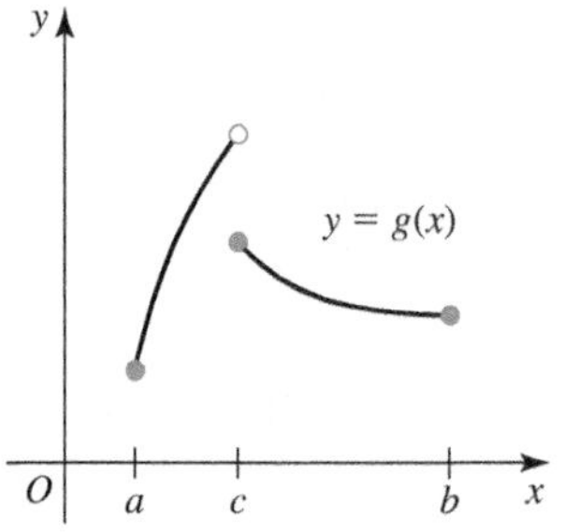

14.

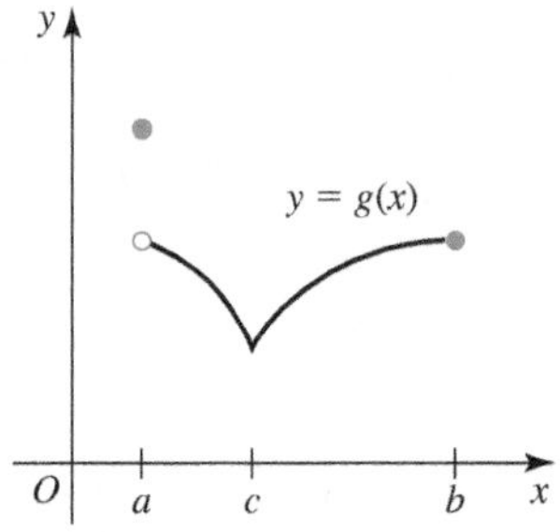

15–18. Local and absolute extreme values *Use the following graphs to identify the points on the interval $[a, b]$ at which local and absolute extreme values occur.*

15.

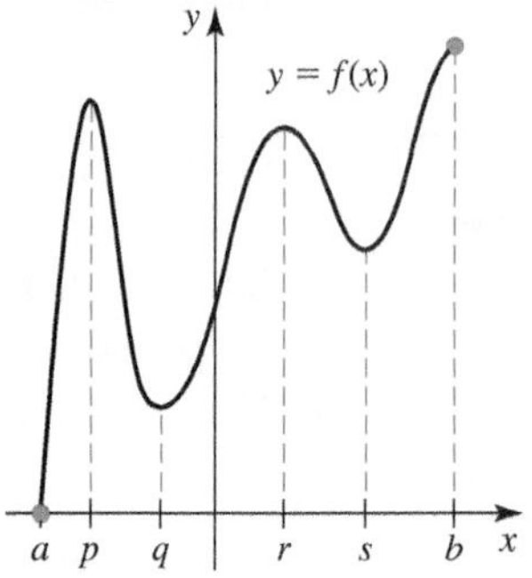

16.

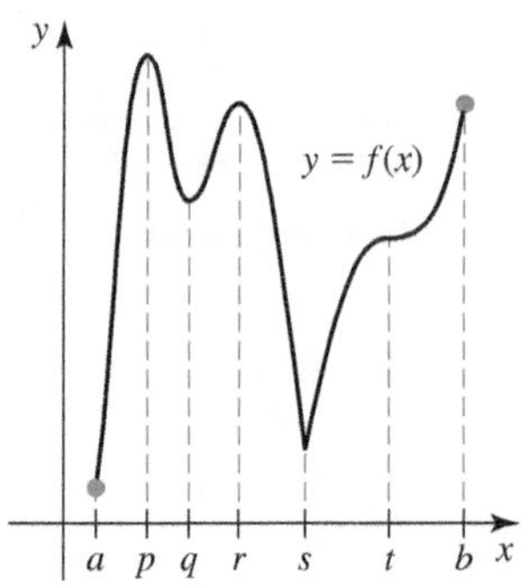

17.

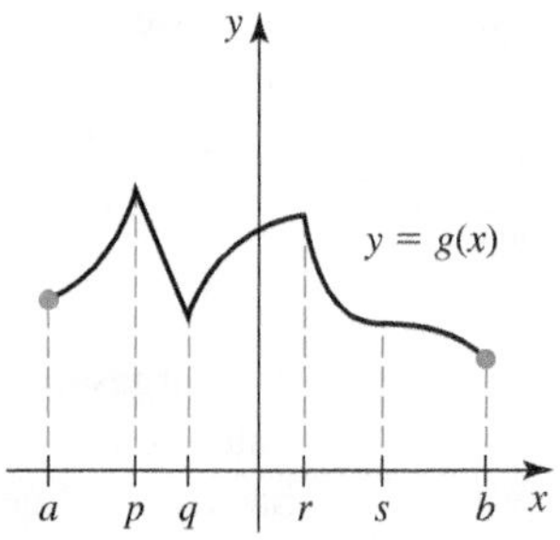

18.

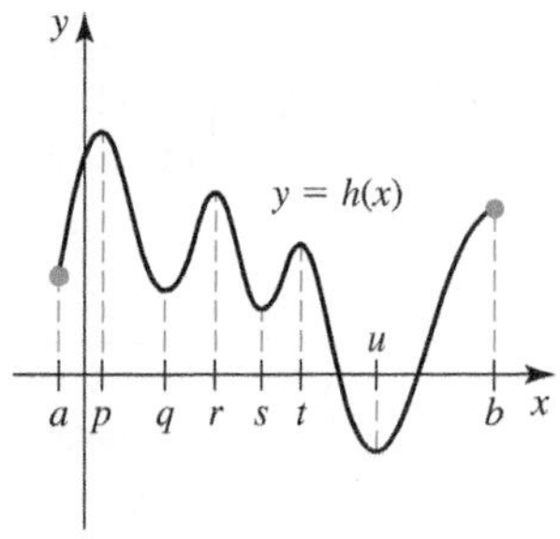

19–22. Designing a function *Sketch a graph of a function f continuous on $[0, 4]$ satisfying the given properties.*

19. $f'(x) = 0$ for $x = 1$ and 2; f has an absolute maximum at $x = 4$; f has an absolute minimum at $x = 0$; and f has a local minimum at $x = 2$.
20. $f'(x) = 0$ for $x = 1$, 2, and 3; f has an absolute minimum at $x = 1$; f has no local extremum at $x = 2$; and f has an absolute maximum at $x = 3$.

21. $f'(1)$ and $f'(3)$ are undefined; $f'(2) = 0$; f has a local maximum at $x = 1$; f has a local minimum at $x = 2$; f has an absolute maximum at $x = 3$; and f has an absolute minimum at $x = 4$.

22. $f'(x) = 0$ at $x = 1$ and 3; $f'(2)$ is undefined; f has an absolute maximum at $x = 2$; f has neither a local maximum nor a local minimum at $x = 1$; and f has an absolute minimum at $x = 3$.

T 23–36. Locating critical points

a. *Find the critical points of the following functions on the domain or on the given interval.*
b. *Use a graphing utility to determine whether each critical point corresponds to a local maximum, local minimum, or neither.*

23. $f(x) = 3x^2 - 4x + 2$

24. $f(x) = \frac{1}{8}x^3 - \frac{1}{2}x$ on $[-1, 3]$

25. $f(x) = \frac{x^3}{3} - 9x$ on $[-7, 7]$

26. $f(x) = \frac{x^4}{4} - \frac{x^3}{3} - 3x^2 + 10$ on $[-4, 4]$

27. $f(x) = 3x^3 + \frac{3x^2}{2} - 2x$ on $[-1, 1]$

28. $f(x) = \frac{4x^5}{5} - 3x^3 + 5$ on $[-2, 2]$

29. $f(x) = x/(x^2 + 1)$

30. $f(x) = 12x^5 - 20x^3$ on $[-2, 2]$

31. $f(x) = (e^x + e^{-x})/2$

32. $f(x) = \sin x \cos x$ on $[0, 2\pi]$

33. $f(x) = 1/x + \ln x$

34. $f(x) = x^2 - 2\ln(x^2 + 1)$

35. $f(x) = x^2\sqrt{x + 1}$ on $[-1, 1]$

36. $f(x) = (\sin^{-1} x)(\cos^{-1} x)$ on $[0, 1]$

T 37–50. Absolute maxima and minima

a. *Find the critical points of f on the given interval.*
b. *Determine the absolute extreme values of f on the given interval when they exist.*
c. *Use a graphing utility to confirm your conclusions.*

37. $f(x) = x^2 - 10$ on $[-2, 3]$

38. $f(x) = (x + 1)^{4/3}$ on $[-9, 7]$

39. $f(x) = \cos^2 x$ on $[0, \pi]$

40. $f(x) = x/(x^2 + 3)^2$ on $[-2, 2]$

41. $f(x) = \sin 3x$ on $[-\pi/4, \pi/3]$

42. $f(x) = x^{2/3}$ on $[-8, 8]$

43. $f(x) = (2x)^x$ on $[0.1, 1]$

44. $f(x) = xe^{1-x/2}$ on $[0, 5]$

45. $f(x) = x^2 + \cos^{-1} x$ on $[-1, 1]$

46. $f(x) = x\sqrt{2 - x^2}$ on $[-\sqrt{2}, \sqrt{2}]$

47. $f(x) = 2x^3 - 15x^2 + 24x$ on $[0, 5]$

48. $f(x) = |2x - x^2|$ on $[-2, 3]$

49. $f(x) = \frac{4x^3}{3} + 5x^2 - 6x$ on $[-4, 1]$

50. $f(x) = 2x^6 - 15x^4 + 24x^2$ on $[-2, 2]$

51. Trajectory high point A stone is launched vertically upward from a cliff 192 feet above the ground at a speed of 64 ft/s. Its height above the ground t seconds after the launch is given by $s = -16t^2 + 64t + 192$, for $0 \le t \le 6$. When does the stone reach its maximum height?

52. Maximizing revenue A sales analyst determines that the revenue from sales of fruit smoothies is given by $R(x) = -60x^2 + 300x$, where x is the price in dollars charged per item, for $0 \le x \le 5$.

a. Find the critical points of the revenue function.
b. Determine the absolute maximum value of the revenue function and the price that maximizes the revenue.

53. Maximizing profit Suppose a tour guide has a bus that holds a maximum of 100 people. Assume his profit (in dollars) for taking n people on a city tour is $P(n) = n(50 - 0.5n) - 100$. (Although P is defined only for positive integers, treat it as a continuous function.)

a. How many people should the guide take on a tour to maximize the profit?
b. Suppose the bus holds a maximum of 45 people. How many people should be taken on a tour to maximize the profit?

54. Maximizing rectangle perimeters All rectangles with an area of 64 have a perimeter given by $P(x) = 2x + 128/x$, where x is the length of one side of the rectangle. Find the absolute minimum value of the perimeter function on the interval $(0, \infty)$. What are the dimensions of the rectangle with minimum perimeter?

Further Explorations

55. Explain why or why not Determine whether the following statements are true and give an explanation or counterexample.

a. The function $f(x) = \sqrt{x}$ has a local maximum on the interval $[0, \infty)$.
b. If a function has an absolute maximum on a closed interval, then the function must be continuous on that interval.
c. A function f has the property that $f'(2) = 0$. Therefore, f has a local extreme value at $x = 2$.
d. Absolute extreme values of a function on a closed interval always occur at a critical point or an endpoint of the interval.

T 56–63. Absolute maxima and minima

a. *Find the critical points of f on the given interval.*
b. *Determine the absolute extreme values of f on the given interval.*
c. *Use a graphing utility to confirm your conclusions.*

56. $f(x) = (x - 2)^{1/2}$ on $[2, 6]$

57. $f(x) = 2^x \sin x$ on $[-2, 6]$

58. $f(x) = x^{1/2}(x^2/5 - 4)$ on $[0, 4]$

59. $f(x) = \sec x$ on $[-\pi/4, \pi/4]$

60. $f(x) = x^{1/3}(x + 4)$ on $[-27, 27]$

61. $f(x) = x^3e^{-x}$ on $[-1, 5]$

62. $f(x) = x\ln(x/5)$ on $[0.1, 5]$

63. $f(x) = x/\sqrt{x - 4}$ on $[6, 12]$

64–67. Critical points of functions with unknown parameters *Find the critical points of f. Assume a is a constant.*

64. $f(x) = x/\sqrt{x - a}$

65. $f(x) = x\sqrt{x - a}$

66. $f(x) = x^3 - 3ax^2 + 3a^2x - a^3$

67. $f(x) = \frac{1}{5}x^5 - a^4x$

T 68–73. Critical points and extreme values

a. Find the critical points of the following functions on the given interval.

b. Use a graphing utility to determine whether the critical points correspond to local maxima, local minima, or neither.

c. Find the absolute maximum and minimum values on the given interval when they exist.

68. $f(x) = 6x^4 - 16x^3 - 45x^2 + 54x + 23$ on $[-5, 5]$

69. $f(\theta) = 2\sin\theta + \cos\theta$ on $[-2\pi, 2\pi]$

70. $f(x) = x^{2/3}(4 - x^2)$ on $[-3, 4]$

71. $g(x) = (x - 3)^{5/3}(x + 2)$ on $[-4, 4]$

72. $f(t) = 3t/(t^2 + 1)$ on $[-2, 2]$

73. $h(x) = (5 - x)/(x^2 + 2x - 3)$ on $[-10, 10]$

T 74–75. Absolute value functions *Graph the following functions and determine the local and absolute extreme values on the given interval.*

74. $f(x) = |x - 3| + |x + 2|$ on $[-4, 4]$

75. $g(x) = |x - 3| - 2|x + 1|$ on $[-2, 3]$

Applications

76. Minimum surface area box All boxes with a square base and a volume of 50 ft^3 have a surface area given by $S(x) = 2x^2 + 200/x$, where x is the length of the sides of the base. Find the absolute minimum of the surface area function on the interval $(0, \infty)$. What are the dimensions of the box with minimum surface area?

T 77. Every second counts You must get from a point P on the straight shore of a lake to a stranded swimmer who is 50 m from a point Q on the shore that is 50 m from you (see figure). If you can swim at a speed of 2 m/s and run at a speed of 4 m/s, at what point along the shore, x meters from Q, should you stop running and start swimming if you want to reach the swimmer in the minimum time?

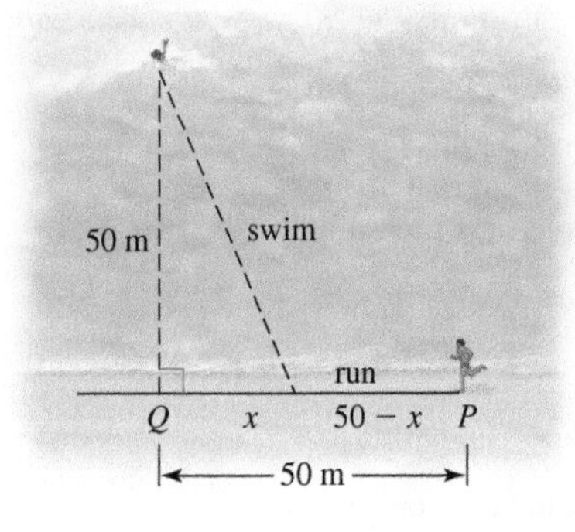

a. Find the function T that gives the travel time as a function of x, where $0 \leq x \leq 50$.

b. Find the critical point of T on $(0, 50)$.

c. Evaluate T at the critical point and the endpoints ($x = 0$ and $x = 50$) to verify that the critical point corresponds to an absolute minimum. What is the minimum travel time?

d. Graph the function T to check your work.

T 78. Dancing on a parabola Two people, A and B, walk along the parabola $y = x^2$ in such a way that the line segment L between them is always perpendicular to the line tangent to the parabola at A's position. What are the positions of A and B when L has minimum length?

a. Assume that A's position is (a, a^2), where $a > 0$. Find the slope of the line tangent to the parabola at A and find the slope of the line that is perpendicular to the tangent line at A.

b. Find the equation of the line joining A and B when A is at (a, a^2).

c. Find the position of B on the parabola when A is at (a, a^2).

d. Write the function $F(a)$ that gives the *square* of the distance between A and B as it varies with a. (The square of the distance is minimized at the same point that the distance is minimized; it is easier to work with the square of the distance.)

e. Find the critical point of F on the interval $a > 0$.

f. Evaluate F at the critical point and verify that it corresponds to an absolute minimum. What are the positions of A and B that minimize the length of L? What is the minimum length?

g. Graph the function F to check your work.

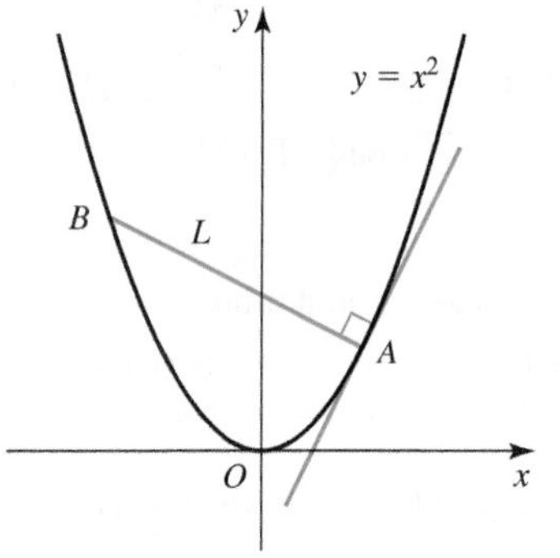

Additional Exercises

79. Values of related functions Suppose f is differentiable on $(-\infty, \infty)$ and assume it has a local extreme value at the point $x = 2$, where $f(2) = 0$. Let $g(x) = xf(x) + 1$ and let $h(x) = xf(x) + x + 1$, for all values of x.

a. Evaluate $g(2)$, $h(2)$, $g'(2)$, and $h'(2)$.

b. Does either g or h have a local extreme value at $x = 2$? Explain.

80. Extreme values of parabolas Consider the function $f(x) = ax^2 + bx + c$, with $a \neq 0$. Explain geometrically why f has exactly one absolute extreme value on $(-\infty, \infty)$. Find the critical point to determine the value of x at which f has an extreme value.

81. Even and odd functions

a. Suppose a nonconstant even function f has a local minimum at c. Does f have a local maximum or minimum at $-c$? Explain. (An even function satisfies $f(-x) = f(x)$.)

b. Suppose a nonconstant odd function f has a local minimum at c. Does f have a local maximum or minimum at $-c$? Explain. (An odd function satisfies $f(-x) = -f(x)$.)

T **82. A family of double-humped functions** Consider the functions $f(x) = x/(x^2 + 1)^n$, where n is a positive integer.

a. Show that these functions are odd for all positive integers n.

b. Show that the critical points of these functions are $x = \pm\dfrac{1}{\sqrt{2n - 1}}$, for all positive integers n. (Start with the special cases $n = 1$ and $n = 2$.)

c. Show that as n increases, the absolute maximum values of these functions decrease.

d. Use a graphing utility to verify your conclusions.

83. Proof of the Local Extreme Value Theorem Prove Theorem 4.2 for a local maximum: If f has a local maximum value at the point c and $f'(c)$ exists, then $f'(c) = 0$. Use the following steps.

a. Suppose f has a local maximum at c. What is the sign of $f(x) - f(c)$ if x is near c and $x > c$? What is the sign of $f(x) - f(c)$ if x is near c and $x < c$?

b. If $f'(c)$ exists, then it is defined by $\lim_{x \to c} \dfrac{f(x) - f(c)}{x - c}$. Examine this limit as $x \to c^+$ and conclude that $f'(c) \le 0$.

c. Examine the limit in part (b) as $x \to c^-$ and conclude that $f'(c) \ge 0$.

d. Combine parts (b) and (c) to conclude that $f'(c) = 0$.

QUICK CHECK ANSWERS

1. The continuous function $f(x) = x$ does not have an absolute minimum on the open interval $(0, 1)$. The function $f(x) = -x$ on $\left[0, \frac{1}{2}\right)$ and $f(x) = 0$ on $\left[\frac{1}{2}, 1\right]$ does not have an absolute minimum on $[0, 1]$. **2.** The critical point is $x = 0$. Although $f'(0) = 0$, the function has neither a local maximum nor minimum at $x = 0$. ◀

4.2 What Derivatives Tell Us

In the previous section, we saw that the derivative is a tool for finding critical points, which are related to local maxima and minima. As we show in this section, derivatives (first *and* second derivatives) tell us much more about the behavior of functions.

Increasing and Decreasing Functions

We have used the terms *increasing* and *decreasing* informally in earlier sections to describe a function or its graph. For example, the graph in Figure 4.13a rises as x increases, so the corresponding function is increasing. In Figure 4.13b, the graph falls as x increases, so the corresponding function is decreasing. The following definition makes these ideas precise.

➤ A function is called **monotonic** if it is either increasing or decreasing. We can make a further distinction by defining **nondecreasing** ($f(x_2) \ge f(x_1)$ whenever $x_2 > x_1$) and **nonincreasing** ($f(x_2) \le f(x_1)$ whenever $x_2 > x_1$).

DEFINITION **Increasing and Decreasing Functions**

Suppose a function f is defined on an interval I. We say that f is **increasing** on I if $f(x_2) > f(x_1)$ whenever x_1 and x_2 are in I and $x_2 > x_1$. We say that f is **decreasing** on I if $f(x_2) < f(x_1)$ whenever x_1 and x_2 are in I and $x_2 > x_1$.

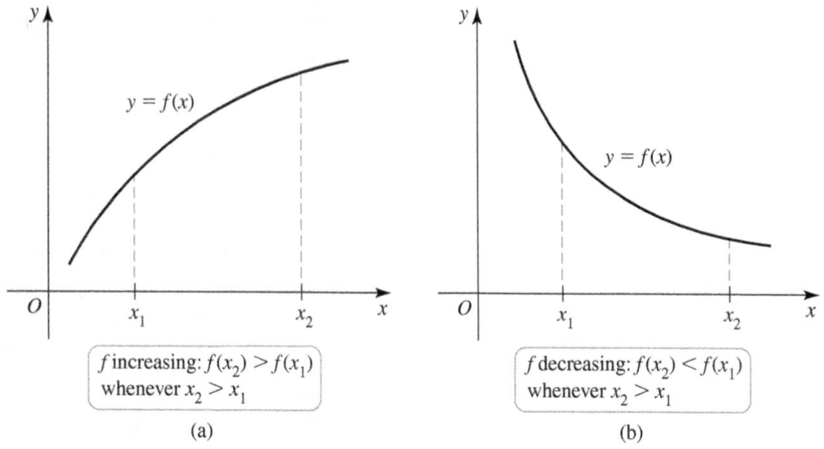

Figure 4.13

Intervals of Increase and Decrease The graph of a function f gives us an idea of the intervals on which f is increasing and decreasing. But how do we determine those intervals precisely? This question is answered by making a connection to the derivative.

Recall that the derivative of a function gives the slopes of tangent lines. If the derivative is positive on an interval, the tangent lines on that interval have positive slopes, and the function is increasing on the interval (Figure 4.14a). Said differently, positive derivatives on an interval imply positive rates of change on the interval, which, in turn, indicate an increase in function values.

Similarly, if the derivative is negative on an interval, the tangent lines on that interval have negative slopes, and the function is decreasing on that interval (Figure 4.14b). These observations are proved in Section 4.6 using a result called the Mean Value Theorem.

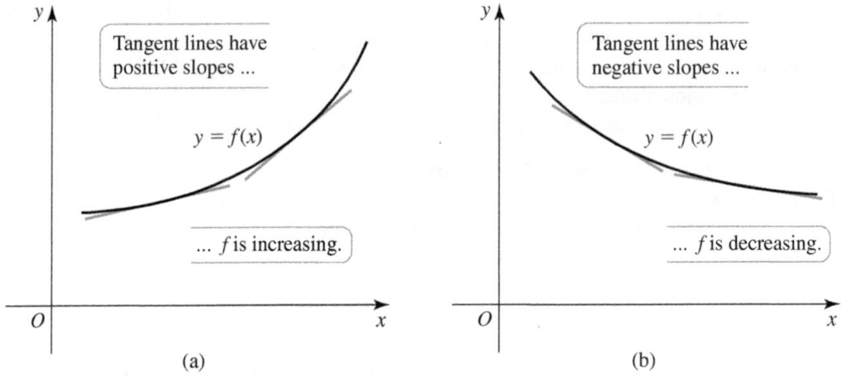

Figure 4.14

➤ The converse of Theorem 4.3 may not be true. According to the definition, $f(x) = x^3$ is increasing on $(-\infty, \infty)$ but it is not true that $f'(x) > 0$ on $(-\infty, \infty)$ (because $f'(0) = 0$).

> **THEOREM 4.3 Test for Intervals of Increase and Decrease**
> Suppose f is continuous on an interval I and differentiable at all interior points of I. If $f'(x) > 0$ at all interior points of I, then f is increasing on I. If $f'(x) < 0$ at all interior points of I, then f is decreasing on I.

QUICK CHECK 1 Explain why a positive derivative on an interval implies that the function is increasing on the interval. ◄

EXAMPLE 1 Sketching a function Sketch a graph of a function f that is continuous on $(-\infty, \infty)$ and satisfies the following conditions.

1. $f' > 0$ on $(-\infty, 0)$, $(4, 6)$, and $(6, \infty)$.
2. $f' < 0$ on $(0, 4)$.
3. $f'(0)$ is undefined.
4. $f'(4) = f'(6) = 0$.

SOLUTION By condition (1), f is increasing on the intervals $(-\infty, 0)$, $(4, 6)$, and $(6, \infty)$. By condition (2), f is decreasing on $(0, 4)$. Continuity of f and condition (3) imply that f has a cusp or corner at $x = 0$, and by condition (4), the graph has a horizontal tangent line at $x = 4$ and $x = 6$. It is useful to summarize these results using a *sign graph* (Figure 4.15).

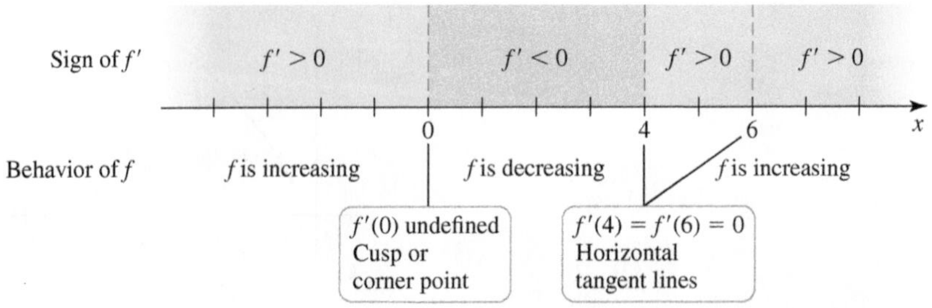

Figure 4.15

One possible graph satisfying these conditions is shown in Figure 4.16. Notice that the graph has a cusp at $x = 0$. Furthermore, although $f'(4) = f'(6) = 0$, f has a local minimum at $x = 4$ but no local extremum at $x = 6$.

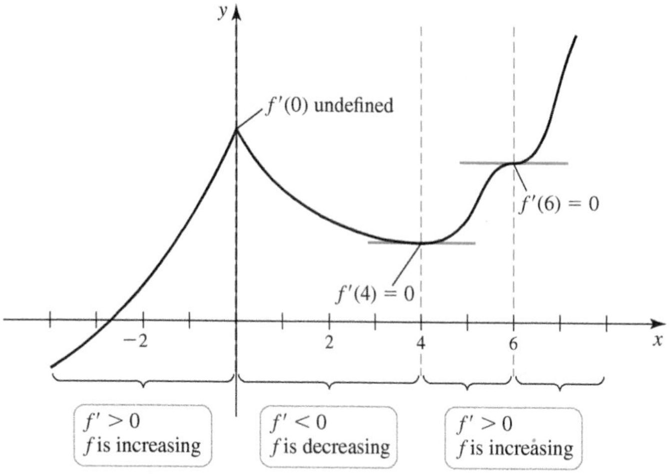

Figure 4.16

Related Exercises 11–16

EXAMPLE 2 **Intervals of increase and decrease** Find the intervals on which the following functions are increasing and decreasing.

a. $f(x) = xe^{-x}$ **b.** $f(x) = 2x^3 + 3x^2 + 1$

SOLUTION

a. By the Product Rule, $f'(x) = e^{-x} + x(-e^{-x}) = (1 - x)e^{-x}$. Solving $f'(x) = 0$ and noting that $e^{-x} \neq 0$ for all x, the sole critical point is $x = 1$. Therefore, if f' changes sign, then it does so at $x = 1$ and nowhere else, which implies f' has the same sign throughout each of the intervals $(-\infty, 1)$ and $(1, \infty)$. We determine the sign of f' on each interval by evaluating f' at selected points in each interval:

- At $x = 0$, $f'(0) = 1 > 0$. So $f' > 0$ on $(-\infty, 1)$, which means that f is increasing on $(-\infty, 1)$.
- At $x = 2$, $f'(2) = -e^{-2} < 0$. So $f' < 0$ on $(1, \infty)$, which means that f is decreasing on $(1, \infty)$.

Note also that the graph of f has a horizontal tangent line at $x = 1$. We verify these conclusions by plotting f and f' (Figure 4.17).

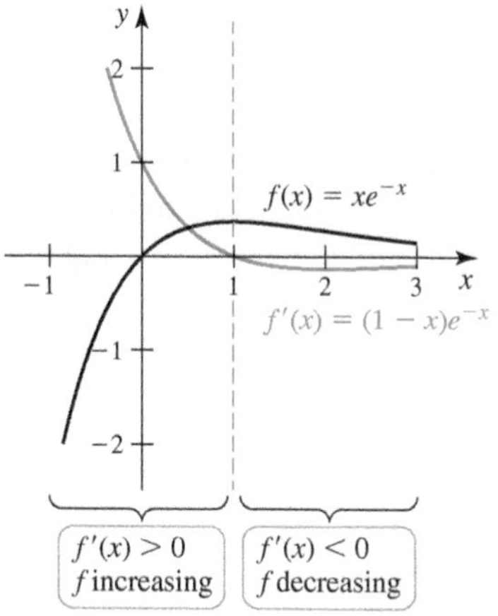

Figure 4.17

➤ Appendix A shows how to solve inequalities using test values.

b. In this case, $f'(x) = 6x^2 + 6x = 6x(x + 1)$. To find the intervals of increase, we first solve $6x(x + 1) = 0$ and determine that the critical points are $x = 0$ and $x = -1$. If f' changes sign, then it does so at these points and nowhere else; that is, f' has the same sign throughout each of the intervals $(-\infty, -1)$, $(-1, 0)$, and $(0, \infty)$. Evaluating f' at selected points of each intervals determines the sign of f' on that interval.

- At $x = -2$, $f'(-2) = 12 > 0$, so $f' > 0$ and f is increasing on $(-\infty, -1)$.
- At $x = -\frac{1}{2}$, $f'(-\frac{1}{2}) = -\frac{3}{2} < 0$, so $f' < 0$ and f is decreasing on $(-1, 0)$.
- At $x = 1$, $f'(1) = 12 > 0$, so $f' > 0$ and f is increasing on $(0, \infty)$.

The graph of f has a horizontal tangent line at $x = -1$ and $x = 0$. Figure 4.18 shows the graph of f superimposed on the graph of f', confirming our conclusions.

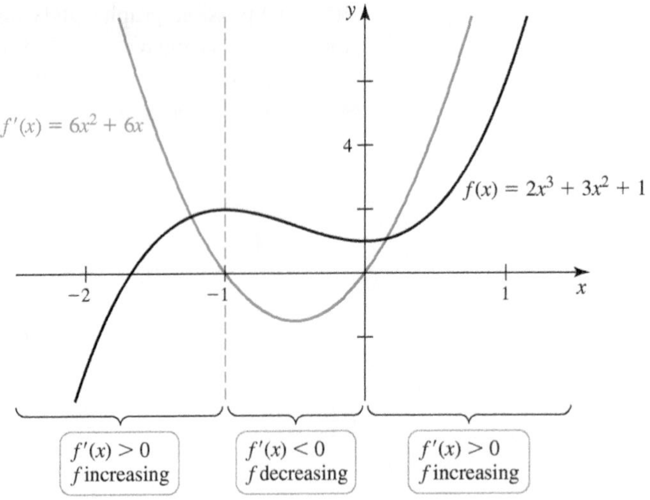

Figure 4.18

Related Exercises 17–38 ◀

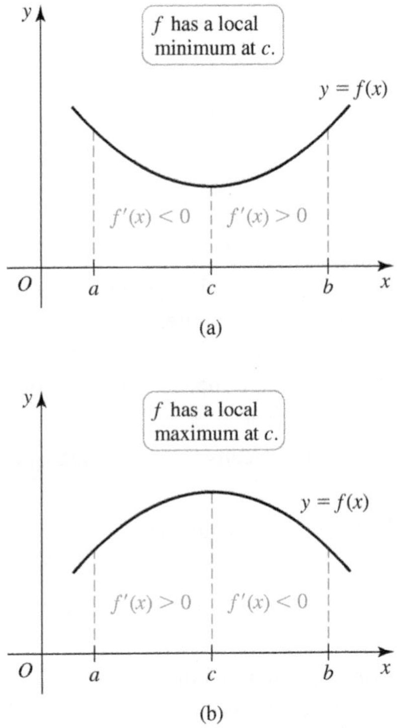

Figure 4.19

Identifying Local Maxima and Minima

Using what we know about increasing and decreasing functions, we can now identify local extrema. Suppose $x = c$ is a critical point of f, where $f'(c) = 0$. Suppose also that f' changes sign at c with $f'(x) < 0$ on an interval (a, c) to the left of c and $f'(x) > 0$ on an interval (c, b) to the right of c. In this case f' is decreasing to the left of c and increasing to the right of c, which means that f has a local minimum at c, as shown in Figure 4.19a.

Similarly, suppose f' changes sign at c with $f'(x) > 0$ on an interval (a, c) to the left of c and $f'(x) < 0$ on an interval (c, b) to the right of c. Then f is increasing to the left of c and decreasing to the right of c, so f has a local maximum at c, as shown in Figure 4.19b.

Figure 4.20 shows typical features of a function on an interval $[a, b]$. At local maxima or minima (c_2, c_3, and c_4), f' changes sign. Although c_1 and c_5 are critical points, the sign of f' is the same on both sides near these points, so there is no local maximum or minimum at these points. As emphasized earlier, *critical points do not always correspond to local extreme values.*

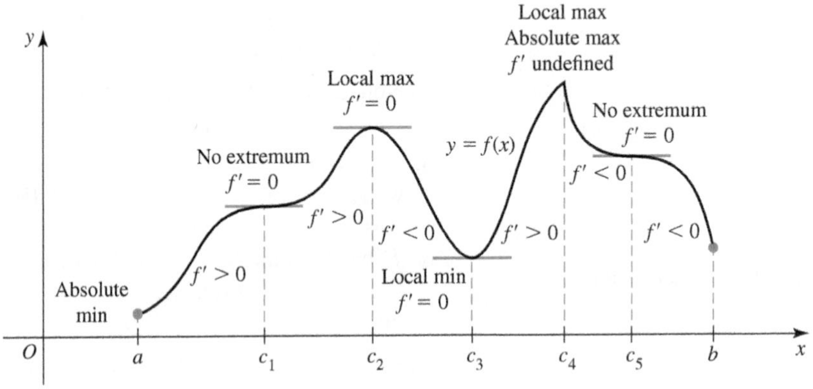

Figure 4.20

QUICK CHECK 2 Sketch a function f that is differentiable on $(-\infty, \infty)$ with the following properties: (i) $x = 0$ and $x = 2$ are critical points; (ii) f is increasing on $(-\infty, 2)$; (iii) f is decreasing on $(2, \infty)$. ◀

First Derivative Test The observations used to interpret Figure 4.20 are summarized in a powerful test for identifying local maxima and minima.

> THEOREM 4.4 **First Derivative Test**
> Suppose that f is continuous on an interval that contains a critical point c and assume f is differentiable on an interval containing c, except perhaps at c itself.
>
> - If f' changes sign from positive to negative as x increases through c, then f has a **local maximum** at c.
> - If f' changes sign from negative to positive as x increases through c, then f has a **local minimum** at c.
> - If f' is positive on both sides near c or negative on both sides near c, then f has no local extreme value at c.

Proof: Suppose that $f'(x) > 0$ on an interval (a, c). By Theorem 4.3, we know that f is increasing on (a, c), which implies that $f(x) < f(c)$ for all x in (a, c). Similarly, suppose that $f'(x) < 0$ on an interval (c, b). This time Theorem 4.3 says that f is decreasing on (c, b), which implies that $f(x) < f(c)$ for all x in (c, b). Therefore, $f(x) \le f(c)$ for all x in (a, b) and f has a local maximum at c. The proofs of the other two cases are similar. ◀

EXAMPLE 3 **Using the First Derivative Test** Consider the function

$$f(x) = 3x^4 - 4x^3 - 6x^2 + 12x + 1.$$

a. Find the intervals on which f is increasing and decreasing.

b. Identify the local extrema of f.

SOLUTION

a. Differentiating f, we find that

$$\begin{aligned} f'(x) &= 12x^3 - 12x^2 - 12x + 12 \\ &= 12(x^3 - x^2 - x + 1) \\ &= 12(x + 1)(x - 1)^2. \end{aligned}$$

Solving $f'(x) = 0$ gives the critical points $x = -1$ and $x = 1$. The critical points determine the intervals $(-\infty, -1)$, $(-1, 1)$, and $(1, \infty)$ on which f' does not change sign. Choosing a test point in each interval, a sign graph of f' is constructed (Figure 4.21) that summarizes the behavior of f.

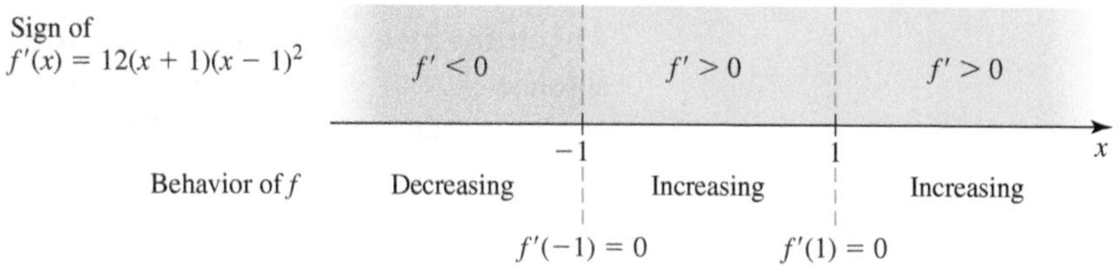

Figure 4.21

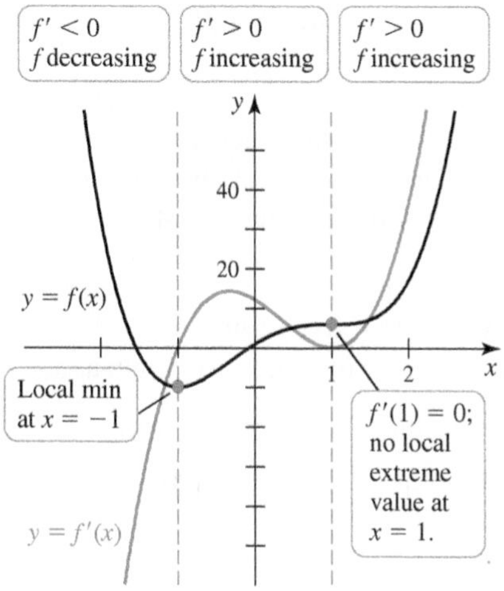

Figure 4.22

b. Note that f is a polynomial, so it is continuous on $(-\infty, \infty)$. Because f' changes sign from negative to positive as x passes through the critical point $x = -1$, it follows by the First Derivative Test that f has a local minimum value of $f(-1) = -10$ at $x = -1$. Observe that f' is positive on both sides near $x = 1$, so f does not have a local extreme value at $x = 1$ (Figure 4.22).

Related Exercises 39–48 ◀

EXAMPLE 4 **Extreme values** Find the local extrema of the function $g(x) = x^{2/3}(2 - x)$.

SOLUTION In Example 4b of Section 4.1, we found that

$$g'(x) = \frac{4}{3}x^{-1/3} - \frac{5}{3}x^{2/3} = \frac{4 - 5x}{3x^{1/3}}$$

and that the critical points of g are $x = 0$ and $x = \frac{4}{5}$. These two critical points are *candidates* for local extrema, and Theorem 4.4 is used to classify each as a local maximum, local minimum, or neither.

On the interval $(-\infty, 0)$, the numerator of g' is positive and the denominator is negative (Figure 4.23). Therefore, $g'(x) < 0$ on $(-\infty, 0)$. On the interval $(0, \frac{4}{5})$, the numerator of g' is positive, as is the denominator. Therefore, $g'(x) > 0$ on $(0, \frac{4}{5})$. We see that as x passes through 0, g' changes sign from negative to positive, which means g has a local minimum at 0. A similar argument shows that g' changes sign from positive to negative as x passes through $\frac{4}{5}$, so g has a local maximum at $\frac{4}{5}$. These observations are confirmed by the graphs of g and g' (Figure 4.24).

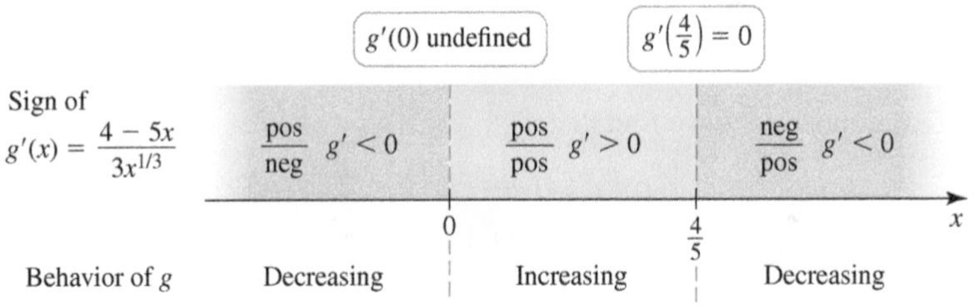

Figure 4.23

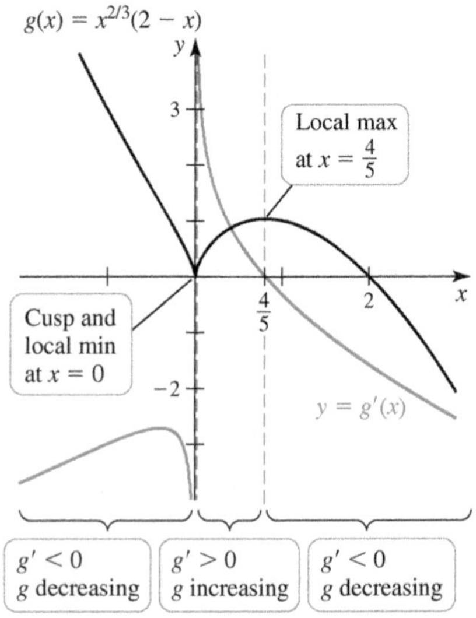

Figure 4.24

Related Exercises 39–48 ◀

QUICK CHECK 3 Explain how the First Derivative Test determines whether $f(x) = x^2$ has a local maximum or local minimum at the critical point $x = 0$. ◀

Absolute Extreme Values on Any Interval Theorem 4.1 guarantees the existence of absolute extreme values only on closed intervals. What can be said about absolute extrema on intervals that are not closed? The following theorem provides a valuable test.

> **THEOREM 4.5** **One Local Extremum Implies Absolute Extremum**
> Suppose f is continuous on an interval I that contains exactly one local extremum at c.
> - If a local maximum occurs at c, then $f(c)$ is the absolute maximum of f on I.
> - If a local minimum occurs at c, then $f(c)$ is the absolute minimum of f on I.

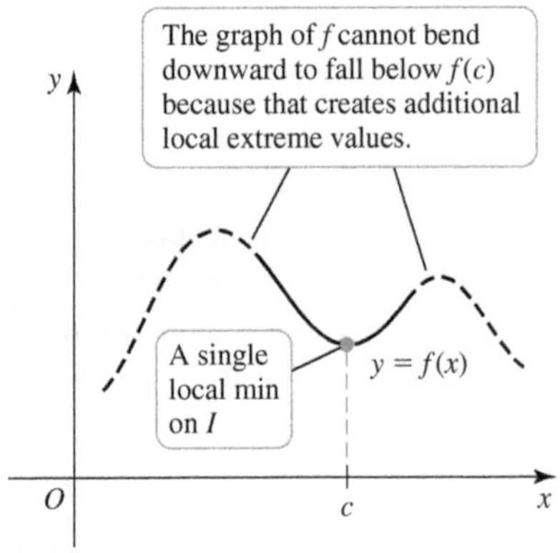

Figure 4.25

The proof of Theorem 4.5 is beyond the scope of this text, although Figure 4.25 illustrates why the theorem is plausible. Assume f has exactly one local minimum on I at c. Notice that there is no other point on the graph at which f has a value less than $f(c)$. If such a point did exist, the graph would have to bend downward to drop below $f(c)$. Because f is continuous, this cannot happen as it implies additional local extreme values on I. A similar argument applies to a solitary local maximum.

EXAMPLE 5 Finding an absolute extremum Verify that $f(x) = x^x$ has an absolute extreme value on its domain.

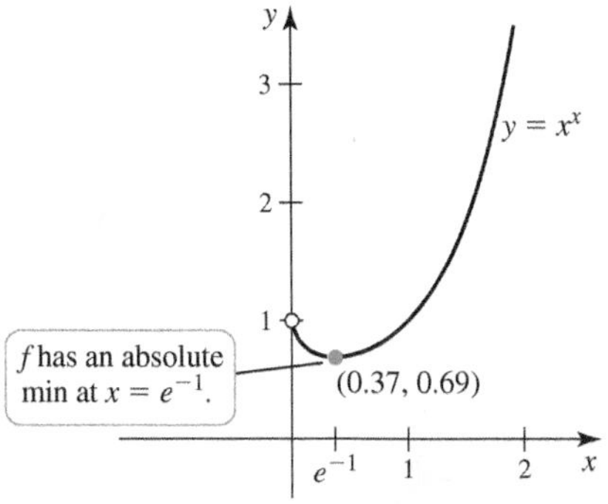

Figure 4.26

SOLUTION First note that f is continuous on its domain $(0, \infty)$. Because $f(x) = x^x = e^{x \ln x}$, it follows that

$$f'(x) = e^{x \ln x}(1 + \ln x) = x^x(1 + \ln x).$$

Solving $f'(x) = 0$ gives a single critical point $x = e^{-1}$; there is no point in the domain at which $f'(x)$ does not exist. The critical point splits the domain of f into the intervals $(0, e^{-1})$ and (e^{-1}, ∞). Evaluating the sign of f' on each interval gives $f'(x) < 0$ on $(0, e^{-1})$ and $f'(x) > 0$ on (e^{-1}, ∞); therefore, by the First Derivative Test, a local minimum occurs at $x = e^{-1}$. Because it is the only local extremum on $(0, \infty)$, it follows from Theorem 4.5 that the absolute minimum of f occurs at $x = e^{-1}$ (Figure 4.26). Its value is $f(e^{-1}) \approx 0.69$.

Related Exercises 49–52 ◀

Concavity and Inflection Points

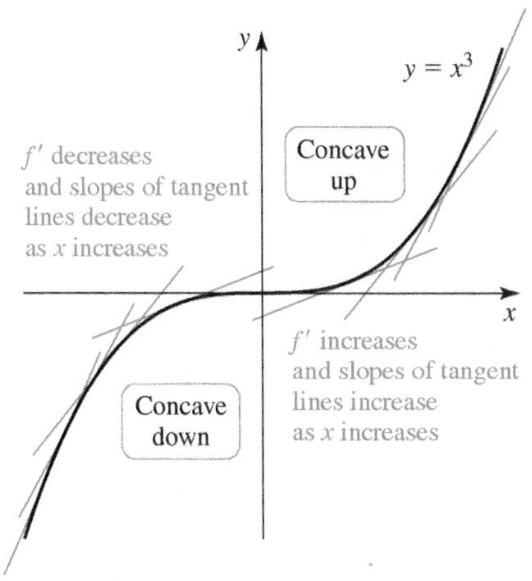

Figure 4.27

Just as the first derivative is related to the slope of tangent lines, the second derivative also has geometric meaning. Consider $f(x) = x^3$, shown in Figure 4.27. Its graph bends upward for $x > 0$, reflecting the fact that the tangent lines get steeper as x increases. It follows that the first derivative is increasing for $x > 0$. A function with the property that f' is increasing on an interval is *concave up* on that interval.

Similarly, $f(x) = x^3$ bends downward for $x < 0$ because it has a decreasing first derivative on that interval. A function with the property that f' is decreasing as x increases on an interval is *concave down* on that interval.

Here is another useful characterization of concavity. If a function is concave up at a point (any point $x > 0$ in Figure 4.27), then its graph near that point lies *above* the tangent line at that point. Similarly, if a function is concave down at a point (any point $x < 0$ in Figure 4.27), then its graph near that point lies *below* the tangent line at that point (Exercise 104).

Finally, imagine a function f that changes concavity (from up to down, or vice versa) at a point c in the domain of f. For example, $f(x) = x^3$ in Figure 4.27 changes from concave down to concave up as x passes through $x = 0$. A point on the graph of f at which f changes concavity is called an *inflection point*.

DEFINITION Concavity and Inflection Point

Let f be differentiable on an open interval I. If f' is increasing on I, then f is **concave up** on I. If f' is decreasing on I, then f is **concave down** on I.

If f is continuous at c and f changes concavity at c (from up to down, or vice versa), then f has an **inflection point** at c.

Applying Theorem 4.3 to f' leads to a test for concavity in terms of the second derivative. Specifically, if $f'' > 0$ on an interval I, then f' is increasing on I and f is concave up on I. Similarly, if $f'' < 0$ on I, then f is concave down on I. In addition, if the values of f'' change sign at a point c (from positive to negative, or vice versa), then the concavity of f changes at c and f has an inflection point at c (Figure 4.28a). We now have a useful interpretation of the second derivative: It measures *concavity*.

THEOREM 4.6 Test for Concavity
Suppose that f'' exists on an open interval I.

- If $f'' > 0$ on I, then f is concave up on I.
- If $f'' < 0$ on I, then f is concave down on I.
- If c is a point of I at which f'' changes sign at c (from positive to negative, or vice versa), then f has an inflection point at c.

There are a few important but subtle points here. The fact that $f''(c) = 0$ does not necessarily imply that f has an inflection point at c. A good example is $f(x) = x^4$. Although $f''(0) = 0$, the concavity does not change at $x = 0$ (a similar function is shown in Figure 4.28b).

Typically, if f has an inflection point at c, then $f''(c) = 0$, reflecting the smooth change in concavity. However, an inflection point may also occur at a point where f'' does not exist. For example, the function $f(x) = x^{1/3}$ has a vertical tangent line and an inflection point at $x = 0$ (a similar function is shown in Figure 4.28c). Finally, note that the function shown in Figure 4.28d, with behavior similar to that of $f(x) = x^{2/3}$, does not have an inflection point at c despite the fact that $f''(c)$ does not exist. In summary, if $f''(c) = 0$ or $f''(c)$ does not exist, then $(c, f(c))$ is a candidate for an inflection point. To be certain an inflection point occurs at c, we must show that the concavity of f changes at c.

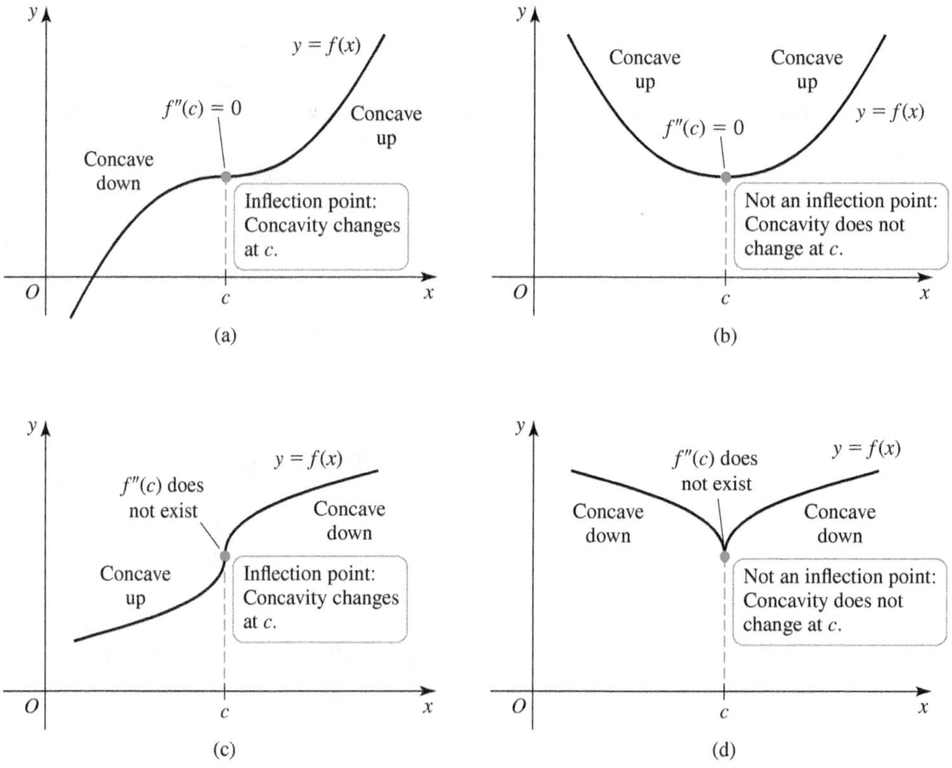

Figure 4.28

QUICK CHECK 4 Verify that the function $f(x) = x^4$ is concave up for $x > 0$ and for $x < 0$. Is $x = 0$ an inflection point? Explain. ◀

EXAMPLE 6 Interpreting concavity Sketch a function satisfying each set of conditions on some interval.

a. $f'(t) > 0$ and $f''(t) > 0$ **b.** $g'(t) > 0$ and $g''(t) < 0$

c. Which of the functions, f or g, could describe a population that increases and approaches a steady state as $t \to \infty$?

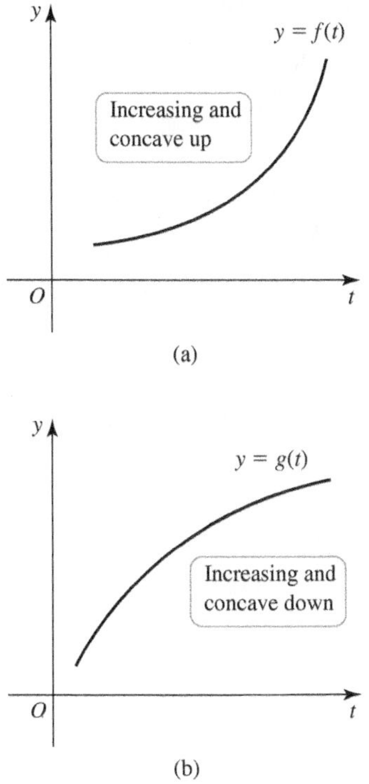

Figure 4.29

SOLUTION

a. Figure 4.29a shows the graph of a function that is increasing $(f'(t) > 0)$ and concave up $(f''(t) > 0)$.

b. Figure 4.29b shows the graph of a function that is increasing $(g'(t) > 0)$ and concave down $(g''(t) < 0)$.

c. Because f increases at an *increasing* rate, the graph of f could not approach a horizontal asymptote, so f could not describe a population that approaches a steady state. On the other hand, g increases at a *decreasing* rate, so its graph could approach a horizontal asymptote, depending on the rate at which g increases.

Related Exercises 53–56 ◀

EXAMPLE 7 **Detecting concavity** Identify the intervals on which the following functions are concave up or concave down. Then locate the inflection points.

a. $f(x) = 3x^4 - 4x^3 - 6x^2 + 12x + 1$

b. $f(x) = \sin^{-1} x$ on $(-1, 1)$

SOLUTION

a. This function was considered in Example 3, where we found that

$$f'(x) = 12(x + 1)(x - 1)^2.$$

It follows that

$$f''(x) = 12(x - 1)(3x + 1).$$

We see that $f''(x) = 0$ at $x = 1$ and $x = -\frac{1}{3}$. These points are *candidates* for inflection points; to be certain that they are inflection points, we must determine whether the concavity changes at these points. The sign graph in Figure 4.30 shows the following:

- $f''(x) > 0$ and f is concave up on $(-\infty, -\frac{1}{3})$ and $(1, \infty)$.
- $f''(x) < 0$ and f is concave down on $(-\frac{1}{3}, 1)$.

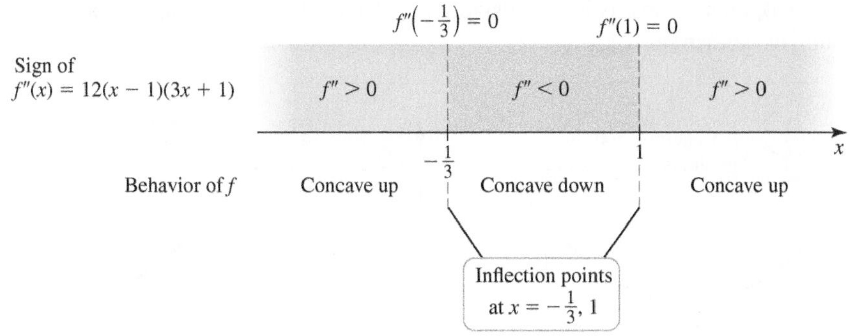

Figure 4.30

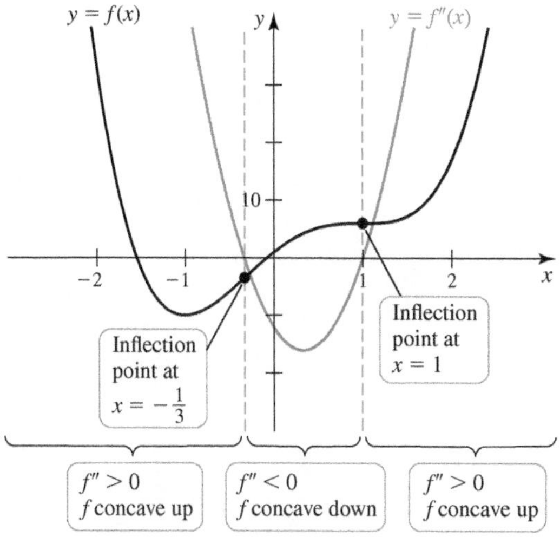

Figure 4.31

We see that the sign of f'' changes at $x = -\frac{1}{3}$ and at $x = 1$, so the concavity of f also changes at these points. Therefore, inflection points occur at $x = -\frac{1}{3}$ and $x = 1$. The graphs of f and f'' (Figure 4.31) show that the concavity of f changes at the zeros of f''.

b. The first derivative of $f(x) = \sin^{-1} x$ is $f'(x) = 1/\sqrt{1 - x^2}$. We use the Chain Rule to compute the second derivative:

$$f''(x) = -\frac{1}{2}(1 - x^2)^{-3/2} \cdot (-2x) = \frac{x}{(1 - x^2)^{3/2}}.$$

The only zero of f'' is $x = 0$, and because its denominator is positive on $(-1, 1)$, f'' changes sign at $x = 0$ from negative to positive. Therefore, f is concave down on $(-1, 0)$ and concave up on $(0, 1)$, with an inflection point at $x = 0$ (Figure 4.32).

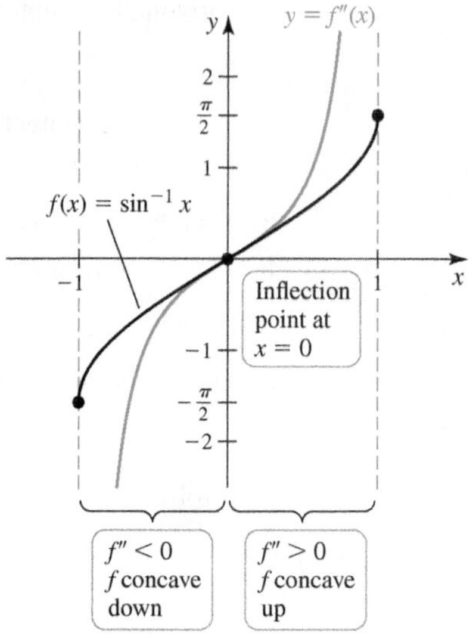

Figure 4.32

Related Exercises 57–70 ◀

Second Derivative Test It is now a short step to a test that uses the second derivative to identify local maxima and minima.

➤ In the inconclusive case of Theorem 4.7 in which $f''(c) = 0$, it is usually best to use the First Derivative Test.

THEOREM 4.7 Second Derivative Test for Local Extrema
Suppose that f'' is continuous on an open interval containing c with $f'(c) = 0$.

- If $f''(c) > 0$, then f has a local minimum at c (Figure 4.33a).
- If $f''(c) < 0$, then f has a local maximum at c (Figure 4.33b).
- If $f''(c) = 0$, then the test is inconclusive; f may have a local maximum, local minimum, or neither at c.

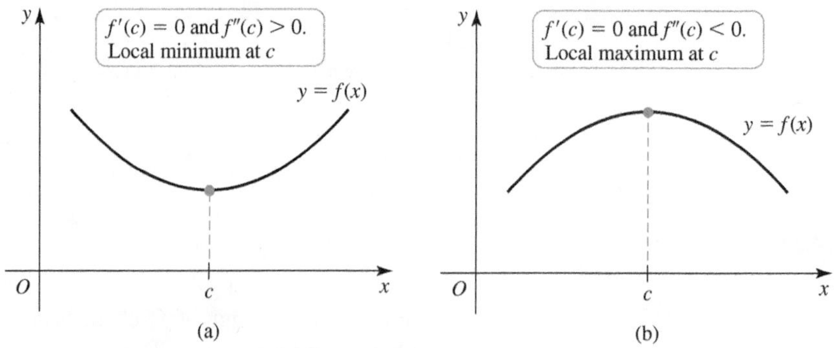

Figure 4.33

Proof: Assume $f''(c) > 0$. Because f'' is continuous on an interval containing c, it follows that $f'' > 0$ on some open interval I containing c and that f' is increasing on I. Because $f'(c) = 0$, it follows that f' changes sign at c from negative to positive, which, by the First Derivative Test, implies that f has a local minimum at c. The proofs of the second and third statements are similar. ◄

QUICK CHECK 5 Sketch a graph of a function with $f'(x) > 0$ and $f''(x) > 0$ on an interval. Sketch a graph of a function with $f'(x) < 0$ and $f''(x) < 0$ on an interval. ◄

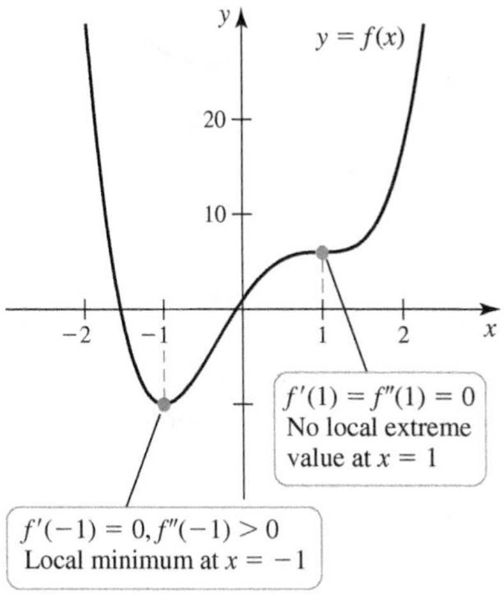

Figure 4.34

EXAMPLE 8 **The Second Derivative Test** Use the Second Derivative Test to locate the local extrema of the following functions.

a. $f(x) = 3x^4 - 4x^3 - 6x^2 + 12x + 1$ on $[-2, 2]$ **b.** $f(x) = \sin^2 x$

SOLUTION

a. This function was considered in Examples 3 and 7, where we found that

$$f'(x) = 12(x + 1)(x - 1)^2 \quad \text{and} \quad f''(x) = 12(x - 1)(3x + 1).$$

Therefore, the critical points of f are $x = -1$ and $x = 1$. Evaluating f'' at the critical points, we find that $f''(-1) = 48 > 0$. By the Second Derivative Test, f has a local minimum at $x = -1$. At the other critical point, $f''(1) = 0$, so the test is inconclusive. You can check that the first derivative does not change sign at $x = 1$, which means f does not have a local maximum or minimum at $x = 1$ (Figure 4.34).

b. Using the Chain Rule and a trigonometric identity, we have $f'(x) = 2\sin x \cos x = \sin 2x$ and $f''(x) = 2\cos 2x$. The critical points occur when $f'(x) = \sin 2x = 0$, or when $x = 0, \pm\pi/2, \pm\pi, \ldots$. To apply the Second Derivative Test, we evaluate f'' at the critical points:

- $f''(0) = 2 > 0$, so f has a local minimum at $x = 0$.
- $f''(\pm\pi/2) = -2 < 0$, so f has a local maximum at $x = \pm\pi/2$.
- $f''(\pm\pi) = 2 > 0$, so f has a local minimum at $x = \pm\pi$.

This pattern continues, and we see that f has alternating local maxima and minima, evenly spaced every $\pi/2$ units (Figure 4.35).

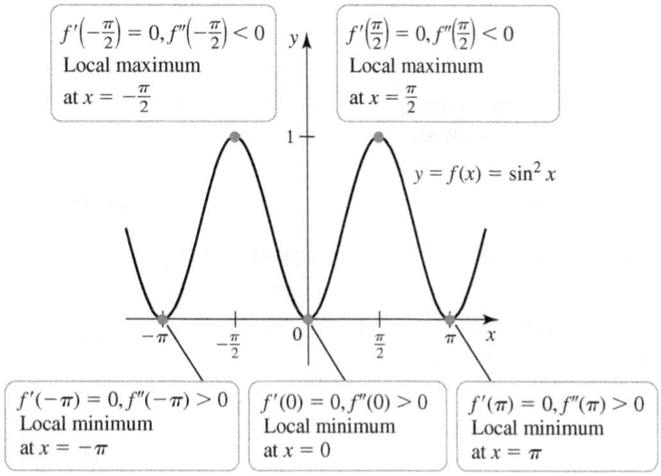

Figure 4.35

Related Exercises 71–82 ◄

Recap of Derivative Properties

This section has demonstrated that the first and second derivatives of a function provide valuable information about its graph. The relationships among a function's derivatives and its extreme values and concavity are summarized in Figure 4.36.

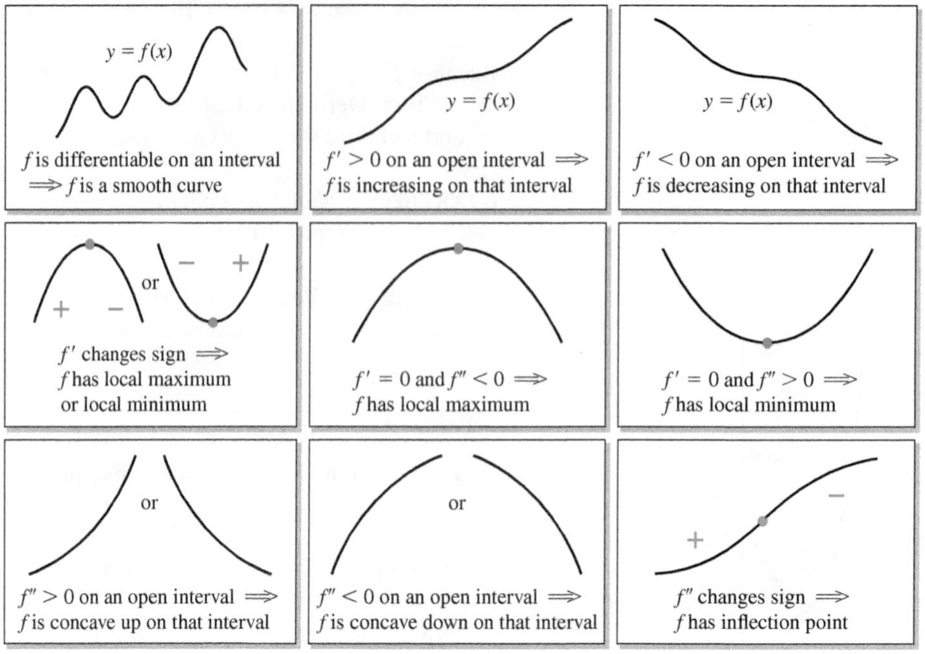

Figure 4.36

SECTION 4.2 EXERCISES

Review Questions

1. Explain how the first derivative of a function determines where the function is increasing and decreasing.
2. Explain how to apply the First Derivative Test.
3. Sketch the graph of a function that has neither a local maximum nor a local minimum at a point where $f'(x) = 0$.
4. Explain how to apply the Second Derivative Test.
5. Suppose f'' exists and is positive on an interval I. Describe the relationship between the graph of f and its tangent lines on the interval I.
6. Sketch a function that changes from concave up to concave down as x increases. Describe how the second derivative of this function changes.
7. What is an inflection point?
8. Give a function that does not have an inflection point at a point where $f''(x) = 0$.
9. Is it possible for a function to satisfy $f(x) > 0, f'(x) > 0$, and $f''(x) < 0$ on an interval? Explain.
10. Suppose f is continuous on an interval containing a critical point c and $f''(c) = 0$. How do you determine whether f has a local extreme value at $x = c$?

Basic Skills

11–14. Sketches from properties *Sketch a graph of a function that is continuous on $(-\infty, \infty)$ and has the following properties. Use a sign graph to summarize information about the function.*

11. $f'(x) < 0$ on $(-\infty, 2)$; $f'(x) > 0$ on $(2, 5)$; $f'(x) < 0$ on $(5, \infty)$
12. $f'(-1)$ is undefined; $f'(x) > 0$ on $(-\infty, -1)$; $f'(x) < 0$ on $(-1, \infty)$
13. $f(0) = f(4) = f'(0) = f'(2) = f'(4) = 0$; $f(x) \geq 0$ on $(-\infty, \infty)$
14. $f'(-2) = f'(2) = f'(6) = 0$; $f'(x) \geq 0$ on $(-\infty, \infty)$

15–16. Functions from derivatives *The following figures give the graph of the derivative of a continuous function f that passes through the origin. Sketch a possible graph of f on the same set of axes.*

15.

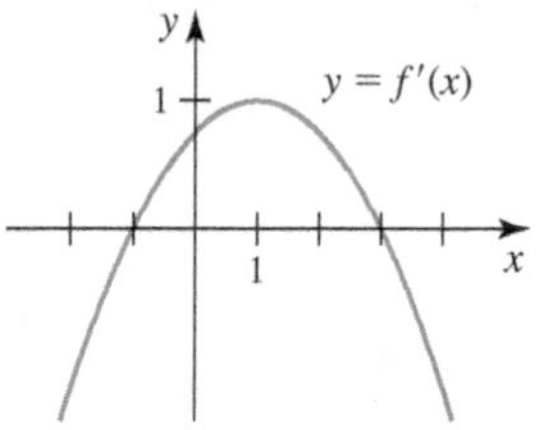

16.

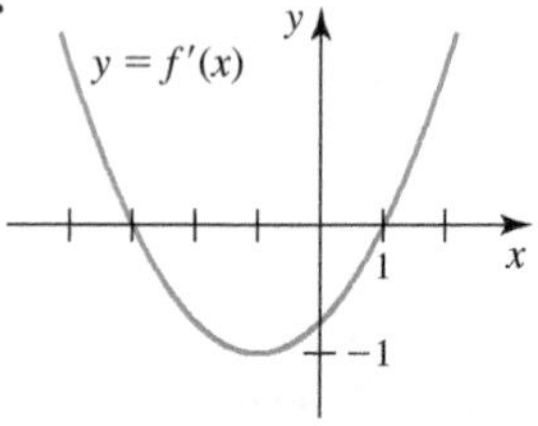

T **17–26. Increasing and decreasing functions** *Find the intervals on which f is increasing and decreasing. Superimpose the graphs of f and f' to verify your work.*

17. $f(x) = 4 - x^2$
18. $f(x) = x^2 - 16$
19. $f(x) = (x - 1)^2$
20. $f(x) = x^3 + 4x$
21. $f(x) = 12 + x - x^2$
22. $f(x) = x^4 - 4x^3 + 4x^2$
23. $f(x) = -\frac{x^4}{4} + x^3 - x^2$
24. $f(x) = 2x^5 - \frac{15x^4}{4} + \frac{5x^3}{3}$
25. $f(x) = x^2 \ln x^2 + 1$
26. $f(x) = \frac{e^x}{e^{2x} + 1}$

27–38. Increasing and decreasing functions *Find the intervals on which f is increasing and decreasing.*

27. $f(x) = 3 \cos 3x$ on $[-\pi, \pi]$
28. $f(x) = \cos^2 x$ on $[-\pi, \pi]$

29. $f(x) = x^{2/3}(x^2 - 4)$

30. $f(x) = x^2\sqrt{9 - x^2}$ on $(-3, 3)$

31. $f(x) = \tan^{-1} x$

32. $f(x) = \ln |x|$

33. $f(x) = -12x^5 + 75x^4 - 80x^3$

34. $f(x) = x^2 - 2 \ln x$

35. $f(x) = -2x^4 + x^2 + 10$

36. $f(x) = \dfrac{x^4}{4} - \dfrac{8x^3}{3} + \dfrac{15x^2}{2} + 8$

37. $f(x) = xe^{-x^2/2}$

38. $f(x) = \tan^{-1}\left(\dfrac{x}{x^2 + 2}\right)$

39–48. First Derivative Test

a. Locate the critical points of f.
b. Use the First Derivative Test to locate the local maximum and minimum values.
c. Identify the absolute maximum and minimum values of the function on the given interval (when they exist).

39. $f(x) = x^2 + 3$ on $[-3, 2]$

40. $f(x) = -x^2 - x + 2$ on $[-4, 4]$

41. $f(x) = x\sqrt{4 - x^2}$ on $[-2, 2]$

42. $f(x) = 2x^3 + 3x^2 - 12x + 1$ on $[-2, 4]$

43. $f(x) = -x^3 + 9x$ on $[-4, 3]$

44. $f(x) = 2x^5 - 5x^4 - 10x^3 + 4$ on $[-2, 4]$

45. $f(x) = x^{2/3}(x - 5)$ on $[-5, 5]$

46. $f(x) = \dfrac{x^2}{x^2 - 1}$ on $[-4, 4]$

47. $f(x) = \sqrt{x} \ln x$ on $(0, \infty)$

T 48. $f(x) = \tan^{-1} x - x^3$ on $[-1, 1]$

49–52. Absolute extreme values *Verify that the following functions satisfy the conditions of Theorem 4.5 on their domains. Then find the location and value of the absolute extremum guaranteed by the theorem.*

49. $f(x) = xe^{-x}$

50. $f(x) = 4x + 1/\sqrt{x}$

51. $A(r) = 24/r + 2\pi r^2, r > 0$

52. $f(x) = x\sqrt{3 - x}$

53–56. Sketching curves *Sketch a graph of a function f that is continuous on $(-\infty, \infty)$ and has the following properties.*

53. $f'(x) > 0, f''(x) > 0$

54. $f'(x) < 0$ and $f''(x) > 0$ on $(-\infty, 0)$; $f'(x) > 0$ and $f''(x) > 0$ on $(0, \infty)$

55. $f'(x) < 0$ and $f''(x) < 0$ on $(-\infty, 0)$; $f'(x) < 0$ and $f''(x) > 0$ on $(0, \infty)$

56. $f'(x) < 0$ and $f''(x) > 0$ on $(-\infty, 0)$; $f'(x) < 0$ and $f''(x) < 0$ on $(0, \infty)$

57–70. Concavity *Determine the intervals on which the following functions are concave up or concave down. Identify any inflection points.*

57. $f(x) = x^4 - 2x^3 + 1$

58. $f(x) = -x^4 - 2x^3 + 12x^2$

59. $f(x) = 5x^4 - 20x^3 + 10$

60. $f(x) = \dfrac{1}{1 + x^2}$

61. $f(x) = e^x(x - 3)$

62. $f(x) = 2x^2 \ln x - 5x^2$

63. $g(t) = \ln (3t^2 + 1)$

64. $g(x) = \sqrt[3]{x - 4}$

65. $f(x) = e^{-x^2/2}$

66. $f(x) = \tan^{-1} x$

67. $f(x) = \sqrt{x} \ln x$

68. $h(t) = 2 + \cos 2t$, for $-\pi \le t \le \pi$

69. $g(t) = 3t^5 - 30t^4 + 80t^3 + 100$

70. $f(x) = 2x^4 + 8x^3 + 12x^2 - x - 2$

71–82. Second Derivative Test *Locate the critical points of the following functions. Then use the Second Derivative Test to determine (if possible) whether they correspond to local maxima or local minima.*

71. $f(x) = x^3 - 3x^2$

72. $f(x) = 6x^2 - x^3$

73. $f(x) = 4 - x^2$

74. $g(x) = x^3 - 6$

75. $f(x) = e^x(x - 7)$

T 76. $f(x) = e^x(x^2 - 7x - 12)$

77. $f(x) = 2x^3 - 3x^2 + 12$

78. $p(x) = x^4e^{-x}$

79. $f(x) = x^2e^{-x}$

80. $g(x) = \dfrac{x^4}{2 - 12x^2}$

81. $f(x) = 2x^2 \ln x - 11x^2$

82. $f(x) = \sqrt{x}\left(\dfrac{12}{7}x^3 - 4x^2\right)$

Further Explorations

83. **Explain why or why not** Determine whether the following statements are true and give an explanation or counterexample.
   a. If $f'(x) > 0$ and $f''(x) < 0$ on an interval, then f is increasing at a decreasing rate on the interval.
   b. If $f'(c) > 0$ and $f''(c) = 0$, then f has a local maximum at c.
   c. Two functions that differ by an additive constant both increase and decrease on the same intervals.
   d. If f and g increase on an interval, then the product fg also increases on that interval.
   e. There exists a function f that is continuous on $(-\infty, \infty)$ with exactly three critical points, all of which correspond to local maxima.

84–85. Functions from derivatives *Consider the following graphs of f' and f''. On the same set of axes, sketch the graph of a possible function f. The graphs of f are not unique.*

84.

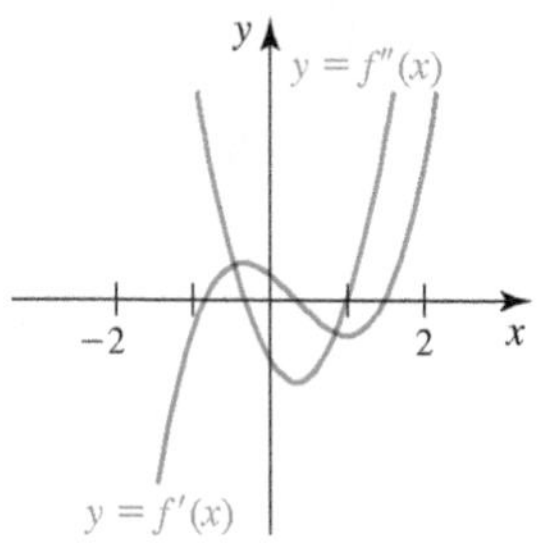

85.

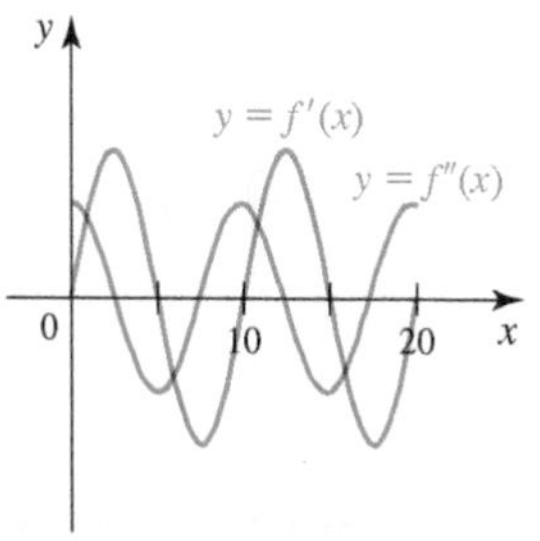

86. **Is it possible?** Determine whether the following properties can be satisfied by a function that is continuous on $(-\infty, \infty)$. If such

a function is possible, provide an example or a sketch of the function. If such a function is not possible, explain why.

a. A function f is concave down and positive everywhere.
b. A function f is increasing and concave down everywhere.
c. A function f has exactly two local extrema and three inflection points.
d. A function f has exactly four zeros and two local extrema.

87. Matching derivatives and functions The following figures show the graphs of three functions (graphs a–c). Match each function with its first derivative (graphs d–f) *and* its second derivative (graphs g–i).

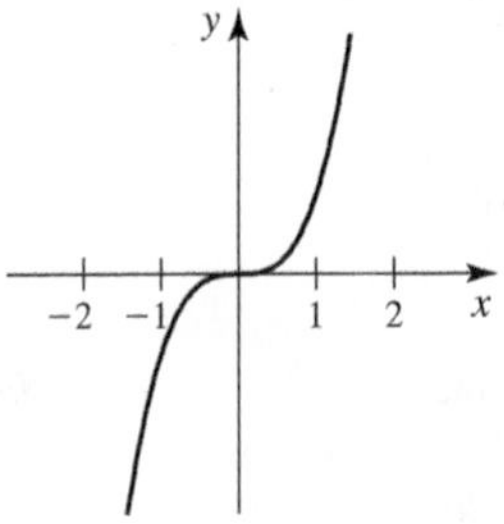

(a)

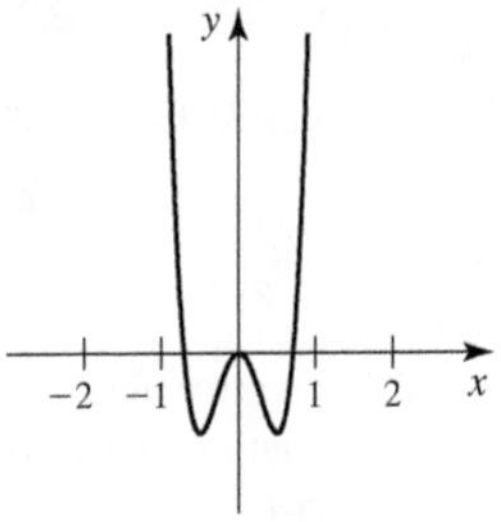

(b)

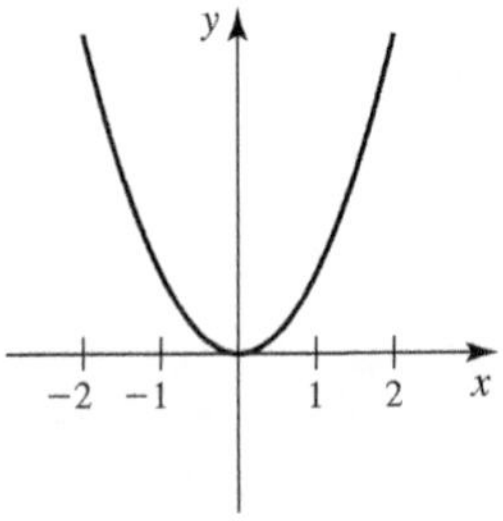

(c)

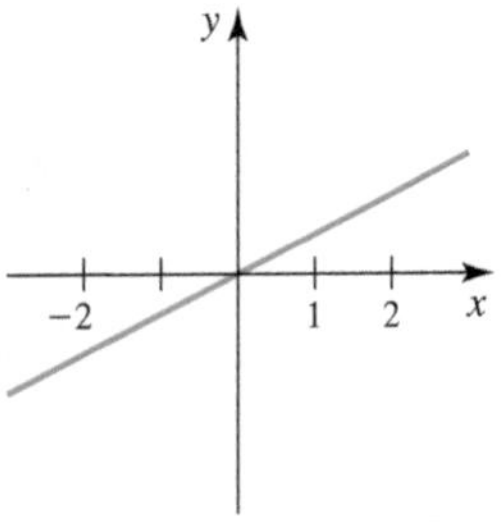

(d)

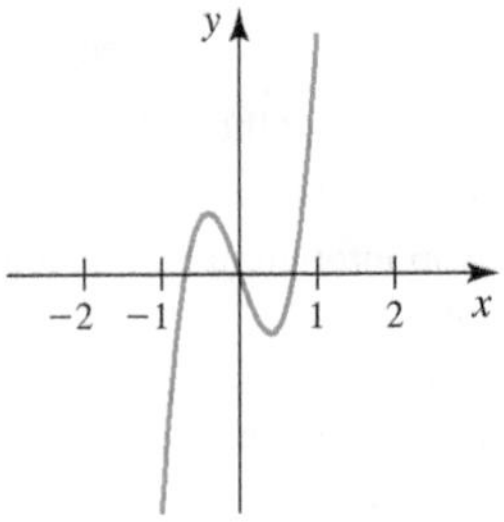

(e)

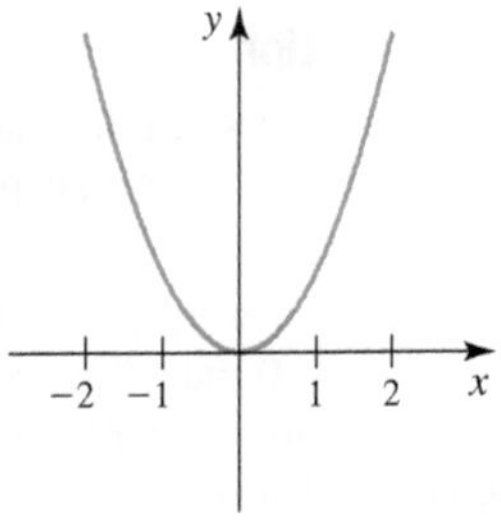

(f)

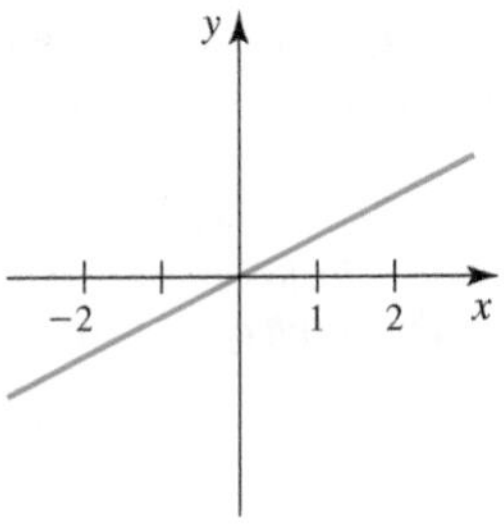

(g)

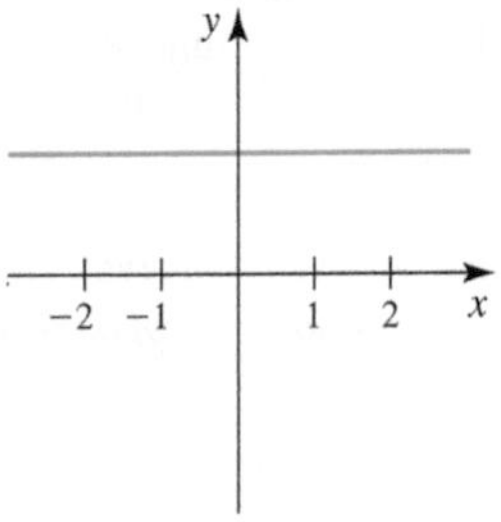

(h)

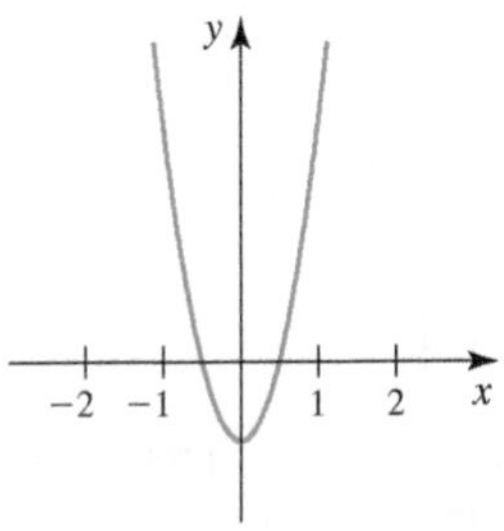

(i)

88. Graphical analysis The figure shows the graphs of f, f', and f''. Which curve is which?

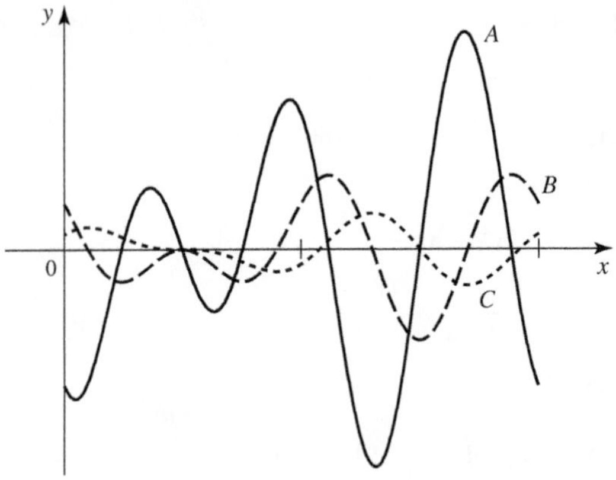

89. Sketching graphs Sketch the graph of a function f continuous on $[a, b]$ such that f, f', and f'' have the signs indicated in the following table on $[a, b]$. There are eight different cases lettered A–H and eight different graphs.

Case	A	B	C	D	E	F	G	H
f	+	+	+	+	−	−	−	−
f'	+	+	−	−	+	+	−	−
f''	+	−	+	−	+	−	+	−

90–93. Designer functions *Sketch the graph of a function that is continuous on* $(-\infty, \infty)$ *and satisfies the following sets of conditions.*

90. $f''(x) > 0$ on $(-\infty, -2)$; $f''(-2) = 0$; $f'(-1) = f'(1) = 0$; $f''(2) = 0$; $f'(3) = 0$; $f''(x) > 0$ on $(4, \infty)$

91. $f(-2) = f''(-1) = 0$; $f'(-\frac{3}{2}) = 0$; $f(0) = f'(0) = 0$; $f(1) = f'(1) = 0$

92. $f'(x) > 0$, for all x in the domain of f'; $f'(-2)$ and $f'(1)$ do not exist; $f''(0) = 0$

93. $f''(x) > 0$ on $(-\infty, -2)$; $f''(x) < 0$ on $(-2, 1)$; $f''(x) > 0$ on $(1, 3)$; $f''(x) < 0$ on $(3, \infty)$

T **94. Graph carefully** Graph the function $f(x) = 60x^5 - 901x^3 + 27x$ in the window $[-4, 4] \times [-10000, 10000]$. How many extreme values do you see? Locate *all* the extreme values by analyzing f'.

95. Interpreting the derivative The graph of f' on the interval $[-3, 2]$ is shown in the figure.

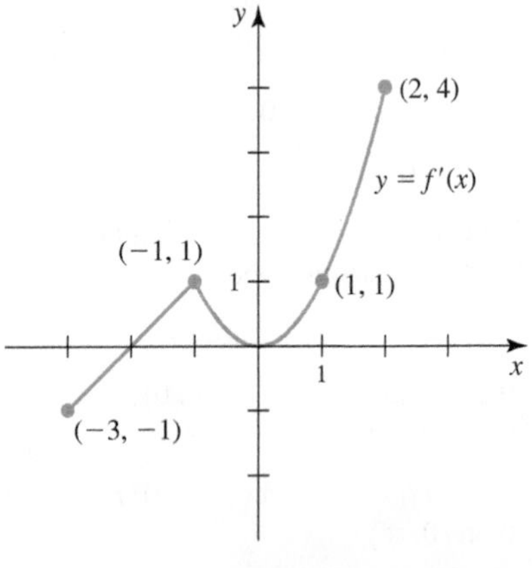

a. On what interval(s) is f increasing? Decreasing?
b. Find the critical points of f. Which critical points correspond to local maxima? Local minima? Neither?

c. At what point(s) does f have an inflection point?
d. On what interval(s) is f concave up? Concave down?
e. Sketch the graph of f''.
f. Sketch one possible graph of f.

96–99. Second Derivative Test *Locate the critical points of the following functions and use the Second Derivative Test to determine (if possible) whether they correspond to local maxima or local minima.*

96. $p(t) = 2t^3 + 3t^2 - 36t$

T **97.** $f(x) = \dfrac{x^4}{4} - \dfrac{5x^3}{3} - 4x^2 + 48x$

98. $h(x) = (x + a)^4$; a constant

99. $f(x) = x^3 + 2x^2 + 4x - 1$

100. Concavity of parabolas Consider the general parabola described by the function $f(x) = ax^2 + bx + c$. For what values of a, b, and c is f concave up? For what values of a, b, and c is f concave down?

Applications

T **101. Demand functions and elasticity** Economists use *demand functions* to describe how much of a commodity can be sold at varying prices. For example, the demand function $D(p) = 500 - 10p$ says that at a price of $p = 10$, a quantity of $D(10) = 400$ units of the commodity can be sold. The elasticity $E = \dfrac{dD}{dp}\dfrac{p}{D}$ of the demand gives the approximate percent change in the demand for every 1% change in the price. (See Section 3.5 or the Guided Project *Elasticity in Economics* for more on demand functions and elasticity.)

a. Compute the elasticity of the demand function $D(p) = 500 - 10p$.
b. If the price is \$12 and increases by 4.5%, what is the approximate percent change in the demand?
c. Show that for the linear demand function $D(p) = a - bp$, where a and b are positive real numbers, the elasticity is a decreasing function, for $p \geq 0$ and $p \neq a/b$.
d. Show that the demand function $D(p) = a/p^b$, where a and b are positive real numbers, has a constant elasticity for all positive prices.

102. Population models A typical population curve is shown in the figure. The population is small at $t = 0$ and increases toward a steady-state level called the *carrying capacity*. Explain why the maximum growth rate occurs at an inflection point of the population curve.

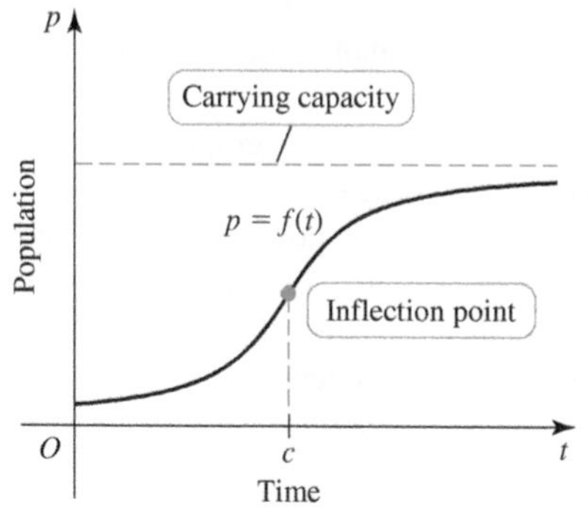

103. Population models The population of a species is given by the function $P(t) = \dfrac{Kt^2}{t^2 + b}$, where $t \geq 0$ is measured in years and K and b are positive real numbers.

a. With $K = 300$ and $b = 30$, what is $\lim_{t\to\infty} P(t)$, the carrying capacity of the population?
b. With $K = 300$ and $b = 30$, when does the maximum growth rate occur?
c. For arbitrary positive values of K and b, when does the maximum growth rate occur (in terms of K and b)?

Additional Exercises

104. Tangent lines and concavity Give an argument to support the claim that if a function is concave up at a point, then the tangent line at that point lies below the curve near that point.

105. Symmetry of cubics Consider the general cubic polynomial $f(x) = x^3 + ax^2 + bx + c$, where a, b, and c are real numbers.

a. Show that f has exactly one inflection point and it occurs at $x^* = -a/3$.
b. Show that f is an odd function with respect to the inflection point $(x^*, f(x^*))$. This means that $f(x^*) - f(x^* + x) = f(x^* - x) - f(x^*)$, for all x.

106. Properties of cubics Consider the general cubic polynomial $f(x) = x^3 + ax^2 + bx + c$, where a, b, and c are real numbers.

a. Prove that f has exactly one local maximum and one local minimum provided that $a^2 > 3b$.
b. Prove that f has no extreme values if $a^2 < 3b$.

T **107. A family of single-humped functions** Consider the functions $f(x) = \dfrac{1}{x^{2n} + 1}$, where n is a positive integer.

a. Show that these functions are even.
b. Show that the graphs of these functions intersect at the points $(\pm 1, \frac{1}{2})$, for all positive values of n.
c. Show that the inflection points of these functions occur at $x = \pm \sqrt[2n]{\dfrac{2n - 1}{2n + 1}}$, for all positive values of n.
d. Use a graphing utility to verify your conclusions.
e. Describe how the inflection points and the shape of the graphs change as n increases.

108. Even quartics Consider the quartic (fourth-degree) polynomial $f(x) = x^4 + bx^2 + d$ consisting only of even-powered terms.

a. Show that the graph of f is symmetric about the y-axis.
b. Show that if $b \geq 0$, then f has one critical point and no inflection points.
c. Show that if $b < 0$, then f has three critical points and two inflection points. Find the critical points and inflection points, and show that they alternate along the x-axis. Explain why one critical point is always $x = 0$.
d. Prove that the number of distinct real roots of f depends on the values of the coefficients b and d, as shown in the figure. The curve that divides the plane is the parabola $d = b^2/4$.
e. Find the number of real roots when $b = 0$ or $d = 0$ or $d = b^2/4$.

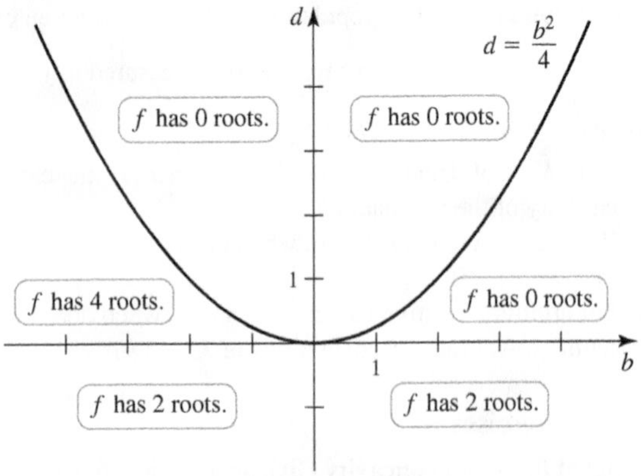

109. General quartic Show that the general quartic (fourth-degree) polynomial $f(x) = x^4 + ax^3 + bx^2 + cx + d$ has either zero or two inflection points, and that the latter case occurs provided that $b < 3a^2/8$.

110. First Derivative Test is not exhaustive Sketch the graph of a (simple) nonconstant function f that has a local maximum at $x = 1$, with $f'(1) = 0$, where f' does not change sign from positive to negative as x increases through 1. Why can't the First Derivative Test be used to classify the critical point at $x = 1$ as a local maximum? How could the test be rephrased to account for such a critical point?

QUICK CHECK ANSWERS

1. Positive derivatives on an interval mean the curve is rising on the interval, which means the function is increasing on the interval. **2.**

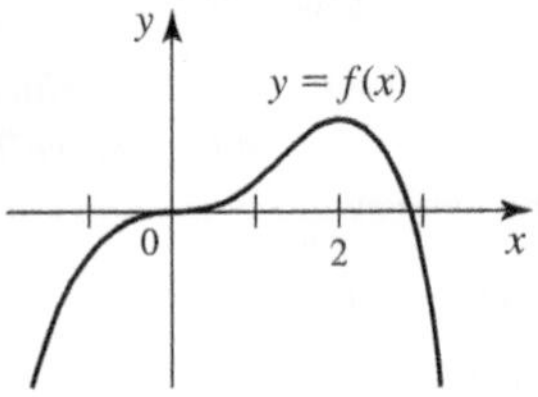

3. $f'(x) < 0$ on $(-\infty, 0)$ and $f'(x) > 0$ on $(0, \infty)$. Therefore, f has a local minimum at $x = 0$ by the First Derivative Test. **4.** $f''(x) = 12x^2$, so $f''(x) > 0$ for $x < 0$ and for $x > 0$. There is no inflection point at $x = 0$ because the second derivative does not change sign. **5.** The first curve should be rising and concave up. The second curve should be falling and concave down.

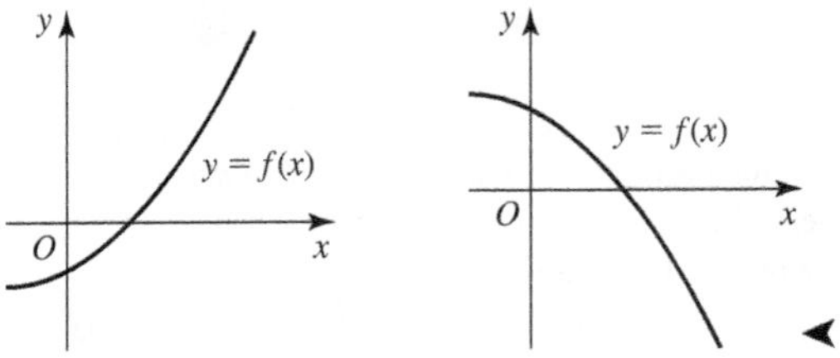

◀

4.3 Graphing Functions

We have now collected the tools required for a comprehensive approach to graphing functions. These *analytical methods* are indispensable, even with the availability of powerful graphing utilities, as illustrated by the following example.

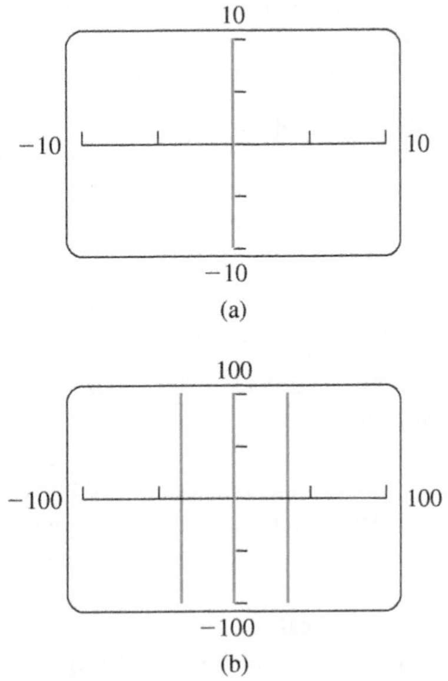

Figure 4.37

Calculators and Analysis

Suppose you want to graph the harmless-looking function $f(x) = x^3/3 - 400x$. The result of plotting f using a graphing calculator with a default window of $[-10, 10] \times [-10, 10]$ is shown in Figure 4.37a; one vertical line appears on the screen. Zooming out to the window $[-100, 100] \times [-100, 100]$ produces three vertical lines (Figure 4.37b); it is still difficult to understand the behavior of the function using only this graph. Expanding the window even more to $[-1000, 1000] \times [-1000, 1000]$ is no better. So what do we do?

QUICK CHECK 1 Graph $f(x) = x^3/3 - 400x$ using various windows on a graphing calculator. Find a window that gives a better graph of f than those in Figure 4.37. ◀

The function $f(x) = x^3/3 - 400x$ has a reasonable graph, but it cannot be found automatically by letting technology do all the work. Here is the message of this section: Graphing utilities are valuable for exploring functions, producing preliminary graphs, and checking your work. But they should not be relied on exclusively because they cannot explain *why* a graph has its shape. Rather, graphing utilities should be used in an interactive way with the analytical methods presented in this chapter.

Graphing Guidelines

The following set of guidelines need not be followed exactly for every function, and you will find that several steps can often be done at once. Depending on the specific problem, some of the steps are best done analytically, while other steps can be done with a graphing utility. Experiment with both approaches and try to find a good balance. We also present a schematic record-keeping procedure to keep track of discoveries as they are made.

Graphing Guidelines for $y = f(x)$

1. **Identify the domain or interval of interest.** On what interval(s) should the function be graphed? It may be the domain of the function or some subset of the domain.
2. **Exploit symmetry.** Take advantage of symmetry. For example, is the function *even* ($f(-x) = f(x)$), *odd* ($f(-x) = -f(x)$), or neither?
3. **Find the first and second derivatives.** They are needed to determine extreme values, concavity, inflection points, and intervals of increase and decrease. Computing derivatives—particularly second derivatives—may not be practical, so some functions may need to be graphed without complete derivative information.
4. **Find critical points and possible inflection points.** Determine points at which $f'(x) = 0$ or f' is undefined. Determine points at which $f''(x) = 0$ or f'' is undefined.
5. **Find intervals on which the function is increasing/decreasing and concave up/down.** The first derivative determines the intervals of increase and decrease. The second derivative determines the intervals on which the function is concave up or concave down.
6. **Identify extreme values and inflection points.** Use either the First or Second Derivative Test to classify the critical points. Both x- and y-coordinates of maxima, minima, and inflection points are needed for graphing.
7. **Locate all asymptotes and determine end behavior.** Vertical asymptotes often occur at zeros of denominators. Horizontal asymptotes require examining limits as $x \to \pm\infty$; these limits determine end behavior.
8. **Find the intercepts.** The y-intercept of the graph is found by setting $x = 0$. The x-intercepts are found by setting $y = 0$; they are the real zeros (or roots) of f (those values of x that satisfy $f(x) = 0$).
9. **Choose an appropriate graphing window and plot a graph.** Use the results of the previous steps to graph the function. If you use graphing software, check for consistency with your analytical work. Is your graph *complete*—that is, does it show all the essential details of the function?

➤ The precise order of these steps may vary from one problem to another.

EXAMPLE 1 **A warm-up** Given the following information about the first and second derivatives of a function f that is continuous on $(-\infty, \infty)$, summarize the information using a sign graph, and then sketch a possible graph of f.

$$f' < 0, f'' > 0 \text{ on } (-\infty, 0) \quad f' > 0, f'' > 0 \text{ on } (0, 1) \quad f' > 0, f'' < 0 \text{ on } (1, 2)$$
$$f' < 0, f'' < 0 \text{ on } (2, 3) \quad f' < 0, f'' > 0 \text{ on } (3, 4) \quad f' > 0, f'' > 0 \text{ on } (4, \infty)$$

SOLUTION Figure 4.38 uses the given information to determine the behavior of f and its graph. For example, on the interval $(-\infty, 0)$, f is decreasing and concave up; so we sketch a segment of a curve with these properties on this interval. Continuing in this manner, we obtain a useful summary of the properties of f.

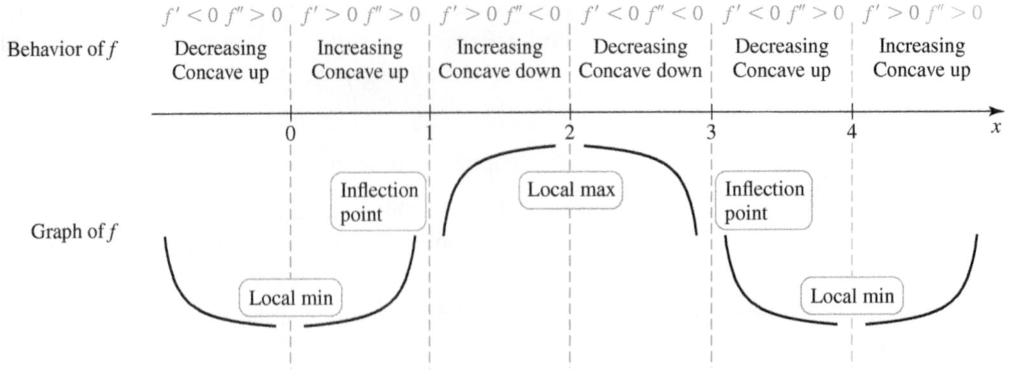

Figure 4.38

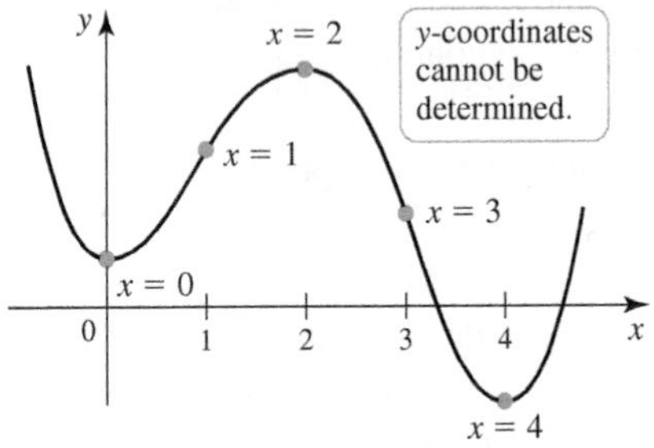

Figure 4.39

Assembling the information shown in Figure 4.38, a possible graph of f is produced (Figure 4.39). Notice that derivative information is not sufficient to determine the y-coordinates of points on the curve.

Related Exercises 7–8 ◀

QUICK CHECK 2 Explain why the function f and $f + C$, where C is a constant, have the same derivative properties. ◀

EXAMPLE 2 **A deceptive polynomial** Use the graphing guidelines to graph $f(x) = \dfrac{x^3}{3} - 400x$ on its domain.

SOLUTION

1. **Domain** The domain of any polynomial is $(-\infty, \infty)$.

➤ Notice that the first derivative of an odd polynomial is an even polynomial and the second derivative is an odd polynomial (assuming the original polynomial is of degree 3 or greater).

2. **Symmetry** Because f consists of odd powers of the variable, it is an odd function. Its graph is symmetric about the origin.
3. **Derivatives** The derivatives of f are

$$f'(x) = x^2 - 400 \quad \text{and} \quad f''(x) = 2x.$$

4. **Critical points and possible inflection points** Solving $f'(x) = 0$, we find that the critical points are $x = \pm 20$. Solving $f''(x) = 0$, we see that a possible inflection point occurs at $x = 0$.

➤ See Appendix A for solving inequalities using test values.

5. **Increasing/decreasing and concavity** Note that

$$f'(x) = x^2 - 400 = (x - 20)(x + 20).$$

Solving the inequality $f'(x) < 0$, we find that f is decreasing on the interval $(-20, 20)$. Solving the inequality $f'(x) > 0$ reveals that f is increasing on the intervals $(-\infty, -20)$ and $(20, \infty)$ (Figure 4.40). By the First Derivative Test, we have enough information to conclude that f has a local maximum at $x = -20$ and a local minimum at $x = 20$.

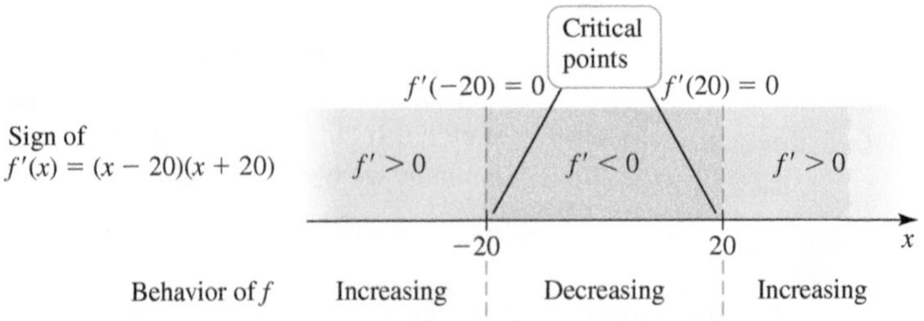

Figure 4.40

Furthermore, $f''(x) = 2x < 0$ on $(-\infty, 0)$, so f is concave down on this interval. Also, $f''(x) > 0$ on $(0, \infty)$, so f is concave up on $(0, \infty)$ (Figure 4.41).

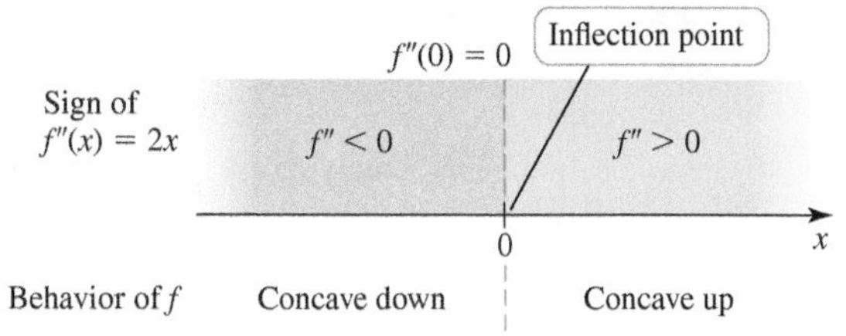

Figure 4.41

The evidence obtained so far is summarized in Figure 4.42.

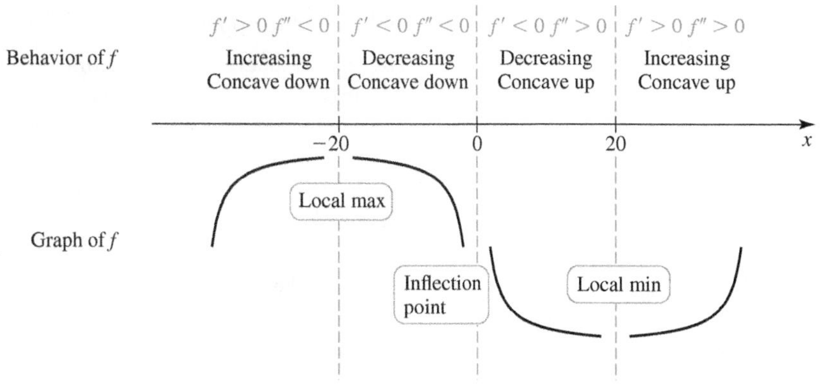

Figure 4.42

6. **Extreme values and inflection points** In this case, the Second Derivative Test is easily applied and it confirms what we have already learned. Because $f''(-20) < 0$ and $f''(20) > 0, f$ has a local maximum at $x = -20$ and a local minimum at $x = 20$. The corresponding function values are $f(-20) = 16{,}000/3 = 5333\frac{1}{3}$ and $f(20) = -f(-20) = -5333\frac{1}{3}$. Finally, we see that f'' changes sign at $x = 0$, making $(0, 0)$ an inflection point.

7. **Asymptotes and end behavior** Polynomials have neither vertical nor horizontal asymptotes. Because the highest-power term in the polynomial is x^3 (an odd power) and the leading coefficient is positive, we have the end behavior

$$\lim_{x\to\infty} f(x) = \infty \quad \text{and} \quad \lim_{x\to-\infty} f(x) = -\infty.$$

8. **Intercepts** The y-intercept is $(0, 0)$. We solve the equation $f(x) = 0$ to find the x-intercepts:

$$\frac{x^3}{3} - 400x = x\left(\frac{x^2}{3} - 400\right) = 0.$$

The roots of this equation are $x = 0$ and $x = \pm\sqrt{1200} \approx \pm 34.6$.

9. **Graph the function** Using the information found in Steps 1–8, we choose the graphing window $[-40, 40] \times [-6000, 6000]$ and produce the graph shown in Figure 4.43. Notice that the symmetry detected in Step 2 is evident in this graph.

Related Exercises 9–14 ◀

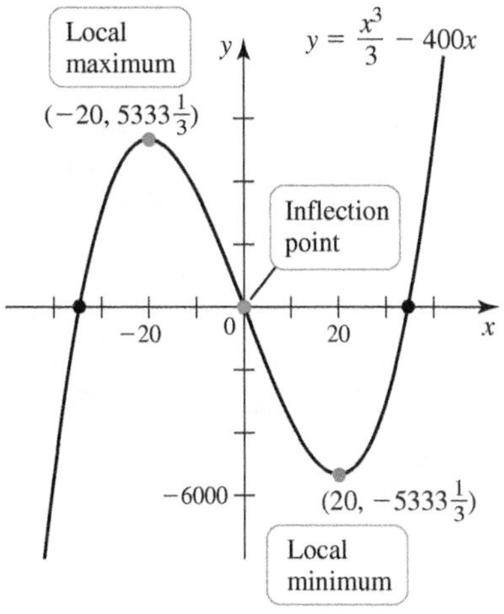

Figure 4.43

EXAMPLE 3 **The surprises of a rational function** Use the graphing guidelines to graph $f(x) = \dfrac{10x^3}{x^2 - 1}$ on its domain.

SOLUTION

1. **Domain** The zeros of the denominator are $x = \pm 1$, so the domain is $\{x: x \neq \pm 1\}$.
2. **Symmetry** This function consists of an odd function divided by an even function. The product or quotient of an even function and an odd function is odd. Therefore, the graph is symmetric about the origin.
3. **Derivatives** The Quotient Rule is used to find the first and second derivatives:
$$f'(x) = \frac{10x^2(x^2 - 3)}{(x^2 - 1)^2} \quad \text{and} \quad f''(x) = \frac{20x(x^2 + 3)}{(x^2 - 1)^3}.$$
4. **Critical points and possible inflection points** The solutions of $f'(x) = 0$ occur where the numerator equals 0, provided the denominator is nonzero at those points. Solving $10x^2(x^2 - 3) = 0$ gives the critical points $x = 0$ and $x = \pm\sqrt{3}$. The solutions of $f''(x) = 0$ are found by solving $20x(x^2 + 3) = 0$; we see that the only possible inflection point occurs at $x = 0$.
5. **Increasing/decreasing and concavity** To find the sign of f', first note that the denominator of f' is nonnegative, as is the factor $10x^2$ in the numerator. So the sign of f' is determined by the sign of the factor $x^2 - 3$, which is negative on $(-\sqrt{3}, \sqrt{3})$ (excluding $x = \pm 1$) and positive on $(-\infty, -\sqrt{3})$ and $(\sqrt{3}, \infty)$. Therefore, f is decreasing on $(-\sqrt{3}, \sqrt{3})$ (excluding $x = \pm 1$) and increasing on $(-\infty, -\sqrt{3})$ and $(\sqrt{3}, \infty)$.

   The sign of f'' is a bit trickier. Because $x^2 + 3$ is positive, the sign of f'' is determined by the sign of $20x$ in the numerator and $(x^2 - 1)^3$ in the denominator. When $20x$ and $(x^2 - 1)^3$ have the same sign, $f''(x) > 0$; when $20x$ and $(x^2 - 1)^3$ have opposite signs, $f''(x) < 0$ (Table 4.1). The results of this analysis are shown in Figure 4.44.

➤ Sign charts and sign graphs (Table 4.1 and Figure 4.44) must be constructed carefully when vertical asymptotes are involved: The sign of f' and f'' may or may not change at an asymptote.

Table 4.1

	$20x$	$x^2 + 3$	$(x^2 - 1)^3$	Sign of f''
$(-\infty, -1)$	−	+	+	−
$(-1, 0)$	−	+	−	+
$(0, 1)$	+	+	−	−
$(1, \infty)$	+	+	+	+

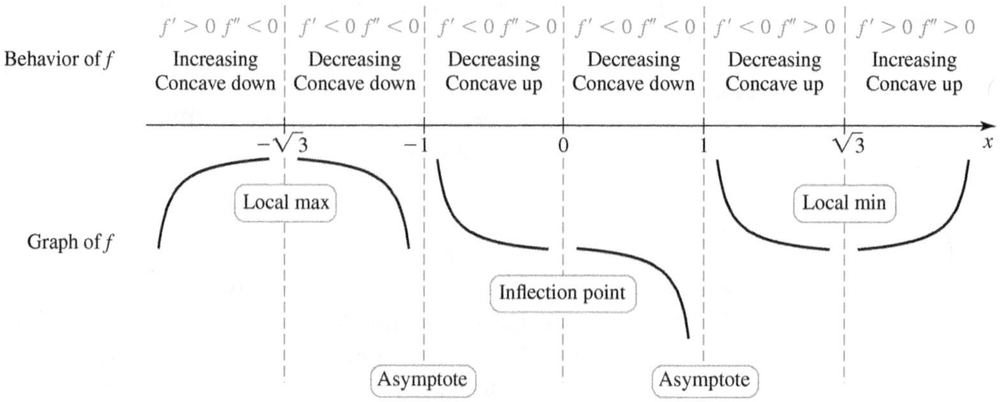

Figure 4.44

6. **Extreme values and inflection points** The First Derivative Test is easily applied by looking at Figure 4.44. The function is increasing on $(-\infty, -\sqrt{3})$ and decreasing on $(-\sqrt{3}, -1)$; therefore, f has a local maximum at $x = -\sqrt{3}$, where $f(-\sqrt{3}) = -15\sqrt{3}$. Similarly, f has a local minimum at $x = \sqrt{3}$, where $f(\sqrt{3}) = 15\sqrt{3}$. (These results could also be obtained with the Second Derivative Test.) There is no local extreme value at the critical point $x = 0$, only a horizontal tangent line.

   Using Table 4.1 from Step 5, we see that f'' changes sign at $x = \pm 1$ and at $x = 0$. The points $x = \pm 1$ are not in the domain of f, so they cannot correspond to inflection points. However, there is an inflection point at $(0, 0)$.

7. **Asymptotes and end behavior** Recall from Section 2.4 that zeros of the denominator, which in this case are $x = \pm 1$, are candidates for vertical asymptotes. Checking the behavior of f on either side of $x = \pm 1$, we find

$$\lim_{x\to -1^-} f(x) = -\infty, \qquad \lim_{x\to -1^+} f(x) = \infty.$$

$$\lim_{x\to 1^-} f(x) = -\infty, \qquad \lim_{x\to 1^+} f(x) = \infty.$$

   It follows that f has vertical asymptotes at $x = \pm 1$. The degree of the numerator is greater than the degree of the denominator, so there is no horizontal asymptote. Using long division, it can be shown that

$$f(x) = 10x + \frac{10x}{x^2 - 1}.$$

   Therefore, as $x \to \pm\infty$, the graph of f approaches the line $y = 10x$. This line is a slant asymptote (Section 2.5).

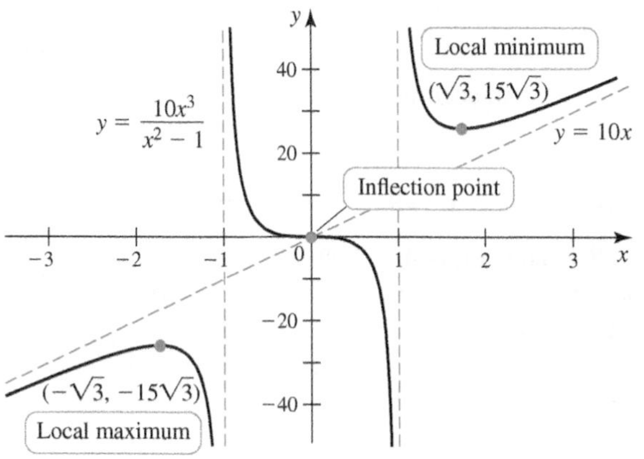

Figure 4.45

8. **Intercepts** The zeros of a rational function coincide with the zeros of the numerator, provided that those points are not also zeros of the denominator. In this case, the zeros of f satisfy $10x^3 = 0$, or $x = 0$ (which is not a zero of the denominator). Therefore, $(0, 0)$ is both the x- and y-intercept.

9. **Graphing** We now assemble an accurate graph of f, as shown in Figure 4.45. A window of $[-3, 3] \times [-40, 40]$ gives a complete graph of the function. Notice that the symmetry about the origin deduced in Step 2 is apparent in the graph.

Related Exercises 15–20 ◄

QUICK CHECK 3 Verify that the function f in Example 3 is symmetric about the origin by showing that $f(-x) = -f(x)$. ◄

In the next two examples, we show how the guidelines may be streamlined to some extent.

➤ The function $f(x) = e^{-x^2}$ and the family of functions $f(x) = ce^{-ax^2}$ are central to the study of statistics. They have bell-shaped graphs and describe Gaussian or normal distributions.

EXAMPLE 4 **The normal distribution** Analyze the function $f(x) = e^{-x^2}$ and draw its graph.

SOLUTION The domain of f is all real numbers, and $f(x) > 0$ for all x. Because $f(-x) = f(x)$, f is an even function and its graph is symmetric about the y-axis.

Extreme values and inflection points follow from the derivatives of f. Using the Chain Rule, we have $f'(x) = -2xe^{-x^2}$. The critical points satisfy $f'(x) = 0$, which has the single root $x = 0$ (because $e^{-x^2} > 0$ for all x). It now follows that

- $f'(x) > 0$, for $x < 0$, so f is increasing on $(-\infty, 0)$.
- $f'(x) < 0$, for $x > 0$, so f is decreasing on $(0, \infty)$.

By the First Derivative Test, we see that f has a local maximum (and an absolute maximum by Theorem 4.5) at $x = 0$ where $f(0) = 1$.

Differentiating $f'(x) = -2xe^{-x^2}$ with the Product Rule yields

$$f''(x) = e^{-x^2}(-2) + (-2x)(-2xe^{-x^2}) \quad \text{Product Rule}$$
$$= 2e^{-x^2}(2x^2 - 1). \quad \text{Simplify.}$$

Again using the fact that $e^{-x^2} > 0$, for all x, we see that $f''(x) = 0$ when $2x^2 - 1 = 0$ or when $x = \pm 1/\sqrt{2}$; these values are candidates for inflection points. Observe that $f''(x) > 0$ and f is concave up on $(-\infty, -1/\sqrt{2})$ and $(1/\sqrt{2}, \infty)$, while $f''(x) < 0$ and f is concave down on $(-1/\sqrt{2}, 1/\sqrt{2})$. Because f'' changes sign at $x = \pm 1/\sqrt{2}$, we have inflection points at $(\pm 1/\sqrt{2}, 1/\sqrt{e})$ (Figure 4.46).

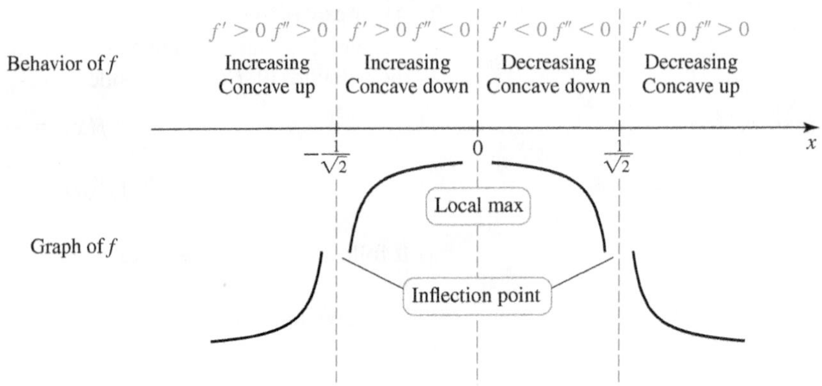

Figure 4.46

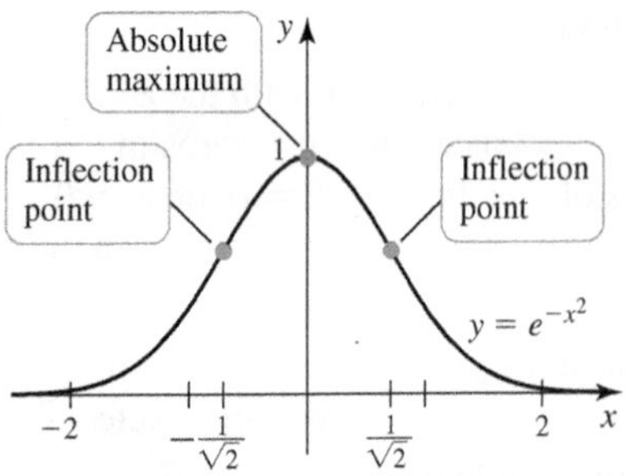

Figure 4.47

To determine the end behavior, notice that $\lim_{x \to \pm\infty} e^{-x^2} = 0$, so $y = 0$ is a horizontal asymptote of f. Assembling all of these facts, an accurate graph can now be drawn (Figure 4.47).

Related Exercises 21–42 ◀

EXAMPLE 5 **Roots and cusps** Graph $f(x) = \frac{1}{8}x^{2/3}(9x^2 - 8x - 16)$ on its domain.

SOLUTION The domain of f is $(-\infty, \infty)$. The polynomial factor in f consists of both even and odd powers, so f has no special symmetry. Computing the first derivative is straightforward if you first expand f as a sum of three terms:

$$f'(x) = \frac{d}{dx}\left(\frac{9x^{8/3}}{8} - x^{5/3} - 2x^{2/3}\right) \quad \text{Expand } f.$$
$$= 3x^{5/3} - \frac{5}{3}x^{2/3} - \frac{4}{3}x^{-1/3} \quad \text{Differentiate.}$$
$$= \frac{(x-1)(9x+4)}{3x^{1/3}}. \quad \text{Simplify.}$$

The critical points are now identified: f' is undefined at $x = 0$ (because $x^{-1/3}$ is undefined there) and $f'(x) = 0$ at $x = 1$ and $x = -\frac{4}{9}$. So we have three critical points to analyze. Table 4.2 tracks the signs of the factors in the numerator and denominator of f', and shows the sign of f' on the relevant intervals; this information is recorded in Figure 4.48.

Table 4.2

	$3x^{1/3}$	$9x + 4$	$x - 1$	Sign of f'
$(-\infty, -\frac{4}{9})$	−	−	−	−
$(-\frac{4}{9}, 0)$	−	+	−	+
$(0, 1)$	+	+	−	−
$(1, \infty)$	+	+	+	+

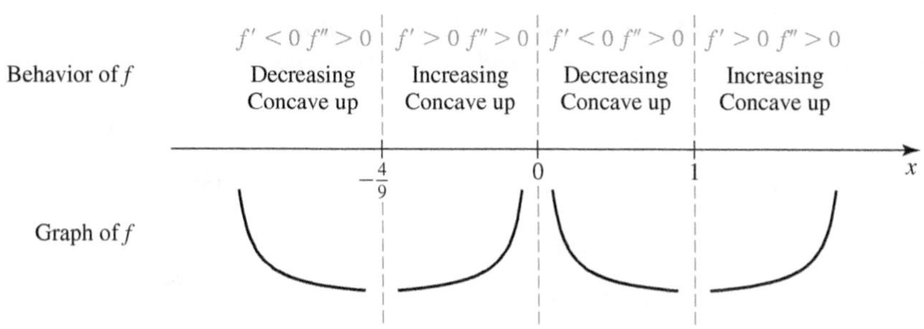

Figure 4.48

➤ To show that $f''(x) > 0$ (for $x \neq 0$), analyze its numerator and denominator.

- The graph of $45x^2 - 10x + 4$ is a parabola that opens upward (its leading coefficient is positive) with no x-intercepts (verified by the quadratic formula). Therefore, the numerator is always positive.
- The denominator is nonnegative because $9x^{4/3} = 9(x^{1/3})^4$ (even powers are nonnegative).

We use the second line in the calculation of f' to compute the second derivative:

$$f''(x) = \frac{d}{dx}\left(3x^{5/3} - \frac{5}{3}x^{2/3} - \frac{4}{3}x^{-1/3}\right)$$

$$= 5x^{2/3} - \frac{10}{9}x^{-1/3} + \frac{4}{9}x^{-4/3} \qquad \text{Differentiate.}$$

$$= \frac{45x^2 - 10x + 4}{9x^{4/3}}. \qquad \text{Simplify.}$$

Solving $f''(x) = 0$, we discover that $f''(x) > 0$, for all x except $x = 0$, where it is undefined. Therefore, f is concave up on $(-\infty, 0)$ and $(0, \infty)$ (Figure 4.48).

By the Second Derivative Test, because $f''(x) > 0$, for $x \neq 0$, the critical points $x = -\frac{4}{9}$ and $x = 1$ correspond to local minima; their y-coordinates are $f\left(-\frac{4}{9}\right) \approx -0.78$ and $f(1) = -\frac{15}{8} = -1.875$.

What about the third critical point $x = 0$? Note that $f(0) = 0$, and f is increasing just to the left of 0 and decreasing just to the right. By the First Derivative Test, f has a local maximum at $x = 0$. Furthermore, $f'(x) \to \infty$ as $x \to 0^-$ and $f'(x) \to -\infty$ as $x \to 0^+$, so the graph of f has a cusp at $x = 0$.

As $x \to \pm\infty$, f is dominated by its highest-power term, which is $9x^{8/3}/8$. This term becomes large and positive as $x \to \pm\infty$; therefore, f has no absolute maximum. Its absolute minimum occurs at $x = 1$ because, comparing the two local minima, $f(1) < f\left(-\frac{4}{9}\right)$.

The roots of f satisfy $\frac{1}{8}x^{2/3}(9x^2 - 8x - 16) = 0$, which gives $x = 0$ and

$$x = \frac{4}{9}(1 \pm \sqrt{10}) \approx -0.96 \quad \text{and} \quad 1.85. \qquad \text{Use the quadratic formula.}$$

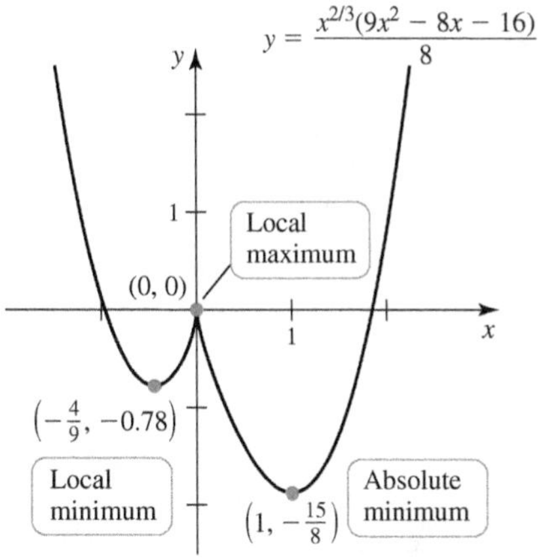

Figure 4.49

With the information gathered in this analysis, we obtain the graph shown in Figure 4.49.

Related Exercises 21–42 ◀

SECTION 4.3 EXERCISES

Review Questions

1. Why is it important to determine the domain of f before graphing f?
2. Explain why it is useful to know about symmetry in a function.
3. Can the graph of a polynomial have vertical or horizontal asymptotes? Explain.
4. Where are the vertical asymptotes of a rational function located?
5. How do you find the absolute maximum and minimum values of a function that is continuous on a closed interval?
6. Describe the possible end behavior of a polynomial.

Basic Skills

7–8. Shape of the curve *Sketch a curve with the following properties.*

7. $f' < 0$ and $f'' < 0$, for $x < 3$
$f' < 0$ and $f'' > 0$, for $x > 3$

8. $f' < 0$ and $f'' < 0$, for $x < -1$
$f' < 0$ and $f'' > 0$, for $-1 < x < 2$
$f' > 0$ and $f'' > 0$, for $2 < x < 8$
$f' > 0$ and $f'' < 0$, for $8 < x < 10$
$f' > 0$ and $f'' > 0$, for $x > 10$

9–14. Graphing polynomials *Sketch a graph of the following polynomials. Identify local extrema, inflection points, and x- and y-intercepts when they exist.*

9. $f(x) = x^3 - 6x^2 + 9x$ **10.** $f(x) = 3x - x^3$

11. $f(x) = x^4 - 6x^2$ **12.** $f(x) = 2x^6 - 3x^4$

13. $f(x) = (x - 6)(x + 6)^2$ **14.** $f(x) = 27(x - 2)^2(x + 2)$

15–20. Graphing rational functions *Use the guidelines of this section to make a complete graph of f.*

15. $f(x) = \dfrac{x^2}{x - 2}$ **16.** $f(x) = \dfrac{x^2}{x^2 - 4}$

17. $f(x) = \dfrac{3x}{x^2 - 1}$ **18.** $f(x) = \dfrac{2x - 3}{2x - 8}$

19. $f(x) = \dfrac{x^2 + 12}{2x + 1}$ T **20.** $f(x) = \dfrac{4x + 4}{x^2 + 3}$

T **21–36. More graphing** *Make a complete graph of the following functions. If an interval is not specified, graph the function on its domain. Use a graphing utility to check your work.*

21. $f(x) = \tan^{-1} x^2$ **22.** $f(x) = \ln (x^2 + 1)$

23. $f(x) = x + 2 \cos x$ on $[-2\pi, 2\pi]$

24. $f(x) = x - 3x^{2/3}$ **25.** $f(x) = x - 3x^{1/3}$

26. $f(x) = 2 - x^{2/3} + x^{4/3}$ **27.** $f(x) = \sin x - x$ on $[0, 2\pi]$

28. $f(x) = x\sqrt{x + 3}$ **29.** $g(t) = e^{-t} \sin t$ on $[-\pi, \pi]$

30. $g(x) = x^2 \ln x$

31. $f(x) = x + \tan x$ on $\left(-\dfrac{3\pi}{2}, \dfrac{3\pi}{2}\right)$

32. $f(x) = (\ln x)/x^2$ **33.** $f(x) = x \ln x$

34. $g(x) = e^{-x^2/2}$ **35.** $p(x) = xe^{-x^2}$

36. $g(x) = 1/(e^{-x} - 1)$

T **37–42. Graphing with technology** *Make a complete graph of the following functions. A graphing utility is useful in locating intercepts, local extreme values, and inflection points.*

37. $f(x) = \dfrac{1}{3}x^3 - 2x^2 - 5x + 2$

38. $f(x) = \dfrac{1}{15}x^3 - x + 1$

39. $f(x) = 3x^4 + 4x^3 - 12x^2$

40. $f(x) = x^3 - 33x^2 + 216x - 2$

41. $f(x) = \dfrac{3x - 5}{x^2 - 1}$

42. $f(x) = x^{1/3}(x - 2)^2$

Further Explorations

43. Explain why or why not Determine whether the following statements are true and give an explanation or counterexample.

a. If the zeros of f' are -3, 1, and 4, then the local extrema of f are located at these points.

b. If the zeros of f'' are -2 and 4, then the inflection points of f are located at these points.

c. If the zeros of the denominator of f are -3 and 4, then f has vertical asymptotes at these points.

d. If a rational function has a finite limit as $x \to \infty$, then it must have a finite limit as $x \to -\infty$.

44–47. Functions from derivatives *Use the derivative f' to determine the x-coordinates of the local maxima and minima of f, and the intervals of increase and decrease. Sketch a possible graph of f (f is not unique).*

44. $f'(x) = (x - 1)(x + 2)(x + 4)$

45. $f'(x) = 10 \sin 2x$ on $[-2\pi, 2\pi]$

46. $f'(x) = \dfrac{1}{6}(x + 1)(x - 2)^2(x - 3)$

47. $f'(x) = x^2(x + 2)(x - 1)$

48–49. Functions from graphs *Use the graphs of f' and f'' to find the critical points and inflection points of f, the intervals on which f is increasing and decreasing, and the intervals of concavity. Then graph f assuming $f(0) = 0$.*

48.

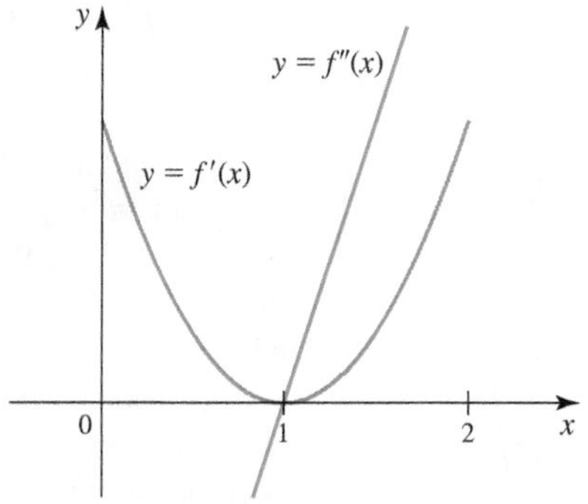

49.

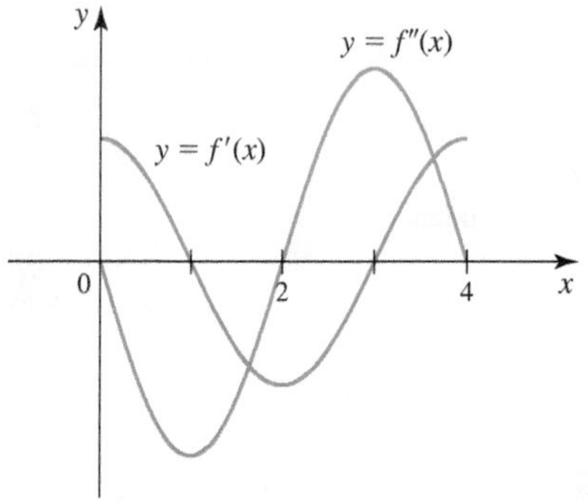

50–53. Nice cubics and quartics *The following third- and fourth-degree polynomials have a property that makes them relatively easy to graph. Make a complete graph and describe the property.*

50. $f(x) = x^4 + 8x^3 - 270x^2 + 1$

51. $f(x) = x^3 - 6x^2 - 135x$

52. $f(x) = x^3 - 147x + 286$

53. $f(x) = x^3 - 3x^2 - 144x - 140$

T **54. Oscillations** Consider the function $f(x) = \cos (\ln x)$, for $x > 0$. Use analytical techniques and a graphing utility.

a. Locate all local extrema on the interval $(0, 4]$.

b. Identify the inflection points on the interval $(0, 4]$.

c. Locate the three smallest zeros of f on the interval $(0.1, \infty)$.

d. Sketch the graph of f.

55. Local max/min of $x^{1/x}$ Use analytical methods to find all local extrema of the function $f(x) = x^{1/x}$, for $x > 0$. Verify your work using a graphing utility.

56. Local max/min of x^x Use analytical methods to find all local extrema of the function $f(x) = x^x$, for $x > 0$. Verify your work using a graphing utility.

57–60. Designer functions *Sketch a continuous function f on some interval that has the properties described.*

57. The function f has one inflection point but no local extrema.

58. The function f has three real zeros and exactly two local minima.

59. The function f satisfies $f'(-2) = 2, f'(0) = 0, f'(1) = -3$, and $f'(4) = 1$.

60. The function f has the same finite limit as $x \to \pm\infty$ and has exactly one absolute minimum and one absolute maximum.

T **61–68. More graphing** *Sketch a complete graph of the following functions. Use analytical methods and a graphing utility together in a complementary way.*

61. $f(x) = \dfrac{-x\sqrt{x^2 - 4}}{x - 2}$

62. $f(x) = 3\sqrt[4]{x} - \sqrt{x} - 2$

63. $f(x) = 3x^4 - 44x^3 + 60x^2$ (*Hint:* Two different graphing windows may be needed.)

64. $f(x) = \dfrac{1}{1 + \cos \pi x}$ on $(1, 3)$

65. $f(x) = 10x^6 - 36x^5 - 75x^4 + 300x^3 + 120x^2 - 720x$

66. $f(x) = \dfrac{\sin \pi x}{1 + \sin \pi x}$ on $[0, 2]$

67. $f(x) = \dfrac{x\sqrt{|x^2 - 1|}}{x^4 + 1}$

68. $f(x) = \sin(3\pi \cos x)$ on $[-\pi/2, \pi/2]$

T **69. Hidden oscillations** Use analytical methods together with a graphing utility to graph the following functions on the interval $[-2\pi, 2\pi]$. Define f at $x = 0$ so that it is continuous there. Be sure to uncover all relevant features of the graph.

a. $f(x) = \dfrac{1 - \cos^3 x}{x^2}$ **b.** $f(x) = \dfrac{1 - \cos^5 x}{x^2}$

70. Cubic with parameters Locate all local maxima and minima of $f(x) = x^3 - 3bx^2 + 3a^2x + 23$, where a and b are constants, in the following cases.

a. $|a| < |b|$ **b.** $|a| > |b|$ **c.** $|a| = |b|$

Applications

71. Height functions The figure shows six containers, each of which is filled from the top. Assume that water is poured into the containers at a constant rate and each container is filled in 10 seconds. Assume also that the horizontal cross sections of the containers are always circles. Let $h(t)$ be the depth of water in the container at time t, for $0 \le t \le 10$.

a. For each container, sketch a graph of the function $y = h(t)$, for $0 \le t \le 10$.
b. Explain why h is an increasing function.
c. Describe the concavity of the function. Identify inflection points when they occur.
d. For each container, where does h' (the derivative of h) have an absolute maximum on $[0, 10]$?

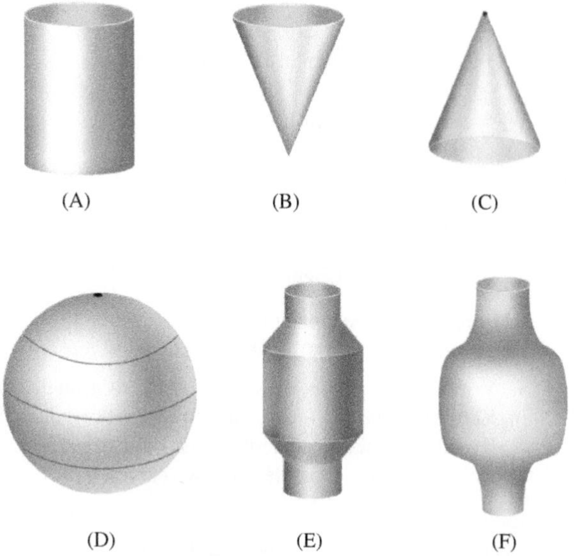

T **72. A pursuit curve** A man is stands 1 mi east of a crossroads. At noon, a dog starts walking north from the crossroads at 1 mi/hr (see figure). At the same instant, the man starts walking and at all times walks directly toward the dog at $s > 1$ mi/hr. The path in the xy plane followed by the man as he pursues his dog is given by the function

$$y = f(x) = \frac{s}{2}\left(\frac{x^{(s+1)/s}}{s + 1} - \frac{x^{(s-1)/s}}{s - 1}\right) + \frac{s}{s^2 - 1}.$$

Select various values of $s > 1$ and graph this pursuit curve. Comment on the changes in the curve as s increases.

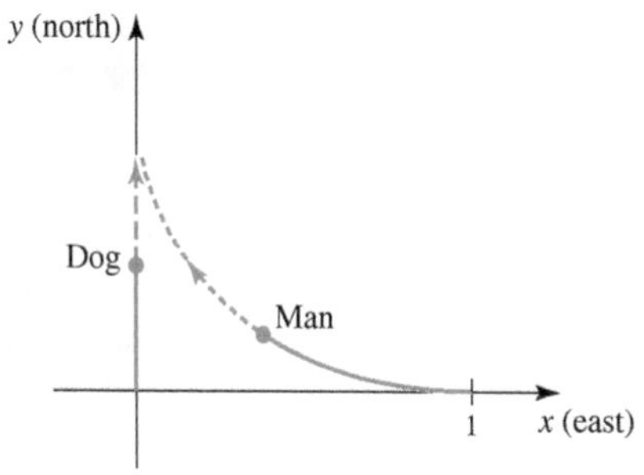

Additional Exercises

73. Derivative information Suppose a continuous function f is concave up on $(-\infty, 0)$ and $(0, \infty)$. Assume f has a local maximum at $x = 0$. What, if anything, do you know about $f'(0)$? Explain with an illustration.

74. $e^\pi > \pi^e$ Prove that $e^\pi > \pi^e$ by first finding the maximum value of $f(x) = \ln x/x$.

T 75–81. Special curves *The following classical curves have been studied by generations of mathematicians. Use analytical methods (including implicit differentiation) and a graphing utility to graph the curves. Include as much detail as possible.*

75. $x^{2/3} + y^{2/3} = 1$ (Astroid or hypocycloid with four cusps)

76. $y = \dfrac{8}{x^2 + 4}$ (Witch of Agnesi)

77. $x^3 + y^3 = 3xy$ (Folium of Descartes)

78. $y^2 = \dfrac{x^3}{2 - x}$ (Cissoid of Diocles)

79. $y^4 - x^4 - 4y^2 + 5x^2 = 0$ (Devil's curve)

80. $y^2 = x^3(1 - x)$ (Pear curve)

81. $x^4 - x^2 + y^2 = 0$ (Figure-8 curve)

T 82. Elliptic curves The equation $y^2 = x^3 - ax + 3$, where a is a parameter, defines a well-known family of *elliptic curves*.

a. Verify that if $a = 3$, the graph consists of a single curve.
b. Verify that if $a = 4$, the graph consists of two distinct curves.
c. By experimentation, determine the value of a $(3 < a < 4)$ at which the graph separates into two curves.

T 83. Lamé curves The equation $|y/a|^n + |x/a|^n = 1$, where n and a are positive real numbers, defines the family of Lamé curves. Make a complete graph of this function with $a = 1$, for $n = \frac{2}{3}, 1, 2, 3$. Describe the progression that you observe as n increases.

T 84. An exotic curve (Putnam Exam 1942) Find the coordinates of four local maxima of the function $f(x) = \dfrac{x}{1 + x^6 \sin^2 x}$ and graph the function, for $0 \le x \le 10$.

T 85. A family of superexponential functions Let $f(x) = (a - x)^x$, where $a > 0$.

a. What is the domain of f (in terms of a)?
b. Describe the end behavior of f (near the boundary of its domain).
c. Compute f'. Then graph f and f' for $a = 0.5, 1, 2$, and 3.
d. Show that f has a single local maximum at the point z that satisfies $z = (a - z) \ln (a - z)$.
e. Describe how z (found in part (d)) varies as a increases. Describe how $f(z)$ varies as a increases.

86. x^y versus y^x Consider positive real numbers x and y. Notice that $4^3 < 3^4$, while $3^2 > 2^3$ and $4^2 = 2^4$. Describe the regions in the first quadrant of the xy-plane in which $x^y > y^x$ and $x^y < y^x$.

T 87–90. Combining technology with analytical methods *Use a graphing utility together with analytical methods to create a complete graph of the following functions. Be sure to find and label the intercepts, local extrema, inflection points, asymptotes, intervals where the function is increasing/decreasing, and intervals of concavity.*

87. $f(x) = \dfrac{\tan^{-1} x}{x^2 + 1}$

88. $f(x) = \dfrac{\sqrt{4x^2 + 1}}{x^2 + 1}$

89. $f(x) = \dfrac{x \sin x}{x^2 + 1}$ on $[-2\pi, 2\pi]$

90. $f(x) = x/\ln x$

QUICK CHECK ANSWERS

1. Make the window larger in the y-direction.
2. Notice that f and $f + C$ have the same derivatives.
3. $f(-x) = \dfrac{10(-x)^3}{(-x)^2 - 1} = -\dfrac{10x^3}{x^2 - 1} = -f(x)$ ◀

4.4 Optimization Problems

The theme of this section is *optimization*, a topic arising in many disciplines that rely on mathematics. A structural engineer may seek the dimensions of a beam that maximize strength for a specified cost. A packaging designer may seek the dimensions of a container that maximize the volume of the container for a given surface area. Airline strategists need to find the best allocation of airliners among several hubs to minimize fuel costs and maximize passenger miles. In all these examples, the challenge is to find an *efficient* way to carry out a task, where "efficient" could mean least expensive, most profitable, least time consuming, or, as you will see, many other measures.

To introduce the ideas behind optimization problems, think about pairs of nonnegative real numbers x and y between 0 and 20 with the property that their sum is 20, that is, $x + y = 20$. Of all possible pairs, which has the greatest product?

Table 4.3 displays a few cases showing how the product of two nonnegative numbers varies while their sum remains constant. The condition that $x + y = 20$ is called a **constraint**: It tells us to consider only (nonnegative) values of x and y satisfying this equation.

The quantity that we wish to maximize (or minimize in other cases) is called the **objective function**; in this case, the objective function is the product $P = xy$. From

Table 4.3

x	y	$x + y$	$P = xy$
1	19	20	19
5.5	14.5	20	79.75
9	11	20	99
13	7	20	91
18	2	20	36

Table 4.3, it appears that the product is greatest if both x and y are near the middle of the interval $[0, 20]$.

This simple problem has all the essential features of optimization problems. At their heart, optimization problems take the following form:

What is the maximum (minimum) value of an objective function subject to the given constraint(s)?

➤ In this problem, it is just as easy to eliminate x as y. In other problems, eliminating one variable may result in less work than eliminating other variables.

For the problem at hand, this question would be stated as, "What pair of nonnegative numbers maximizes $P = xy$ subject to the constraint $x + y = 20$?" The first step is to use the constraint to express the objective function $P = xy$ in terms of a single variable. In this case, the constraint is

$$x + y = 20, \quad \text{or} \quad y = 20 - x.$$

Substituting for y, the objective function becomes

$$P = xy = x(20 - x) = 20x - x^2,$$

which is a function of the single variable x. Notice that the values of x lie in the interval $0 \le x \le 20$ with $P(0) = P(20) = 0$.

To maximize P, we first find the critical points by solving

$$P'(x) = 20 - 2x = 0$$

to obtain the solution $x = 10$. To find the absolute maximum value of P on the interval $[0, 20]$, we check the endpoints and the critical points. Because $P(0) = P(20) = 0$ and $P(10) = 100$, we conclude that P has its absolute maximum value at $x = 10$. By the constraint $x + y = 20$, the numbers with the greatest product are $x = y = 10$, and their product is $P = 100$.

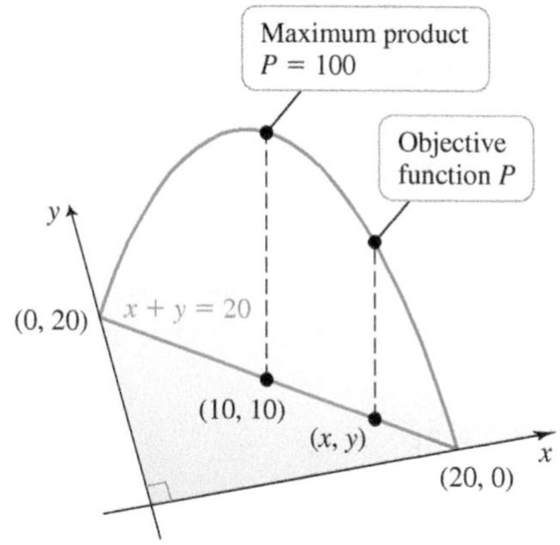

Figure 4.50

Figure 4.50 summarizes this problem. We see the constraint line $x + y = 20$ in the xy-plane. Above the line is the objective function $P = xy$. As x and y vary along the constraint line, the objective function changes, reaching a maximum value of 100 when $x = y = 10$.

QUICK CHECK 1 Verify that in the previous example, the same result is obtained if the constraint $x + y = 20$ is used to eliminate x rather than y. ◀

Most optimization problems have the same basic structure as the preceding example: There is an objective function, which may involve several variables, and one or more constraints. The methods of calculus (Sections 4.1 and 4.2) are used to find the minimum or maximum values of the objective function.

EXAMPLE 1 Rancher's dilemma A rancher has 400 ft of fence for constructing a rectangular corral. One side of the corral will be formed by a barn and requires no fence. Three exterior fences and two interior fences partition the corral into three rectangular regions as shown in Figure 4.51. What are the dimensions of the corral that maximize the enclosed area? What is the area of that corral?

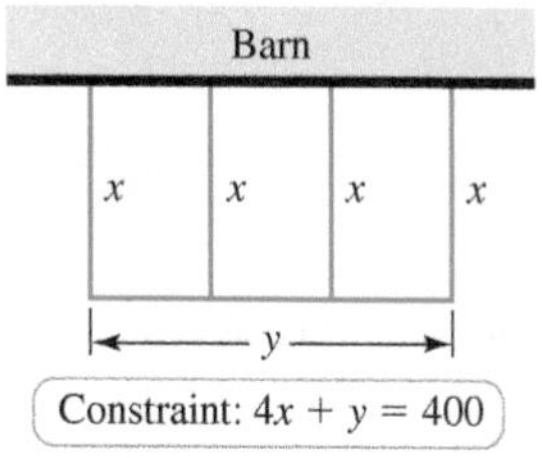

Figure 4.51

SOLUTION We first sketch the corral (Figure 4.51), where $x \ge 0$ is the width and $y \ge 0$ is the length of the corral. The amount of fence required is $4x + y$, so the constraint is $4x + y = 400$, or $y = 400 - 4x$.

The objective function to be maximized is the area of the corral, $A = xy$. Using $y = 400 - 4x$, we eliminate y and express A as a function of x:

$$A = xy = x(400 - 4x) = 400x - 4x^2.$$

➤ Recall from Section 4.1 that the absolute extreme values occur at critical points or endpoints.

Notice that the width of the corral must be at least $x = 0$, and it cannot exceed $x = 100$ (because 400 ft of fence are available). Therefore, we maximize $A(x) = 400x - 4x^2$, for $0 \le x \le 100$. The critical points of the objective function satisfy

$$A'(x) = 400 - 8x = 0,$$

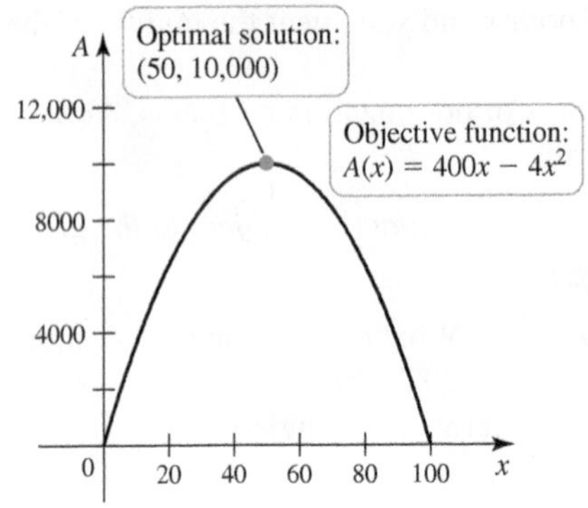

Figure 4.52

which has the solution $x = 50$. To find the absolute maximum value of A, we check the endpoints of $[0, 100]$ and the critical point $x = 50$. Because $A(0) = A(100) = 0$ and $A(50) = 10{,}000$, the absolute maximum value of A occurs when $x = 50$. Using the constraint, the optimal length of the corral is $y = 400 - 4(50) = 200$. Therefore, the maximum area of $10{,}000 \text{ ft}^2$ is achieved with dimensions $x = 50$ ft and $y = 200$ ft. The objective function A is shown in Figure 4.52.

Related Exercises 5–14 ◀

QUICK CHECK 2 Find the objective function in Example 1 (in terms of x) (i) if there is no interior fence and (ii) if there is one interior fence that forms a right angle with the barn, as in Figure 4.51. ◀

EXAMPLE 2 Airline regulations Suppose an airline policy states that all baggage must be box-shaped with a sum of length, width, and height not exceeding 64 in. What are the dimensions and volume of a square-based box with the greatest volume under these conditions?

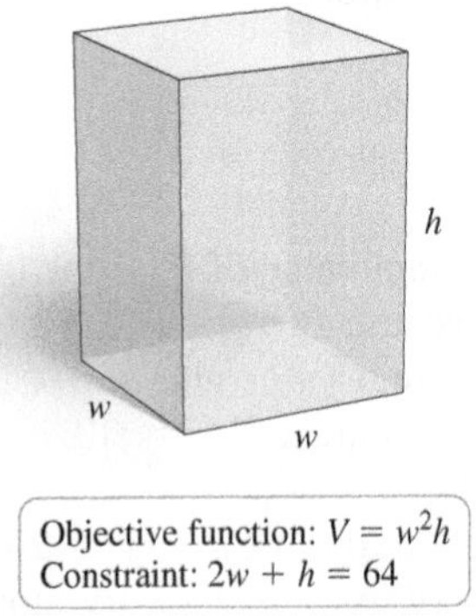

Figure 4.53

SOLUTION We sketch a square-based box whose length and width are w and whose height is h (Figure 4.53). By the airline policy, the constraint is $2w + h = 64$. The objective function is the volume, $V = w^2h$. Either w or h may be eliminated from the objective function; the constraint $h = 64 - 2w$ implies that the volume is

$$V = w^2h = w^2(64 - 2w) = 64w^2 - 2w^3.$$

The objective function has now been expressed in terms of a single variable. Notice that w is nonnegative and cannot exceed 32, so the domain of V is $0 \le w \le 32$. The critical points satisfy

$$V'(w) = 128w - 6w^2 = 2w(64 - 3w) = 0,$$

which has roots $w = 0$ and $w = \frac{64}{3}$. By the First (or Second) Derivative Test, $w = \frac{64}{3}$ corresponds to a local maximum. At the endpoints, $V(0) = V(32) = 0$. Therefore, the volume function has an absolute maximum of $V(64/3) \approx 9709 \text{ in}^3$. The dimensions of the optimal box are $w = 64/3$ in and $h = 64 - 2w = 64/3$ in, so the optimal box is a cube. A graph of the volume function is shown in Figure 4.54.

Related Exercises 15–17 ◀

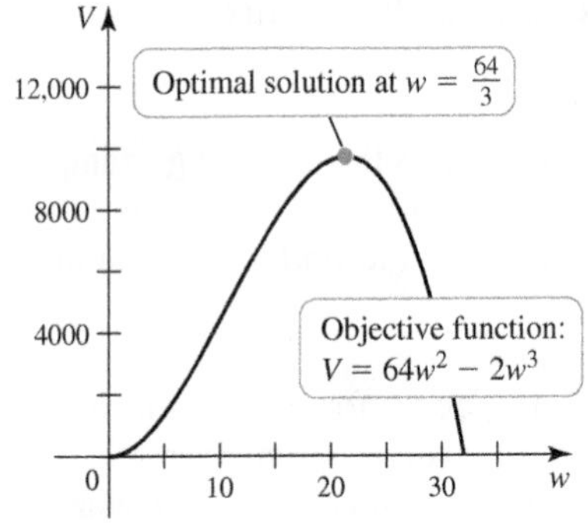

Figure 4.54

QUICK CHECK 3 Find the objective function in Example 2 (in terms of w) if the constraint is that the sum of length and width and height cannot exceed 108 in. ◀

Optimization Guidelines With two examples providing some insight, we present a procedure for solving optimization problems. These guidelines provide a general framework, but the details may vary depending on the problem.

Guidelines for Optimization Problems

1. Read the problem carefully, identify the variables, and organize the given information with a picture.
2. Identify the objective function (the function to be optimized). Write it in terms of the variables of the problem.
3. Identify the constraint(s). Write them in terms of the variables of the problem.
4. Use the constraint(s) to eliminate all but one independent variable of the objective function.
5. With the objective function expressed in terms of a single variable, find the interval of interest for that variable.
6. Use methods of calculus to find the absolute maximum or minimum value of the objective function on the interval of interest. If necessary, check the endpoints.

EXAMPLE 3 Walking and swimming Suppose you are standing on the shore of a circular pond with a radius of 1 mile and you want to get to a point on the shore directly opposite your position (on the other end of a diameter). You plan to swim at 2 mi/hr from your current position to another point P on the shore and then walk at 3 mi/hr along the shore to the terminal point (Figure 4.55). How should you choose P to minimize the total time for the trip?

SOLUTION As shown in Figure 4.55, the initial point is chosen arbitrarily, and the terminal point is at the other end of a diameter. The easiest way to describe the transition point P is to refer to the central angle θ. If $\theta = 0$, then the entire trip is done by walking; if $\theta = \pi$, the entire trip is done by swimming. So the interval of interest is $0 \le \theta \le \pi$.

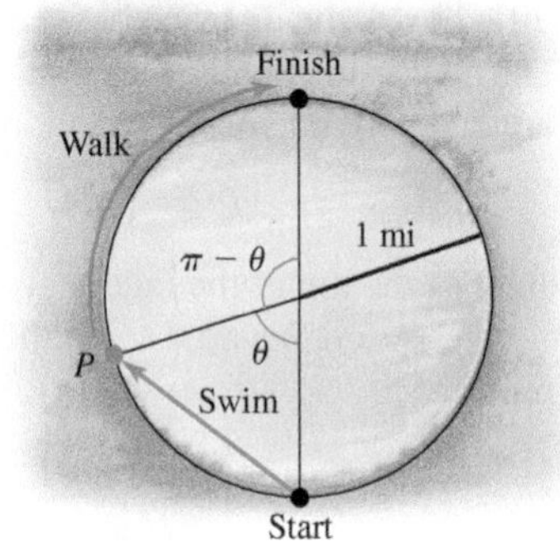

Figure 4.55

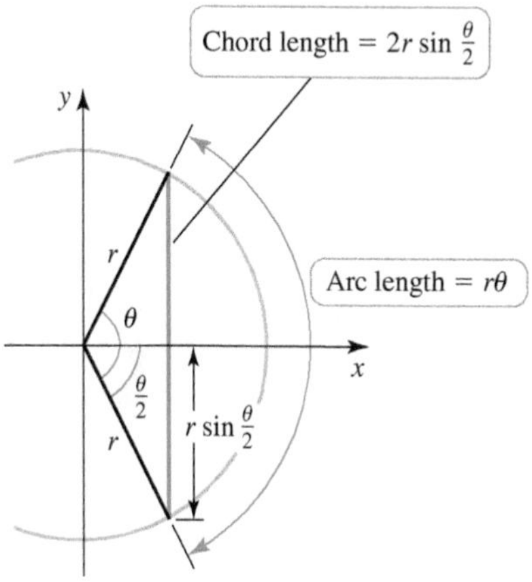

Figure 4.56

The objective function is the total travel time as it varies with θ. For each leg of the trip (swim and walk), the travel time is the distance traveled divided by the speed. We need a few facts from circular geometry. The length of the swimming leg is the length of the chord of the circle corresponding to the angle θ. For a circle of radius r, this chord length is given by $2r \sin(\theta/2)$ (Figure 4.56). So the time for the swimming leg (with $r = 1$ and a speed of 2 mi/hr) is

> To show that the chord length of a circle is $2r \sin(\theta/2)$, draw a line from the center of the circle to the midpoint of the chord. This line bisects the angle θ. Using a right triangle, half the length of the chord is $r \sin(\theta/2)$.

$$\text{time} = \frac{\text{distance}}{\text{rate}} = \frac{2\sin(\theta/2)}{2} = \sin\frac{\theta}{2}.$$

The length of the walking leg is the length of the arc of the circle corresponding to the angle $\pi - \theta$. For a circle of radius r, the arc length corresponding to an angle θ is $r\theta$ (Figure 4.56). Therefore, the time for the walking leg (with an angle $\pi - \theta$, $r = 1$, and a speed of 3 mi/hr) is

$$\text{time} = \frac{\text{distance}}{\text{rate}} = \frac{\pi - \theta}{3}.$$

The total travel time for the trip (in hours) is the objective function

$$T(\theta) = \sin\frac{\theta}{2} + \frac{\pi - \theta}{3}, \quad \text{for} \quad 0 \le \theta \le \pi.$$

> You can check two special cases: If the entire trip is done walking, the travel time is $(\pi \text{ mi})/(3 \text{ mi/hr}) \approx 1.05$ hr. If the entire trip is done swimming, the travel time is $(2 \text{ mi})/(2 \text{ mi/hr}) = 1$ hr.

We now analyze the objective function. The critical points of T satisfy

$$\frac{dT}{d\theta} = \frac{1}{2}\cos\frac{\theta}{2} - \frac{1}{3} = 0 \quad \text{or} \quad \cos\frac{\theta}{2} = \frac{2}{3}.$$

Using a calculator, the only solution in the interval $[0, \pi]$ is $\theta = 2\cos^{-1}\left(\frac{2}{3}\right) \approx 1.68 \text{ rad} \approx 96°$, which is the critical point.

Evaluating the objective function at the critical point and at the endpoints, we find that $T(1.68) \approx 1.23$ hr, $T(0) = \pi/3 \approx 1.05$ hr, and $T(\pi) = 1$ hr. We conclude that the minimum travel time is $T(\pi) = 1$ hr when the entire trip is done swimming. The *maximum* travel time, corresponding to $\theta \approx 96°$, is $T \approx 1.23$ hr.

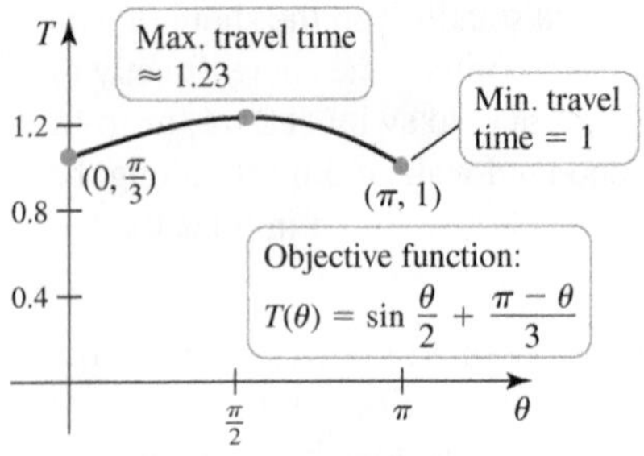

Figure 4.57

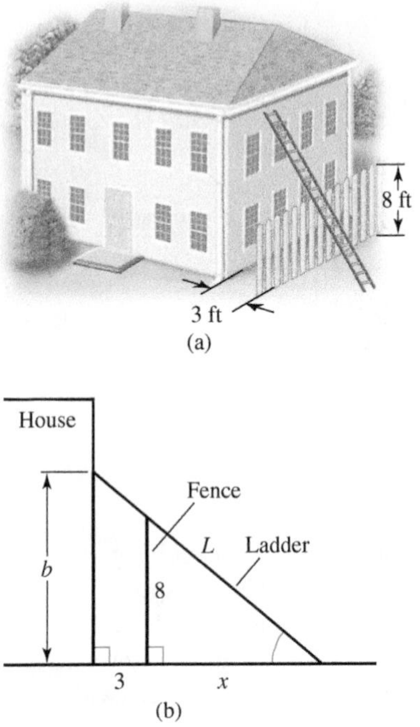

Figure 4.58

The objective function is shown in Figure 4.57. In general, the maximum and minimum travel times depend on the walking and swimming speeds (Exercise 18).

Related Exercises 18–21 ◀

EXAMPLE 4 Ladder over the fence An 8-foot-tall fence runs parallel to the side of a house 3 feet away (Figure 4.58a). What is the length of the shortest ladder that clears the fence and reaches the house? Assume that the vertical wall of the house and the horizontal ground have infinite extent (see Exercise 23 for more realistic assumptions).

SOLUTION Let's first ask why we expect a minimum ladder length. You could put the foot of the ladder far from the fence, so it clears the fence at a shallow angle; but the ladder would be long. Or you could put the foot of the ladder close to the fence, so it clears the fence at a steep angle; but again, the ladder would be long. Somewhere between these extremes, there is a ladder position that minimizes the ladder length.

The objective function in this problem is the ladder length L. The position of the ladder is specified by x, the distance between the foot of the ladder and the fence (Figure 4.58b). The goal is to express L as a function of x, where $x > 0$.

The Pythagorean theorem gives the relationship

$$L^2 = (x + 3)^2 + b^2,$$

where b is the height of the top of the ladder above the ground. Similar triangles give the constraint $8/x = b/(3 + x)$. We now solve the constraint equation for b and substitute to express L^2 in terms of x:

$$L^2 = (x + 3)^2 + \Bigg(\underbrace{\frac{8(x + 3)}{x}}_{b}\Bigg)^2 = (x + 3)^2\left(1 + \frac{64}{x^2}\right).$$

At this juncture, we could find the critical points of L by first solving the preceding equation for L and then solving $L' = 0$. However, the solution is simplified considerably if we note that L is a nonnegative function. Therefore, L and L^2 have local extrema at the same points, so we choose to minimize L^2. The derivative of L^2 is

$$\frac{d}{dx}\left[(x + 3)^2\left(1 + \frac{64}{x^2}\right)\right] = 2(x + 3)\left(1 + \frac{64}{x^2}\right) + (x + 3)^2\left(-\frac{128}{x^3}\right) \quad \text{Chain Rule and Product Rule}$$

$$= 2(x + 3)\left(1 + \frac{64}{x^2} - (x + 3)\frac{64}{x^3}\right) \quad \text{Factor.}$$

$$= \frac{2(x + 3)(x^3 - 192)}{x^3}. \quad \text{Simplify.}$$

Because $x > 0$, we have $x + 3 \neq 0$; therefore, the condition $\frac{d}{dx}(L^2) = 0$ becomes $x^3 - 192 = 0$, or $x = 4\sqrt[3]{3} \approx 5.77$. By the First Derivative Test, this critical point corresponds to a local minimum. By Theorem 4.5, this solitary local minimum is also the absolute minimum on the interval $(0, \infty)$. Therefore, the minimum ladder length occurs when the foot of the ladder is approximately 5.77 ft from the fence. We find that $L^2(5.77) \approx 224.77$ and the minimum ladder length is $\sqrt{224.77} \approx 15$ ft.

Related Exercises 22–23 ◀

SECTION 4.4 EXERCISES

Review Questions

1. Fill in the blanks: The goal of an optimization problem is to find the maximum or minimum value of the ________ function subject to the ________.

2. If the objective function involves more than one independent variable, how are the extra variables eliminated?

3. Suppose the objective function is $Q = x^2y$ and you know that $x + y = 10$. Write the objective function first in terms of x and then in terms of y.

4. Suppose you wish to minimize a continuous objective function on a closed interval, but you find that it has only a single local maximum. Where should you look for the solution to the problem?

Basic Skills

5. **Maximum area rectangles** Of all rectangles with a perimeter of 10, which one has the maximum area? (Give the dimensions.)

6. **Maximum area rectangles** Of all rectangles with a fixed perimeter of P, which one has the maximum area? (Give the dimensions in terms of P.)

7. **Minimum perimeter rectangles** Of all rectangles of area 100, which one has the minimum perimeter?

8. **Minimum perimeter rectangles** Of all rectangles with a fixed area A, which one has the minimum perimeter? (Give the dimensions in terms of A.)

9. **Maximum product** What two nonnegative real numbers with a sum of 23 have the largest possible product?

10. **Sum of squares** What two nonnegative real numbers a and b whose sum is 23 maximize $a^2 + b^2$? Minimize $a^2 + b^2$?

11. **Minimum sum** What two positive real numbers whose product is 50 have the smallest possible sum?

12. **Maximum product** Find numbers x and y satisfying the equation $3x + y = 12$ such that the product of x and y is as large as possible.

13. **Minimum sum** Find positive numbers x and y satisfying the equation $xy = 12$ such that the sum $2x + y$ is as small as possible.

14. **Pen problems**
    a. A rectangular pen is built with one side against a barn. Two hundred meters of fencing are used for the other three sides of the pen. What dimensions maximize the area of the pen?
    b. A rancher plans to make four identical and adjacent rectangular pens against a barn, each with an area of 100 m^2 (see figure). What are the dimensions of each pen that minimize the amount of fence that must be used?

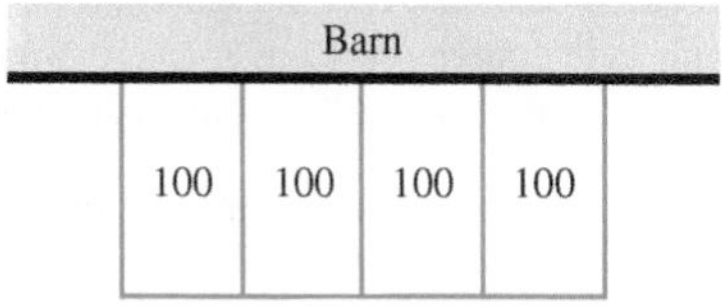

15. **Minimum-surface-area box** Of all boxes with a square base and a volume of 100 m^3, which one has the minimum surface area? (Give its dimensions.)

16. **Maximum-volume box** Suppose an airline policy states that all baggage must be box-shaped with a sum of length, width, and height not exceeding 108 in. What are the dimensions and volume of a square-based box with the greatest volume under these conditions?

17. **Shipping crates** A square-based, box-shaped shipping crate is designed to have a volume of 16 ft^3. The material used to make the base costs twice as much (per square foot) as the material in the sides, and the material used to make the top costs half as much (per square foot) as the material in the sides. What are the dimensions of the crate that minimize the cost of materials?

18. **Walking and swimming** A man wishes to get from an initial point on the shore of a circular lake with radius 1 mi to a point on the shore directly opposite (on the other end of the diameter). He plans to swim from the initial point to another point on the shore and then walk along the shore to the terminal point.
    a. If he swims at 2 mi/hr and walks at 4 mi/hr, what are the minimum and maximum times for the trip?
    b. If he swims at 2 mi/hr and walks at 1.5 mi/hr, what are the minimum and maximum times for the trip?
    c. If he swims at 2 mi/hr, what is the minimum walking speed for which it is quickest to walk the entire distance?

19. **Minimum distance** Find the point P on the line $y = 3x$ that is closest to the point $(50, 0)$. What is the least distance between P and $(50, 0)$?

20. **Minimum distance** Find the point P on the curve $y = x^2$ that is closet to the point $(18, 0)$. What is the least distance between P and $(18, 0)$?

21. **Walking and rowing** A boat on the ocean is 4 mi from the nearest point on a straight shoreline; that point is 6 mi from a restaurant on the shore. A woman plans to row the boat straight to a point on the shore and then walk along the shore to the restaurant.

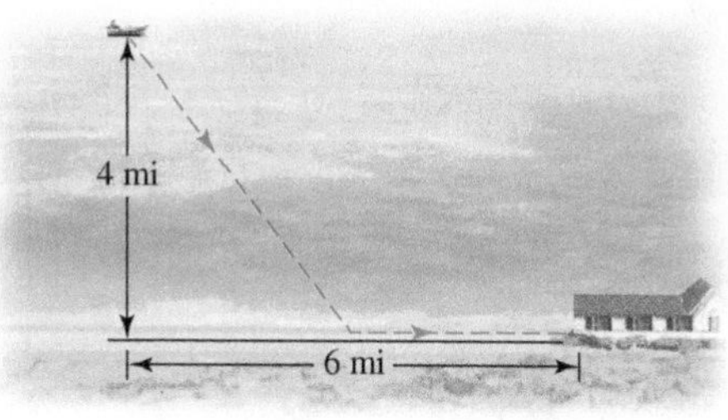

    a. If she walks at 3 mi/hr and rows at 2 mi/hr, at which point on the shore should she land to minimize the total travel time?
    b. If she walks at 3 mi/hr, what is the minimum speed at which she must row so that the quickest way to the restaurant is to row directly (with no walking)?

22. **Shortest ladder** A 10-ft-tall fence runs parallel to the wall of a house at a distance of 4 ft. Find the length of the shortest ladder that extends from the ground to the house without touching the fence. Assume the vertical wall of the house and the horizontal ground have infinite extent.

23. **Shortest ladder—more realistic** An 8-ft-tall fence runs parallel to the wall of a house at a distance of 5 ft. Find the length of the shortest ladder that extends from the ground to the house without touching the fence. Assume that the vertical wall of the house is 20 ft high and the horizontal ground extends 20 ft from the fence.

Further Explorations and Applications

24. **Rectangles beneath a parabola** A rectangle is constructed with its base on the x-axis and two of its vertices on the parabola $y = 16 - x^2$. What are the dimensions of the rectangle with the maximum area? What is that area?

25. **Rectangles beneath a semicircle** A rectangle is constructed with its base on the diameter of a semicircle with radius 5 and its two other vertices on the semicircle. What are the dimensions of the rectangle with maximum area?

26. **Circle and square** A piece of wire of length 60 is cut, and the resulting two pieces are formed to make a circle and a square. Where should the wire be cut to (a) minimize and (b) maximize the combined area of the circle and the square?

27. **Maximum-volume cone** A cone is constructed by cutting a sector from a circular sheet of metal with radius 20. The cut sheet is then folded up and welded (see figure). Find the radius and height of the cone with maximum volume that can be formed in this way.

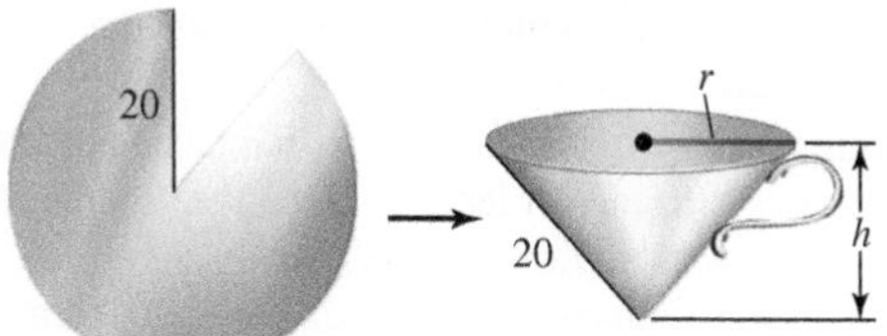

28. Covering a marble Imagine a flat-bottomed cylindrical pot with a circular cross section of radius 4. A marble with radius $0 < r < 4$ is placed in the bottom of the pot. What is the radius of the marble that requires the most water to cover it completely?

29. Optimal garden A rectangular flower garden with an area of 30 m^2 is surrounded by a grass border 1 m wide on two sides and 2 m wide on the other two sides (see figure). What dimensions of the garden minimize the combined area of the garden and borders?

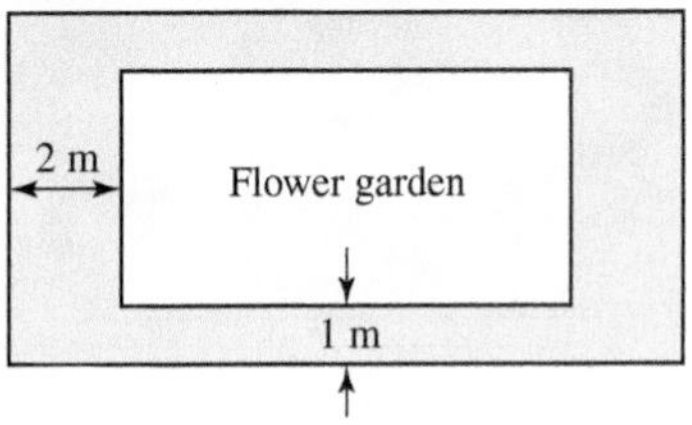

30. Rectangles beneath a line

a. A rectangle is constructed with one side on the positive x-axis, one side on the positive y-axis, and the vertex opposite the origin on the line $y = 10 - 2x$. What dimensions maximize the area of the rectangle? What is the maximum area?

b. Is it possible to construct a rectangle with a greater area than that found in part (a) by placing one side of the rectangle on the line $y = 10 - 2x$ and the two vertices not on that line on the positive x- and y-axes? Find the dimensions of the rectangle of maximum area that can be constructed in this way.

31. Kepler's wine barrel Several mathematical stories originated with the second wedding of the mathematician and astronomer Johannes Kepler. Here is one: While shopping for wine for his wedding, Kepler noticed that the price of a barrel of wine (here assumed to be a cylinder) was determined solely by the length d of a dipstick that was inserted diagonally through a centered hole in the top of the barrel to the edge of the base of the barrel (see figure). Kepler realized that this measurement does not determine the volume of the barrel and that for a fixed value of d, the volume varies with the radius r and height h of the barrel. For a fixed value of d, what is the ratio r/h that maximizes the volume of the barrel?

32. Folded boxes

a. Squares with sides of length x are cut out of each corner of a rectangular piece of cardboard measuring 3 ft by 4 ft. The resulting piece of cardboard is then folded into a box without a lid. Find the volume of the largest box that can be formed in this way.

b. Suppose that in part (a) the original piece of cardboard is a square with sides of length ℓ. Find the volume of the largest box that can be formed in this way.

c. Suppose that in part (a) the original piece of cardboard is a rectangle with sides of length ℓ and L. Holding ℓ fixed, find the size of the corner squares x that maximizes the volume of the box as $L \to \infty$. (*Source: Mathematics Teacher*, Nov 2002)

33. Making silos A grain silo consists of a cylindrical concrete tower surmounted by a metal hemispherical dome. The metal in the dome costs 1.5 times as much as the concrete (per unit of surface area). If the volume of the silo is 750 m^3, what are the dimensions of the silo (radius and height of the cylindrical tower) that minimize the cost of the materials? Assume the silo has no floor and no flat ceiling under the dome.

34. Suspension system A load must be suspended 6 m below a high ceiling using cables attached to two supports that are 2 m apart (see figure). How far below the ceiling (x in the figure) should the cables be joined to minimize the total length of cable used?

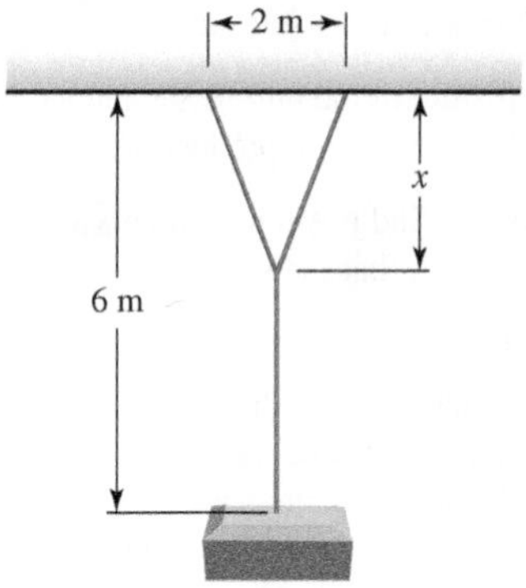

35. Light sources The intensity of a light source at a distance is directly proportional to the strength of the source and inversely proportional to the square of the distance from the source. Two light sources, one twice as strong as the other, are 12 m apart. At what point on the line segment joining the sources is the intensity the weakest?

36. Crease-length problem A rectangular sheet of paper of width a and length b, where $0 < a < b$, is folded by taking one corner of the sheet and placing it at a point P on the opposite long side of the sheet (see figure). The fold is then flattened to form a crease across the sheet. Assuming that the fold is made so that there is no flap extending beyond the original sheet, find the point P that produces the crease of minimum length. What is the length of that crease?

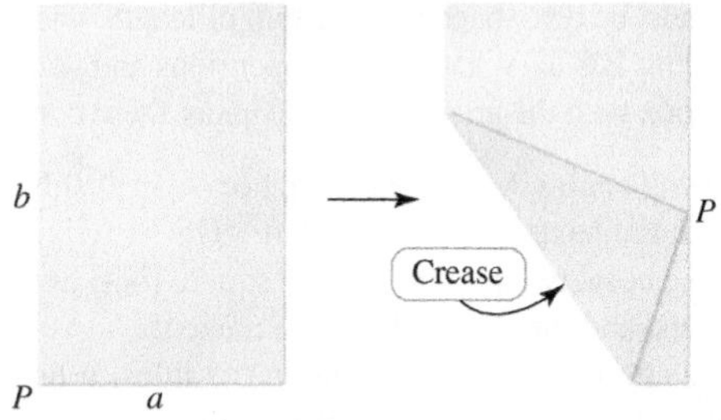

37. Laying cable An island is 3.5 mi from the nearest point on a straight shoreline; that point is 8 mi from a power station (see figure). A utility company plans to lay electrical cable underwater from the island to the shore and then underground along the shore to the power station. Assume that it costs \$2400/mi to lay underwater cable and \$1200/mi to lay underground cable. At what point should the underwater cable meet the shore to minimize the cost of the project?

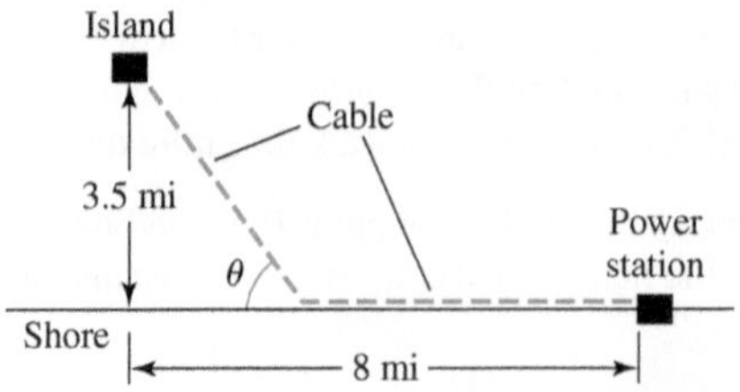

38. Laying cable again Solve the problem in Exercise 37, but this time minimize the cost with respect to the smaller angle θ between the underwater cable and the shore. (You should get the same answer.)

39. Sum of isosceles distances

a. An isosceles triangle has a base of length 4 and two sides of length $2\sqrt{2}$. Let P be a point on the perpendicular bisector of the base. Find the location P that minimizes the sum of the distances between P and the three vertices.

b. Assume in part (a) that the height of the isosceles triangle is $h > 0$ and its base has length 4. Show that the location of P that gives a minimum solution is independent of h for $h \geq \frac{2}{\sqrt{3}}$.

40. Circle in a triangle What are the radius and area of the circle of maximum area that can be inscribed in an isosceles triangle whose two equal sides have length 1?

41. Slant height and cones Among all right circular cones with a slant height of 3, what are the dimensions (radius and height) that maximize the volume of the cone? The slant height of a cone is the distance from the outer edge of the base to the vertex.

T **42. Blood testing** Suppose that a blood test for a disease is given to a population of N people, where N is large. At most, N individual blood tests must be done. The following strategy reduces the number of tests. Suppose 100 people are selected from the population and their blood samples are pooled. One test determines whether any of the 100 people test positive. If the test is positive, those 100 people are tested individually, making 101 tests necessary. However, if the pooled sample tests negative, then 100 people have been tested with one test. This procedure is then repeated. Probability theory shows that if the group size is x (for example, $x = 100$, as described here), then the average number of blood tests required to test N people is $N(1 - q^x + 1/x)$, where q is the probability that any one person tests negative. What group size x minimizes the average number of tests in the case that $N = 10{,}000$ and $q = 0.95$? Assume that x is a nonnegative real number.

43. Crankshaft A crank of radius r rotates with an angular frequency ω. It is connected to a piston by a connecting rod of length L (see figure). The acceleration of the piston varies with the position of the crank according to the function

$$a(\theta) = \omega^2 r\left(\cos\theta + \frac{r\cos 2\theta}{L}\right).$$

For fixed ω and r, find the values of θ, with $0 \leq \theta \leq 2\pi$, for which the acceleration of the piston is a maximum and minimum.

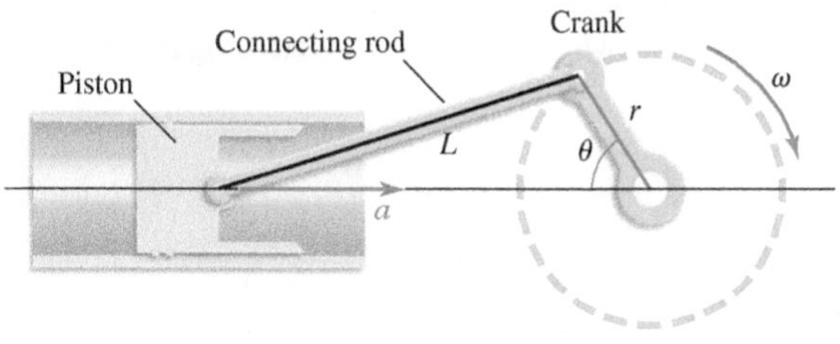

44. Metal rain gutters A rain gutter is made from sheets of metal 9 in wide. The gutters have a 3-in base and two 3-in sides, folded up at an angle θ (see figure). What angle θ maximizes the cross-sectional area of the gutter?

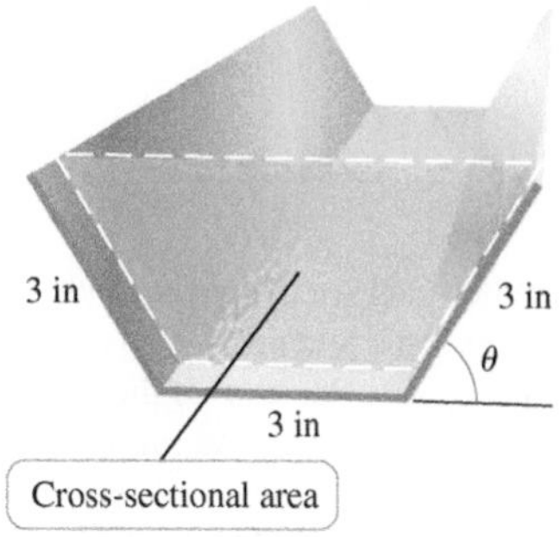

45. Optimal soda can

a. Classical problem Find the radius and height of a cylindrical soda can with a volume of 354 cm^3 that minimize the surface area.

b. Real problem Compare your answer in part (a) to a real soda can, which has a volume of 354 cm^3, a radius of 3.1 cm, and a height of 12.0 cm, to conclude that real soda cans do not seem to have an optimal design. Then use the fact that real soda cans have a double thickness in their top and bottom surfaces to find the radius and height that minimizes the surface area of a real can (the surface areas of the top and bottom are now twice their values in part (a)). Are these dimensions closer to the dimensions of a real soda can?

46. Cylinder and cones (Putnam Exam 1938) Right circular cones of height h and radius r are attached to each end of a right circular cylinder of height h and radius r, forming a double-pointed object. For a given surface area A, what are the dimensions r and h that maximize the volume of the object?

47. Viewing angles An auditorium with a flat floor has a large screen on one wall. The lower edge of the screen is 3 ft above eye level, and the upper edge of the screen is 10 ft above eye level (see figure). How far from the screen should you stand to maximize your viewing angle θ?

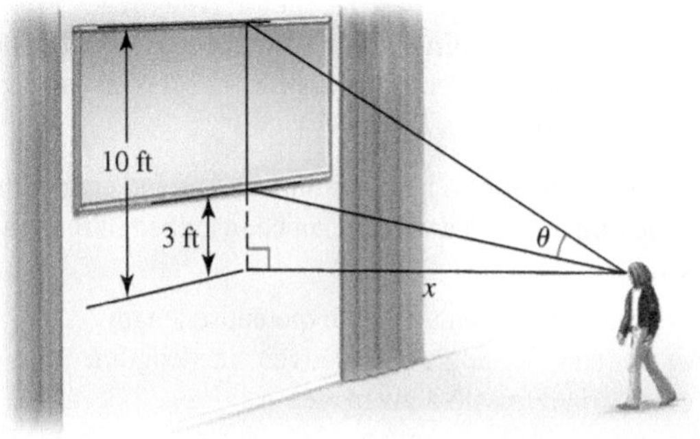

48. Searchlight problem—narrow beam A searchlight is 100 m from the nearest point on a straight highway (see figure). As it rotates, the searchlight casts a horizontal beam that intersects the highway in a point. If the light revolves at a rate of $\pi/6$ rad/s, find the rate at which the beam sweeps along the highway as a function of θ. For what value of θ is this rate maximized?

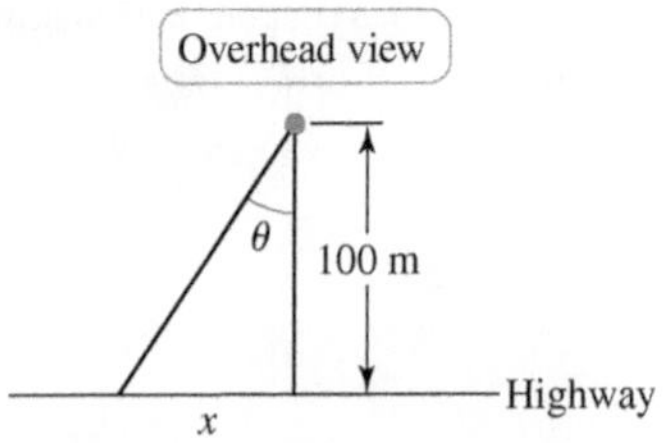

T **49. Watching a Ferris wheel** An observer stands 20 m from the bottom of a Ferris wheel on a line that is perpendicular to the face of the wheel, with her eyes at the level of the bottom of the wheel. The wheel revolves at a rate of π rad/min, and the observer's line of sight with a specific seat on the Ferris wheel makes an angle θ with the horizontal (see figure). At what time during a full revolution is θ changing most rapidly?

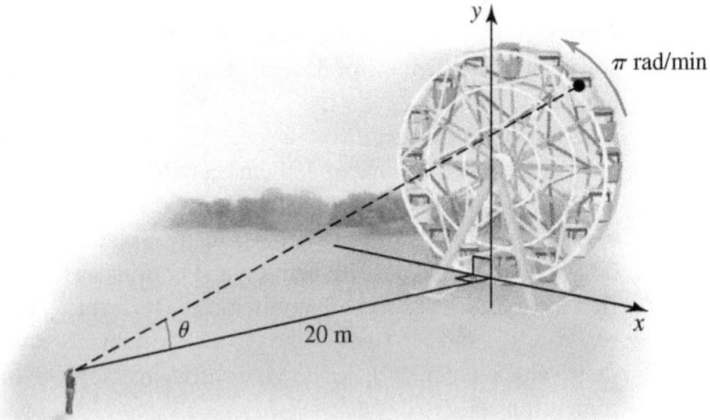

50. Maximum angle Find the value of x that maximizes θ in the figure.

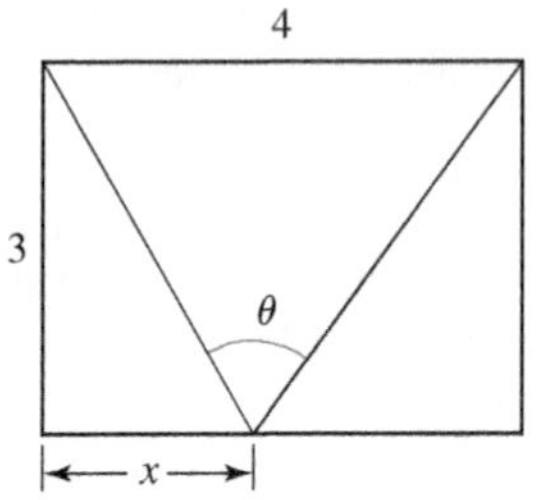

51. Maximum-volume cylinder in a sphere Find the dimensions of the right circular cylinder of maximum volume that can be placed inside a sphere of radius R.

52. Rectangles in triangles Find the dimensions and area of the rectangle of maximum area that can be inscribed in the following figures.

a. A right triangle with a given hypotenuse length L

b. An equilateral triangle with a given side length L

c. A right triangle with a given area A

d. An arbitrary triangle with a given area A (The result applies to any triangle, but first consider triangles for which all the angles are less than or equal to 90°.)

53. Cylinder in a cone A right circular cylinder is placed inside a cone of radius R and height H so that the base of the cylinder lies on the base of the cone.

a. Find the dimensions of the cylinder with maximum volume. Specifically, show that the volume of the maximum-volume cylinder is $\frac{4}{9}$ the volume of the cone.

b. Find the dimensions of the cylinder with maximum lateral surface area (area of the curved surface).

54. Maximizing profit Suppose you own a tour bus and you book groups of 20 to 70 people for a day tour. The cost per person is \$30 minus \$0.25 for every ticket sold. If gas and other miscellaneous costs are \$200, how many tickets should you sell to maximize your profit? Treat the number of tickets as a nonnegative real number.

55. Cone in a cone A right circular cone is inscribed inside a larger right circular cone with a volume of 150 cm^3. The axes of the cones coincide and the vertex of the inner cone touches the center of the base of the outer cone. Find the ratio of the heights of the cones that maximizes the volume of the inner cone.

56. Another pen problem A rancher is building a horse pen on the corner of her property using 1000 ft of fencing. Because of the unusual shape of her property, the pen must be built in the shape of a trapezoid (see figure).

a. Determine the lengths of the sides that maximize the area of the pen.

b. Suppose there is already a fence along the side of the property opposite the side of length y. Find the lengths of the sides that maximize the area of the pen, using 1000 ft of fencing.

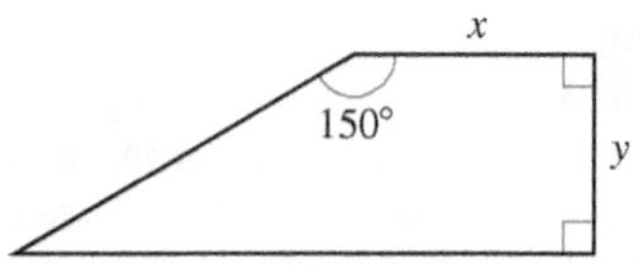

57. Minimum-length roads A house is located at each corner of a square with side lengths of 1 mi. What is the length of the shortest road system with straight roads that connects all of the houses by roads (that is, a road system that allows one to drive from any house to any other house)? (*Hint:* Place two points inside the square at which roads meet.) (*Source: Problems for Mathematicians Young and Old*, P. Halmos, MAA, 1991)

58. Light transmission A window consists of a rectangular pane of clear glass surmounted by a semicircular pane of tinted glass. The clear glass transmits twice as much light per unit of surface area as the tinted glass. Of all such windows with a fixed perimeter P, what are the dimensions of the window that transmits the most light?

59. Slowest shortcut Suppose you are standing in a field near a straight section of railroad tracks just as the locomotive of a train passes the point nearest to you, which is $\frac{1}{4}$ mi away. The train, with length $\frac{1}{3}$ mi, is traveling at 20 mi/hr. If you start running in a straight line across the field, how slowly can you run and still catch the train? In which direction should you run?

60. The arbelos An arbelos is the region enclosed by three mutually tangent semicircles; it is the region inside the larger semicircle and outside the two smaller semicircles (see figure).

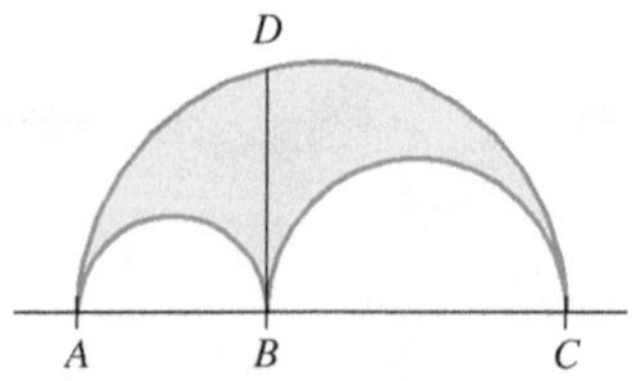

a. Given an arbelos in which the diameter of the largest circle is 1, what positions of point B maximize the area of the arbelos?
b. Show that the area of the arbelos is the area of a circle whose diameter is the distance BD in the figure.

61. **Proximity questions**
a. What point on the line $y = 3x + 4$ is closest to the origin?
b. What point on the parabola $y = 1 - x^2$ is closest to the point $(1, 1)$?
c. Find the point on the graph of $y = \sqrt{x}$ that is nearest the point $(p, 0)$ if (i) $p > \frac{1}{2}$; and (ii) $0 < p < \frac{1}{2}$. Express the answer in terms of p.

62. **Turning a corner with a pole**
a. What is the length of the longest pole that can be carried horizontally around a corner at which a 3-ft corridor and a 4-ft corridor meet at right angles?
b. What is the length of the longest pole that can be carried horizontally around a corner at which a corridor that is a feet wide and a corridor that is b feet wide meet at right angles?
c. What is the length of the longest pole that can be carried horizontally around a corner at which a corridor that is $a = 5$ ft wide and a corridor that is $b = 5$ ft wide meet at an angle of 120°?
d. What is the length of the longest pole that can be carried around a corner at which a corridor that is a feet wide and a corridor that is b feet wide meet at right angles, assuming there is an 8-ft ceiling and that you may tilt the pole at any angle?

63. **Travel costs** A simple model for travel costs involves the cost of gasoline and the cost of a driver. Specifically, assume that gasoline costs \$ p/gallon and the vehicle gets g miles per gallon. Also assume that the driver earns \$ w/hour.
a. A plausible function to describe how gas mileage (in mi/gal) varies with speed v is $g(v) = v(85 - v)/60$. Evaluate $g(0)$, $g(40)$, and $g(60)$ and explain why these values are reasonable.
b. At what speed does the gas mileage function have its maximum?
c. Explain why the formula $C(v) = Lp/g(v) + Lw/v$ gives the cost of the trip in dollars, where L is the length of the trip and v is the constant speed. Show that the dimensions are consistent.
d. Let $L = 400$ mi, $p = \$4$/gal, and $w = \$20$/hr. At what (constant) speed should the vehicle be driven to minimize the cost of the trip?
e. Should the optimal speed be increased or decreased (compared with part (d)) if L is increased from 400 mi to 500 mi? Explain.
f. Should the optimal speed be increased or decreased (compared with part (d)) if p is increased from \$4/gal to \$4.20/gal? Explain.
g. Should the optimal speed be increased or decreased (compared with part (d)) if w is decreased from \$20/hr to \$15/hr? Explain.

64. **Do dogs know calculus?** A mathematician stands on a beach with his dog at point A. He throws a tennis ball so that it hits the water at point B. The dog, wanting to get to the tennis ball as quickly as possible, runs along the straight beach line to point D and then swims from point D to point B to retrieve his ball. Assume C is the point on the edge of the beach closest to the tennis ball (see figure).

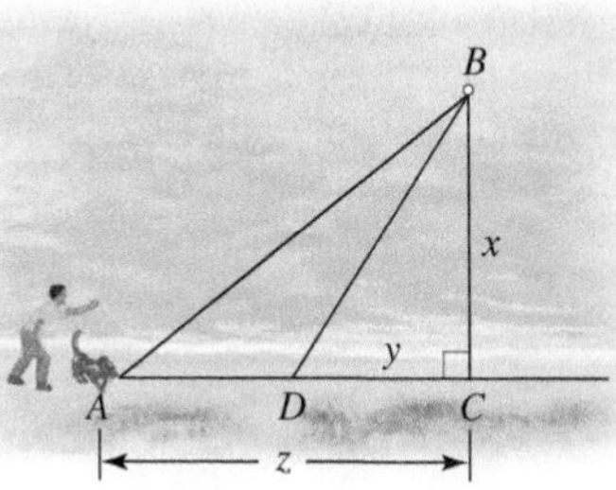

a. Assume the dog runs at speed r and swims at speed s, where $r > s$ and both are measured in meters/second. Also assume the lengths of BC, CD, and AC are x, y, and z, respectively. Find a function $T(y)$ representing the total time it takes the dog to get to the ball.
b. Verify that the value of y that minimizes the time it takes to retrieve the ball is $y = \dfrac{x}{\sqrt{r/s + 1}\sqrt{r/s - 1}}$.
c. If the dog runs at 8 m/s and swims at 1 m/s, what ratio y/x produces the fastest retrieving time?
d. A dog named Elvis who runs at 6.4 m/s and swims at 0.910 m/s was found to use an average ratio y/x of 0.144 to retrieve his ball. Does Elvis appear to know calculus? (*Source: Do Dogs Know Calculus?* T. Pennings, *The College Mathematics Journal*, 34, 3, May 2003)

65. **Fermat's Principle**
a. Two poles of heights m and n are separated by a horizontal distance d. A rope is stretched from the top of one pole to the ground and then to the top of the other pole. Show that the configuration that requires the least amount of rope occurs when $\theta_1 = \theta_2$ (see figure).

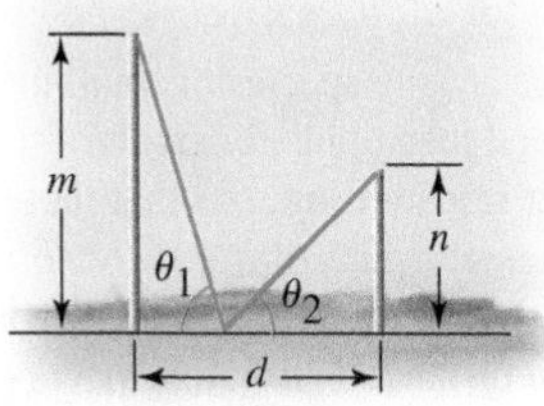

(a)

b. Fermat's Principle states that when light travels between two points in the same medium (at a constant speed), it travels on the path that minimizes the travel time. Show that when light from a source A reflects off a surface and is received at point B, the angle of incidence equals the angle of reflection, or $\theta_1 = \theta_2$ (see figure).

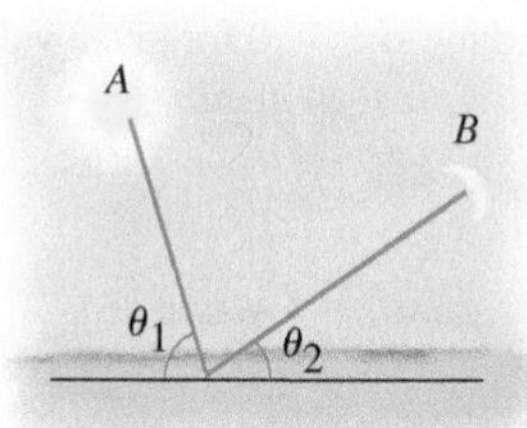

(b)

66. Snell's Law Suppose that a light source at A is in a medium in which light travels at speed v_1 and the point B is in a medium in which light travels at speed v_2 (see figure). Using Fermat's Principle, which states that light travels along the path that requires the minimum travel time (Exercise 65), show that the path taken between points A and B satisfies $(\sin \theta_1)/v_1 = (\sin \theta_2)/v_2$.

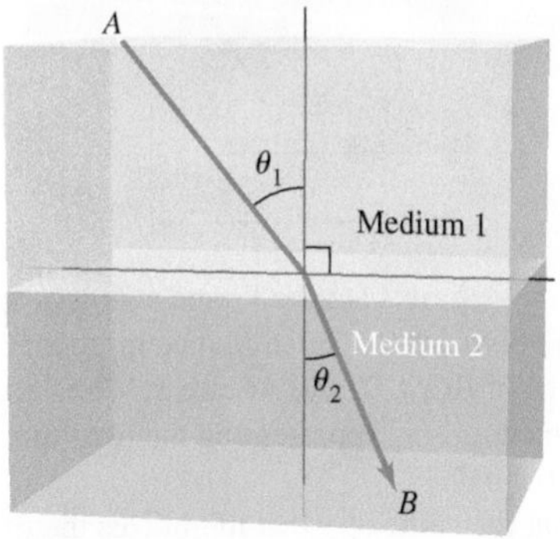

67. Tree notch (Putnam Exam 1938, rephrased) A notch is cut in a cylindrical vertical tree trunk. The notch penetrates to the axis of the cylinder and is bounded by two half-planes that intersect on a diameter D of the tree. The angle between the two half-planes is θ. Prove that for a given tree and fixed angle θ, the volume of the notch is minimized by taking the bounding planes at equal angles to the horizontal plane that also passes through D.

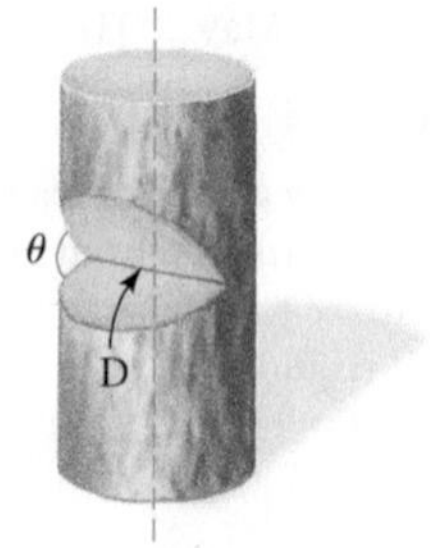

T **68. Gliding mammals** Many species of small mammals (such as flying squirrels and marsupial gliders) have the ability to walk and glide. Recent research suggests that these animals choose the most energy-efficient means of travel. According to one empirical model, the energy required for a glider with body mass m to walk a horizontal distance D is $8.46\, Dm^{2/3}$ (where m is measured in grams, D is measured in meters, and energy is measured in microliters of oxygen consumed in respiration). The energy cost of climbing to a height $D \tan \theta$ and gliding a distance D at an angle θ below the horizontal is modeled by $1.36\, m\, D \tan \theta$ (where $\theta = 0$ represents horizontal flight and $\theta > 45°$ represents controlled falling). Therefore, the function

$$S(m, \theta) = 8.46m^{2/3} - 1.36m \tan \theta$$

gives the energy difference per horizontal meter traveled between walking and gliding: If $S > 0$ for given values of m and θ, then it is more costly to walk than glide.

a. For what glide angles is it more efficient for a 200-gram animal to glide rather that walk?

b. Find the threshold function $\theta = g(m)$ that gives the curve along which walking and gliding are equally efficient. Is it an increasing or decreasing function of body mass?

c. To make gliding more efficient than walking, do larger gliders have a larger or smaller selection of glide angles than smaller gliders?

d. Let $\theta = 25°$ (a typical glide angle). Graph S as a function of m, for $0 \le m \le 3000$. For what values of m is gliding more efficient?

e. For $\theta = 25°$, what value of m (call it m^*) maximizes S?

f. Does m^*, as defined in part (e), increase or decrease with increasing θ? That is, as a glider reduces its glide angle, does its optimal size become larger or smaller?

g. Assuming Dumbo is a gliding elephant whose weight is 1 metric ton (10^6 g), what glide angle would Dumbo use to be more efficient at gliding than walking?

(*Source: Energetic savings and the body size distribution of gliding mammals*, R. Dial, *Evolutionary Ecology Research* 5, 2003)

69. A challenging pen problem Two triangular pens are built against a barn. Two hundred meters of fencing are to be used for the three sides and the diagonal dividing fence (see figure). What dimensions maximize the area of the pen?

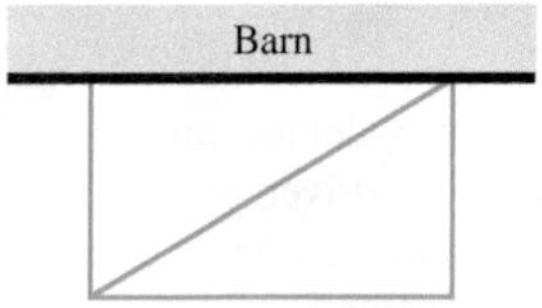

70. Minimizing related functions Find the values of x that minimize each function.

a. $f(x) = (x - 1)^2 + (x - 5)^2$

b. $f(x) = (x - a)^2 + (x - b)^2$, for constants a and b

c. $f(x) = \sum_{k=1}^{n} (x - a_k)^2$, for a positive integer n and constants $a_1, a_2, \ldots, a_n$.

(*Source: Calculus*, Vol. 1, T. Apostol, John Wiley and Sons, 1967)

QUICK CHECK ANSWERS

2. (i) $A = 400x - 2x^2$ (ii) $A = 400x - 3x^2$
3. $V = 108w^2 - 2w^3$ ◄

4.5 Linear Approximation and Differentials

Imagine plotting a smooth curve with a graphing utility. Now pick a point P on the curve, draw the line tangent to the curve at P, and zoom in on it several times. As you successively enlarge the curve near P, it looks more and more like the tangent line (Figure 4.59a). This fundamental observation—that smooth curves appear straighter on smaller scales—is called *local linearity*; it is the basis of many important mathematical ideas, one of which is *linear approximation.*

Now consider a curve with a corner or cusp at a point Q (Figure 4.59b). No amount of magnification "straightens out" the curve or removes the corner at Q. The different behavior at P and Q is related to the idea of differentiability: The function in Figure 4.59a is differentiable at P, whereas the function in Figure 4.59b is not differentiable at Q. One of the requirements for the techniques presented in this section is that the function be differentiable at the point in question.

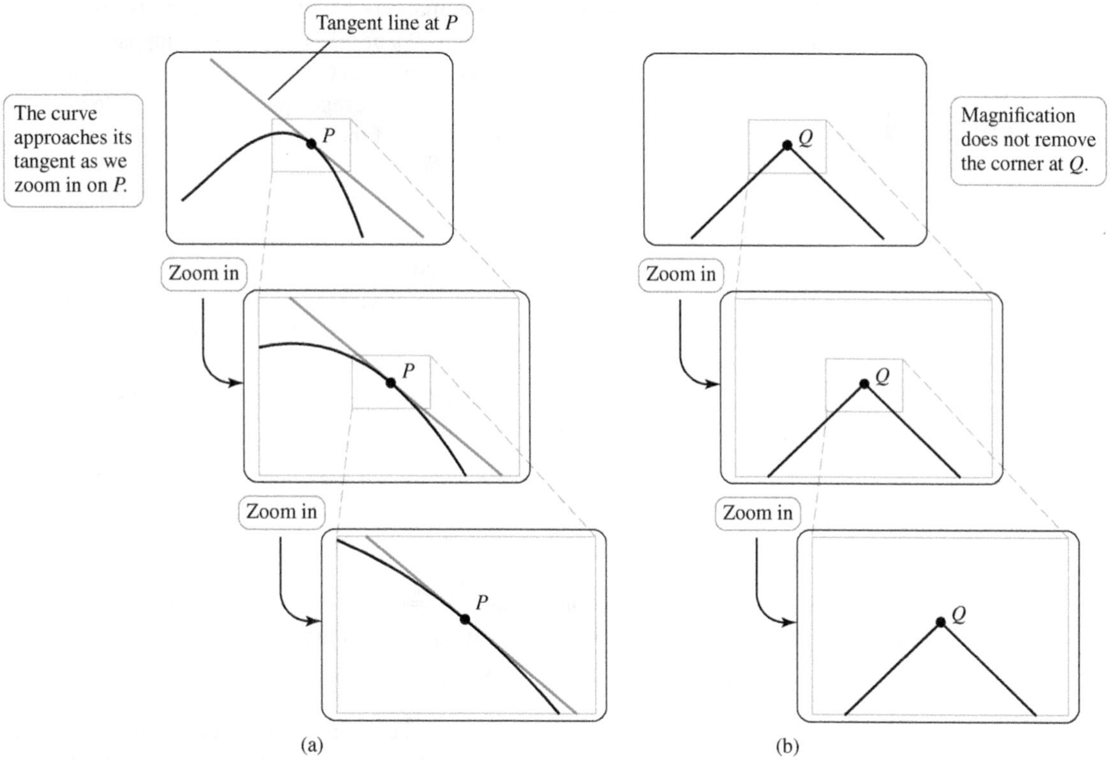

Figure 4.59

Linear Approximation

Figure 4.59a suggests that when we zoom in on the graph of a smooth function at a point P, the curve approaches its tangent line at P. This fact is the key to understanding linear approximation. The idea is to use the line tangent to the curve at P to approximate the value of the function at points near P. Here's how it works.

Assume f is differentiable on an interval containing the point a. The slope of the line tangent to the curve at the point $(a, f(a))$ is $f'(a)$. Therefore, an equation of the tangent line is

$$y - f(a) = f'(a)(x - a) \quad \text{or} \quad y = \underbrace{f(a) + f'(a)(x - a)}_{L(x)}.$$

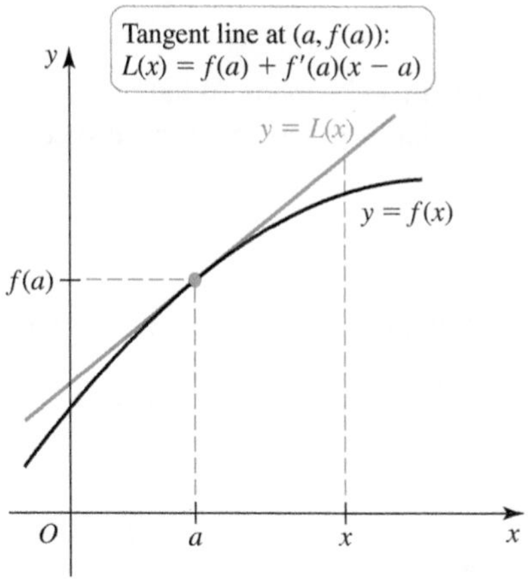

Figure 4.60

This tangent line represents a new function L that we call the *linear approximation* to f at the point a (Figure 4.60). If f and f' are easy to evaluate at a, then the value of f at points near a is easily approximated using the linear approximation L. That is,

$$f(x) \approx L(x) = f(a) + f'(a)(x - a).$$

This approximation improves as x approaches a.

DEFINITION Linear Approximation to f at a

Suppose f is differentiable on an interval I containing the point a. The **linear approximation** to f at a is the linear function

$$L(x) = f(a) + f'(a)(x - a), \quad \text{for } x \text{ in } I.$$

QUICK CHECK 1 Sketch the graph of a function f that is concave up on an interval containing the point a. Sketch the linear approximation to f at a. Is the graph of the linear approximation above or below the graph of f? ◀

> In Example 1, notice that when x is positive, you are driving slower than 60 mi/hr; when x is negative, you are driving faster than 60 mi/hr.

EXAMPLE 1 Useful driving math Suppose you are driving along a highway at a nearly constant speed and you record the number of seconds it takes to travel between two consecutive mile markers. If it takes 60 seconds, to travel one mile, then your average speed is 1 mi/60 s or 60 mi/hr. Now suppose that you travel one mile in $60 + x$ seconds; for example, if it takes 62 seconds, then $x = 2$, and if it takes 57 seconds, then $x = -3$. In this case, your average speed over one mile is $1 \text{ mi}/(60 + x)\text{s}$. Because there are 3600 s in 1 hr, the function

$$s(x) = \frac{3600}{60 + x} = 3600(60 + x)^{-1}$$

gives your average speed in mi/hr if you travel one mile in x seconds more or less than 60 seconds. For example, if you travel one mile in 62 seconds, then $x = 2$ and your average speed is $s(2) \approx 58.06$ mi/hr. If you travel one mile in 57 seconds, then $x = -3$ and your average speed is $s(-3) \approx 63.16$ mi/hr. Because you don't want to use a calculator while driving, you need an easy approximation to this function. Use linear approximation to derive such a formula.

SOLUTION The idea is to find the linear approximation to s at the point 0. We first use the Chain Rule to compute

$$s'(x) = -3600(60 + x)^{-2},$$

and then note that $s(0) = 60$ and $s'(0) = -3600 \cdot 60^{-2} = -1$. Using the linear approximation formula, we find that

$$s(x) \approx L(x) = s(0) + s'(0)(x - 0) = 60 - x.$$

For example, if you travel one mile in 62 seconds, then $x = 2$ and your average speed is approximately $L(2) = 58$ mi/hr, which is very close to the exact value given previously. If you travel one mile in 57 seconds, then $x = -3$ and your average speed is approximately $L(-3) = 63$ mi/hr, which again is close to the exact value.

Related Exercises 7–12 ◀

QUICK CHECK 2 In Example 1, suppose you travel one mile in 75 seconds. What is the average speed given by the linear approximation formula? What is the exact average speed? Explain the discrepancy between the two values. ◀

EXAMPLE 2 Linear approximations and errors

a. Find the linear approximation to $f(x) = \sqrt{x}$ at $x = 1$ and use it to approximate $\sqrt{1.1}$.

b. Use linear approximation to estimate the value of $\sqrt{0.1}$.

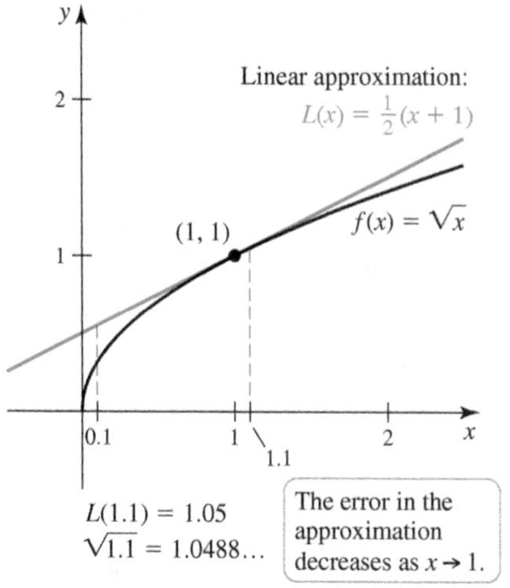

Figure 4.61

Table 4.4

x	$L(x)$	Exact $\sqrt{x}$	Error
1.2	1.1	1.0954 . . .	4.6×10^{-3}
1.1	1.05	1.0488 . . .	1.2×10^{-3}
1.01	1.005	1.0049 . . .	1.2×10^{-5}
1.001	1.0005	1.0005 . . .	1.2×10^{-7}

SOLUTION

a. We construct the linear approximation

$$L(x) = f(a) + f'(a)(x - a),$$

where $f(x) = \sqrt{x}$, $f'(x) = 1/(2\sqrt{x})$, and $a = 1$. Noting that $f(a) = f(1) = 1$ and $f'(a) = f'(1) = \frac{1}{2}$, we have

$$L(x) = 1 + \frac{1}{2}(x - 1) = \frac{1}{2}(x + 1),$$

which is an equation of the line tangent to the curve at the point $(1, 1)$ (Figure 4.61). Because $x = 1.1$ is near $x = 1$, we approximate $\sqrt{1.1}$ by $L(1.1)$:

$$\sqrt{1.1} \approx L(1.1) = \frac{1}{2}(1.1 + 1) = 1.05.$$

The exact value is $f(1.1) = \sqrt{1.1} = 1.0488\ldots$; therefore, the linear approximation has an error of about 0.0012. Furthermore, our approximation is an *overestimate* because the tangent line lies above the graph of f. In Table 4.4, we see several approximations to $\sqrt{x}$ for x near 1 and the associated errors $|L(x) - \sqrt{x}|$. Clearly, the errors decrease as x approaches 1.

b. If the linear approximation $L(x) = \frac{1}{2}(x + 1)$ obtained in part (a) is used to approximate $\sqrt{0.1}$, we have

$$\sqrt{0.1} \approx L(0.1) = \frac{1}{2}(0.1 + 1) = 0.55.$$

A calculator gives $\sqrt{0.1} = 0.3162\ldots$, which shows that the approximation is well off the mark. The error arises because the tangent line through $(1, 1)$ is not close to the curve at $x = 0.1$ (Figure 4.61). For this reason, we seek a different value of a, with the requirement that it is near $x = 0.1$, and both $f(a)$ and $f'(a)$ are easily computed. It is tempting to try $a = 0$, but $f'(0)$ is undefined. One choice that works well is $a = \frac{9}{100} = 0.09$. Using the linear approximation $L(x) = f(a) + f'(a)(x - a)$, we have

➤ We choose $a = \frac{9}{100}$ because it is close to 0.1 and its square root is easy to evaluate.

$$\begin{aligned}\sqrt{0.1} \approx L(0.1) &= \overbrace{\sqrt{\frac{9}{100}}}^{f(a)} + \overbrace{\frac{1}{2\sqrt{9/100}}}^{f'(a)}\overbrace{\left(\frac{1}{10} - \frac{9}{100}\right)}^{(x-a)} \\ &= \frac{3}{10} + \frac{10}{6}\left(\frac{1}{100}\right) \\ &= \frac{19}{60} \approx 0.3167.\end{aligned}$$

This approximation agrees with the exact value to three decimal places.

Related Exercises 13–20 ◀

QUICK CHECK 3 Suppose you want to use linear approximation to estimate $\sqrt{0.18}$. What is a good choice for a? ◀

EXAMPLE 3 Linear approximation for the sine function Find the linear approximation to $f(x) = \sin x$ at $x = 0$ and use it to approximate $\sin 2.5°$.

SOLUTION We first construct a linear approximation $L(x) = f(a) + f'(a)(x - a)$, where $f(x) = \sin x$ and $a = 0$. Noting that $f(0) = 0$ and $f'(0) = \cos(0) = 1$, we have

$$L(x) = 0 + 1(x - 0) = x.$$

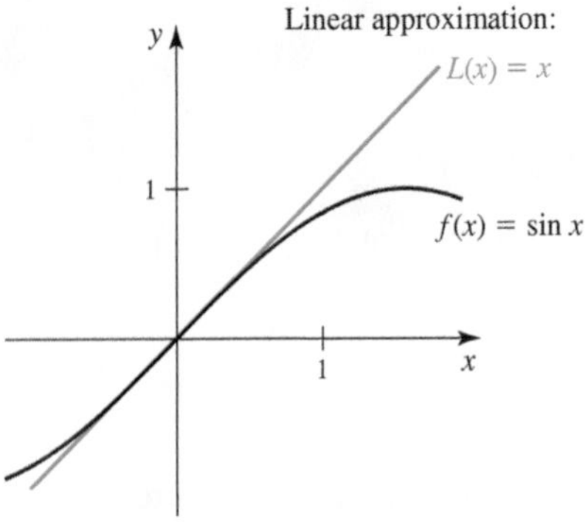

Figure 4.62

Again, the linear approximation is the line tangent to the curve at the point $(0, 2)$ (Figure 4.62). Before using $L(x)$ to approximate sin 2.5°, we convert to radian measure (the derivative formulas for trigonometric functions require angles in radians):

$$2.5° = 2.5°\left(\frac{\pi}{180°}\right) = \frac{\pi}{72} \approx 0.04363 \text{ rad.}$$

Therefore, $\sin 2.5° \approx L(0.04363) = 0.04363$. A calculator gives $\sin 2.5° \approx 0.04362$, so the approximation is accurate to four decimal places.

Related Exercises 21–30 ◀

In Examples 2 and 3, we used a calculator to check the accuracy of our approximations. This raises the question: Why bother with linear approximation when a calculator does a better job? There are some good answers to that question.

Linear approximation is actually just the first step in the process of *polynomial approximation*. While linear approximation does a decent job of estimating function values when x is near a, we can generally do better with higher-degree polynomials. These ideas are explored further in Chapter 9.

Linear approximation also allows us to discover simple approximations to complicated functions. In Example 3, we found the *small-angle approximation to the sine function*: $\sin x \approx x$ for x near 0.

QUICK CHECK 4 Explain why the linear approximation to $f(x) = \cos x$ at $x = 0$ is $L(x) = 1$. ◀

Linear Approximation and Concavity

Additional insight into linear approximation is gained by bringing concavity into the picture. Figure 4.63a shows the graph of a function f and its linear approximation (tangent line) at the point $(a, f(a))$. In this particular case, f is concave up on an interval containing a, and the graph of L lies below the graph of f near a. As a result, the linear approximation evaluated at a point near a is less than the exact value of f at that point. In other words, the linear approximation *underestimates* values of f near a.

The contrasting case is shown in Figure 4.63b, where we see graphs of f and L when f is concave down on an interval containing a. Now the graph of L lies above the graph of f, which means the linear approximation *overestimates* values of f near a.

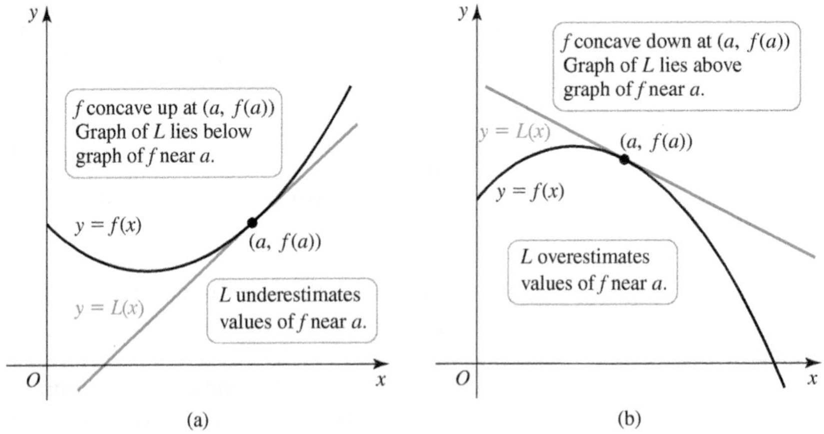

Figure 4.63

We can make another observation related to the degree of concavity (also called *curvature*). A large value of $|f''(a)|$ (large curvature) means that near $(a, f(a))$, the slope of the curve changes rapidly and the graph of f separates quickly from the tangent line. A small value of $|f''(a)|$ (small curvature) means the slope of the curve changes slowly and the curve is relatively flat near $(a, f(a))$; therefore, the curve remains close to the tangent line. As a result, absolute errors in linear approximation are larger when $|f''(a)|$ is large.

EXAMPLE 4 Linear approximation and concavity

a. Find the linear approximation to $f(x) = x^{1/3}$ at $x = 1$ and $x = 27$.

b. Use the linear approximations of part (a) to approximate $\sqrt[3]{2}$ and $\sqrt[3]{26}$

c. Are the approximations in part (b) overestimates or underestimates?

d. Compute the error in the approximations of part (b). Which error is greater? Explain.

SOLUTION

a. Note that

$$f(1) = 1, \quad f(27) = 3, \quad f'(x) = \frac{1}{3x^{2/3}}, \quad f'(1) = \frac{1}{3}, \quad \text{and} \quad f'(27) = \frac{1}{27}.$$

Therefore, the linear approximation at $x = 1$ is

$$L_1(x) = 1 + \frac{1}{3}(x - 1) = \frac{1}{3}x + \frac{2}{3},$$

and the linear approximation at $x = 27$ is

$$L_2(x) = 3 + \frac{1}{27}(x - 27) = \frac{1}{27}x + 2.$$

b. Using the results of part (a), we find that

$$\sqrt[3]{2} \approx L_1(2) = \frac{1}{3}\cdot 2 + \frac{2}{3} = \frac{4}{3} \approx 1.333$$

and

$$\sqrt[3]{26} \approx L_2(26) = \frac{1}{27}\cdot 26 + 2 \approx 2.963.$$

c. Figure 4.64 shows the graphs of f and the linear approximations L_1 and L_2 at $x = 1$ and $x = 27$, respectively (note the different scales on the x-axes). We see that f is concave down at both points, which is confirmed by the fact that

$$f''(x) = -\frac{2}{9}x^{-5/3} < 0, \quad \text{for} \quad x > 0.$$

As a result, the linear approximations lie above the graph of f and both approximations are overestimates.

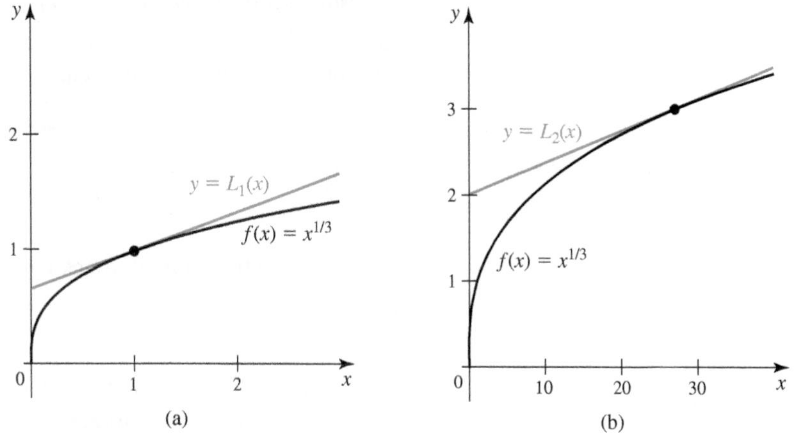

Figure 4.64

d. The error in the two linear approximations are

$$|L_1(2) - 2^{1/3}| \approx 0.073 \quad \text{and} \quad |L_2(26) - 26^{1/3}| \approx 0.00047.$$

Because $|f''(1)| \approx 0.22$ and $|f''(27)| \approx 0.00091$, the curvature of f is much greater at $x = 1$ than at $x = 27$, explaining why the approximation of $\sqrt[3]{26}$ is more accurate than the approximation of $\sqrt[3]{2}$.

Related Exercises 31–34 ◄

A Variation on Linear Approximation Linear approximation says that a function f can be approximated as

$$f(x) \approx f(a) + f'(a)(x - a),$$

where a is fixed and x is a nearby point. We first rewrite this expression as

$$\underbrace{f(x) - f(a)}_{\Delta y} \approx f'(a)\underbrace{(x - a)}_{\Delta x}.$$

It is customary to use the notation Δ (capital Greek delta) to denote a change. The factor $x - a$ is the change in the x-coordinate between a and a nearby point x. Similarly, $f(x) - f(a)$ is the corresponding change in the y-coordinate (Figure 4.65). So we write this approximation as

$$\Delta y \approx f'(a)\,\Delta x.$$

In other words, a change in y (the function value) can be approximated by the corresponding change in x magnified or diminished by a factor of $f'(a)$. This interpretation states the familiar fact that $f'(a)$ is the rate of change of y with respect to x.

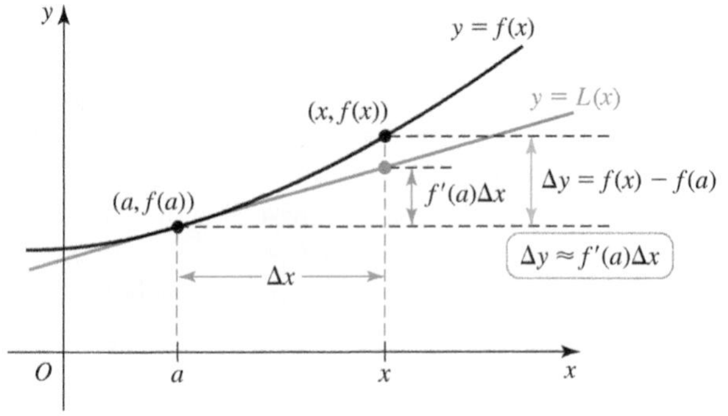

Figure 4.65

> **Relationship Between Δx and Δy**
>
> Suppose f is differentiable on an interval I containing the point a. The change in the value of f between two points a and $a + \Delta x$ is approximately
>
> $$\Delta y \approx f'(a)\,\Delta x,$$
>
> where $a + \Delta x$ is in I.

EXAMPLE 5 Estimating changes with linear approximations

a. Approximate the change in $y = f(x) = x^9 - 2x + 1$ when x changes from 1.00 to 1.05.

b. Approximate the change in the surface area of a spherical hot-air balloon when the radius decreases from 4 m to 3.9 m.

SOLUTION

a. The change in y is $\Delta y \approx f'(a)\,\Delta x$, where $a = 1$, $\Delta x = 0.05$, and $f'(x) = 9x^8 - 2$. Substituting these values, we find that

$$\Delta y \approx f'(a)\,\Delta x = f'(1)\cdot 0.05 = 7\cdot 0.05 = 0.35.$$

If x increases from 1.00 to 1.05, then y increases by approximately 0.35.

➤ Notice that the units in these calculations are consistent. If r has units of meters (m), S' has units of $m^2/m = m$, so ΔS has units of m^2, as it should.

QUICK CHECK 5 Given that the volume of a sphere is $V = 4\pi r^3/3$, find an expression for the approximate change in the volume when the radius changes from a to $a + \Delta r$. ◄

b. The surface area of a sphere is $S = 4\pi r^2$, so the change in the surface area when the radius changes by Δr is $\Delta S \approx S'(a)\,\Delta r$. Substituting $S'(r) = 8\pi r$, $a = 4$, and $\Delta r = -0.1$, the approximate change in the surface area is

$$\Delta S \approx S'(a)\,\Delta r = S'(4)\cdot(-0.1) = 32\pi\cdot(-0.1) \approx -10.05.$$

The change in surface area is approximately $-10.05\ m^2$; it is negative, reflecting a decrease.

Related Exercises 35–40 ◄

SUMMARY Uses of Linear Approximation

- To approximate f near $x = a$, use

$$f(x) \approx L(x) = f(a) + f'(a)(x - a).$$

- To approximate the change Δy in the dependent variable when x changes from a to $a + \Delta x$, use

$$\Delta y \approx f'(a)\,\Delta x.$$

Differentials

We now introduce an important concept that allows us to distinguish two related quantities:

- the change in the function $y = f(x)$ as x changes from a to $a + \Delta x$ (which we call Δy, as before), and
- the change in the linear approximation $y = L(x)$ as x changes from a to $a + \Delta x$ (which we call the *differential dy*).

Consider a function $y = f(x)$ differentiable on an interval containing a. If the x-coordinate changes from a to $a + \Delta x$, the corresponding change in the function is *exactly*

$$\Delta y = f(a + \Delta x) - f(a).$$

Using the linear approximation $L(x) = f(a) + f'(a)(x - a)$, the change in L as x changes from a to $a + \Delta x$ is

$$\begin{aligned}\Delta L &= L(a + \Delta x) - L(a)\\ &= \underbrace{(f(a) + f'(a)(a + \Delta x - a))}_{L(a+\Delta x)} - \underbrace{(f(a) + f'(a)(a - a))}_{L(a)}\\ &= f'(a)\,\Delta x.\end{aligned}$$

To distinguish Δy and ΔL, we define two new variables called *differentials*. The differential dx is simply Δx; the differential dy is the change in the linear approximation, which is $\Delta L = f'(a)\,\Delta x$. Using this notation,

$$\Delta L = \underbrace{dy}_{\text{same as } \Delta L} = f'(a)\,\Delta x = f'(a)\underbrace{dx}_{\text{same as } \Delta x}.$$

Therefore, at the point a, we have $dy = f'(a)\,dx$. More generally, we replace the fixed point a by a variable point x and write

$$dy = f'(x)\,dx.$$

DEFINITION Differentials

Let f be differentiable on an interval containing x. A small change in x is denoted by the **differential** dx. The corresponding change in f is approximated by the **differential** $dy = f'(x)\,dx$; that is,

$$\Delta y = f(x + dx) - f(x) \approx dy = f'(x)\,dx.$$

Figure 4.66 shows that if $\Delta x = dx$ is small, then the change in f, which is Δy, is well approximated by the change in the linear approximation, which is dy. Furthermore, the approximation $\Delta y \approx dy$ improves as dx approaches 0. The notation for differentials is consistent with the notation for the derivative: If we divide both sides of $dy = f'(x)\,dx$ by dx, we have

$$\frac{dy}{dx} = \frac{f'(x)\,dx}{dx} = f'(x).$$

➤ Of the two coinventors of calculus, Gottfried Leibniz relied on the idea of differentials in his development of calculus. Leibniz's notation for differentials is essentially the same as the notation we use today. An Irish philosopher of the day, Bishop Berkeley, called differentials "the ghost of departed quantities."

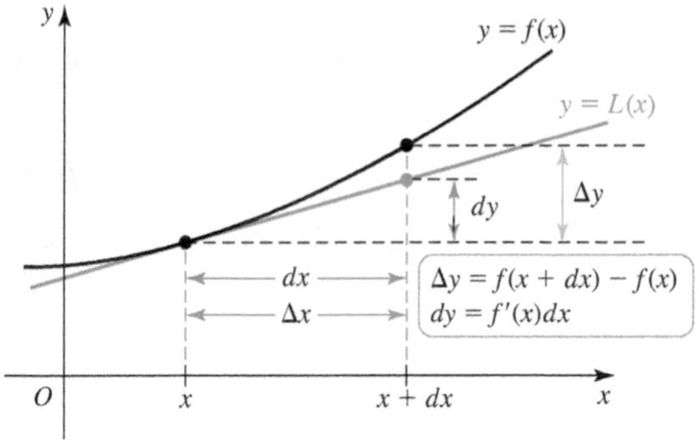

Figure 4.66

EXAMPLE 6 **Differentials as change** Use the notation of differentials to write the approximate change in $f(x) = 3\cos^2 x$ given a small change dx.

SOLUTION With $f(x) = 3\cos^2 x$, we have $f'(x) = -6\cos x \sin x = -3\sin 2x$. Therefore,

$$dy = f'(x)\,dx = -3\sin 2x\,dx.$$

➤ Recall that $\sin 2x = 2\sin x \cos x$.

The interpretation is that a small change dx in the independent variable x produces an approximate change in the dependent variable of $dy = -3\sin 2x\,dx$ in y. For example, if x increases from $x = \pi/4$ to $x = \pi/4 + 0.1$, then $dx = 0.1$ and

$$dy = -3\sin(\pi/2)(0.1) = -0.3.$$

The approximate change in the function is -0.3, which means a decrease of approximately 0.3.

Related Exercises 41–50 ◀

SECTION 4.5 EXERCISES

Review Questions

1. Sketch the graph of a smooth function f and label a point $P(a, (f(a))$ on the curve. Draw the line that represents the linear approximation to f at P.

2. Suppose you find the linear approximation to a differentiable function at a local maximum of that function. Describe the graph of the linear approximation.

3. How is linear approximation used to approximate the value of a function f near a point at which f and f' are easily evaluated?

4. How can linear approximation be used to approximate the change in $y = f(x)$ given a change in x?

5. Given a function f that is differentiable on its domain, write and explain the relationship between the differentials dx and dy.

6. Does the differential dy represent the change in f or the change in the linear approximation to f? Explain.

Basic Skills

7–8. Estimating speed *Use the linear approximation given in Example 1 to answer the following questions.*

7. If you travel one mile in 59 seconds, what is your approximate average speed? What is your exact speed?

8. If you travel one mile in 63 seconds, what is your approximate average speed? What is your exact speed?

9–12. Estimating time *Suppose you want to travel D miles at a constant speed of $(60 + x)$ mi/hr, where x could be positive or negative. The time in minutes required to travel D miles is $T(x) = 60D(60 + x)^{-1}$.*

9. Show that the linear approximation to T at the point $x = 0$ is
$$T(x) \approx L(x) = D\left(1 - \frac{x}{60}\right).$$

10. Use the result of Exercise 9 to approximate the amount of time it takes to drive 45 miles at 62 mi/hr. What is the exact time required?

11. Use the result of Exercise 9 to approximate the amount of time it takes to drive 80 miles at 57 mi/hr. What is the exact time required?

12. Use the result of Exercise 9 to approximate the amount of time it takes to drive 93 miles at 63 mi/hr. What is the exact time required?

T 13–20. Linear approximation

a. Write the equation of the line that represents the linear approximation to the following functions at the given point a.
b. Graph the function and the linear approximation at a.
c. Use the linear approximation to estimate the given function value.
d. Compute the percent error in your approximation, $100\,|\text{approximation} - \text{exact}|/|\text{exact}|$, *where the exact value is given by a calculator.*

13. $f(x) = 12 - x^2;\ a = 2;\ f(2.1)$

14. $f(x) = \sin x;\ a = \pi/4;\ f(0.75)$

15. $f(x) = \ln(1 + x);\ a = 0;\ f(0.9)$

16. $f(x) = x/(x + 1);\ a = 1;\ f(1.1)$

17. $f(x) = \cos x;\ a = 0;\ f(-0.01)$

18. $f(x) = e^x;\ a = 0;\ f(0.05)$

19. $f(x) = (8 + x)^{-1/3};\ a = 0;\ f(-0.1)$

20. $f(x) = \sqrt[4]{x};\ a = 81;\ f(85)$

21–30. Estimations with linear approximation *Use linear approximations to estimate the following quantities. Choose a value of a that produces a small error.*

21. $1/203$ 22. $\tan 3°$ 23. $\sqrt{146}$ 24. $\sqrt[3]{65}$

25. $\ln(1.05)$ 26. $\sqrt{5/29}$ 27. $e^{0.06}$ 28. $1/\sqrt{119}$

29. $1/\sqrt[3]{510}$ 30. $\cos 31°$

31–34. Linear approximation and concavity *Carry out the following steps for the given functions f and points a.*

a. Find the linear approximation L to the function f at the point a.
b. Graph f and L on the same set of axes.
c. Based on the graphs in part (a), state whether linear approximations to f near a are underestimates or overestimates.
d. Compute f″(a) to confirm your conclusion in part (c).

31. $f(x) = \dfrac{2}{x}, a = 1$ 32. $f(x) = 5 - x^2, a = 2$

33. $f(x) = e^{-x}, a = \ln 2$ 34. $f(x) = \sqrt{2}\cos x, a = \dfrac{\pi}{4}$

35–40. Approximating changes

35. Approximate the change in the volume of a sphere when its radius changes from $r = 5$ ft to $r = 5.1$ ft $(V(r) = \frac{4}{3}\pi r^3)$.

36. Approximate the change in the atmospheric pressure when the altitude increases from $z = 2$ km to $z = 2.01$ km $(P(z) = 1000\,e^{-z/10})$.

37. Approximate the change in the volume of a right circular cylinder of fixed radius $r = 20$ cm when its height decreases from $h = 12$ cm to $h = 11.9$ cm $(V(h) = \pi r^2 h)$.

38. Approximate the change in the volume of a right circular cone of fixed height $h = 4$ m when its radius increases from $r = 3$ m to $r = 3.05$ m $(V(r) = \pi r^2 h/3)$.

39. Approximate the change in the lateral surface area (excluding the area of the base) of a right circular cone with fixed height $h = 6$ m when its radius decreases from $r = 10$ m to $r = 9.9$ m $(S = \pi r\sqrt{r^2 + h^2})$.

40. Approximate the change in the magnitude of the electrostatic force between two charges when the distance between them increases from $r = 20$ m to $r = 21$ m $(F(r) = 0.01/r^2)$.

41–50. Differentials *Consider the following functions and express the relationship between a small change in x and the corresponding change in y in the form* $dy = f'(x)\,dx$.

41. $f(x) = 2x + 1$ 42. $f(x) = \sin^2 x$

43. $f(x) = 1/x^3$ 44. $f(x) = e^{2x}$

45. $f(x) = 2 - a\cos x$, a constant

46. $f(x) = (4 + x)/(4 - x)$

47. $f(x) = 3x^3 - 4x$ 48. $f(x) = \sin^{-1} x$

49. $f(x) = \tan x$ 50. $f(x) = \ln(1 - x)$

Further Explorations

51. **Explain why or why not** Determine whether the following statements are true and give an explanation or counterexample.
    a. The linear approximation to $f(x) = x^2$ at $x = 0$ is $L(x) = 0$.
    b. Linear approximation at $x = 0$ provides a good approximation to $f(x) = |x|$.
    c. If $f(x) = mx + b$, then the linear approximation to f at any point is $L(x) = f(x)$.
    d. When linear approximation is used to estimate values of $\ln x$ near $x = e$, the approximations are overestimates of the true values.

52. **Linear approximation** Estimate $f(5.1)$ given that $f(5) = 10$ and $f'(5) = -2$.

53. **Linear approximation** Estimate $f(3.85)$ given that $f(4) = 3$ and $f'(4) = 2$.

T 54–57. Linear approximation

a. Write an equation of the line that represents the linear approximation to the following functions at a.
b. Graph the function and the linear approximation at a.
c. Use the linear approximation to estimate the given quantity.
d. Compute the percent error in your approximation.

54. $f(x) = \tan x;\ a = 0;\ \tan 3°$

55. $f(x) = 1/(x + 1);\ a = 0;\ 1/1.1$

56. $f(x) = \cos x;\ a = \pi/4;\ \cos 0.8$

57. $f(x) = e^{-x};\ a = 0;\ e^{-0.03}$

Applications

58. **Ideal Gas Law** The pressure P, temperature T, and volume V of an ideal gas are related by $PV = nRT$, where n is the number of moles of the gas and R is the universal gas constant. For the purposes of this exercise, let $nR = 1$; therefore $P = T/V$.
    a. Suppose that the volume is held constant and the temperature increases by $\Delta T = 0.05$. What is the approximate change in the pressure? Does the pressure increase or decrease?
    b. Suppose that the temperature is held constant and the volume increases by $\Delta V = 0.1$. What is the approximate change in the pressure? Does the pressure increase or decrease?

c. Suppose that the pressure is held constant and the volume increases by $\Delta V = 0.1$. What is the approximate change in the temperature? Does the temperature increase or decrease?

T **59. Error in driving speed** Consider again the average speed $s(x)$ and its linear approximation $L(x)$ discussed in Example 1. The error in using $L(x)$ to approximates $s(x)$ is given by $E(x) = |L(x) - s(x)|$. Use a graphing utility to determine the (approximate) values of x for which $E(x) \leq 1$. What does your answer say about the accuracy of the average speeds estimated by $L(x)$ over this interval?

60. Time function Show that the function $T(x) = 60\,D(60 + x)^{-1}$ gives the time in minutes required to drive D miles at $60 + x$ miles per hour.

T **61. Errors in approximations** Suppose $f(x) = \sqrt[3]{x}$ is to be approximated near $x = 8$. Find the linear approximation to f at 8. Then complete the following table, showing the errors in various approximations. Use a calculator to obtain the exact values. The percent error is $100|\text{approximation} - \text{exact}|/|\text{exact}|$. Comment on the behavior of the errors as x approaches 8.

x	Linear approx.	Exact value	Percent error
8.1			
8.01			
8.001			
8.0001			
7.9999			
7.999			
7.99			
7.9			

T **62. Errors in approximations** Suppose $f(x) = 1/(1 + x)$ is to be approximated near $x = 0$. Find the linear approximation to f at 0. Then complete the following table showing the errors in various approximations. Use a calculator to obtain the exact values. The percent error is $100|\text{approximation} - \text{exact}|/|\text{exact}|$. Comment on the behavior of the errors as x approaches 0.

x	Linear approx.	Exact value	Percent error
0.1			
0.01			
0.001			
0.0001			
−0.0001			
−0.001			
−0.01			
−0.1			

Additional Exercises

63. Linear approximation and the second derivative Draw the graph of a function f such that $f(1) = f'(1) = f''(1) = 1$. Draw the linear approximation to the function at the point $(1, 1)$. Now draw the graph of another function g such that $g(1) = g'(1) = 1$ and $g''(1) = 10$. (It is not possible to represent the second derivative exactly, but your graphs should reflect the fact that $f''(1)$ is relatively small and $g''(1)$ is relatively large.) Now suppose that linear approximations are used to approximate $f(1.1)$ and $g(1.1)$.

a. Which function value has the more accurate linear approximation near $x = 1$ and why?

b. Explain why the error in the linear approximation to f near a point a is proportional to the magnitude of $f''(a)$.

QUICK CHECK ANSWERS

1. The linear approximation lies below the graph of f for x near a. **2.** $L(15) = 45$, $s(15) = 48$; $x = 15$ is not close to 0. **3.** $a = 0.16$ **4.** Note that $f(0) = 1$ and $f'(0) = 0$, so $L(x) = 1$ (this is the line tangent to $y = \cos x$ at $(0, 1)$). **5.** $\Delta V \approx 4\pi a^2\,\Delta r$ ◄

4.6 Mean Value Theorem

➤ Michel Rolle (1652–1719) is one of the less celebrated mathematicians whose name is nevertheless attached to a theorem. He worked in Paris most of his life as a scribe and published his theorem in 1691.

The *Mean Value Theorem* is a cornerstone in the theoretical framework of calculus. Several critical theorems (some stated in previous sections) rely on the Mean Value Theorem; this theorem also appears in practical applications. We begin with a preliminary result known as Rolle's Theorem.

Rolle's Theorem

Consider a function f that is continuous on a closed interval $[a, b]$ and differentiable on the open interval (a, b). Furthermore, assume f has the special property that $f(a) = f(b)$ (Figure 4.67). The statement of Rolle's Theorem is not surprising: It says that somewhere between a and b, there is at least one point at which f has a horizontal tangent line.

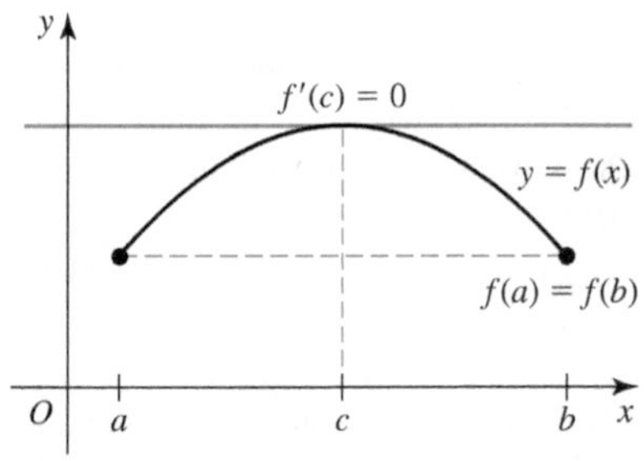

Figure 4.67

THEOREM 4.8 Rolle's Theorem
Let f be continuous on a closed interval $[a, b]$ and differentiable on (a, b) with $f(a) = f(b)$. There is at least one point c in (a, b) such that $f'(c) = 0$.

Proof: The function f satisfies the conditions of Theorem 4.1 (Extreme Value Theorem); therefore, it attains its absolute maximum and minimum values on $[a, b]$. Those values are attained either at an endpoint or at an interior point c.

➤ The Extreme Value Theorem, discussed in Section 4.1, states that a function that is continuous on a closed bounded interval attains its absolute maximum and minimum values on that interval.

Case 1: First suppose that f attains both its absolute maximum and minimum values at the endpoints. Because $f(a) = f(b)$, the maximum and minimum values are equal, and it follows that f is a constant function on $[a, b]$. Therefore, $f'(x) = 0$ for all x in (a, b), and the conclusion of the theorem holds.

Case 2: Assume at least one of the absolute extreme values of f does not occur at an endpoint. Then f must attain an absolute extreme value at an interior point of $[a, b]$; therefore, f must have either a local maximum or a local minimum at a point c in (a, b). We know from Theorem 4.2 that at a local extremum, the derivative is zero. Therefore, $f'(c) = 0$ for at least one point c of (a, b), and again the conclusion of the theorem holds. ◀

Why does Rolle's Theorem require continuity? A function that is not continuous on $[a, b]$ may have identical values at both endpoints and still not have a horizontal tangent line at any point on the interval (Figure 4.68a). Similarly, a function that is continuous on $[a, b]$ but not differentiable at a point of (a, b) may also fail to have a horizontal tangent line (Figure 4.68b).

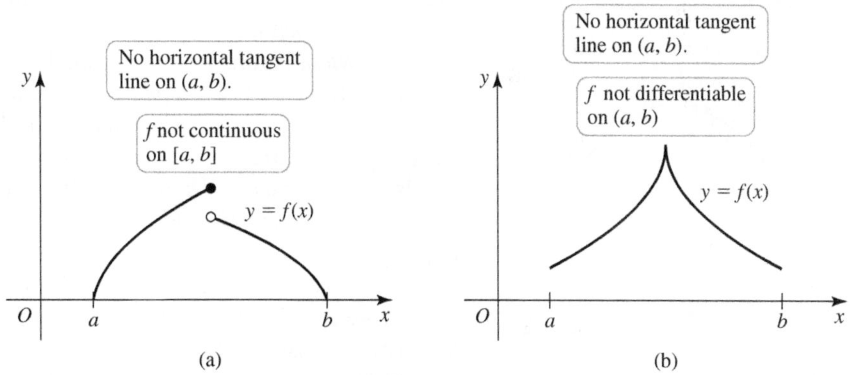

Figure 4.68

QUICK CHECK 1 Where on the interval $[0, 4]$ does $f(x) = 4x - x^2$ have a horizontal tangent line? ◀

EXAMPLE 1 **Verifying Rolle's Theorem** Find an interval I on which Rolle's Theorem applies to $f(x) = x^3 - 7x^2 + 10x$. Then find all points c in I at which $f'(c) = 0$.

SOLUTION Because f is a polynomial, it is everywhere continuous and differentiable. We need an interval $[a, b]$ with the property that $f(a) = f(b)$. Noting that $f(x) = x(x - 2)(x - 5)$, we choose the interval $[0, 5]$, because $f(0) = f(5) = 0$ (other intervals are possible). The goal is to find points c in the interval $(0, 5)$ at which $f'(c) = 0$, which amounts to the familiar task of finding the critical points of f. The critical points satisfy

$$f'(x) = 3x^2 - 14x + 10 = 0.$$

Using the quadratic formula, the roots are

$$x = \frac{7 \pm \sqrt{19}}{3}, \quad \text{or} \quad x \approx 0.88 \quad \text{and} \quad x \approx 3.79.$$

As shown in Figure 4.69, the graph of f has two points at which the tangent line is horizontal.

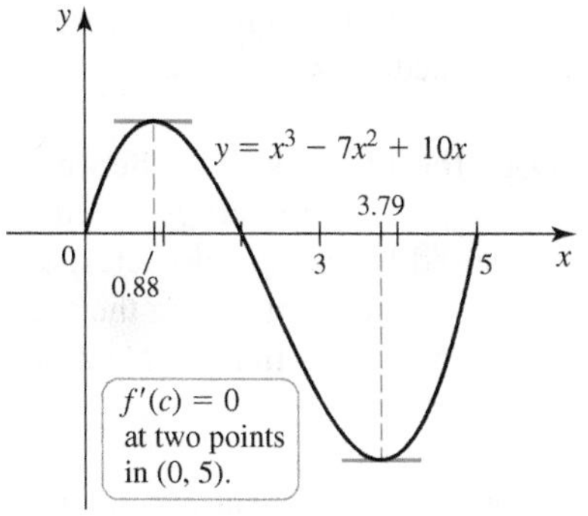

Figure 4.69

Related Exercises 7–14 ◀

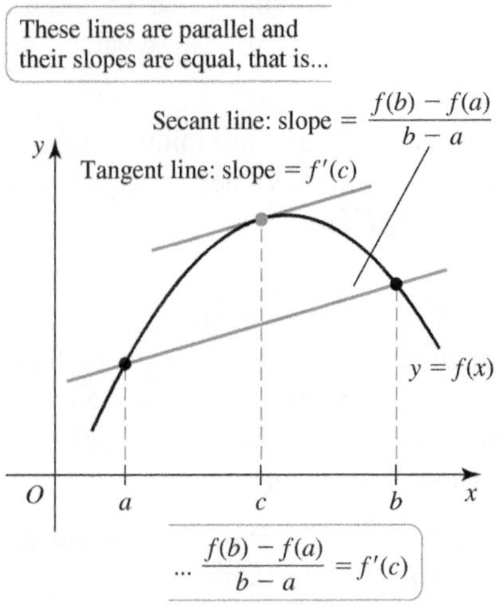

Figure 4.70

Mean Value Theorem

The Mean Value Theorem is easily understood with the aid of a picture. Figure 4.70 shows a function f differentiable on (a, b) with a secant line passing through $(a, f(a))$ and $(b, f(b))$; the slope of the secant line is the average rate of change of f over $[a, b]$. The Mean Value Theorem claims that there exists a point c in (a, b) at which the slope of the tangent line at c is equal to the slope of the secant line. In other words, we can find a point on the graph of f where the tangent line is parallel to the secant line.

THEOREM 4.9 Mean Value Theorem
If f is continuous on the closed interval $[a, b]$ and differentiable on (a, b), then there is at least one point c in (a, b) such that

$$\frac{f(b) - f(a)}{b - a} = f'(c).$$

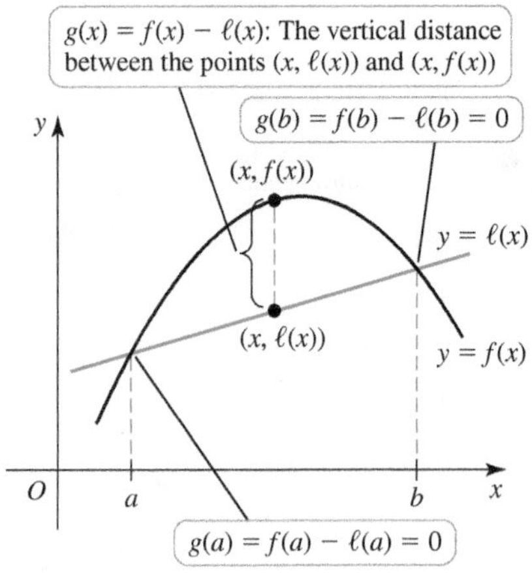

Figure 4.71

Proof: The strategy of the proof is to use the function f of the Mean Value Theorem to form a new function g that satisfies Rolle's Theorem. Notice that the continuity and differentiability conditions of Rolle's Theorem and the Mean Value Theorem are the same. We devise g so that it satisfies the conditions $g(a) = g(b) = 0$.

As shown in Figure 4.71, the secant line passing through $(a, f(a))$ and $(b, f(b))$ is described by a function ℓ. We now define a new function g that measures the vertical distance between the given function f and the line ℓ. This function is simply $g(x) = f(x) - \ell(x)$. Because f and ℓ are continuous on $[a, b]$ and differentiable on (a, b), it follows that g is also continuous on $[a, b]$ and differentiable on (a, b). Furthermore, because the graphs of f and ℓ intersect at $x = a$ and $x = b$, we have $g(a) = f(a) - \ell(a) = 0$ and $g(b) = f(b) - \ell(b) = 0$.

We now have a function g that satisfies the conditions of Rolle's Theorem. By that theorem, we are guaranteed the existence of at least one point c in the interval (a, b) such that $g'(c) = 0$. By the definition of g, this condition implies that $f'(c) - \ell'(c) = 0$, or $f'(c) = \ell'(c)$.

We are almost finished. What is $\ell'(c)$? It is just the slope of the secant line, which is

$$\frac{f(b) - f(a)}{b - a}.$$

Therefore, $f'(c) = \ell'(c)$ implies that

$$\frac{f(b) - f(a)}{b - a} = f'(c).$$ ◀

➤ The proofs of Rolle's Theorem and the Mean Value Theorem are nonconstructive: The theorems claim that a certain point exists, but their proofs do not say how to find it.

QUICK CHECK 2 Sketch the graph of a function that illustrates why the continuity condition of the Mean Value Theorem is needed. Sketch the graph of a function that illustrates why the differentiability condition of the Mean Value Theorem is needed. ◀

The following situation offers an interpretation of the Mean Value Theorem. Imagine driving for 2 hours to a town 100 miles away. While your average speed is 100 mi/2 hr = 50 mi/hr, your instantaneous speed (measured by the speedometer) almost certainly varies. The Mean Value Theorem says that at some point during the trip, your instantaneous speed equals your average speed, which is 50 mi/hr. In Example 2, we apply these ideas to the science of weather forecasting.

EXAMPLE 2 Mean Value Theorem in action The *lapse rate* is the rate at which the temperature T decreases in the atmosphere with respect to increasing altitude z. It is typically reported in units of °C/km and is defined by $\gamma = -dT/dz$. When the lapse rate rises above 7°C/km in a certain layer of the atmosphere, it indicates favorable conditions for thunderstorm and tornado formation, provided other atmospheric conditions are also present.

Suppose the temperature at $z = 2.9$ km is $T = 7.6°C$ and the temperature at $z = 5.6$ km is $T = -14.3°C$. Assume also that the temperature function is continuous and differentiable at all altitudes of interest. What can a meteorologist conclude from these data?

➤ Meteorologists look for "steep" lapse rates in the layer of the atmosphere where the pressure is between 700 and 500 hPa (hectopascals). This range of pressure typically corresponds to altitudes between 3 km and 5.5 km. The data in Example 2 were recorded in Denver at nearly the same time a tornado struck 50 mi to the north.

SOLUTION Figure 4.72 shows the two data points plotted on a graph of altitude and temperature. The slope of the line joining these points is

$$\frac{-14.3°C - 7.6°C}{5.6 \text{ km} - 2.9 \text{ km}} = -8.1°C/\text{km},$$

which means, on average, the temperature is decreasing at $8.1°C/\text{km}$ in the layer of air between 2.9 km and 5.6 km. With only two data points, we cannot know the entire temperature profile. The Mean Value Theorem, however, guarantees that there is at least one altitude at which $dT/dz = -8.1°C/\text{km}$. At each such altitude, the lapse rate is $\gamma = -dT/dz = 8.1°C/\text{km}$. Because this lapse rate is above the $7°C/\text{km}$ threshold associated with unstable weather, the meteorologist might expect an increased likelihood of severe storms.

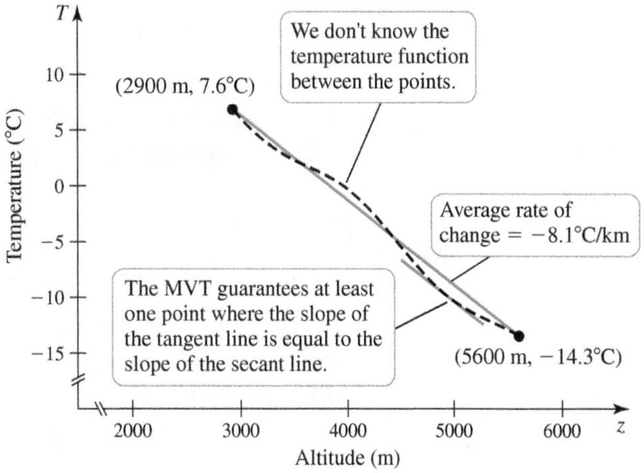

Figure 4.72

Related Exercises 15–16 ◀

EXAMPLE 3 Verifying the Mean Value Theorem Determine whether the function $f(x) = 2x^3 - 3x + 1$ satisfies the conditions of the Mean Value Theorem on the interval $[-2, 2]$. If so, find the point(s) guaranteed to exist by the theorem.

SOLUTION The polynomial f is everywhere continuous and differentiable, so it satisfies the conditions of the Mean Value Theorem. The average rate of change of the function on the interval $[-2, 2]$ is

$$\frac{f(2) - f(-2)}{2 - (-2)} = \frac{11 - (-9)}{4} = 5.$$

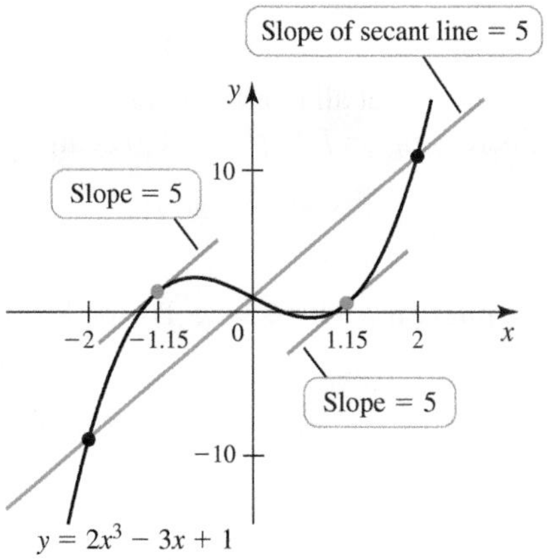

Figure 4.73

The goal is to find points in $(-2, 2)$ at which the line tangent to the curve has a slope of 5—that is, to find points at which $f'(x) = 5$. Differentiating f, this condition becomes

$$f'(x) = 6x^2 - 3 = 5 \quad \text{or} \quad x^2 = \frac{4}{3}.$$

Therefore, the points guaranteed to exist by the Mean Value Theorem are $x = \pm 2/\sqrt{3} \approx \pm 1.15$. The tangent lines have slope 5 at the corresponding points on the curve (Figure 4.73).

Related Exercises 17–24 ◀

Consequences of the Mean Value Theorem

We close with several results—some postponed from previous sections—that follow from the Mean Value Theorem.

We already know that the derivative of a constant function is zero; that is, if $f(x) = C$, then $f'(x) = 0$ (Theorem 3.2). Theorem 4.10 states the converse of this result.

THEOREM 4.10 Zero Derivative Implies Constant Function
If f is differentiable and $f'(x) = 0$ at all points of an interval I, then f is a constant function on I.

Proof: Suppose $f'(x) = 0$ on $[a, b]$, where a and b are distinct points of I. By the Mean Value Theorem, there exists a point c in (a, b) such that

$$\frac{f(b) - f(a)}{b - a} = \underbrace{f'(c) = 0}_{f'(x) = 0 \text{ for all } x \text{ in } I}.$$

Multiplying both sides of this equation by $b - a \neq 0$, it follows that $f(b) = f(a)$, and this is true for every pair of points a and b in I. If $f(b) = f(a)$ for every pair of points in an interval, then f is a constant function on that interval. ◄

Theorem 4.11 builds on the conclusion of Theorem 4.10.

THEOREM 4.11 Functions with Equal Derivatives Differ by a Constant
If two functions have the property that $f'(x) = g'(x)$, for all x of an interval I, then $f(x) - g(x) = C$ on I, where C is a constant; that is, f and g differ by a constant.

Proof: The fact that $f'(x) = g'(x)$ on I implies that $f'(x) - g'(x) = 0$ on I. Recall that the derivative of a difference of two functions equals the difference of the derivatives, so we can write

$$f'(x) - g'(x) = (f - g)'(x) = 0.$$

Now we have a function $f - g$ whose derivative is zero on I. By Theorem 4.10, $f(x) - g(x) = C$, for all x in I, where C is a constant; that is, f and g differ by a constant. ◄

QUICK CHECK 3 Give two distinct linear functions f and g that satisfy $f'(x) = g'(x)$; that is, the lines have equal slopes. Show that f and g differ by a constant. ◄

In Section 4.2, we stated and gave an argument to support the test for intervals of increase and decrease. With the Mean Value Theorem, we can prove this important result.

THEOREM 4.12 Intervals of Increase and Decrease
Suppose f is continuous on an interval I and differentiable at all interior points of I. If $f'(x) > 0$ at all interior points of I, then f is increasing on I. If $f'(x) < 0$ at all interior points of I, then f is decreasing on I.

Proof: Let a and b be any two distinct points in the interval I with $b > a$. By the Mean Value Theorem,

$$\frac{f(b) - f(a)}{b - a} = f'(c),$$

for some c between a and b. Equivalently,

$$f(b) - f(a) = f'(c)(b - a).$$

Notice that $b - a > 0$ by assumption. So if $f'(c) > 0$, then $f(b) - f(a) > 0$. Therefore, for all a and b in I with $b > a$, we have $f(b) > f(a)$, which implies that f is increasing on I. Similarly, if $f'(c) < 0$, then $f(b) - f(a) < 0$ or $f(b) < f(a)$. It follows that f is decreasing on I. ◄

SECTION 4.6 EXERCISES

Review Questions

1. Explain Rolle's Theorem with a sketch.

2. Draw the graph of a function for which the conclusion of Rolle's Theorem does not hold.

3. Explain why Rolle's Theorem cannot be applied to the function $f(x) = |x|$ on the interval $[-a, a]$, for any $a > 0$.

4. Explain the Mean Value Theorem with a sketch.

5. Draw the graph of a function for which the conclusion of the Mean Value Theorem does not hold.

6. At what points c does the conclusion of the Mean Value Theorem hold for $f(x) = x^3$ on the interval $[-10, 10]$?

Basic Skills

7–14. Rolle's Theorem *Determine whether Rolle's Theorem applies to the following functions on the given interval. If so, find the point(s) that are guaranteed to exist by Rolle's Theorem.*

7. $f(x) = x(x-1)^2;\ [0, 1]$

8. $f(x) = \sin 2x;\ [0, \pi/2]$

9. $f(x) = \cos 4x;\ [\pi/8, 3\pi/8]$

10. $f(x) = 1 - |x|;\ [-1, 1]$

11. $f(x) = 1 - x^{2/3};\ [-1, 1]$

12. $f(x) = x^3 - 2x^2 - 8x;\ [-2, 4]$

13. $g(x) = x^3 - x^2 - 5x - 3;\ [-1, 3]$

14. $h(x) = e^{-x^2};\ [-a, a]$, where $a > 0$

15. **Lapse rates in the atmosphere** Concurrent measurements indicate that at an elevation of 6.1 km, the temperature is $-10.3°C$, and at an elevation of 3.2 km, the temperature is $8.0°C$. Based on the Mean Value Theorem, can you conclude that the lapse rate exceeds the threshold value of $7°C/km$ at some intermediate elevation? Explain.

16. **Drag racer acceleration** The fastest drag racers can reach a speed of 330 mi/hr over a quarter-mile strip in 4.45 seconds (from a standing start). Complete the following sentence about such a drag racer: At some point during the race, the maximum acceleration of the drag racer is at least _______ mi/hr/s.

17–24. Mean Value Theorem

a. *Determine whether the Mean Value Theorem applies to the following functions on the given interval* $[a, b]$.

b. *If so, find the point(s) that are guaranteed to exist by the Mean Value Theorem.*

c. *For those cases in which the Mean Value Theorem applies, make a sketch of the function and the line that passes through* $(a, f(a))$ *and* $(b, f(b))$. *Mark the points P at which the slope of the function equals the slope of the secant line. Then sketch the tangent line at P.*

17. $f(x) = 7 - x^2;\ [-1, 2]$

18. $f(x) = 3\sin 2x;\ [0, \pi/4]$

19. $f(x) = e^x;\ [0, \ln 4]$

20. $f(x) = \ln 2x;\ [1, e]$

21. $f(x) = \sin^{-1} x;\ [0, 1/2]$

22. $f(x) = x + 1/x;\ [1, 3]$

23. $f(x) = 2x^{1/3};\ [-8, 8]$

24. $f(x) = x/(x+2);\ [-1, 2]$

Further Explorations

25. **Explain why or why not** Determine whether the following statements are true and give an explanation or counterexample.
    a. The continuous function $f(x) = 1 - |x|$ satisfies the conditions of the Mean Value Theorem on the interval $[-1, 1]$.
    b. Two differentiable functions that differ by a constant always have the same derivative.
    c. If $f'(x) = 0$, then $f(x) = 10$.

26–28. Questions about derivatives

26. Without evaluating derivatives, which of the functions $f(x) = \ln x$, $g(x) = \ln 2x$, $h(x) = \ln x^2$, and $p(x) = \ln 10x^2$ have the same derivative?

27. Without evaluating derivatives, which of the functions $g(x) = 2x^{10}$, $h(x) = x^{10} + 2$, and $p(x) = x^{10} - \ln 2$ have the same derivative as $f(x) = x^{10}$?

28. Find all functions f whose derivative is $f'(x) = x + 1$.

29. **Mean Value Theorem and graphs** By visual inspection, locate all points on the interval $[-4, 4]$ at which the slope of the tangent line equals the average rate of change of the function on the interval $[-4, 4]$.

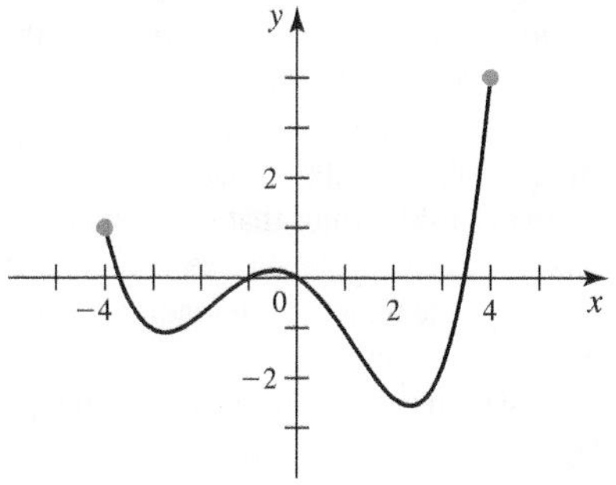

30–31. Mean Value Theorem and graphs *Find all points on the interval* $(1, 3)$ *at which the slope of the tangent line equals the average rate of change of f on* $[1, 3]$. *Reconcile your results with the Mean Value Theorem.*

30.

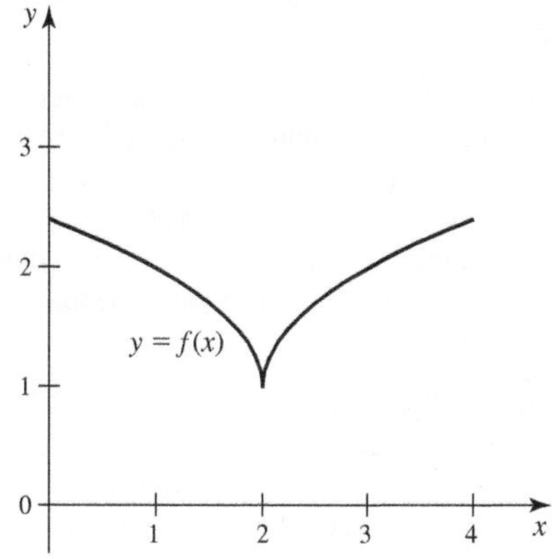

31.

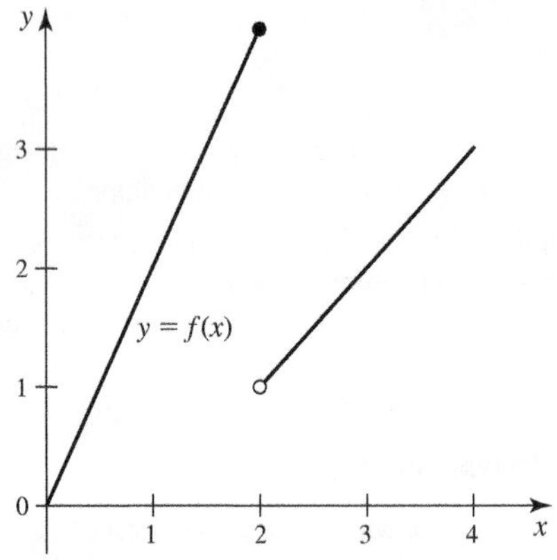

Applications

32. **Avalanche forecasting** Avalanche forecasters measure the *temperature gradient* dT/dh, which is the rate at which the temperature in a snowpack T changes with respect to its depth h. A large temperature gradient may lead to a weak layer in the snowpack. When these weak layers collapse, avalanches occur. Avalanche forecasters use the following rule of thumb: If dT/dh exceeds 10°C/m anywhere in the snowpack, conditions are favorable for weak-layer formation, and the risk of avalanche increases. Assume the temperature function is continuous and differentiable.
    - **a.** An avalanche forecaster digs a snow pit and takes two temperature measurements. At the surface ($h = 0$), the temperature is -12°C. At a depth of 1.1 m, the temperature is 2°C. Using the Mean Value Theorem, what can he conclude about the temperature gradient? Is the formation of a weak layer likely?
    - **b.** One mile away, a skier finds that the temperature at a depth of 1.4 m is -1°C, and at the surface, it is -12°C. What can be concluded about the temperature gradient? Is the formation of a weak layer in her location likely?
    - **c.** Because snow is an excellent insulator, the temperature of snow-covered ground is often near 0°C. Furthermore, the surface temperature of snow in a particular area does not vary much from one location to the next. Explain why a weak layer is more likely to form in places where the snowpack is not too deep.
    - **d.** The term *isothermal* is used to describe the situation where all layers of the snowpack are at the same temperature (typically near the freezing point). Is a weak layer likely to form in isothermal snow? Explain.

33. **Mean Value Theorem and the police** A state patrol officer saw a car start from rest at a highway on-ramp. She radioed ahead to a patrol officer 30 mi along the highway. When the car reached the location of the second officer 28 min later, it was clocked going 60 mi/hr. The driver of the car was given a ticket for exceeding the 60-mi/hr speed limit. Why can the officer conclude that the driver exceeded the speed limit?

34. **Mean Value Theorem and the police again** Compare carefully to Exercise 33. A state patrol officer saw a car start from rest at a highway on-ramp. She radioed ahead to another officer 30 mi along the highway. When the car reached the location of the second officer 30 min later, it was clocked going 60 mi/hr. Can the patrol officer conclude that the driver exceeded the speed limit?

35. **Running pace** Explain why if a runner completes a 6.2-mi (10-km) race in 32 min, then he must have been running at exactly 11 mi/hr at least twice in the race. Assume the runner's speed at the finish line is zero.

Additional Exercises

36. **Mean Value Theorem for linear functions** Interpret the Mean Value Theorem when it is applied to any linear function.

37. **Mean Value Theorem for quadratic functions** Consider the quadratic function $f(x) = Ax^2 + Bx + C$, where A, B, and C are real numbers with $A \neq 0$. Show that when the Mean Value Theorem is applied to f on the interval $[a, b]$, the number c guaranteed by the theorem is the midpoint of the interval.

38. **Means**
    - **a.** Show that the point c guaranteed to exist by the Mean Value Theorem for $f(x) = x^2$ on $[a, b]$ is the arithmetic mean of a and b; that is, $c = (a + b)/2$.
    - **b.** Show that the point c guaranteed to exist by the Mean Value Theorem for $f(x) = 1/x$ on $[a, b]$, where $0 < a < b$, is the geometric mean of a and b; that is, $c = \sqrt{ab}$.

39. **Equal derivatives** Verify that the functions $f(x) = \tan^2 x$ and $g(x) = \sec^2 x$ have the same derivative. What can you say about the difference $f - g$? Explain.

40. **Equal derivatives** Verify that the functions $f(x) = \sin^2 x$ and $g(x) = -\cos^2 x$ have the same derivative. What can you say about the difference $f - g$? Explain.

41. **100-m speed** The Jamaican sprinter Usain Bolt set a world record of 9.58 s in the 100-m dash in the summer of 2009. Did his speed ever exceed 37 km/hr during the race? Explain.

42. **Condition for nondifferentiability** Suppose $f'(x) < 0 < f''(x)$, for $x < a$, and $f'(x) > 0 > f''(x)$, for $x > a$. Prove that f is not differentiable at a. (*Hint:* Assume f is differentiable at a and apply the Mean Value Theorem to f'.) More generally, show that if f' and f'' change sign at the same point, then f is not differentiable at that point.

43. **Generalized Mean Value Theorem** Suppose the functions f and g are continuous on $[a, b]$ and differentiable on (a, b), where $g(a) \neq g(b)$. Then there is a point c in (a, b) at which

$$\frac{f(b) - f(a)}{g(b) - g(a)} = \frac{f'(c)}{g'(c)}.$$

This result is known as the **Generalized (or Cauchy's) Mean Value Theorem.**
    - **a.** If $g(x) = x$, then show that the Generalized Mean Value Theorem reduces to the Mean Value Theorem.
    - **b.** Suppose $f(x) = x^2 - 1$, $g(x) = 4x + 2$, and $[a, b] = [0, 1]$. Find a value of c satisfying the Generalized Mean Value Theorem.

QUICK CHECK ANSWERS

1. $x = 2$ **2.** The functions shown in Figure 4.68 provide examples. **3.** The graphs of $f(x) = 3x$ and $g(x) = 3x + 2$ have the same slope. Note that $f(x) - g(x) = -2$, a constant. ◄

4.7 L'Hôpital's Rule

The study of limits in Chapter 2 was thorough but not exhaustive. Some limits, called *indeterminate forms*, cannot generally be evaluated using the techniques presented in Chapter 2. These limits tend to be the more interesting limits that arise in practice. A powerful result called *l'Hôpital's Rule* enables us to evaluate such limits with relative ease.

Here is how indeterminate forms arise. If f is a *continuous* function at a point a, then we know that $\lim_{x \to a} f(x) = f(a)$, allowing the limit to be evaluated by computing $f(a)$. But there are many limits that cannot be evaluated by substitution. In fact, we encountered such a limit in Section 3.4:

$$\lim_{x \to 0} \frac{\sin x}{x} = 1.$$

If we attempt to substitute $x = 0$ into $(\sin x)/x$, we get $0/0$, which has no meaning. Yet we proved that $(\sin x)/x$ has the limit 1 at $x = 0$ (Theorem 3.11). This limit is an example of an *indeterminate form*; specifically, $\lim_{x \to 0} \frac{\sin x}{x}$ has the form $0/0$ because the numerator and denominator both approach 0 as $x \to 0$.

The meaning of an *indeterminate form* is further illustrated by $\lim_{x \to \infty} \frac{ax}{x + 1}$, where $a \neq 0$. This limit has the indeterminate form ∞/∞ (meaning that the numerator and denominator become arbitrarily large in magnitude as $x \to \infty$), but the actual value of the limit is $\lim_{x \to \infty} \frac{ax}{x + 1} = a \lim_{x \to \infty} \frac{x}{x + 1} = a$, where a is any nonzero real number. In general, a limit with the form ∞/∞ or $0/0$ can have *any* value—which is why these limits must be handled carefully.

➤ The notations $0/0$ and ∞/∞ are merely symbols used to describe various types of indeterminate forms. The notation $0/0$ does not imply division by 0.

L'Hôpital's Rule for the Form 0/0

Consider a function of the form $f(x)/g(x)$ and assume that $\lim_{x \to a} f(x) = \lim_{x \to a} g(x) = 0$. Then the limit $\lim_{x \to a} \frac{f(x)}{g(x)}$ has the indeterminate form $0/0$. We first state l'Hôpital's Rule and then prove a special case.

➤ Guillaume François l'Hôpital (lo-pee-tal) (1661–1704) is credited with writing the first calculus textbook. Much of the material in his book, including l'Hôpital's Rule, was provided by the Swiss mathematician Johann Bernoulli (1667–1748).

THEOREM 4.13 L'Hôpital's Rule
Suppose f and g are differentiable on an open interval I containing a with $g'(x) \neq 0$ on I when $x \neq a$. If $\lim_{x \to a} f(x) = \lim_{x \to a} g(x) = 0$, then

$$\lim_{x \to a} \frac{f(x)}{g(x)} = \lim_{x \to a} \frac{f'(x)}{g'(x)},$$

provided the limit on the right exists (or is $\pm\infty$). The rule also applies if $x \to a$ is replaced with $x \to \pm\infty$, $x \to a^+$, or $x \to a^-$.

Proof (special case): The proof of this theorem relies on the Generalized Mean Value Theorem (Exercise 43 of Section 4.6). We prove a special case of the theorem in which we assume that f' and g' are continuous at a, $f(a) = g(a) = 0$, and $g'(a) \neq 0$. We have

$$\lim_{x \to a} \frac{f'(x)}{g'(x)} = \frac{f'(a)}{g'(a)} \quad \text{Continuity of } f' \text{ and } g'$$

$$= \frac{\lim_{x \to a} \frac{f(x) - f(a)}{x - a}}{\lim_{x \to a} \frac{g(x) - g(a)}{x - a}} \quad \text{Definition of } f'(a) \text{ and } g'(a)$$

➤ The definition of the derivative provides an example of an indeterminate form. Assuming f is differentiable at x,

$$f'(x) = \lim_{h \to 0} \frac{f(x + h) - f(x)}{h}$$

has the form $0/0$.

$$= \lim_{x \to a} \frac{\dfrac{f(x) - f(a)}{x - a}}{\dfrac{g(x) - g(a)}{x - a}} \quad \text{Limit of a quotient, } g'(a) \neq 0$$

$$= \lim_{x \to a} \frac{f(x) - f(a)}{g(x) - g(a)} \quad \text{Cancel } x - a.$$

$$= \lim_{x \to a} \frac{f(x)}{g(x)}. \quad f(a) = g(a) = 0$$

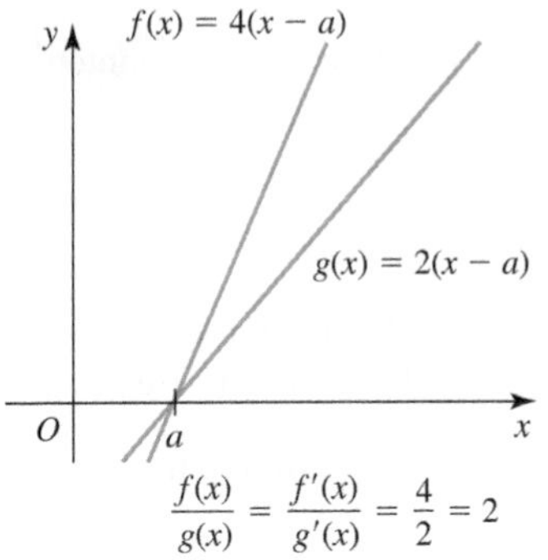

Figure 4.74

The geometry of l'Hôpital's Rule offers some insight. First consider two *linear* functions, f and g, whose graphs both pass through the point $(a, 0)$ with slopes 4 and 2, respectively; this means that

$$f(x) = 4(x - a) \quad \text{and} \quad g(x) = 2(x - a).$$

Furthermore, $f(a) = g(a) = 0, f'(x) = 4$, and $g'(x) = 2$ (Figure 4.74).

Looking at the quotient f/g, we see that

$$\frac{f(x)}{g(x)} = \frac{4(x - a)}{2(x - a)} = \frac{4}{2} = \frac{f'(x)}{g'(x)}. \quad \text{Exactly}$$

This argument may be generalized, and we find that for any linear functions f and g with $f(a) = g(a) = 0$,

$$\lim_{x \to a} \frac{f(x)}{g(x)} = \lim_{x \to a} \frac{f'(x)}{g'(x)},$$

provided $g'(a) \neq 0$.

If f and g are not linear functions, we replace them with their linear approximations at a (Figure 4.75). Zooming in on the point a, the curves are close to their respective tangent lines $y = f'(a)(x - a)$ and $y = g'(a)(x - a)$, which have slopes $f'(a)$ and $g'(a) \neq 0$, respectively. Near $x = a$, we have

$$\frac{f(x)}{g(x)} \approx \frac{f'(a)(x - a)}{g'(a)(x - a)} = \frac{f'(a)}{g'(a)}.$$

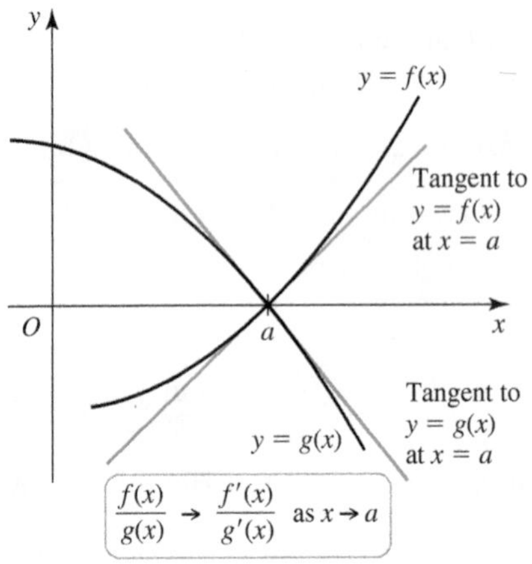

Figure 4.75

Therefore, the ratio of the functions is well approximated by the ratio of the derivatives. In the limit as $x \to a$, we again have

$$\lim_{x \to a} \frac{f(x)}{g(x)} = \lim_{x \to a} \frac{f'(x)}{g'(x)}.$$

QUICK CHECK 1 Which of the following functions lead to an indeterminate form as $x \to 0$: $f(x) = x^2/(x + 2)$, $g(x) = (\tan 3x)/x$, or $h(x) = (1 - \cos x)/x^2$? ◄

EXAMPLE 1 **Using l'Hôpital's Rule** Evaluate the following limits.

a. $\displaystyle\lim_{x \to 1} \frac{x^3 + x^2 - 2x}{x - 1}$ **b.** $\displaystyle\lim_{x \to 0} \frac{\sqrt{9 + 3x} - 3}{x}$

SOLUTION

a. Direct substitution of $x = 1$ into $\dfrac{x^3 + x^2 - 2x}{x - 1}$ produces the indeterminate form $0/0$. Applying l'Hôpital's Rule with $f(x) = x^3 + x^2 - 2x$ and $g(x) = x - 1$ gives

$$\lim_{x \to 1} \frac{x^3 + x^2 - 2x}{x - 1} = \lim_{x \to 1} \frac{f'(x)}{g'(x)} = \lim_{x \to 1} \frac{3x^2 + 2x - 2}{1} = 3.$$

➤ The limit in part (a) can also be evaluated by factoring the numerator and canceling $(x - 1)$:

$$\lim_{x \to 1} \frac{x^3 + x^2 - 2x}{x - 1} = \lim_{x \to 1} \frac{x(x - 1)(x + 2)}{x - 1} = \lim_{x \to 1} x(x + 2) = 3.$$

b. Substituting $x = 0$ into this function produces the indeterminate form $0/0$. Let $f(x) = \sqrt{9 + 3x} - 3$ and $g(x) = x$, and note that $f'(x) = \dfrac{3}{2\sqrt{9 + 3x}}$ and $g'(x) = 1$. Applying l'Hôpital's Rule, we have

$$\underbrace{\lim_{x \to 0} \frac{\sqrt{9 + 3x} - 3}{x}}_{f/g} = \underbrace{\lim_{x \to 0} \frac{\frac{3}{2\sqrt{9 + 3x}}}{1}}_{f'/g'} = \frac{1}{2}.$$

Related Exercises 13–22 ◀

L'Hôpital's Rule requires evaluating $\lim_{x \to a} f'(x)/g'(x)$. It may happen that this second limit is another indeterminate form to which l'Hôpital's Rule may again be applied.

EXAMPLE 2 **L'Hôpital's Rule repeated** Evaluate the following limits.

a. $\lim_{x \to 0} \dfrac{e^x - x - 1}{x^2}$ **b.** $\lim_{x \to 2} \dfrac{x^3 - 3x^2 + 4}{x^4 - 4x^3 + 7x^2 - 12x + 12}$

SOLUTION

a. This limit has the indeterminate form $0/0$. Applying l'Hôpital's Rule, we have

$$\lim_{x \to 0} \frac{e^x - x - 1}{x^2} = \lim_{x \to 0} \frac{e^x - 1}{2x},$$

which is another limit of the form $0/0$. Therefore, we apply l'Hôpital's Rule again:

$$\begin{aligned}
\lim_{x \to 0} \frac{e^x - x - 1}{x^2} &= \lim_{x \to 0} \frac{e^x - 1}{2x} && \text{L'Hôpital's Rule} \\
&= \lim_{x \to 0} \frac{e^x}{2} && \text{L'Hôpital's Rule again} \\
&= \frac{1}{2}. && \text{Evaluate limit.}
\end{aligned}$$

b. Evaluating the numerator and denominator at $x = 2$, we see that this limit has the form $0/0$. Applying l'Hôpital's Rule twice, we have

$$\begin{aligned}
\lim_{x \to 2} \frac{x^3 - 3x^2 + 4}{x^4 - 4x^3 + 7x^2 - 12x + 12} &= \underbrace{\lim_{x \to 2} \frac{3x^2 - 6x}{4x^3 - 12x^2 + 14x - 12}}_{\text{limit of the form } 0/0} && \text{L'Hôpital's Rule} \\
&= \lim_{x \to 2} \frac{6x - 6}{12x^2 - 24x + 14} && \text{L'Hôpital's Rule again} \\
&= \frac{3}{7}. && \text{Evaluate limit.}
\end{aligned}$$

It is easy to overlook a crucial step in this computation: After applying l'Hôpital's Rule the first time, you *must* establish that the new limit is an indeterminate form before applying l'Hôpital's Rule a second time.

Related Exercises 23–36 ◀

Indeterminate Form ∞/∞

L'Hôpital's Rule also applies directly to limits of the form $\lim_{x\to a} f(x)/g(x)$, where $\lim_{x\to a} f(x) = \pm\infty$ and $\lim_{x\to a} g(x) = \pm\infty$; this indeterminate form is denoted ∞/∞. The proof of this result is found in advanced books.

> **THEOREM 4.14 L'Hôpital's Rule (∞/∞)**
> Suppose that f and g are differentiable on an open interval I containing a, with $g'(x) \neq 0$ on I when $x \neq a$. If $\lim_{x\to a} f(x) = \pm\infty$ and $\lim_{x\to a} g(x) = \pm\infty$, then
> $$\lim_{x\to a} \frac{f(x)}{g(x)} = \lim_{x\to a} \frac{f'(x)}{g'(x)},$$
> provided the limit on the right exists (or is $\pm\infty$). The rule also applies for $x \to \pm\infty$, $x \to a^+$, or $x \to a^-$.

QUICK CHECK 2 Which of the following functions lead to an indeterminate form as $x \to \infty$: $f(x) = \sin x/x$, $g(x) = 2^x/x^2$, or $h(x) = (3x^2 + 4)/x^2$? ◄

EXAMPLE 3 L'Hôpital's Rule for ∞/∞ Evaluate the following limits.

a. $\displaystyle\lim_{x\to\infty} \frac{4x^3 - 6x^2 + 1}{2x^3 - 10x + 3}$ **b.** $\displaystyle\lim_{x\to\pi/2^-} \frac{1 + \tan x}{\sec x}$

SOLUTION

➤ As shown in Section 2.5, the limit in Example 3a could also be evaluated by first dividing the numerator and denominator by x^3 or by using Theorem 2.7.

a. This limit has the indeterminate form ∞/∞ because both the numerator and the denominator approach ∞ as $x \to \infty$. Applying l'Hôpital's Rule three times, we have

$$\underbrace{\lim_{x\to\infty} \frac{4x^3 - 6x^2 + 1}{2x^3 - 10x + 3}}_{\infty/\infty} = \underbrace{\lim_{x\to\infty} \frac{12x^2 - 12x}{6x^2 - 10}}_{\infty/\infty} = \underbrace{\lim_{x\to\infty} \frac{24x - 12}{12x}}_{\infty/\infty} = \lim_{x\to\infty} \frac{24}{12} = 2.$$

b. In this limit, both the numerator and denominator approach ∞ as $x \to \pi/2^-$. L'Hôpital's Rule gives us

➤ In Exercise 3b, notice that we simplify $\sec^2 x/(\sec x \tan x)$ before taking the final limit. This step is important.

$$\lim_{x\to\pi/2^-} \frac{1 + \tan x}{\sec x} = \lim_{x\to\pi/2^-} \frac{\sec^2 x}{\sec x \tan x} \quad \text{L'Hôpital's Rule}$$
$$= \lim_{x\to\pi/2^-} \frac{1}{\sin x} \quad \text{Simplify.}$$
$$= 1. \quad \text{Evaluate limit.}$$

Related Exercises 37–44 ◄

Related Indeterminate Forms: $0 \cdot \infty$ and $\infty - \infty$

We now consider limits of the form $\lim_{x\to a} f(x)g(x)$, where $\lim_{x\to a} f(x) = 0$ and $\lim_{x\to a} g(x) = \pm\infty$; such limits are denoted $0 \cdot \infty$. *L'Hôpital's Rule cannot be directly applied to limits of this form.* Furthermore, it's risky to jump to conclusions about such limits. Suppose $f(x) = x$ and $g(x) = \dfrac{1}{x^2}$, in which case $\lim_{x\to 0} f(x) = 0$, $\lim_{x\to 0} g(x) = \infty$, and $\lim_{x\to 0} f(x)g(x) = \lim_{x\to 0} \dfrac{1}{x}$ does not exist. On the other hand, if $f(x) = x$ and $g(x) = \dfrac{1}{\sqrt{x}}$, we have $\lim_{x\to 0^+} f(x) = 0$, $\lim_{x\to 0^+} g(x) = \infty$, and $\lim_{x\to 0^+} f(x)g(x) = \lim_{x\to 0^+} \sqrt{x} = 0$. So a limit of the form $0 \cdot \infty$, in which the two functions compete with each other, may have any value or may not exist. The following example illustrates how this indeterminate form can be recast in the form $0/0$ or ∞/∞.

EXAMPLE 4 L'Hôpital's Rule for $0 \cdot \infty$ Evaluate $\lim_{x\to\infty} x^2 \sin\left(\frac{1}{4x^2}\right)$.

SOLUTION This limit has the form $0 \cdot \infty$. A common technique that converts this form to either $0/0$ or ∞/∞ is to *divide by the reciprocal*. We rewrite the limit and apply l'Hôpital's Rule:

$$\underbrace{\lim_{x\to\infty} x^2 \sin\left(\frac{1}{4x^2}\right)}_{0\cdot\infty \text{ form}} = \underbrace{\lim_{x\to\infty} \frac{\sin\left(\frac{1}{4x^2}\right)}{\frac{1}{x^2}}}_{\text{recast in } 0/0 \text{ form}} \qquad x^2 = \frac{1}{1/x^2}$$

$$= \lim_{x\to\infty} \frac{\cos\left(\frac{1}{4x^2}\right)\frac{1}{4}(-2x^{-3})}{-2x^{-3}} \qquad \text{L'Hôpital's Rule}$$

$$= \frac{1}{4}\lim_{x\to\infty} \cos\left(\frac{1}{4x^2}\right) \qquad \text{Simplify.}$$

$$= \frac{1}{4}. \qquad \frac{1}{4x^2} \to 0,\ \cos 0 = 1$$

Related Exercises 45–50 ◀

QUICK CHECK 3 What is the form of the limit $\lim_{x\to\pi/2^-} (x - \pi/2)(\tan x)$? Write it in the form $0/0$. ◀

Limits of the form $\lim_{x\to a} (f(x) - g(x))$, where $\lim_{x\to a} f(x) = \infty$ and $\lim_{x\to a} g(x) = \infty$, are indeterminate forms that we denote $\infty - \infty$. L'Hôpital's Rule cannot be applied directly to an $\infty - \infty$ form. It must first be expressed in the form $0/0$ or ∞/∞. With the $\infty - \infty$ form, it is easy to reach erroneous conclusions. For example, if $f(x) = 3x + 5$ and $g(x) = 3x$, then

$$\lim_{x\to\infty} ((3x + 5) - (3x)) = 5.$$

However, if $f(x) = 3x$ and $g(x) = 2x$, then

$$\lim_{x\to\infty} (3x - 2x) = \lim_{x\to\infty} x = \infty.$$

These examples show again why indeterminate forms are deceptive. Before proceeding, we introduce another useful technique.

Occasionally, it helps to convert a limit as $x \to \infty$ to a limit as $t \to 0^+$ (or vice versa) by a *change of variables*. To evaluate $\lim_{x\to\infty} f(x)$, we define $t = 1/x$ and note that as $x \to \infty$, $t \to 0^+$. Then

$$\lim_{x\to\infty} f(x) = \lim_{t\to 0^+} f\left(\frac{1}{t}\right).$$

This idea is illustrated in the next example.

EXAMPLE 5 **L'Hôpital's Rule for $\infty - \infty$** Evaluate $\lim_{x\to\infty}(x - \sqrt{x^2 - 3x})$.

SOLUTION As $x \to \infty$, both terms in the difference $x - \sqrt{x^2 - 3x}$ approach ∞ and this limit has the form $\infty - \infty$. We first factor x from the expression and form a quotient:

$$\begin{aligned}\lim_{x\to\infty}(x - \sqrt{x^2 - 3x}) &= \lim_{x\to\infty}(x - \sqrt{x^2(1 - 3/x)}) && \text{Factor } x^2 \text{ under square root.}\\ &= \lim_{x\to\infty} x(1 - \sqrt{1 - 3/x}) && x > 0, \text{ so } \sqrt{x^2} = x\\ &= \lim_{x\to\infty}\frac{1 - \sqrt{1 - 3/x}}{1/x}. && \text{Write } 0 \cdot \infty \text{ form as } 0/0 \text{ form; } x = \frac{1}{1/x}.\end{aligned}$$

This new limit has the form $0/0$, and l'Hôpital's Rule may be applied. One way to proceed is to use the change of variables $t = 1/x$:

$$\begin{aligned}\lim_{x\to\infty}\frac{1 - \sqrt{1 - 3/x}}{1/x} &= \lim_{t\to 0^+}\frac{1 - \sqrt{1 - 3t}}{t} && \text{Let } t = 1/x\text{; replace } \lim_{x\to\infty} \text{ with } \lim_{t\to 0^+}.\\ &= \lim_{t\to 0^+}\frac{\frac{3}{2\sqrt{1 - 3t}}}{1} && \text{L'Hôpital's Rule}\\ &= \frac{3}{2}. && \text{Evaluate limit.}\end{aligned}$$

Related Exercises 51–54 ◀

Indeterminate Forms 1^∞, 0^0, and ∞^0

The indeterminate forms 1^∞, 0^0, and ∞^0 all arise in limits of the form $\lim_{x\to a} f(x)^{g(x)}$, where $x \to a$ could be replaced with $x \to a^\pm$ or $x \to \pm\infty$. L'Hôpital's Rule cannot be applied directly to the indeterminate forms 1^∞, 0^0, and ∞^0. They must first be expressed in the form $0/0$ or ∞/∞. Here is how we proceed.

The inverse relationship between $\ln x$ and e^x says that $f^g = e^{g \ln f}$, so we first write

$$\lim_{x\to a} f(x)^{g(x)} = \lim_{x\to a} e^{g(x)\ln f(x)}.$$

By the continuity of the exponential function, we switch the order of the limit and the exponential function (Theorem 2.12); therefore,

$$\lim_{x\to a} f(x)^{g(x)} = \lim_{x\to a} e^{g(x)\ln f(x)} = e^{\lim_{x\to a} g(x)\ln f(x)},$$

provided $\lim_{x\to a} g(x)\ln f(x)$ exists. Therefore, $\lim_{x\to a} f(x)^{g(x)}$ is evaluated using the following two steps.

> ➤ Notice the following:
> - For 1^∞, L has the form $\infty \cdot \ln 1 = \infty \cdot 0$.
> - For 0^0, L has the form $0 \cdot \ln 0 = 0 \cdot -\infty$.
> - For ∞^0, L has the form $0 \cdot \ln \infty = 0 \cdot \infty$.

PROCEDURE **Indeterminate forms 1^∞, 0^0, and ∞^0**

Assume $\lim_{x\to a} f(x)^{g(x)}$ has the indeterminate form 1^∞, 0^0, or ∞^0.

1. Analyze $L = \lim_{x\to a} g(x)\ln f(x)$. This limit can be put in the form $0/0$ or ∞/∞, both of which are handled by l'Hôpital's Rule.
2. When L is finite, $\lim_{x\to a} f(x)^{g(x)} = e^L$. If $L = \infty$ or $-\infty$, then $\lim_{x\to a} f(x)^{g(x)} = \infty$ or $\lim_{x\to a} f(x)^{g(x)} = 0$, respectively.

QUICK CHECK 4 Explain why a limit of the form 0^∞ is not an indeterminate form. ◀

EXAMPLE 6 **Indeterminate forms 0^0 and 1^∞** Evaluate the following limits.

a. $\lim_{x \to 0^+} x^x$ **b.** $\lim_{x \to \infty} \left(1 + \frac{1}{x}\right)^x$

SOLUTION

a. This limit has the form 0^0. Using the given two-step procedure, we note that $x^x = e^{x \ln x}$ and first evaluate

$$L = \lim_{x \to 0^+} x \ln x.$$

This limit has the form $0 \cdot \infty$, which may be put in the form ∞ / ∞ so that l'Hôpital's Rule can be applied:

$$L = \lim_{x \to 0^+} x \ln x = \lim_{x \to 0^+} \frac{\ln x}{1/x} \qquad x = \frac{1}{1/x}$$

$$= \lim_{x \to 0^+} \frac{1/x}{-1/x^2} \qquad \text{L'Hôpital's Rule for } \infty/\infty \text{ form}$$

$$= \lim_{x \to 0^+} (-x) = 0. \qquad \text{Simplify and evaluate the limit.}$$

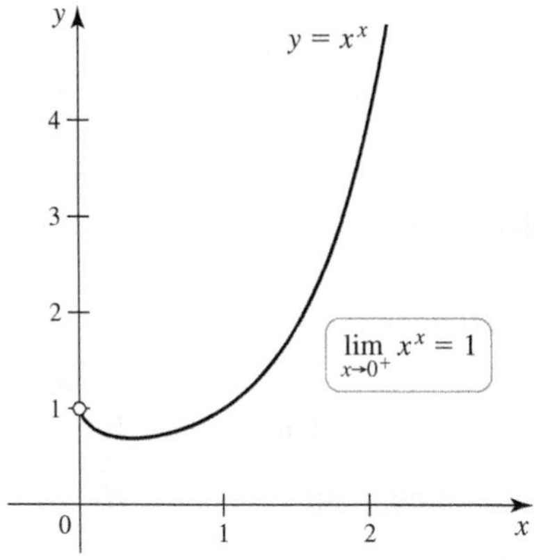

Figure 4.76

The second step is to exponentiate the limit:

$$\lim_{x \to 0^+} x^x = e^L = e^0 = 1.$$

We conclude that $\lim_{x \to 0^+} x^x = 1$ (Figure 4.76).

➤ The limit in Example 6b is often given as a definition of e. It is a special case of the more general limit

$$\lim_{x \to \infty} \left(1 + \frac{a}{x}\right)^x = e^a.$$

See Exercise 119.

b. This limit has the form 1^∞. Noting that $(1 + 1/x)^x = e^{x \ln (1 + 1/x)}$, the first step is to evaluate

$$L = \lim_{x \to \infty} x \ln \left(1 + \frac{1}{x}\right),$$

which has the form $0 \cdot \infty$. Proceeding as in part (a), we have

$$L = \lim_{x \to \infty} x \ln \left(1 + \frac{1}{x}\right) = \lim_{x \to \infty} \frac{\ln (1 + 1/x)}{1/x} \qquad x = \frac{1}{1/x}$$

$$= \lim_{x \to \infty} \frac{\frac{1}{1 + 1/x} \cdot \left(-\frac{1}{x^2}\right)}{\left(-\frac{1}{x^2}\right)} \qquad \text{L'Hôpital's Rule for } 0/0 \text{ form}$$

$$= \lim_{x \to \infty} \frac{1}{1 + 1/x} = 1. \qquad \text{Simplify and evaluate.}$$

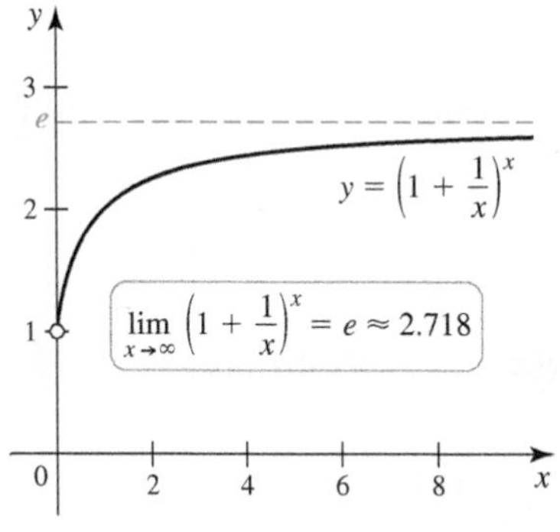

Figure 4.77

The second step is to exponentiate the limit:

$$\lim_{x \to \infty} \left(1 + \frac{1}{x}\right)^x = e^L = e^1 = e.$$

The function $y = (1 + 1/x)^x$ (Figure 4.77) has a horizontal asymptote $y = e \approx 2.71828$.

Related Exercises 55–68 ◀

Growth Rates of Functions

An important use of l'Hôpital's Rule is to compare the growth rates of functions. Here are two questions—one practical and one theoretical—that demonstrate the importance of comparative growth rates of functions.

➤ Models of epidemics produce more complicated functions than the one given here, but they have the same general features.

- A particular theory for modeling the spread of an epidemic predicts that the number of infected people t days after the start of the epidemic is given by the function

$$N(t) = 2.5t^2e^{-0.01t} = 2.5\frac{t^2}{e^{0.01t}}.$$

Question: In the long run (as $t \to \infty$), does the epidemic spread or does it die out?

➤ The Prime Number Theorem was proved simultaneously (two different proofs) in 1896 by Jacques Hadamard and Charles de la Vallée Poussin, relying on fundamental ideas contributed by Riemann.

- A prime number is an integer $p \geq 2$ that has only two divisors, 1 and itself. The first few prime numbers are 2, 3, 5, 7, and 11. A celebrated theorem states that the number of prime numbers less than x is approximately

$$P(x) = \frac{x}{\ln x}, \quad \text{for large values of } x.$$

Question: According to this theorem, is the number of prime numbers infinite?

These two questions involve a comparison of two functions. In the first question, if t^2 grows faster than $e^{0.01t}$ as $t \to \infty$, then $\lim_{t\to\infty} N(t) = \infty$ and the epidemic grows. If $e^{0.01t}$ grows faster than t^2 as $t \to \infty$, then $\lim_{t\to\infty} N(t) = 0$ and the epidemic dies out. We will explain what is meant by *grows faster than* in a moment.

In the second question, the comparison is between x and $\ln x$. If x grows faster than $\ln x$ as $x \to \infty$, then $\lim_{x\to\infty} P(x) = \infty$ and the number of prime numbers is infinite.

Our goal is to obtain a ranking of the following families of functions based on their growth rates:

➤ Another function with a large growth rate is the factorial function, defined for integers as $f(n) = n! = n(n-1)\cdots 2\cdot 1$. See Exercise 116.

- mx, where $m > 0$ (represents linear functions)
- x^p, where $p > 0$ (represents polynomials and algebraic functions)
- x^x (sometimes called a *superexponential* or *tower function*)
- $\ln x$ (represents logarithmic functions)
- $\ln^q x$, where $q > 0$ (represents powers of logarithmic functions)
- $x^p \ln x$, where $p > 0$ (a combination of powers and logarithms)
- e^x (represents exponential functions).

QUICK CHECK 5 Before proceeding, use your intuition and rank these classes of functions in order of their growth rates. ◄

We need to be precise about growth rates and what it means for f to grow faster than g as $x \to \infty$. We work with the following definitions.

DEFINITION Growth Rates of Functions (as $x \to \infty$)

Suppose f and g are functions with $\lim_{x\to\infty} f(x) = \lim_{x\to\infty} g(x) = \infty$. Then **$f$ grows faster than g** as $x \to \infty$ if

$$\lim_{x\to\infty}\frac{g(x)}{f(x)} = 0 \quad \text{or, equivalently, if} \quad \lim_{x\to\infty}\frac{f(x)}{g(x)} = \infty.$$

The functions f and g have **comparable growth rates** if

$$\lim_{x\to\infty}\frac{f(x)}{g(x)} = M,$$

where $0 < M < \infty$ (M is nonzero and finite).

The idea of growth rates is illustrated nicely with graphs. Figure 4.78 shows a family of linear functions of the form $y = mx$, where $m > 0$, and powers of x of the form $y = x^p$, where $p > 1$. We see that powers of x grow faster (their curves rise at a greater rate) than the linear functions as $x \to \infty$.

Figure 4.79 shows that exponential functions of the form $y = b^x$, where $b > 1$, grow faster than powers of x of the form $y = x^p$, where $p > 0$, as $x \to \infty$ (Example 8).

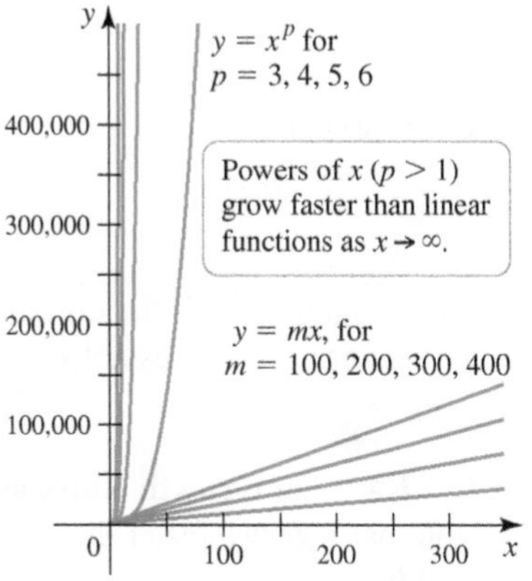

Figure 4.78

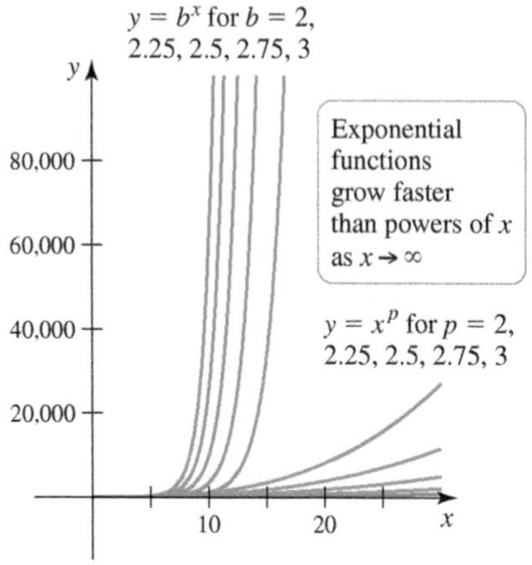

Figure 4.79

QUICK CHECK 6 Compare the growth rates of $f(x) = x^2$ and $g(x) = x^3$ as $x \to \infty$. Compare the growth rates of $f(x) = x^2$ and $g(x) = 10x^2$ as $x \to \infty$. ◄

We now begin a systematic comparison of growth rates. Note that a growth rate limit involves an indeterminate form ∞/∞, so l'Hôpital's Rule is always in the picture.

EXAMPLE 7 Powers of x vs. powers of $\ln x$ Compare the growth rates as $x \to \infty$ of the following pairs of functions.

a. $f(x) = \ln x$ and $g(x) = x^p$, where $p > 0$

b. $f(x) = \ln^q x$ and $g(x) = x^p$, where $p > 0$ and $q > 0$

SOLUTION

a. The limit of the ratio of the two functions is

$$\lim_{x\to\infty} \frac{\ln x}{x^p} = \lim_{x\to\infty} \frac{1/x}{px^{p-1}} \quad \text{L'Hôpital's Rule}$$

$$= \lim_{x\to\infty} \frac{1}{px^p} \quad \text{Simplify.}$$

$$= 0. \quad \text{Evaluate the limit.}$$

We see that any positive power of x grows faster than $\ln x$.

b. We compare $\ln^q x$ and x^p by observing that

$$\lim_{x\to\infty} \frac{\ln^q x}{x^p} = \lim_{x\to\infty} \left(\frac{\ln x}{x^{p/q}}\right)^q = \Bigg(\underbrace{\lim_{x\to\infty} \frac{\ln x}{x^{p/q}}}_{0}\Bigg)^q.$$

By part (a), $\lim_{x\to\infty} \frac{\ln x}{x^{p/q}} = 0$ (because $p/q > 0$). Therefore, $\lim_{x\to\infty} \frac{\ln^q x}{x^p} = 0$ (because $q > 0$). We conclude that any positive power of x grows faster than any positive power of $\ln x$.

Related Exercises 69–80 ◄

EXAMPLE 8 **Powers of x vs. exponentials** Compare the rates of growth of $f(x) = x^p$ and $g(x) = e^x$ as $x \to \infty$, where p is a positive real number.

SOLUTION The goal is to evaluate $\lim_{x\to\infty} \frac{x^p}{e^x}$, for $p > 0$. This comparison is most easily done using Example 7 and a change of variables. We let $x = \ln t$ and note that as $x \to \infty$, we also have $t \to \infty$. With this substitution, $x^p = \ln^p t$ and $e^x = e^{\ln t} = t$. Therefore,

$$\lim_{x\to\infty} \frac{x^p}{e^x} = \lim_{t\to\infty} \frac{\ln^p t}{t} = 0. \quad \text{Example 7}$$

We see that increasing exponential functions grow faster than positive powers of x (Figure 4.79).

Related Exercises 69–80 ◀

These examples, together with the comparison of exponential functions b^x and the superexponential x^x (Exercise 120), establish a ranking of growth rates.

THEOREM 4.15 **Ranking Growth Rates as $x \to \infty$**
Let $f \ll g$ mean that g grows faster than f as $x \to \infty$. With positive real numbers p, q, r, and s and $b > 1$,

$$\ln^q x \ll x^p \ll x^p \ln^r x \ll x^{p+s} \ll b^x \ll x^x.$$

You should try to build these relative growth rates into your intuition. They are useful in future chapters (Chapter 8 on sequences, in particular), and they can be used to evaluate limits at infinity quickly.

Pitfalls in Using l'Hôpital's Rule

We close with a list of common pitfalls when using l'Hôpital's Rule.

1. L'Hôpital's Rule says $\lim_{x\to a} \frac{f(x)}{g(x)} = \lim_{x\to a} \frac{f'(x)}{g'(x)}$, not

$$\lim_{x\to a} \frac{f(x)}{g(x)} = \lim_{x\to a} \left(\frac{f(x)}{g(x)}\right)' \quad \text{or} \quad \lim_{x\to a} \frac{f(x)}{g(x)} = \lim_{x\to a} \left(\frac{1}{g(x)}\right)' f'(x).$$

   In other words, you should evaluate $f'(x)$ and $g'(x)$, form their quotient, and then take the limit. Don't confuse l'Hôpital's Rule with the Quotient Rule.

2. Be sure that the given limit involves the indeterminate form $0/0$ or ∞/∞ before applying l'Hôpital's Rule. For example, consider the following erroneous use of l'Hôpital's Rule:

$$\lim_{x\to 0} \frac{1 - \sin x}{\cos x} = \lim_{x\to 0} \frac{-\cos x}{\sin x},$$

   which does not exist. The original limit is not an indeterminate form in the first place. This limit should be evaluated by direct substitution:

$$\lim_{x\to 0} \frac{1 - \sin x}{\cos x} = \frac{1 - \sin 0}{1} = 1.$$

3. When using l'Hôpital's Rule repeatedly, be sure to simplify expressions as much as possible at each step and evaluate the limit as soon as the new limit is no longer an indeterminate form.

4. Repeated use of l'Hôpital's Rule occasionally leads to unending cycles, in which case other methods must be used. For example, limits of the form $\lim_{x\to\infty} \frac{\sqrt{ax + 1}}{\sqrt{bx + 1}}$, where a and b are real numbers, lead to such behavior (Exercise 111).

5. Be sure that the limit produced by l'Hôpital's Rule exists. Consider $\lim_{x\to\infty} \frac{3x + \cos x}{x}$, which has the form ∞/∞. Applying l'Hôpital's Rule, we have

$$\lim_{x\to\infty} \frac{3x + \cos x}{x} = \lim_{x\to\infty} \frac{3 - \sin x}{1}.$$

It is tempting to conclude that because the limit on the right side does not exist, the original limit also does not exist. In fact, the original limit has a value of 3 (divide numerator and denominator by x). To reach a conclusion from l'Hôpital's Rule, the limit produced by l'Hôpital's Rule must exist (or be $\pm\infty$).

SECTION 4.7 EXERCISES

Review Questions

1. Explain with examples what is meant by the indeterminate form $0/0$.
2. Why are special methods, such as l'Hôpital's Rule, needed to evaluate indeterminate forms (as opposed to substitution)?
3. Explain the steps used to apply l'Hôpital's Rule to a limit of the form $0/0$.
4. To which indeterminate forms does l'Hôpital's Rule apply *directly*?
5. Explain how to convert a limit of the form $0 \cdot \infty$ to a limit of the form $0/0$ or ∞/∞.
6. Give an example of a limit of the form ∞/∞ as $x \to 0$.
7. Explain why the form 1^∞ is indeterminate and cannot be evaluated by substitution. Explain how the competing functions behave.
8. Give the two-step method for attacking an indeterminate limit of the form $\lim_{x\to a} f(x)^{g(x)}$.
9. In terms of limits, what does it mean for f to grow faster than g as $x \to \infty$?
10. In terms of limits, what does it mean for the rates of growth of f and g to be comparable as $x \to \infty$?
11. Rank the functions x^3, $\ln x$, x^x, and 2^x in order of increasing growth rates as $x \to \infty$.
12. Rank the functions x^{100}, $\ln x^{10}$, x^x, and 10^x in order of increasing growth rates as $x \to \infty$.

Basic Skills

13–22. 0/0 form *Evaluate the following limits using l'Hôpital's Rule.*

13. $\lim_{x\to 2} \frac{x^2 - 2x}{8 - 6x + x^2}$
14. $\lim_{x\to -1} \frac{x^4 + x^3 + 2x + 2}{x + 1}$
15. $\lim_{x\to 1} \frac{\ln x}{4x - x^2 - 3}$
16. $\lim_{x\to 0} \frac{e^x - 1}{x^2 + 3x}$
17. $\lim_{x\to e} \frac{\ln x - 1}{x - e}$
18. $\lim_{x\to 1} \frac{4\tan^{-1} x - \pi}{x - 1}$
19. $\lim_{x\to 0} \frac{3\sin 4x}{5x}$
20. $\lim_{x\to 2\pi} \frac{x\sin x + x^2 - 4\pi^2}{x - 2\pi}$
21. $\lim_{u\to \pi/4} \frac{\tan u - \cot u}{u - \pi/4}$
22. $\lim_{z\to 0} \frac{\tan 4z}{\tan 7z}$

23–36. 0/0 form *Evaluate the following limits.*

23. $\lim_{x\to 0} \frac{1 - \cos 3x}{8x^2}$
24. $\lim_{x\to 0} \frac{\sin^2 3x}{x^2}$
25. $\lim_{x\to \pi} \frac{\cos x + 1}{(x - \pi)^2}$
26. $\lim_{x\to 0} \frac{e^x - x - 1}{5x^2}$
27. $\lim_{x\to 0} \frac{e^x - \sin x - 1}{x^4 + 8x^3 + 12x^2}$
28. $\lim_{x\to 0} \frac{\sin x - x}{7x^3}$
29. $\lim_{x\to \infty} \frac{e^{1/x} - 1}{1/x}$
30. $\lim_{x\to \infty} \frac{\tan^{-1} x - \pi/2}{1/x}$
31. $\lim_{x\to -1} \frac{x^3 - x^2 - 5x - 3}{x^4 + 2x^3 - x^2 - 4x - 2}$
32. $\lim_{x\to 1} \frac{x^n - 1}{x - 1}$, n is a positive integer
33. $\lim_{v\to 3} \frac{v - 1 - \sqrt{v^2 - 5}}{v - 3}$
34. $\lim_{y\to 2} \frac{y^2 + y - 6}{\sqrt{8 - y^2} - y}$
35. $\lim_{x\to 2} \frac{x^2 - 4x + 4}{\sin^2(\pi x)}$
36. $\lim_{x\to 2} \frac{\sqrt[3]{3x + 2} - 2}{x - 2}$

37–44. ∞/∞ form *Evaluate the following limits.*

37. $\lim_{x\to \infty} \frac{3x^4 - x^2}{6x^4 + 12}$
38. $\lim_{x\to \infty} \frac{4x^3 - 2x^2 + 6}{\pi x^3 + 4}$
39. $\lim_{x\to \pi/2^-} \frac{\tan x}{3/(2x - \pi)}$
40. $\lim_{x\to \infty} \frac{e^{3x}}{3e^{3x} + 5}$
41. $\lim_{x\to \infty} \frac{\ln(3x + 5)}{\ln(7x + 3) + 1}$
42. $\lim_{x\to \infty} \frac{\ln(3x + 5e^x)}{\ln(7x + 3e^{2x})}$
43. $\lim_{x\to \infty} \frac{x^2 - \ln(2/x)}{3x^2 + 2x}$
44. $\lim_{x\to \pi/2} \frac{2\tan x}{\sec^2 x}$

45–50. 0 · ∞ form *Evaluate the following limits.*

45. $\lim_{x\to 0} x\csc x$
46. $\lim_{x\to 1^-} (1 - x)\tan\left(\frac{\pi x}{2}\right)$
47. $\lim_{x\to 0} \csc 6x \sin 7x$
48. $\lim_{x\to \infty} (\csc(1/x)(e^{1/x} - 1))$
49. $\lim_{x\to \pi/2^-} \left(\frac{\pi}{2} - x\right)\sec x$
50. $\lim_{x\to 0^+} (\sin x)\sqrt{\frac{1 - x}{x}}$

51–54. $\infty - \infty$ form *Evaluate the following limits.*

51. $\lim_{x\to 0^+}\left(\cot x - \frac{1}{x}\right)$

52. $\lim_{x\to\infty}\left(x - \sqrt{x^2+1}\right)$

53. $\lim_{\theta\to\pi/2^-}(\tan\theta - \sec\theta)$

54. $\lim_{x\to\infty}\left(x - \sqrt{x^2+4x}\right)$

55–68. 1^∞, 0^0, ∞^0 forms *Evaluate the following limits or explain why they do not exist. Check your results by graphing.*

55. $\lim_{x\to 0^+} x^{2x}$

56. $\lim_{x\to 0}(1+4x)^{3/x}$

57. $\lim_{\theta\to\pi/2^-}(\tan\theta)^{\cos\theta}$

58. $\lim_{\theta\to 0^+}(\sin\theta)^{\tan\theta}$

59. $\lim_{x\to 0^+}(1+x)^{\cot x}$

60. $\lim_{x\to\infty}\left(1+\frac{1}{x}\right)^{\ln x}$

61. $\lim_{x\to\infty}\left(1+\frac{a}{x}\right)^{x}$, for a constant a

62. $\lim_{x\to 0}(e^{5x}+x)^{1/x}$

63. $\lim_{x\to 0}(e^{ax}+x)^{1/x}$, for a constant a

64. $\lim_{x\to 0}(2^{ax}+x)^{1/x}$, for a constant a

65. $\lim_{x\to 0^+}(\tan x)^{x}$

66. $\lim_{z\to\infty}\left(1+\frac{10}{z^2}\right)^{z^2}$

67. $\lim_{x\to 0}(x+\cos x)^{1/x}$

68. $\lim_{x\to 0^+}\left(\frac{1}{3}\cdot 3^x + \frac{2}{3}\cdot 2^x\right)^{1/x}$

69–80. Comparing growth rates *Use limit methods to determine which of the two given functions grows faster or state that they have comparable growth rates.*

69. x^{10}; $e^{0.01x}$

70. $x^2\ln x$; $\ln^2 x$

71. $\ln x^{20}$; $\ln x$

72. $\ln x$; $\ln(\ln x)$

73. 100^x; x^x

74. $x^2\ln x$; x^3

75. x^{20}; 1.00001^x

76. $x^{10}\ln^{10}x$; x^{11}

77. x^x; $(x/2)^x$

78. $\ln\sqrt{x}$; $\ln^2 x$

79. e^{x^2}; e^{10x}

80. e^{x^2}; $x^{x/10}$

Further Explorations

81. Explain why or why not Determine whether the following statements are true and give an explanation or counterexample.

a. By l'Hôpital's Rule, $\lim_{x\to 2}\frac{x-2}{x^2-1} = \lim_{x\to 2}\frac{1}{2x} = \frac{1}{4}$.

b. $\lim_{x\to 0}(x\sin x) = \lim_{x\to 0} f(x)g(x) = \lim_{x\to 0} f'(x)\lim_{x\to 0} g'(x) = \left(\lim_{x\to 0} 1\right)\left(\lim_{x\to 0}\cos x\right) = 1.$

c. $\lim_{x\to 0^+} x^{1/x}$ is an indeterminate form.

d. The number 1 raised to any fixed power is 1. Therefore, because $(1+x)\to 1$ as $x\to 0$, $(1+x)^{1/x}\to 1$ as $x\to 0$.

e. The functions $\ln x^{100}$ and $\ln x$ have comparable growth rates as $x\to\infty$.

f. The function e^x grows faster than 2^x as $x\to\infty$.

82–83. Two methods *Evaluate the following limits in two different ways: Use the methods of Chapter 2 and use l'Hôpital's Rule.*

82. $\lim_{x\to\infty}\frac{100x^3-3}{x^4-2}$

83. $\lim_{x\to\infty}\frac{2x^3-x^2+1}{5x^3+2x}$

84. L'Hôpital's example Evaluate one of the limits l'Hôpital used in his own textbook in about 1700:

$$\lim_{x\to a}\frac{\sqrt{2a^3x - x^4} - a\sqrt[3]{a^2x}}{a - \sqrt[4]{ax^3}},\ \text{where } a \text{ is a real number.}$$

85–102. Miscellaneous limits by any means *Use analytical methods to evaluate the following limits.*

85. $\lim_{x\to 6}\frac{\sqrt[5]{5x+2}-2}{1/x - 1/6}$

86. $\lim_{x\to\infty} x^2\ln\left(\cos\frac{1}{x}\right)$

87. $\lim_{x\to\infty}\left(\sqrt{x-2}-\sqrt{x-4}\right)$

88. $\lim_{x\to\pi/2}(\pi - 2x)\tan x$

89. $\lim_{x\to\infty} x^3\left(\frac{1}{x} - \sin\frac{1}{x}\right)$

90. $\lim_{x\to\infty}\left(x^2e^{1/x} - x^2 - x\right)$

91. $\lim_{x\to 1^+}\left(\frac{1}{x-1} - \frac{1}{\sqrt{x}-1}\right)$

92. $\lim_{x\to 0^+} x^{1/\ln x}$

93. $\lim_{x\to\infty}\frac{\log_2 x}{\log_3 x}$

94. $\lim_{x\to\infty}(\log_2 x - \log_3 x)$

95. $\lim_{n\to\infty}\frac{1+2+\cdots+n}{n^2}$

$\left(\textit{Hint: } \text{Use } 1+2+\cdots+n = \frac{n(n+1)}{2}.\right)$

96. $\lim_{x\to 0}\left(\frac{\sin x}{x}\right)^{1/x^2}$

97. $\lim_{x\to 1}\frac{x\ln x - x + 1}{x\ln^2 x}$

98. $\lim_{x\to 1}\frac{x\ln x + \ln x - 2x + 2}{x^2\ln^3 x}$

99. $\lim_{x\to 0^+} x^{1/(1+\ln x)}$

100. $\lim_{n\to\infty}\left(\cot\frac{1}{n} - n\right)$

101. $\lim_{n\to\infty}\left(n\cot\frac{1}{n} - n^2\right)$

102. $\lim_{n\to\infty} n^2\ln\left(n\sin\frac{1}{n}\right)$

T **103. It may take time** The ranking of growth rates given in the text applies for $x\to\infty$. However, these rates may not be evident for small values of x. For example, an exponential grows faster than any power of x. However, for $1 < x < 19{,}800$, x^2 is greater than $e^{x/1000}$. For the following pairs of functions, estimate the point at which the faster-growing function overtakes the slower-growing function (for the last time).

a. $\ln^3 x$ and $x^{0.3}$

b. $2^{x/100}$ and x^3

c. $x^{x/100}$ and e^x

d. $\ln^{10} x$ and $e^{x/10}$

T **104–107. Limits with parameters** *Evaluate the following limits in terms of the parameters a and b, which are positive real numbers. In each case, graph the function for specific values of the parameters to check your results.*

104. $\lim_{x\to 0}(1+ax)^{b/x}$

105. $\lim_{x\to 0^+}(a^x - b^x)^x$, $a > b > 0$

106. $\lim_{x\to 0^+}(a^x - b^x)^{1/x}$, $a > b > 0$

107. $\lim_{x\to 0}\frac{a^x - b^x}{x}$

Applications

108. An optics limit The theory of interference of coherent oscillators requires the limit $\lim_{\delta \to 2m\pi} \dfrac{\sin^2(N\delta/2)}{\sin^2(\delta/2)}$, where N is a positive integer and m is any integer. Show that the value of this limit is N^2.

109. Compound interest Suppose you make a deposit of $\$P$ into a savings account that earns interest at a rate of 100 r% per year.

a. Show that if interest is compounded once per year, then the balance after t years is $B(t) = P(1 + r)^t$.

b. If interest is compounded m times per year, then the balance after t years is $B(t) = P(1 + r/m)^{mt}$. For example, $m = 12$ corresponds to monthly compounding, and the interest rate for each month is $r/12$. In the limit $m \to \infty$, the compounding is said to be *continuous*. Show that with continuous compounding, the balance after t years is $B(t) = Pe^{rt}$.

T **110. Algorithm complexity** The complexity of a computer algorithm is the number of operations or steps the algorithm needs to complete its task assuming there are n pieces of input (for example, the number of steps needed to put n numbers in ascending order). Four algorithms for doing the same task have complexities of A: $n^{3/2}$, B: $n \log_2 n$, C: $n(\log_2 n)^2$, and D: $\sqrt{n} \log_2 n$. Rank the algorithms in order of increasing efficiency for large values of n. Graph the complexities as they vary with n and comment on your observations.

Additional Exercises

111. L'Hôpital loops Consider the limit $\lim_{x \to \infty} \dfrac{\sqrt{ax + b}}{\sqrt{cx + d}}$, where a, b, c, and d are positive real numbers. Show that l'Hôpital's Rule fails for this limit. Find the limit using another method.

112. General $\infty - \infty$ result Let a and b be positive real numbers. Evaluate $\lim_{x \to \infty} (ax - \sqrt{a^2x^2 - bx})$ in terms of a and b.

113. Exponential functions and powers Show that any exponential function b^x, for $b > 1$, grows faster than x^p, for $p > 0$.

114. Exponentials with different bases Show that $f(x) = a^x$ grows faster than $g(x) = b^x$ as $x \to \infty$ if $1 < b < a$.

115. Logs with different bases Show that $f(x) = \log_a x$ and $g(x) = \log_b x$, where $a > 1$ and $b > 1$, grow at a comparable rate as $x \to \infty$.

T **116. Factorial growth rate** The factorial function is defined for positive integers as $n! = n(n - 1)(n - 2) \cdots 3 \cdot 2 \cdot 1$. For example, $5! = 5 \cdot 4 \cdot 3 \cdot 2 \cdot 1 = 120$. A valuable result that gives good approximations to $n!$ for large values of n is *Stirling's formula*, $n! \approx \sqrt{2\pi n}\, n^n e^{-n}$. Use this formula and a calculator to determine where the factorial function appears in the ranking of growth rates given in Theorem 4.15. (See the Guided Project *Stirling's Formula*.)

117. A geometric limit Let $f(\theta)$ be the area of the triangle ABP (see figure) and let $g(\theta)$ be the area of the region between the chord PB and the arc PB. Evaluate $\lim_{\theta \to 0} g(\theta)/f(\theta)$.

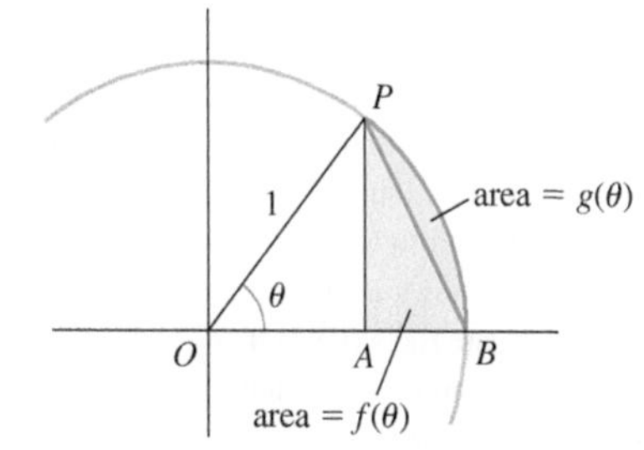

T **118. A fascinating function** Consider the function $f(x) = (ab^x + (1 - a)c^x)^{1/x}$, where a, b, and c are positive real numbers with $0 < a < 1$.

a. Graph f for several sets of (a, b, c). Verify that in all cases f is an increasing function with a single inflection point, for all x.

b. Use analytical methods to determine $\lim_{x \to 0} f(x)$ in terms of a, b, and c.

c. Show that $\lim_{x \to \infty} f(x) = \max\{b, c\}$ and $\lim_{x \to -\infty} f(x) = \min\{b, c\}$, for any $0 < a < 1$.

d. Estimate the location of the inflection point of f.

119. Exponential limit Prove that $\lim_{x \to \infty} \left(1 + \dfrac{a}{x}\right)^x = e^a$, for $a \neq 0$.

120. Exponentials vs. super exponentials Show that x^x grows faster than b^x as $x \to \infty$, for $b > 1$.

121. Exponential growth rates

a. For what values of $b > 0$ does b^x grow faster than e^x as $x \to \infty$?

b. Compare the growth rates of e^x and e^{ax} as $x \to \infty$, for $a > 0$.

QUICK CHECK ANSWERS

1. g and h **2.** g and h **3.** $0 \cdot \infty$; $(x - \pi/2)/\cot x$ **4.** The form 0^∞ (for example, $\lim_{x \to 0^+} x^{1/x}$) is not indeterminate, because as the base goes to zero, raising it to larger and larger powers drives the entire function to zero. **6.** x^3 grows faster than x^2 as $x \to \infty$, whereas x^2 and $10x^2$ have comparable growth rates as $x \to \infty$. ◄

4.8 Newton's Method

A common problem that arises in mathematics is finding the *roots*, or *zeros*, of a function. The roots of a function are the values of x that satisfy the equation $f(x) = 0$. Equivalently, they correspond to the x-intercepts of the graph of f. You have already seen an important example of a root-finding problem. To find the critical points of a function f, we must solve the equation $f'(x) = 0$; that is, we find the roots of f'. Newton's method, which we discuss in this section, is one of the most effective methods for *approximating* the roots of a function.

➤ Newton's method is attributed to Sir Isaac Newton, who devised the method in 1669. However, similar methods were known prior to Newton's time. A special case of Newton's method for approximating square roots is called the Babylonian method and was probably invented by Greek mathematicians.

Why Approximate?

A little background about roots of functions explains why a method is needed to approximate roots. If you are given a linear function, such as $f(x) = 2x - 9$, you know how to use algebraic methods to solve $f(x) = 0$ and find the single root $x = \frac{9}{2}$. Similarly, given the quadratic function $f(x) = x^2 - 6x - 72$, you know how to factor or use the quadratic formula to discover that the roots are $x = 12$ and $x = -6$. It turns out that formulas also exist for finding the roots of cubic (third-degree) and quartic (fourth-degree) polynomials. Methods such as factoring and algebra are called *analytical methods*; when they work, they give the roots of a function *exactly* in terms of arithmetic operations and radicals.

Here is an important fact: Apart from the functions we have listed—polynomials of degree four or less—analytical methods do not give the roots of most functions. To be sure, there are special cases in which analytical methods work. For example, you should verify that the single real root of $f(x) = e^{2x} + 2e^x - 3$ is $x = 0$ and that the two real roots of $f(x) = x^{10} - 1$ are $x = 1$ and $x = -1$. But in general, the roots of even relatively simple functions such as $f(x) = e^{-x} - x$ cannot be found exactly using analytical methods.

When analytical methods do not work, which is the majority of cases, we need another approach. That approach is to approximate roots using *numerical methods*, such as Newton's method.

Deriving Newton's Method

Newton's method is most easily derived geometrically. Assume that r is a root of f that we wish to approximate; this means that $f(r) = 0$. We also assume that f is differentiable on some interval containing r. Suppose x_0 is an initial approximation to r that is generally obtained by some preliminary analysis. A better approximation to r is often obtained by carrying out the following two steps:

- A line tangent to the curve $y = f(x)$ at the point $(x_0, f(x_0))$ is drawn.
- The point $(x_1, 0)$ at which the tangent line intersects the x-axis is found and x_1 becomes the new approximation to r.

For the curve shown in Figure 4.80a, x_1 is a better approximation to the root r than x_0.

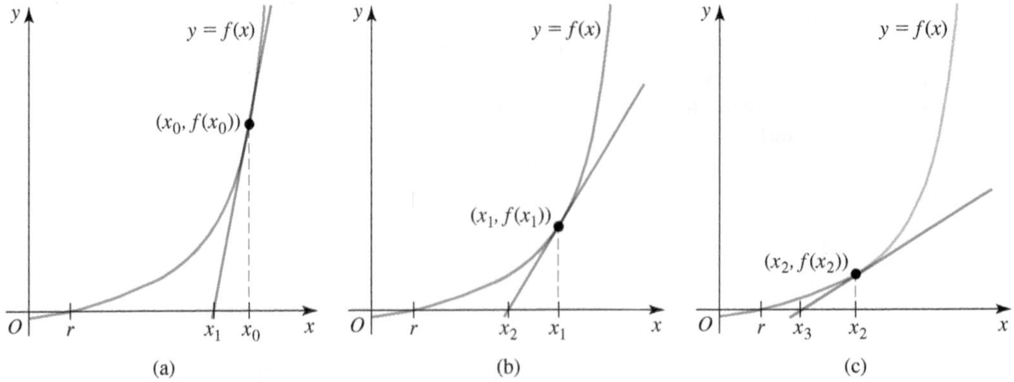

Figure 4.80

➤ Sequences are the subject of Chapter 8. An ordered set of numbers

$$\{x_1, x_2, x_3, \ldots\}$$

is a sequence, and if its values approach a number r, we say that the sequence *converges* to r. If a sequence fails to approach a single number, the sequence *diverges*.

To improve the approximation x_1, we repeat the two-step process, using x_1 to determine the next estimate x_2 (Figure 4.80b). Then x_2 is used to obtain x_3 (Figure 4.80c), and so forth. Continuing in this fashion, we obtain a *sequence* of approximations $\{x_1, x_2, x_3, \ldots\}$

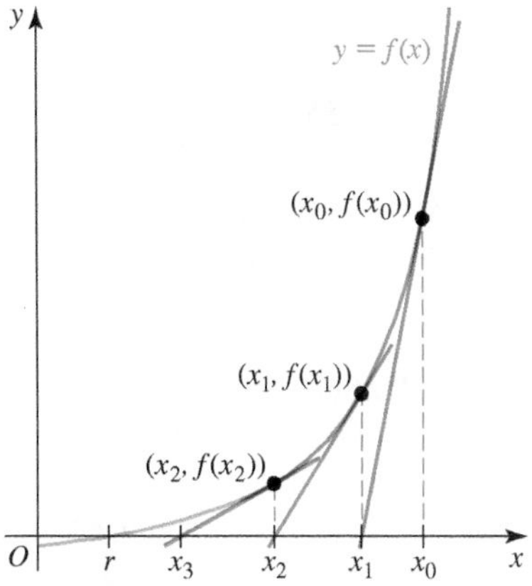

Figure 4.81

that ideally get closer and closer, or *converge*, to the root r. Several steps of Newton's method and the convergence of the approximations to the root are shown in Figure 4.81.

All that remains is to find a formula that captures the process just described. Assume that we have computed the nth approximation x_n to the root r and we want to obtain the next approximation x_{n+1}. We first draw the line tangent to the curve at the point $(x_n, f(x_n))$; its slope is $m = f'(x_n)$. Using the point-slope form of the equation of a line, an equation of the tangent line at the point $(x_n, f(x_n))$ is

$$y - f(x_n) = \underbrace{f'(x_n)}_{m}(x - x_n).$$

➤ Recall that the point-slope form of the equation of a line with slope m passing through (x_n, y_n) is

$$y - y_n = m(x - x_n).$$

We find the point at which this line intersects the x-axis by setting $y = 0$ in the equation of the line and solving for x. This value of x becomes the new approximation x_{n+1}:

$$\underbrace{0}_{\text{set } y \text{ to } 0} - f(x_n) = f'(x_n)(\underbrace{x}_{\substack{\text{becomes}\\ x_{n+1}}} - x_n).$$

Solving for x and calling it x_{n+1}, we find that

$$\underbrace{x_{n+1}}_{\substack{\text{new}\\ \text{approximation}}} = \underbrace{x_n}_{\substack{\text{current}\\ \text{approximation}}} - \frac{f(x_n)}{f'(x_n)}, \quad \text{provided } f'(x_n) \neq 0.$$

We have derived the general step of Newton's method for approximating roots of a function f. This step is repeated for $n = 0, 1, 2, \ldots$, until a termination condition is met (to be discussed).

PROCEDURE Newton's Method for Approximating Roots of $f(x) = 0$

1. Choose an initial approximation x_0 as close to a root as possible.
2. For $n = 0, 1, 2, \ldots$

$$x_{n+1} = x_n - \frac{f(x_n)}{f'(x_n)},$$

provided $f'(x_n) \neq 0$.

3. End the calculations when a termination condition is met.

➤ Newton's method is an example of a repetitive loop calculation called an *iteration*. The most efficient way to implement the method is with a calculator or computer. The method is also included in many software packages.

QUICK CHECK 1 Verify that setting $y = 0$ in the equation $y - f(x_n) = f'(x_n)(x - x_n)$ and solving for x gives the formula for Newton's method. ◄

EXAMPLE 1 Applying Newton's method Approximate the roots of $f(x) = x^3 - 5x + 1$ (Figure 4.82) using seven steps of Newton's method. Use $x_0 = -3$, $x_0 = 1$, and $x_0 = 4$ as initial approximations.

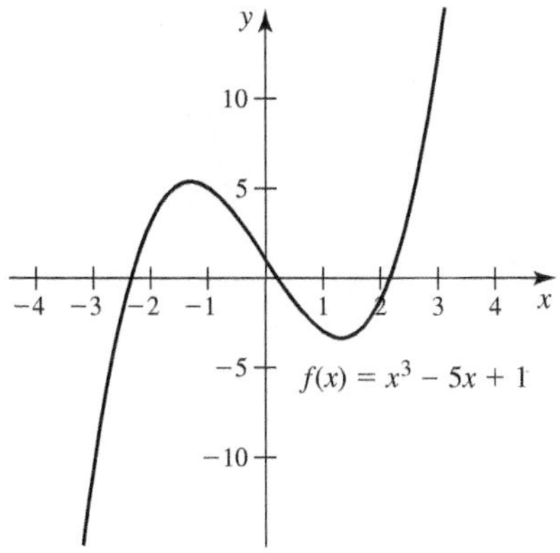

Figure 4.82

SOLUTION Noting that $f'(x) = 3x^2 - 5$, Newton's method takes the form

$$x_{n+1} = x_n - \frac{\overbrace{x_n^3 - 5x_n + 1}^{f(x_n)}}{\underbrace{3x_n^2 - 5}_{f'(x_n)}} = \frac{2x_n^3 - 1}{3x_n^2 - 5},$$

where $n = 0, 1, 2, \ldots$, and x_0 is specified. With an initial approximation of $x_0 = -3$, the first approximation is

$$x_1 = \frac{2x_0^3 - 1}{3x_0^2 - 5} = \frac{2(-3)^3 - 1}{3(-3)^2 - 5} = -2.5.$$

Table 4.5

n	x_n	x_n	x_n
0	−3	1	4
1	−2.500000	−0.500000	2.953488
2	−2.345455	0.294118	2.386813
3	−2.330203	0.200215	2.166534
4	−2.330059	0.201639	2.129453
5	−2.330059	0.201640	2.128420
6	−2.330059	0.201640	2.128419
7	−2.330059	0.201640	2.128419

➤ The numbers in Table 4.5 were computed with 16 decimal digits of precision. The results are displayed with 6 digits to the right of the decimal point.

QUICK CHECK 2 What happens if you apply Newton's method to the function $f(x) = x$? ◄

The second approximation is

$$x_2 = \frac{2x_1^3 - 1}{3x_1^2 - 5} = \frac{2(-2.5)^3 - 1}{3(-2.5)^2 - 5} \approx -2.345455.$$

Continuing in this fashion, we generate the first seven approximations shown in Table 4.5. The approximations generated from the initial approximations $x_0 = 1$ and $x_0 = 4$ are also shown in the table.

Notice that with the initial approximation $x_0 = -3$ (second column), the resulting sequence of approximations settles on the value -2.330059 after four iterations, and then there are no further changes in these digits. A similar behavior is seen with the initial approximations $x_0 = 1$ and $x_0 = 4$. Based on this evidence, we conclude that -2.330059, 0.201640, and 2.128419 are approximations to the roots of f with at least six digits (to the right of the decimal point) of accuracy.

A graph of f (Figure 4.83) confirms that f has three real roots and that the Newton approximations to the three roots are reasonable. The figure also shows the first three Newton approximations at each root. *Related Exercises 5–14* ◄

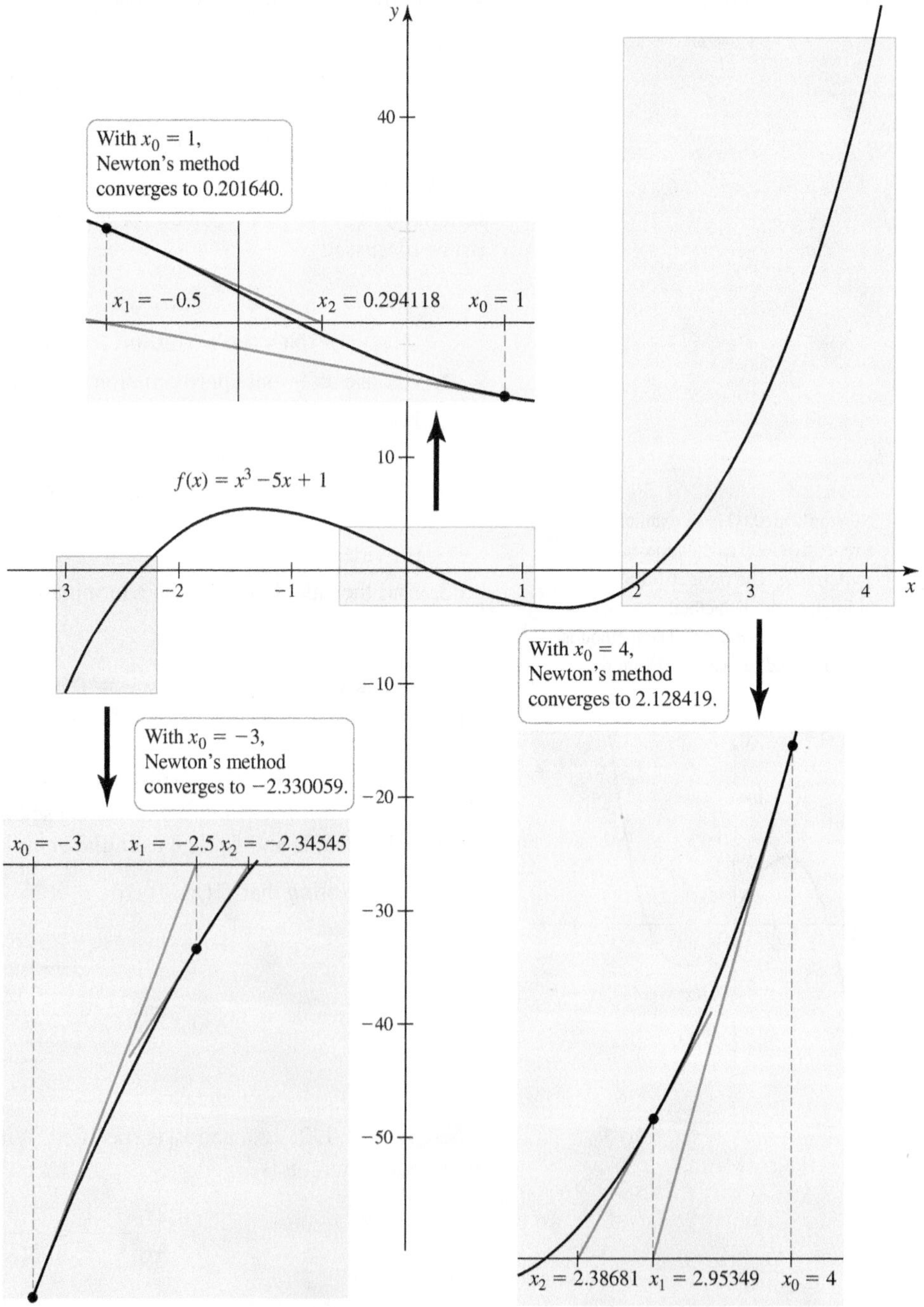

Figure 4.83

➤ If you write a program for Newton's method, it is a good idea to specify a maximum number of iterations as an escape clause in case the method does not converge.

➤ Small residuals do not always imply small errors: The function shown below has a zero at $x = 0$. An approximation such as 0.5 has a small residual but a large error.

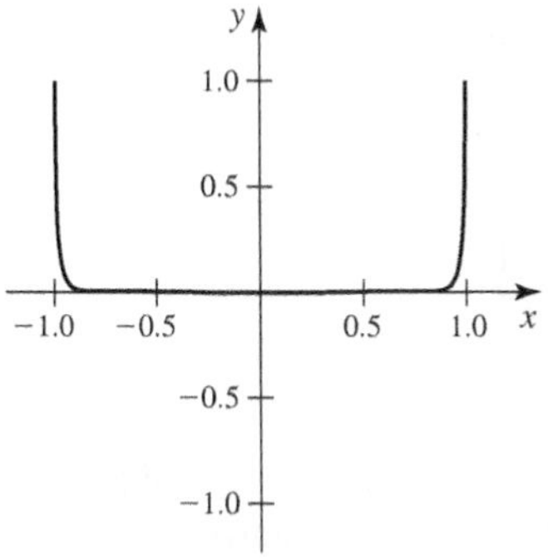

When Do You Stop?

Example 1 raises an important question and gives a practical answer: How many Newton approximations should you compute? Ideally, we would like to compute the **error** in x_n as an approximation to the root r, which is the quantity $|x_n - r|$. Unfortunately, we don't know r in practice; it is the quantity that we are trying to approximate. So we need a practical way to estimate the error.

In the second column of Table 4.5, we see that x_4 and x_5 agree in their seven digits, -2.330059. A general rule of thumb is that if two successive approximations agree to, say, seven digits, then those common digits are accurate (as an approximation to the root). So if you want p digits of accuracy in your approximation, you should compute until either two successive approximations agree to p digits or until some maximum number of iterations is exceeded (in which case Newton's method has failed to find an approximation of the root with the desired accuracy).

There is another practical way to gauge the accuracy of approximations. Because Newton's method generates approximations to a root of f, it follows that as the approximations x_n approach the root, $f(x_n)$ should approach zero. The quantity $f(x_n)$ is called a **residual**, and small residuals usually (but not always) suggest that the approximations have small errors. In Example 1, we find that for the approximations in the second column, $f(x_7) = -1.8 \times 10^{-15}$; for the approximations in the third column, $f(x_7) = 1.1 \times 10^{-16}$; and for the approximations in the fourth column, $f(x_7) = -1.8 \times 10^{-15}$. All these residuals (computed in full precision) are small in magnitude, giving additional confidence that the approximations have small errors.

EXAMPLE 2 **Finding intersection points** Find the points at which the curves $y = \cos x$ and $y = x$ intersect.

SOLUTION The graphs of two functions g and h intersect at points whose x-coordinates satisfy $g(x) = h(x)$, or, equivalently, where

$$f(x) = g(x) - h(x) = 0.$$

We see that finding intersection points is a root-finding problem. In this case, the intersection points of the curves $y = \cos x$ and $y = x$ satisfy

$$f(x) = \cos x - x = 0.$$

A preliminary graph is advisable to determine the number of intersection points and good initial approximations. From Figure 4.84a, we see that the two curves have one intersection point, and its x-coordinate is between 0 and 1. Equivalently, the function f has a zero between 0 and 1 (Figure 4.84b). A reasonable initial approximation is $x_0 = 0.5$.

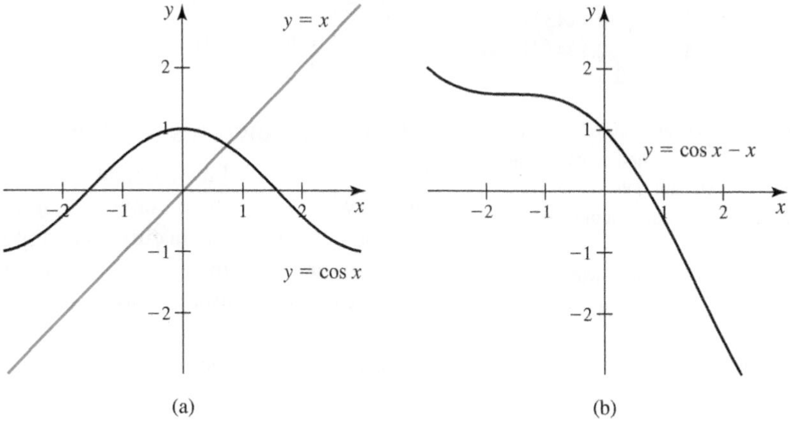

Figure 4.84

Newton's method takes the form

$$x_{n+1} = x_n - \underbrace{\overbrace{\frac{\cos x_n - x_n}{-\sin x_n - 1}}^{f(x_n)}}_{f'(x_n)} = \frac{x_n \sin x_n + \cos x_n}{\sin x_n + 1}.$$

The results of Newton's method, using an initial approximation of $x_0 = 0.5$, are shown in Table 4.6.

Table 4.6

n	x_n	Residual
0	0.5	0.377583
1	0.755222	−0.0271033
2	0.739142	−0.0000946154
3	0.739085	-1.18098×10^{-9}
4	0.739085	0
5	0.739085	0

We see that after four iterations, the approximations agree to six digits; so we take 0.739085 as the approximation to the root. Furthermore, the residuals, shown in the last column and computed with full precision, are essentially zero, which confirms the accuracy of the approximation. Therefore, the intersection point is approximately (0.739085, 0.739085) (because the point lies on the line $y = x$).

Related Exercises 15–20 ◀

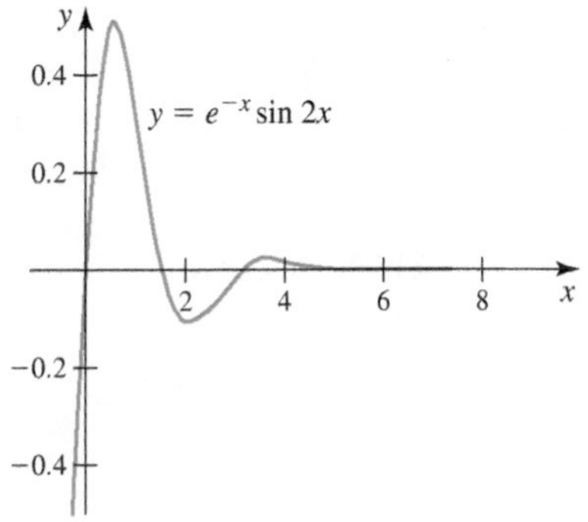

Figure 4.85

EXAMPLE 3 **Finding local extrema** Find the x-coordinate of the first local maximum and the first local minimum of the function $f(x) = e^{-x} \sin 2x$ on the interval $(0, \infty)$.

SOLUTION A graph of the function provides some guidance. Figure 4.85 shows that f has an infinite number of local extrema for $x > 0$. The first local maximum occurs on the interval $[0, 1]$, and the first local minimum occurs on the interval $[2, 3]$.

To locate the local extrema, we must find the critical points by solving

$$f'(x) = e^{-x}(2 \cos 2x - \sin 2x) = 0.$$

To this equation, we apply Newton's method. The results of the calculations, using initial approximations of $x_0 = 0.2$ and $x_0 = 2.5$, are shown in Table 4.7.

Table 4.7

n	x_n	x_n
0	0.200000	2.500000
1	0.499372	1.623915
2	0.550979	2.062202
3	0.553568	2.121018
4	0.553574	2.124360
5	0.553574	2.124371
6	0.553574	2.124371

Newton's method finds the two critical points quickly, and they are consistent with the graph of f. We conclude that the first local maximum occurs at $x \approx 0.553574$ and the first local minimum occurs at $x \approx 2.124371$.

Related Exercises 21–24 ◀

Pitfalls of Newton's Method

Given a good initial approximation, Newton's method usually converges to a root. In addition, when the method converges, it usually does so quickly. However, when Newton's method fails, it does so in curious and spectacular ways. The formula for Newton's method suggests one way in which the method could encounter difficulties: The term $f'(x_n)$ appears in a denominator, so if at any step $f'(x_n) = 0$, then the method breaks down. Furthermore, if $f'(x_n)$ is close to zero at any step, then the method may converge slowly or may fail to converge. The following example shows three ways in which Newton's method may go awry.

➤ A more thorough analysis of the rate at which Newton's method converges and the ways in which it fails to converge is presented in a course in numerical analysis.

Newton's method is widely used because in general, it has a remarkable rate of convergence; the number of digits of accuracy roughly doubles with each iteration.

EXAMPLE 4 Difficulties with Newton's method Find the root of $f(x) = \dfrac{8x^2}{3x^2 + 1}$ using Newton's method with initial approximations of $x_0 = 1, x_0 = 0.15$, and $x_0 = 1.1$.

SOLUTION Notice that f has the single root $x = 0$. So the point of the example is not to find the root, but to investigate the performance of Newton's method. Computing f' and doing a few steps of algebra show that the formula for Newton's method is

$$x_{n+1} = x_n - \frac{f(x_n)}{f'(x_n)} = \frac{x_n}{2}(1 - 3x_n^2).$$

The results of five iterations of Newton's method are displayed in Table 4.8, and they tell three different stories.

Table 4.8

n	x_n	x_n	x_n
0	1	0.15	1.1
1	−1	0.0699375	−1.4465
2	1	0.0344556	3.81665
3	−1	0.0171665	−81.4865
4	1	0.00857564	8.11572×10^5
5	−1	0.00428687	-8.01692×10^{17}

The approximations generated using $x_0 = 1$ (second column) get stuck in a cycle that alternates between $+1$ and -1. The geometry underlying this rare occurrence is illustrated in Figure 4.86.

The approximations generated using $x_0 = 0.15$ (third column) actually converge to the root 0, but they converge slowly (Figure 4.87). Notice that the error is reduced by a factor of approximately 2 with each step. Newton's method usually has a faster rate of error reduction. The slow convergence is due to the fact that both f and f' have zeros at 0. As mentioned earlier, if the approximations x_n approach a zero of f', the rate of convergence is often compromised.

The approximations generated using $x_0 = 1.1$ (fourth column) increase in magnitude quickly and do not converge to a finite value, even though this initial approximation seems reasonable. The geometry of this case is shown in Figure 4.88.

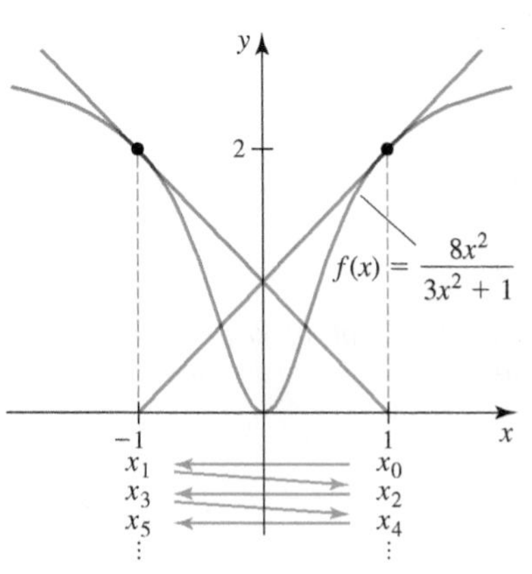

Figure 4.86

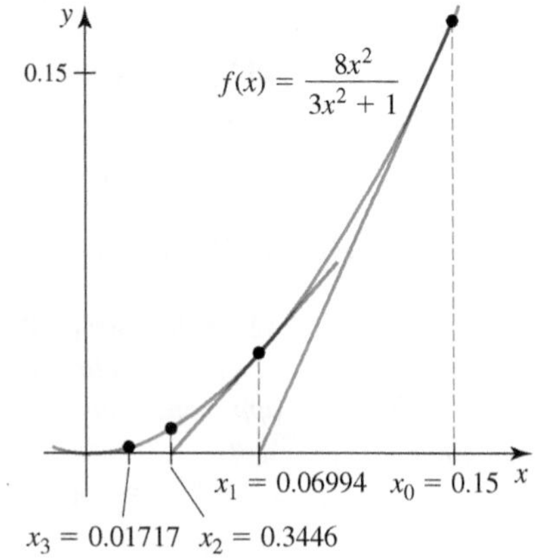

Figure 4.87

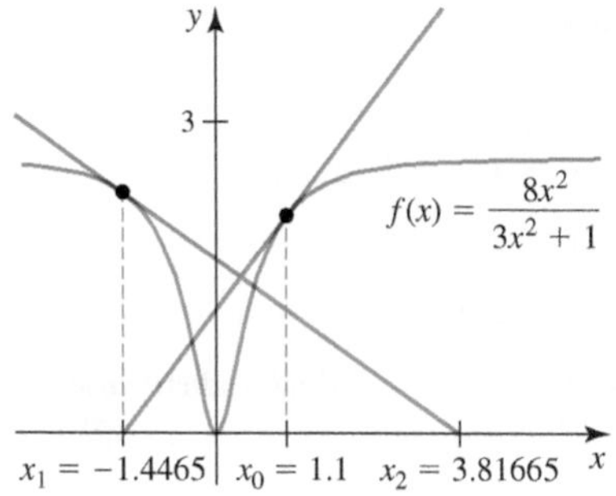

Figure 4.88

The three cases in this example illustrate several ways that Newton's method may fail to converge at its usual rate: The approximations may cycle or wander, they may converge slowly, or they may diverge (often at a rapid rate).

Related Exercises 25–26 ◀

SECTION 4.8 EXERCISES

Review Questions

1. Give a geometric explanation of Newton's method.
2. Explain how the iteration formula for Newton's method works.
3. How do you decide when to terminate Newton's method?
4. Give the formula for Newton's method for the function $f(x) = x^2 - 5$.

Basic Skills

T **5–8. Formulating Newton's method** *Write the formula for Newton's method and use the given initial approximation to compute the approximations x_1 and x_2.*

5. $f(x) = x^2 - 6$; $x_0 = 3$
6. $f(x) = x^2 - 2x - 3$; $x_0 = 2$
7. $f(x) = e^{-x} - x$; $x_0 = \ln 2$
8. $f(x) = x^3 - 2$; $x_0 = 2$

T **9–14. Finding roots with Newton's method** *Use a calculator or program to compute the first 10 iterations of Newton's method when it is applied to the following functions with the given initial approximation. Make a table similar to that in Example 1.*

9. $f(x) = x^2 - 10$; $x_0 = 4$
10. $f(x) = x^3 + x^2 + 1$; $x_0 = -2$
11. $f(x) = \sin x + x - 1$; $x_0 = 1.5$
12. $f(x) = e^x - 5$; $x_0 = 2$
13. $f(x) = \tan x - 2x$; $x_0 = 1.5$
14. $f(x) = \ln(x + 1) - 1$; $x_0 = 1.7$

T **15–20. Finding intersection points** *Use Newton's method to approximate all the intersection points of the following pairs of curves. Some preliminary graphing or analysis may help in choosing good initial approximations.*

15. $y = \sin x$ and $y = \frac{x}{2}$
16. $y = e^x$ and $y = x^3$
17. $y = \frac{1}{x}$ and $y = 4 - x^2$
18. $y = x^3$ and $y = x^2 + 1$
19. $y = 4\sqrt{x}$ and $y = x^2 + 1$
20. $y = \ln x$ and $y = x^3 - 2$

T **21–24. Newton's method and curve sketching** *Use Newton's method to find approximate answers to the following questions.*

21. Where is the first local minimum of $f(x) = \frac{\cos x}{x}$ on the interval $(0, \infty)$ located?
22. Where are all the local extrema of $f(x) = 3x^4 + 8x^3 + 12x^2 + 48x$ located?
23. Where are the inflection points of $f(x) = \frac{9}{5}x^5 - \frac{15}{2}x^4 + \frac{7}{3}x^3 + 30x^2 + 1$ located?
24. Where is the local extremum of $f(x) = \frac{e^x}{x}$ located? (Use Newton's method.)

T **25–26. Slow convergence**

25. The functions $f(x) = (x - 1)^2$ and $g(x) = x^2 - 1$ both have a root at $x = 1$. Apply Newton's method to both functions with an initial approximation $x_0 = 2$. Compare the rate at which the method converges in each case and give an explanation.
26. Consider the function $f(x) = x^5 + 4x^4 + x^3 - 10x^2 - 4x + 8$, which has zeros at $x = 1$ and $x = -2$. Apply Newton's method to this function with initial approximations of $x_0 = -1$, $x_0 = -0.2$, $x_0 = 0.2$, and $x_0 = 2$. Discuss and compare the results of the calculations.

Further Explorations

27. **Explain why or why not** Determine whether the following statements are true and give an explanation or counterexample.
    a. Newton's method is an example of a numerical method for approximating the roots of a function.
    b. Newton's method gives a better approximation to the roots of a quadratic equation than the quadratic formula.
    c. Newton's method always finds an approximate root of a function.

T **28–31. Fixed points** *An important question about many functions concerns the existence and location of fixed points. A* **fixed point** *of f is a value of x that satisfies the equation $f(x) = x$; it corresponds to a point at which the graph of f intersects the line $y = x$. Find all the fixed points of the following functions. Use preliminary analysis and graphing to determine good initial approximations.*

28. $f(x) = 5 - x^2$
29. $f(x) = \frac{x^3}{10} + 1$
30. $f(x) = \tan\frac{x}{2}$ on $(-\pi, \pi)$
31. $f(x) = 2x\cos x$ on $[0, 2]$

T **32–38. More root finding** *Find all the roots of the following functions. Use preliminary analysis and graphing to determine good initial approximations.*

32. $f(x) = \cos x - \frac{x}{7}$
33. $f(x) = \cos 2x - x^2 + 2x$
34. $f(x) = \frac{x}{6} - \sec x$ on $[0, 8]$
35. $f(x) = e^{-x} - \frac{x + 4}{5}$

36. $f(x) = \dfrac{x^5}{5} - \dfrac{x^3}{4} - \dfrac{1}{20}$

37. $f(x) = \ln x - x^2 + 3x - 1$

38. $f(x) = x^2(x - 100) + 1$

39. Residuals and errors Approximate the root of $f(x) = x^{10}$ at $x = 0$ using Newton's method with an initial approximation of $x_0 = 0.5$. Make a table showing the first 10 approximations, the error in these approximations (which is $|x_n - 0| = |x_n|$), and the residual of these approximations (which is $f(x_n)$). Comment on the relative size of the errors and the residuals and give an explanation.

40. A tangent question Verify by graphing that the graphs of $y = \sin x$ and $y = x/2$ have one point of intersection, for $x > 0$, whereas the graphs of $y = \sin x$ and $y = x/9$ have three points of intersection, for $x > 0$. Approximate the value of a such that the graphs of $y = \sin x$ and $y = x/a$ have exactly two points of intersection, for $x > 0$.

41. A tangent question Verify by graphing that the graphs of $y = e^x$ and $y = x$ have no points of intersection, whereas the graphs of $y = e^{x/3}$ and $y = x$ have two points of intersection. Approximate the value of $a > 0$ such that the graphs of $y = e^{x/a}$ and $y = x$ have exactly one point of intersection.

42. Approximating square roots Let $a > 0$ be given and suppose we want to approximate $\sqrt{a}$ using Newton's method.

a. Explain why the square root problem is equivalent to finding the positive root of $f(x) = x^2 - a$.

b. Show that Newton's method applied to this function takes the form (sometimes called the Babylonian method)

$$x_{n+1} = \frac{1}{2}\left(x_n + \frac{a}{x_n}\right), \quad \text{for } n = 0, 1, 2, \ldots.$$

c. How would you choose initial approximations to approximate $\sqrt{13}$ and $\sqrt{73}$?

d. Approximate $\sqrt{13}$ and $\sqrt{73}$ with at least 10 significant digits.

43. Approximating reciprocals To approximate the reciprocal of a number a without using division, we can apply Newton's method to the function $f(x) = \dfrac{1}{x} - a$.

a. Verify that Newton's method gives the formula $x_{n+1} = (2 - ax_n)x_n$.

b. Apply Newton's method with $a = 7$ using a starting value of your choice. Compute an approximation with eight digits of accuracy. What number does Newton's method approximate in this case?

44. Modified Newton's method The function f has a root of *multiplicity* 2 at r if $f(r) = f'(r) = 0$ and $f''(r) \neq 0$. In this case, a slight modification of Newton's method, known as the *modified* (or *accelerated*) Newton's method, is given by the formula

$$x_{n+1} = x_n - \frac{2f(x_n)}{f'(x_n)}, \quad \text{for } n = 0, 1, 2, \ldots.$$

This modified form generally increases the rate of convergence.

a. Verify that 0 is a root of multiplicity 2 of the function $f(x) = e^{2\sin x} - 2x - 1$.

b. Apply Newton's method and the modified Newton's method using $x_0 = 0.1$ to find the value of x_3 in each case. Compare the accuracy of each value of x_3.

c. Consider the function $f(x) = \dfrac{8x^2}{3x^2 + 1}$ given in Example 4. Use the modified Newton's method to find the value of x_3 using $x_0 = 0.15$. Compare this value to the value of x_3 found in Example 4 with $x_0 = 0.15$.

Applications

45. A damped oscillator The displacement of a particular object as it bounces vertically up and down on a spring is given by $y(t) = 2.5e^{-t}\cos 2t$, where the initial displacement is $y(0) = 2.5$ and $y = 0$ corresponds to the rest position (see figure).

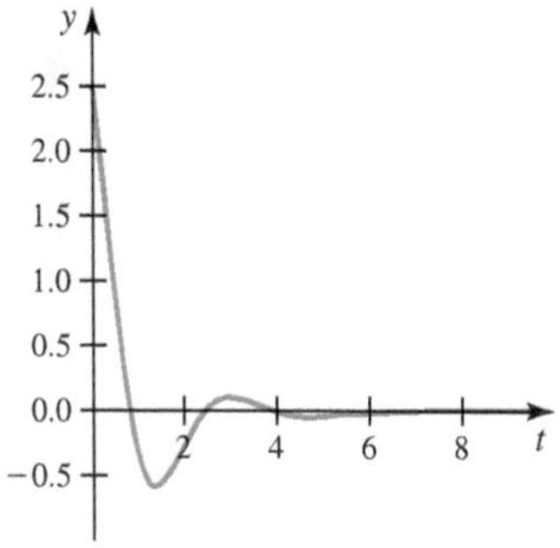

a. Find the time at which the object first passes the rest position, $y = 0$.

b. Find the time and the displacement when the object reaches its lowest point.

c. Find the time at which the object passes the rest position for the second time.

d. Find the time and the displacement when the object reaches its high point for the second time.

46. The sinc function The sinc function, $\operatorname{sinc}(x) = \dfrac{\sin x}{x}$ for $x \neq 0$, $\operatorname{sinc}(0) = 1$, appears frequently in signal-processing applications.

a. Graph the sinc function on $[-2\pi, 2\pi]$.

b. Locate the first local minimum and the first local maximum of $\operatorname{sinc}(x)$, for $x > 0$.

47. An eigenvalue problem A certain kind of differential equation (see Section 7.9) leads to the root-finding problem $\tan \pi\lambda = \lambda$, where the roots λ are called **eigenvalues**. Find the first three positive eigenvalues of this problem.

Additional Exercises

48. Fixed points of quadratics and quartics Let $f(x) = ax(1 - x)$, where a is a real number and $0 \le x \le 1$. Recall that the fixed point of a function is a value of x such that $f(x) = x$ (Exercises 28–31).

a. Without using a calculator, find the values of a, with $0 < a \le 4$, such that f has a fixed point. Give the fixed point in terms of a.

b. Consider the polynomial $g(x) = f(f(x))$. Write g in terms of a and powers of x. What is its degree?

c. Graph g for $a = 2, 3$, and 4.

d. Find the number and location of the fixed points of g for $a = 2, 3$, and 4 on the interval $0 \le x \le 1$.

T **49. Basins of attraction** Suppose f has a real root r and Newton's method is used to approximate r with an initial approximation x_0. The **basin of attraction** of r is the set of initial approximations that produce a sequence that converges to r. Points near r are often in the basin of attraction of r—but not always. Sometimes an initial approximation x_0 may produce a sequence that doesn't converge, and sometimes an initial approximation x_0 may produce a sequence that converges to a distant root. Let $f(x) = (x + 2)(x + 1)(x - 3)$, which has roots $x = -2, -1$, and 3. Use Newton's method with initial approximations on the interval $[-4, 4]$ to determine (approximately) the basin of each root.

QUICK CHECK ANSWERS

1. $0 - f(x_n) = f'(x_n)(x - x_n) \Rightarrow -\frac{f(x_n)}{f'(x_n)} = x - x_n \Rightarrow x = x_n - \frac{f(x_n)}{f'(x_n)}$ **2.** Newton's method will find the root $x = 0$ exactly in one step. ◄

4.9 Antiderivatives

The goal of differentiation is to find the derivative f' of a given function f. The reverse process, called *antidifferentiation*, is equally important: Given a function f, we look for an *antiderivative* function F whose derivative is f; that is, a function F such that $F' = f$.

> **DEFINITION Antiderivative**
>
> A function F is an **antiderivative** of f on an interval I provided $F'(x) = f(x)$, for all x in I.

In this section, we revisit derivative formulas developed in previous chapters to discover corresponding antiderivative formulas.

Thinking Backward

Consider the derivative formula $\frac{d}{dx}(x) = 1$. It implies that an antiderivative of $f(x) = 1$ is $F(x) = x$ because $F'(x) = f(x)$. Using the same logic, we can write

$$\frac{d}{dx}(x^2) = 2x \quad \Rightarrow \quad \text{an antiderivative of } f(x) = 2x \text{ is } F(x) = x^2 \text{ and}$$

$$\frac{d}{dx}(\sin x) = \cos x \quad \Rightarrow \quad \text{an antiderivative of } f(x) = \cos x \text{ is } F(x) = \sin x.$$

QUICK CHECK 1 Verify by differentiation that x^3 is an antiderivative of $3x^2$ and $-\cos x$ is an antiderivative of $\sin x$. ◄

Each of these proposed antiderivative formulas is easily checked by showing that $F' = f$.

An immediate question arises: Does a function have more than one antiderivative? To answer this question, let's focus on $f(x) = 1$ and the antiderivative $F(x) = x$. Because the derivative of a constant C is zero, we see that $F(x) = x + C$ is also an antiderivative of $f(x) = 1$, which is easy to check:

$$F'(x) = \frac{d}{dx}(x + C) = 1 = f(x).$$

Therefore, $f(x) = 1$ actually has an infinite number of antiderivatives. For the same reason, any function of the form $F(x) = x^2 + C$ is an antiderivative of $f(x) = 2x$, and any function of the form $F(x) = \sin x + C$ is an antiderivative of $f(x) = \cos x$, where C is an arbitrary constant.

We might ask whether there are still *more* antiderivatives of a given function. The following theorem provides the answer.

THEOREM 4.16 The Family of Antiderivatives
Let F be any antiderivative of f on an interval I. Then *all* the antiderivatives of f on I have the form $F + C$, where C is an arbitrary constant.

Proof: Suppose that F and G are antiderivatives of f on an interval I. Then $F' = f$ and $G' = f$, which implies that $F' = G'$ on I. Theorem 4.11 states that functions with equal derivatives differ by a constant. Therefore, $G = F + C$, and all antiderivatives of f have the form $F + C$, where C is an arbitrary constant. ◀

Theorem 4.16 says that while there are infinitely many antiderivatives of a function, they are all of one family, namely, those functions of the form $F + C$. Because the antiderivatives of a particular function differ by a constant, the antiderivatives are vertical translations of one another (Figure 4.89).

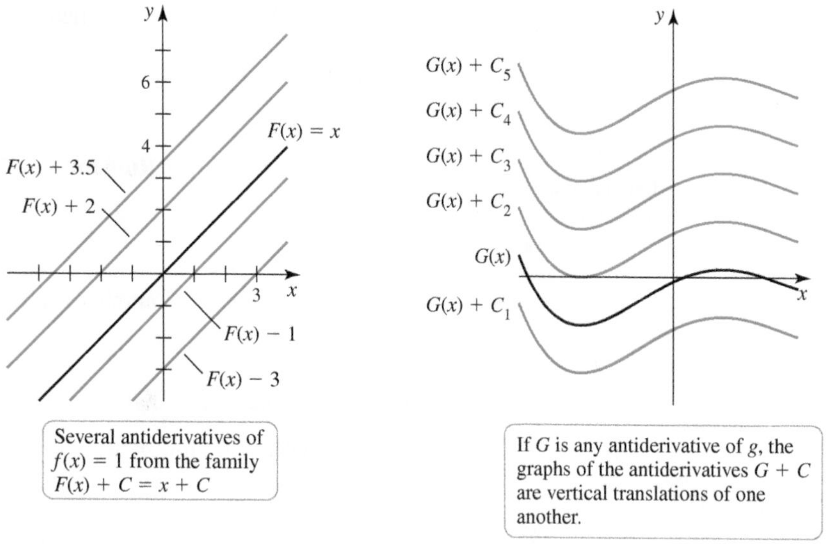

Figure 4.89

EXAMPLE 1 Finding antiderivatives Use what you know about derivatives to find all antiderivatives of the following functions.

a. $f(x) = 3x^2$ **b.** $f(x) = \dfrac{1}{1 + x^2}$ **c.** $f(t) = \sin t$

SOLUTION

a. Note that $\dfrac{d}{dx}(x^3) = 3x^2$. Therefore, an antiderivative of $f(x) = 3x^2$ is x^3. By Theorem 4.16, the complete family of antiderivatives is $F(x) = x^3 + C$, where C is an arbitrary constant.

b. Because $\dfrac{d}{dx}(\tan^{-1} x) = \dfrac{1}{1 + x^2}$, all antiderivatives of f are of the form $F(x) = \tan^{-1} x + C$, where C is an arbitrary constant.

c. Recall that $\dfrac{d}{dt}(\cos t) = -\sin t$. We seek a function whose derivative is $\sin t$, not $-\sin t$. Observing that $\dfrac{d}{dt}(-\cos t) = \sin t$, it follows that the antiderivatives of $\sin t$ are $F(t) = -\cos t + C$, where C is an arbitrary constant.

Related Exercises 11–22 ◀

QUICK CHECK 2 Find the family of antiderivatives for each of $f(x) = e^x$, $g(x) = 4x^3$, and $h(x) = \sec^2 x$. ◄

Indefinite Integrals

The notation $\frac{d}{dx}(f(x))$ means *take the derivative of* $f(x)$ *with respect to* x. We need analogous notation for antiderivatives. For historical reasons that become apparent in the next chapter, the notation that means *find the antiderivatives of f* is the **indefinite integral** $\int f(x)\,dx$. Every time an indefinite integral sign $\int$ appears, it is followed by a function called the **integrand**, which in turn is followed by the differential dx. For now, dx simply means that x is the independent variable, or the **variable of integration**. The notation $\int f(x)\,dx$ represents *all* the antiderivatives of f. When the integrand is a function of a variable different from x—say, $g(t)$—then we write $\int g(t)\,dt$ to represent the antiderivatives of g.

Using this new notation, the three results of Example 1 are written

$$\int 3x^2\,dx = x^3 + C, \quad \int \frac{1}{1+x^2}\,dx = \tan^{-1} x + C, \quad \text{and} \quad \int \sin t\,dt = -\cos t + C,$$

where C is an arbitrary constant called a **constant of integration**. The derivative formulas presented earlier in the text may be written in terms of indefinite integrals. We begin with the Power Rule.

➤ Notice that if $p = -1$ in Theorem 4.17, then $F(x)$ is undefined. The antiderivative of $f(x) = x^{-1}$ is discussed in Example 5. The case $p = 0$ says that $\int 1\,dx = x + C$.

THEOREM 4.17 Power Rule for Indefinite Integrals

$$\int x^p\,dx = \frac{x^{p+1}}{p+1} + C,$$

where $p \neq -1$ is a real number and C is an arbitrary constant.

Proof: The theorem says that the antiderivatives of $f(x) = x^p$ have the form $F(x) = \frac{x^{p+1}}{p+1} + C$. Differentiating F, we verify that $F'(x) = f(x)$, provided $p \neq -1$:

➤ Any indefinite integral calculation can be checked by differentiation: The derivative of the alleged indefinite integral must equal the integrand.

$$\begin{aligned} F'(x) &= \frac{d}{dx}\left(\frac{x^{p+1}}{p+1} + C\right) \\ &= \frac{d}{dx}\left(\frac{x^{p+1}}{p+1}\right) + \underbrace{\frac{d}{dx}(C)}_{0} \\ &= \frac{(p+1)x^{(p+1)-1}}{p+1} + 0 = x^p. \end{aligned}$$ ◄

Theorems 3.4 and 3.5 (Section 3.2) state the Constant Multiple and Sum Rules for derivatives. Here are the corresponding antiderivative rules, which are proved by differentiation.

THEOREM 4.18 Constant Multiple and Sum Rules

Constant Multiple Rule: $\int cf(x)\,dx = c\int f(x)\,dx$, for real numbers c

Sum Rule: $\int (f(x) + g(x))\,dx = \int f(x)\,dx + \int g(x)\,dx$

The following example shows how Theorems 4.17 and 4.18 are used.

EXAMPLE 2 **Indefinite integrals** Determine the following indefinite integrals.

a. $\int (3x^5 + 2 - 5\sqrt{x})\,dx$ **b.** $\int \left(\frac{4x^{19} - 5x^{-8}}{x^2}\right) dx$ **c.** $\int (z^2 + 1)(2z - 5)\,dz$

SOLUTION

➤ $\int dx$ means $\int 1\,dx$, which is the indefinite integral of the constant function $f(x) = 1$, so $\int dx = x + C$.

➤ Each indefinite integral in Example 2a produces an arbitrary constant, all of which may be combined in one arbitrary constant called C.

a.
$$\int (3x^5 + 2 - 5\sqrt{x})\,dx = \int 3x^5\,dx + \int 2\,dx - \int 5x^{1/2}\,dx \quad \text{Sum Rule}$$
$$= 3\int x^5\,dx + 2\int dx - 5\int x^{1/2}\,dx \quad \text{Constant Multiple Rule}$$
$$= 3\cdot\frac{x^6}{6} + 2\cdot x - 5\cdot\frac{x^{3/2}}{3/2} + C \quad \text{Power Rule}$$
$$= \frac{x^6}{2} + 2x - \frac{10}{3}x^{3/2} + C \quad \text{Simplify.}$$

b.
$$\int \left(\frac{4x^{19} - 5x^{-8}}{x^2}\right) dx = \int (4x^{17} - 5x^{-10})\,dx \quad \text{Simplify the integrand.}$$
$$= 4\int x^{17}\,dx - 5\int x^{-10}\,dx \quad \text{Sum and Constant Multiple Rules}$$
$$= 4\cdot\frac{x^{18}}{18} - 5\cdot\frac{x^{-9}}{-9} + C \quad \text{Power Rule}$$
$$= \frac{2x^{18}}{9} + \frac{5x^{-9}}{9} + C \quad \text{Simplify.}$$

➤ Examples 2b and 2c show that in general, the indefinite integral of a product or quotient is not the product or quotient of indefinite integrals.

c.
$$\int (z^2 + 1)(2z - 5)\,dz = \int (2z^3 - 5z^2 + 2z - 5)\,dz \quad \text{Expand integrand.}$$
$$= \frac{1}{2}z^4 - \frac{5}{3}z^3 + z^2 - 5z + C \quad \text{Integrate each term.}$$

All these results should be checked by differentiation.

Related Exercises 23–36 ◀

Indefinite Integrals of Trigonometric Functions

In this section, we have two goals that can be accomplished at the same time. The first goal is to write the familiar derivative results for trigonometric functions as indefinite integrals. The second goal is to show how these results are generalized using the Chain Rule. The following example illustrates the key ideas.

EXAMPLE 3 **Indefinite integrals of trigonometric functions** Evaluate the following indefinite integrals.

a. $\int \sec^2 x\,dx$ **b.** $\int \sin 3x\,dx$

c. $\int \sec ax \tan ax\,dx$, where $a \neq 0$ is a real number

➤ Remember the words that go with antiderivatives and indefinite integrals. The statement $\frac{d}{dx}(\tan x) = \sec^2 x$ says that $\tan x$ can be differentiated to get $\sec^2 x$. Therefore,
$$\int \sec^2 x\,dx = \tan x + C.$$

SOLUTION

a. The derivative result $\frac{d}{dx}(\tan x) = \sec^2 x$ is reversed to produce the indefinite integral
$$\int \sec^2 x\,dx = \tan x + C.$$

> The statement $\frac{d}{dx}(\cos 3x) = -3 \sin 3x$ says that $\cos 3x$ can be differentiated to get $-3 \sin 3x$. Therefore, $\int(-3 \sin 3x)\, dx = \cos 3x + C$.

b. From Example 1c, we know that $\int \sin x\, dx = -\cos x + C$. The complication in the given integral is the factor of 3 in $\sin 3x$. Here is the thinking that allows us to handle this factor. A derivative result that appears related to the given indefinite integral is $\frac{d}{dx}(\cos 3x) = -3 \sin 3x$, which is obtained using the Chain Rule. We write this derivative result as the indefinite integral

$$\int (-3 \sin 3x)\, dx = \cos 3x + C, \quad \text{or} \quad -3 \int \sin 3x\, dx = \cos 3x + C.$$

Dividing both sides of this equation by -3 gives the desired result,

$$\int \sin 3x\, dx = -\frac{1}{3} \cos 3x + C,$$

> If C is an arbitrary constant and $a \neq 0$ is a real number, then C/a is also an arbitrary constant and we continue to call it C.

which can be checked by differentiation. Notice that 3 could be replaced in this example with any constant $a \neq 0$ to produce the more general result

$$\int \sin ax\, dx = -\frac{1}{a} \cos ax + C.$$

c. A derivative result that appears related to this indefinite integral is $\frac{d}{dx}(\sec x) = \sec x \tan x$, or more generally, using the Chain Rule,

$$\frac{d}{dx}(\sec ax) = a \sec ax \tan ax.$$

Writing this derivative result as an indefinite integral, we have

$$\int a \sec ax \tan ax\, dx = \sec ax + C.$$

After dividing through by a, we have

$$\int \sec ax \tan ax\, dx = \frac{1}{a} \sec ax + C.$$

Related Exercises 37–46 ◀

The technique used in Example 3 of writing a Chain Rule result as an indefinite integral can be used to obtain the integrals in Table 4.9. We assume that $a \neq 0$ is a real number and that C is an arbitrary constant.

> In Section 5.5, we show how to derive the results in Tables 4.9 and 4.10 using the Substitution Rule.

Table 4.9 Indefinite Integrals of Trigonometric Functions

1. $\frac{d}{dx}(\sin ax) = a \cos ax \quad \Rightarrow \quad \int \cos ax\, dx = \frac{1}{a} \sin ax + C$
2. $\frac{d}{dx}(\cos ax) = -a \sin ax \quad \Rightarrow \quad \int \sin ax\, dx = -\frac{1}{a} \cos ax + C$
3. $\frac{d}{dx}(\tan ax) = a \sec^2 ax \quad \Rightarrow \quad \int \sec^2 ax\, dx = \frac{1}{a} \tan ax + C$
4. $\frac{d}{dx}(\cot ax) = -a \csc^2 ax \quad \Rightarrow \quad \int \csc^2 ax\, dx = -\frac{1}{a} \cot ax + C$
5. $\frac{d}{dx}(\sec ax) = a \sec ax \tan ax \quad \Rightarrow \quad \int \sec ax \tan ax\, dx = \frac{1}{a} \sec ax + C$
6. $\frac{d}{dx}(\csc ax) = -a \csc ax \cot ax \quad \Rightarrow \quad \int \csc ax \cot ax\, dx = -\frac{1}{a} \csc ax + C$

QUICK CHECK 3 Use differentiation to verify that $\int \sin 2x\, dx = -\frac{1}{2} \cos 2x + C$. ◀

EXAMPLE 4 Indefinite integrals of trigonometric functions Determine the following indefinite integrals.

a. $\int \sec^2 3x\,dx$ **b.** $\int \cos\frac{x}{2}\,dx$

SOLUTION These integrals follow directly from Table 4.9 and can be verified by differentiation.

a. Letting $a = 3$ in result (3) of Table 4.9, we have

$$\int \sec^2 3x\,dx = \frac{\tan 3x}{3} + C.$$

b. We let $a = \frac{1}{2}$ in result (1) of Table 4.9, which says that

$$\int \cos\frac{x}{2}\,dx = \frac{\sin(x/2)}{1/2} + C = 2\sin\frac{x}{2} + C.$$

Related Exercises 37–46 ◀

Other Indefinite Integrals

We now continue the process of rewriting familiar derivative results as indefinite integrals. As in Example 3, we generally begin with a derivative based on the Chain Rule and then express it as an indefinite integral.

EXAMPLE 5 Additional indefinite integrals Evaluate the following indefinite integrals. Assume a is a nonzero real number.

a. $\int \frac{dx}{x}$ **b.** $\int e^{ax}\,dx$ **c.** $\int \frac{dx}{a^2 + x^2}$

SOLUTION

a. In this case, we know that $\frac{d}{dx}(\ln|x|) = \frac{1}{x}$, for $x \neq 0$. The corresponding indefinite integral follows immediately:

$$\int \frac{dx}{x} = \ln|x| + C.$$

This result fills the gap in the Power Rule for the case $p = -1$.

b. By the Chain Rule, we know that $\frac{d}{dx}(e^{ax}) = ae^{ax}$. Written as an indefinite integral, this result is equivalent to $\int ae^{ax}\,dx = e^{ax} + C$. We divide through by a to obtain

$$\int e^{ax}\,dx = \frac{1}{a}e^{ax} + C,$$

which can be verified by differentiation.

c. The integrand $\frac{1}{a^2 + x^2}$ looks familiar (see Example 1b); it suggests that we begin with the derivative formula $\frac{d}{dx}(\tan^{-1} x) = \frac{1}{1 + x^2}$. As before, we call on the Chain Rule to generalize this result and write

$$\frac{d}{dx}\left(\tan^{-1}\frac{x}{a}\right) = \frac{1/a}{1 + \left(\frac{x}{a}\right)^2} = \frac{a}{a^2 + x^2}.$$

➤ In Example 5c, we could have applied the Chain Rule to $\tan^{-1} ax$ and derived a useful indefinite integral. However, working with $\tan^{-1}\frac{x}{a}$ produces a more common form of the integral.

Expressed as an indefinite integral, we find that

$$\int \frac{a}{a^2 + x^2}\,dx = \tan^{-1}\frac{x}{a} + C.$$

Dividing through by a gives

$$\int \frac{dx}{a^2 + x^2} = \frac{1}{a}\tan^{-1}\frac{x}{a} + C.$$

Related Exercises 47–58 ◀

The ideas used in Example 5 lead to the results in Table 4.10, where $a \neq 0$ is a real number and C is an arbitrary constant.

➤ Tables 4.9 and 4.10 are subsets of the table of integrals at the end of the book.

Table 4.10 Other Indefinite Integrals

7. $\frac{d}{dx}(e^{ax}) = ae^{ax}$	$\Rightarrow \int e^{ax}\,dx = \frac{1}{a}e^{ax} + C$
8. $\frac{d}{dx}(b^x) = b^x \ln b$	$\Rightarrow \int b^x\,dx = \frac{1}{\ln b}b^x + C, b > 0, b \neq 1$
9. $\frac{d}{dx}(\ln\lvert x\rvert) = \frac{1}{x}$	$\Rightarrow \int \frac{dx}{x} = \ln\lvert x\rvert + C$
10. $\frac{d}{dx}\left(\sin^{-1}\frac{x}{a}\right) = \frac{1}{\sqrt{a^2 - x^2}}$	$\Rightarrow \int \frac{dx}{\sqrt{a^2 - x^2}} = \sin^{-1}\frac{x}{a} + C$
11. $\frac{d}{dx}\left(\tan^{-1}\frac{x}{a}\right) = \frac{a}{a^2 + x^2}$	$\Rightarrow \int \frac{dx}{a^2 + x^2} = \frac{1}{a}\tan^{-1}\frac{x}{a} + C$
12. $\frac{d}{dx}\left(\sec^{-1}\left\lvert\frac{x}{a}\right\rvert\right) = \frac{a}{x\sqrt{x^2 - a^2}}$	$\Rightarrow \int \frac{dx}{x\sqrt{x^2 - a^2}} = \frac{1}{a}\sec^{-1}\left\lvert\frac{x}{a}\right\rvert + C, a > 0$

EXAMPLE 6 **Indefinite integrals** Determine the following indefinite integrals.

a. $\int e^{-10t}\,dt$ **b.** $\int \frac{4}{\sqrt{9 - x^2}}\,dx$ **c.** $\int \frac{dx}{16x^2 + 1}$

SOLUTION

➤ The results in Tables 4.9 and 4.10 apply regardless of what we call the variable of integration.

a. Setting $a = -10$ in result (7) of Table 4.10, we find that

$$\int e^{-10t}\,dt = -\frac{1}{10}e^{-10t} + C.$$

b. Setting $a = 3$ in result (10) of Table 4.10, we have

$$\int \frac{4}{\sqrt{9 - x^2}}\,dx = 4\int \frac{dx}{\sqrt{3^2 - x^2}} = 4\sin^{-1}\frac{x}{3} + C.$$

c. An algebra step is needed to put this integral in a form that matches Table 4.10. We first write

$$\int \frac{dx}{16x^2 + 1} = \frac{1}{16}\int \frac{dx}{x^2 + \frac{1}{16}} = \frac{1}{16}\int \frac{dx}{x^2 + \left(\frac{1}{4}\right)^2}.$$

Setting $a = \frac{1}{4}$ in result (11) of Table 4.10 gives

$$\int \frac{dx}{16x^2 + 1} = \frac{1}{16}\int \frac{dx}{x^2 + \left(\frac{1}{4}\right)^2} = \frac{1}{16}\cdot 4\tan^{-1}4x + C = \frac{1}{4}\tan^{-1}4x + C.$$

Related Exercises 47–58 ◀

Introduction to Differential Equations

An equation involving an unknown function and its derivatives is called a **differential equation**. Here is an example to get us started.

Suppose you know that the derivative of a function f satisfies the equation

$$f'(x) = 2x + 10.$$

To find a function f that satisfies this equation, we note that the solutions are antiderivatives of $2x + 10$, which are $x^2 + 10x + C$, where C is an arbitrary constant. So we have found an infinite number of solutions, all of the form $f(x) = x^2 + 10x + C$.

QUICK CHECK 4 Explain why an antiderivative of f' is f. ◀

Now consider a more general differential equation of the form $f'(x) = g(x)$, where g is given and f is unknown. The solution f consists of the antiderivatives of g, which involve an arbitrary constant. In most practical cases, the differential equation is accompanied by an **initial condition** that allows us to determine the arbitrary constant. Therefore, we consider problems of the form

$$f'(x) = g(x), \quad \text{where } g \text{ is given, and} \qquad \text{Differential equation}$$
$$f(a) = b, \quad \text{where } a \text{ and } b \text{ are given.} \qquad \text{Initial condition}$$

A differential equation coupled with an initial condition is called an **initial value problem**.

EXAMPLE 7 An initial value problem Solve the initial value problem $f'(x) = x^2 - 2x$ with $f(1) = \frac{1}{3}$.

SOLUTION The solution f is an antiderivative of $x^2 - 2x$. Therefore,

$$f(x) = \frac{x^3}{3} - x^2 + C,$$

where C is an arbitrary constant. We have determined that the solution is a member of a family of functions, all of which differ by a constant. This family of functions, called the **general solution**, is shown in Figure 4.90, where we see curves for various choices of C.

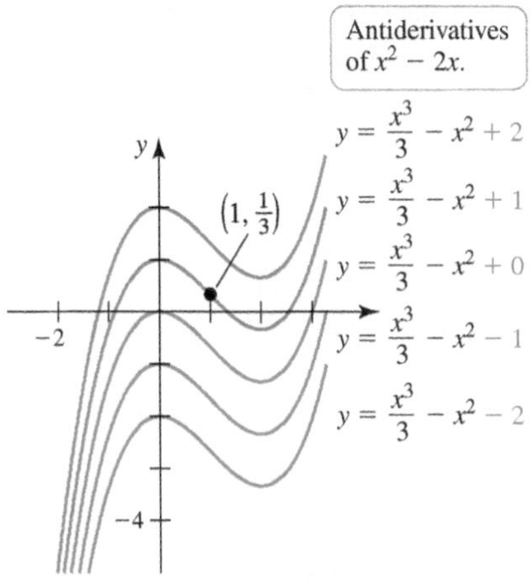

Figure 4.90

Using the initial condition $f(1) = \frac{1}{3}$, we must find the particular function in the general solution whose graph passes through the point $\left(1, \frac{1}{3}\right)$. Imposing the condition $f(1) = \frac{1}{3}$, we reason as follows:

$$\begin{aligned} f(x) &= \frac{x^3}{3} - x^2 + C && \text{General solution} \\ f(1) &= \frac{1}{3} - 1 + C && \text{Substitute } x = 1. \\ \frac{1}{3} &= \frac{1}{3} - 1 + C && f(1) = \tfrac{1}{3} \\ C &= 1. && \text{Solve for } C. \end{aligned}$$

Therefore, the solution to the initial value problem is

$$f(x) = \frac{x^3}{3} - x^2 + 1,$$

which is just one of the curves in the family shown in Figure 4.90.

➤ It is advisable to check that the solution satisfies the original problem: $f'(x) = x^2 - 2x$ and $f(1) = \frac{1}{3} - 1 + 1 = \frac{1}{3}$.

Related Exercises 59–82 ◀

Motion Problems Revisited

Antiderivatives allow us to revisit the topic of one-dimensional motion introduced in Section 3.6. Suppose the position of an object that moves along a line relative to an origin is $s(t)$, where $t \geq 0$ measures elapsed time. The velocity of the object is $v(t) = s'(t)$, which may now be read in terms of antiderivatives: *The position function is an antiderivative of the velocity*. If we are given the velocity function of an object and its position at a particular time, we can determine its position at all future times by solving an initial value problem.

QUICK CHECK 5 Position is an antiderivative of velocity. But there are infinitely many antiderivatives that differ by a constant. Explain how two objects can have the same velocity function but two different position functions. ◀

➤ The convention with motion problems is to assume that motion begins at $t = 0$. This means that initial conditions are specified at $t = 0$.

We also know that the acceleration $a(t)$ of an object moving in one dimension is the rate of change of the velocity, which means $a(t) = v'(t)$. In antiderivative terms, this says that the velocity is an antiderivative of the acceleration. Therefore, if we are given the acceleration of an object and its velocity at a particular time, we can determine its velocity at all times. These ideas lie at the heart of modeling the motion of objects.

Initial Value Problems for Velocity and Position

Suppose an object moves along a line with a (known) velocity $v(t)$, for $t \geq 0$. Then its position is found by solving the initial value problem

$$s'(t) = v(t), \ s(0) = s_0, \text{ where } s_0 \text{ is the (known) initial position.}$$

If the (known) acceleration of the object $a(t)$ is given, then its velocity is found by solving the initial value problem

$$v'(t) = a(t), \ v(0) = v_0, \text{ where } v_0 \text{ is the (known) initial velocity.}$$

EXAMPLE 8 A race Runner A begins at the point $s(0) = 0$ and runs with velocity $v(t) = 2t$. Runner B begins with a head start at the point $S(0) = 8$ and runs with velocity $V(t) = 2$. Find the positions of the runners for $t \geq 0$ and determine who is ahead at $t = 6$ time units.

SOLUTION Let the position of Runner A be $s(t)$, with an initial position $s(0) = 0$. Then the position function satisfies the initial value problem

$$s'(t) = 2t, \ s(0) = 0.$$

The solution is an antiderivative of $s'(t) = 2t$, which has the form $s(t) = t^2 + C$. Substituting $s(0) = 0$, we find that $C = 0$. Therefore, the position of Runner A is given by $s(t) = t^2$, for $t \geq 0$.

Let the position of Runner B be $S(t)$, with an initial position $S(0) = 8$. This position function satisfies the initial value problem

$$S'(t) = 2, \ S(0) = 8.$$

The antiderivatives of $S'(t) = 2$ are $S(t) = 2t + C$. Substituting $S(0) = 8$ implies that $C = 8$. Therefore, the position of Runner B is given by $S(t) = 2t + 8$, for $t \geq 0$.

The graphs of the position functions are shown in Figure 4.91. Runner B begins with a head start but is overtaken when $s(t) = S(t)$, or when $t^2 = 2t + 8$. The solutions of this equation are $t = 4$ and $t = -2$. Only the positive solution is relevant because the race takes place for $t \geq 0$, so Runner A overtakes Runner B at $t = 4$, when $s = S = 16$. When $t = 6$, Runner A has the lead.

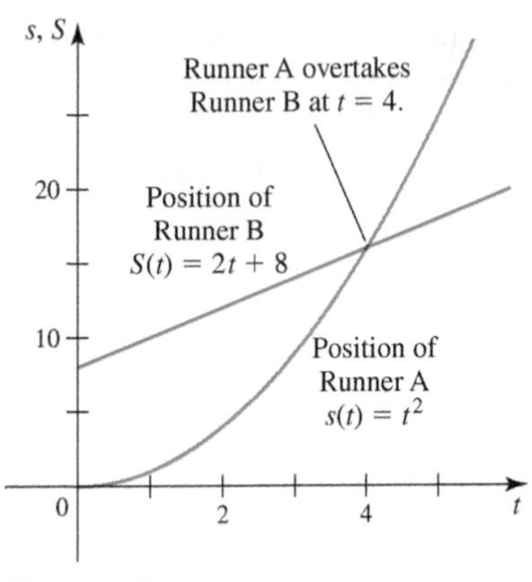

Figure 4.91

Related Exercises 83–96 ◀

EXAMPLE 9 Motion with gravity Neglecting air resistance, the motion of an object moving vertically near Earth's surface is determined by the acceleration due to gravity, which is approximately $9.8\ \text{m/s}^2$. Suppose a stone is thrown vertically upward at $t = 0$ with a velocity of 40 m/s from the edge of a cliff that is 100 m above a river.

a. Find the velocity $v(t)$ of the object, for $t \geq 0$.

b. Find the position $s(t)$ of the object, for $t \geq 0$.

c. Find the maximum height of the object above the river.

d. With what speed does the object strike the river?

SOLUTION We establish a coordinate system in which the positive s-axis points vertically upward with $s = 0$ corresponding to the river (Figure 4.92). Let $s(t)$ be the position of the stone measured relative to the river, for $t \geq 0$. The initial velocity of the stone is $v(0) = 40$ m/s and the initial position of the stone is $s(0) = 100$ m.

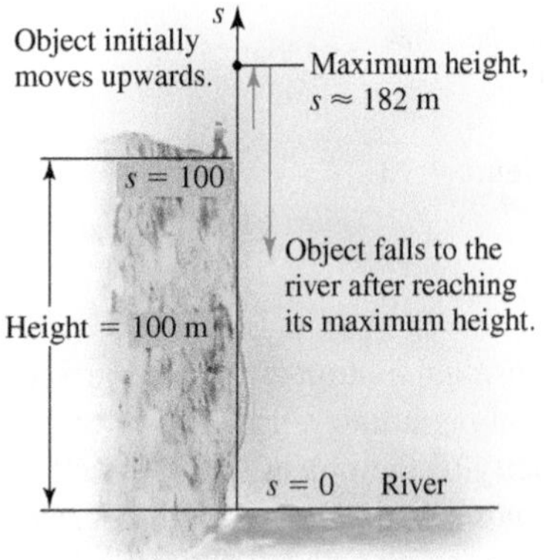

Figure 4.92

➤ The acceleration due to gravity at Earth's surface is approximately $g = 9.8\ \text{m/s}^2$, or $g = 32\ \text{ft/s}^2$. It varies even at sea level from about 9.8640 at the poles to 9.7982 at the equator. The equation $v'(t) = -g$ is an instance of Newton's Second Law of Motion and assumes no other forces (such as air resistance) are present.

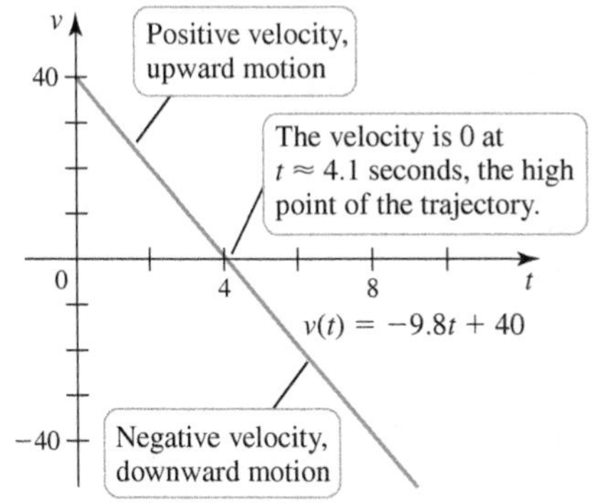

Figure 4.93

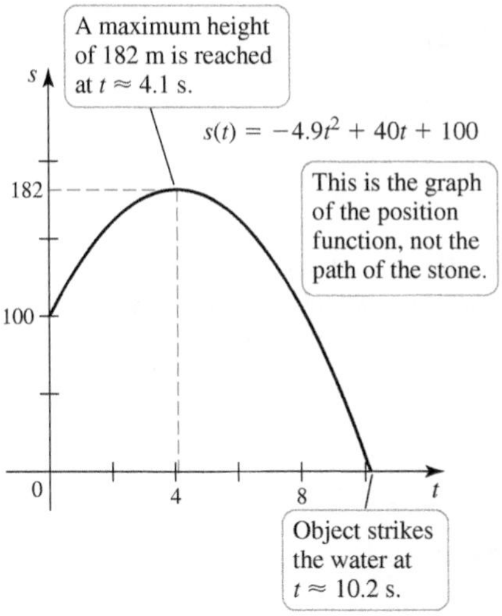

Figure 4.94

a. The acceleration due to gravity points in the *negative* s-direction. Therefore, the initial value problem governing the motion of the object is

$$\text{acceleration} = v'(t) = -9.8,\ v(0) = 40.$$

The antiderivatives of -9.8 are $v(t) = -9.8t + C$. The initial condition $v(0) = 40$ gives $C = 40$. Therefore, the velocity of the stone is

$$v(t) = -9.8t + 40.$$

As shown in Figure 4.93, the velocity decreases from its initial value $v(0) = 40$ until it reaches zero at the high point of the trajectory. This point is reached when

$$v(t) = -9.8t + 40 = 0$$

or when $t \approx 4.1$ s. For $t > 4.1$, the velocity is negative and increases in magnitude as the stone falls to Earth.

b. Knowing the velocity function of the stone, we can determine its position. The position function satisfies the initial value problem

$$v(t) = s'(t) = -9.8t + 40,\ s(0) = 100.$$

The antiderivatives of $-9.8t + 40$ are

$$s(t) = -4.9t^2 + 40t + C.$$

The initial condition $s(0) = 100$ implies $C = 100$, so the position function of the stone is

$$s(t) = -4.9t^2 + 40t + 100,$$

as shown in Figure 4.94. The parabolic graph of the position function is not the actual trajectory of the stone; the stone moves vertically along the s-axis.

c. The position function of the stone increases for $0 < t < 4.1$. At $t \approx 4.1$, the stone reaches a high point of $s(4.1) \approx 182$ m.

d. For $t > 4.1$, the position function decreases, and the stone strikes the river when $s(t) = 0$. The roots of this equation are $t \approx 10.2$ and $t \approx -2.0$. Only the first root is relevant because the motion starts at $t = 0$. Therefore, the stone strikes the ground at $t \approx 10.2$ s. Its speed (in m/s) at this instant is $|v(10.2)| \approx |-60| = 60$.

Related Exercises 97–100 ◀

SECTION 4.9 EXERCISES

Review Questions

1. Fill in the blanks with either of the words *the derivative* or *an antiderivative*: If $F'(x) = f(x)$, then f is ________ of F and F is ________ of f.

2. Describe the set of antiderivatives of $f(x) = 0$.

3. Describe the set of antiderivatives of $f(x) = 1$.

4. Why do two different antiderivatives of a function differ by a constant?

5. Give the antiderivatives of x^p. For what values of p does your answer apply?

6. Give the antiderivatives of e^{-x}.

7. Give the antiderivatives of $1/x$.

8. Evaluate $\int \cos ax\,dx$ and $\int \sin ax\,dx$, where a is a constant.

9. If $F(x) = x^2 - 3x + C$ and $F(-1) = 4$, what is the value of C?

10. For a given function f, explain the steps used to solve the initial value problem $F'(t) = f(t)$, $F(0) = 10$.

Basic Skills

11–22. Finding antiderivatives *Find all the antiderivatives of the following functions. Check your work by taking derivatives.*

11. $f(x) = 5x^4$

12. $g(x) = 11x^{10}$

13. $f(x) = \sin 2x$

14. $g(x) = -4\cos 4x$

15. $P(x) = 3\sec^2 x$

16. $Q(s) = \csc^2 s$

17. $f(y) = -2/y^3$

18. $H(z) = -6z^{-7}$

19. $f(x) = e^x$

20. $h(y) = y^{-1}$

21. $G(s) = \dfrac{1}{s^2 + 1}$

22. $F(t) = \pi$

23–36. Indefinite integrals *Determine the following indefinite integrals. Check your work by differentiation.*

23. $\int (3x^5 - 5x^9)\,dx$

24. $\int (3u^{-2} - 4u^2 + 1)\,du$

25. $\int \left(4\sqrt{x} - \frac{4}{\sqrt{x}}\right) dx$

26. $\int \left(\frac{5}{t^2} + 4t^2\right) dt$

27. $\int (5s + 3)^2\,ds$

28. $\int 5m(12m^3 - 10m)\,dm$

29. $\int (3x^{1/3} + 4x^{-1/3} + 6)\,dx$

30. $\int 6\sqrt[3]{x}\,dx$

31. $\int (3x + 1)(4 - x)\,dx$

32. $\int (4z^{1/3} - z^{-1/3})\,dz$

33. $\int \left(\frac{3}{x^4} + 2 - \frac{3}{x^2}\right) dx$

34. $\int \sqrt[5]{r^2}\,dr$

35. $\int \frac{4x^4 - 6x^2}{x}\,dx$

36. $\int \frac{12t^8 - t}{t^3}\,dt$

37–46. Indefinite integrals involving trigonometric functions *Determine the following indefinite integrals. Check your work by differentiation.*

37. $\int (\sin 2y + \cos 3y)\,dy$

38. $\int \left(\sin 4t - \sin\frac{t}{4}\right) dt$

39. $\int (\sec^2 x - 1)\,dx$

40. $\int 2\sec^2 2v\,dv$

41. $\int (\sec^2\theta + \sec\theta\tan\theta)\,d\theta$

42. $\int \frac{\sin\theta - 1}{\cos^2\theta}\,d\theta$

43. $\int (3t^2 + \sec^2 2t)\,dt$

44. $\int \csc 3\varphi \cot 3\varphi\,d\varphi$

45. $\int \sec 4\theta \tan 4\theta\,d\theta$

46. $\int \csc^2 6x\,dx$

47–58. Other indefinite integrals *Determine the following indefinite integrals. Check your work by differentiation.*

47. $\int \frac{1}{2y}\,dy$

48. $\int (e^{2t} + 2\sqrt{t})\,dt$

49. $\int \frac{6}{\sqrt{25 - x^2}}\,dx$

50. $\int \frac{3}{4 + v^2}\,dv$

51. $\int \frac{dx}{x\sqrt{x^2 - 100}}$

52. $\int \frac{2}{16z^2 + 25}\,dz$

53. $\int \frac{1}{x\sqrt{x^2 - 25}}\,dx$

54. $\int (49 - x^2)^{-1/2}\,dx$

55. $\int \frac{t + 1}{t}\,dt$

56. $\int (22x^{10} - 24e^{12x})\,dx$

57. $\int e^{x+2}\,dx$

58. $\int \frac{10t^5 - 3}{t}\,dt$

59–66. Particular antiderivatives *For the following functions f, find the antiderivative F that satisfies the given condition.*

59. $f(x) = x^5 - 2x^{-2} + 1;\ F(1) = 0$

60. $f(t) = \sec^2 t;\ F(\pi/4) = 1$

61. $f(v) = \sec v \tan v;\ F(0) = 2$

62. $f(x) = (4\sqrt{x} + 6/\sqrt{x})/x^2;\ F(1) = 4$

63. $f(x) = 8x^3 - 2x^{-2};\ F(1) = 5$

64. $f(u) = 2e^u + 3;\ F(0) = 8$

65. $f(y) = \frac{3y^3 + 5}{y};\ F(1) = 3$

66. $f(\theta) = 2\sin 2\theta - 4\cos 4\theta;\ F\left(\frac{\pi}{4}\right) = 2$

67–76. Solving initial value problems *Find the solution of the following initial value problems.*

67. $f'(x) = 2x - 3;\ f(0) = 4$

68. $g'(x) = 7x^6 - 4x^3 + 12;\ g(1) = 24$

69. $g'(x) = 7x\left(x^6 - \frac{1}{7}\right);\ g(1) = 2$

70. $h'(t) = 6\sin 3t;\ h(\pi/6) = 6$

71. $f'(u) = 4(\cos u - \sin 2u);\ f(\pi/6) = 0$

72. $p'(t) = 10e^{-t};\ p(0) = 100$

73. $y'(t) = \frac{3}{t} + 6;\ y(1) = 8$

74. $u'(x) = \frac{e^{2x} + 4e^{-x}}{e^x};\ u(\ln 2) = 2$

75. $y'(\theta) = \frac{\sqrt{2}\cos^3\theta + 1}{\cos^2\theta};\ y\left(\frac{\pi}{4}\right) = 3$

76. $v'(x) = 4x^{1/3} + 2x^{-1/3};\ v(8) = 40$

T **77–82. Graphing general solutions** *Graph several functions that satisfy the following differential equations. Then find and graph the particular function that satisfies the given initial condition.*

77. $f'(x) = 2x - 5;\ f(0) = 4$

78. $f'(x) = 3x^2 - 1;\ f(1) = 2$

79. $f'(x) = 3x + \sin \pi x;\ f(2) = 3$

80. $f'(s) = 4\sec s \tan s;\ f(\pi/4) = 1$

81. $f'(t) = 1/t;\ f(1) = 4$

82. $f'(x) = 2\cos 2x;\ f(0) = 1$

T **83–88. Velocity to position** *Given the following velocity functions of an object moving along a line, find the position function with the given initial position. Then graph both the velocity and position functions.*

83. $v(t) = 2t + 4;\ s(0) = 0$

84. $v(t) = e^{-2t} + 4;\ s(0) = 2$

85. $v(t) = 2\sqrt{t};\ s(0) = 1$

86. $v(t) = 2\cos t;\ s(0) = 0$

87. $v(t) = 6t^2 + 4t - 10;\ s(0) = 0$

88. $v(t) = 2\sin 2t;\ s(0) = 0$

89–94. Acceleration to position *Given the following acceleration functions of an object moving along a line, find the position function with the given initial velocity and position.*

89. $a(t) = -32;\ v(0) = 20, s(0) = 0$

90. $a(t) = 4;\ v(0) = -3, s(0) = 2$

91. $a(t) = 0.2\,t;\ v(0) = 0, s(0) = 1$

92. $a(t) = 2\cos t$; $v(0) = 1, s(0) = 0$

93. $a(t) = 3\sin 2t$; $v(0) = 1, s(0) = 10$

94. $a(t) = 2e^{-t/6}$; $v(0) = 1, s(0) = 0$

T **95–96. Races** *The velocity function and initial position of Runners A and B are given. Analyze the race that results by graphing the position functions of the runners and finding the time and positions (if any) at which they first pass each other.*

95. A: $v(t) = \sin t$, $s(0) = 0$; B: $V(t) = \cos t$, $S(0) = 0$

96. A: $v(t) = 2e^{-t}$, $s(0) = 0$; B: $V(t) = 4e^{-4t}$, $S(0) = 10$

97–100. Motion with gravity *Consider the following descriptions of the vertical motion of an object subject only to the acceleration due to gravity. Begin with the acceleration equation $a(t) = v'(t) = g$, where $g = -9.8\ m/s^2$.*

a. Find the velocity of the object for all relevant times.
b. Find the position of the object for all relevant times.
c. Find the time when the object reaches its highest point. What is the height?
d. Find the time when the object strikes the ground.

97. A softball is popped up vertically (from the ground) with a velocity of 30 m/s.

98. A stone is thrown vertically upward with a velocity of 30 m/s from the edge of a cliff 200 m above a river.

99. A payload is released at an elevation of 400 m from a hot-air balloon that is rising at a rate of 10 m/s.

100. A payload is dropped at an elevation of 400 m from a hot-air balloon that is descending at a rate of 10 m/s.

Further Explorations

101. Explain why or why not Determine whether the following statements are true and give an explanation or counterexample.

a. $F(x) = x^3 - 4x + 100$ and $G(x) = x^3 - 4x - 100$ are antiderivatives of the same function.
b. If $F'(x) = f(x)$, then f is an antiderivative of F.
c. If $F'(x) = f(x)$, then $\int f(x)\,dx = F(x) + C$.
d. $f(x) = x^3 + 3$ and $g(x) = x^3 - 4$ are derivatives of the same function.
e. If $F'(x) = G'(x)$, then $F(x) = G(x)$.

102–109. Miscellaneous indefinite integrals *Determine the following indefinite integrals. Check your work by differentiation.*

102. $\int (\sqrt[3]{x^2} + \sqrt{x^3})\,dx$ **103.** $\int \frac{e^{2x} - e^{-2x}}{2}\,dx$

104. $\int (4\cos 4w - 3\sin 3w)\,dw$ **105.** $\int (\csc^2\theta + 2\theta^2 - 3\theta)\,d\theta$

106. $\int (\csc^2\theta + 1)\,d\theta$ **107.** $\int \frac{1 + \sqrt{x}}{x}\,dx$

108. $\int \frac{2 + x^2}{1 + x^2}\,dx$ **109.** $\int \sqrt{x}\,(2x^6 - 4\sqrt[3]{x})\,dx$

110–113. Functions from higher derivatives *Find the function F that satisfies the following differential equations and initial conditions.*

110. $F''(x) = 1, F'(0) = 3, F(0) = 4$

111. $F''(x) = \cos x, F'(0) = 3, F(\pi) = 4$

112. $F'''(x) = 4x, F''(0) = 0, F'(0) = 1, F(0) = 3$

113. $F'''(x) = 672x^5 + 24x, F''(0) = 0, F'(0) = 2, F(0) = 1$

Applications

114. Mass on a spring A mass oscillates up and down on the end of a spring. Find its position s relative to the equilibrium position if its acceleration is $a(t) = \sin \pi t$ and its initial velocity and position are $v(0) = 3$ and $s(0) = 0$, respectively.

115. Flow rate A large tank is filled with water when an outflow valve is opened at $t = 0$. Water flows out at a rate, in gal/min, given by $Q'(t) = 0.1(100 - t^2)$, for $0 \le t \le 10$.

a. Find the amount of water $Q(t)$ that has flowed out of the tank after t minutes, given the initial condition $Q(0) = 0$.
b. Graph the flow function Q, for $0 \le t \le 10$.
c. How much water flows out of the tank in 10 min?

116. General headstart problem Suppose that object A is located at $s = 0$ at time $t = 0$ and starts moving along the s-axis with a velocity given by $v(t) = 2at$, where $a > 0$. Object B is located at $s = c > 0$ at $t = 0$ and starts moving along the s-axis with a constant velocity given by $V(t) = b > 0$. Show that A always overtakes B at time

$$t = \frac{b + \sqrt{b^2 + 4ac}}{2a}.$$

Additional Exercises

117. Using identities Use the identities $\sin^2 x = (1 - \cos 2x)/2$ and $\cos^2 x = (1 + \cos 2x)/2$ to find $\int \sin^2 x\,dx$ and $\int \cos^2 x\,dx$.

118–121. Verifying indefinite integrals *Verify the following indefinite integrals by differentiation. These integrals are derived in later chapters.*

118. $\int \frac{\cos\sqrt{x}}{\sqrt{x}}\,dx = 2\sin\sqrt{x} + C$

119. $\int \frac{x}{\sqrt{x^2 + 1}}\,dx = \sqrt{x^2 + 1} + C$

120. $\int x^2 \cos x^3\,dx = \frac{1}{3}\sin x^3 + C$

121. $\int \frac{x}{(x^2 - 1)^2}\,dx = -\frac{1}{2(x^2 - 1)} + C$

QUICK CHECK ANSWERS

1. $d/dx(x^3) = 3x^2$ and $d/dx(-\cos x) = \sin x$
2. $e^x + C, x^4 + C, \tan x + C$
3. $d/dx(-(\cos 2x)/2 + C) = \sin 2x$ **4.** One function that can be differentiated to get f' is f. Therefore, f is an antiderivative of f'. **5.** The two position functions involve two different initial positions; they differ by a constant. ◀

CHAPTER 4 REVIEW EXERCISES

1. **Explain why or why not** Determine whether the following statements are true and give an explanation or counterexample.
   a. If $f'(c) = 0$, then f has a local maximum or minimum at c.
   b. If $f''(c) = 0$, then f has an inflection point at c.
   c. $F(x) = x^2 + 10$ and $G(x) = x^2 - 100$ are antiderivatives of the same function.
   d. Between two local minima of a function continuous on $(-\infty, \infty)$, there must be a local maximum.
   e. The linear approximation to $f(x) = \sin x$ at $x = 0$ is $L(x) = x$.
   f. If $\lim_{x\to\infty} f(x) = \infty$ and $\lim_{x\to\infty} g(x) = \infty$, then $\lim_{x\to\infty} (f(x) - g(x)) = 0$.

2. **Locating extrema** Consider the graph of a function f on the interval $[-3, 3]$.
   a. Give the approximate coordinates of the local maxima and minima of f.
   b. Give the approximate coordinates of the absolute maximum and minimum of f (if they exist).
   c. Give the approximate coordinates of the inflection point(s) of f.
   d. Give the approximate coordinates of the zero(s) of f.
   e. On what intervals (approximately) is f concave up?
   f. On what intervals (approximately) is f concave down?

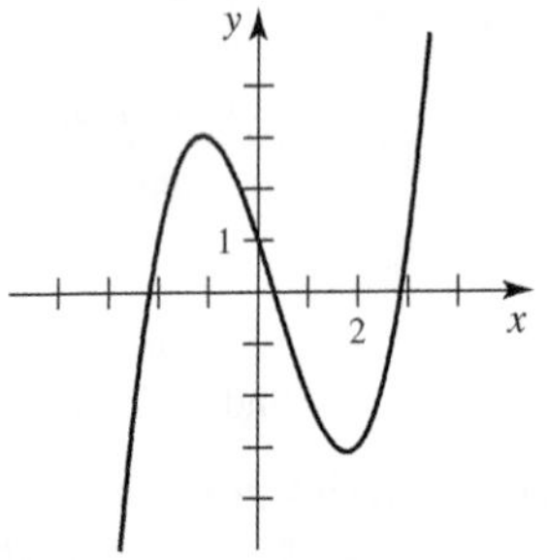

3–4. Designer functions *Sketch the graph of a function continuous on the given interval that satisfies the following conditions.*

3. f is continuous on the interval $[-4, 4]$; $f'(x) = 0$ for $x = -2$, 0, and 3; f has an absolute minimum at $x = 3$; f has a local minimum at $x = -2$; f has a local maximum at $x = 0$; f has an absolute maximum at $x = -4$.

4. f is continuous on $(-\infty, \infty)$; $f'(x) < 0$ and $f''(x) < 0$ on $(-\infty, 0)$; $f'(x) > 0$ and $f''(x) > 0$ on $(0, \infty)$.

5. **Functions from derivatives** Given the graphs of f' and f'', sketch a possible graph of f.

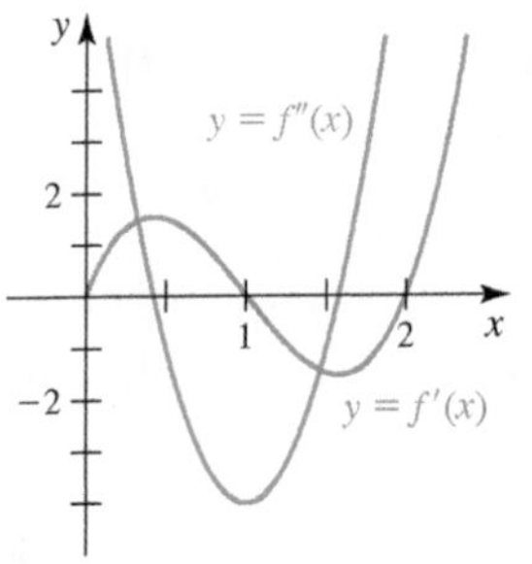

6–10. Critical points *Find the critical points of the following functions on the given intervals. Identify the absolute maximum and minimum values (if they exist). Graph the function to confirm your conclusions.*

6. $f(x) = \sin 2x + 3$ on $[-\pi, \pi]$
7. $f(x) = 2x^3 - 3x^2 - 36x + 12$ on $(-\infty, \infty)$
8. $f(x) = 4x^{1/2} - x^{5/2}$ on $[0, 4]$
9. $f(x) = 2x \ln x + 10$ on $(0, 4)$
10. $g(x) = x \sin^{-1} x$ on $[-1, 1]$

11. **Absolute values** Consider the function $f(x) = |x - 2| + |x + 3|$ on $[-4, 4]$. Graph f, identify the critical points, and give the coordinates of the local and absolute extreme values.

12. **Inflection points** Does $f(x) = 2x^5 - 10x^4 + 20x^3 + x + 1$ have any inflection points? If so, identify them.

13–20. Curve sketching *Use the guidelines given in Section 4.3 to make a complete graph of the following functions on their domains or on the given interval. Use a graphing utility to check your work.*

13. $f(x) = x^4/2 - 3x^2 + 4x + 1$
14. $f(x) = \dfrac{3x}{x^2 + 3}$
15. $f(x) = 4 \cos (\pi(x - 1))$ on $[0, 2]$
16. $f(x) = \dfrac{x^2 + x}{4 - x^2}$
17. $f(x) = \sqrt[3]{x} - \sqrt{x} + 2$
18. $f(x) = \dfrac{\cos \pi x}{1 + x^2}$ on $[-2, 2]$
19. $f(x) = x^{2/3} + (x + 2)^{1/3}$
20. $f(x) = x(x - 1) e^{-x}$

21. **Optimization** A right triangle has legs of length h and r, and a hypotenuse of length 4 (see figure). It is revolved about the leg of length h to sweep out a right circular cone. What values of h and r maximize the volume of the cone? (Volume of a cone $= \pi r^2 h/3$.)

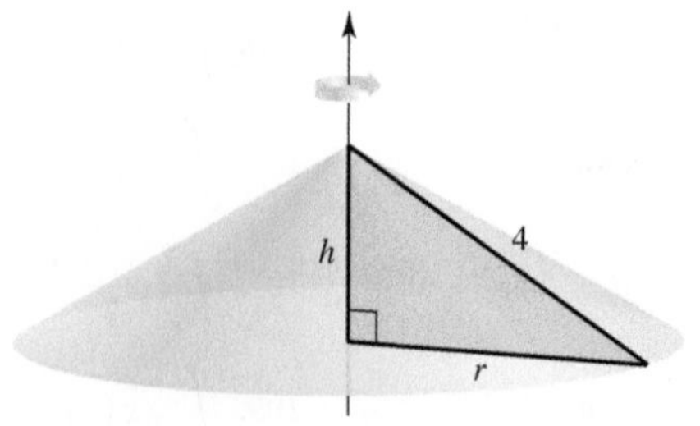

22. **Rectangles beneath a curve** A rectangle is constructed with one side on the positive x-axis, one side on the positive y-axis, and the vertex opposite the origin on the curve $y = \cos x$, for $0 < x < \pi/2$. Approximate the dimensions of the rectangle that maximize the area of the rectangle. What is the area?

23. Maximum printable area A rectangular page in a textbook (with width x and length y) has an area of $98\ \text{in}^2$, top and bottom margins set at 1 in, and left and right margins set at $\frac{1}{2}$ in. The printable area of the page is the rectangle that lies within the margins. What are the dimensions of the page that maximize the printable area?

24. Nearest point What point on the graph of $f(x) = \frac{5}{2} - x^2$ is closest to the origin? (*Hint*: You can minimize the square of the distance.)

25. Maximum area A line segment of length 10 joins the points $(0, p)$ and $(q, 0)$ to form a triangle in the first quadrant. Find the values of p and q that maximize the area of the triangle.

26. Minimum painting surface A metal cistern in the shape of a right circular cylinder with volume $V = 50\ \text{m}^3$ needs to be painted each year to reduce corrosion. The paint is applied only to surfaces exposed to the elements (the outside cylinder wall and the circular top). Find the dimensions r and h of the cylinder that minimize the area of the painted surfaces.

27–28. Linear approximation

a. *Find the linear approximation to f at the given point a.*
b. *Use your answer from part (a) to estimate the given function value. Does your approximation underestimate or overestimate the exact function value?*

27. $f(x) = x^{2/3};\ a = 27;\ f(29)$

28. $f(x) = \sin^{-1} x;\ a = 1/2;\ f(0.48)$

29–30. Estimations with linear approximation *Use linear approximation to estimate the following quantities. Choose a value of a to produce a small error.*

29. $1/4.2^2$

30. $\tan^{-1} 1.05$

31. Change in elevation The elevation h (in feet above the ground) of a stone dropped from a height of 1000 ft is modeled by the equation $h(t) = 1000 - 16t^2$, where t is measured in seconds and air resistance is neglected. Approximate the change in elevation over the interval $5 \le t \le 5.7$ (recall that $\Delta h \approx h'(a)\Delta t$).

32. Change in energy The energy E (in joules) released by an earthquake of magnitude M is modeled by the equation $E(M) = 25{,}000 \cdot 10^{1.5M}$. Approximate the change in energy released when the magnitude changes from 7.0 to 7.5 (recall that $\Delta E \approx E'(a)\Delta M$).

33. Mean Value Theorem The population of a culture of cells grows according to the function $P(t) = \dfrac{100t}{t+1}$, where $t \ge 0$ is measured in weeks.

a. What is the average rate of change in the population over the interval $[0, 8]$?
b. At what point of the interval $[0, 8]$ is the instantaneous rate of change equal to the average rate of change?

34. Growth rate of bamboo Bamboo belongs to the grass family and is one of the fastest-growing plants in the world.

a. A bamboo shoot was 500 cm tall at 10.00 A.M. and 515 cm at 3:00 P.M. Compute the average growth rate of the bamboo shoot in cm/hr over the period of time from 10:00 A.M. to 3:00 P.M.
b. Based on the Mean Value Theorem, what can you conclude about the instantaneous growth rate of bamboo measured in *millimeters per second* between 10:00 A.M. and 3:00 P.M.?

T **35. Newton's method** Use Newton's method to approximate the roots of $f(x) = 3x^3 - 4x^2 + 1$ to six digits.

T **36. Newton's method** Use Newton's method to approximate the roots of $f(x) = e^{-2x} + 2e^x - 6$ to six digits. Make a table showing the first five approximations for each root using an initial estimate of your choice.

T **37. Newton's method** Use Newton's method to approximate the x-coordinate of the inflection points of $f(x) = 2x^5 - 6x^3 - 4x + 2$ to six digits.

38–51. Limits *Evaluate the following limits. Use l'Hôpital's Rule when needed.*

38. $\displaystyle\lim_{t\to 2} \frac{t^3 - t^2 - 2t}{t^2 - 4}$

39. $\displaystyle\lim_{t\to 0} \frac{1 - \cos 6t}{2t}$

40. $\displaystyle\lim_{x\to\infty} \frac{5x^2 + 2x - 5}{\sqrt{x^4 - 1}}$

41. $\displaystyle\lim_{\theta\to 0} \frac{3\sin^2 2\theta}{\theta^2}$

42. $\displaystyle\lim_{x\to\infty} \left(\sqrt{x^2 + x + 1} - \sqrt{x^2 - x}\right)$

43. $\displaystyle\lim_{\theta\to 0} 2\theta \cot 3\theta$

44. $\displaystyle\lim_{x\to 0} \frac{e^{-2x} - 1 + 2x}{x^2}$

45. $\displaystyle\lim_{y\to 0^+} \frac{\ln^{10} y}{\sqrt{y}}$

46. $\displaystyle\lim_{\theta\to 0} \frac{3\sin 8\theta}{8\sin 3\theta}$

47. $\displaystyle\lim_{x\to 1} \frac{x^4 - x^3 - 3x^2 + 5x - 2}{x^3 + x^2 - 5x + 3}$

48. $\displaystyle\lim_{x\to\infty} \frac{\ln x^{100}}{\sqrt{x}}$

49. $\displaystyle\lim_{x\to 0} \csc x \sin^{-1} x$

50. $\displaystyle\lim_{x\to\infty} \frac{\ln^3 x}{\sqrt{x}}$

51. $\displaystyle\lim_{x\to\infty} \ln\left(\frac{x+1}{x-1}\right)$

52–59. 1^∞, 0^0, ∞^0 forms *Evaluate the following limits. Check your results by graphing.*

52. $\displaystyle\lim_{x\to 0^+} (1 + x)^{\cot x}$

53. $\displaystyle\lim_{x\to \pi/2^-} (\sin x)^{\tan x}$

54. $\displaystyle\lim_{x\to\infty} (\sqrt{x} + 1)^{1/x}$

55. $\displaystyle\lim_{x\to 0^+} |\ln x|^x$

56. $\displaystyle\lim_{x\to\infty} x^{1/x}$

57. $\displaystyle\lim_{x\to\infty} \left(1 - \frac{3}{x}\right)^x$

58. $\displaystyle\lim_{x\to\infty} \left(\frac{2}{\pi}\tan^{-1} x\right)^x$

59. $\displaystyle\lim_{x\to 1} (x - 1)^{\sin \pi x}$

60–67. Comparing growth rates *Determine which of the two functions grows faster or state that they have comparable growth rates.*

60. x^{100} and 1.1^x

61. $x^{1/2}$ and $x^{1/3}$

62. $\ln x$ and $\log_{10} x$

63. $\sqrt{x}$ and $\ln^{10} x$

64. $10x$ and $\ln x^2$

65. e^x and 3^x

66. $\sqrt{x^6 + 10}$ and x^3

67. 2^x and $4^{x/2}$

68–81. Indefinite integrals *Determine the following indefinite integrals.*

68. $\int (x^8 - 3x^3 + 1)\, dx$

69. $\int (2x + 1)^2 dx$

70. $\int \frac{x+1}{x}\, dx$

71. $\int \left(\frac{1}{x^2} - \frac{2}{x^{5/2}}\right) dx$

72. $\int \frac{x^4 - 2\sqrt{x} + 2}{x^2}\, dx$

73. $\int (1 + \cos 3\theta)\, d\theta$

74. $\int 2 \sec^2 \theta\, d\theta$

75. $\int \sec 2x \tan 2x\, dx$

76. $\int 2e^{2x}\, dx$

77. $\int \frac{12}{x}\, dx$

78. $\int \frac{dx}{\sqrt{1 - x^2}}$

79. $\int \frac{dx}{x^2 + 1}$

80. $\int \frac{1 + \tan \theta}{\sec \theta}\, d\theta$

81. $\int (\sqrt[4]{x^3} + \sqrt{x^5})\, dx$

82–85. Functions from derivatives *Find the function with the following properties.*

82. $f'(x) = 3x^2 - 1$ and $f(0) = 10$

83. $f'(t) = \sin t + 2t$ and $f(0) = 5$

84. $g'(t) = t^2 + t^{-2}$ and $g(1) = 1$

85. $h'(x) = \sin^2 x$ and $h(1) = 1$ (*Hint:* $\sin^2 x = (1 - \cos 2x)/2$.)

86. Motion along a line Two objects move along the x-axis with position functions $x_1(t) = 2 \sin t$ and $x_2(t) = \sin(t - \pi/2)$. At what times on the interval $[0, 2\pi]$ are the objects closest to each other and farthest from each other?

87. Vertical motion with gravity A rocket is launched vertically upward with an initial velocity of 120 m/s from a platform that is 125 m above the ground. Assume that the only force at work is gravity. Determine and graph the velocity and position functions of the rocket, for $t \geq 0$. Then describe the motion in words.

88. Logs of logs Compare the growth rates of $\ln x$, $\ln(\ln x)$, and $\ln(\ln(\ln x))$.

89. Two limits with exponentials Evaluate $\lim_{x\to 0^+} \frac{x}{\sqrt{1 - e^{-x^2}}}$ and $\lim_{x\to 0^+} \frac{x^2}{1 - e^{-x^2}}$ and confirm your result by graphing.

90. Geometric mean Prove that $\lim_{r\to 0} \left(\frac{a^r + b^r + c^r}{3}\right)^{1/r} = \sqrt[3]{abc}$, where a, b, and c are positive real numbers.

91–92. Two methods *Evaluate the following limits in two different ways: Use the methods of Chapter 2 and use l'Hôpital's Rule.*

91. $\lim_{x\to\infty} \frac{2x^5 - x + 1}{5x^6 + x}$

92. $\lim_{x\to\infty} \frac{4x^4 - \sqrt{x}}{2x^4 + x^{-1}}$

93. Towers of exponents The functions

$$f(x) = (x^x)^x \quad \text{and} \quad g(x) = x^{(x^x)}$$

are different functions. For example, $f(3) = 19{,}683$ and $g(3) \approx 7.6 \times 10^{12}$. Determine whether $\lim_{x\to 0^+} f(x)$ and $\lim_{x\to 0^+} g(x)$ are indeterminate forms and evaluate the limits.

94. Cosine limits Let n be a positive integer. Use graphical and/or analytical methods to verify the following limits.

a. $\lim_{x\to 0} \frac{1 - \cos x^n}{x^{2n}} = \frac{1}{2}$

b. $\lim_{x\to 0} \frac{1 - \cos^n x}{x^2} = \frac{n}{2}$

95. Limits for *e* Consider the function $g(x) = (1 + 1/x)^{x+a}$. Show that if $0 \leq a < \frac{1}{2}$, then $g(x) \to e$ from *below* as $x \to \infty$; if $\frac{1}{2} \leq a < 1$, then $g(x) \to e$ from *above* as $x \to \infty$.

T **96. A family of super-exponential functions** Let $f(x) = (a + x)^x$, where $a > 0$.

a. What is the domain of f (in terms of a)?

b. Describe the end behavior of f (near the left boundary of its domain and as $x \to \infty$).

c. Compute f'. Then graph f and f', for $a = 0.5, 1, 2$, and 3.

d. Show that f has a single local minimum at the point z that satisfies $(z + a)\ln(z + a) + z = 0$.

e. Describe how z (found in part (d)) varies as a increases. Describe how $f(z)$ varies as a increases.

Chapter 4 Guided Projects

Applications of the material in this chapter and related topics can be found in the following Guided Projects. For additional information, see the Preface.

- Oscillators
- Ice cream, geometry, and calculus
- Newton's method

5

Integration

Chapter Preview We are now at a critical point in the calculus story. Many would argue that this chapter is the cornerstone of calculus because it explains the relationship between the two processes of calculus: differentiation and integration. We begin by explaining why finding the area of regions bounded by the graphs of functions is such an important problem in calculus. Then you will see how antiderivatives lead to definite integrals, which are used to solve the area problem. But there is more to the story. You will also see the remarkable connection between derivatives and integrals, which is expressed in the Fundamental Theorem of Calculus. In this chapter, we develop key properties of definite integrals, investigate a few of their many applications, and present the first of several powerful techniques for evaluating definite integrals.

5.1 Approximating Areas under Curves

The derivative of a function is associated with rates of change and slopes of tangent lines. We also know that antiderivatives (or indefinite integrals) reverse the derivative operation. Figure 5.1 summarizes our current understanding and raises the question: What is the geometric meaning of the integral? The following example reveals a clue.

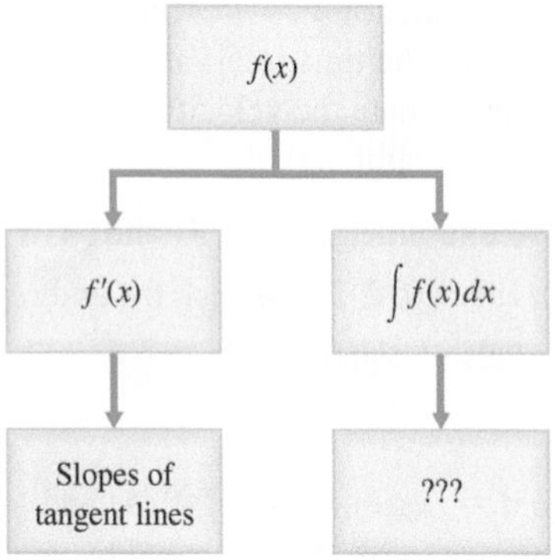

Figure 5.1

Area under a Velocity Curve

Consider an object moving along a line with a known position function. You learned in previous chapters that the slope of the line tangent to the graph of the position function at a certain time gives the velocity v at that time. We now turn the situation around. If we know the velocity function of a moving object, what can we learn about its position function?

➤ Recall from Section 3.5 that the *displacement* of an object moving along a line is the difference between its initial and final position. If the velocity of an object is positive, its displacement equals the distance traveled.

Imagine a car traveling at a constant velocity of 60 mi/hr along a straight highway over a two-hour period. The graph of the velocity function $v = 60$ on the interval $0 \le t \le 2$ is a horizontal line (Figure 5.2). The displacement of the car between $t = 0$ and $t = 2$ is found by a familiar formula:

$$\begin{aligned}\text{displacement} &= \text{rate} \cdot \text{time} \\ &= 60\text{ mi/hr} \cdot 2\text{ hr} = 120\text{ mi}.\end{aligned}$$

This product is the area of the rectangle formed by the velocity curve and the t-axis between $t = 0$ and $t = 2$ (Figure 5.3). In the case of constant positive velocity, we see that the area between the velocity curve and the t-axis is the displacement of the moving object.

➤ The side lengths of the rectangle in Figure 5.3 have units mi/hr and hr. Therefore, the units of the area are mi/hr · hr = mi, which is a unit of displacement.

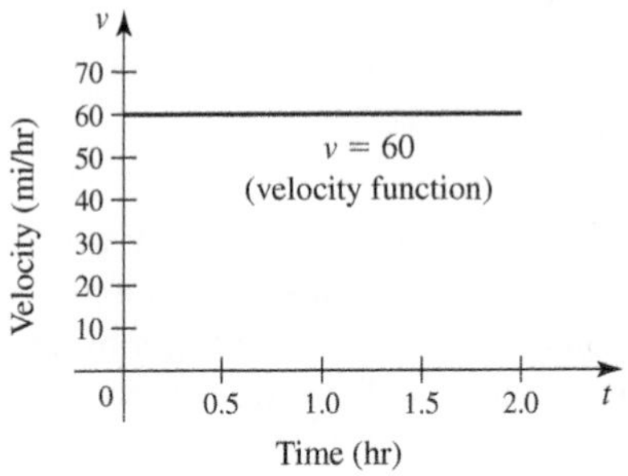

Figure 5.2

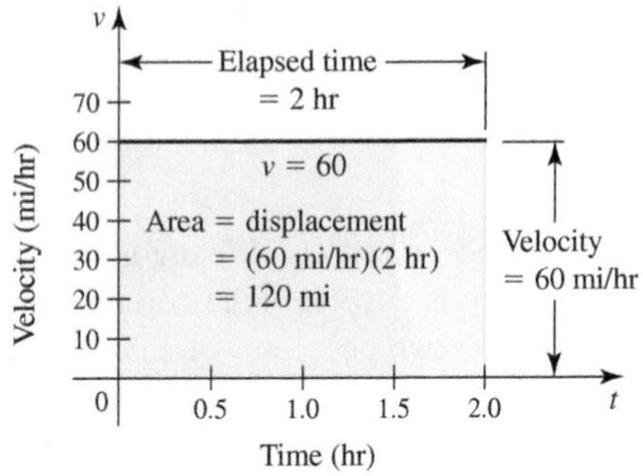

Figure 5.3

QUICK CHECK 1 What is the displacement of an object that travels at a constant velocity of 10 mi/hr for a half hour, 20 mi/hr for the next half hour, and 30 mi/hr for the next hour? ◄

Because objects do not necessarily move at a constant velocity, we first extend these ideas to positive velocities that *change* over an interval of time. One strategy is to divide the time interval into many subintervals and approximate the velocity on each subinterval with a constant velocity. Then the displacements on each subinterval are calculated and summed. This strategy produces only an approximation to the displacement; however, this approximation generally improves as the number of subintervals increases.

EXAMPLE 1 Approximating the displacement Suppose the velocity in m/s of an object moving along a line is given by the function $v = t^2$, where $0 \le t \le 8$. Approximate the displacement of the object by dividing the time interval $[0, 8]$ into n subintervals of equal length. On each subinterval, approximate the velocity with a constant equal to the value of v evaluated at the midpoint of the subinterval.

a. Begin by dividing $[0, 8]$ into $n = 2$ subintervals: $[0, 4]$ and $[4, 8]$.

b. Divide $[0, 8]$ into $n = 4$ subintervals: $[0, 2]$, $[2, 4]$, $[4, 6]$, and $[6, 8]$.

c. Divide $[0, 8]$ into $n = 8$ subintervals of equal length.

SOLUTION

a. We divide the interval $[0, 8]$ into $n = 2$ subintervals, $[0, 4]$ and $[4, 8]$, each with length 4. The velocity on each subinterval is approximated by evaluating v at the midpoint of that subinterval (Figure 5.4a).

- We approximate the velocity on $[0, 4]$ by $v(2) = 2^2 = 4$ m/s. Traveling at 4 m/s for 4 s results in a displacement of 4 m/s · 4 s = 16 m.
- We approximate the velocity on $[4, 8]$ by $v(6) = 6^2 = 36$ m/s. Traveling at 36 m/s for 4 s results in a displacement of 36 m/s · 4 s = 144 m.

Therefore, an approximation to the displacement over the entire interval $[0, 8]$ is

$$(v(2) \cdot 4\text{ s}) + (v(6) \cdot 4\text{ s}) = (4\text{ m/s} \cdot 4\text{ s}) + (36\text{ m/s} \cdot 4\text{ s}) = 160\text{ m}.$$

b. With $n = 4$ (Figure 5.4b), each subinterval has length 2. The approximate displacement over the entire interval is

$$\underbrace{(1\text{ m/s}\cdot 2\text{ s})}_{v(1)} + \underbrace{(9\text{ m/s}\cdot 2\text{ s})}_{v(3)} + \underbrace{(25\text{ m/s}\cdot 2\text{ s})}_{v(5)} + \underbrace{(49\text{ m/s}\cdot 2\text{ s})}_{v(7)} = 168\text{ m}.$$

c. With $n = 8$ subintervals (Figure 5.4c), the approximation to the displacement is 170 m. In each case, the approximate displacement is the sum of the areas of the rectangles under the velocity curve.

The midpoint of each subinterval is used to approximate the velocity over that subinterval.

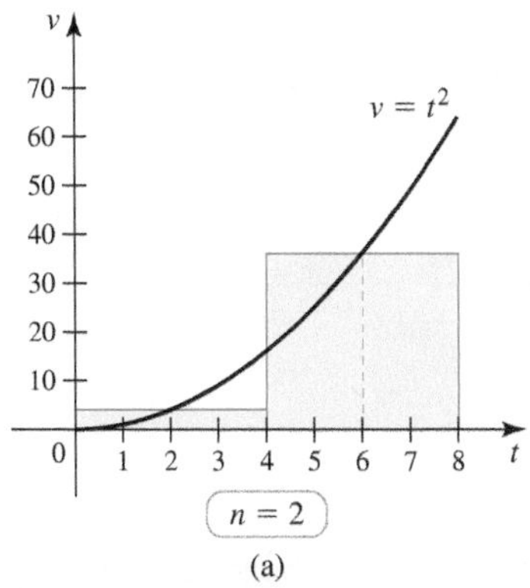

Figure 5.4

Related Exercises 9–16 ◀

QUICK CHECK 2 In Example 1, if we used $n = 32$ subintervals of equal length, what would be the length of each subinterval? Find the midpoint of the first and last subinterval. ◀

The progression in Example 1 may be continued. Larger values of n mean more rectangles; in general, more rectangles give a better fit to the region under the curve (Figure 5.5). With the help of a calculator, we can generate the approximations in Table 5.1 using $n = 1, 2, 4, 8, 16, 32$, and 64 subintervals. Observe that as n increases, the approximations appear to approach a limit of approximately 170.7 m. The limit is the exact displacement, which is represented by the area of the region under the velocity curve. This strategy of taking limits of sums is developed fully in Section 5.2.

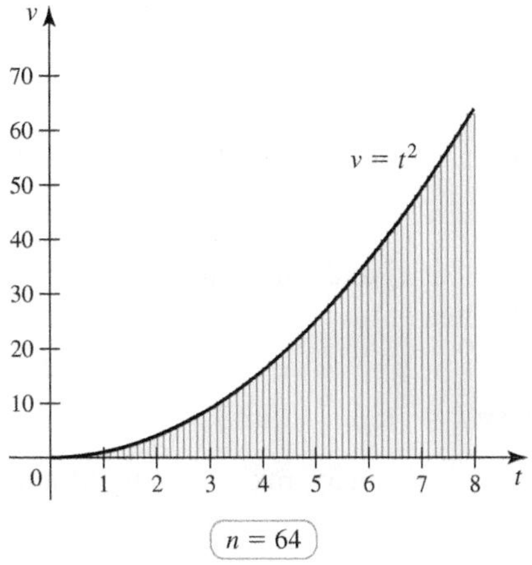

Figure 5.5

Table 5.1 **Approximations to the area under the velocity curve $v = t^2$ on $[0, 8]$**

Number of subintervals	Length of each subinterval	Approximate displacement (area under curve)
1	8 s	128.0 m
2	4 s	160.0 m
4	2 s	168.0 m
8	1 s	170.0 m
16	0.5 s	170.5 m
32	0.25 s	170.625 m
64	0.125 s	170.65625 m

➤ The language "the area of the region bounded by the graph of a function" is often abbreviated as "the area under the curve."

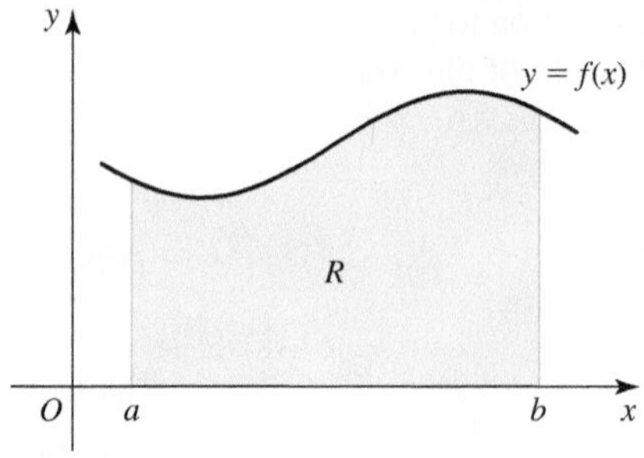

Figure 5.6

Approximating Areas by Riemann Sums

We wouldn't spend much time investigating areas under curves if the idea applied only to computing displacements from velocity curves. However, the problem of finding areas under curves arises frequently and turns out to be immensely important—as you will see in the next two chapters. For this reason, we now develop a systematic method for approximating areas under curves. Consider a function f that is continuous and nonnegative on an interval $[a, b]$. The goal is to approximate the area of the region R bounded by the graph of f and the x-axis from $x = a$ to $x = b$ (Figure 5.6). We begin by dividing the interval $[a, b]$ into n subintervals of equal length,

$$[x_0, x_1], [x_1, x_2], \ldots, [x_{n-1}, x_n],$$

where $a = x_0$ and $b = x_n$ (Figure 5.7). The length of each subinterval, denoted Δx, is found by dividing the length of the entire interval by n:

$$\Delta x = \frac{b - a}{n}.$$

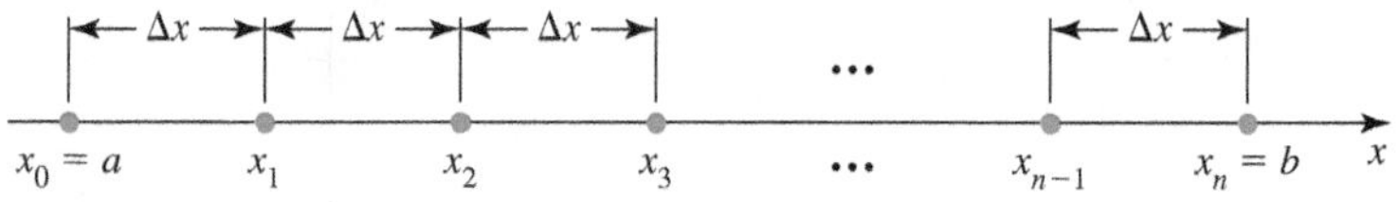

Figure 5.7

DEFINITION Regular Partition

Suppose $[a, b]$ is a closed interval containing n subintervals

$$[x_0, x_1], [x_1, x_2], \ldots, [x_{n-1}, x_n]$$

of equal length $\Delta x = \frac{b - a}{n}$ with $a = x_0$ and $b = x_n$. The endpoints $x_0, x_1, x_2, \ldots, x_{n-1}, x_n$ of the subintervals are called **grid points**, and they create a **regular partition** of the interval $[a, b]$. In general, the kth grid point is

$$x_k = a + k\Delta x, \text{ for } k = 0, 1, 2, \ldots, n.$$

QUICK CHECK 3 If the interval $[1, 9]$ is partitioned into 4 subintervals of equal length, what is Δx? List the grid points x_0, x_1, x_2, x_3, and x_4. ◀

In the kth subinterval $[x_{k-1}, x_k]$, we choose any point x_k^* and build a rectangle whose height is $f(x_k^*)$, the value of f at x_k^* (Figure 5.8). The area of the rectangle on the kth subinterval is

$$\text{height} \cdot \text{base} = f(x_k^*)\Delta x, \qquad \text{where } k = 1, 2, \ldots, n.$$

Summing the areas of the rectangles in Figure 5.8, we obtain an approximation to the area of R, which is called a **Riemann sum**:

$$f(x_1^*)\Delta x + f(x_2^*)\Delta x + \cdots + f(x_n^*)\Delta x.$$

Three notable Riemann sums are the *left*, *right*, and *midpoint Riemann sums*.

➤ Although the idea of integration was developed in the 17th century, it was almost 200 years later that the German mathematician Bernhard Riemann (1826–1866) worked on the mathematical theory underlying integration.

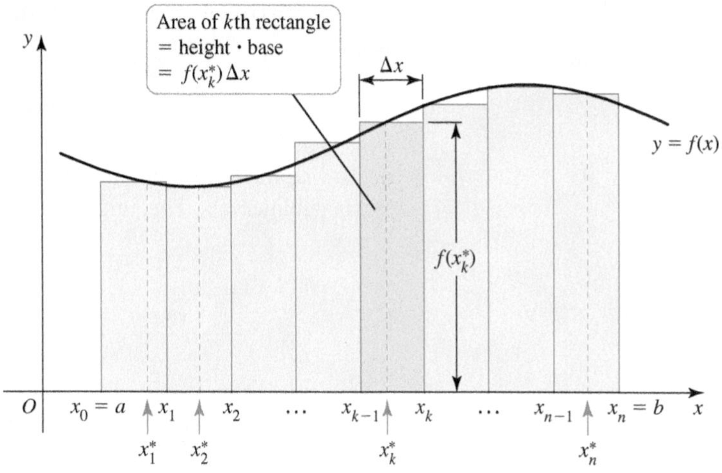

Figure 5.8

➤ For the left Riemann sum, $x_1^* = a + 0 \cdot \Delta x, x_2^* = a + 1 \cdot \Delta x$, $x_3^* = a + 2 \cdot \Delta x$, and in general, $x_k^* = a + (k - 1)\Delta x$, for $k = 1, \ldots, n$.

For the right Riemann sum, $x_1^* = a + 1 \cdot \Delta x, x_2^* = a + 2 \cdot \Delta x$, $x_3^* = a + 3 \cdot \Delta x$, and in general $x_k^* = a + k\Delta x$, for $k = 1, \ldots, n$.

For the midpoint Riemann sum,

$$x_1^* = a + \tfrac{1}{2}\Delta x, x_2^* = a + \tfrac{3}{2}\Delta x,$$

and in general,

$$x_k^* = a + \left(k - \tfrac{1}{2}\right)\Delta x = \frac{x_k + x_{k-1}}{2},$$

for $k = 1, \ldots, n$.

DEFINITION Riemann Sum

Suppose f is defined on a closed interval $[a, b]$, which is divided into n subintervals of equal length Δx. If x_k^* is any point in the kth subinterval $[x_{k-1}, x_k]$, for $k = 1, 2, \ldots, n$, then

$$f(x_1^*)\Delta x + f(x_2^*)\Delta x + \cdots + f(x_n^*)\Delta x$$

is called a **Riemann sum** for f on $[a, b]$. This sum is called

- a **left Riemann sum** if x_k^* is the left endpoint of $[x_{k-1}, x_k]$ (Figure 5.9);
- a **right Riemann sum** if x_k^* is the right endpoint of $[x_{k-1}, x_k]$ (Figure 5.10); and
- a **midpoint Riemann sum** if x_k^* is the midpoint of $[x_{k-1}, x_k]$ (Figure 5.11), for $k = 1, 2, \ldots, n$.

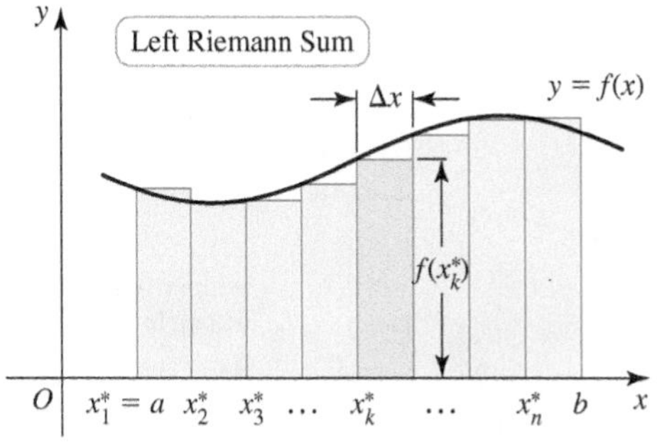

Figure 5.9

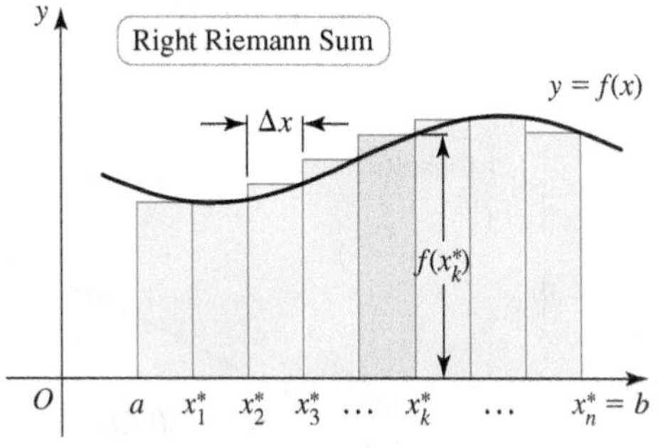

Figure 5.10

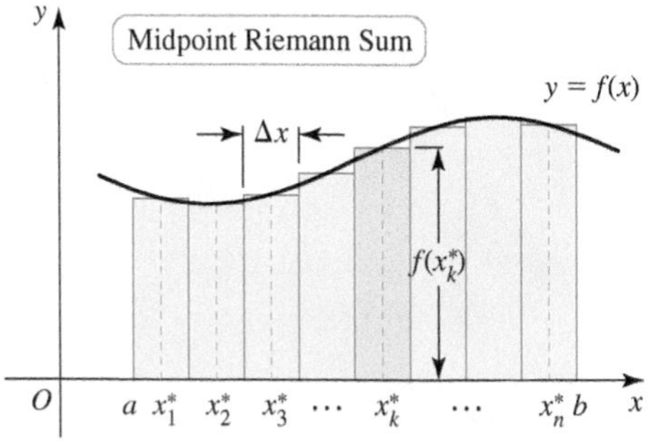

Figure 5.11

We now use this definition to approximate the area under the curve $y = \sin x$.

EXAMPLE 2 Left and right Riemann sums Let R be the region bounded by the graph of $f(x) = \sin x$ and the x-axis between $x = 0$ and $x = \pi/2$.

a. Approximate the area of R using a left Riemann sum with $n = 6$ subintervals. Illustrate the sum with the appropriate rectangles.

b. Approximate the area of R using a right Riemann sum with $n = 6$ subintervals. Illustrate the sum with the appropriate rectangles.

c. Do the area approximations in parts (a) and (b) underestimate or overestimate the actual area under the curve?

SOLUTION Dividing the interval $[a, b] = [0, \pi/2]$ into $n = 6$ subintervals means the length of each subinterval is

$$\Delta x = \frac{b-a}{n} = \frac{\pi/2 - 0}{6} = \frac{\pi}{12}.$$

a. To find the left Riemann sum, we set $x_1^*, x_2^*, \ldots, x_6^*$ equal to the left endpoints of the six subintervals. The heights of the rectangles are $f(x_k^*)$, for $k = 1, \ldots, 6$.

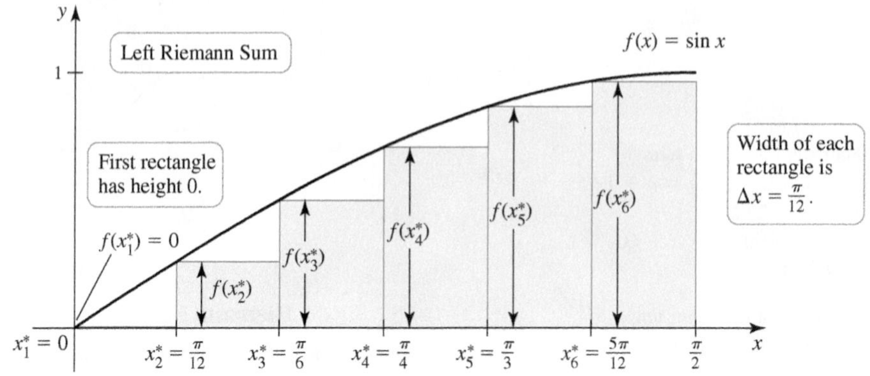

Figure 5.12

The resulting left Riemann sum (Figure 5.12) is

$$\begin{aligned} &f(x_1^*)\Delta x + f(x_2^*)\Delta x + \cdots + f(x_6^*)\Delta x \\ &= (\sin 0)\cdot\frac{\pi}{12} + \left(\sin\frac{\pi}{12}\right)\cdot\frac{\pi}{12} + \left(\sin\frac{\pi}{6}\right)\cdot\frac{\pi}{12} \\ &\quad + \left(\sin\frac{\pi}{4}\right)\cdot\frac{\pi}{12} + \left(\sin\frac{\pi}{3}\right)\cdot\frac{\pi}{12} + \left(\sin\frac{5\pi}{12}\right)\cdot\frac{\pi}{12} \\ &\approx 0.863. \end{aligned}$$

b. In a right Riemann sum, the right endpoints are used for $x_1^*, x_2^*, \ldots, x_6^*$, and the heights of the rectangles are $f(x_k^*)$, for $k = 1, \ldots, 6$.

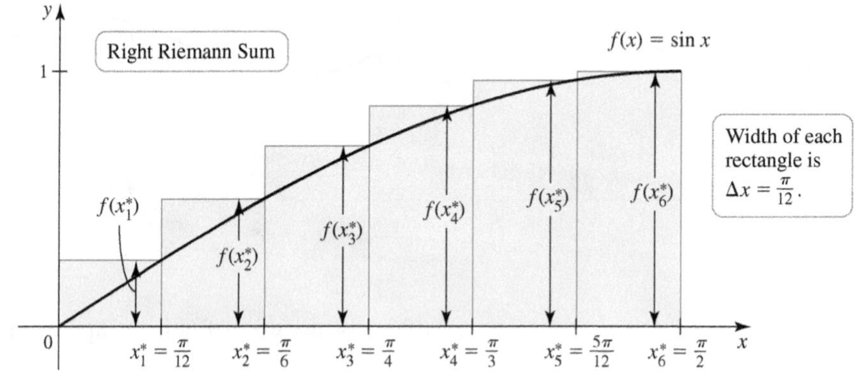

Figure 5.13

The resulting right Riemann sum (Figure 5.13) is

$$\begin{aligned} &f(x_1^*)\Delta x + f(x_2^*)\Delta x + \cdots + f(x_6^*)\Delta x \\ &= \left(\sin\frac{\pi}{12}\right)\cdot\frac{\pi}{12} + \left(\sin\frac{\pi}{6}\right)\cdot\frac{\pi}{12} + \left(\sin\frac{\pi}{4}\right)\cdot\frac{\pi}{12} \\ &\quad + \left(\sin\frac{\pi}{3}\right)\cdot\frac{\pi}{12} + \left(\sin\frac{5\pi}{12}\right)\cdot\frac{\pi}{12} + \left(\sin\frac{\pi}{2}\right)\cdot\frac{\pi}{12} \\ &\approx 1.125. \end{aligned}$$

QUICK CHECK 4 If the function in Example 2 is replaced with $f(x) = \cos x$, does the left Riemann sum or the right Riemann sum overestimate the area under the curve? ◄

c. Looking at the graphs, we see that the left Riemann sum in part (a) underestimates the actual area of R, whereas the right Riemann sum in part (b) overestimates the area of R. Therefore, the area of R is between 0.863 and 1.125. As the number of rectangles increases, these approximations improve.

Related Exercises 17–26 ◄

EXAMPLE 3 A midpoint Riemann sum Let R be the region bounded by the graph of $f(x) = \sin x$ and the x-axis between $x = 0$ and $x = \pi/2$. Approximate the area of R using a midpoint Riemann sum with $n = 6$ subintervals. Illustrate the sum with the appropriate rectangles.

SOLUTION The grid points and the length of the subintervals $\Delta x = \pi/12$ are the same as in Example 2. To find the midpoint Riemann sum, we set $x_1^*, x_2^*, \ldots, x_6^*$ equal to the midpoints of the subintervals. The midpoint of the first subinterval is the average of x_0 and x_1, which is

$$x_1^* = \frac{x_1 + x_0}{2} = \frac{\pi/12 + 0}{2} = \frac{\pi}{24}.$$

The remaining midpoints are also computed by averaging the two nearest grid points.

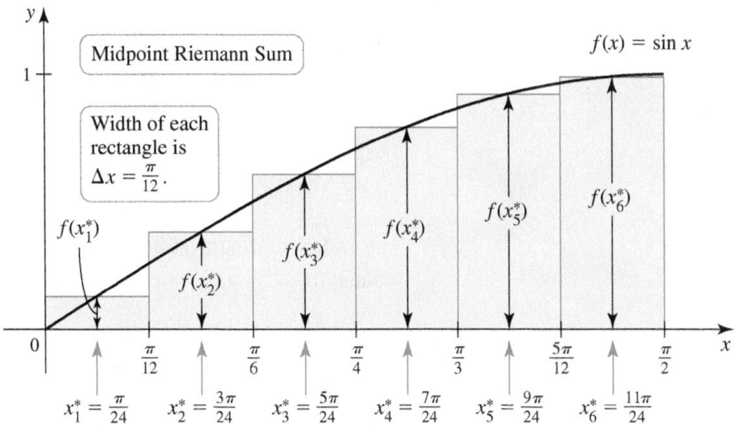

Figure 5.14

The resulting midpoint Riemann sum (Figure 5.14) is

$$\begin{aligned} &f(x_1^*)\Delta x + f(x_2^*)\Delta x + \cdots + f(x_6^*)\Delta x \\ &= \left(\sin\frac{\pi}{24}\right)\cdot\frac{\pi}{12} + \left(\sin\frac{3\pi}{24}\right)\cdot\frac{\pi}{12} + \left(\sin\frac{5\pi}{24}\right)\cdot\frac{\pi}{12} \\ &\quad + \left(\sin\frac{7\pi}{24}\right)\cdot\frac{\pi}{12} + \left(\sin\frac{9\pi}{24}\right)\cdot\frac{\pi}{12} + \left(\sin\frac{11\pi}{24}\right)\cdot\frac{\pi}{12} \\ &\approx 1.003. \end{aligned}$$

Comparing the midpoint Riemann sum (Figure 5.14) with the left (Figure 5.12) and right (Figure 5.13) Riemann sums suggests that the midpoint sum is a more accurate estimate of the area under the curve.

Related Exercises 27–34 ◄

EXAMPLE 4 Riemann sums from tables Estimate the area A under the graph of f on the interval $[0, 2]$ using left and right Riemann sums with $n = 4$, where f is continuous but known only at the points in Table 5.2.

Table 5.2

x	$f(x)$
0	1
0.5	3
1.0	4.5
1.5	5.5
2.0	6.0

SOLUTION With $n = 4$ subintervals on the interval $[0, 2]$, $\Delta x = 2/4 = 0.5$. Using the left endpoint of each subinterval, the left Riemann sum is

$$A \approx (f(0) + f(0.5) + f(1.0) + f(1.5))\Delta x = (1 + 3 + 4.5 + 5.5)0.5 = 7.0.$$

Using the right endpoint of each subinterval, the right Riemann sum is

$$A \approx (f(0.5) + f(1.0) + f(1.5) + f(2.0))\Delta x = (3 + 4.5 + 5.5 + 6.0)0.5 = 9.5.$$

With only five function values, these estimates of the area are necessarily crude. Better estimates are obtained by using more subintervals and more function values.

Related Exercises 35–38 ◀

Sigma (Summation) Notation

Working with Riemann sums is cumbersome with large numbers of subintervals. Therefore, we pause for a moment to introduce some notation that simplifies our work.

Sigma (or **summation**) **notation** is used to express sums in a compact way. For example, the sum $1 + 2 + 3 + \cdots + 10$ is represented in sigma notation as $\sum_{k=1}^{10} k$. Here is how the notation works. The symbol Σ (*sigma*, the Greek capital S) stands for *sum*. The **index** k takes on all integer values from the lower limit ($k = 1$) to the upper limit ($k = 10$). The expression that immediately follows Σ (the **summand**) is evaluated for each value of k, and the resulting values are summed. Here are some examples.

$$\sum_{k=1}^{99} k = 1 + 2 + 3 + \cdots + 99 = 4950 \qquad \sum_{k=1}^{n} k = 1 + 2 + \cdots + n$$

$$\sum_{k=0}^{3} k^2 = 0^2 + 1^2 + 2^2 + 3^2 = 14 \qquad \sum_{k=1}^{4} (2k + 1) = 3 + 5 + 7 + 9 = 24$$

$$\sum_{k=-1}^{2} (k^2 + k) = ((-1)^2 + (-1)) + (0^2 + 0) + (1^2 + 1) + (2^2 + 2) = 8.$$

The index in a sum is a *dummy variable*. It is internal to the sum, so it does not matter what symbol you choose as an index. For example,

$$\sum_{k=1}^{99} k = \sum_{n=1}^{99} n = \sum_{p=1}^{99} p.$$

Two properties of sums and sigma notation are useful in upcoming work. Suppose that $\{a_1, a_2, \ldots, a_n\}$ and $\{b_1, b_2, \ldots, b_n\}$ are two sets of real numbers, and suppose that c is a real number. Then we can factor multiplicative constants out of a sum:

Constant Multiple Rule $\quad \sum_{k=1}^{n} ca_k = c\sum_{k=1}^{n} a_k.$

We can also split a sum into two sums:

Addition Rule $\quad \sum_{k=1}^{n} (a_k + b_k) = \sum_{k=1}^{n} a_k + \sum_{k=1}^{n} b_k.$

In the coming examples and exercises, the following formulas for sums of powers of integers are essential.

> Formulas for $\sum_{k=1}^{n} k^p$, where p is a positive integer, have been known for centuries. The formulas for $p = 0, 1, 2,$ and 3 are relatively simple. The formulas become complicated as p increases.

THEOREM 5.1 Sums of Powers of Integers

Let n be a positive integer and c a real number.

$$\sum_{k=1}^{n} c = cn \qquad \sum_{k=1}^{n} k = \frac{n(n + 1)}{2}$$

$$\sum_{k=1}^{n} k^2 = \frac{n(n + 1)(2n + 1)}{6} \qquad \sum_{k=1}^{n} k^3 = \frac{n^2(n + 1)^2}{4}$$

Related Exercises 39–42 ◀

Riemann Sums Using Sigma Notation

With sigma notation, a Riemann sum has the convenient compact form

$$f(x_1^*)\Delta x + f(x_2^*)\Delta x + \cdots + f(x_n^*)\Delta x = \sum_{k=1}^{n} f(x_k^*)\Delta x.$$

To express left, right, and midpoint Riemann sums in sigma notation, we must identify the points x_k^*.

- For left Riemann sums, the left endpoints of the subintervals are $x_k^* = a + (k - 1)\Delta x$, for $k = 1, \ldots, n$.
- For right Riemann sums, the right endpoints of the subintervals are $x_k^* = a + k\Delta x$, for $k = 1, \ldots, n$.
- For midpoint Riemann sums, the midpoints of the subintervals are $x_k^* = a + (k - \frac{1}{2})\Delta x$, for $k = 1, \ldots, n$.

The three Riemann sums are written compactly as follows.

> DEFINITION **Left, Right, and Midpoint Riemann Sums in Sigma Notation**
>
> Suppose f is defined on a closed interval $[a, b]$, which is divided into n subintervals of equal length Δx. If x_k^* is a point in the kth subinterval $[x_{k-1}, x_k]$, for $k = 1, 2, \ldots, n$, then the **Riemann sum** for f on $[a, b]$ is $\sum_{k=1}^{n} f(x_k^*)\Delta x$. Three cases arise in practice.
>
> - **Left Riemann sum** if $x_k^* = a + (k - 1)\Delta x$
> - **Right Riemann sum** if $x_k^* = a + k\Delta x$
> - **Midpoint Riemann sum** if $x_k^* = a + (k - \frac{1}{2})\Delta x$

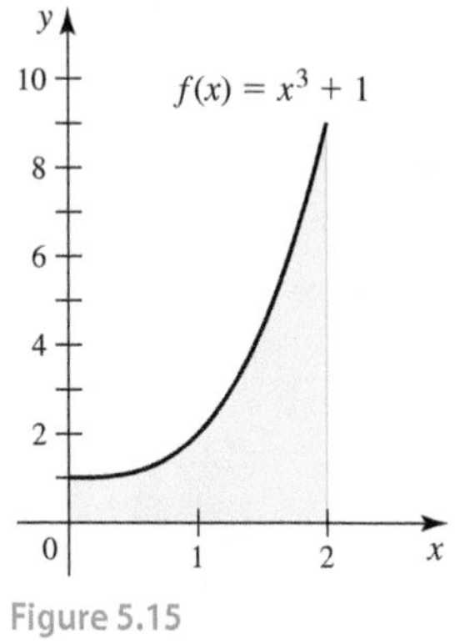

Figure 5.15

EXAMPLE 5 **Calculating Riemann sums** Evaluate the left, right, and midpoint Riemann sums for $f(x) = x^3 + 1$ between $a = 0$ and $b = 2$ using $n = 50$ subintervals. Make a conjecture about the exact area of the region under the curve (Figure 5.15).

SOLUTION With $n = 50$, the length of each subinterval is

$$\Delta x = \frac{b - a}{n} = \frac{2 - 0}{50} = \frac{1}{25} = 0.04.$$

The value of x_k^* for the left Riemann sum is

$$x_k^* = a + (k - 1)\Delta x = 0 + 0.04(k - 1) = 0.04k - 0.04,$$

for $k = 1, 2, \ldots, 50$. Therefore, the left Riemann sum, evaluated with a calculator, is

$$\sum_{k=1}^{n} f(x_k^*)\Delta x = \sum_{k=1}^{50} f(0.04k - 0.04)0.04 = 5.8416.$$

To evaluate the right Riemann sum, we let $x_k^* = a + k\Delta x = 0.04k$ and find that

$$\sum_{k=1}^{n} f(x_k^*)\Delta x = \sum_{k=1}^{50} f(0.04k)0.04 = 6.1616.$$

For the midpoint Riemann sum, we let

$$x_k^* = a + \left(k - \frac{1}{2}\right)\Delta x = 0 + 0.04\left(k - \frac{1}{2}\right) = 0.04k - 0.02.$$

The value of the sum is

$$\sum_{k=1}^{n} f(x_k^*)\,\Delta x = \sum_{k=1}^{50} f(0.04k - 0.02)0.04 = 5.9992.$$

Because f is increasing on $[0, 2]$, the left Riemann sum underestimates the area of the shaded region in Figure 5.15 and the right Riemann sum overestimates the area. Therefore, the exact area lies between 5.8416 and 6.1616. The midpoint Riemann sum usually gives the best estimate for increasing or decreasing functions.

Table 5.3 shows the left, right, and midpoint Riemann sum approximations for values of n up to 200. All three sets of approximations approach a value near 6, which is a reasonable estimate of the area under the curve. In Section 5.2, we show rigorously that the limit of all three Riemann sums as $n \to \infty$ is 6.

Table 5.3 Left, right, and midpoint Riemann sum approximations

n	L_n	R_n	M_n
20	5.61	6.41	5.995
40	5.8025	6.2025	5.99875
60	5.86778	6.13444	5.99944
80	5.90063	6.10063	5.99969
100	5.9204	6.0804	5.9998
120	5.93361	6.06694	5.99986
140	5.94306	6.05735	5.9999
160	5.95016	6.05016	5.99992
180	5.95568	6.04457	5.99994
200	5.9601	6.0401	5.99995

ALTERNATIVE SOLUTION It is worth examining another approach to Example 5. Consider the right Riemann sum given previously:

$$\sum_{k=1}^{n} f(x_k^*)\,\Delta x = \sum_{k=1}^{50} f(0.04k)0.04.$$

Rather than evaluating this sum with a calculator, we note that $f(0.04k) = (0.04k)^3 + 1$ and use the properties of sums:

$$\sum_{k=1}^{n} f(x_k^*)\Delta x = \sum_{k=1}^{50} \underbrace{((0.04k)^3 + 1)}_{f(x_k^*)}\underbrace{0.04}_{\Delta x}$$

$$= \sum_{k=1}^{50} (0.04k)^3\,0.04 + \sum_{k=1}^{50} 1 \cdot 0.04 \qquad \sum (a_k + b_k) = \sum a_k + \sum b_k$$

$$= (0.04)^4 \sum_{k=1}^{50} k^3 + 0.04 \sum_{k=1}^{50} 1. \qquad \sum c a_k = c \sum a_k$$

Using the summation formulas for powers of integers in Theorem 5.1, we find that

$$\sum_{k=1}^{50} 1 = 50 \quad \text{and} \quad \sum_{k=1}^{50} k^3 = \frac{50^2 \cdot 51^2}{4}.$$

Substituting the values of these sums into the right Riemann sum, its value is

$$\sum_{k=1}^{50} f(x_k^*)\,\Delta x = \frac{3851}{625} = 6.1616,$$

confirming the result given by a calculator. The idea of evaluating Riemann sums for *arbitrary* values of n is used in Section 5.2, where we evaluate the limit of the Riemann sum as $n \to \infty$.

Related Exercises 43–52 ◄

SECTION 5.1 EXERCISES

Review Questions

1. Suppose an object moves along a line at 15 m/s, for $0 \le t < 2$, and at 25 m/s, for $2 \le t \le 5$, where t is measured in seconds. Sketch the graph of the velocity function and find the displacement of the object for $0 \le t \le 5$.

2. Given the graph of the positive velocity of an object moving along a line, what is the geometrical representation of its displacement over a time interval $[a, b]$?

3. Suppose you want to approximate the area of the region bounded by the graph of $f(x) = \cos x$ and the x-axis between $x = 0$ and $x = \pi/2$. Explain a possible strategy.

4. Explain how Riemann sum approximations to the area of a region under a curve change as the number of subintervals increases.

5. Suppose the interval $[1, 3]$ is partitioned into $n = 4$ subintervals. What is the subinterval length Δx? List the grid points x_0, x_1, x_2, x_3, and x_4. Which points are used for the left, right, and midpoint Riemann sums?

6. Suppose the interval $[2, 6]$ is partitioned into $n = 4$ subintervals with grid points $x_0 = 2, x_1 = 3, x_2 = 4, x_3 = 5$, and $x_4 = 6$. Write, but do not evaluate, the left, right, and midpoint Riemann sums for $f(x) = x^2$.

7. Does a right Riemann sum underestimate or overestimate the area of the region under the graph of a function that is positive and decreasing on an interval $[a, b]$? Explain.

8. Does a left Riemann sum underestimate or overestimate the area of the region under the graph of a function that is positive and increasing on an interval $[a, b]$? Explain.

Basic Skills

9. **Approximating displacement** The velocity in ft/s of an object moving along a line is given by $v = 3t^2 + 1$ on the interval $0 \le t \le 4$.
   a. Divide the interval $[0, 4]$ into $n = 4$ subintervals, $[0, 1]$, $[1, 2]$, $[2, 3]$, and $[3, 4]$. On each subinterval, assume the object moves at a constant velocity equal to v evaluated at the midpoint of the subinterval and use these approximations to estimate the displacement of the object on $[0, 4]$ (see part (a) of the figure).
   b. Repeat part (a) for $n = 8$ subintervals (see part (b) of the figure).

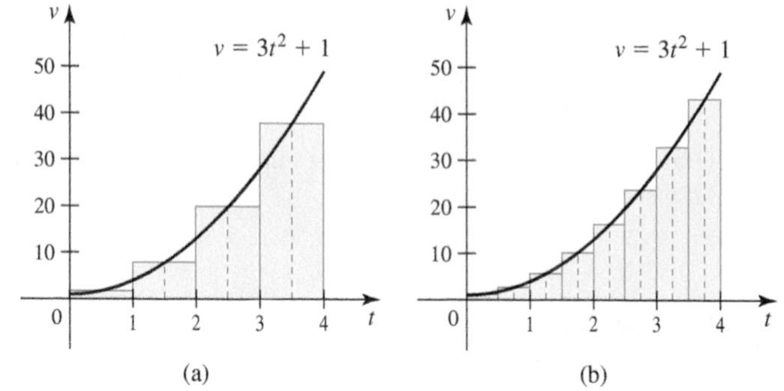

T 10. **Approximating displacement** The velocity in ft/s of an object moving along a line is given by $v = \sqrt{10t}$ on the interval $1 \le t \le 7$.
   a. Divide the time interval $[1, 7]$ into $n = 3$ subintervals, $[1, 3]$, $[3, 5]$, and $[5, 7]$. On each subinterval, assume the object moves at a constant velocity equal to v evaluated at the midpoint of the subinterval and use these approximations to estimate the displacement of the object on $[1, 7]$ (see part (a) of the figure).
   b. Repeat part (a) for $n = 6$ subintervals (see part (b) of the figure).

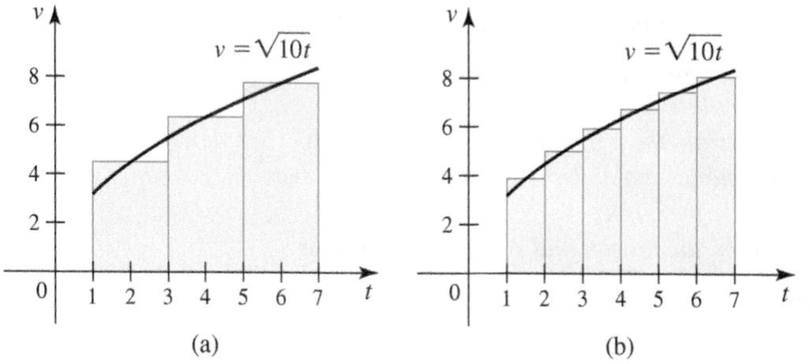

11–16. Approximating displacement *The velocity of an object is given by the following functions on a specified interval. Approximate the displacement of the object on this interval by subdividing the interval into n subintervals. Use the left endpoint of each subinterval to compute the height of the rectangles.*

11. $v = 2t + 1$ (m/s), for $0 \le t \le 8$; $n = 2$

T 12. $v = e^t$ (m/s), for $0 \le t \le 3$; $n = 3$

13. $v = \dfrac{1}{2t + 1}$ (m/s), for $0 \le t \le 8$; $n = 4$

14. $v = t^2/2 + 4$ (ft/s), for $0 \le t \le 12$; $n = 6$

T 15. $v = 4\sqrt{t + 1}$ (mi/hr), for $0 \le t \le 15$; $n = 5$

16. $v = \dfrac{t + 3}{6}$ (m/s), for $0 \le t \le 4$; $n = 4$

17–18. Left and right Riemann sums *Use the figures to calculate the left and right Riemann sums for f on the given interval and for the given value of n.*

17. $f(x) = x + 1$ on $[1, 6]$; $n = 5$

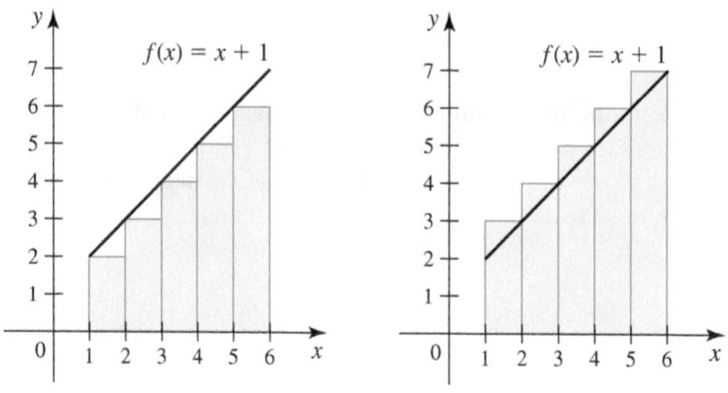

18. $f(x) = \dfrac{1}{x}$ on $[1, 5]$; $n = 4$

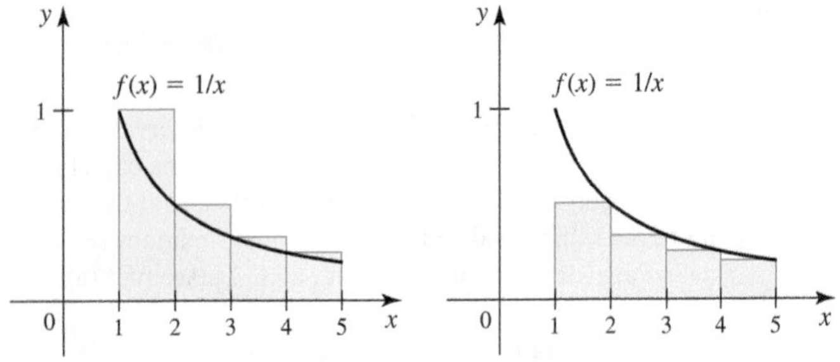

19–26. Left and right Riemann sums *Complete the following steps for the given function, interval, and value of n.*

a. *Sketch the graph of the function on the given interval.*
b. *Calculate Δx and the grid points $x_0, x_1, \ldots, x_n$.*
c. *Illustrate the left and right Riemann sums. Then determine which Riemann sum underestimates and which sum overestimates the area under the curve.*
d. *Calculate the left and right Riemann sums.*

19. $f(x) = x + 1$ on $[0, 4]$; $n = 4$

20. $f(x) = 9 - x$ on $[3, 8]$; $n = 5$

21. $f(x) = \cos x$ on $[0, \pi/2]$; $n = 4$

T **22.** $f(x) = \sin^{-1}(x/3)$ on $[0, 3]$; $n = 6$

23. $f(x) = x^2 - 1$ on $[2, 4]$; $n = 4$

24. $f(x) = 2x^2$ on $[1, 6]$; $n = 5$

T **25.** $f(x) = e^{x/2}$ on $[1, 4]$; $n = 6$

T **26.** $f(x) = \ln 4x$ on $[1, 3]$; $n = 5$

27. A midpoint Riemann sum Approximate the area of the region bounded by the graph of $f(x) = 100 - x^2$ and the x-axis on $[0, 10]$ with $n = 5$ subintervals. Use the midpoint of each subinterval to determine the height of each rectangle (see figure).

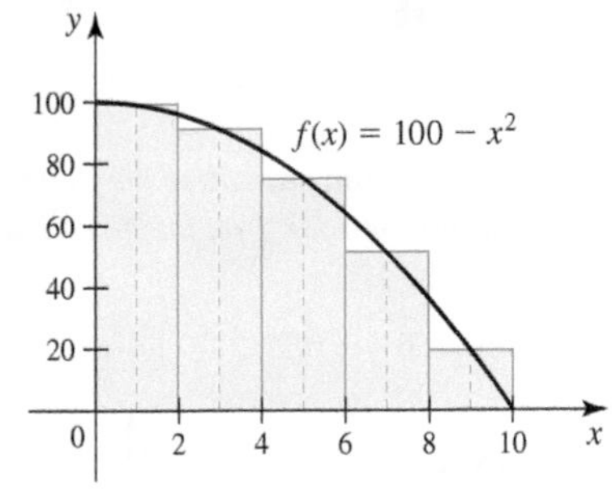

T **28. A midpoint Riemann sum** Approximate the area of the region bounded by the graph of $f(t) = \cos(t/2)$ and the t-axis on $[0, \pi]$ with $n = 4$ subintervals. Use the midpoint of each subinterval to determine the height of each rectangle (see figure).

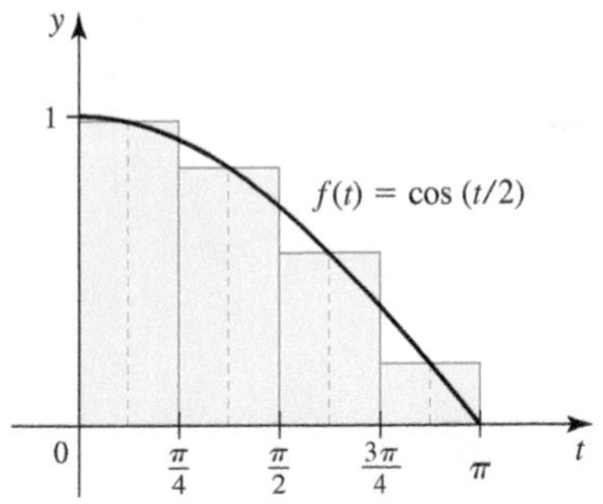

29–34. Midpoint Riemann sums *Complete the following steps for the given function, interval, and value of n.*

a. *Sketch the graph of the function on the given interval.*
b. *Calculate Δx and the grid points $x_0, x_1, \ldots, x_n$.*
c. *Illustrate the midpoint Riemann sum by sketching the appropriate rectangles.*
d. *Calculate the midpoint Riemann sum.*

29. $f(x) = 2x + 1$ on $[0, 4]$; $n = 4$

T **30.** $f(x) = 2\cos^{-1} x$ on $[0, 1]$; $n = 5$

T **31.** $f(x) = \sqrt{x}$ on $[1, 3]$; $n = 4$

32. $f(x) = x^2$ on $[0, 4]$; $n = 4$

33. $f(x) = \dfrac{1}{x}$ on $[1, 6]$; $n = 5$

34. $f(x) = 4 - x$ on $[-1, 4]$; $n = 5$

35–36. Riemann sums from tables *Evaluate the left and right Riemann sums for f over the given interval for the given value of n.*

35. $n = 4$; $[0, 2]$

x	0	0.5	1	1.5	2
$f(x)$	5	3	2	1	1

36. $n = 8$; $[1, 5]$

x	1	1.5	2	2.5	3	3.5	4	4.5	5
$f(x)$	0	2	3	2	2	1	0	2	3

37. Displacement from a table of velocities The velocities (in mi/hr) of an automobile moving along a straight highway over a two-hour period are given in the following table.

t (hr)	0	0.25	0.5	0.75	1	1.25	1.5	1.75	2
v (mi/hr)	50	50	60	60	55	65	50	60	70

a. Sketch a smooth curve passing through the data points.
b. Find the midpoint Riemann sum approximation to the displacement on $[0, 2]$ with $n = 2$ and $n = 4$.

38. Displacement from a table of velocities The velocities (in m/s) of an automobile moving along a straight freeway over a four-second period are given in the following table.

t (s)	0	0.5	1	1.5	2	2.5	3	3.5	4
v (m/s)	20	25	30	35	30	30	35	40	40

a. Sketch a smooth curve passing through the data points.
b. Find the midpoint Riemann sum approximation to the displacement on $[0, 4]$ with $n = 2$ and $n = 4$ subintervals.

39. Sigma notation Express the following sums using sigma notation. (Answers are not unique.)

a. $1 + 2 + 3 + 4 + 5$
b. $4 + 5 + 6 + 7 + 8 + 9$
c. $1^2 + 2^2 + 3^2 + 4^2$
d. $1 + \frac{1}{2} + \frac{1}{3} + \frac{1}{4}$

40. Sigma notation Express the following sums using sigma notation. (Answers are not unique.)

a. $1 + 3 + 5 + 7 + \cdots + 99$
b. $4 + 9 + 14 + \cdots + 44$
c. $3 + 8 + 13 + \cdots + 63$
d. $\dfrac{1}{1 \cdot 2} + \dfrac{1}{2 \cdot 3} + \dfrac{1}{3 \cdot 4} + \cdots + \dfrac{1}{49 \cdot 50}$

41. Sigma notation Evaluate the following expressions.

a. $\sum_{k=1}^{10} k$ b. $\sum_{k=1}^{6} (2k + 1)$

c. $\sum_{k=1}^{4} k^2$ d. $\sum_{n=1}^{5} (1 + n^2)$

e. $\sum_{m=1}^{3} \frac{2m + 2}{3}$ f. $\sum_{j=1}^{3} (3j - 4)$

g. $\sum_{p=1}^{5} (2p + p^2)$ h. $\sum_{n=0}^{4} \sin \frac{n\pi}{2}$

T **42. Evaluating sums** Evaluate the following expressions by two methods.

(i) Use Theorem 5.1. (ii) Use a calculator.

a. $\sum_{k=1}^{45} k$ b. $\sum_{k=1}^{45} (5k - 1)$ c. $\sum_{k=1}^{75} 2k^2$

d. $\sum_{n=1}^{50} (1 + n^2)$ e. $\sum_{m=1}^{75} \frac{2m + 2}{3}$ f. $\sum_{j=1}^{20} (3j - 4)$

g. $\sum_{p=1}^{35} (2p + p^2)$ h. $\sum_{n=0}^{40} (n^2 + 3n - 1)$

T **43–46. Riemann sums for larger values of** n *Complete the following steps for the given function f and interval.*

a. *For the given value of n, use sigma notation to write the left, right, and midpoint Riemann sums. Then evaluate each sum using a calculator.*

b. *Based on the approximations found in part (a), estimate the area of the region bounded by the graph of f and the x-axis on the interval.*

43. $f(x) = \sqrt{x}$ on $[0, 4]$; $n = 40$

44. $f(x) = x^2 + 1$ on $[-1, 1]$; $n = 50$

45. $f(x) = x^2 - 1$ on $[2, 7]$; $n = 75$

46. $f(x) = \cos 2x$ on $[0, \pi/4]$; $n = 60$

T **47–52. Approximating areas with a calculator** *Use a calculator and right Riemann sums to approximate the area of the given region. Present your calculations in a table showing the approximations for n = 10, 30, 60, and 80 subintervals. Comment on whether your approximations appear to approach a limit.*

47. The region bounded by the graph of $f(x) = 4 - x^2$ and the x-axis on the interval $[-2, 2]$

48. The region bounded by the graph of $f(x) = x^2 + 1$ and the x-axis on the interval $[0, 2]$

49. The region bounded by the graph of $f(x) = 2 - 2\sin x$ and the x-axis on the interval $[-\pi/2, \pi/2]$

50. The region bounded by the graph of $f(x) = 2^x$ and the x-axis on the interval $[1, 2]$

51. The region bounded by the graph of $f(x) = \ln x$ and the x-axis on the interval $[1, e]$

52. The region bounded by the graph of $f(x) = \sqrt{x + 1}$ and the x-axis on the interval $[0, 3]$

Further Explorations

53. Explain why or why not Determine whether the following statements are true and give an explanation or counterexample.

a. Consider the linear function $f(x) = 2x + 5$ and the region bounded by its graph and the x-axis on the interval $[3, 6]$. Suppose the area of this region is approximated using midpoint Riemann sums. Then the approximations give the exact area of the region for any number of subintervals.

b. A left Riemann sum always overestimates the area of a region bounded by a positive increasing function and the x-axis on an interval $[a, b]$.

c. For an increasing or decreasing nonconstant function on an interval $[a, b]$ and a given value of n, the value of the midpoint Riemann sum always lies between the values of the left and right Riemann sums.

T **54. Riemann sums for a semicircle** Let $f(x) = \sqrt{1 - x^2}$.

a. Show that the graph of f is the upper half of a circle of radius 1 centered at the origin.

b. Estimate the area between the graph of f and the x-axis on the interval $[-1, 1]$ using a midpoint Riemann sum with $n = 25$.

c. Repeat part (b) using $n = 75$ rectangles.

d. What happens to the midpoint Riemann sums on $[-1, 1]$ as $n \to \infty$?

T **55–58. Sigma notation for Riemann sums** *Use sigma notation to write the following Riemann sums. Then evaluate each Riemann sum using Theorem 5.1 or a calculator.*

55. The right Riemann sum for $f(x) = x + 1$ on $[0, 4]$ with $n = 50$

56. The left Riemann sum for $f(x) = e^x$ on $[0, \ln 2]$ with $n = 40$

57. The midpoint Riemann sum for $f(x) = x^3$ on $[3, 11]$ with $n = 32$

58. The midpoint Riemann sum for $f(x) = 1 + \cos \pi x$ on $[0, 2]$ with $n = 50$

59–62. Identifying Riemann sums *Fill in the blanks with right or midpoint, an interval, and a value of n. In some cases, more than one answer may work.*

59. $\sum_{k=1}^{4} f(1 + k) \cdot 1$ is a ______ Riemann sum for f on the interval [___, ___] with $n =$ ______.

60. $\sum_{k=1}^{4} f(2 + k) \cdot 1$ is a ______ Riemann sum for f on the interval [___, ___] with $n =$ ______.

61. $\sum_{k=1}^{4} f(1.5 + k) \cdot 1$ is a ______ Riemann sum for f on the interval [___, ___] with $n =$ ______.

62. $\sum_{k=1}^{8} f\left(1.5 + \frac{k}{2}\right) \cdot \frac{1}{2}$ is a ______ Riemann sum for f on the interval [___, ___] with $n =$ ______.

63. Approximating areas Estimate the area of the region bounded by the graph of $f(x) = x^2 + 2$ and the x-axis on $[0, 2]$ in the following ways.

a. Divide $[0, 2]$ into $n = 4$ subintervals and approximate the area of the region using a left Riemann sum. Illustrate the solution geometrically.

b. Divide $[0, 2]$ into $n = 4$ subintervals and approximate the area of the region using a midpoint Riemann sum. Illustrate the solution geometrically.

c. Divide $[0, 2]$ into $n = 4$ subintervals and approximate the area of the region using a right Riemann sum. Illustrate the solution geometrically.

64. Approximating area from a graph Approximate the area of the region bounded by the graph (see figure) and the x-axis by dividing the interval $[0, 6]$ into $n = 3$ subintervals. Use a left and right Riemann sum to obtain two different approximations.

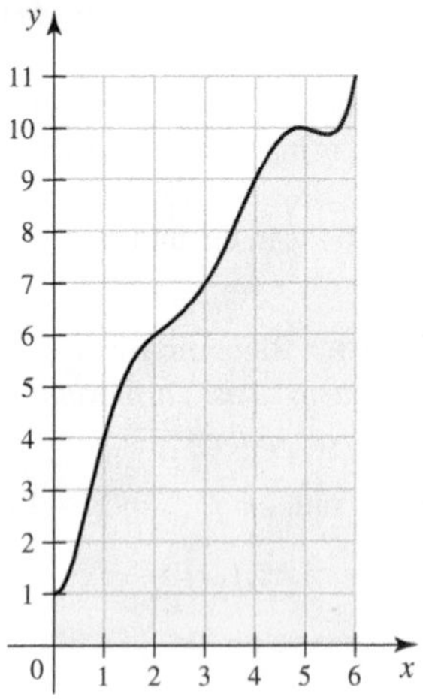

65. Approximating area from a graph Approximate the area of the region bounded by the graph (see figure) and the x-axis by dividing the interval $[1, 7]$ into $n = 6$ subintervals. Use a left and right Riemann sum to obtain two different approximations.

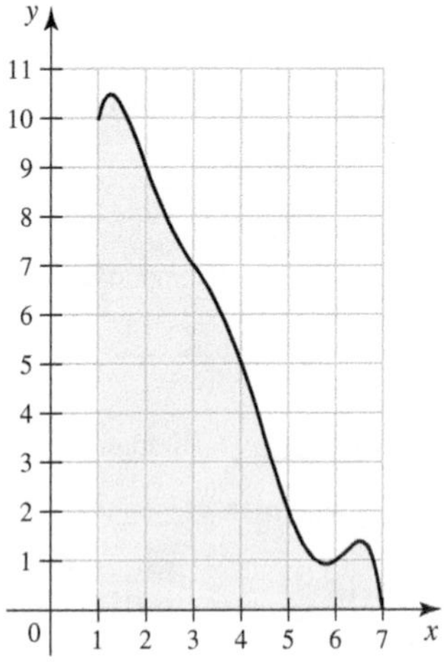

Applications

66. Displacement from a velocity graph Consider the velocity function for an object moving along a line (see figure).

a. Describe the motion of the object over the interval $[0, 6]$.

b. Use geometry to find the displacement of the object between $t = 0$ and $t = 3$.

c. Use geometry to find the displacement of the object between $t = 3$ and $t = 5$.

d. Assuming that the velocity remains 30 m/s, for $t \geq 4$, find the function that gives the displacement between $t = 0$ and any time $t \geq 5$.

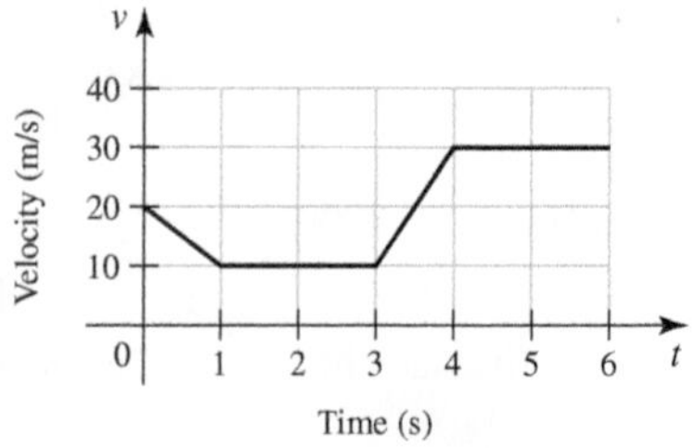

67. Displacement from a velocity graph Consider the velocity function for an object moving along a line (see figure).

a. Describe the motion of the object over the interval $[0, 6]$.

b. Use geometry to find the displacement of the object between $t = 0$ and $t = 2$.

c. Use geometry to find the displacement of the object between $t = 2$ and $t = 5$.

d. Assuming that the velocity remains 10 m/s, for $t \geq 5$, find the function that gives the displacement between $t = 0$ and any time $t \geq 5$.

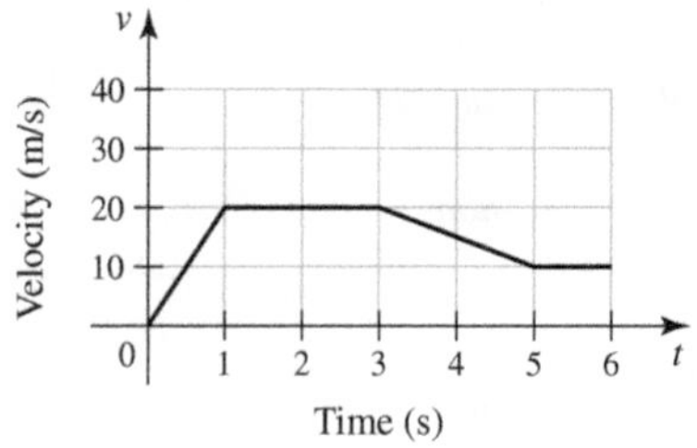

68. Flow rates Suppose a gauge at the outflow of a reservoir measures the flow rate of water in units of ft^3/hr. In Chapter 6, we show that the total amount of water that flows out of the reservoir is the area under the flow rate curve. Consider the flow-rate function shown in the figure.

a. Find the amount of water (in units of ft^3) that flows out of the reservoir over the interval $[0, 4]$.

b. Find the amount of water that flows out of the reservoir over the interval $[8, 10]$.

c. Does more water flow out of the reservoir over the interval $[0, 4]$ or $[4, 6]$?

d. Show that the units of your answer are consistent with the units of the variables on the axes.

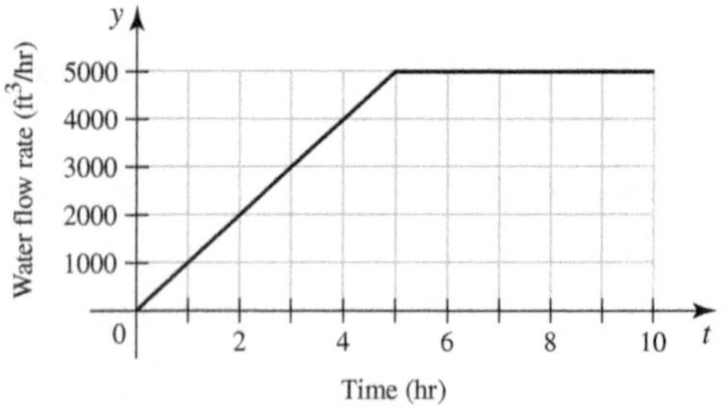

69. Mass from density A thin 10-cm rod is made of an alloy whose density varies along its length according to the function shown in the figure. Assume density is measured in units of g/cm.

In Chapter 6, we show that the mass of the rod is the area under the density curve.

a. Find the mass of the left half of the rod ($0 \le x \le 5$).
b. Find the mass of the right half of the rod ($5 \le x \le 10$).
c. Find the mass of the entire rod ($0 \le x \le 10$).
d. Find the point along the rod at which it will balance (called the center of mass).

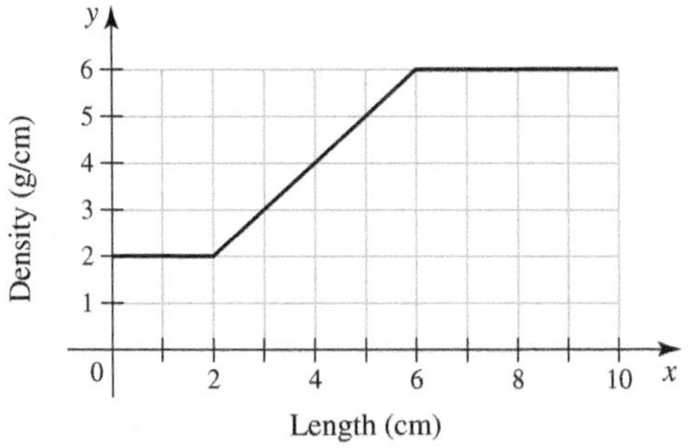

70–71. Displacement from velocity *The following functions describe the velocity of a car (in mi/hr) moving along a straight highway for a 3-hr interval. In each case, find the function that gives the displacement of the car over the interval $[0, t]$, where $0 \le t \le 3$.*

70. $v(t) = \begin{cases} 40 & \text{if } 0 \le t \le 1.5 \\ 50 & \text{if } 1.5 < t \le 3 \end{cases}$

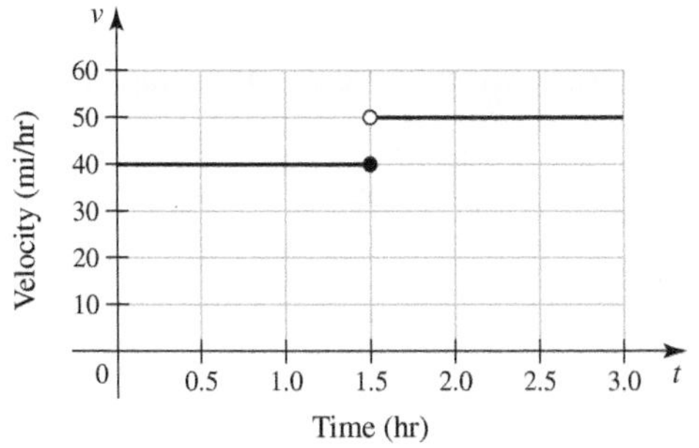

71. $v(t) = \begin{cases} 30 & \text{if } 0 \le t \le 2 \\ 50 & \text{if } 2 < t \le 2.5 \\ 44 & \text{if } 2.5 < t \le 3 \end{cases}$

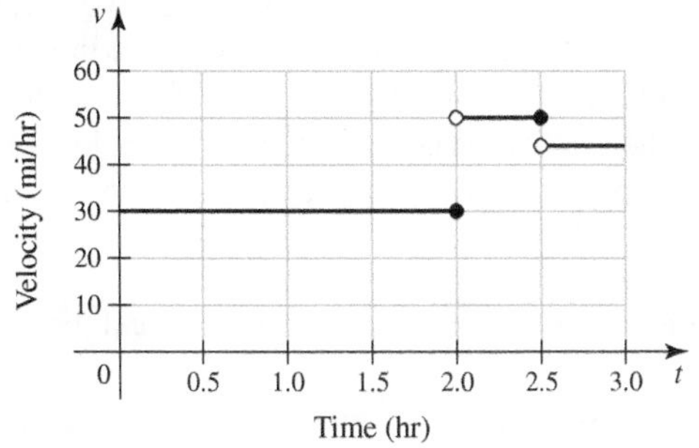

T **72–75. Functions with absolute value** *Use a calculator and the method of your choice to approximate the area of the following regions. Present your calculations in a table, showing approximations using $n = 16, 32,$ and 64 subintervals. Comment on whether your approximations appear to approach a limit.*

72. The region bounded by the graph of $f(x) = |25 - x^2|$ and the x-axis on the interval $[0, 10]$

73. The region bounded by the graph of $f(x) = |x(x^2 - 1)|$ and the x-axis on the interval $[-1, 1]$

74. The region bounded by the graph of $f(x) = |\cos 2x|$ and the x-axis on the interval $[0, \pi]$

75. The region bounded by the graph of $f(x) = |1 - x^3|$ and the x-axis on the interval $[-1, 2]$

Additional Exercises

76. Riemann sums for constant functions Let $f(x) = c$, where $c > 0$, be a constant function on $[a, b]$. Prove that any Riemann sum for any value of n gives the exact area of the region between the graph of f and the x-axis on $[a, b]$.

77. Riemann sums for linear functions Assume that the linear function $f(x) = mx + c$ is positive on the interval $[a, b]$. Prove that the midpoint Riemann sum with any value of n gives the exact area of the region between the graph of f and the x-axis on $[a, b]$.

78. Shape of the graph for left Riemann sums Suppose a left Riemann sum is used to approximate the area of the region bounded by the graph of a positive function and the x-axis on the interval $[a, b]$. Fill in the following table to indicate whether the resulting approximation underestimates or overestimates the exact area in the four cases shown. Use a sketch to explain your reasoning in each case.

	Increasing on $[a, b]$	Decreasing on $[a, b]$
Concave up on $[a, b]$		
Concave down on $[a, b]$		

79. Shape of the graph for right Riemann sums Suppose a right Riemann sum is used to approximate the area of the region bounded by the graph of a positive function and the x-axis on the interval $[a, b]$. Fill in the following table to indicate whether the resulting approximation underestimates or overestimates the exact area in the four cases shown. Use a sketch to explain your reasoning in each case.

	Increasing on $[a, b]$	Decreasing on $[a, b]$
Concave up on $[a, b]$		
Concave down on $[a, b]$		

QUICK CHECK ANSWERS

1. 45 mi **2.** 0.25, 0.125, 7.875
3. $\Delta x = 2$; $\{1, 3, 5, 7, 9\}$
4. The left sum overestimates the area.

5.2 Definite Integrals

We introduced Riemann sums in Section 5.1 as a way to approximate the area of a region bounded by a curve $y = f(x)$ and the x-axis on an interval $[a, b]$. In that discussion, we assumed f to be nonnegative on the interval. Our next task is to discover the geometric meaning of Riemann sums when f is negative on some or all of $[a, b]$. Once this matter is settled, we proceed to the main event of this section, which is to define the *definite integral*. With definite integrals, the approximations given by Riemann sums become exact.

Net Area

How do we interpret Riemann sums when f is negative at some or all points of $[a, b]$? The answer follows directly from the Riemann sum definition.

EXAMPLE 1 **Interpreting Riemann sums** Evaluate and interpret the following Riemann sums for $f(x) = 1 - x^2$ on the interval $[a, b]$ with n equally spaced subintervals.

a. A midpoint Riemann sum with $[a, b] = [1, 3]$ and $n = 4$

b. A left Riemann sum with $[a, b] = [0, 3]$ and $n = 6$

SOLUTION

a. The length of each subinterval is $\Delta x = \dfrac{b - a}{n} = \dfrac{3 - 1}{4} = 0.5$. So the grid points are

$$x_0 = 1, \quad x_1 = 1.5, \quad x_2 = 2, \quad \text{and} \quad x_3 = 2.5, \quad \text{and} \quad x_4 = 3.$$

To compute the midpoint Riemann sum, we evaluate f at the midpoints of the subintervals, which are

$$x_1^* = 1.25, \quad x_2^* = 1.75, \quad x_3^* = 2.25, \quad \text{and} \quad x_4^* = 2.75.$$

The resulting midpoint Riemann sum is

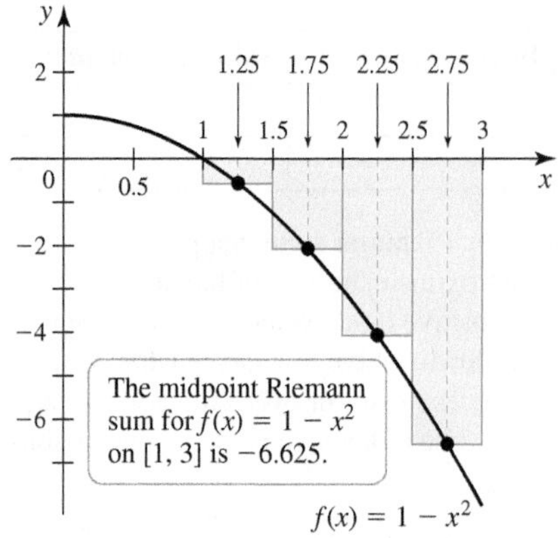

Figure 5.16

$$\begin{aligned}\sum_{k=1}^{n} f(x_k^*)\,\Delta x &= \sum_{k=1}^{4} f(x_k^*)(0.5)\\ &= f(1.25)(0.5) + f(1.75)(0.5) + f(2.25)(0.5) + f(2.75)(0.5)\\ &= (-0.5625 - 2.0625 - 4.0625 - 6.5625)0.5\\ &= -6.625.\end{aligned}$$

All values of $f(x_k^*)$ are negative, so the Riemann sum is also negative. Because area is always a nonnegative quantity, this Riemann sum does not approximate the area of the region between the curve and the x-axis on $[1, 3]$. Notice, however, that the values of $f(x_k^*)$ are the *negative* of the heights of the corresponding rectangles (Figure 5.16). Therefore, the Riemann sum approximates the *negative* of the area of the region bounded by the curve.

b. The length of each subinterval is $\Delta x = \dfrac{b - a}{n} = \dfrac{3 - 0}{6} = 0.5$, and the grid points are

$$x_0 = 0, \quad x_1 = 0.5, \quad x_2 = 1, \quad x_3 = 1.5, \quad x_4 = 2, \quad x_5 = 2.5, \quad \text{and} \quad x_6 = 3.$$

To calculate the left Riemann sum, we set $x_1^*, x_2^*, \ldots, x_6^*$ equal to the left endpoints of the subintervals:

$$x_1^* = 0, \quad x_2^* = 0.5, \quad x_3^* = 1, \quad x_4^* = 1.5, \quad x_5^* = 2, \quad \text{and} \quad x_6^* = 2.5.$$

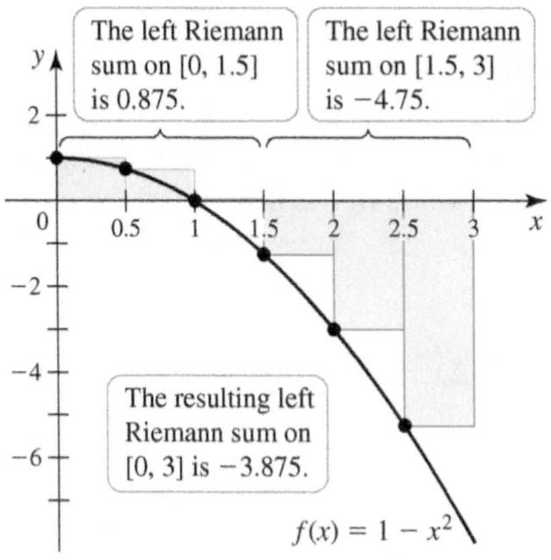

Figure 5.17

The resulting left Riemann sum is

$$\sum_{k=1}^{n} f(x_k^*)\Delta x = \sum_{k=1}^{6} f(x_k^*)(0.5)$$
$$= (\underbrace{f(0) + f(0.5) + f(1)}_{\text{nonnegative contribution}} + \underbrace{f(1.5) + f(2) + f(2.5)}_{\text{negative contribution}})0.5$$
$$= (1 + 0.75 + 0 - 1.25 - 3 - 5.25)0.5$$
$$= -3.875.$$

In this case, the values of $f(x_k^*)$ are nonnegative for $k = 1, 2,$ and 3, and negative for $k = 4, 5,$ and 6 (Figure 5.17). Where f is positive, we get positive contributions to the Riemann sum, and where f is negative, we get negative contributions to the sum.

Related Exercises 11–20 ◀

Let's recap what we learned in Example 1. On intervals where $f(x) < 0$, Riemann sums approximate the *negative* of the area of the region bounded by the curve (Figure 5.18).

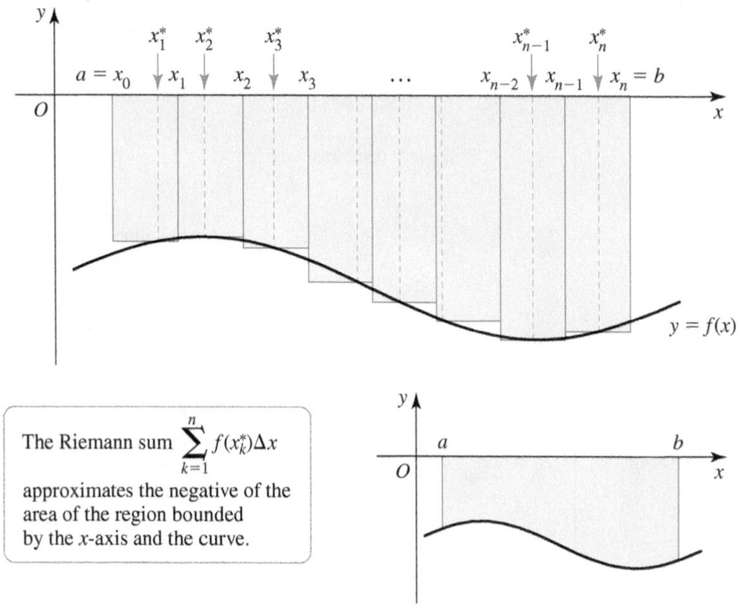

Figure 5.18

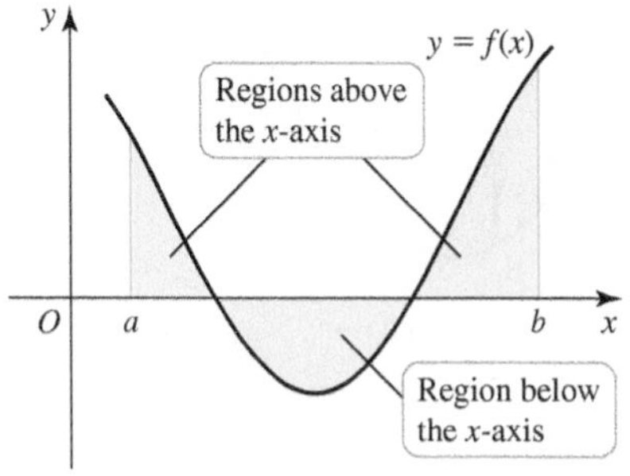

Figure 5.19

In the more general case that f is positive on only part of $[a, b]$, we get positive contributions to the sum where f is positive and negative contributions to the sum where f is negative. In this case, Riemann sums approximate the area of the regions that lie above the x-axis *minus* the area of the regions that lie *below* the x-axis (Figure 5.19). This difference between the positive and negative contributions is called the *net area*; it can be positive, negative, or zero.

➤ Net area suggests the difference between positive and negative contributions much like net change or net profit. Some texts use the term **signed area** for net area.

DEFINITION Net Area

Consider the region R bounded by the graph of a continuous function f and the x-axis between $x = a$ and $x = b$. The **net area** of R is the sum of the areas of the parts of R that lie above the x-axis *minus* the sum of the areas of the parts of R that lie below the x-axis on $[a, b]$.

QUICK CHECK 1 Suppose $f(x) = -5$. What is the net area of the region bounded by the graph of f and the x-axis on the interval $[1, 5]$? Make a sketch of the function and the region. ◀

QUICK CHECK 2 Sketch a continuous function f that is positive over the interval $[0, 1)$ and negative over the interval $(1, 2]$, such that the net area of the region bounded by the graph of f and the x-axis on $[0, 2]$ is zero. ◄

The Definite Integral

Riemann sums for f on $[a, b]$ give *approximations* to the net area of the region bounded by the graph of f and the x-axis between $x = a$ and $x = b$, where $a < b$. How can we make these approximations exact? If f is continuous on $[a, b]$, it is reasonable to expect the Riemann sum approximations to approach the exact value of the net area as the number of subintervals $n \to \infty$ and as the length of the subintervals $\Delta x \to 0$ (Figure 5.20). In terms of limits, we write

$$\text{net area} = \lim_{n \to \infty} \sum_{k=1}^{n} f(x_k^*)\,\Delta x.$$

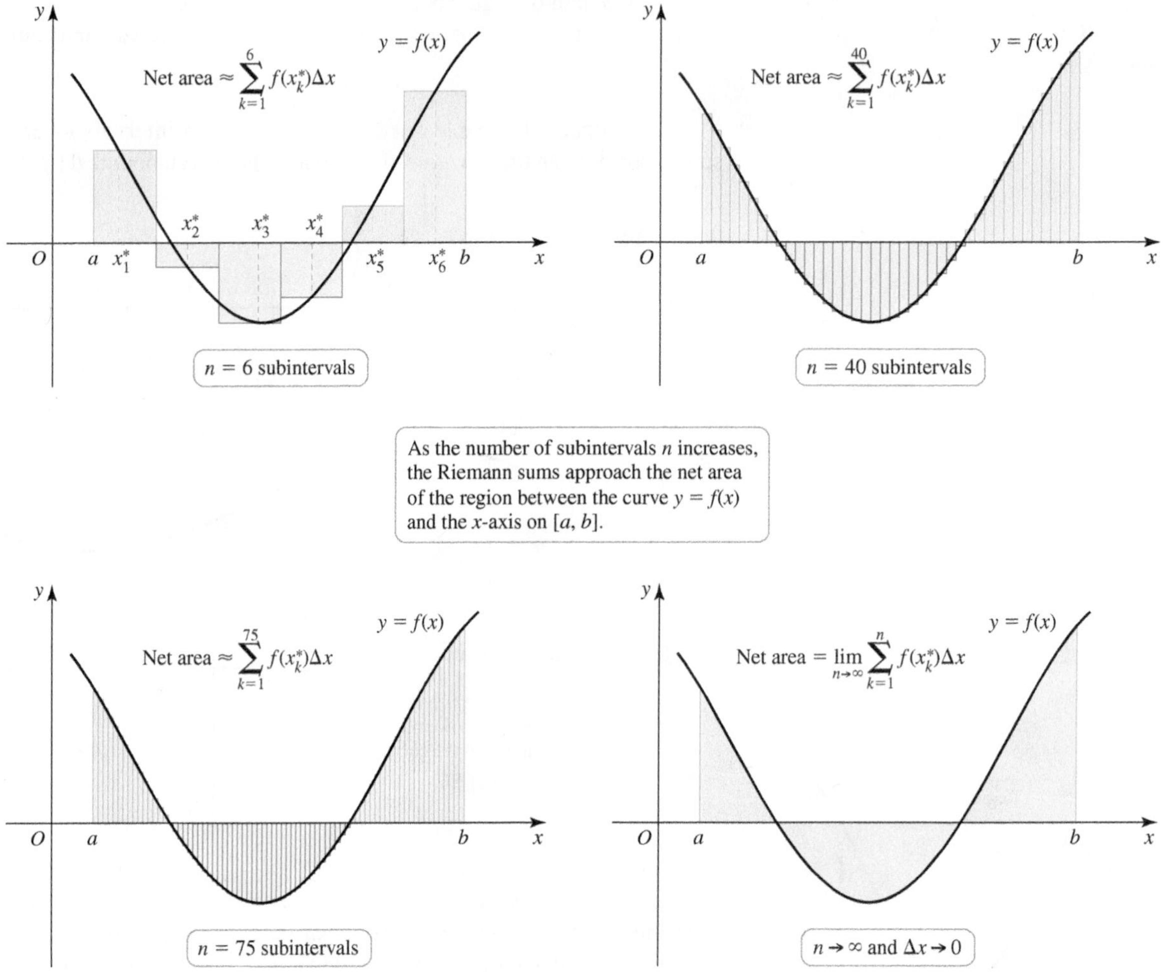

Figure 5.20

The Riemann sums we have used so far involve regular partitions in which the subintervals have the same length Δx. We now introduce partitions of $[a, b]$ in which the lengths of the subintervals are not necessarily equal. A **general partition** of $[a, b]$ consists of the n subintervals

$$[x_0, x_1], [x_1, x_2], \ldots, [x_{n-1}, x_n],$$

where $x_0 = a$ and $x_n = b$. The length of the kth subinterval is $\Delta x_k = x_k - x_{k-1}$, for $k = 1, \ldots, n$. We let x_k^* be any point in the subinterval $[x_{k-1}, x_k]$. This general partition is used to define the *general Riemann sum*.

DEFINITION General Riemann Sum

Suppose $[x_0, x_1], [x_1, x_2], \ldots, [x_{n-1}, x_n]$ are subintervals of $[a, b]$ with

$$a = x_0 < x_1 < x_2 < \cdots < x_{n-1} < x_n = b.$$

Let Δx_k be the length of the subinterval $[x_{k-1}, x_k]$ and let x_k^* be any point in $[x_{k-1}, x_k]$, for $k = 1, 2, \ldots, n$.

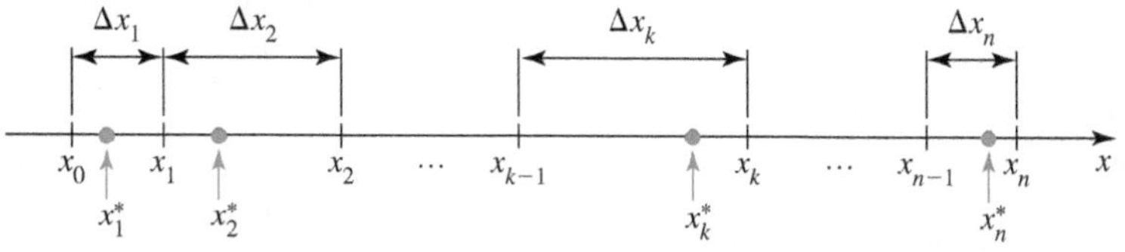

If f is defined on $[a, b]$, the sum

$$\sum_{k=1}^{n} f(x_k^*)\,\Delta x_k = f(x_1^*)\,\Delta x_1 + f(x_2^*)\,\Delta x_2 + \cdots + f(x_n^*)\,\Delta x_n$$

is called a **general Riemann sum for f on $[a, b]$**.

As was the case for regular Riemann sums, if we choose x_k^* to be the left endpoint of $[x_{k-1}, x_k]$, for $k = 1, 2, \ldots, n$, then the general Riemann sum is a left Riemann sum. Similarly, if we choose x_k^* to be the right endpoint $[x_{k-1}, x_k]$, for $k = 1, 2, \ldots, n$, then the general Riemann sum is a right Riemann sum, and if we choose x_k^* to be the midpoint of the interval $[x_{k-1}, x_k]$, for $k = 1, 2, \ldots, n$, then the general Riemann sum is a midpoint Riemann sum.

Now consider the limit of $\sum_{k=1}^{n} f(x_k^*)\,\Delta x_k$ as $n \to \infty$ and as *all* the $\Delta x_k \to 0$. We let Δ denote the largest value of Δx_k; that is, $\Delta = \max\{\Delta x_1, \Delta x_2, \ldots, \Delta x_n\}$. Observe that if $\Delta \to 0$, then $\Delta x_k \to 0$, for $k = 1, 2, \ldots, n$. For the limit $\lim_{\Delta \to 0} \sum_{k=1}^{n} f(x_k^*)\Delta x_k$ to exist, it must have the same value over all general partitions of $[a, b]$ and for all choices of x_k^* on a partition.

➤ Note that $\Delta \to 0$ forces all $\Delta x_k \to 0$, which forces $n \to \infty$. Therefore, it suffices to write $\Delta \to 0$ in the limit.

DEFINITION Definite Integral

A function f defined on $[a, b]$ is **integrable** on $[a, b]$ if $\lim_{\Delta \to 0} \sum_{k=1}^{n} f(x_k^*)\Delta x_k$ exists and is unique over all partitions of $[a, b]$ and all choices of x_k^* on a partition. This limit is the **definite integral of f from a to b**, which we write

$$\int_a^b f(x)\,dx = \lim_{\Delta \to 0} \sum_{k=1}^{n} f(x_k^*)\Delta x_k.$$

When the limit defining the definite integral of f exists, it equals the net area of the region bounded by the graph of f and the x-axis on $[a, b]$. It is imperative to remember that the indefinite integral $\int f(x)\,dx$ is a family of functions of x (the antiderivatives of f) and that the definite integral $\int_a^b f(x)\,dx$ is a real number (the net area of a region).

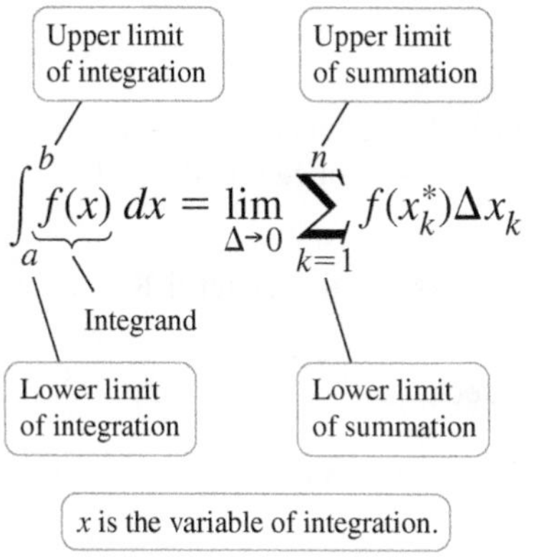

Figure 5.21

Notation The notation for the definite integral requires some explanation. There is a direct match between the notation on either side of the equation in the definition (Figure 5.21). In the limit as $\Delta \to 0$, the finite sum, denoted Σ, becomes a sum with an infinite number of terms, denoted $\int$. The integral sign $\int$ is an elongated S for sum. The **limits of integration**, a and b, and the limits of summation also match: The lower limit in the sum,

$k = 1$, corresponds to the left endpoint of the interval, $x = a$, and the upper limit in the sum, $k = n$, corresponds to the right endpoint of the interval, $x = b$. The function under the integral sign is called the **integrand**. Finally, the differential dx in the integral (which corresponds to Δx_k in the sum) is an essential part of the notation; it tells us that the **variable of integration** is x.

The variable of integration is a dummy variable that is completely internal to the integral. It does not matter what the variable of integration is called, as long as it does not conflict with other variables that are in use. Therefore, the integrals in Figure 5.22 all have the same meaning.

➤ For Leibniz, who introduced this notation in 1675, dx represented the width of an infinitesimally thin rectangle and $f(x)\,dx$ represented the area of such a rectangle. He used $\int_a^b f(x)\,dx$ to denote the sum of these areas from a to b.

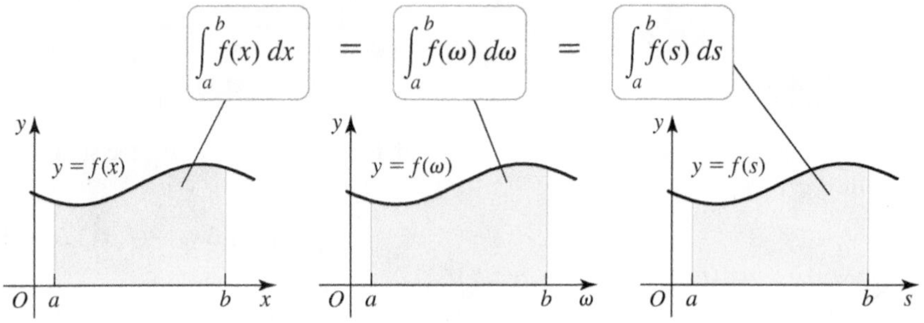

Figure 5.22

The strategy of slicing a region into smaller parts, summing the results from the parts, and taking a limit is used repeatedly in calculus and its applications. We call this strategy the **slice-and-sum method**. It often results in a Riemann sum whose limit is a definite integral.

Evaluating Definite Integrals

➤ A function f is bounded on an interval I if there is a number M such that $|f(x)| < M$ for all x in I.

Most of the functions encountered in this text are integrable (see Exercise 83 for an exception). In fact, if f is continuous on $[a, b]$ or if f is bounded on $[a, b]$ with a finite number of discontinuities, then f is integrable on $[a, b]$. The proof of this result goes beyond the scope of this text.

THEOREM 5.2 Integrable Functions
If f is continuous on $[a, b]$ or bounded on $[a, b]$ with a finite number of discontinuities, then f is integrable on $[a, b]$.

When f is continuous on $[a, b]$, we have seen that the definite integral $\int_a^b f(x)\,dx$ is the net area bounded by the graph of f and the x-axis on $[a, b]$. Figure 5.23 illustrates how the idea of net area carries over to piecewise continuous functions (Exercises 76–80).

Net area $= \int_a^b f(x)\,dx$
= area above x-axis (Regions 1 and 3)
− area below x-axis (Region 2)

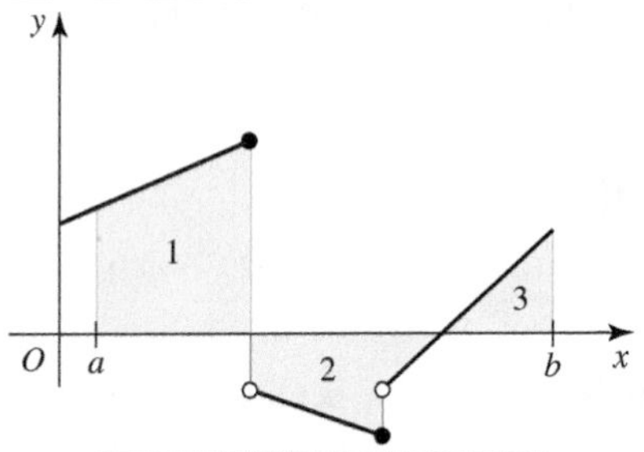

Figure 5.23

QUICK CHECK 3 Graph $f(x) = x$ and use geometry to evaluate $\int_{-1}^{1} x\,dx$. ◄

EXAMPLE 2 Identifying the limit of a sum Assume that

$$\lim_{\Delta \to 0} \sum_{k=1}^{n} (3x_k^{*2} + 2x_k^* + 1)\Delta x_k$$

is the limit of a Riemann sum for a function f on $[1, 3]$. Identify the function f and express the limit as a definite integral. What does the definite integral represent geometrically?

SOLUTION By comparing the sum $\sum_{k=1}^{n} (3x_k^{*2} + 2x_k^* + 1)\Delta x_k$ to the general Riemann sum $\sum_{k=1}^{n} f(x_k^*)\Delta x_k$, we see that $f(x) = 3x^2 + 2x + 1$. Because f is a polynomial, it is continuous on $[1, 3]$ and is, therefore, integrable on $[1, 3]$. It follows that

$$\lim_{\Delta \to 0} \sum_{k=1}^{n} (3x_k^{*2} + 2x_k^* + 1)\,\Delta x_k = \int_1^3 (3x^2 + 2x + 1)\,dx.$$

Because f is positive on $[1, 3]$, the definite integral $\int_1^3 (3x^2 + 2x + 1)\,dx$ is the area of the region bounded by the curve $y = 3x^2 + 2x + 1$ and the x-axis on $[1, 3]$ (Figure 5.24).

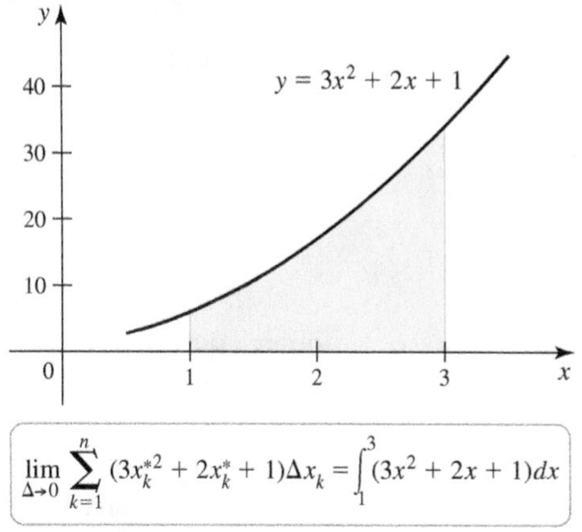

Figure 5.24

Related Exercises 21–24 ◀

EXAMPLE 3 **Evaluating definite integrals using geometry** Use familiar area formulas to evaluate the following definite integrals.

a. $\displaystyle\int_2^4 (2x + 3)\,dx$ **b.** $\displaystyle\int_1^6 (2x - 6)\,dx$ **c.** $\displaystyle\int_3^4 \sqrt{1 - (x - 3)^2}\,dx$

SOLUTION To evaluate these definite integrals geometrically, a sketch of the corresponding region is essential.

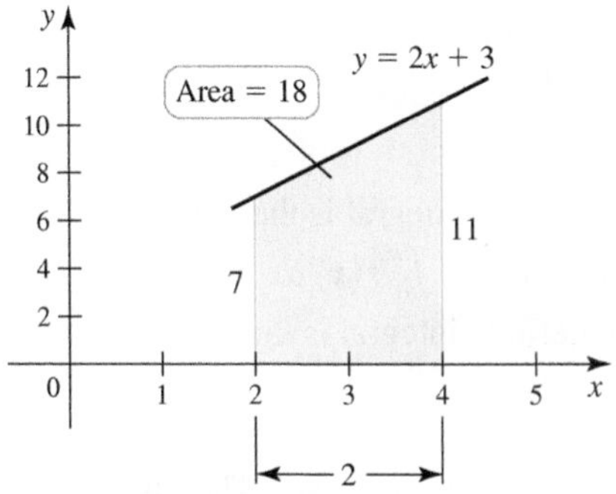

Figure 5.25

a. The definite integral $\int_2^4 (2x + 3)\,dx$ is the area of the trapezoid bounded by the x-axis and the line $y = 2x + 3$ from $x = 2$ to $x = 4$ (Figure 5.25). The width of its base is 2 and the lengths of its two parallel sides are $f(2) = 7$ and $f(4) = 11$. Using the area formula for a trapezoid, we have

$$\int_2^4 (2x + 3)\,dx = \frac{1}{2}\cdot 2(11 + 7) = 18.$$

➤ **A trapezoid and its area** When $a = 0$, we get the area of a triangle. When $a = b$, we get the area of a rectangle.

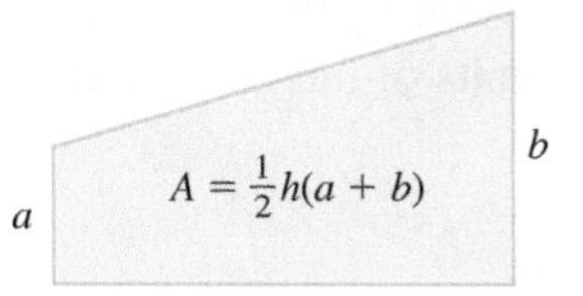

b. A sketch shows that the regions bounded by the line $y = 2x - 6$ and the x-axis are triangles (Figure 5.26). The area of the triangle on the interval $[1, 3]$ is $\frac{1}{2}\cdot 2 \cdot 4 = 4$. Similarly, the area of the triangle on $[3, 6]$ is $\frac{1}{2}\cdot 3 \cdot 6 = 9$. The definite integral is the net area of the entire region, which is the area of the triangle above the x-axis minus the area of the triangle below the x-axis:

$$\int_1^6 (2x - 6)\,dx = \text{net area} = 9 - 4 = 5.$$

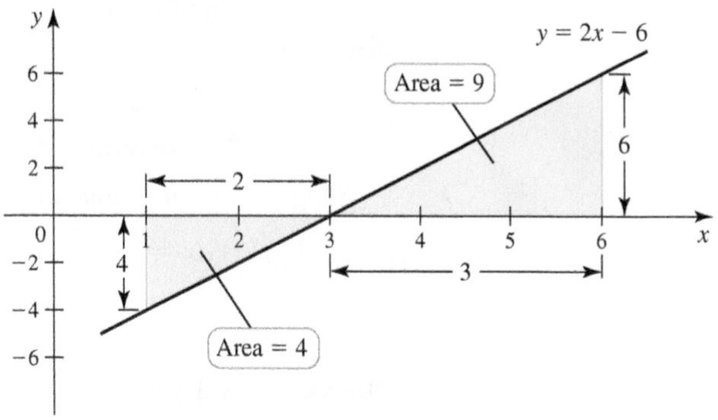

Figure 5.26

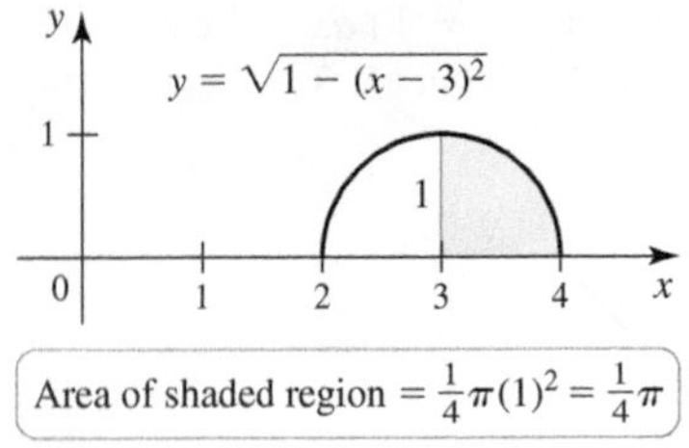

Figure 5.27

c. We first let $y = \sqrt{1 - (x - 3)^2}$ and observe that $y \geq 0$ when $2 \leq x \leq 4$. Squaring both sides leads to the equation $(x - 3)^2 + y^2 = 1$, whose graph is a circle of radius 1 centered at (3, 0). Because $y \geq 0$, the graph of $y = \sqrt{1 - (x - 3)^2}$ is the upper half of the circle. It follows that the integral $\int_3^4 \sqrt{1 - (x - 3)^2}\, dx$ is the area of a quarter circle of radius 1 (Figure 5.27). Therefore,

$$\int_3^4 \sqrt{1 - (x - 3)^2}\, dx = \frac{1}{4}\pi(1)^2 = \frac{\pi}{4}.$$

Related Exercises 25–32 ◄

QUICK CHECK 4 Let $f(x) = 5$ and use geometry to evaluate $\int_1^3 f(x)\, dx$. What is the value of $\int_a^b c\, dx$, where c is a real number? ◄

EXAMPLE 4 Definite integrals from graphs Figure 5.28 shows the graph of a function f with the areas of the regions bounded by its graph and the x-axis given. Find the values of the following definite integrals.

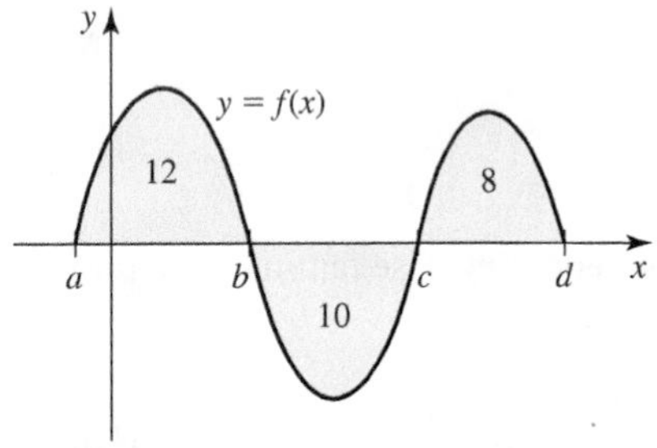

Figure 5.28

a. $\int_a^b f(x)\, dx$ **b.** $\int_b^c f(x)\, dx$ **c.** $\int_a^c f(x)\, dx$ **d.** $\int_b^d f(x)\, dx$

SOLUTION

a. Because f is positive on $[a, b]$, the value of the definite integral is the area of the region between the graph and the x-axis on $[a, b]$; that is, $\int_a^b f(x)\, dx = 12$.

b. Because f is negative on $[b, c]$, the value of the definite integral is the negative of the area of the corresponding region; that is, $\int_b^c f(x)\, dx = -10$.

c. The value of the definite integral is the area of the region on $[a, b]$ (where f is positive) minus the area of the region on $[b, c]$ (where f is negative). Therefore, $\int_a^c f(x)\, dx = 12 - 10 = 2$.

d. Reasoning as in part (c), we have $\int_b^d f(x)\, dx = -10 + 8 = -2$.

Related Exercises 33–40 ◄

Properties of Definite Integrals

Recall that the definite integral $\int_a^b f(x)\, dx$ was defined assuming that $a < b$. There are, however, occasions when it is necessary to reverse the limits of integration. If f is integrable on $[a, b]$, we define

$$\int_b^a f(x)\, dx = -\int_a^b f(x)\, dx.$$

In other words, reversing the limits of integration changes the sign of the integral.

Another fundamental property of integrals is that if we integrate from a point to itself, then the length of the interval of integration is zero, which means the definite integral is also zero.

> **DEFINITION Reversing Limits and Identical Limits of Integration**
>
> Suppose f is integrable on $[a, b]$.
>
> **1.** $\int_b^a f(x)\, dx = -\int_a^b f(x)\, dx$ **2.** $\int_a^a f(x)\, dx = 0$

QUICK CHECK 5 Evaluate $\int_a^b f(x)\, dx + \int_b^a f(x)\, dx$ assuming f is integrable on $[a, b]$. ◄

Integral of a Sum Definite integrals possess other properties that often simplify their evaluation. Assume f and g are integrable on $[a, b]$. The first property states that their sum $f + g$ is integrable on $[a, b]$ and the integral of their sum is the sum of their integrals:

$$\int_a^b (f(x) + g(x))\,dx = \int_a^b f(x)\,dx + \int_a^b g(x)\,dx.$$

We prove this property assuming that f and g are continuous. In this case, $f + g$ is continuous and, therefore, integrable. We then have

$$\int_a^b (f(x) + g(x))\,dx = \lim_{\Delta \to 0} \sum_{k=1}^{n} (f(x_k^*) + g(x_k^*))\Delta x_k \quad \text{Definition of definite integral}$$

$$= \lim_{\Delta \to 0} \left(\sum_{k=1}^{n} f(x_k^*)\Delta x_k + \sum_{k=1}^{n} g(x_k^*)\Delta x_k \right) \quad \text{Split into two finite sums.}$$

$$= \lim_{\Delta \to 0} \sum_{k=1}^{n} f(x_k^*)\Delta x_k + \lim_{\Delta \to 0} \sum_{k=1}^{n} g(x_k^*)\Delta x_k \quad \text{Split into two limits.}$$

$$= \int_a^b f(x)\,dx + \int_a^b g(x)\,dx. \quad \text{Definition of definite integral}$$

Constants in Integrals Another property of definite integrals is that constants can be factored out of the integral. If f is integrable on $[a, b]$ and c is a constant, then cf is integrable on $[a, b]$ and

$$\int_a^b cf(x)\,dx = c\int_a^b f(x)\,dx.$$

The justification for this property (Exercise 81) is based on the fact that for finite sums,

$$\sum_{k=1}^{n} cf(x_k^*)\Delta x_k = c\sum_{k=1}^{n} f(x_k^*)\Delta x_k.$$

Integrals over Subintervals If the point p lies between a and b, then the integral on $[a, b]$ may be split into two integrals. As shown in Figure 5.29, we have the property

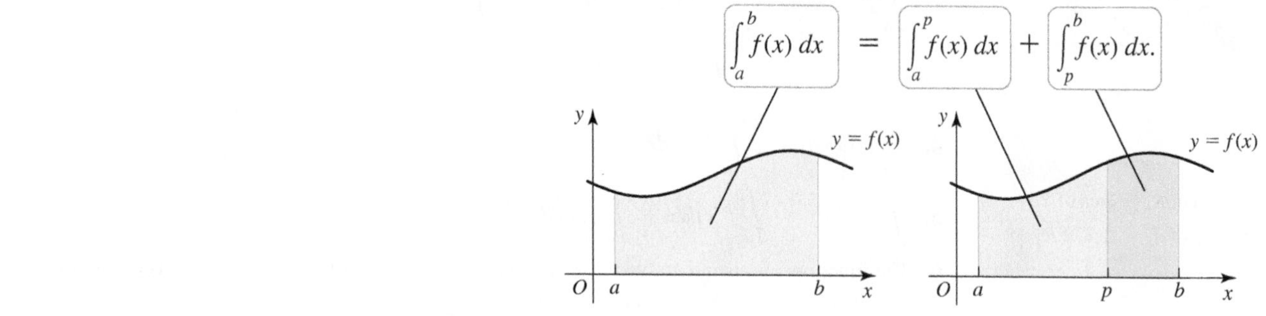

Figure 5.29

It is surprising that this property also holds when p lies outside the interval $[a, b]$. For example, if $a < b < p$ and f is integrable on $[a, p]$, then it follows (Figure 5.30) that

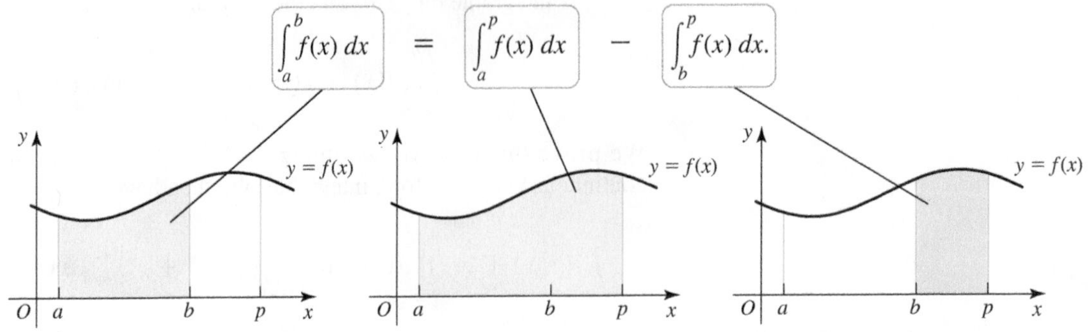

Figure 5.30

Because $\int_p^b f(x)\,dx = -\int_b^p f(x)\,dx$, we have the original property:

$$\int_a^b f(x)\,dx = \int_a^p f(x)\,dx + \int_p^b f(x)\,dx.$$

Integrals of Absolute Values Finally, how do we interpret $\int_a^b |f(x)|\,dx$, the integral of the absolute value of an integrable function? The graphs f and $|f|$ are shown in Figure 5.31. The integral $\int_a^b |f(x)|\,dx$ gives the area of regions R_1^* and R_2. But R_1 and R_1^* have the same area; therefore, $\int_a^b |f(x)|\,dx$ also gives the area of R_1 and R_2. The conclusion is that $\int_a^b |f(x)|\,dx$ is the area of the entire region (above and below the x-axis) that lies between the graph of f and the x-axis on $[a, b]$.

All these properties will be used frequently in upcoming work. It's worth collecting them in one table (Table 5.4).

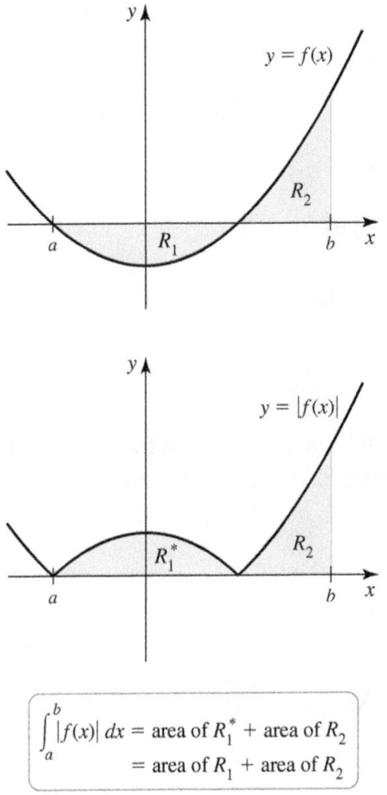

Figure 5.31

Table 5.4 Properties of definite integrals

Let f and g be integrable functions on an interval that contains a, b, and p.

1. $\int_a^a f(x)\,dx = 0$ Definition
2. $\int_b^a f(x)\,dx = -\int_a^b f(x)\,dx$ Definition
3. $\int_a^b (f(x) + g(x))\,dx = \int_a^b f(x)\,dx + \int_a^b g(x)\,dx$
4. $\int_a^b cf(x)\,dx = c\int_a^b f(x)\,dx$ For any constant c
5. $\int_a^b f(x)\,dx = \int_a^p f(x)\,dx + \int_p^b f(x)\,dx$
6. The function $|f|$ is integrable on $[a, b]$, and $\int_a^b |f(x)|\,dx$ is the sum of the areas of the regions bounded by the graph of f and the x-axis on $[a, b]$.

EXAMPLE 5 **Properties of integrals** Assume that $\int_0^5 f(x)\,dx = 3$ and $\int_0^7 f(x)\,dx = -10$. Evaluate the following integrals, if possible.

a. $\int_0^7 2f(x)\,dx$ **b.** $\int_5^7 f(x)\,dx$ **c.** $\int_5^0 f(x)\,dx$ **d.** $\int_7^0 6f(x)\,dx$ **e.** $\int_0^7 |f(x)|\,dx$

SOLUTION

a. By Property 4 of Table 5.4,

$$\int_0^7 2f(x)\,dx = 2\int_0^7 f(x)\,dx = 2\cdot(-10) = -20.$$

b. By Property 5 of Table 5.4, $\int_0^7 f(x)\,dx = \int_0^5 f(x)\,dx + \int_5^7 f(x)\,dx$. Therefore,

$$\int_5^7 f(x)\,dx = \int_0^7 f(x)\,dx - \int_0^5 f(x)\,dx = -10 - 3 = -13.$$

c. By Property 2 of Table 5.4,

$$\int_5^0 f(x)\,dx = -\int_0^5 f(x)\,dx = -3.$$

d. Using Properties 2 and 4 of Table 5.4, we have

$$\int_7^0 6f(x)\,dx = -\int_0^7 6f(x)\,dx = -6\int_0^7 f(x)\,dx = (-6)(-10) = 60.$$

e. This integral cannot be evaluated without knowing the intervals on which f is positive and negative. It could have any value greater than or equal to 10.

Related Exercises 41–46 ◄

QUICK CHECK 6 Evaluate $\int_{-1}^2 x\,dx$ and $\int_{-1}^2 |x|\,dx$ using geometry. ◄

Evaluating Definite Integrals Using Limits

In Example 3, we used area formulas for trapezoids, triangles, and circles to evaluate definite integrals. Regions bounded by more general functions have curved boundaries for which conventional geometrical methods do not work. At the moment, the only way to handle such integrals is to appeal to the definition of the definite integral and the summation formulas given in Theorem 5.1.

We know that if f is integrable on $[a, b]$, then $\int_a^b f(x)\,dx = \lim_{\Delta\to 0}\sum_{k=1}^{n} f(x_k^*)\Delta x_k$, for any partition of $[a, b]$ and any points x_k^*. To simplify these calculations, we use equally spaced grid points and right Riemann sums. That is, for each value of n, we let $\Delta x_k = \Delta x = \dfrac{b-a}{n}$ and $x_k^* = a + k\,\Delta x$, for $k = 1, 2, \ldots, n$. Then as $n \to \infty$ and $\Delta \to 0$,

$$\int_a^b f(x)\,dx = \lim_{\Delta\to 0}\sum_{k=1}^{n} f(x_k^*)\Delta x_k = \lim_{n\to\infty}\sum_{k=1}^{n} f(a + k\Delta x)\Delta x.$$

EXAMPLE 6 Evaluating definite integrals Find the value of $\int_0^2 (x^3 + 1)\,dx$ by evaluating a right Riemann sum and letting $n \to \infty$.

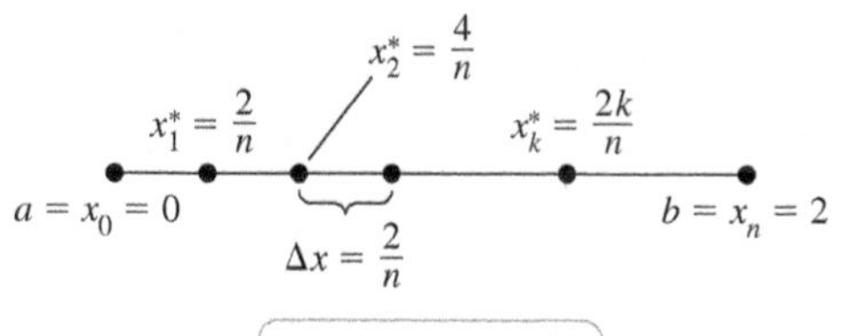

$x_k^* = a + k\Delta x = \frac{2k}{n}$
$k = 1, \ldots, n$

SOLUTION Based on approximations found in Example 5, Section 5.1, we conjectured that the value of this integral is 6. To verify this conjecture, we now evaluate the integral exactly. The interval $[a, b] = [0, 2]$ is divided into n subintervals of length $\Delta x = \dfrac{b-a}{n} = \dfrac{2}{n}$, which produces the grid points

$$x_k^* = a + k\Delta x = 0 + k\cdot\frac{2}{n} = \frac{2k}{n}, \qquad \text{for } k = 1, 2, \ldots, n.$$

Letting $f(x) = x^3 + 1$, the right Riemann sum is

$$\sum_{k=1}^{n} f(x_k^*)\Delta x = \sum_{k=1}^{n}\left(\left(\frac{2k}{n}\right)^3 + 1\right)\frac{2}{n}$$

$$= \frac{2}{n}\sum_{k=1}^{n}\left(\frac{8k^3}{n^3} + 1\right) \qquad \sum_{k=1}^{n} ca_k = c\sum_{k=1}^{n} a_k$$

$$= \frac{2}{n}\left(\frac{8}{n^3}\sum_{k=1}^{n} k^3 + \sum_{k=1}^{n} 1\right) \qquad \sum_{k=1}^{n}(a_k + b_k) = \sum_{k=1}^{n} a_k + \sum_{k=1}^{n} b_k$$

$$= \frac{2}{n}\left(\frac{8}{n^3}\left(\frac{n^2(n+1)^2}{4}\right) + n\right) \qquad \sum_{k=1}^{n} k^3 = \frac{n^2(n+1)^2}{4} \text{ and } \sum_{k=1}^{n} 1 = n; \text{ Theorem 5.1}$$

$$= \frac{4(n^2 + 2n + 1)}{n^2} + 2. \qquad \text{Simplify.}$$

➤ An analogous calculation could be done using left Riemann sums or midpoint Riemann sums.

Now we evaluate $\int_0^2 (x^3 + 1)\,dx$ by letting $n \to \infty$ in the Riemann sum:

$$\int_0^2 (x^3 + 1)\,dx = \lim_{n\to\infty}\sum_{k=1}^{n} f(x_k^*)\Delta x$$

$$= \lim_{n\to\infty}\left(\frac{4(n^2 + 2n + 1)}{n^2} + 2\right)$$

$$= 4\underbrace{\lim_{n\to\infty}\left(\frac{n^2 + 2n + 1}{n^2}\right)}_{1} + \lim_{n\to\infty} 2$$

$$= 4(1) + 2 = 6.$$

Therefore, $\int_0^2 (x^3 + 1)\,dx = 6$, confirming our conjecture in Example 5, Section 5.1.

Related Exercises 47–52 ◀

The Riemann sum calculations in Example 6 are tedious even if f is a simple function. For polynomials of degree 4 and higher, the calculations are more challenging, and for rational and transcendental functions, advanced mathematical results are needed. The next section introduces more efficient methods for evaluating definite integrals.

SECTION 5.2 EXERCISES

Review Questions

1. What does net area measure?

2. What is the geometric meaning of a definite integral if the integrand changes sign on the interval of integration?

3. Under what conditions does the net area of a region equal the area of a region? When does the net area of a region differ from the area of a region?

4. Suppose that $f(x) < 0$ on the interval $[a, b]$. Using Riemann sums, explain why the definite integral $\int_a^b f(x)\,dx$ is negative.

5. Use graphs to evaluate $\int_0^{2\pi} \sin x\,dx$ and $\int_0^{2\pi} \cos x\,dx$.

6. Explain how the notation for Riemann sums, $\sum_{k=1}^{n} f(x_k^*)\Delta x$, corresponds to the notation for the definite integral, $\int_a^b f(x)\,dx$.

7. Give a geometrical explanation of why $\int_a^a f(x)\,dx = 0$.

8. Use Table 5.4 to rewrite $\int_1^6 (2x^3 - 4x)\,dx$ as the difference of two integrals.

9. Use geometry to find a formula for $\int_0^a x\,dx$, in terms of a.

10. If f is continuous on $[a, b]$ and $\int_a^b |f(x)|\,dx = 0$, what can you conclude about f?

Basic Skills

11–14. Approximating net area *The following functions are negative on the given interval.*

a. Sketch the function on the given interval.

b. Approximate the net area bounded by the graph of f and the x-axis on the interval using a left, right, and midpoint Riemann sum with $n = 4$.

11. $f(x) = -2x - 1$ on $[0, 4]$

T 12. $f(x) = -4 - x^3$ on $[3, 7]$

T 13. $f(x) = \sin 2x$ on $[\pi/2, \pi]$

T 14. $f(x) = x^3 - 1$ on $[-2, 0]$

T 15–20. Approximating net area *The following functions are positive and negative on the given interval.*

a. Sketch the function on the given interval.

b. Approximate the net area bounded by the graph of f and the x-axis on the interval using a left, right, and midpoint Riemann sum with $n = 4$.

c. Use the sketch in part (a) to show which intervals of $[a, b]$ *make positive and negative contributions to the net area.*

15. $f(x) = 4 - 2x$ on $[0, 4]$

16. $f(x) = 8 - 2x^2$ on $[0, 4]$

17. $f(x) = \sin 2x$ on $[0, 3\pi/4]$

18. $f(x) = x^3$ on $[-1, 2]$

19. $f(x) = \tan^{-1}(3x - 1)$ on $[0, 1]$

20. $f(x) = xe^{-x}$ on $[-1, 1]$

21–24. Identifying definite integrals as limits of sums *Consider the following limits of Riemann sums for a function f on* $[a, b]$. *Identify f and express the limit as a definite integral.*

21. $\lim_{\Delta \to 0} \sum_{k=1}^{n} (x_k^{*2} + 1)\Delta x_k$ on $[0, 2]$

22. $\lim_{\Delta \to 0} \sum_{k=1}^{n} (4 - x_k^{*2})\Delta x_k$ on $[-2, 2]$

23. $\lim_{\Delta \to 0} \sum_{k=1}^{n} x_k^* \ln x_k^* \Delta x_k$ on $[1, 2]$

24. $\lim_{\Delta \to 0} \sum_{k=1}^{n} |x_k^{*2} - 1|\Delta x_k$ on $[-2, 2]$

25–32. Net area and definite integrals *Use geometry (not Riemann sums) to evaluate the following definite integrals. Sketch a graph of the integrand, show the region in question, and interpret your result.*

25. $\int_0^4 (8 - 2x)\,dx$

26. $\int_{-4}^2 (2x + 4)\,dx$

27. $\int_{-1}^2 (-|x|)\,dx$

28. $\int_0^2 (1 - x)\,dx$

29. $\int_0^4 \sqrt{16 - x^2}\,dx$

30. $\int_{-1}^3 \sqrt{4 - (x - 1)^2}\,dx$

31. $\int_0^4 f(x)\,dx$, where $f(x) = \begin{cases} 5 & \text{if } x \le 2 \\ 3x - 1 & \text{if } x > 2 \end{cases}$

32. $\int_1^{10} g(x)\,dx$, where $g(x) = \begin{cases} 4x & \text{if } 0 \le x \le 2 \\ -8x + 16 & \text{if } 2 < x \le 3 \\ -8 & \text{if } x > 3 \end{cases}$

33–36. Net area from graphs *The figure shows the areas of regions bounded by the graph of f and the x-axis. Evaluate the following integrals.*

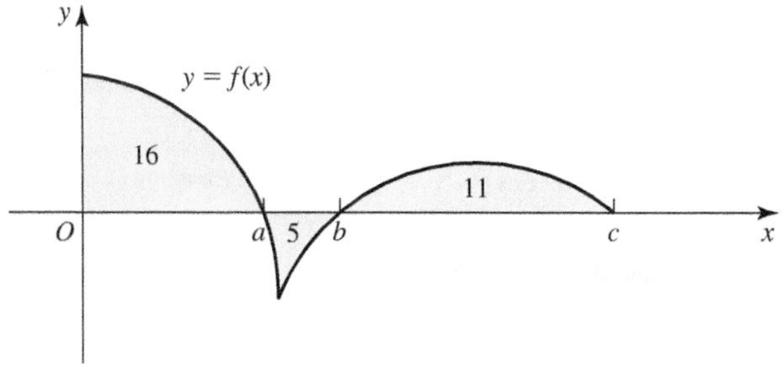

33. $\int_0^a f(x)\,dx$

34. $\int_0^b f(x)\,dx$

35. $\int_a^c f(x)\,dx$

36. $\int_0^c f(x)\,dx$

37–40. Net area from graphs *The accompanying figure shows four regions bounded by the graph of* $y = x \sin x$: R_1, R_2, R_3, *and* R_4, *whose areas are* $1, \pi - 1, \pi + 1$, *and* $2\pi - 1$, *respectively. (We verify these results later in the text.) Use this information to evaluate the following integrals.*

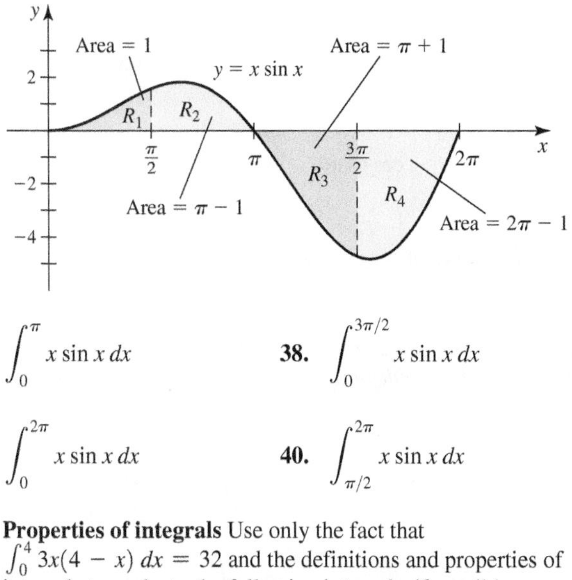

37. $\int_0^{\pi} x \sin x\,dx$

38. $\int_0^{3\pi/2} x \sin x\,dx$

39. $\int_0^{2\pi} x \sin x\,dx$

40. $\int_{\pi/2}^{2\pi} x \sin x\,dx$

41. Properties of integrals Use only the fact that $\int_0^4 3x(4 - x)\,dx = 32$ and the definitions and properties of integrals to evaluate the following integrals, if possible.

a. $\int_4^0 3x(4 - x)\,dx$

b. $\int_0^4 x(x - 4)\,dx$

c. $\int_4^0 6x(4 - x)\,dx$

d. $\int_0^8 3x(4 - x)\,dx$

42. Properties of integrals Suppose $\int_1^4 f(x)\,dx = 8$ and $\int_1^6 f(x)\,dx = 5$. Evaluate the following integrals.

a. $\int_1^4 (-3f(x))\,dx$

b. $\int_1^4 3f(x)\,dx$

c. $\int_6^4 12f(x)\,dx$

d. $\int_4^6 3f(x)\,dx$

43. Properties of integrals Suppose $\int_0^3 f(x)\,dx = 2$, $\int_3^6 f(x)\,dx = -5$, and $\int_3^6 g(x)\,dx = 1$. Evaluate the following integrals.

a. $\int_0^3 5f(x)\,dx$ **b.** $\int_3^6 (-3g(x))\,dx$

c. $\int_3^6 (3f(x) - g(x))\,dx$ **d.** $\int_6^3 (f(x) + 2g(x))\,dx$

44. Properties of integrals Suppose $f(x) \geq 0$ on $[0, 2]$, $f(x) \leq 0$ on $[2, 5]$, $\int_0^2 f(x)\,dx = 6$, and $\int_2^5 f(x)\,dx = -8$. Evaluate the following integrals.

a. $\int_0^5 f(x)\,dx$ **b.** $\int_0^5 |f(x)|\,dx$

c. $\int_2^5 4|f(x)|\,dx$ **d.** $\int_0^5 (f(x) + |f(x)|)\,dx$

45–46. Using properties of integrals *Use the value of the first integral I to evaluate the two given integrals.*

45. $I = \int_0^1 (x^3 - 2x)\,dx = -\frac{3}{4}$

a. $\int_0^1 (4x - 2x^3)\,dx$ **b.** $\int_1^0 (2x - x^3)\,dx$

46. $\int_0^{\pi/2} (2\sin\theta - \cos\theta)\,d\theta$

a. $\int_0^{\pi/2} (2\sin\theta - \cos\theta)\,d\theta$ **b.** $\int_{\pi/2}^0 (4\cos\theta - 8\sin\theta)\,d\theta$

47–52. Limits of sums *Use the definition of the definite integral to evaluate the following definite integrals. Use right Riemann sums and Theorem 5.1.*

47. $\int_0^2 (2x + 1)\,dx$ **48.** $\int_1^5 (1 - x)\,dx$

49. $\int_3^7 (4x + 6)\,dx$ **50.** $\int_0^2 (x^2 - 1)\,dx$

51. $\int_1^4 (x^2 - 1)\,dx$ **52.** $\int_0^2 4x^3\,dx$

Further Explorations

53. Explain why or why not Determine whether the following statements are true and give an explanation or counterexample.

a. If f is a constant function on the interval $[a, b]$, then the right and left Riemann sums give the exact value of $\int_a^b f(x)\,dx$, for any positive integer n.

b. If f is a linear function on the interval $[a, b]$, then a midpoint Riemann sum gives the exact value of $\int_a^b f(x)\,dx$, for any positive integer n.

c. $\int_0^{2\pi/a} \sin ax\,dx = \int_0^{2\pi/a} \cos ax\,dx = 0$. (*Hint:* Graph the functions and use properties of trigonometric functions.)

d. If $\int_a^b f(x)\,dx = \int_b^a f(x)\,dx$, then f is a constant function.

e. Property 4 of Table 5.4 implies that $\int_a^b xf(x)\,dx = x\int_a^b f(x)\,dx$.

T 54–57. Approximating definite integrals *Complete the following steps for the given integral and the given value of n.*

a. Sketch the graph of the integrand on the interval of integration.

b. Calculate Δx and the grid points $x_0, x_1, \ldots, x_n$, assuming a regular partition.

c. Calculate the left and right Riemann sums for the given value of n.

d. Determine which Riemann sum (left or right) underestimates the value of the definite integral and which overestimates the value of the definite integral.

54. $\int_0^2 (x^2 - 2)\,dx;\ n = 4$ **55.** $\int_3^6 (1 - 2x)\,dx;\ n = 6$

56. $\int_0^{\pi/2} \cos x\,dx;\ n = 4$ **57.** $\int_1^7 \frac{1}{x}\,dx;\ n = 6$

T 58–62. Approximating definite integrals with a calculator *Consider the following definite integrals.*

a. Write the left and right Riemann sums in sigma notation, for n = 20, 50, and 100. Then evaluate the sums using a calculator.

b. Based on your answers to part (a), make a conjecture about the value of the definite integral.

58. $\int_4^9 3\sqrt{x}\,dx$ **59.** $\int_0^1 (x^2 + 1)\,dx$

60. $\int_1^e \ln x\,dx$ **61.** $\int_0^1 \cos^{-1} x\,dx$

62. $\int_{-1}^1 \pi\cos\left(\frac{\pi x}{2}\right)dx$

T 63–66. Midpoint Riemann sums with a calculator *Consider the following definite integrals.*

a. Write the midpoint Riemann sum in sigma notation for an arbitrary value of n.

b. Evaluate each sum using a calculator with n = 20, 50, and 100. Use these values to estimate the value of the integral.

63. $\int_1^4 2\sqrt{x}\,dx$ **64.** $\int_{-1}^2 \sin\left(\frac{\pi x}{4}\right)dx$

65. $\int_0^4 (4x - x^2)\,dx$ **66.** $\int_0^{1/2} \sin^{-1} x\,dx$

67. More properties of integrals Consider two functions f and g on $[1, 6]$ such that $\int_1^6 f(x)\,dx = 10$, $\int_1^6 g(x)\,dx = 5$, $\int_4^6 f(x)\,dx = 5$, and $\int_1^4 g(x)\,dx = 2$. Evaluate the following integrals.

a. $\int_1^4 3f(x)\,dx$ **b.** $\int_1^6 (f(x) - g(x))\,dx$

c. $\int_1^4 (f(x) - g(x))\,dx$ d. $\int_4^6 (g(x) - f(x))\,dx$

e. $\int_4^6 8g(x)\,dx$ f. $\int_4^1 2f(x)\,dx$

68–71. Area versus net area *Graph the following functions. Then use geometry (not Riemann sums) to find the area and the net area of the region described.*

68. The region between the graph of $y = 4x - 8$ and the x-axis, for $-4 \le x \le 8$

69. The region between the graph of $y = -3x$ and the x-axis, for $-2 \le x \le 2$

70. The region between the graph of $y = 3x - 6$ and the x-axis, for $0 \le x \le 6$

71. The region between the graph of $y = 1 - |x|$ and the x-axis, for $-2 \le x \le 2$

72–75. Area by geometry *Use geometry to evaluate the following integrals.*

72. $\int_{-2}^{3} |x + 1|\,dx$ **73.** $\int_1^6 |2x - 4|\,dx$

74. $\int_1^6 (3x - 6)\,dx$ **75.** $\int_{-6}^{4} \sqrt{24 - 2x - x^2}\,dx$

Additional Exercises

76. Integrating piecewise continuous functions Suppose f is continuous on the intervals $[a, p]$ and $(p, b]$, where $a < p < b$, with a finite jump at p. Form a uniform partition on the interval $[a, p]$ with n grid points and another uniform partition on the interval $[p, b]$ with m grid points, where p is a grid point of both partitions. Write a Riemann sum for $\int_a^b f(x)\,dx$ and separate it into two pieces for $[a, p]$ and $[p, b]$. Explain why $\int_a^b f(x)\,dx = \int_a^p f(x)\,dx + \int_p^b f(x)\,dx$.

77–78. Integrating piecewise continuous functions *Use geometry and the result of Exercise 76 to evaluate the following integrals.*

77. $\int_0^{10} f(x)\,dx$, where $f(x) = \begin{cases} 2 & \text{if } 0 \le x \le 5 \\ 3 & \text{if } 5 < x \le 10 \end{cases}$

78. $\int_1^6 f(x)\,dx$, where $f(x) = \begin{cases} 2x & \text{if } 1 \le x < 4 \\ 10 - 2x & \text{if } 4 \le x \le 6 \end{cases}$

79–80. Integrating piecewise continuous functions *Recall that the* floor function $\lfloor x \rfloor$ *is the greatest integer less than or equal to x and that the* ceiling function $\lceil x \rceil$ *is the least integer greater than or equal to x. Use the result of Exercise 76 and the graphs to evaluate the following integrals.*

79. $\int_1^5 x\lfloor x \rfloor\,dx$

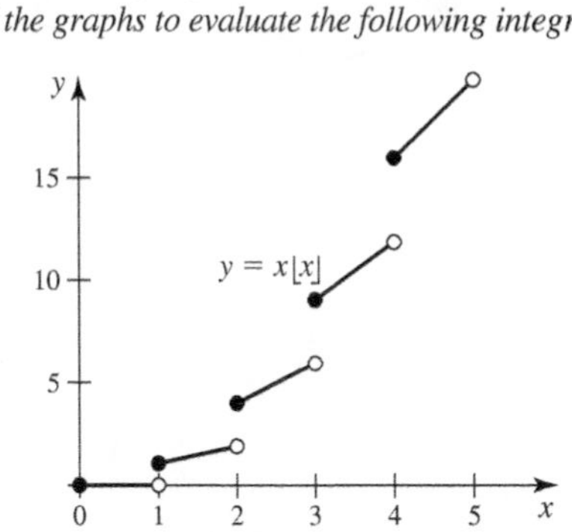

80. $\int_0^4 \frac{x}{\lceil x \rceil}\,dx$

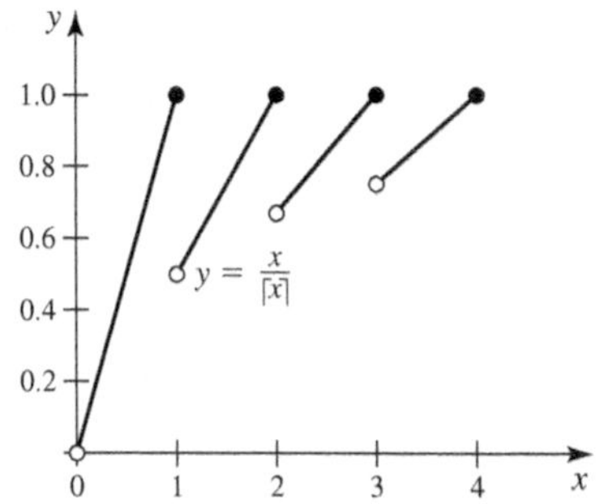

81. Constants in integrals Use the definition of the definite integral to justify the property $\int_a^b cf(x)\,dx = c\int_a^b f(x)\,dx$, where f is continuous and c is a real number.

82. Zero net area If $0 < c < d$, then find the value of b (in terms of c and d) for which $\int_c^d (x + b)\,dx = 0$.

83. A nonintegrable function Consider the function defined on $[0, 1]$ such that $f(x) = 1$ if x is a rational number and $f(x) = 0$ if x is irrational. This function has an infinite number of discontinuities, and the integral $\int_0^1 f(x)\,dx$ does not exist. Show that the right, left, and midpoint Riemann sums on *regular* partitions with n subintervals equal 1 for all n. (*Hint:* Between any two real numbers lie a rational and an irrational number.)

84. Powers of x by Riemann sums Consider the integral $I(p) = \int_0^1 x^p\,dx$, where p is a positive integer.

a. Write the left Riemann sum for the integral with n subintervals.

b. It is a fact (proved by the 17th-century mathematicians Fermat and Pascal) that $\lim_{n\to\infty} \frac{1}{n}\sum_{k=0}^{n-1}\left(\frac{k}{n}\right)^p = \frac{1}{p+1}$. Use this fact to evaluate $I(p)$.

85. An exact integration formula Evaluate $\int_a^b \frac{dx}{x^2}$, where $0 < a < b$, using the definition of the definite integral and the following steps.

a. Assume $\{x_0, x_1, \ldots, x_n\}$ is a partition of $[a, b]$ with $\Delta x_k = x_k - x_{k-1}$, for $k = 1, 2, \ldots, n$. Show that $x_{k-1} \le \sqrt{x_{k-1}x_k} \le x_k$, for $k = 1, 2, \ldots, n$.

b. Show that $\frac{1}{x_{k-1}} - \frac{1}{x_k} = \frac{\Delta x_k}{x_{k-1}x_k}$, for $k = 1, 2, \ldots, n$.

c. Simplify the general Riemann sum for $\int_a^b \frac{dx}{x^2}$ using $\bar{x}_k^* = \sqrt{x_{k-1}x_k}$.

d. Conclude that $\int_a^b \frac{dx}{x^2} = \frac{1}{a} - \frac{1}{b}$.

(*Source: The College Mathematics Journal,* 32, 4, Sep 2001)

QUICK CHECK ANSWERS

1. -20 **2.** $f(x) = 1 - x$ is one possibility. **3.** 0 **4.** 10; $c(b - a)$ **5.** 0 **6.** $\frac{3}{2}; \frac{5}{2}$ ◄

5.3 Fundamental Theorem of Calculus

Evaluating definite integrals using limits of Riemann sums, as described in Section 5.2, is usually not possible or practical. Fortunately, there is a powerful and practical method for evaluating definite integrals, which is developed in this section. Along the way, we discover the inverse relationship between differentiation and integration, expressed in the most important result of calculus, the Fundamental Theorem of Calculus. The first step in this process is to introduce *area functions* (first seen in Section 1.2).

Area Functions

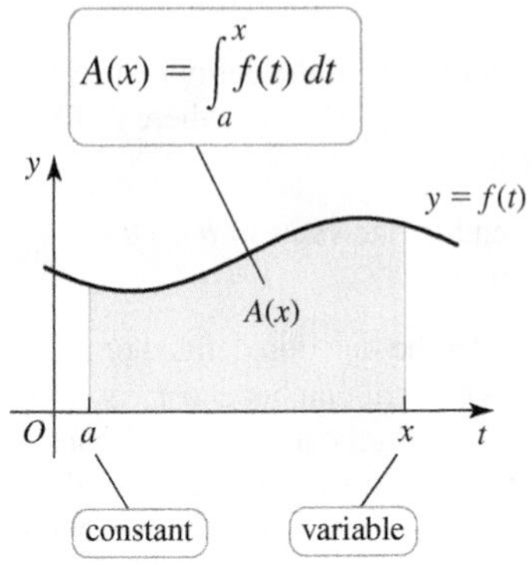

Figure 5.32

The concept of an area function is crucial to the discussion about the connection between derivatives and integrals. We start with a continuous function $y = f(t)$ defined for $t \geq a$, where a is a fixed number. The *area function* for f with left endpoint a is denoted $A(x)$; it gives the net area of the region bounded by the graph of f and the t-axis between $t = a$ and $t = x$ (Figure 5.32). The net area of this region is also given by the definite integral

Independent variable of the area function

$$A(x) = \int_a^x f(t)\,dt.$$

Variable of integration (dummy variable)

➤ Suppose you want to devise a function A whose value is the sum of the first n positive integers, $1 + 2 + \cdots + n$. The most compact way to write this function is $A(n) = \sum_{k=1}^{n} k$, for $n \geq 1$. In this function, n is the independent variable of the function A, and k, which is internal to the sum, is a dummy variable. This function involving a sum is analogous to an area function involving an integral.

Notice that x is the upper limit of the integral *and* the independent variable of the area function: As x changes, so does the net area under the curve. Because the symbol x is already in use as the independent variable for A, we must choose another symbol for the variable of integration. Any symbol—except x—can be used because it is a *dummy variable*; we have chosen t as the integration variable.

Figure 5.33 gives a general view of how an area function is generated. Suppose that f is a continuous function and a is a fixed number. Now choose a point $b > a$. The net area

➤ Notice that t is the independent variable when we plot f and x is the independent variable when we plot A.

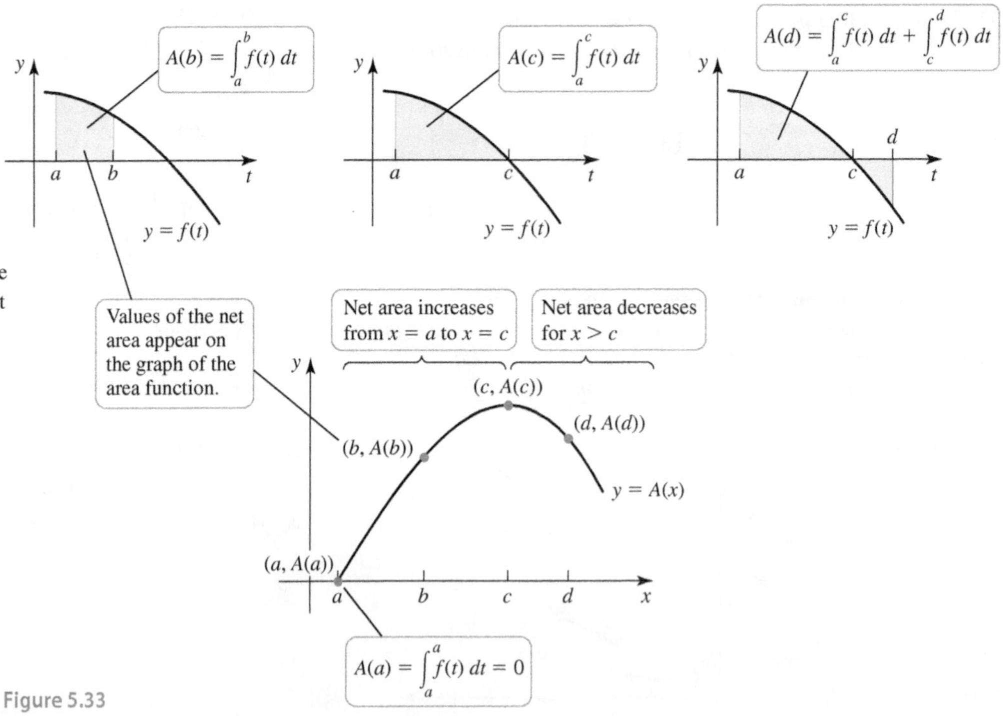

Figure 5.33

of the region between the graph of f and the t-axis on the interval $[a, b]$ is $A(b)$. Moving the right endpoint to $(c, 0)$ or $(d, 0)$ produces different regions with net areas $A(c)$ and $A(d)$, respectively. In general, if $x > a$ is a variable point, then $A(x) = \int_a^x f(t)\,dt$ is the net area of the region between the graph of f and the t-axis on the interval $[a, x]$.

Figure 5.33 shows how $A(x)$ varies with respect to x. Notice that $A(a) = \int_a^a f(t)\,dt = 0$. Then for $x > a$, the net area increases for $x < c$, at which point $f(c) = 0$. For $x > c$, the function f is negative, which produces a negative contribution to the area function. As a result, the area function decreases for $x > c$.

> **DEFINITION Area Function**
>
> Let f be a continuous function, for $t \geq a$. The **area function for f with left endpoint a** is
>
> $$A(x) = \int_a^x f(t)\,dt,$$
>
> where $x \geq a$. The area function gives the net area of the region bounded by the graph of f and the t-axis on the interval $[a, x]$.

The following two examples illustrate the idea of area functions.

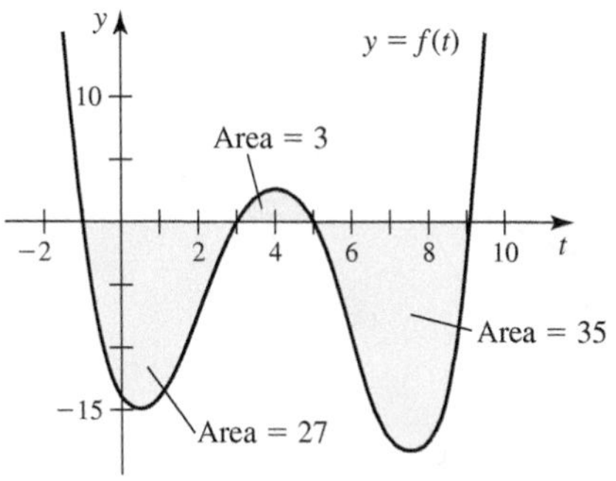

Figure 5.34

EXAMPLE 1 Comparing area functions The graph of f is shown in Figure 5.34 with areas of various regions marked. Let $A(x) = \int_{-1}^x f(t)\,dt$ and $F(x) = \int_3^x f(t)\,dt$ be two area functions for f (note the different left endpoints). Evaluate the following area functions.

a. $A(3)$ and $F(3)$ **b.** $A(5)$ and $F(5)$ **c.** $A(9)$ and $F(9)$

SOLUTION

a. The value of $A(3) = \int_{-1}^3 f(t)\,dt$ is the net area of the region bounded by the graph of f and the t-axis on the interval $[-1, 3]$. Using the graph of f, we see that $A(3) = -27$ (because this region has an area of 27 and lies below the t-axis). On the other hand, $F(3) = \int_3^3 f(t)\,dt = 0$ by Property 1 of Table 5.4. Notice that $A(3) - F(3) = -27$.

b. The value of $A(5) = \int_{-1}^5 f(t)\,dt$ is found by subtracting the area of the region that lies below the t-axis on $[-1, 3]$ from the area of the region that lies above the t-axis on $[3, 5]$. Therefore, $A(5) = 3 - 27 = -24$. Similarly, $F(5)$ is the net area of the region bounded by the graph of f and the t-axis on the interval $[3, 5]$; therefore, $F(5) = 3$. Notice that $A(5) - F(5) = -27$.

c. Reasoning as in parts (a) and (b), we see that $A(9) = -27 + 3 - 35 = -59$ and $F(9) = 3 - 35 = -32$. As before, observe that $A(9) - F(9) = -27$.

Related Exercises 11–12 ◀

Example 1 illustrates the important fact (to be explained shortly) that two area functions of the same function differ by a constant; in Example 1, the constant is -27.

QUICK CHECK 1 In Example 1, let $B(x)$ be the area function for f with left endpoint 5. Evaluate $B(5)$ and $B(9)$. ◀

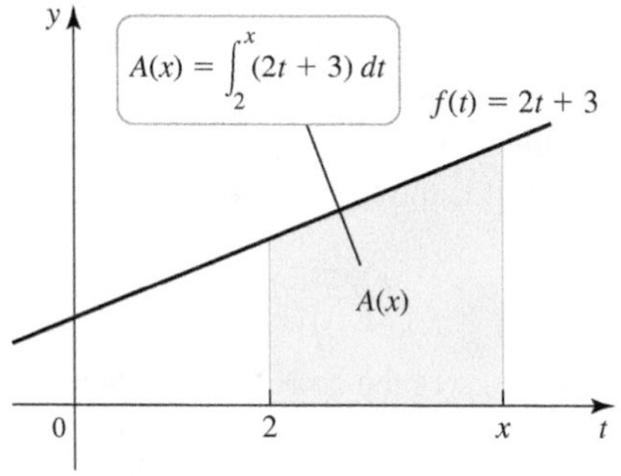

Figure 5.35

EXAMPLE 2 Area of a trapezoid Consider the trapezoid bounded by the line $f(t) = 2t + 3$ and the t-axis from $t = 2$ to $t = x$ (Figure 5.35). The area function $A(x) = \int_2^x f(t)\,dt$ gives the area of the trapezoid, for $x \geq 2$.

a. Evaluate $A(2)$. **b.** Evaluate $A(5)$.

c. Find and graph the area function $y = A(x)$, for $x \geq 2$.

d. Compare the derivative of A to f.

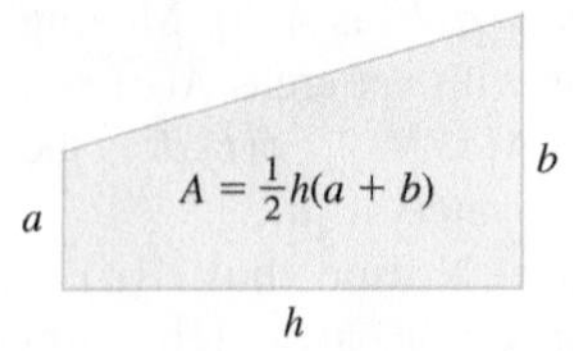

Figure 5.36

SOLUTION

a. By Property 1 of Table 5.4, $A(2) = \int_2^2 (2t + 3)\, dt = 0$.

b. Notice that $A(5)$ is the area of the trapezoid (Figure 5.35) bounded by the line $y = 2t + 3$ and the t-axis on the interval $[2, 5]$. Using the area formula for a trapezoid (Figure 5.36), we find that

$$A(5) = \int_2^5 (2t + 3)\, dt = \frac{1}{2} \underbrace{(5 - 2)}_{\substack{\text{distance between} \\ \text{parallel sides}}} \cdot \underbrace{(f(2) + f(5))}_{\substack{\text{sum of parallel} \\ \text{side lengths}}} = \frac{1}{2} \cdot 3(7 + 13) = 30.$$

c. Now the right endpoint of the base is a variable $x \geq 2$ (Figure 5.37). The distance between the parallel sides of the trapezoid is $x - 2$. By the area formula for a trapezoid, the area of this trapezoid for any $x \geq 2$ is

$$\begin{aligned} A(x) &= \frac{1}{2} \underbrace{(x - 2)}_{\substack{\text{distance between} \\ \text{parallel sides}}} \cdot \underbrace{(f(2) + f(x))}_{\substack{\text{sum of parallel} \\ \text{side lengths}}} \\ &= \frac{1}{2}(x - 2)(7 + 2x + 3) \\ &= (x - 2)(x + 5) \\ &= x^2 + 3x - 10. \end{aligned}$$

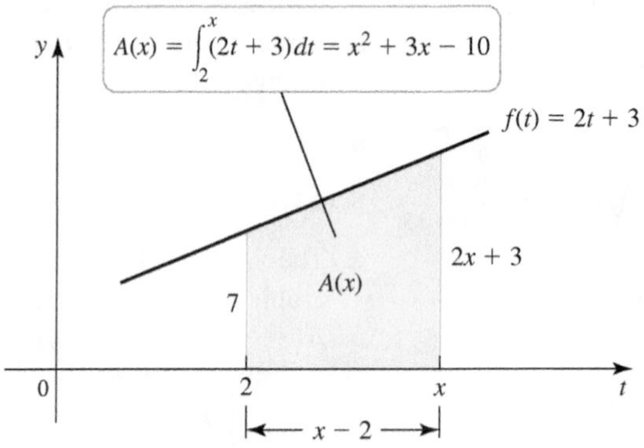

Figure 5.37

Expressing the area function in terms of an integral with a variable upper limit we have

$$A(x) = \int_2^x (2t + 3)\, dt = x^2 + 3x - 10.$$

Because the line $f(t) = 2t + 3$ is above the t-axis, for $t \geq 2$, the area function $A(x) = x^2 + 3x - 10$ is an increasing function of x with $A(2) = 0$ (Figure 5.38).

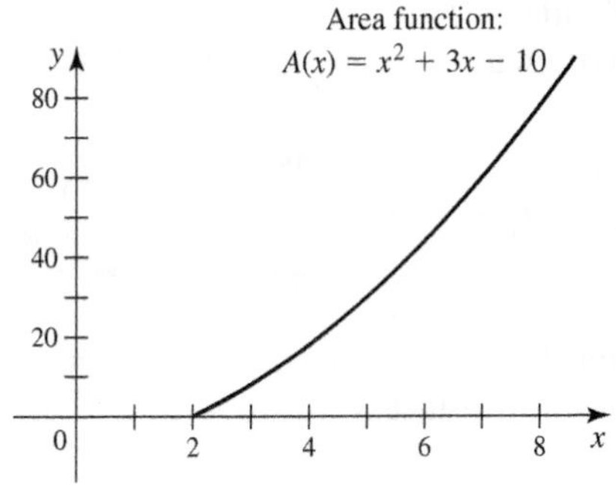

Figure 5.38

d. Differentiating the area function, we find that

$$A'(x) = \frac{d}{dx}(x^2 + 3x - 10) = 2x + 3 = f(x).$$

Therefore, $A'(x) = f(x)$, or equivalently, the area function A is an antiderivative of f. We soon show that this relationship is not an accident; it is the first part of the Fundamental Theorem of Calculus.

➤ Recall that if $A'(x) = f(x)$, then f is the derivative of A; equivalently, A is an antiderivative of f.

Related Exercises 13–22 ◀

QUICK CHECK 2 Verify that the area function in Example 2c gives the correct area when $x = 6$ and $x = 10$. ◀

Fundamental Theorem of Calculus

Example 2 suggests that the area function A for a linear function f is an antiderivative of f; that is, $A'(x) = f(x)$. Our goal is to show that this conjecture holds for more general functions. Let's start with an intuitive argument; a formal proof is given at the end of the section.

Assume that f is a continuous function defined on an interval $[a, b]$. As before, $A(x) = \int_a^x f(t)\,dt$ is the area function for f with a left endpoint a: It gives the net area of the region bounded by the graph of f and the t-axis on the interval $[a, x]$, for $x \geq a$. Figure 5.39 is the key to the argument.

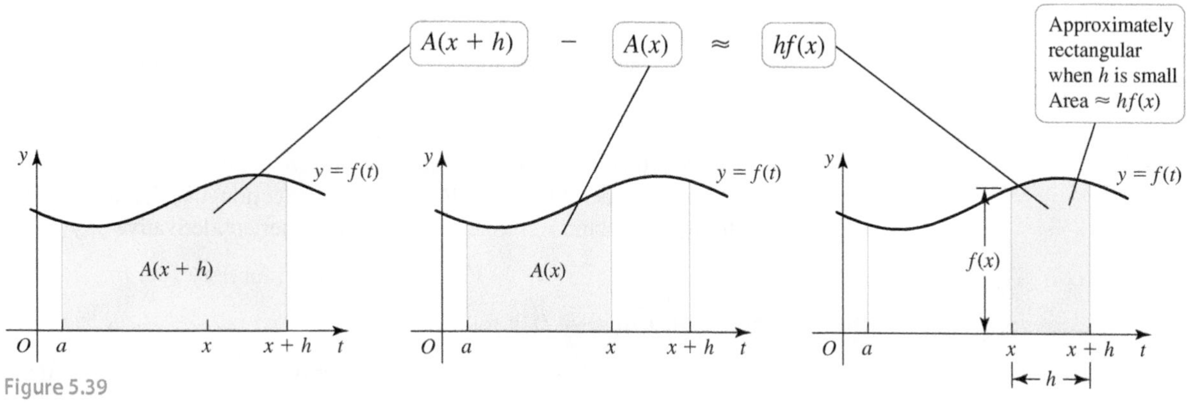

Figure 5.39

Note that with $h > 0$, $A(x + h)$ is the net area of the region whose base is the interval $[a, x + h]$ and $A(x)$ is the net area of the region whose base is the interval $[a, x]$. So the difference $A(x + h) - A(x)$ is the net area of the region whose base is the interval $[x, x + h]$. If h is small, the region in question is nearly rectangular with a base of length h and a height $f(x)$. Therefore, the net area of this region is

$$A(x + h) - A(x) \approx h f(x).$$

Dividing by h, we have

$$\frac{A(x + h) - A(x)}{h} \approx f(x).$$

An analogous argument can be made with $h < 0$. Now observe that as h tends to zero, this approximation improves. In the limit as $h \to 0$, we have

$$\underbrace{\lim_{h \to 0} \frac{A(x + h) - A(x)}{h}}_{A'(x)} = \underbrace{\lim_{h \to 0} f(x)}_{f(x)}.$$

➤ Recall that

$$f'(x) = \lim_{h \to 0} \frac{f(x + h) - f(x)}{h}.$$

If the function f is replaced with A, then

$$A'(x) = \lim_{h \to 0} \frac{A(x + h) - A(x)}{h}.$$

We see that indeed $A'(x) = f(x)$. Because $A(x) = \int_a^x f(t)\,dt$, the result can also be written

$$A'(x) = \frac{d}{dx} \underbrace{\int_a^x f(t)\,dt}_{A(x)} = f(x),$$

which says that the derivative of the integral of f is f. This conclusion is the first part of the Fundamental Theorem of Calculus.

THEOREM 5.3 (PART 1) Fundamental Theorem of Calculus
If f is continuous on $[a, b]$, then the area function

$$A(x) = \int_a^x f(t)\,dt, \quad \text{for} \quad a \le x \le b,$$

is continuous on $[a, b]$ and differentiable on (a, b). The area function satisfies $A'(x) = f(x)$. Equivalently,

$$A'(x) = \frac{d}{dx}\int_a^x f(t)\,dt = f(x),$$

which means that the area function of f is an antiderivative of f on $[a, b]$.

Given that A is an antiderivative of f on $[a, b]$, it is one short step to a powerful method for evaluating definite integrals. Remember (Section 4.9) that any two antiderivatives of f differ by a constant. Assuming that F is any other antiderivative of f on $[a, b]$, we have

$$F(x) = A(x) + C, \text{ for } a \le x \le b.$$

Noting that $A(a) = 0$, it follows that

$$F(b) - F(a) = (A(b) + C) - (A(a) + C) = A(b).$$

Writing $A(b)$ in terms of a definite integral leads to the remarkable result

$$A(b) = \int_a^b f(x)\,dx = F(b) - F(a).$$

We have shown that to evaluate a definite integral of f, we

- find any antiderivative of f, which we call F; and
- compute $F(b) - F(a)$, the difference in the values of F between the upper and lower limits of integration.

This process is the essence of the second part of the Fundamental Theorem of Calculus.

THEOREM 5.3 (PART 2) Fundamental Theorem of Calculus
If f is continuous on $[a, b]$ and F is any antiderivative of f on $[a, b]$, then

$$\int_a^b f(x)\,dx = F(b) - F(a).$$

It is customary and convenient to denote the difference $F(b) - F(a)$ by $F(x)\big|_a^b$. Using this shorthand, the Fundamental Theorem is summarized in Figure 5.40.

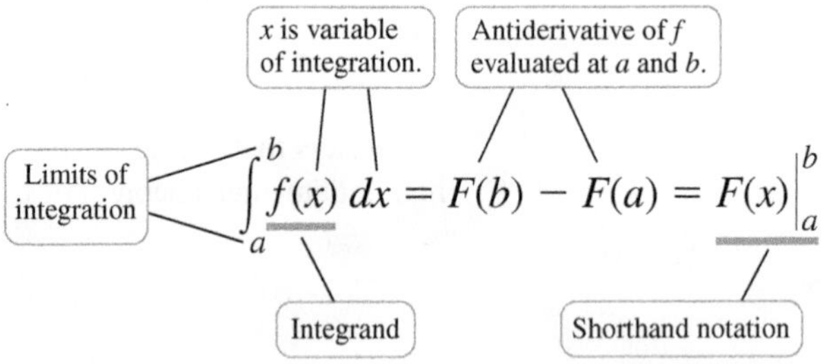

Figure 5.40

QUICK CHECK 3 Evaluate $\left(\dfrac{x}{x+1}\right)\Bigg|_1^2$. ◄

The Inverse Relationship between Differentiation and Integration It is worth pausing to observe that the two parts of the Fundamental Theorem express the inverse relationship between differentiation and integration. Part 1 of the Fundamental Theorem says

$$\frac{d}{dx}\int_a^x f(t)\,dt = f(x),$$

or the derivative of the integral of f is f itself.

Noting that f is an antiderivative of f', Part 2 of the Fundamental Theorem says

$$\int_a^b f'(x)\,dx = f(b) - f(a),$$

or the definite integral of the derivative of f is given in terms of f evaluated at two points. In other words, the integral "undoes" the derivative.

QUICK CHECK 4 Explain why f is an antiderivative of f'. ◂

This last relationship is important because it expresses the integral as an *accumulation* operation. Suppose we know the rate of change of f (which is f') on an interval $[a, b]$. The Fundamental Theorem says that we can integrate (that is, sum or accumulate) the rate of change over that interval and the result is simply the difference in f evaluated at the endpoints. You will see this accumulation property used many times in the next chapter. Now let's use the Fundamental Theorem to evaluate definite integrals.

EXAMPLE 3 Evaluating definite integrals Evaluate the following definite integrals using the Fundamental Theorem of Calculus, Part 2. Interpret each result geometrically.

a. $\int_0^{10} (60x - 6x^2)\,dx$ **b.** $\int_0^{2\pi} 3\sin x\,dx$ **c.** $\int_{1/16}^{1/4} \frac{\sqrt{t} - 1}{t}\,dt$

SOLUTION

a. Using the antiderivative rules of Section 4.9, an antiderivative of $60x - 6x^2$ is $30x^2 - 2x^3$. By the Fundamental Theorem, the value of the definite integral is

$$\int_0^{10} (60x - 6x^2)\,dx = (30x^2 - 2x^3)\Big|_0^{10} \quad \text{Fundamental Theorem}$$
$$= (30\cdot 10^2 - 2\cdot 10^3) - (30\cdot 0^2 - 2\cdot 0^3) \quad \text{Evaluate at } x = 10 \text{ and } x = 0.$$
$$= (3000 - 2000) - 0$$
$$= 1000. \quad \text{Simplify.}$$

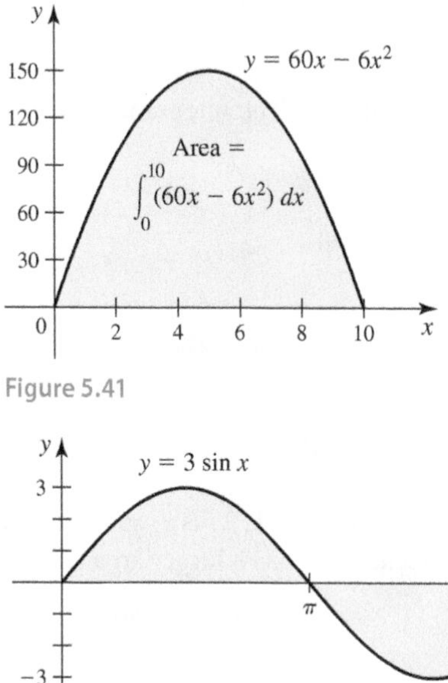

Figure 5.41

Because f is positive on $[0, 10]$, the definite integral $\int_0^{10}(60x - 6x^2)\,dx$ is the area of the region between the graph of f and the x-axis on the interval $[0, 10]$ (Figure 5.41).

b. As shown in Figure 5.42, the region bounded by the graph of $f(x) = 3\sin x$ and the x-axis on $[0, 2\pi]$ consists of two parts, one above the x-axis and one below the x-axis. By the symmetry of f, these two regions have the same area, so the definite integral over $[0, 2\pi]$ is zero. Let's confirm this fact. An antiderivative of $f(x) = 3\sin x$ is $-3\cos x$. Therefore, the value of the definite integral is

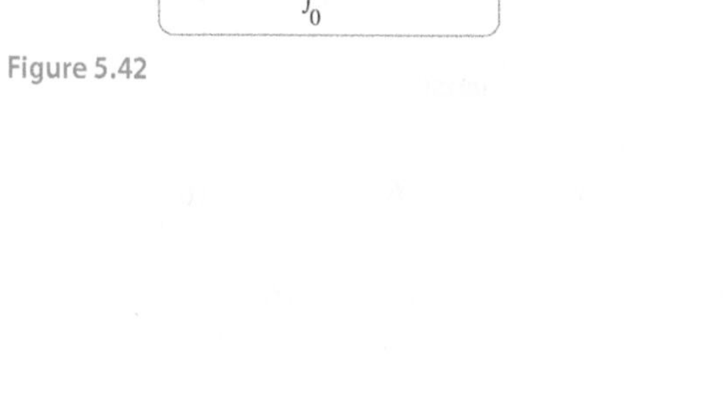

Figure 5.42

$$\int_0^{2\pi} 3\sin x\,dx = -3\cos x\Big|_0^{2\pi} \quad \text{Fundamental Theorem}$$
$$= (-3\cos(2\pi)) - (-3\cos(0)) \quad \text{Substitute.}$$
$$= -3 - (-3) = 0. \quad \text{Simplify.}$$

c. Although the variable of integration is t, rather than x, we proceed as in parts (a) and (b) after simplifying the integrand:

$$\frac{\sqrt{t} - 1}{t} = \frac{1}{\sqrt{t}} - \frac{1}{t}.$$

➤ We know that

$$\frac{d}{dt}(t^{1/2}) = \frac{1}{2}t^{-1/2}.$$

Therefore, $\int \frac{1}{2}t^{-1/2}\,dt = t^{1/2} + C$

and $\int \frac{dt}{\sqrt{t}} = \int t^{-1/2}\,dt = 2t^{1/2} + C.$

Finding antiderivatives with respect to t and applying the Fundamental Theorem, we have

$$\begin{aligned}
\int_{1/16}^{1/4} \frac{\sqrt{t}-1}{t}\,dt &= \int_{1/16}^{1/4}\left(t^{-1/2} - \frac{1}{t}\right)dt && \text{Simplify the integrand.}\\
&= \left(2t^{1/2} - \ln|t|\right)\Big|_{1/16}^{1/4} && \text{Fundamental Theorem}\\
&= \left(2\left(\frac{1}{4}\right)^{1/2} - \ln\frac{1}{4}\right) - \left(2\left(\frac{1}{16}\right)^{1/2} - \ln\frac{1}{16}\right) && \text{Evaluate.}\\
&= 1 - \ln\frac{1}{4} - \frac{1}{2} + \ln\frac{1}{16} && \text{Simplify.}\\
&= \frac{1}{2} - \ln 4 \approx -0.8863.
\end{aligned}$$

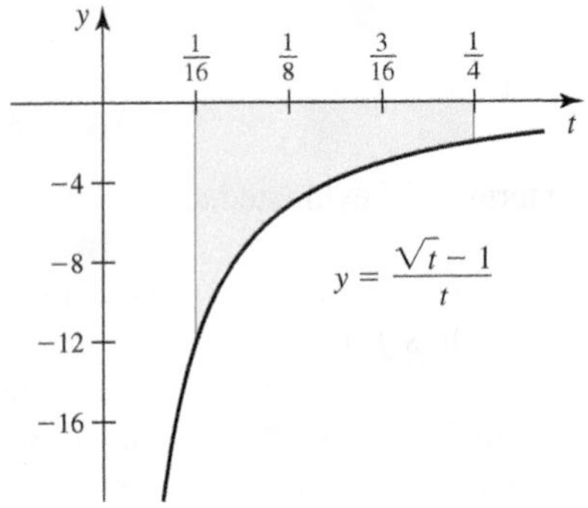

Figure 5.43

The definite integral is negative because the graph of f lies below the t-axis (Figure 5.43). *Related Exercises 23–50* ◀

EXAMPLE 4 **Net areas and definite integrals** The graph of $f(x) = 6x(x+1)(x-2)$ is shown in Figure 5.44. The region R_1 is bounded by the curve and the x-axis on the interval $[-1, 0]$, and R_2 is bounded by the curve and the x-axis on the interval $[0, 2]$.

a. Find the *net area* of the region between the curve and the x-axis on $[-1, 2]$.

b. Find the *area* of the region between the curve and the x-axis on $[-1, 2]$.

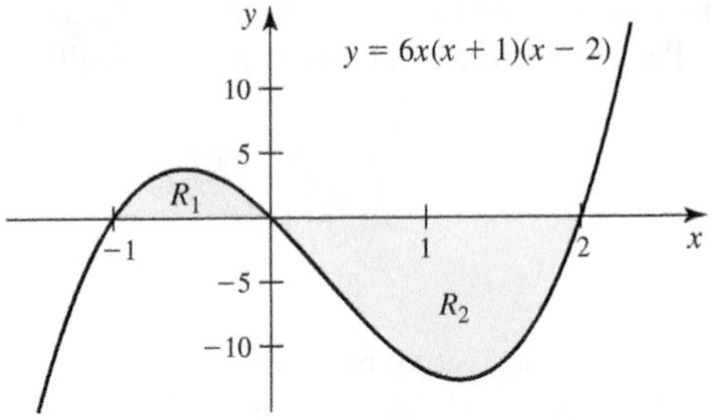

Figure 5.44

SOLUTION

a. The net area of the region is given by a definite integral. The integrand f is first expanded to find an antiderivative:

$$\begin{aligned}
\int_{-1}^{2} f(x)\,dx &= \int_{-1}^{2}(6x^3 - 6x^2 - 12x)\,dx. && \text{Expand } f.\\
&= \left(\frac{3}{2}x^4 - 2x^3 - 6x^2\right)\Big|_{-1}^{2} && \text{Fundamental Theorem}\\
&= -\frac{27}{2}. && \text{Simplify.}
\end{aligned}$$

The net area of the region between the curve and the x-axis on $[-1, 2]$ is $-\frac{27}{2}$, which is the area of R_1 *minus* the area of R_2 (Figure 5.44). Because R_2 has a larger area than R_1, the net area is negative.

b. The region R_1 lies above the x-axis, so its area is

$$\int_{-1}^{0}(6x^3 - 6x^2 - 12x)\,dx = \left(\frac{3}{2}x^4 - 2x^3 - 6x^2\right)\Big|_{-1}^{0} = \frac{5}{2}.$$

The region R_2 lies below the x-axis, so its net area is negative:

$$\int_{0}^{2}(6x^3 - 6x^2 - 12x)\,dx = \left(\frac{3}{2}x^4 - 2x^3 - 6x^2\right)\Big|_{0}^{2} = -16.$$

Therefore, the *area* of R_2 is $-(-16) = 16$. The combined area of R_1 and R_2 is $\frac{5}{2} + 16 = \frac{37}{2}$. We could also find the area of this region directly by evaluating $\int_{-1}^{2}|f(x)|\,dx$. *Related Exercises 51–60* ◀

Examples 3 and 4 make use of Part 2 of the Fundamental Theorem, which is the most potent tool for evaluating definite integrals. The remaining examples illustrate the use of the equally important Part 1 of the Fundamental Theorem.

EXAMPLE 5 Derivatives of integrals Use Part 1 of the Fundamental Theorem to simplify the following expressions.

a. $\dfrac{d}{dx}\displaystyle\int_1^x \sin^2 t\,dt$ **b.** $\dfrac{d}{dx}\displaystyle\int_x^5 \sqrt{t^2+1}\,dt$ **c.** $\dfrac{d}{dx}\displaystyle\int_0^{x^2} \cos t^2\,dt$

SOLUTION

a. Using Part 1 of the Fundamental Theorem, we see that

$$\frac{d}{dx}\int_1^x \sin^2 t\,dt = \sin^2 x.$$

b. To apply Part 1 of the Fundamental Theorem, the variable must appear in the upper limit. Therefore, we use the fact that $\int_a^b f(t)\,dt = -\int_b^a f(t)\,dt$ and then apply the Fundamental Theorem:

$$\frac{d}{dx}\int_x^5 \sqrt{t^2+1}\,dt = -\frac{d}{dx}\int_5^x \sqrt{t^2+1}\,dt = -\sqrt{x^2+1}.$$

c. The upper limit of the integral is not x, but a function of x. Therefore, the function to be differentiated is a composite function, which requires the Chain Rule. We let $u = x^2$ to produce

$$y = g(u) = \int_0^u \cos t^2\,dt.$$

By the Chain Rule,

$$\begin{aligned}
\frac{d}{dx}\int_0^{x^2} \cos t^2\,dt &= \frac{dy}{dx} = \frac{dy}{du}\frac{du}{dx} && \text{Chain Rule}\\
&= \left(\frac{d}{du}\int_0^u \cos t^2\,dt\right)(2x) && \text{Substitute for } g\text{; note that } u'(x) = 2x.\\
&= (\cos u^2)(2x) && \text{Fundamental Theorem}\\
&= 2x\cos x^4. && \text{Substitute } u = x^2.
\end{aligned}$$

Related Exercises 61–68

➤ Example 5c illustrates one case of Leibniz's Rule:

$$\frac{d}{dx}\int_a^{g(x)} f(t)\,dt = f(g(x))g'(x).$$

EXAMPLE 6 Working with area functions Consider the function f shown in Figure 5.45 and its area function $A(x) = \int_0^x f(t)\,dt$, for $0 \le x \le 17$. Assume that the four regions R_1, R_2, R_3, and R_4 have the same area. Based on the graph of f, do the following.

a. Find the zeros of A on $[0, 17]$.

b. Find the points on $[0, 17]$ at which A has local maxima or local minima.

c. Sketch a graph of A, for $0 \le x \le 17$.

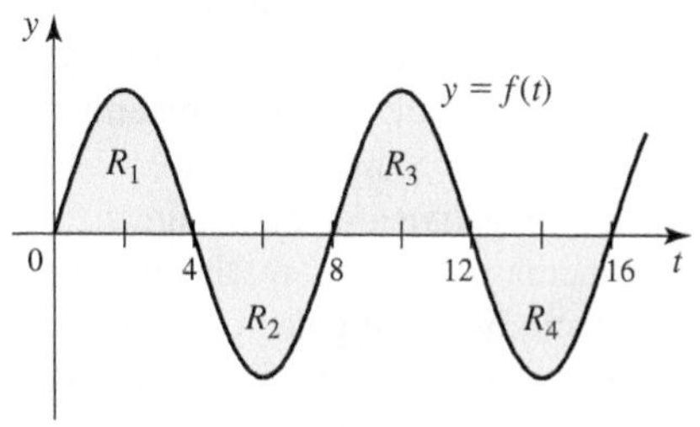

Figure 5.45

SOLUTION

a. The area function $A(x) = \int_0^x f(t)\,dt$ gives the net area bounded by the graph of f and the t-axis on the interval $[0, x]$ (Figure 5.46a). Therefore, $A(0) = \int_0^0 f(t)\,dt = 0$. Because R_1 and R_2 have the same area but lie on opposite sides of the t-axis, it follows that $A(8) = \int_0^8 f(t)\,dt = 0$. Similarly, $A(16) = \int_0^{16} f(t)\,dt = 0$. Therefore, the zeros of A are $x = 0$, 8, and 16.

b. Observe that the function f is positive, for $0 < t < 4$, which implies that $A(x)$ increases as x increases from 0 to 4 (Figure 5.46b). Then as x increases from 4 to 8, $A(x)$ decreases because f is negative, for $4 < t < 8$ (Figure 5.46c). Similarly, $A(x)$ increases as x increases from $x = 8$ to $x = 12$ (Figure 5.46d) and decreases from $x = 12$ to $x = 16$. By the First Derivative Test, A has local minima at $x = 8$ and $x = 16$ and local maxima at $x = 4$ and $x = 12$ (Figure 5.46e).

➤ Recall that local extrema occur only at interior points of the domain.

c. Combining the observations in parts (a) and (b) leads to a qualitative sketch of A (Figure 5.46e). Note that $A(x) \geq 0$, for all $x \geq 0$. It is not possible to determine function values (y-coordinates) on the graph of A.

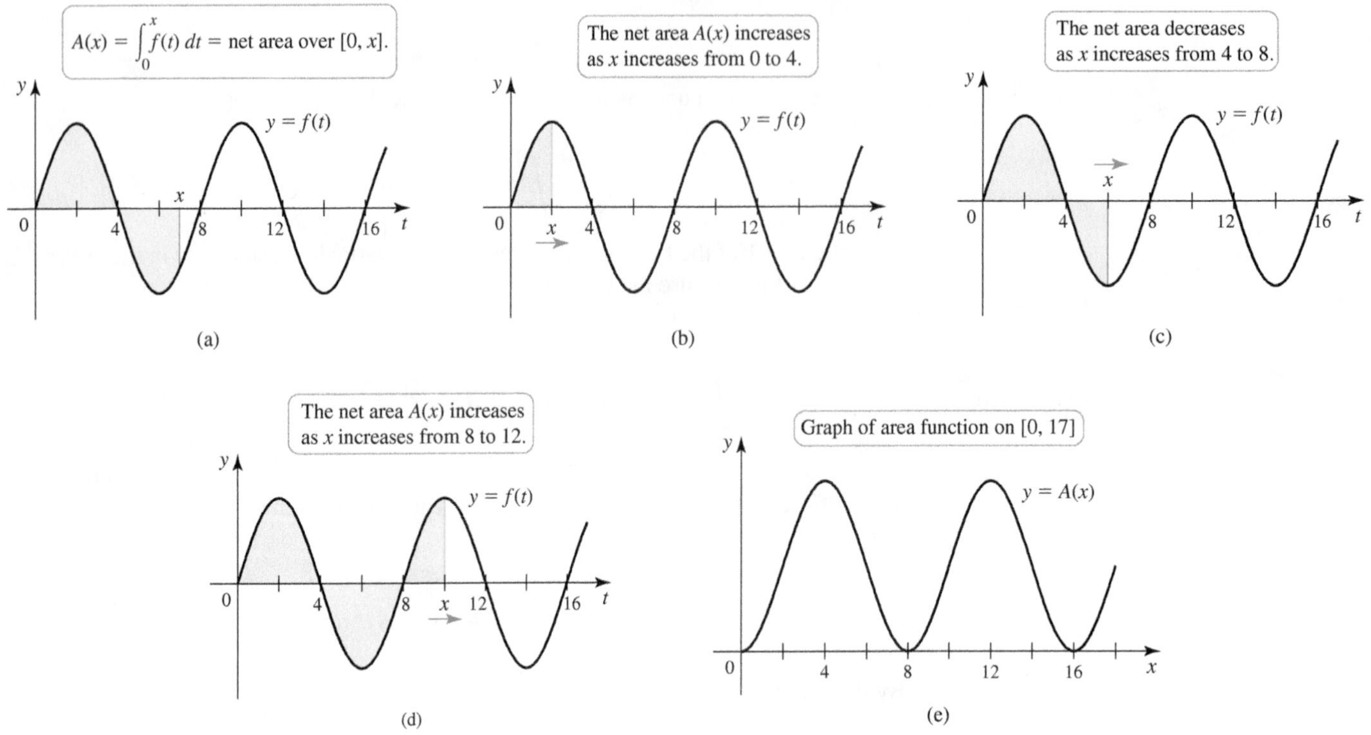

Figure 5.46

Related Exercises 69–80 ◀

EXAMPLE 7 **The sine integral function** Let

$$g(t) = \begin{cases} \dfrac{\sin t}{t} & \text{if } t > 0 \\ 1 & \text{if } t = 0. \end{cases}$$

Graph the *sine integral function* $S(x) = \int_0^x g(t)\,dt$, for $x \geq 0$.

SOLUTION Notice that S is an area function for g. The independent variable of S is x, and t has been chosen as the (dummy) variable of integration. A good way to start is by graphing the integrand g (Figure 5.47a). The function oscillates with a decreasing amplitude with $g(0) = 1$. Beginning with $S(0) = 0$, the area function S increases until $x = \pi$ because g is positive on $(0, \pi)$. However, on $(\pi, 2\pi)$, g is negative and the net area decreases. On $(2\pi, 3\pi)$, g is positive again, so S again increases. Therefore, the graph of S has alternating local maxima and minima. Because the amplitude of g decreases, each maximum of S is less than the previous maximum and each minimum of S is greater than the previous minimum (Figure 5.47b). Determining the exact value of S at these maxima and minima is difficult.

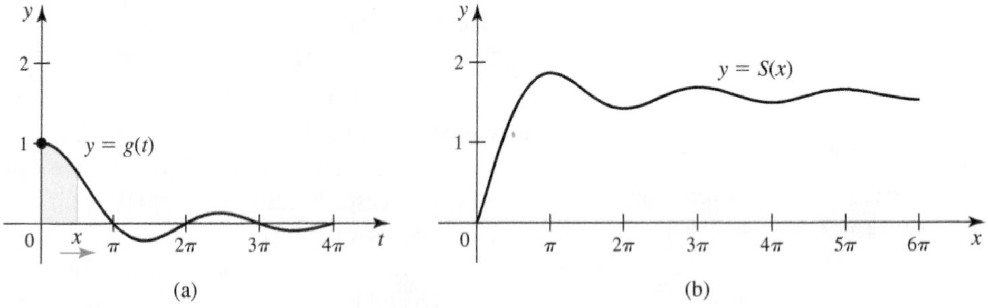

Figure 5.47

Appealing to Part 1 of the Fundamental Theorem, we find that

$$S'(x) = \frac{d}{dx}\int_0^x g(t)\,dt = \frac{\sin x}{x}, \text{ for } x > 0.$$

➤ Note that

$$\lim_{x\to\infty} S'(x) = \lim_{x\to\infty} g(x) = 0.$$

As anticipated, the derivative of S changes sign at integer multiples of π. Specifically, S' is positive and S increases on the intervals $(0, \pi), (2\pi, 3\pi), \ldots, (2n\pi, (2n + 1)\pi), \ldots$, while S' is negative and S decreases on the remaining intervals. Clearly, S has local maxima at $x = \pi, 3\pi, 5\pi, \ldots$, and it has local minima at $x = 2\pi, 4\pi, 6\pi, \ldots$.

One more observation is helpful. It can be shown that although S oscillates for increasing x, its graph gradually flattens out and approaches a horizontal asymptote. (Finding the exact value of this horizontal asymptote is challenging; see Exercise 111.) Assembling all these observations, the graph of the sine integral function emerges (Figure 5.47b).

Related Exercises 81–84 ◀

We conclude this section with a formal proof of the Fundamental Theorem of Calculus.

Proof of the Fundamental Theorem: Let f be continuous on $[a, b]$ and let A be the area function for f with left endpoint a. The first step is to prove that A is differentiable on (a, b) and $A'(x) = f(x)$, which is Part 1 of the Fundamental Theorem. The proof of Part 2 then follows.

Step 1. We assume that $a < x < b$ and use the definition of the derivative,

$$A'(x) = \lim_{h\to 0} \frac{A(x + h) - A(x)}{h}.$$

First assume that $h > 0$. Using Figure 5.48 and Property 5 of Table 5.4, we have

$$A(x + h) - A(x) = \int_a^{x+h} f(t)\,dt - \int_a^x f(t)\,dt = \int_x^{x+h} f(t)\,dt.$$

That is, $A(x + h) - A(x)$ is the net area of the region bounded by the curve on the interval $[x, x + h]$.

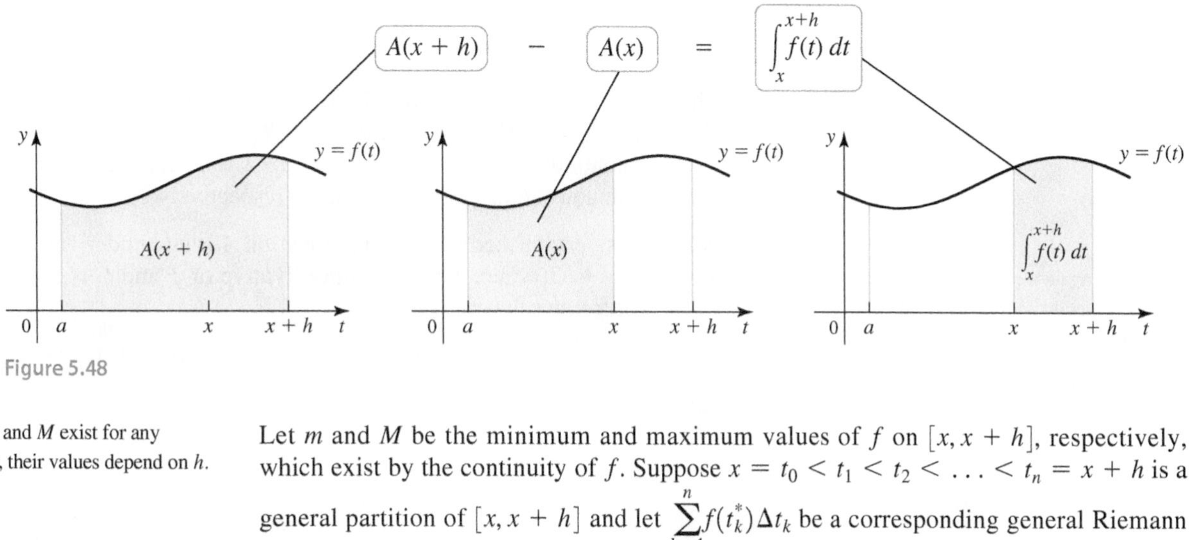

Figure 5.48

➤ The quantities m and M exist for any $h > 0$; however, their values depend on h.

Let m and M be the minimum and maximum values of f on $[x, x + h]$, respectively, which exist by the continuity of f. Suppose $x = t_0 < t_1 < t_2 < \ldots < t_n = x + h$ is a general partition of $[x, x + h]$ and let $\sum_{k=1}^{n} f(t_k^*)\Delta t_k$ be a corresponding general Riemann sum, where $\Delta t_k = t_k - t_{k-1}$. Because $m \le f(t) \le M$ on $[x, x + h]$, it follows that

$$\underbrace{\sum_{k=1}^{n} m\Delta t_k}_{mh} \le \sum_{k=1}^{n} f(t_k^*)\Delta t_k \le \underbrace{\sum_{k=1}^{n} M\Delta t_k}_{Mh}$$

or

$$mh \le \sum_{k=1}^{n} f(t_k^*)\Delta t_k \le Mh.$$

We have used the facts that $\sum_{k=1}^{n} m\Delta t_k = m\sum_{k=1}^{n} \Delta t_k = mh$ and similarly, $\sum_{k=1}^{n} M\Delta t_k = Mh$. Notice that these inequalities hold for every Riemann sum for f on $[x, x + h]$; that is, for all partitions and for all n. Therefore, we are justified in taking the limit as $n \to \infty$ across these inequalities to obtain

$$\lim_{n\to\infty} mh \le \underbrace{\lim_{n\to\infty} \sum_{k=1}^{n} f(t_k^*)\Delta t_k}_{\int_x^{x+h} f(t)\,dt} \le \lim_{n\to\infty} Mh.$$

Evaluating each of these three limits results in

$$mh \le \underbrace{\int_x^{x+h} f(t)\,dt}_{A(x+h)-A(x)} \le Mh.$$

Substituting for the integral, we find that

$$mh \le A(x + h) - A(x) \le Mh.$$

Dividing these inequalities by $h > 0$, we have

$$m \le \frac{A(x + h) - A(x)}{h} \le M.$$

The case $h < 0$ is handled similarly and leads to the same conclusion.

We now take the limit as $h \to 0$ across these inequalities. As $h \to 0$, m and M approach $f(x)$, because f is continuous at x. At the same time, as $h \to 0$, the quotient that is sandwiched between m and M approaches $A'(x)$:

$$\underbrace{\lim_{h\to 0} m}_{f(x)} = \underbrace{\lim_{h\to 0} \frac{A(x + h) - A(x)}{h}}_{A'(x)} = \underbrace{\lim_{h\to 0} M}_{f(x)}.$$

By the Squeeze Theorem (Theorem 2.5), we conclude that $A'(x)$ exists and A is differentiable for $a < x < b$. Furthermore, $A'(x) = f(x)$. Finally, because A is differentiable on (a, b), A is continuous on (a, b) by Theorem 3.1. Exercise 116 shows that A is also right- and left-continuous at the endpoints a and b, respectively.

➤ Once again we use an important fact: Two antiderivatives of the same function differ by a constant.

Step 2. Having established that the area function A is an antiderivative of f, we know that $F(x) = A(x) + C$, where F is any antiderivative of f and C is a constant. Noting that $A(a) = 0$, it follows that

$$F(b) - F(a) = (A(b) + C) - (A(a) + C) = A(b).$$

Writing $A(b)$ in terms of a definite integral, we have

$$A(b) = \int_a^b f(x)\,dx = F(b) - F(a),$$

which is Part 2 of the Fundamental Theorem. ◄

SECTION 5.3 EXERCISES

Review Questions

1. Suppose A is an area function of f. What is the relationship between f and A?

2. Suppose F is an antiderivative of f and A is an area function of f. What is the relationship between F and A?

3. Explain in words and write mathematically how the Fundamental Theorem of Calculus is used to evaluate definite integrals.

4. Let $f(x) = c$, where c is a positive constant. Explain why an area function of f is an increasing function.

5. The linear function $f(x) = 3 - x$ is decreasing on the interval $[0, 3]$. Is the area function for f (with left endpoint 0) increasing or decreasing on the interval $[0, 3]$? Draw a picture and explain.

6. Evaluate $\int_0^2 3x^2\,dx$ and $\int_{-2}^2 3x^2\,dx$.

7. Explain in words and express mathematically the inverse relationship between differentiation and integration as given by Part 1 of the Fundamental Theorem of Calculus.

8. Why can the constant of integration be omitted from the antiderivative when evaluating a definite integral?

9. Evaluate $\frac{d}{dx}\int_a^x f(t)\,dt$ and $\frac{d}{dx}\int_a^b f(t)\,dt$, where a and b are constants.

10. Explain why $\int_a^b f'(x)\,dx = f(b) - f(a)$.

Basic Skills

11. **Area functions** The graph of f is shown in the figure. Let $A(x) = \int_{-2}^x f(t)\,dt$ and $F(x) = \int_4^x f(t)\,dt$ be two area functions for f. Evaluate the following area functions.

a. $A(-2)$ **b.** $F(8)$ **c.** $A(4)$ **d.** $F(4)$ **e.** $A(8)$

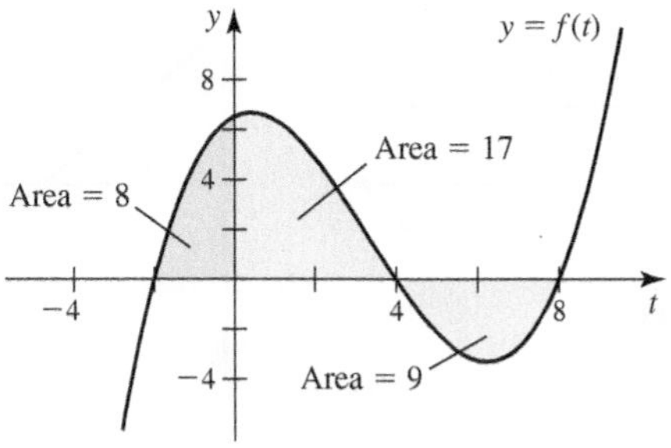

12. **Area functions** The graph of f is shown in the figure. Let $A(x) = \int_0^x f(t)\,dt$ and $F(x) = \int_2^x f(t)\,dt$ be two area functions for f. Evaluate the following area functions.

a. $A(2)$ **b.** $F(5)$ **c.** $A(0)$ **d.** $F(8)$
e. $A(8)$ **f.** $A(5)$ **g.** $F(2)$

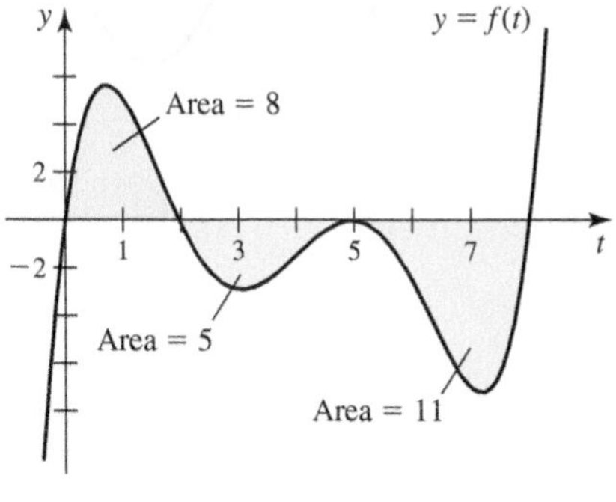

13–16. Area functions for constant functions *Consider the following functions f and real numbers a (see figure).*

a. Find and graph the area function $A(x) = \int_a^x f(t)\,dt$ for f.

b. Verify that $A'(x) = f(x)$.

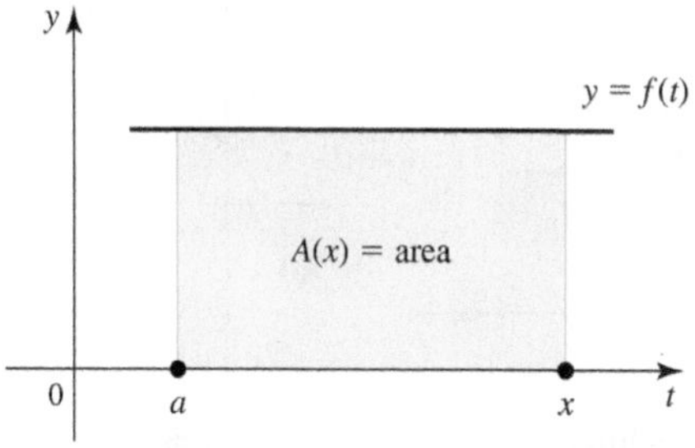

13. $f(t) = 5,\ a = 0$

14. $f(t) = 10,\ a = 4$

15. $f(t) = 5,\ a = -5$

16. $f(t) = 2,\ a = -3$

17. **Area functions for the same linear function** Let $f(t) = t$ and consider the two area functions $A(x) = \int_0^x f(t)\,dt$ and $F(x) = \int_2^x f(t)\,dt$.
   a. Evaluate $A(2)$ and $A(4)$. Then use geometry to find an expression for $A(x)$, for $x \geq 0$.
   b. Evaluate $F(4)$ and $F(6)$. Then use geometry to find an expression for $F(x)$, for $x \geq 2$.
   c. Show that $A(x) - F(x)$ is a constant and that $A'(x) = F'(x) = f(x)$.

18. **Area functions for the same linear function** Let $f(t) = 2t - 2$ and consider the two area functions $A(x) = \int_1^x f(t)\,dt$ and $F(x) = \int_4^x f(t)\,dt$.
   a. Evaluate $A(2)$ and $A(3)$. Then use geometry to find an expression for $A(x)$, for $x \geq 1$.
   b. Evaluate $F(5)$ and $F(6)$. Then use geometry to find an expression for $F(x)$, for $x \geq 4$.
   c. Show that $A(x) - F(x)$ is a constant and that $A'(x) = F'(x) = f(x)$.

19–22. Area functions for linear functions *Consider the following functions f and real numbers a (see figure).*

a. Find and graph the area function $A(x) = \int_a^x f(t)\,dt$.

b. Verify that $A'(x) = f(x)$.

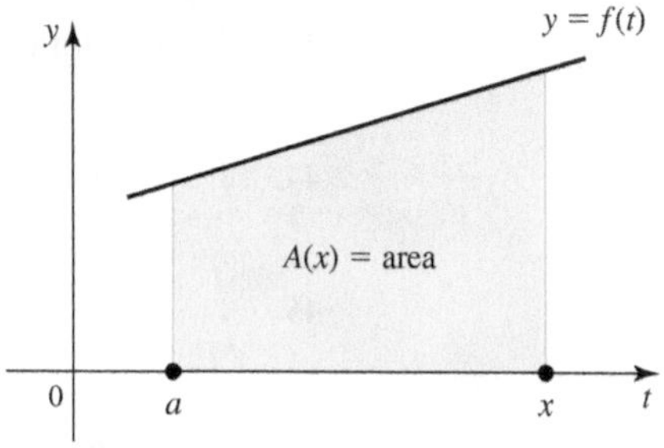

19. $f(t) = t + 5,\ a = -5$

20. $f(t) = 2t + 5,\ a = 0$

21. $f(t) = 3t + 1,\ a = 2$

22. $f(t) = 4t + 2,\ a = 0$

23–24. Definite integrals *Evaluate the following integrals using the Fundamental Theorem of Calculus. Explain why your result is consistent with the figure.*

23. $\displaystyle\int_0^1 (x^2 - 2x + 3)\,dx$

24. $\displaystyle\int_{-\pi/4}^{7\pi/4} (\sin x + \cos x)\,dx$

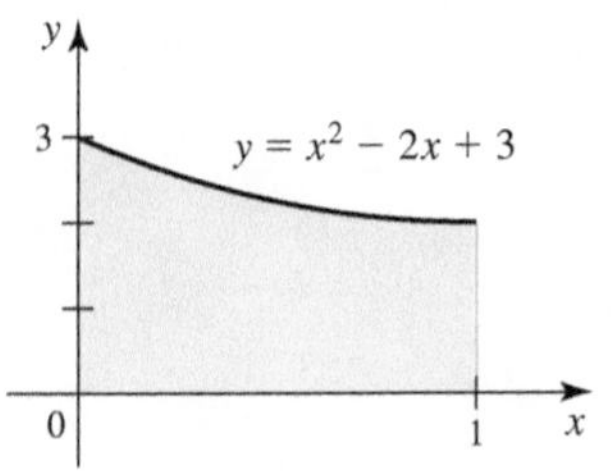

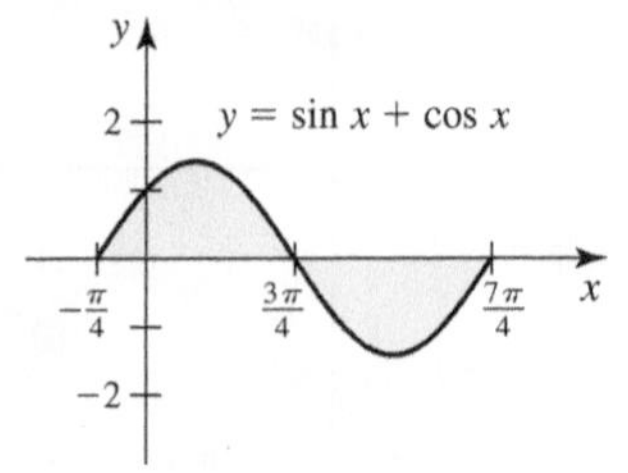

25–28. Definite integrals *Evaluate the following integrals using the Fundamental Theorem of Calculus. Sketch the graph of the integrand and shade the region whose net area you have found.*

25. $\displaystyle\int_{-2}^{3} (x^2 - x - 6)\,dx$

26. $\displaystyle\int_0^1 (x - \sqrt{x})\,dx$

27. $\displaystyle\int_0^5 (x^2 - 9)\,dx$

28. $\displaystyle\int_{1/2}^{2} \left(1 - \frac{1}{x^2}\right) dx$

29–50. Definite integrals *Evaluate the following integrals using the Fundamental Theorem of Calculus.*

29. $\displaystyle\int_0^2 4x^3\,dx$

30. $\displaystyle\int_0^2 (3x^2 + 2x)\,dx$

31. $\displaystyle\int_0^1 (x + \sqrt{x})\,dx$

32. $\displaystyle\int_0^{\pi/4} 2\cos x\,dx$

33. $\displaystyle\int_1^9 \frac{2}{\sqrt{x}}\,dx$

34. $\displaystyle\int_4^9 \frac{2 + \sqrt{t}}{t}\,dt$

35. $\displaystyle\int_{-2}^{2} (x^2 - 4)\,dx$

36. $\displaystyle\int_0^{\ln 8} e^x\,dx$

37. $\displaystyle\int_{1/2}^{1} (x^{-3} - 8)\,dx$

38. $\displaystyle\int_0^4 x(x - 2)(x - 4)\,dx$

39. $\displaystyle\int_0^{\pi/4} \sec^2\theta\,d\theta$

40. $\displaystyle\int_0^{1/2} \frac{dx}{\sqrt{1 - x^2}}$

41. $\displaystyle\int_{-2}^{-1} x^{-3}\,dx$

42. $\displaystyle\int_0^{\pi} (1 - \sin x)\,dx$

43. $\displaystyle\int_1^4 (1 - x)(x - 4)\,dx$

44. $\displaystyle\int_{-\pi/2}^{\pi/2} (\cos x - 1)\,dx$

45. $\displaystyle\int_1^2 \frac{3}{t}\,dt$

46. $\displaystyle\int_4^9 \frac{x - \sqrt{x}}{x^3}\,dx$

47. $\displaystyle\int_0^{\pi/8} \cos 2x\,dx$

48. $\displaystyle\int_0^1 10e^{2x}\,dx$

49. $\displaystyle\int_1^{\sqrt{3}} \frac{dx}{1 + x^2}$

50. $\displaystyle\int_{\pi/16}^{\pi/8} 8\csc^2 4x\,dx$

51–54. Areas *Find (i) the net area and (ii) the area of the following regions. Graph the function and indicate the region in question.*

51. The region bounded by $y = x^{1/2}$ and the x-axis between $x = 1$ and $x = 4$

52. The region above the x-axis bounded by $y = 4 - x^2$

53. The region below the x-axis bounded by $y = x^4 - 16$

54. The region bounded by $y = 6\cos x$ and the x-axis between $x = -\pi/2$ and $x = \pi$

55–60. Areas of regions *Find the area of the region bounded by the graph of f and the x-axis on the given interval.*

55. $f(x) = x^2 - 25$ on $[2, 4]$

56. $f(x) = x^3 - 1$ on $[-1, 2]$

57. $f(x) = \dfrac{1}{x}$ on $[-2, -1]$

58. $f(x) = x(x + 1)(x - 2)$ on $[-1, 2]$

59. $f(x) = \sin x$ on $[-\pi/4, 3\pi/4]$

60. $f(x) = \cos x$ on $[\pi/2, \pi]$

61–68. Derivatives of integrals *Simplify the following expressions.*

61. $\displaystyle\frac{d}{dx}\int_3^x (t^2 + t + 1)\,dt$

62. $\displaystyle\frac{d}{dx}\int_0^x e^t\,dt$

63. $\displaystyle\frac{d}{dx}\int_2^{x^3} \frac{dp}{p^2}$

64. $\displaystyle\frac{d}{dx}\int_{x^2}^{10} \frac{dz}{z^2 + 1}$

65. $\displaystyle\frac{d}{dx}\int_x^1 \sqrt{t^4 + 1}\,dt$

66. $\displaystyle\frac{d}{dx}\int_x^0 \frac{dp}{p^2 + 1}$

67. $\displaystyle\frac{d}{dx}\int_{-x}^{x} \sqrt{1 + t^2}\,dt$

68. $\displaystyle\frac{d}{dx}\int_{e^x}^{e^{2x}} \ln t^2\,dt$

69. Matching functions with area functions Match the functions f, whose graphs are given in a–d, with the area functions $A(x) = \int_0^x f(t)\,dt$, whose graphs are given in A–D.

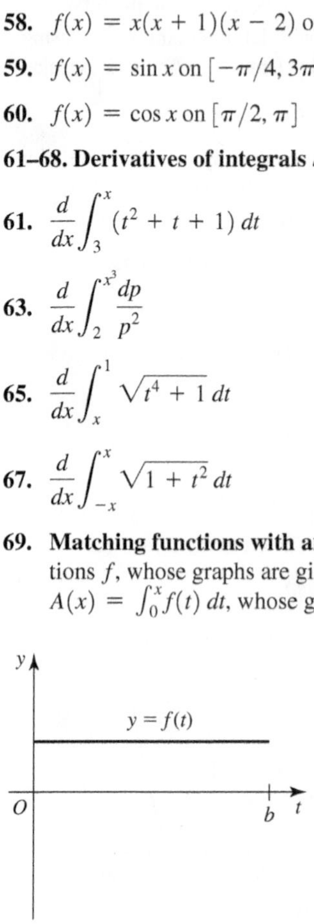

(a)

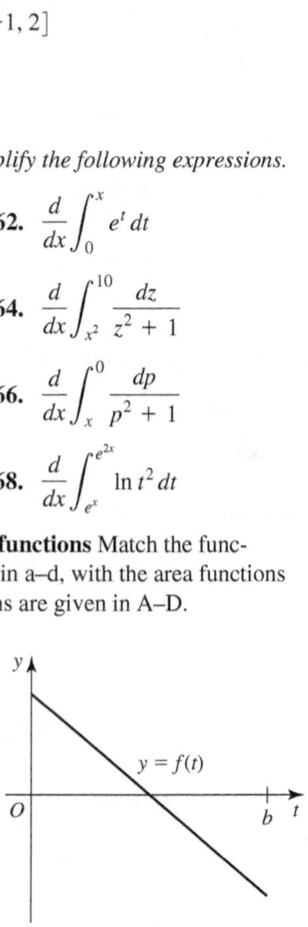

(b)

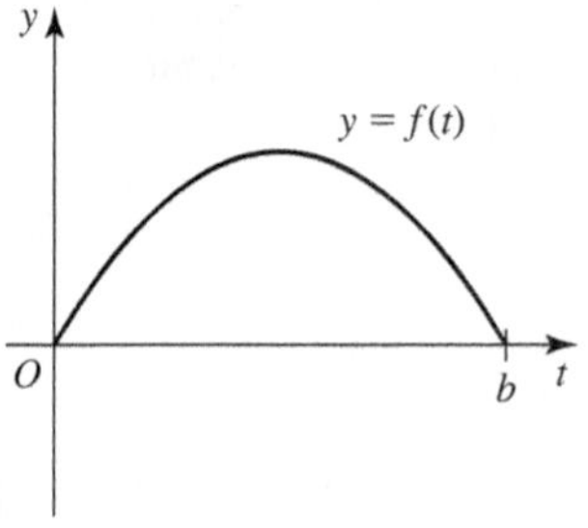

(c)

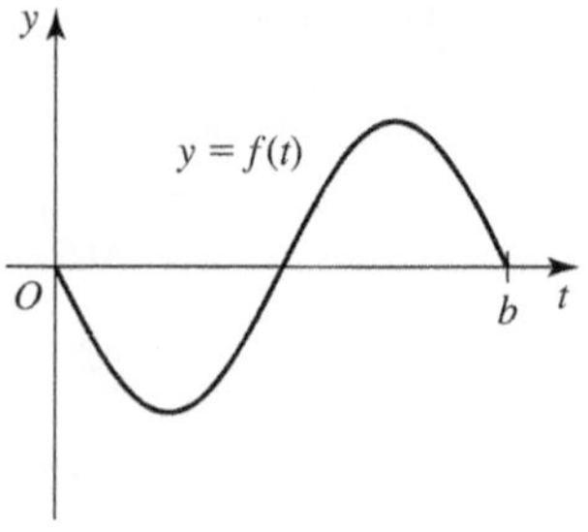

(d)

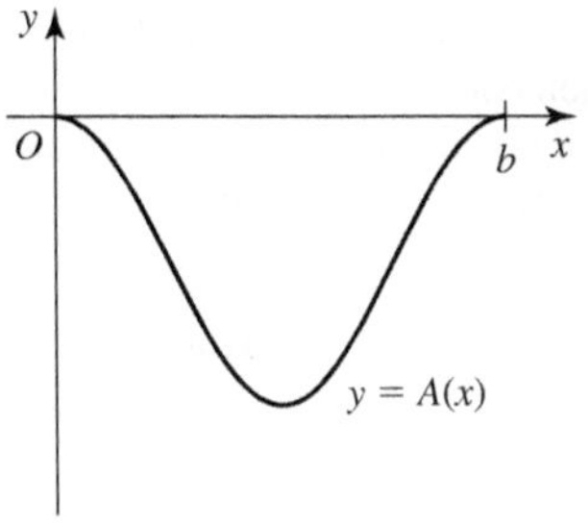

(A)

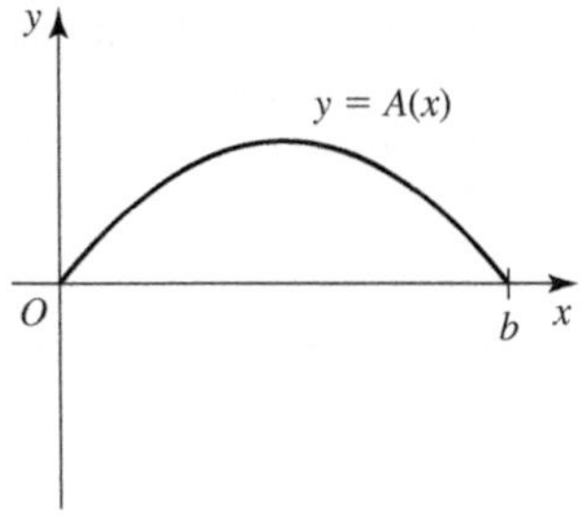

(B)

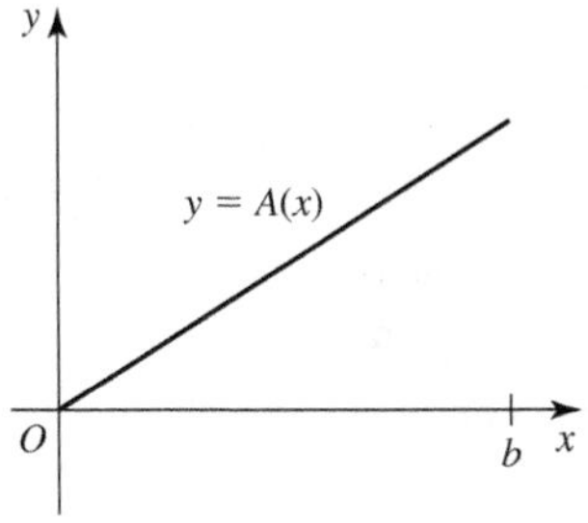

(C)

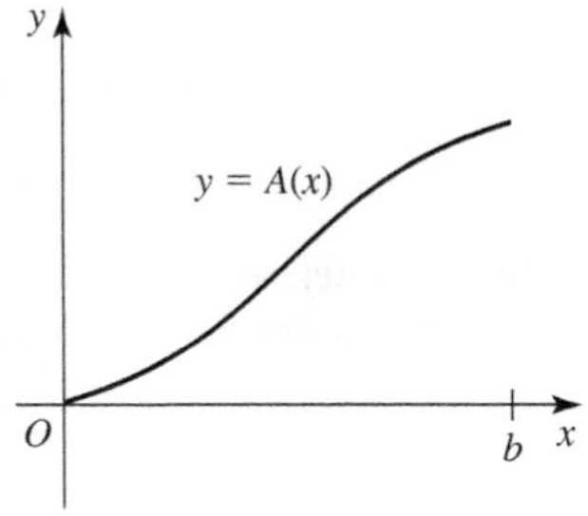

(D)

70–73. Working with area functions *Consider the function f and its graph.*

a. *Estimate the zeros of the area function* $A(x) = \int_0^x f(t)\,dt$, *for* $0 \le x \le 10$.

b. *Estimate the points (if any) at which A has a local maximum or minimum.*

c. *Sketch a graph of A, for* $0 \le x \le 10$, *without a scale on the y-axis.*

70.

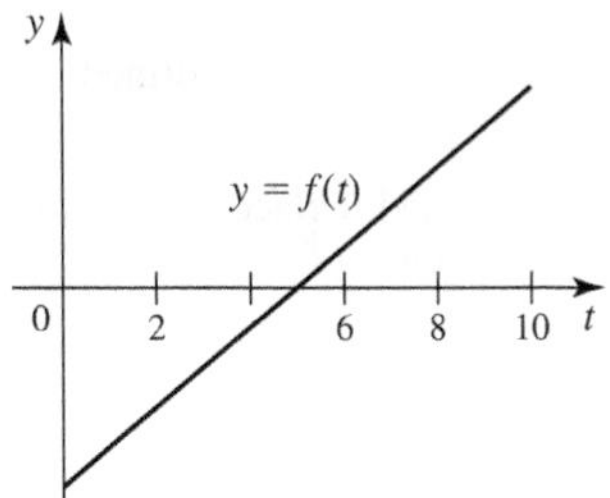

71.

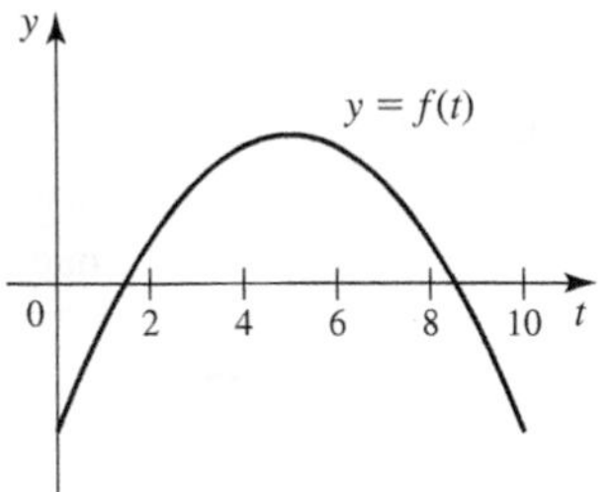

72.

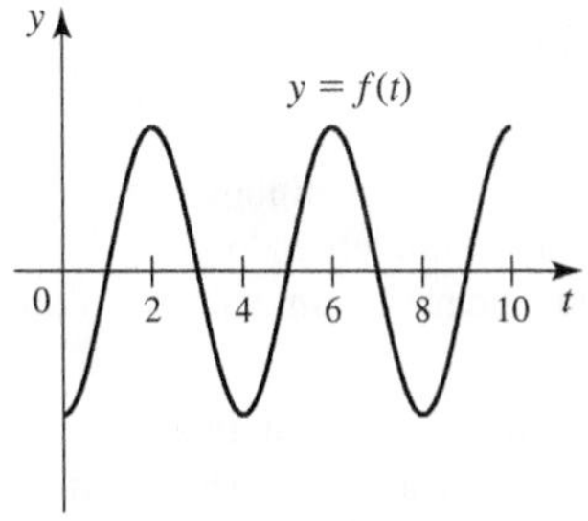

73.

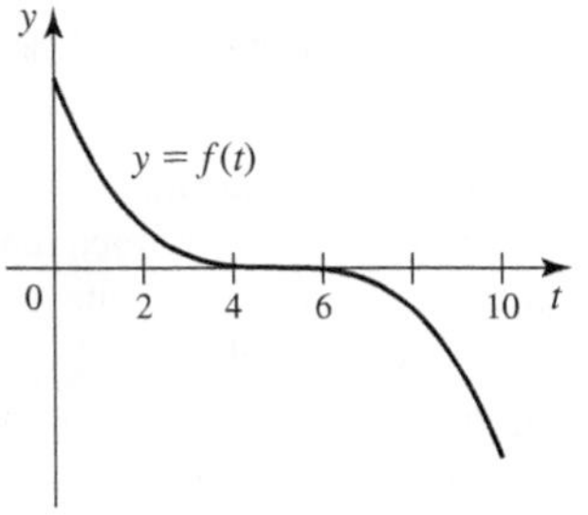

74. Area functions from graphs The graph of f is given in the figure. Let $A(x) = \int_0^x f(t)\,dt$ and evaluate $A(1)$, $A(2)$, $A(4)$, and $A(6)$.

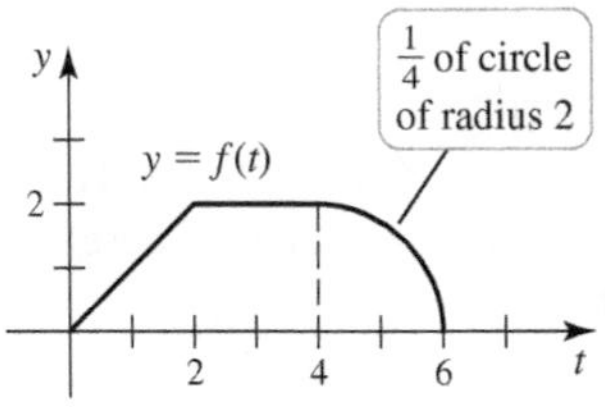

75. Area functions from graphs The graph of f is given in the figure. Let $A(x) = \int_0^x f(t)\,dt$ and evaluate $A(2)$, $A(5)$, $A(8)$, and $A(12)$.

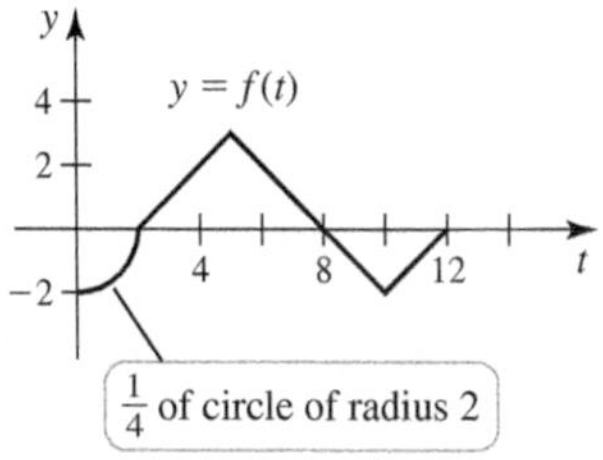

76–80. Working with area functions *Consider the function f and the points a, b, and c.*

a. *Find the area function* $A(x) = \int_a^x f(t)\,dt$ *using the Fundamental Theorem.*

b. *Graph f and A.*

c. *Evaluate* $A(b)$ *and* $A(c)$. *Interpret the results using the graphs of part (b).*

76. $f(x) = \sin x;\ a = 0, b = \pi/2, c = \pi$

77. $f(x) = e^x;\ a = 0, b = \ln 2, c = \ln 4$

78. $f(x) = -12x(x-1)(x-2);\ a = 0, b = 1, c = 2$

79. $f(x) = \cos \pi x;\ a = 0, b = \frac{1}{2}, c = 1$

80. $f(x) = \dfrac{1}{x};\ a = 1, b = 4, c = 6$

T **81–84. Functions defined by integrals** *Consider the function g, which is given in terms of a definite integral with a variable upper limit.*

a. *Graph the integrand.*

b. *Calculate* $g'(x)$.

c. *Graph g, showing all your work and reasoning.*

81. $g(x) = \displaystyle\int_0^x \sin^2 t\,dt$

82. $g(x) = \displaystyle\int_0^x (t^2 + 1)\,dt$

83. $g(x) = \displaystyle\int_0^x \sin(\pi t^2)\,dt$ (a Fresnel integral)

84. $g(x) = \displaystyle\int_0^x \cos(\pi\sqrt{t})\,dt$

Further Explorations

85. Explain why or why not Determine whether the following statements are true and give an explanation or counterexample.

a. Suppose that f is a positive decreasing function, for $x > 0$. Then the area function $A(x) = \int_0^x f(t)\,dt$ is an increasing function of x.

b. Suppose that f is a negative increasing function, for $x > 0$. Then the area function $A(x) = \int_0^x f(t)\,dt$ is a decreasing function of x.

c. The functions $p(x) = \sin 3x$ and $q(x) = 4\sin 3x$ are antiderivatives of the same function.

d. If $A(x) = 3x^2 - x - 3$ is an area function for f, then $B(x) = 3x^2 - x$ is also an area function for f.

e. $\dfrac{d}{dx}\displaystyle\int_a^b f(t)\,dt = 0.$

86–94. Definite integrals *Evaluate the following definite integrals using the Fundamental Theorem of Calculus.*

86. $\frac{1}{2}\int_0^{\ln 2} e^x\,dx$ **87.** $\int_1^4 \frac{x-2}{\sqrt{x}}\,dx$ **88.** $\int_1^2 \left(\frac{2}{s} - \frac{4}{s^3}\right) ds$

89. $\int_0^{\pi/3} \sec x \tan x\,dx$ **90.** $\int_{\pi/4}^{\pi/2} \csc^2\theta\,d\theta$ **91.** $\int_1^8 \sqrt[3]{y}\,dy$

92. $\int_{\sqrt{2}}^2 \frac{dx}{x\sqrt{x^2-1}}$ **93.** $\int_1^2 \frac{z^2+4}{z}\,dz$ **94.** $\int_0^{\sqrt{3}} \frac{3\,dx}{9+x^2}$

T **95–98. Areas of regions** *Find the area of the region R bounded by the graph of f and the x-axis on the given interval. Graph f and show the region R.*

95. $f(x) = 2 - |x|$ on $[-2, 4]$

96. $f(x) = (1 - x^2)^{-1/2}$ on $[-1/2, \sqrt{3}/2]$

97. $f(x) = x^4 - 4$ on $[1, 4]$ **98.** $f(x) = x^2(x-2)$ on $[-1, 3]$

99–102. Derivatives and integrals *Simplify the given expressions.*

99. $\int_3^8 f'(t)\,dt$, where f' is continuous on $[3, 8]$

100. $\frac{d}{dx}\int_0^{x^2} \frac{dt}{t^2+4}$ **101.** $\frac{d}{dx}\int_0^{\cos x} (t^4 + 6)\,dt$

102. $\frac{d}{dx}\int_x^1 e^{t^2}\,dt$ **103.** $\frac{d}{dt}\left(\int_1^t \frac{3}{x}\,dx - \int_{t^2}^1 \frac{3}{x}\,dx\right)$

104. $\frac{d}{dt}\left(\int_0^t \frac{dx}{1+x^2} + \int_0^{1/t} \frac{dx}{1+x^2}\right)$

Additional Exercises

105. Zero net area Consider the function $f(x) = x^2 - 4x$.

a. Graph f on the interval $x \ge 0$.
b. For what value of $b > 0$ is $\int_0^b f(x)\,dx = 0$?
c. In general, for the function $f(x) = x^2 - ax$, where $a > 0$, for what value of $b > 0$ (as a function of a) is $\int_0^b f(x)\,dx = 0$?

106. Cubic zero net area Consider the graph of the cubic $y = x(x-a)(x-b)$, where $0 < a < b$. Verify that the graph bounds a region above the x-axis, for $0 < x < a$, and bounds a region below the x-axis, for $a < x < b$. What is the relationship between a and b if the areas of these two regions are equal?

107. Maximum net area What value of $b > -1$ maximizes the integral

$$\int_{-1}^b x^2(3-x)\,dx?$$

108. Maximum net area Graph the function $f(x) = 8 + 2x - x^2$ and determine the values of a and b that maximize the value of the integral

$$\int_a^b (8 + 2x - x^2)\,dx.$$

109. An integral equation Use the Fundamental Theorem of Calculus, Part 1, to find the function f that satisfies the equation

$$\int_0^x f(t)\,dt = 2\cos x + 3x - 2.$$

Verify the result by substitution into the equation.

110. Max/min of area functions Suppose f is continuous on $[0, \infty)$ and $A(x)$ is the net area of the region bounded by the graph of f and the t-axis on $[0, x]$. Show that the local maxima and minima of A occur at the zeros of f. Verify this fact with the function $f(x) = x^2 - 10x$.

T **111. Asymptote of sine integral** Use a calculator to approximate

$$\lim_{x\to\infty} S(x) = \lim_{x\to\infty} \int_0^x \frac{\sin t}{t}\,dt,$$

where S is the sine integral function (see Example 7). Explain your reasoning.

112. Sine integral Show that the sine integral $S(x) = \int_0^x \frac{\sin t}{t}\,dt$ satisfies the (differential) equation $xS'(x) + 2S''(x) + xS'''(x) = 0$.

113. Fresnel integral Show that the Fresnel integral $S(x) = \int_0^x \sin t^2\,dt$ satisfies the (differential) equation

$$(S'(x))^2 + \left(\frac{S''(x)}{2x}\right)^2 = 1.$$

114. Variable integration limits Evaluate $\frac{d}{dx}\int_{-x}^x (t^2 + t)\,dt$. (*Hint:* Separate the integral into two pieces.)

115. Discrete version of the Fundamental Theorem In this exercise, we work with a discrete problem and show why the relationship $\int_a^b f'(x)\,dx = f(b) - f(a)$ makes sense. Suppose we have a set of equally spaced grid points

$$\{a = x_0 < x_1 < x_2 < \ldots < x_{n-1} < x_n = b\},$$

where the distance between any two grid points is Δx. Suppose also that at each grid point x_k, a function value $f(x_k)$ is defined, for $k = 0, \ldots, n$.

a. We now replace the integral with a sum and replace the derivative with a difference quotient. Explain why $\int_a^b f'(x)\,dx$ is analogous to $\sum_{k=1}^{n} \underbrace{\frac{f(x_k) - f(x_{k-1})}{\Delta x}}_{\approx f'(x_k)} \Delta x$.
b. Simplify the sum in part (a) and show that it is equal to $f(b) - f(a)$.
c. Explain the correspondence between the integral relationship and the summation relationship.

116. Continuity at the endpoints Assume that f is continuous on $[a, b]$ and let A be the area function for f with left endpoint a. Let m^* and M^* be the absolute minimum and maximum values of f on $[a, b]$, respectively.

a. Prove that $m^*(x-a) \le A(x) \le M^*(x-a)$ for all x in $[a, b]$. Use this result and the Squeeze Theorem to show that A is continuous from the right at $x = a$.
b. Prove that $m^*(b-x) \le A(b) - A(x) \le M^*(b-x)$ for all x in $[a, b]$. Use this result to show that A is continuous from the left at $x = b$.

QUICK CHECK ANSWERS

1. $0, -35$ **2.** $A(6) = 44$; $A(10) = 120$ **3.** $\frac{2}{3} - \frac{1}{2} = \frac{1}{6}$
4. If f is differentiated, we get f'. Therefore, f is an antiderivative of f'. ◄

5.4 Working with Integrals

With the Fundamental Theorem of Calculus in hand, we may begin an investigation of integration and its applications. In this section, we discuss the role of symmetry in integrals, we use the slice-and-sum strategy to define the average value of a function, and we explore a theoretical result called the Mean Value Theorem for Integrals.

Integrating Even and Odd Functions

Symmetry appears throughout mathematics in many different forms, and its use often leads to insights and efficiencies. Here we use the symmetry of a function to simplify integral calculations.

Section 1.1 introduced the symmetry of even and odd functions. An **even function** satisfies the property $f(-x) = f(x)$, which means that its graph is symmetric about the y-axis (Figure 5.49a). Examples of even functions are $f(x) = \cos x$ and $f(x) = x^n$, where n is an even integer. An **odd function** satisfies the property $f(-x) = -f(x)$, which means that its graph is symmetric about the origin (Figure 5.49b). Examples of odd functions are $f(x) = \sin x$ and $f(x) = x^n$, where n is an odd integer.

Special things happen when we integrate even and odd functions on intervals centered at the origin. First suppose f is an even function and consider $\int_{-a}^{a} f(x)\,dx$. From Figure 5.49a, we see that the integral of f on $[-a, 0]$ equals the integral of f on $[0, a]$. Therefore, the integral on $[-a, a]$ is twice the integral on $[0, a]$, or

$$\int_{-a}^{a} f(x)\,dx = 2\int_{0}^{a} f(x)\,dx.$$

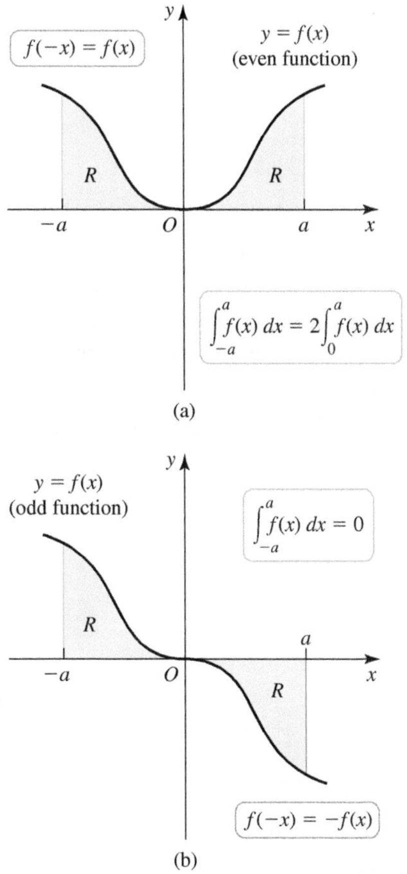

Figure 5.49

On the other hand, suppose f is an odd function and consider $\int_{-a}^{a} f(x)\,dx$. As shown in Figure 5.49b, the integral on the interval $[-a, 0]$ is the negative of the integral on $[0, a]$. Therefore, the integral on $[-a, a]$ is zero, or

$$\int_{-a}^{a} f(x)\,dx = 0.$$

We summarize these results in the following theorem.

> **THEOREM 5.4 Integrals of Even and Odd Functions**
> Let a be a positive real number and let f be an integrable function on the interval $[-a, a]$.
>
> - If f is even, $\int_{-a}^{a} f(x)\,dx = 2\int_{0}^{a} f(x)\,dx$.
> - If f is odd, $\int_{-a}^{a} f(x)\,dx = 0$.

QUICK CHECK 1 If f and g are both even functions, is the product fg even or odd? Use the facts that $f(-x) = f(x)$ and $g(-x) = g(x)$. ◄

The following example shows how symmetry can simplify integration.

EXAMPLE 1 Integrating symmetric functions Evaluate the following integrals using symmetry arguments.

a. $\displaystyle\int_{-2}^{2} (x^4 - 3x^3)\,dx$ **b.** $\displaystyle\int_{-\pi/2}^{\pi/2} (\cos x - 4\sin^3 x)\,dx$

SOLUTION

a. Note that $x^4 - 3x^3$ is neither odd nor even so Theorem 5.4 cannot be applied directly. However, we can split the integral and then use symmetry:

$$\int_{-2}^{2} (x^4 - 3x^3)\,dx = \int_{-2}^{2} x^4\,dx - 3\underbrace{\int_{-2}^{2} x^3\,dx}_{0} \qquad \text{Properties 3 and 4 of Table 5.4}$$

$$= 2\int_{0}^{2} x^4\,dx - 0 \qquad x^4 \text{ is even; } x^3 \text{ is odd.}$$

$$= 2\left(\frac{x^5}{5}\right)\Bigg|_0^2 \qquad \text{Fundamental Theorem}$$

$$= 2\left(\frac{32}{5}\right) = \frac{64}{5}. \qquad \text{Simplify.}$$

Notice how the odd-powered term of the integrand is eliminated by symmetry. Integration of the even-powered term is simplified because the lower limit is zero.

b. The $\cos x$ term is an even function, so it can be integrated on the interval $[0, \pi/2]$. What about $\sin^3 x$? It is an odd function raised to an odd power, which results in an odd function; its integral on $[-\pi/2, \pi/2]$ is zero. Therefore,

➤ There are a couple of ways to see that $\sin^3 x$ is an odd function. Its graph is symmetric about the origin, indicating that $\sin^3(-x) = -\sin^3 x$. Or by analogy, take an odd power of x and raise it to an odd power. For example, $(x^5)^3 = x^{15}$, which is odd. See Exercises 53–56 for direct proofs of symmetry in composite functions.

$$\int_{-\pi/2}^{\pi/2} (\cos x - 4\sin^3 x)\,dx = 2\int_{0}^{\pi/2} \cos x\,dx - 0 \qquad \text{Symmetry}$$

$$= 2\sin x\Bigg|_0^{\pi/2} \qquad \text{Fundamental Theorem}$$

$$= 2(1 - 0) = 2. \qquad \text{Simplify.}$$

Related Exercises 7–20 ◀

Average Value of a Function

If five people weigh 155, 143, 180, 105, and 123 lb, their average (mean) weight is

$$\frac{155 + 143 + 180 + 105 + 123}{5} = 141.2 \text{ lb}.$$

This idea generalizes quite naturally to functions. Consider a function f that is continuous on $[a, b]$. Using a regular partition $x_0 = a, x_1, x_2, \ldots, x_n = b$ with $\Delta x = \dfrac{b-a}{n}$, we select a point x_k^* in each subinterval and compute $f(x_k^*)$, for $k = 1, \ldots, n$. The values of $f(x_k^*)$ may be viewed as a sampling of f on $[a, b]$. The average of these function values is

$$\frac{f(x_1^*) + f(x_2^*) + \cdots + f(x_n^*)}{n}.$$

Noting that $n = \dfrac{b-a}{\Delta x}$, we write the average of the n sample values as the Riemann sum

$$\frac{f(x_1^*) + f(x_2^*) + \cdots + f(x_n^*)}{(b-a)/\Delta x} = \frac{1}{b-a}\sum_{k=1}^{n} f(x_k^*)\Delta x.$$

Now suppose we increase n, taking more and more samples of f, while Δx decreases to zero. The limit of this sum is a definite integral that gives the average value $\bar{f}$ on $[a, b]$:

$$\bar{f} = \frac{1}{b-a}\lim_{n\to\infty}\sum_{k=1}^{n} f(x_k^*)\Delta x$$

$$= \frac{1}{b-a}\int_a^b f(x)\,dx.$$

This definition of the average value of a function is analogous to the definition of the average of a finite set of numbers.

> **DEFINITION Average Value of a Function**
>
> The average value of an integrable function f on the interval $[a, b]$ is
>
> $$\bar{f} = \frac{1}{b-a}\int_a^b f(x)\,dx.$$

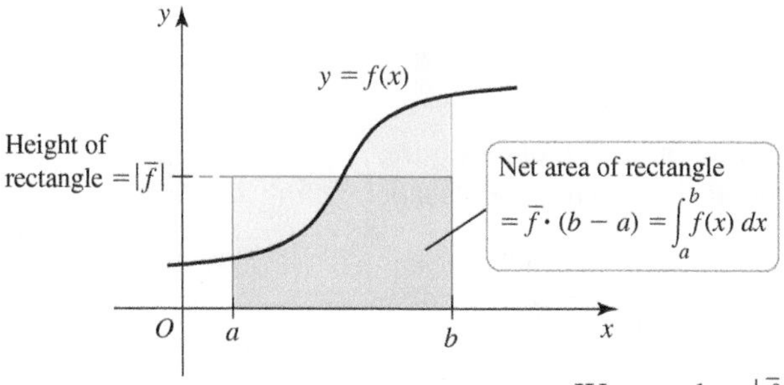

Figure 5.50

The average value of a function f on an interval $[a, b]$ has a clear geometrical interpretation. Multiplying both sides of the definition of average value by $(b - a)$, we have

$$\underbrace{(b-a)\bar{f}}_{\text{net area of rectangle}} = \underbrace{\int_a^b f(x)\,dx.}_{\text{net area of region bounded by curve}}$$

We see that $|\bar{f}|$ is the height of a rectangle with base $[a, b]$, and that rectangle has the same net area as the region bounded by the graph of f on the interval $[a, b]$ (Figure 5.50). Note that $\bar{f}$ may be zero or negative.

QUICK CHECK 2 What is the average value of a constant function on an interval? What is the average value of an odd function on an interval $[-a, a]$? ◀

EXAMPLE 2 Average elevation A hiking trail has an elevation given by

$$f(x) = 60x^3 - 650x^2 + 1200x + 4500,$$

where f is measured in feet above sea level and x represents horizontal distance along the trail in miles, with $0 \le x \le 5$. What is the average elevation of the trail?

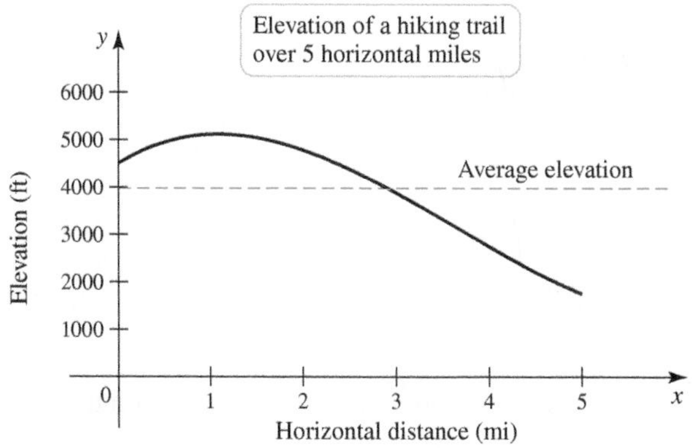

Figure 5.51

SOLUTION The trail ranges between elevations of about 2000 and 5000 ft (Figure 5.51). If we let the endpoints of the trail correspond to the horizontal distances $a = 0$ and $b = 5$, the average elevation of the trail in feet is

$$\bar{f} = \frac{1}{5}\int_0^5 (60x^3 - 650x^2 + 1200x + 4500)\,dx$$

$$= \frac{1}{5}\left(60\frac{x^4}{4} - 650\frac{x^3}{3} + 1200\frac{x^2}{2} + 4500x\right)\bigg|_0^5 \qquad \text{Fundamental Theorem}$$

$$= 3958\tfrac{1}{3}. \qquad \text{Simplify.}$$

The average elevation of the trail is slightly less than 3960 ft.

Related Exercises 21–34 ◀

Mean Value Theorem for Integrals

➤ Compare this statement to that of the Mean Value Theorem for Derivatives: There is at least one point c in (a, b) such that $f'(c)$ equals the average slope of f.

The average value of a function brings us close to an important theoretical result. The Mean Value Theorem for Integrals says that if f is continuous on $[a, b]$, then there is at least one point c in the interval (a, b) such that $f(c)$ equals the average value of f on

(a, b). In other words, the horizontal line $y = \bar{f}$ intersects the graph of f for some point c in (a, b) (Figure 5.52). If f were not continuous, such a point might not exist.

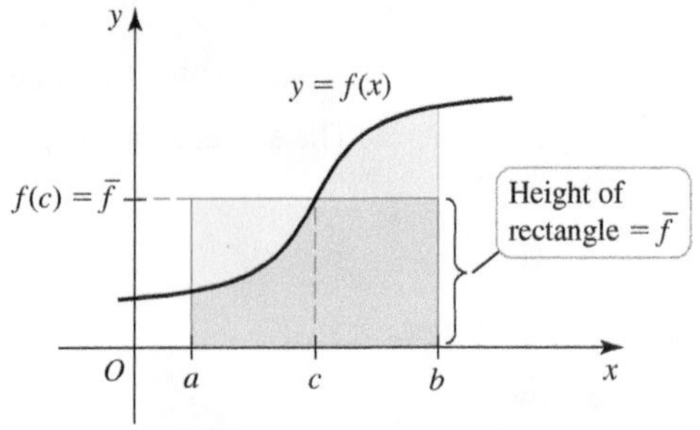

Figure 5.52

➤ Theorem 5.5 guarantees a point c in the open interval (a, b) at which f equals its average value. However, f may also equal its average value at an endpoint of that interval.

THEOREM 5.5 Mean Value Theorem for Integrals
Let f be continuous on the interval $[a, b]$. There exists a point c in (a, b) such that

$$f(c) = \bar{f} = \frac{1}{b-a}\int_a^b f(t)\,dt.$$

Proof: We begin by letting $F(x) = \int_a^x f(t)\,dt$ and noting that F is continuous on $[a, b]$ and differentiable on (a, b) (by Theorem 5.3, Part 1). We now apply the Mean Value Theorem for derivatives (Theorem 4.9) to F and conclude that there exists at least one point c in (a, b) such that

$$\underbrace{F'(c)}_{f(c)} = \frac{F(b) - F(a)}{b - a}.$$

By Theorem 5.3, Part 1, we know that $F'(c) = f(c)$, and by Theorem 5.3, Part 2, we know that

$$F(b) - F(a) = \int_a^b f(t)\,dt.$$

Combining these observations, we have

$$f(c) = \frac{1}{b-a}\int_a^b f(t)\,dt,$$

where c is a point in (a, b). ◀

➤ A more general form of the Mean Value Theorem states that if f and g are continuous on $[a, b]$ with $g(x) \geq 0$ on $[a, b]$, then there exists a number c in (a, b) such that

$$\int_a^b f(x)g(x)\,dx = f(c)\int_a^b g(x)\,dx.$$

QUICK CHECK 3 Explain why $f(x) = 0$ for at least one point of (a, b) if f is continuous and $\int_a^b f(x)\,dx = 0$. ◀

EXAMPLE 3 Average value equals function value Find the point(s) on the interval $(0, 1)$ at which $f(x) = 2x(1 - x)$ equals its average value on $[0, 1]$.

SOLUTION The average value of f on $[0, 1]$ is

$$\bar{f} = \frac{1}{1-0}\int_0^1 2x(1 - x)\,dx = \left(x^2 - \frac{2}{3}x^3\right)\Big|_0^1 = \frac{1}{3}.$$

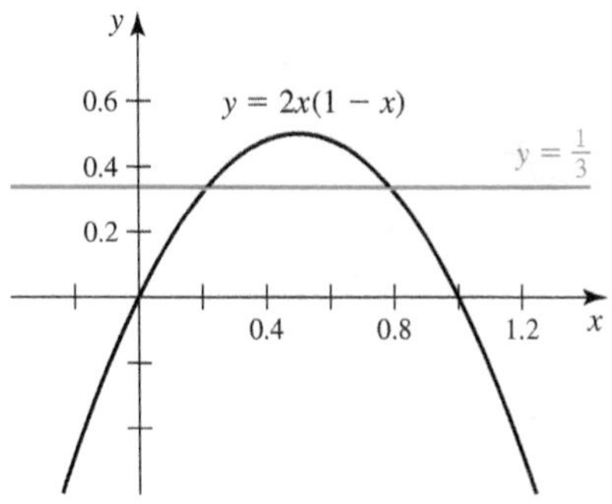

Figure 5.53

We must find the points on $(0, 1)$ at which $f(x) = \frac{1}{3}$ (Figure 5.53). Using the quadratic formula, the two solutions of $f(x) = 2x(1 - x) = \frac{1}{3}$ are

$$\frac{1 - \sqrt{1/3}}{2} \approx 0.211 \quad \text{and} \quad \frac{1 + \sqrt{1/3}}{2} \approx 0.789.$$

These two points are located symmetrically on either side of $x = \frac{1}{2}$. The two solutions, 0.211 and 0.789, are the same for $f(x) = ax(1 - x)$ for any nonzero value of a (Exercise 57).

Related Exercises 35–40 ◄

SECTION 5.4 EXERCISES

Review Questions

1. If f is an odd function, why is $\int_{-a}^{a} f(x)\,dx = 0$?
2. If f is an even function, why is $\int_{-a}^{a} f(x)\,dx = 2\int_{0}^{a} f(x)\,dx$?
3. Is x^{12} an even or odd function? Is $\sin x^2$ an even or odd function?
4. Explain how to find the average value of a function on an interval $[a, b]$ and why this definition is analogous to the definition of the average of a set of numbers.
5. Explain the statement that a continuous function on an interval $[a, b]$ equals its average value at some point on (a, b).
6. Sketch the function $y = x$ on the interval $[0, 2]$ and let R be the region bounded by $y = x$ and the x-axis on $[0, 2]$. Now sketch a rectangle in the first quadrant whose base is $[0, 2]$ and whose area equals the area of R.

Basic Skills

7–16. Symmetry in integrals *Use symmetry to evaluate the following integrals.*

7. $\int_{-2}^{2} x^9\,dx$

8. $\int_{-200}^{200} 2x^5\,dx$

9. $\int_{-2}^{2} (3x^8 - 2)\,dx$

10. $\int_{-\pi/4}^{\pi/4} \cos x\,dx$

11. $\int_{-2}^{2} (x^9 - 3x^5 + 2x^2 - 10)\,dx$

12. $\int_{-\pi/2}^{\pi/2} 5\sin x\,dx$

13. $\int_{-10}^{10} \frac{x}{\sqrt{200 - x^2}}\,dx$

14. $\int_{-\pi/2}^{\pi/2} (\cos 2x + \cos x \sin x - 3\sin x^5)\,dx$

15. $\int_{-\pi/4}^{\pi/4} \sin^5 x\,dx$

16. $\int_{-1}^{1} (1 - |x|)\,dx$

17–20. Symmetry and definite integrals *Use symmetry to evaluate the following integrals. Draw a figure to interpret your result.*

17. $\int_{-\pi}^{\pi} \sin x\,dx$

18. $\int_{0}^{2\pi} \cos x\,dx$

19. $\int_{0}^{\pi} \cos x\,dx$

20. $\int_{0}^{2\pi} \sin x\,dx$

21–30. Average values *Find the average value of the following functions on the given interval. Draw a graph of the function and indicate the average value.*

21. $f(x) = x^3$ on $[-1, 1]$

22. $f(x) = x^2 + 1$ on $[-2, 2]$

23. $f(x) = \frac{1}{x^2 + 1}$ on $[-1, 1]$

24. $f(x) = \cos 2x$ on $[-\frac{\pi}{4}, \frac{\pi}{4}]$

25. $f(x) = 1/x$ on $[1, e]$

26. $f(x) = e^{2x}$ on $[0, \ln 2]$

27. $f(x) = \cos x$ on $[-\frac{\pi}{2}, \frac{\pi}{2}]$

28. $f(x) = x(1 - x)$ on $[0, 1]$

29. $f(x) = x^n$ on $[0, 1]$, for any positive integer n

30. $f(x) = x^{1/n}$ on $[0, 1]$, for any positive integer n

31. **Average distance on a parabola** What is the average distance between the parabola $y = 30x(20 - x)$ and the x-axis on the interval $[0, 20]$?

T 32. **Average elevation** The elevation of a path is given by $f(x) = x^3 - 5x^2 + 30$, where x measures horizontal distances. Draw a graph of the elevation function and find its average value, for $0 \le x \le 4$.

33. **Average height of an arch** The height of an arch above the ground is given by the function $y = 10\sin x$, for $0 \le x \le \pi$. What is the average height of the arch above the ground?

34. **Average height of a wave** The surface of a water wave is described by $y = 5(1 + \cos x)$, for $-\pi \le x \le \pi$, where $y = 0$ corresponds to a trough of the wave (see figure). Find the average height of the wave above the trough on $[-\pi, \pi]$.

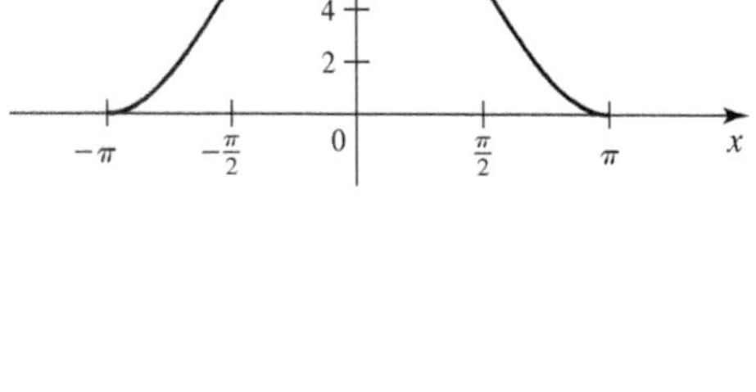

T 35–40. Mean Value Theorem for Integrals *Find or approximate all points at which the given function equals its average value on the given interval.*

35. $f(x) = 8 - 2x$ on $[0, 4]$ **36.** $f(x) = e^x$ on $[0, 2]$

37. $f(x) = 1 - x^2/a^2$ on $[0, a]$, where a is a positive real number

38. $f(x) = \frac{\pi}{4}\sin x$ on $[0, \pi]$ **39.** $f(x) = 1 - |x|$ on $[-1, 1]$

40. $f(x) = 1/x$ on $[1, 4]$

Further Explorations

41. Explain why or why not Determine whether the following statements are true and give an explanation or counterexample.

a. If f is symmetric about the line $x = 2$, then $\int_0^4 f(x)\,dx = 2\int_0^2 f(x)\,dx$.

b. If f has the property $f(a + x) = -f(a - x)$, for all x, where a is a constant, then $\int_{a-2}^{a+2} f(x)\,dx = 0$.

c. The average value of a linear function on an interval $[a, b]$ is the function value at the midpoint of $[a, b]$.

d. Consider the function $f(x) = x(a - x)$ on the interval $[0, a]$, for $a > 0$. Its average value on $[0, a]$ is $\frac{1}{2}$ of its maximum value.

42–45. Symmetry in integrals *Use symmetry to evaluate the following integrals.*

42. $\displaystyle\int_{-\pi/4}^{\pi/4} \tan x\,dx$ **43.** $\displaystyle\int_{-\pi/4}^{\pi/4} \sec^2 x\,dx$

44. $\displaystyle\int_{-2}^{2} (1 - |x|^3)\,dx$ **45.** $\displaystyle\int_{-2}^{2} \frac{x^3 - 4x}{x^2 + 1}\,dx$

Applications

46. Root mean square The root mean square (or RMS) is another measure of average value, often used with oscillating functions (for example, sine and cosine functions that describe the current, voltage, or power in an alternating circuit). The RMS of a function f on the interval $[0, T]$ is

$$\bar{f}_{\text{RMS}} = \sqrt{\frac{1}{T}\int_0^T f(t)^2\,dt}.$$

Compute the RMS of $f(t) = A\sin(\omega t)$, where A and ω are positive constants and T is any integer multiple of the period of f, which is $2\pi/\omega$.

47. Gateway Arch The Gateway Arch in St. Louis is 630 ft high and has a 630-ft base. Its shape can be modeled by the parabola

$$y = 630\left(1 - \left(\frac{x}{315}\right)^2\right).$$

Find the average height of the arch above the ground.

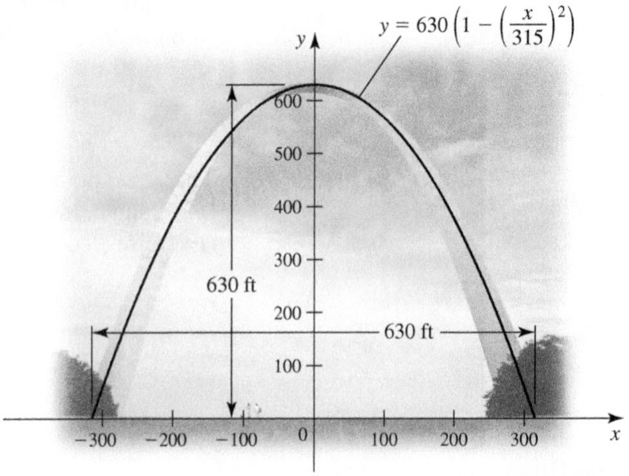

48. Another Gateway Arch Another description of the Gateway Arch is

$$y = 1260 - 315(e^{0.00418x} + e^{-0.00418x}),$$

where the base of the arch is $[-315, 315]$ and x and y are measured in feet. Find the average height of the arch above the ground.

49. Planetary orbits The planets orbit the Sun in elliptical orbits with the Sun at one focus (see Section 10.4 for more on ellipses). The equation of an ellipse whose dimensions are $2a$ in the x-direction and $2b$ in the y-direction is $\frac{x^2}{a^2} + \frac{y^2}{b^2} = 1$.

a. Let d^2 denote the square of the distance from a planet to the center of the ellipse at $(0, 0)$. Integrate over the interval $[-a, a]$ to show that the average value of d^2 is $(a^2 + 2b^2)/3$.

b. Show that in the case of a circle ($a = b = R$), the average value in part (a) is R^2.

c. Assuming $0 < b < a$, the coordinates of the Sun are $(\sqrt{a^2 - b^2}, 0)$. Let D^2 denote the square of the distance from the planet to the Sun. Integrate over the interval $[-a, a]$ to show that the average value of D^2 is $(4a^2 - b^2)/3$.

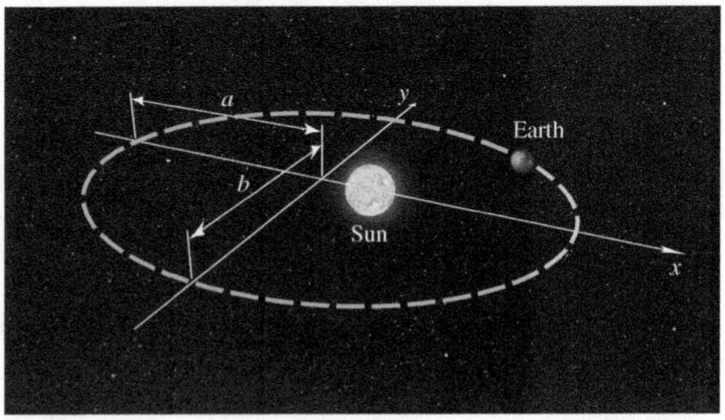

Additional Exercises

50. Comparing a sine and a quadratic function Consider the functions $f(x) = \sin x$ and $g(x) = \frac{4}{\pi^2}x(\pi - x)$.

a. Carefully graph f and g on the same set of axes. Verify that both functions have a single local maximum on the interval $[0, \pi]$ and that they have the same maximum value on $[0, \pi]$.
b. On the interval $[0, \pi]$, which is true: $f(x) \geq g(x)$, $g(x) \geq f(x)$, or neither?
c. Compute and compare the average values of f and g on $[0, \pi]$.

51. Using symmetry Suppose f is an even function and

$$\int_{-8}^{8} f(x)\,dx = 18.$$

a. Evaluate $\int_0^8 f(x)\,dx$ **b.** Evaluate $\int_{-8}^{8} xf(x)\,dx$

52. Using symmetry Suppose f is an odd function, $\int_0^4 f(x)\,dx = 3$, and $\int_0^8 f(x)\,dx = 9$.

a. Evaluate $\int_{-4}^{8} f(x)\,dx$ **b.** Evaluate $\int_{-8}^{4} f(x)\,dx$

53–56. Symmetry of composite functions *Prove that the integrand is either even or odd. Then give the value of the integral or show how it can be simplified. Assume that f and g are even functions and p and q are odd functions.*

53. $\int_{-a}^{a} f(g(x))\,dx$ **54.** $\int_{-a}^{a} f(p(x))\,dx$

55. $\int_{-a}^{a} p(g(x))\,dx$ **56.** $\int_{-a}^{a} p(q(x))\,dx$

57. Average value with a parameter Consider the function $f(x) = ax(1 - x)$ on the interval $[0, 1]$, where a is a positive real number.

a. Find the average value of f as a function of a.
b. Find the points at which the value of f equals its average value and prove that they are independent of a.

58. Square of the average For what polynomials f is it true that the square of the average value of f equals the average value of the square of f over all intervals $[a, b]$?

59. Problems of antiquity Several calculus problems were solved by Greek mathematicians long before the discovery of calculus. The following problems were solved by Archimedes using methods that predated calculus by 2000 years.

a. Show that the area of a segment of a parabola is $\frac{4}{3}$ that of its inscribed triangle of greatest area. In other words, the area bounded by the parabola $y = a^2 - x^2$ and the x-axis is $\frac{4}{3}$ the area of the triangle with vertices $(\pm a, 0)$ and $(0, a^2)$. Assume that $a > 0$ but is unspecified.
b. Show that the area bounded by the parabola $y = a^2 - x^2$ and the x-axis is $\frac{2}{3}$ the area of the rectangle with vertices $(\pm a, 0)$ and $(\pm a, a^2)$. Assume that $a > 0$ but is unspecified.

60. Unit area sine curve Find the value of c such that the region bounded by $y = c \sin x$ and the x-axis on the interval $[0, \pi]$ has area 1.

61. Unit area cubic Find the value of $c > 0$ such that the region bounded by the cubic $y = x(x - c)^2$ and the x-axis on the interval $[0, c]$ has area 1.

62. Unit area

a. Consider the curve $y = 1/x$, for $x \geq 1$. For what value of $b > 0$ does the region bounded by this curve and the x-axis on the interval $[1, b]$ have an area of 1?
b. Consider the curve $y = 1/x^p$, where $x \geq 1$, and $p < 2$ with $p \neq 1$. For what value of b (as a function of p) does the region bounded by this curve and the x-axis on the interval $[1, b]$ have unit area?
c. Is $b(p)$ in part (b) an increasing or decreasing function of p? Explain.

63. A sine integral by Riemann sums Consider the integral $I = \int_0^{\pi/2} \sin x\,dx$.

a. Write the left Riemann sum for I with n subintervals.
b. Show that $\lim_{\theta \to 0} \theta\left(\frac{\cos\theta + \sin\theta - 1}{2(1 - \cos\theta)}\right) = 1$.
c. It is a fact that $\sum_{k=0}^{n-1} \sin\left(\frac{\pi k}{2n}\right) = \frac{\cos\left(\frac{\pi}{2n}\right) + \sin\left(\frac{\pi}{2n}\right) - 1}{2\left(1 - \cos\left(\frac{\pi}{2n}\right)\right)}$.

Use this fact and part (b) to evaluate I by taking the limit of the Riemann sum as $n \to \infty$.

64. Alternate definitions of means Consider the function

$$f(t) = \frac{\int_a^b x^{t+1}\,dx}{\int_a^b x^t\,dx}.$$

Show that the following means can be defined in terms of f.

a. Arithmetic mean: $f(0) = \frac{a + b}{2}$
b. Geometric mean: $f\left(-\frac{3}{2}\right) = \sqrt{ab}$
c. Harmonic mean: $f(-3) = \frac{2ab}{a + b}$
d. Logarithmic mean: $f(-1) = \frac{b - a}{\ln b - \ln a}$

(*Source: Mathematics Magazine* 78, 5, Dec 2005)

65. Symmetry of powers Fill in the following table with either **even** or **odd**, and prove each result. Assume n is a nonnegative integer and f^n means the nth power of f.

	***f* is even**	***f* is odd**
***n* is even**	f^n is ____	f^n is ____
***n* is odd**	f^n is ____	f^n is ____

66. Average value of the derivative Suppose that f' is a continuous function for all real numbers. Show that the average value of the derivative on an interval $[a, b]$ is $\overline{f'} = \frac{f(b) - f(a)}{b - a}$. Interpret this result in terms of secant lines.

67. Symmetry about a point A function f is symmetric about a point (c, d) if whenever $(c - x, d - y)$ is on the graph, then so is $(c + x, d + y)$. Functions that are symmetric about a point (c, d) are easily integrated on an interval with midpoint c.

a. Show that if f is symmetric about (c, d) and $a > 0$, then $\int_{c-a}^{c+a} f(x)\,dx = 2af(c) = 2ad$.

b. Graph the function $f(x) = \sin^2 x$ on the interval $[0, \pi/2]$ and show that the function is symmetric about the point $(\frac{\pi}{4}, \frac{1}{2})$.

c. Using only the graph of f (and no integration), show that $\int_0^{\pi/2} \sin^2 x\,dx = \frac{\pi}{4}$. (See the Guided Project *Symmetry in Integrals.*)

68. Bounds on an integral Suppose f is continuous on $[a, b]$ with $f''(x) > 0$ on the interval. It can be shown that

$$(b - a)f\left(\frac{a + b}{2}\right) \leq \int_a^b f(x)\,dx \leq (b - a)\frac{f(a) + f(b)}{2}.$$

a. Assuming f is nonnegative on $[a, b]$, draw a figure to illustrate the geometric meaning of these inequalities. Discuss your conclusions.

b. Divide these inequalities by $(b - a)$ and interpret the resulting inequalities in terms of the average value of f on $[a, b]$.

69. Generalizing the Mean Value Theorem for Integrals Suppose f and g are continuous on $[a, b]$ and let

$$h(x) = (x - b)\int_a^x f(t)\,dt + (x - a)\int_x^b g(t)\,dt.$$

a. Use Rolle's theorem to show that there is a number c in (a, b) such that

$$\int_a^c f(t)\,dt + \int_c^b g(t)\,dt = f(c)(b - c) + g(c)(c - a),$$

which is a generalization of the Mean Value Theorem for Integrals.

b. Show that there a number c in (a, b) such that $\int_a^x f(t)\,dt = f(c)(b - c)$.

c. Use a sketch to interpret part (b) geometrically.

d. Use the result of part (a) to give an alternate proof of the Mean Value Theorem for Integrals.

(*Source: The College Mathematics Journal,* 33, 5, Nov 2002)

QUICK CHECK ANSWERS

1. $f(-x)g(-x) = f(x)g(x)$; therefore, fg is even. **2.** The average value is the constant; the average value is 0. **3.** The average value is zero on the interval; by the Mean Value Theorem for Integrals, $f(x) = 0$ at some point on the interval. ◄

5.5 Substitution Rule

Given just about any differentiable function, with enough know-how and persistence, you can compute its derivative. But the same cannot be said of antiderivatives. Many functions, even relatively simple ones, do not have antiderivatives that can be expressed in terms of familiar functions. Examples are $\sin x^2$, $(\sin x)/x$, and x^x. The immediate goal of this section is to enlarge the family of functions for which we can find antiderivatives. This campaign resumes in Chapter 7, where additional integration methods are developed.

Indefinite Integrals

One way to find new antiderivative rules is to start with familiar derivative rules and work backward. When applied to the Chain Rule, this strategy leads to the Substitution Rule. A few examples illustrate the technique.

EXAMPLE 1 Antiderivatives by trial and error Find $\int \cos 2x\,dx$.

SOLUTION The closest familiar indefinite integral related to this problem is

➤ We assume C is an arbitrary constant without stating so each time it appears.

$$\int \cos x\,dx = \sin x + C,$$

which is true because

$$\frac{d}{dx}(\sin x + C) = \cos x.$$

Therefore, we might *incorrectly* conclude that the indefinite integral of $\cos 2x$ is $\sin 2x + C$. However, by the Chain Rule,

$$\frac{d}{dx}(\sin 2x + C) = 2\cos 2x \neq \cos 2x.$$

Note that $\sin 2x$ fails to be an antiderivative of $\cos 2x$ by a multiplicative factor of 2. A small adjustment corrects this problem. Let's try $\frac{1}{2}\sin 2x$:

$$\frac{d}{dx}\left(\frac{1}{2}\sin 2x\right) = \frac{1}{2}\cdot 2\cos 2x = \cos 2x.$$

It works! So we have

$$\int \cos 2x\, dx = \frac{1}{2}\sin 2x + C.$$

Related Exercises 9–12 ◀

The trial-and-error approach of Example 1 is impractical for complicated integrals. To develop a systematic method, consider a composite function $F(g(x))$, where F is an antiderivative of f; that is, $F' = f$. Using the Chain Rule to differentiate the composite function $F(g(x))$, we find that

$$\frac{d}{dx}(F(g(x))) = \underbrace{F'(g(x))}_{f(g(x))}g'(x) = f(g(x))g'(x).$$

This equation says that $F(g(x))$ is an antiderivative of $f(g(x))g'(x)$, which is written

$$\int f(g(x))g'(x)\, dx = F(g(x)) + C, \tag{1}$$

where F is any antiderivative of f.

➤ You can call the new variable anything you want because it is just another variable of integration. Typically, u is the standard choice for the new variable.

Why is this approach called the *Substitution Rule* (or *Change of Variables Rule*)? In the composite function $f(g(x))$ in equation (1), we identify the "inner function" as $u = g(x)$, which implies that $du = g'(x)\,dx$. Making this identification, the integral in equation (1) is written

$$\int \underbrace{f(g(x))}_{f(u)}\underbrace{g'(x)dx}_{du} = \int f(u)\, du = F(u) + C.$$

We see that the integral $\int f(g(x))g'(x)\,dx$ with respect to x is replaced with a new integral $\int f(u)du$ with respect to the new variable u. In other words, we have substituted the new variable u for the old variable x. Of course, if the new integral with respect to u is no easier to find than the original integral, then the change of variables has not helped. The Substitution Rule requires plenty of practice until certain patterns become familiar.

THEOREM 5.6 Substitution Rule for Indefinite Integrals

Let $u = g(x)$, where g' is continuous on an interval, and let f be continuous on the corresponding range of g. On that interval,

$$\int f(g(x))g'(x)\, dx = \int f(u)\, du.$$

In practice, Theorem 5.6 is applied using the following procedure.

PROCEDURE Substitution Rule (Change of Variables)

1. Given an indefinite integral involving a composite function $f(g(x))$, identify an inner function $u = g(x)$ such that a constant multiple of $g'(x)$ appears in the integrand.
2. Substitute $u = g(x)$ and $du = g'(x)\,dx$ in the integral.
3. Evaluate the new indefinite integral with respect to u.
4. Write the result in terms of x using $u = g(x)$.

Disclaimer: Not all integrals yield to the Substitution Rule.

EXAMPLE 2 Perfect substitutions Use the Substitution Rule to find the following indefinite integrals. Check your work by differentiating.

a. $\int 2(2x + 1)^3\,dx$ **b.** $\int 10e^{10x}\,dx$

SOLUTION

a. We identify $u = 2x + 1$ as the inner function of the composite function $(2x + 1)^3$. Therefore, we choose the new variable $u = 2x + 1$, which implies that $\frac{du}{dx} = 2$, or $du = 2\,dx$. Notice that $du = 2\,dx$ appears as a factor in the integrand. The change of variables looks like this:

$$\int \underbrace{(2x + 1)^3}_{u^3} \cdot \underbrace{2\,dx}_{du} = \int u^3\,du \quad \text{Substitute } u = 2x + 1,\ du = 2\,dx.$$

$$= \frac{u^4}{4} + C \quad \text{Antiderivative}$$

$$= \frac{(2x + 1)^4}{4} + C. \quad \text{Replace } u \text{ with } 2x + 1.$$

➤ Use the Chain Rule to check that $\frac{d}{dx}\left(\frac{(2x + 1)^4}{4} + C\right) = 2(2x + 1)^3$.

Notice that the final step uses $u = 2x + 1$ to return to the original variable.

b. The composite function e^{10x} has the inner function $u = 10x$, which implies that $du = 10\,dx$. The change of variables appears as

$$\int \underbrace{e^{10x}}_{e^u}\,\underbrace{10\,dx}_{du} = \int e^u\,du \quad \text{Substitute } u = 10x,\ du = 10\,dx.$$

$$= e^u + C \quad \text{Antiderivative}$$

$$= e^{10x} + C. \quad \text{Replace } u \text{ with } 10x.$$

In checking, we see that $\frac{d}{dx}(e^{10x} + C) = e^{10x} \cdot 10 = 10e^{10x}$.

Related Exercises 13–16 ◀

QUICK CHECK 1 Find a new variable u so that $\int 4x^3(x^4 + 5)^{10}\,dx = \int u^{10}\,du$. ◀

Most substitutions are not perfect. The remaining examples show more typical situations that require introducing a constant factor.

EXAMPLE 3 Introducing a constant Find the following indefinite integrals.

a. $\int x^4(x^5 + 6)^9\,dx$ **b.** $\int \cos^3 x \sin x\,dx$

SOLUTION

a. The inner function of the composite function $(x^5+6)^9$ is x^5+6 and its derivative $5x^4$ also appears in the integrand (up to a multiplicative factor). Therefore, we use the substitution $u = x^5 + 6$, which implies that $du = 5x^4\,dx$, or $x^4\,dx = \frac{1}{5}\,du$. By the Substitution Rule,

$$\int \underbrace{(x^5+6)^9}_{u^9}\,\underbrace{x^4\,dx}_{\frac{1}{5}du} = \int u^9 \cdot \frac{1}{5}\,du \qquad \text{Substitute } u = x^5+6,\ du = 5x^4\,dx \Rightarrow x^4\,dx = \frac{1}{5}\,du.$$

$$= \frac{1}{5}\int u^9\,du \qquad \int cf(x)\,dx = c\int f(x)\,dx$$

$$= \frac{1}{5}\cdot\frac{u^{10}}{10} + C \qquad \text{Antiderivative}$$

$$= \frac{1}{50}(x^5+6)^{10} + C. \qquad \text{Replace } u \text{ with } x^5+6.$$

b. The integrand can be written as $(\cos x)^3 \sin x$. The inner function in the composition $(\cos x)^3$ is $\cos x$, which suggests the substitution $u = \cos x$. Note that $du = -\sin x\,dx$ or $\sin x\,dx = -du$. The change of variables appears as

$$\int \underbrace{\cos^3 x}_{u^3}\,\underbrace{\sin x\,dx}_{-du} = -\int u^3\,du \qquad \text{Substitute } u = \cos x,\ du = -\sin x\,dx.$$

$$= -\frac{u^4}{4} + C \qquad \text{Antiderivative}$$

$$= -\frac{\cos^4 x}{4} + C. \qquad \text{Replace } u \text{ with } \cos x.$$

Related Exercises 17–32 ◀

QUICK CHECK 2 In Example 3a, explain why the same substitution would not work as well for the integral $\int x^3(x^5+6)^9\,dx$. ◀

Sometimes the choice for a u-substitution is not so obvious *or* more than one u-substitution works. The following example illustrates both of these points.

EXAMPLE 4 Variations on the substitution method Find $\int \frac{x}{\sqrt{x+1}}\,dx$.

SOLUTION

Substitution 1 The composite function $\sqrt{x+1}$ suggests the new variable $u = x+1$. You might doubt whether this choice will work because $du = dx$, which leaves the x in the numerator of the integrand unaccounted for. But let's proceed. Letting $u = x+1$, we have $x = u-1$, $du = dx$, and

$$\int \frac{x}{\sqrt{x+1}}\,dx = \int \frac{u-1}{\sqrt{u}}\,du \qquad \text{Substitute } u = x+1,\ du = dx.$$

$$= \int\left(\sqrt{u} - \frac{1}{\sqrt{u}}\right)du \qquad \text{Rewrite integrand.}$$

$$= \int (u^{1/2} - u^{-1/2})\,du. \qquad \text{Fractional powers}$$

We integrate each term individually and then return to the original variable x:

$$\int (u^{1/2} - u^{-1/2})\,du = \frac{2}{3}u^{3/2} - 2u^{1/2} + C \quad \text{Antiderivatives}$$

$$= \frac{2}{3}(x+1)^{3/2} - 2(x+1)^{1/2} + C \quad \text{Replace } u \text{ with } x+1.$$

$$= \frac{2}{3}(x+1)^{1/2}(x-2) + C. \quad \text{Factor out } (x+1)^{1/2} \text{ and simplify.}$$

➤ In Substitution 2, you could also use the fact that

$$u'(x) = \frac{1}{2\sqrt{x+1}},$$

which implies

$$du = \frac{1}{2\sqrt{x+1}}\,dx.$$

Substitution 2 Another possible substitution is $u = \sqrt{x+1}$. Now $u^2 = x + 1$, $x = u^2 - 1$, and $dx = 2u\,du$. Making these substitutions leads to

$$\int \frac{x}{\sqrt{x+1}}\,dx = \int \frac{u^2-1}{u}\,2u\,du \quad \text{Substitute } u = \sqrt{x+1}, x = u^2 - 1.$$

$$= 2\int (u^2 - 1)\,du \quad \text{Simplify the integrand.}$$

$$= 2\left(\frac{u^3}{3} - u\right) + C \quad \text{Antiderivatives}$$

$$= \frac{2}{3}(x+1)^{3/2} - 2(x+1)^{1/2} + C \quad \text{Replace } u \text{ with } \sqrt{x+1}.$$

$$= \frac{2}{3}(x+1)^{1/2}(x-2) + C. \quad \text{Factor out } (x+1)^{1/2} \text{ and simplify.}$$

Observe that the same indefinite integral is found using either substitution.

Related Exercises 33–38 ◀

Definite Integrals

The Substitution Rule is also used for definite integrals; in fact, there are two ways to proceed.

- You may use the Substitution Rule to find an antiderivative F and then use the Fundamental Theorem to evaluate $F(b) - F(a)$.
- Alternatively, once you have changed variables from x to u, you also may change the limits of integration and complete the integration with respect to u. Specifically, if $u = g(x)$, the lower limit $x = a$ is replaced with $u = g(a)$ and the upper limit $x = b$ is replaced with $u = g(b)$.

The second option tends to be more efficient, and we use it whenever possible. This approach is summarized in the following theorem, which is then applied to several definite integrals.

> **THEOREM 5.7 Substitution Rule for Definite Integrals**
> Let $u = g(x)$, where g' is continuous on $[a, b]$, and let f be continuous on the range of g. Then
>
> $$\int_a^b f(g(x))g'(x)\,dx = \int_{g(a)}^{g(b)} f(u)\,du.$$

EXAMPLE 5 Definite integrals Evaluate the following integrals.

a. $\displaystyle\int_0^2 \frac{dx}{(x+3)^3}$ **b.** $\displaystyle\int_0^4 \frac{x}{x^2+1}\,dx$ **c.** $\displaystyle\int_0^{\pi/2} \sin^4 x \cos x\,dx$

SOLUTION

➤ When the integrand has the form $f(ax + b)$, the substitution $u = ax + b$ is often effective.

a. Let the new variable be $u = x + 3$ and then $du = dx$. Because we have changed the variable of integration from x to u, the limits of integration must also be expressed in terms of u. In this case,

$$x = 0 \text{ implies } u = 0 + 3 = 3, \quad \text{Lower limit}$$
$$x = 2 \text{ implies } u = 2 + 3 = 5. \quad \text{Upper limit}$$

The entire integration is carried out as follows:

$$\int_0^2 \frac{dx}{(x+3)^3} = \int_3^5 u^{-3}\,du \qquad \text{Substitute } u = x + 3,\ du = dx.$$
$$= -\frac{u^{-2}}{2}\bigg|_3^5 \qquad \text{Fundamental Theorem}$$
$$= -\frac{1}{2}(5^{-2} - 3^{-2}) = \frac{8}{225}. \qquad \text{Simplify.}$$

b. Notice that a multiple of the derivative of the denominator appears in the numerator; therefore, we let $u = x^2 + 1$, which implies that $du = 2x\,dx$, or $x\,dx = \frac{1}{2}\,du$. Changing limits of integration,

$$x = 0 \text{ implies } u = 0 + 1 = 1, \quad \text{Lower limit}$$
$$x = 4 \text{ implies } u = 4^2 + 1 = 17. \quad \text{Upper limit}$$

Changing variables, we have

$$\int_0^4 \frac{x}{x^2+1}\,dx = \frac{1}{2}\int_1^{17} u^{-1}\,du \qquad \text{Substitute } u = x^2 + 1,\ du = 2x\,dx.$$
$$= \frac{1}{2}\ln|u|\bigg|_1^{17} \qquad \text{Fundamental Theorem}$$
$$= \frac{1}{2}(\ln 17 - \ln 1) \qquad \text{Simplify.}$$
$$= \frac{1}{2}\ln 17 \approx 1.417. \qquad \ln 1 = 0$$

c. Let $u = \sin x$, which implies that $du = \cos x\,dx$. The lower limit of integration becomes $u = 0$ and the upper limit becomes $u = 1$. Changing variables, we have

$$\int_0^{\pi/2} \sin^4 x \cos x\,dx = \int_0^1 u^4\,du \qquad u = \sin x,\ du = \cos x\,dx$$
$$= \left(\frac{u^5}{5}\right)\bigg|_0^1 = \frac{1}{5}. \qquad \text{Fundamental Theorem}$$

Related Exercises 39–52 ◀

The Substitution Rule enables us to find two standard integrals that appear frequently in practice, $\int \sin^2 x\,dx$ and $\int \cos^2 x\,dx$. These integrals are handled using the identities

$$\sin^2 x = \frac{1 - \cos 2x}{2} \quad \text{and} \quad \cos^2 x = \frac{1 + \cos 2x}{2}.$$

EXAMPLE 6 **Integral of $\cos^2\theta$** Evaluate $\int_0^{\pi/2} \cos^2\theta\, d\theta$.

SOLUTION Working with the indefinite integral first, we use the identity for $\cos^2\theta$:

$$\int \cos^2\theta\, d\theta = \int \frac{1+\cos 2\theta}{2}\, d\theta = \frac{1}{2}\int d\theta + \frac{1}{2}\int \cos 2\theta\, d\theta.$$

➤ See Exercise 102 for a generalization of Example 6. Trigonometric integrals involving powers of sin *x* and cos *x* are explored in greater detail in Section 7.3.

The change of variables $u = 2\theta$ (or Table 4.9) is now used for the second integral, and we have

$$\begin{aligned}\int \cos^2\theta\, d\theta &= \frac{1}{2}\int d\theta + \frac{1}{2}\int \cos 2\theta\, d\theta \\ &= \frac{1}{2}\int d\theta + \frac{1}{2}\cdot\frac{1}{2}\int \cos u\, du && u = 2\theta,\ du = 2\, d\theta \\ &= \frac{\theta}{2} + \frac{1}{4}\sin 2\theta + C. && \text{Evaluate integrals; } u = 2\theta.\end{aligned}$$

Using the Fundamental Theorem of Calculus, the value of the definite integral is

$$\begin{aligned}\int_0^{\pi/2} \cos^2\theta\, d\theta &= \left(\frac{\theta}{2} + \frac{1}{4}\sin 2\theta\right)\Bigg|_0^{\pi/2} \\ &= \left(\frac{\pi}{4} + \frac{1}{4}\sin\pi\right) - \left(0 + \frac{1}{4}\sin 0\right) = \frac{\pi}{4}.\end{aligned}$$

Related Exercises 53–60 ◄

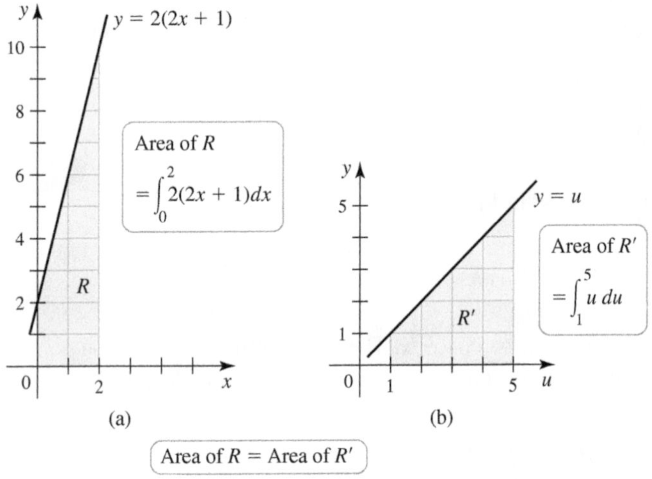

Figure 5.54

Geometry of Substitution

The Substitution Rule has a geometric interpretation. To keep matters simple, consider the integral $\int_0^2 2(2x+1)\, dx$. The graph of the integrand $y = 2(2x+1)$ on the interval $[0, 2]$ is shown in Figure 5.54a, along with the region *R* whose area is given by the integral. The change of variables $u = 2x + 1$, $du = 2\, dx$, $u(0) = 1$, and $u(2) = 5$ leads to the new integral

$$\int_0^2 2(2x+1)\, dx = \int_1^5 u\, du.$$

Figure 5.54b also shows the graph of the new integrand $y = u$ on the interval $[1, 5]$ and the region R' whose area is given by the new integral. You can check that the areas of *R* and R' are equal. An analogous interpretation may be given to more complicated integrands and substitutions.

QUICK CHECK 3 Changes of variables occur frequently in mathematics. For example, suppose you want to solve the equation $x^4 - 13x^2 + 36 = 0$. If you use the substitution $u = x^2$, what is the new equation that must be solved for *u*? What are the roots of the original equation? ◄

SECTION 5.5 EXERCISES

Review Questions

1. On which derivative rule is the Substitution Rule based?
2. Why is the Substitution Rule referred to as a change of variables?
3. The composite function $f(g(x))$ consists of an inner function *g* and an outer function *f*. If an integrand includes $f(g(x))$, which function is often a likely choice for a new variable *u*?
4. Find a suitable substitution for evaluating $\int \tan x \sec^2 x\, dx$ and explain your choice.
5. When using a change of variables $u = g(x)$ to evaluate the definite integral $\int_a^b f(g(x))g'(x)\, dx$, how are the limits of integration transformed?
6. If the change of variables $u = x^2 - 4$ is used to evaluate the definite integral $\int_2^4 f(x)\, dx$, what are the new limits of integration?
7. Find $\int \cos^2 x\, dx$.
8. What identity is needed to find $\int \sin^2 x\, dx$?

Basic Skills

9–12. Trial and error *Find an antiderivative of the following functions by trial and error. Check your answer by differentiating.*

9. $f(x) = (x + 1)^{12}$

10. $f(x) = e^{3x+1}$

11. $f(x) = \sqrt{2x + 1}$

12. $f(x) = \cos(2x + 5)$

13–16. Substitution given *Use the given substitution to find the following indefinite integrals. Check your answer by differentiating.*

13. $\int 2x(x^2 + 1)^4\, dx,\ u = x^2 + 1$

14. $\int 8x \cos(4x^2 + 3)\, dx,\ u = 4x^2 + 3$

15. $\int \sin^3 x \cos x\, dx,\ u = \sin x$

16. $\int (6x + 1)\sqrt{3x^2 + x}\, dx,\ u = 3x^2 + x$

17–32. Indefinite integrals *Use a change of variables to find the following indefinite integrals. Check your work by differentiating.*

17. $\int 2x(x^2 - 1)^{99}\, dx$

18. $\int xe^{x^2}\, dx$

19. $\int \frac{2x^2}{\sqrt{1 - 4x^3}}\, dx$

20. $\int \frac{(\sqrt{x} + 1)^4}{2\sqrt{x}}\, dx$

21. $\int (x^2 + x)^{10}(2x + 1)\, dx$

22. $\int \frac{1}{10x - 3}\, dx$

23. $\int x^3(x^4 + 16)^6\, dx$

24. $\int \sin^{10}\theta \cos\theta\, d\theta$

25. $\int \frac{dx}{\sqrt{1 - 9x^2}}$

26. $\int x^9 \sin x^{10}\, dx$

27. $\int (x^6 - 3x^2)^4(x^5 - x)\, dx$

28. $\int \frac{x}{x - 2}\, dx$ (*Hint:* Let $u = x - 2$.)

29. $\int \frac{dx}{1 + 4x^2}$

30. $\int \frac{3}{1 + 25y^2}\, dy$

31. $\int \frac{2}{x\sqrt{4x^2 - 1}}\, dx,\ x > \frac{1}{2}$

32. $\int \frac{8x + 6}{2x^2 + 3x}\, dx$

33–38. Variations on the substitution method *Find the following integrals.*

33. $\int \frac{x}{\sqrt{x - 4}}\, dx$

34. $\int \frac{y^2}{(y + 1)^4}\, dy$

35. $\int \frac{x}{\sqrt[3]{x + 4}}\, dx$

36. $\int \frac{e^x - e^{-x}}{e^x + e^{-x}}\, dx$

37. $\int x\sqrt[3]{2x + 1}\, dx$

38. $\int (z + 1)\sqrt{3z + 2}\, dz$

39–52. Definite integrals *Use a change of variables to evaluate the following definite integrals.*

39. $\int_0^1 2x(4 - x^2)\, dx$

40. $\int_0^2 \frac{2x}{(x^2 + 1)^2}\, dx$

41. $\int_0^{\pi/2} \sin^2\theta \cos\theta\, d\theta$

42. $\int_0^{\pi/4} \frac{\sin x}{\cos^2 x}\, dx$

43. $\int_{-1}^2 x^2 e^{x^3+1}\, dx$

44. $\int_0^4 \frac{p}{\sqrt{9 + p^2}}\, dp$

45. $\int_{\pi/4}^{\pi/2} \frac{\cos x}{\sin^2 x}\, dx$

46. $\int_0^{\pi/4} \frac{\sin\theta}{\cos^3\theta}\, d\theta$

47. $\int_{2/(5\sqrt{3})}^{2/5} \frac{dx}{x\sqrt{25x^2 - 1}}$

48. $\int_0^3 \frac{v^2 + 1}{\sqrt{v^3 + 3v + 4}}\, dv$

49. $\int_0^4 \frac{x}{x^2 + 1}\, dx$

50. $\int_0^{1/4} \frac{x}{\sqrt{1 - 16x^2}}\, dx$

51. $\int_{1/3}^{1/\sqrt{3}} \frac{4}{9x^2 + 1}\, dx$

52. $\int_0^{\ln 4} \frac{e^x}{3 + 2e^x}\, dx$

53–60. Integrals with $\sin^2 x$ and $\cos^2 x$ *Evaluate the following integrals.*

53. $\int_{-\pi}^{\pi} \cos^2 x\, dx$

54. $\int \sin^2 x\, dx$

55. $\int \sin^2\left(\theta + \frac{\pi}{6}\right) d\theta$

56. $\int_0^{\pi/4} \cos^2 8\theta\, d\theta$

57. $\int_{-\pi/4}^{\pi/4} \sin^2 2\theta\, d\theta$

58. $\int x \cos^2(x^2)\, dx$

59. $\int_0^{\pi/6} \frac{\sin 2y}{\sin^2 y + 2}\, dy$ (*Hint:* $\sin 2y = 2 \sin y \cos y$.)

60. $\int_0^{\pi/2} \sin^4\theta\, d\theta$

Further Explorations

61. Explain why or why not Determine whether the following statements are true and give an explanation or counterexample. Assume that f, f', and f'' are continuous functions for all real numbers.

a. $\int f(x)f'(x)\, dx = \frac{1}{2}(f(x))^2 + C.$

b. $\int (f(x))^n f'(x)\, dx = \frac{1}{n + 1}(f(x))^{n+1} + C,\ n \neq -1.$

c. $\int \sin 2x\, dx = 2\int \sin x\, dx.$

d. $\int (x^2 + 1)^9 dx = \frac{(x^2 + 1)^{10}}{10} + C.$

e. $\int_a^b f'(x)f''(x)\, dx = f'(b) - f'(a).$

62–78. Additional integrals *Use a change of variables to evaluate the following integrals.*

62. $\int \sec 4w \tan 4w\, dw$

63. $\int \sec^2 10x\, dx$

64. $\int (\sin^5 x + 3\sin^3 x - \sin x)\cos x\, dx$

65. $\int \frac{\csc^2 x}{\cot^3 x}\, dx$

66. $\int (x^{3/2} + 8)^5 \sqrt{x}\, dx$

67. $\int \sin x \sec^8 x\, dx$

68. $\int \frac{e^{2x}}{e^{2x} + 1}\, dx$

69. $\int_0^1 x\sqrt{1 - x^2}\, dx$

70. $\int_1^{e^2} \frac{\ln p}{p}\, dp$

71. $\int_2^3 \frac{x}{\sqrt[3]{x^2 - 1}}\, dx$

72. $\int_0^{6/5} \frac{dx}{25x^2 + 36}$

73. $\int_0^2 x^3 \sqrt{16 - x^4}\, dx$

74. $\int_{-1}^1 (x - 1)(x^2 - 2x)^7\, dx$

75. $\int_{-\pi}^0 \frac{\sin x}{2 + \cos x}\, dx$

76. $\int_0^1 \frac{(v + 1)(v + 2)}{2v^3 + 9v^2 + 12v + 36}\, dv$

77. $\int_1^2 \frac{4}{9x^2 + 6x + 1}\, dx$

78. $\int_0^{\pi/4} e^{\sin^2 x} \sin 2x\, dx$

79–82. Areas of regions *Find the area of the following regions.*

79. The region bounded by the graph of $f(x) = x \sin x^2$ and the x-axis between $x = 0$ and $x = \sqrt{\pi}$

80. The region bounded by the graph of $f(\theta) = \cos\theta \sin\theta$ and the θ-axis between $\theta = 0$ and $\theta = \pi/2$

81. The region bounded by the graph of $f(x) = (x - 4)^4$ and the x-axis between $x = 2$ and $x = 6$

82. The region bounded by the graph of $f(x) = \frac{x}{\sqrt{x^2 - 9}}$ and the x-axis between $x = 4$ and $x = 5$

83. **Morphing parabolas** The family of parabolas $y = (1/a) - x^2/a^3$, where $a > 0$, has the property that for $x \geq 0$, the x-intercept is $(a, 0)$ and the y-intercept is $(0, 1/a)$. Let $A(a)$ be the area of the region in the first quadrant bounded by the parabola and the x-axis. Find $A(a)$ and determine whether it is an increasing, decreasing, or constant function of a.

84. **Substitutions** Suppose that f is an even function with $\int_0^8 f(x)\, dx = 9$. Evaluate each integral.

  a. $\int_{-1}^1 x f(x^2)\, dx$

  b. $\int_{-2}^2 x^2 f(x^3)\, dx$

85. **Substitutions** Suppose that p is a nonzero real number and f is an odd integrable function with $\int_0^1 f(x)\, dx = \pi$. Evaluate each integral.

  a. $\int_0^{\pi/(2p)} \cos px\, f(\sin px)\, dx$

  b. $\int_{-\pi/2}^{\pi/2} \cos x\, f(\sin x)\, dx$

Applications

T 86. **Periodic motion** An object moves along a line with a velocity in m/s given by $v(t) = 8\cos(\pi t/6)$. Its initial position is $s(0) = 0$.

  a. Graph the velocity function.

  b. As discussed in Chapter 6, the position of the object is given by $s(t) = \int_0^t v(y)\, dy$, for $t \geq 0$. Find the position function, for $t \geq 0$.

  c. What is the period of the motion—that is, starting at any point, how long does it take the object to return to that position?

87. **Population models** The population of a culture of bacteria has a growth rate given by $p'(t) = \frac{200}{(t + 1)^r}$ bacteria per hour, for $t \geq 0$, where $r > 1$ is a real number. In Chapter 6 it is shown that the increase in the population over the time interval $[0, t]$ is given by $\int_0^t p'(s)\, ds$. (Note that the growth rate decreases in time, reflecting competition for space and food.)

  a. Using the population model with $r = 2$, what is the increase in the population over the time interval $0 \leq t \leq 4$?

  b. Using the population model with $r = 3$, what is the increase in the population over the time interval $0 \leq t \leq 6$?

  c. Let ΔP be the increase in the population over a fixed time interval $[0, T]$. For fixed T, does ΔP increase or decrease with the parameter r? Explain.

  d. A lab technician measures an increase in the population of 350 bacteria over the 10-hr period $[0, 10]$. Estimate the value of r that best fits this data point.

  e. Looking ahead: Use the population model in part (b) to find the increase in population over the time interval $[0, T]$, for any $T > 0$. If the culture is allowed to grow indefinitely ($T \to \infty$), does the bacteria population increase without bound? Or does it approach a finite limit?

88. **Average distance on a triangle** Consider the right triangle with vertices $(0, 0)$, $(0, b)$, and $(a, 0)$, where $a > 0$ and $b > 0$. Show that the average vertical distance from points on the x-axis to the hypotenuse is $b/2$, for all $a > 0$.

T 89. **Average value of sine functions** Use a graphing utility to verify that the functions $f(x) = \sin kx$ have a period of $2\pi/k$, where $k = 1, 2, 3, \ldots$. Equivalently, the first "hump" of $f(x) = \sin kx$ occurs on the interval $[0, \pi/k]$. Verify that the average value of the first hump of $f(x) = \sin kx$ is independent of k. What is the average value?

Additional Exercises

90. **Looking ahead: Integrals of $\tan x$ and $\cot x$** Use a change of variables to verify each integral.

  a. $\int \tan x\, dx = -\ln|\cos x| + C = \ln|\sec x| + C$

  b. $\int \cot x\, dx = \ln|\sin x| + C$

91. **Looking ahead: Integrals of $\sec x$ and $\csc x$**

  a. Multiply the numerator and denominator of $\sec x$ by $\sec x + \tan x$; then use a change of variables to show that

$$\int \sec x\, dx = \ln|\sec x + \tan x| + C.$$

  b. Use a change of variables to show that

$$\int \csc x\, dx = -\ln|\csc x + \cot x| + C.$$

92. Equal areas The area of the shaded region under the curve $y = 2 \sin 2x$ in (a) equals the area of the shaded region under the curve $y = \sin x$ in (b). Explain why this is true without computing areas.

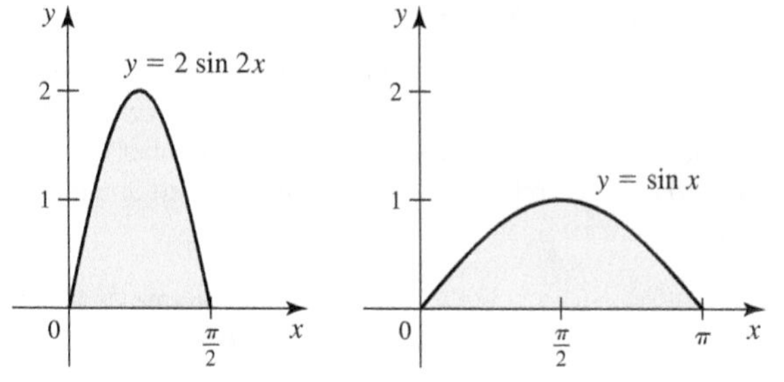

(a) (b)

93. Equal areas The area of the shaded region under the curve $y = \dfrac{(\sqrt{x} - 1)^2}{2\sqrt{x}}$ on the interval $[4, 9]$ in (a) equals the area of the shaded region under the curve $y = x^2$ on the interval $[1, 2]$ in (b). Without computing areas, explain why.

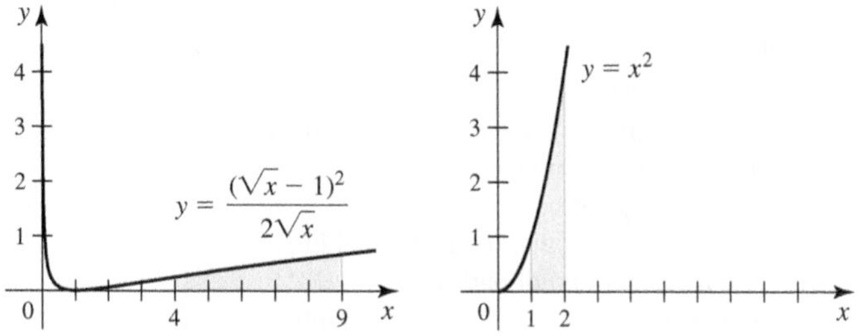

(a) (b)

94–98. General results *Evaluate the following integrals in which the function f is unspecified. Note that $f^{(p)}$ is the pth derivative of f and f^p is the pth power of f. Assume f and its derivatives are continuous for all real numbers.*

94. $\displaystyle\int (5f^3(x) + 7f^2(x) + f(x))\, f'(x)\, dx$

95. $\displaystyle\int_1^2 (5f^3(x) + 7f^2(x) + f(x))f'(x)\, dx$, where $f(1) = 4$, $f(2) = 5$

96. $\displaystyle\int_0^1 f'(x)f''(x)\, dx$, where $f'(0) = 3$ and $f'(1) = 2$

97. $\displaystyle\int (f^{(p)}(x))^n f^{(p+1)}(x)\, dx$, where p is a positive integer, $n \neq -1$

98. $\displaystyle\int 2(f^2(x) + 2f(x))\, f(x)\, f'(x)\, dx$

99–101. More than one way *Occasionally, two different substitutions do the job. Use each substitution to evaluate the following integrals.*

99. $\displaystyle\int_0^1 x\sqrt{x + a}\, dx;\ a > 0 \qquad (u = \sqrt{x + a} \text{ and } u = x + a)$

100. $\displaystyle\int_0^1 x\sqrt[p]{x + a}\, dx;\ a > 0 \qquad (u = \sqrt[p]{x + a} \text{ and } u = x + a)$

101. $\displaystyle\int \sec^3 \theta \tan \theta\, d\theta \qquad (u = \cos \theta \text{ and } u = \sec \theta)$

102. $\sin^2 ax$ and $\cos^2 ax$ integrals Use the Substitution Rule to prove that

$$\int \sin^2 ax\, dx = \frac{x}{2} - \frac{\sin(2ax)}{4a} + C \quad \text{and}$$

$$\int \cos^2 ax\, dx = \frac{x}{2} + \frac{\sin(2ax)}{4a} + C.$$

103. Integral of $\sin^2 x \cos^2 x$ Consider the integral $I = \int \sin^2 x \cos^2 x\, dx$.

- **a.** Find I using the identity $\sin 2x = 2 \sin x \cos x$.
- **b.** Find I using the identity $\cos^2 x = 1 - \sin^2 x$.
- **c.** Confirm that the results in parts (a) and (b) are consistent and compare the work involved in each method.

104. Substitution: shift Perhaps the simplest change of variables is the shift or translation given by $u = x + c$, where c is a real number.

- **a.** Prove that shifting a function does not change the net area under the curve, in the sense that

$$\int_a^b f(x + c)\, dx = \int_{a+c}^{b+c} f(u)\, du.$$

- **b.** Draw a picture to illustrate this change of variables in the case that $f(x) = \sin x$, $a = 0$, $b = \pi$, and $c = \pi/2$.

105. Substitution: scaling Another change of variables that can be interpreted geometrically is the scaling $u = cx$, where c is a real number. Prove and interpret the fact that

$$\int_a^b f(cx)\, dx = \frac{1}{c}\int_{ac}^{bc} f(u)\, du.$$

Draw a picture to illustrate this change of variables in the case that $f(x) = \sin x$, $a = 0$, $b = \pi$, and $c = \frac{1}{2}$.

106–109. Multiple substitutions *If necessary, use two or more substitutions to find the following integrals.*

106. $\displaystyle\int x \sin^4 x^2 \cos x^2\, dx$ (*Hint:* Begin with $u = x^2$, then use $v = \sin u$.)

107. $\displaystyle\int \frac{dx}{\sqrt{1 + \sqrt{1 + x}}}$ (*Hint:* Begin with $u = \sqrt{1 + x}$.)

108. $\displaystyle\int_0^1 x\sqrt{1 - \sqrt{x}}\, dx$

109. $\displaystyle\int_0^1 \sqrt{x - x\sqrt{x}}\, dx$

110. $\displaystyle\int \tan^{10} 4x \sec^2 4x\, dx$ (*Hint:* Begin with $u = 4x$.)

111. $\displaystyle\int_0^{\pi/2} \frac{\cos \theta \sin \theta}{\sqrt{\cos^2 \theta + 16}}\, d\theta$ (*Hint:* Begin with $u = \cos \theta$.)

QUICK CHECK ANSWERS

1. $u = x^4 + 5$ **2.** With $u = x^5 + 6$, we have $du = 5x^4$, and x^4 does not appear in the integrand. **3.** New equation: $u^2 - 13u + 36 = 0$; roots: $x = \pm 2, \pm 3$ ◄

CHAPTER 5 REVIEW EXERCISES

1. **Explain why or why not** Determine whether the following statements are true and give an explanation or counterexample. Assume f and f' are continuous functions for all real numbers.
   a. If $A(x) = \int_a^x f(t)\,dt$ and $f(t) = 2t - 3$, then A is a quadratic function.
   b. Given an area function $A(x) = \int_a^x f(t)\,dt$ and an antiderivative F of f, it follows that $A'(x) = F(x)$.
   c. $\int_a^b f'(x)\,dx = f(b) - f(a)$.
   d. If f is continuous on $[a, b]$ and $\int_a^b |f(x)|\,dx = 0$, then $f(x) = 0$ on $[a, b]$.
   e. If the average value of f on $[a, b]$ is zero, then $f(x) = 0$ on $[a, b]$.
   f. $\int_a^b (2f(x) - 3g(x))\,dx = 2\int_a^b f(x)\,dx + 3\int_b^a g(x)\,dx$.
   g. $\int f'(g(x))g'(x)\,dx = f(g(x)) + C$.

2. **Velocity to displacement** An object travels on the x-axis with a velocity given by $v(t) = 2t + 5$, for $0 \le t \le 4$.
   a. How far does the object travel, for $0 \le t \le 4$?
   b. What is the average value of v on the interval $[0, 4]$?
   c. True or false: The object would travel as far as in part (a) if it traveled at its average velocity (a constant), for $0 \le t \le 4$.

3. **Area by geometry** Use geometry to evaluate the following definite integrals, where the graph of f is given in the figure.

   a. $\displaystyle\int_0^4 f(x)\,dx$ b. $\displaystyle\int_6^4 f(x)\,dx$

   c. $\displaystyle\int_5^7 f(x)\,dx$ d. $\displaystyle\int_0^7 f(x)\,dx$

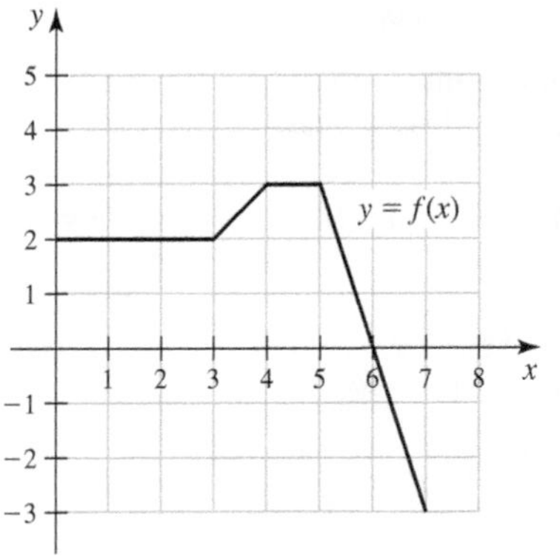

4. **Displacement by geometry** Use geometry to find the displacement of an object moving along a line for the time intervals (*i*) $0 \le t \le 5$, (*ii*) $3 \le t \le 7$, and (*iii*) $0 \le t \le 8$, where the graph of its velocity $v = g(t)$ is given in the figure.

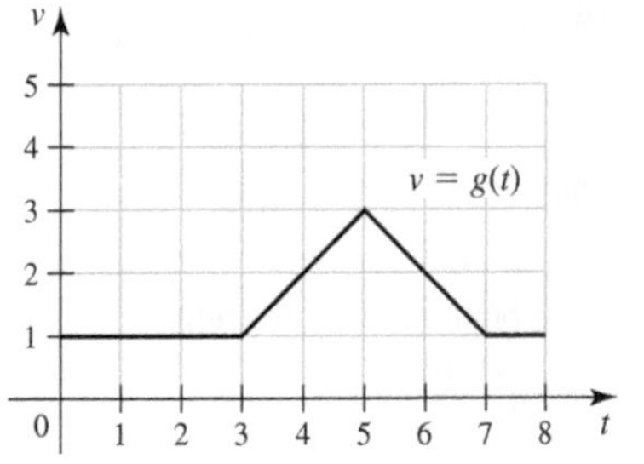

5. **Area by geometry** Use geometry to evaluate $\int_0^4 \sqrt{8x - x^2}\,dx$. (*Hint:* Complete the square.)

6. **Bagel output** The manager of a bagel bakery collects the following production rate data (in bagels per minute) at seven different times during the morning. Estimate the total number of bagels produced between 6:00 and 7:30 A.M., using a left and right Riemann sum.

Time of day (A.M.)	Production rate (bagels/min)
6:00	45
6:15	60
6:30	75
6:45	60
7:00	50
7:15	40
7:30	30

7. **Integration by Riemann sums** Consider the integral $\int_1^4 (3x - 2)\,dx$.
   a. Evaluate the right Riemann sum for the integral with $n = 3$.
   b. Use summation notation to express the right Riemann sum in terms of a positive integer n.
   c. Evaluate the definite integral by taking the limit as $n \to \infty$ of the Riemann sum of part (b).
   d. Confirm the result of part (c) by graphing $y = 3x - 2$ and using geometry to evaluate the integral. Then evaluate $\int_1^4 (3x - 2)\,dx$ with the Fundamental Theorem of Calculus.

8–11. Limit definition of the definite integral *Use the limit definition of the definite integral with right Riemann sums and a regular partition to evaluate the following definite integrals. Use the Fundamental Theorem of Calculus to check your answer.*

8. $\displaystyle\int_0^1 (4x - 2)\,dx$

9. $\displaystyle\int_0^2 (x^2 - 4)\,dx$

10. $\displaystyle\int_1^2 (3x^2 + x)\,dx$

11. $\displaystyle\int_0^4 (x^3 - x)\,dx$

12. **Evaluating Riemann sums** Consider the function $f(x) = 3x + 4$ on the interval $[3, 7]$. Show that the midpoint Riemann sum with $n = 4$ gives the exact area of the region bounded by the graph.

13. **Sum to integral** Evaluate the following limit by identifying the integral that it represents:

$$\lim_{n\to\infty} \sum_{k=1}^{n} \left(\left(\frac{4k}{n}\right)^5 + 1\right)\left(\frac{4}{n}\right).$$

14. **Area function by geometry** Use geometry to find the area $A(x)$ that is bounded by the graph of $f(t) = 2t - 4$ and the t-axis between the point $(2, 0)$ and the variable point $(x, 0)$, where $x \ge 2$. Verify that $A'(x) = f(x)$.

15–30. Evaluating integrals *Evaluate the following integrals.*

15. $\int_{-2}^{2} (3x^4 - 2x + 1)\,dx$

16. $\int \cos 3x\,dx$

17. $\int_{0}^{2} (x+1)^3\,dx$

18. $\int_{0}^{1} (4x^{21} - 2x^{16} + 1)\,dx$

19. $\int (9x^8 - 7x^6)\,dx$

20. $\int_{-2}^{2} e^{4x+8}\,dx$

21. $\int_{0}^{1} \sqrt{x}(\sqrt{x}+1)\,dx$

22. $\int \frac{y^2}{y^3+27}\,dy$

23. $\int_{0}^{1} \frac{dx}{\sqrt{4-x^2}}$

24. $\int y^2(3y^3+1)^4\,dy$

25. $\int_{0}^{3} \frac{x}{\sqrt{25-x^2}}\,dx$

26. $\int x \sin x^2 \cos^8 x^2\,dx$

27. $\int_{0}^{\pi} \sin^2 5\theta\,d\theta$

28. $\int_{0}^{\pi} (1 - \cos^2 3\theta)\,d\theta$

29. $\int_{2}^{3} \frac{x^2+2x-2}{x^3+3x^2-6x}\,dx$

30. $\int_{0}^{\ln 2} \frac{e^x}{1+e^{2x}}\,dx$

31–34. Area of regions *Compute the area of the region bounded by the graph of f and the x-axis on the given interval. You may find it useful to sketch the region.*

31. $f(x) = 16 - x^2$ on $[-4, 4]$

32. $f(x) = x^3 - x$ on $[-1, 0]$

33. $f(x) = 2\sin(x/4)$ on $[0, 2\pi]$

34. $f(x) = 1/(x^2+1)$ on $[-1, \sqrt{3}]$

35–36. Area versus net area *Find (i) the net area and (ii) the area of the region bounded by the graph of f and the x-axis on the given interval. You may find it useful to sketch the region.*

35. $f(x) = x^4 - x^2$ on $[-1, 1]$

36. $f(x) = x^2 - x$ on $[0, 3]$

37. **Symmetry properties** Suppose that $\int_0^4 f(x)\,dx = 10$ and $\int_0^4 g(x)\,dx = 20$. Furthermore, suppose that f is an even function and g is an odd function. Evaluate the following integrals.

a. $\int_{-4}^{4} f(x)\,dx$

b. $\int_{-4}^{4} 3g(x)\,dx$

c. $\int_{-4}^{4} (4f(x) - 3g(x))\,dx$

d. $\int_{0}^{1} 8xf(4x^2)\,dx$

e. $\int_{-2}^{2} 3xf(x)\,dx$

38. **Properties of integrals** The figure shows the areas of regions bounded by the graph of f and the x-axis. Evaluate the following integrals.

a. $\int_{a}^{c} f(x)\,dx$

b. $\int_{b}^{d} f(x)\,dx$

c. $\int_{c}^{b} 2f(x)\,dx$

d. $\int_{a}^{d} 4f(x)\,dx$

e. $\int_{a}^{b} 3f(x)\,dx$

f. $\int_{b}^{d} 2f(x)\,dx$

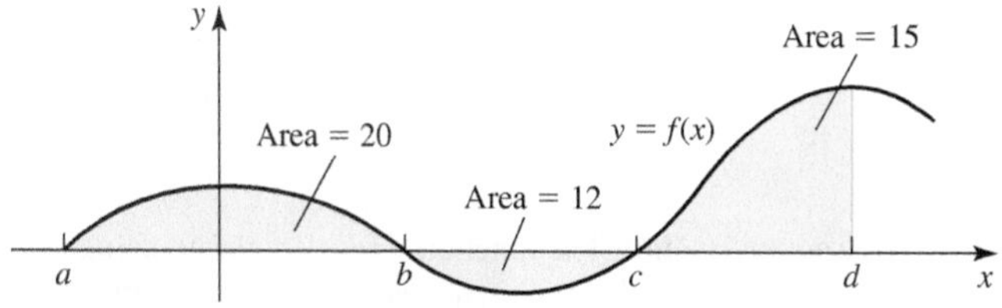

39–44. Properties of integrals *Suppose that* $\int_1^4 f(x)\,dx = 6$, $\int_1^4 g(x)\,dx = 4$, *and* $\int_3^4 f(x)\,dx = 2$. *Evaluate the following integrals or state that there is not enough information.*

39. $\int_{1}^{4} 3f(x)\,dx$

40. $-\int_{4}^{1} 2f(x)\,dx$

41. $\int_{1}^{4} (3f(x) - 2g(x))\,dx$

42. $\int_{1}^{4} f(x)g(x)\,dx$

43. $\int_{1}^{3} \frac{f(x)}{g(x)}\,dx$

44. $\int_{4}^{1} (f(x) - g(x))\,dx$

45. **Displacement from velocity** A particle moves along a line with a velocity given by $v(t) = 5\sin \pi t$ starting with an initial position $s(0) = 0$. Find the displacement of the particle between $t = 0$ and $t = 2$, which is given by $s(t) = \int_0^2 v(t)\,dt$. Find the distance traveled by the particle during this interval, which is $\int_0^2 |v(t)|\,dt$.

46. **Average height** A baseball is launched into the outfield on a parabolic trajectory given by $y = 0.01x(200 - x)$. Find the average height of the baseball over the horizontal extent of its flight.

47. **Average values** Integration is not needed.

a. Find the average value of f shown in the figure on the interval $[1, 6]$ and then find the point(s) c in $(1, 6)$ guaranteed to exist by the Mean Value Theorem for Integrals.

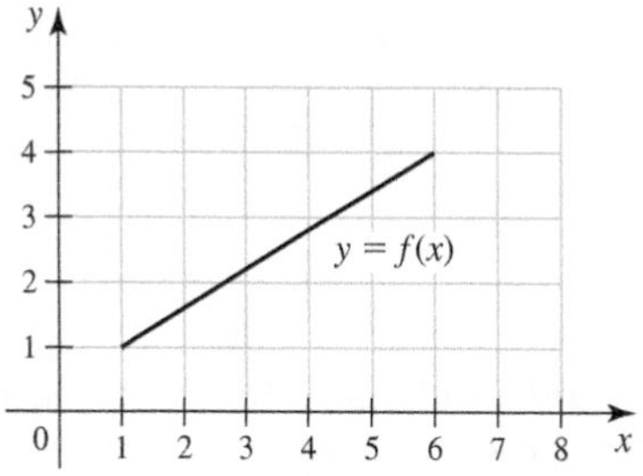

(a)

b. Find the average value of f shown in the figure on the interval $[2, 6]$ and then find the point(s) c in $(2, 6)$ guaranteed to exist by the Mean Value Theorem for Integrals.

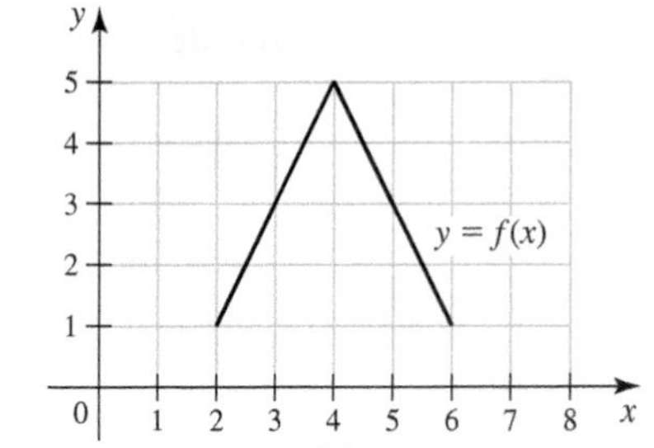

(b)

48. An unknown function The function f satisfies the equation $3x^4 - 48 = \int_2^x f(t)\,dt$. Find f and check your answer by substitution.

49. An unknown function Assume f' is continuous on $[2, 4]$, $\int_1^2 f'(2x)\,dx = 10$, and $f(2) = 4$. Evaluate $f(4)$.

50. Function defined by an integral Let $H(x) = \int_0^x \sqrt{4 - t^2}\,dt$, for $-2 \le x \le 2$.

a. Evaluate $H(0)$.
b. Evaluate $H'(1)$.
c. Evaluate $H'(2)$.
d. Use geometry to evaluate $H(2)$.
e. Find the value of s such that $H(x) = sH(-x)$.

51. Function defined by an integral Make a graph of the function $f(x) = \int_1^x \frac{dt}{t}$, for $x \ge 1$. Be sure to include all of the evidence you used to arrive at the graph.

52. Identifying functions Match the graphs A, B, and C in the figure with the functions $f(x)$, $f'(x)$, and $\int_0^x f(t)\,dt$.

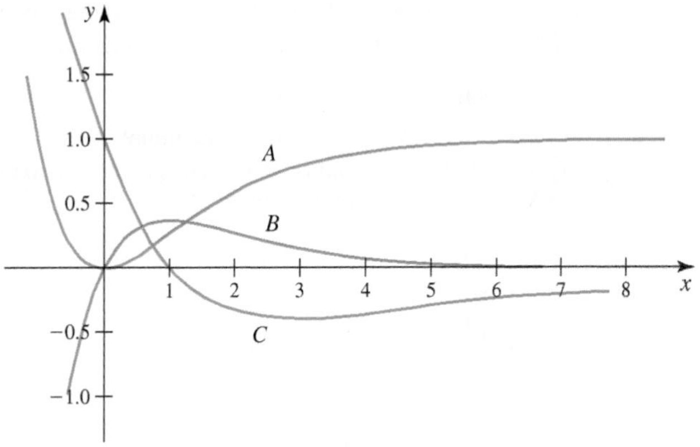

53. Ascent rate of a scuba diver Divers who ascend too quickly in the water risk *decompression illness*. A common recommendation for a maximum rate of ascent is 30 feet/minute with a 5-minute safety stop 15 feet below the surface of the water. Suppose that a diver ascends to the surface in 8 minutes according to the velocity function

$$v(t) = \begin{cases} 30 & \text{if } 0 \le t \le 2 \\ 0 & \text{if } 2 < t \le 7 \\ 15 & \text{if } 7 < t \le 8. \end{cases}$$

a. Graph the velocity function v.
b. Compute the area under the velocity curve.
c. Interpret the physical meaning of the area under the velocity curve.

54. Area functions Consider the graph of the continuous function f in the figure and let $F(x) = \int_0^x f(t)\,dt$ and $G(x) = \int_1^x f(t)\,dt$. Assume the graph consists of a line segment from $(0, -2)$ to $(2, 2)$ and two quarter circles of radius 2.

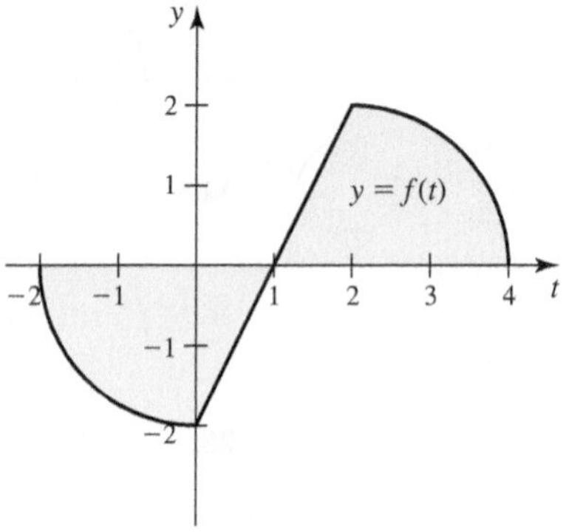

a. Evaluate $F(2)$, $F(-2)$, and $F(4)$.
b. Evaluate $G(-2)$, $G(0)$, and $G(4)$.
c. Explain why there is a constant C such that $F(x) = G(x) + C$, for $-2 \le x \le 4$. Fill in the blank with a number: $F(x) = G(x) +$ ____, for $-2 \le x \le 4$.

55–56. Area functions and the Fundamental Theorem *Consider the function*

$$f(t) = \begin{cases} t & \text{if } -2 \le t < 0 \\ \dfrac{t^2}{2} & \text{if } 0 \le t \le 2 \end{cases}$$

and its graph shown below.

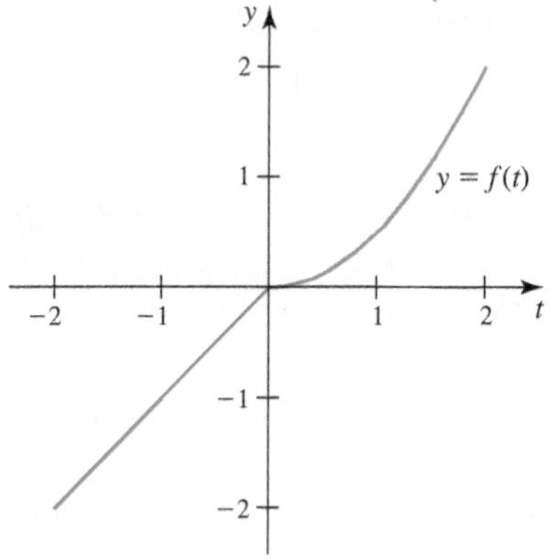

Let $F(x) = \int_{-1}^x f(t)\,dt$ and $G(x) = \int_{-2}^x f(t)\,dt$.

55. a. Evaluate $F(-2)$ and $F(2)$.
b. Use the Fundamental Theorem to find an expression for $F'(x)$, for $-2 \le x < 0$.
c. Use the Fundamental Theorem to find an expression for $F'(x)$, for $0 \le x \le 2$.
d. Evaluate $F'(-1)$ and $F'(1)$. Interpret these values.
e. Evaluate $F''(-1)$ and $F''(1)$.
f. Find a constant C such that $F(x) = G(x) + C$.

56. **a.** Evaluate $G(-1)$ and $G(1)$.
b. Use the Fundamental Theorem to find an expression for $G'(x)$, for $-2 \le x < 0$.
c. Use the Fundamental Theorem to find an expression for $G'(x)$, for $0 \le x \le 2$.
d. Evaluate $G'(0)$ and $G'(1)$. Interpret these values.
e. Find a constant C such that $F(x) = G(x) + C$.

57–58. Limits with integrals *Evaluate the following limits.*

57. $\displaystyle\lim_{x\to 2} \frac{\int_2^x e^{t^2}\,dt}{x-2}$

58. $\displaystyle\lim_{x\to 1} \frac{\int_1^{x^2} e^{t^3}\,dt}{x-1}$

59. Geometry of integrals Without evaluating the integrals, explain why the following statement is true for positive integers n:

$$\int_0^1 x^n\,dx + \int_0^1 \sqrt[n]{x}\,dx = 1.$$

60. Change of variables Use the change of variables $u^3 = x^2 - 1$ to evaluate the integral $\int_1^3 x\sqrt[3]{x^2-1}\,dx$.

61. Inverse tangent integral Prove that for nonzero constants a and b,
$$\int \frac{dx}{a^2x^2+b^2} = \frac{1}{ab}\tan^{-1}\left(\frac{ax}{b}\right) + C.$$

62–67. Additional integrals *Evaluate the following integrals.*

62. $\displaystyle\int \frac{\sin 2x}{1+\cos^2 x}\,dx$ (*Hint:* $\sin 2x = 2\sin x\cos x$.)

63. $\displaystyle\int \frac{1}{x^2}\sin\frac{1}{x}\,dx$

64. $\displaystyle\int \frac{(\tan^{-1} x)^5}{1+x^2}\,dx$

65. $\displaystyle\int \frac{dx}{(\tan^{-1} x)(1+x^2)}$

66. $\displaystyle\int \frac{\sin^{-1} x}{\sqrt{1-x^2}}\,dx$

67. $\displaystyle\int \frac{e^x - e^{-x}}{e^x + e^{-x}}\,dx$

68. Area with a parameter Let $a > 0$ be a real number and consider the family of functions $f(x) = \sin ax$ on the interval $[0, \pi/a]$.
a. Graph f, for $a = 1, 2, 3$.
b. Let $g(a)$ be the area of the region bounded by the graph of f and the x-axis on the interval $[0, \pi/a]$. Graph g for $0 < a < \infty$. Is g an increasing function, a decreasing function, or neither?

69. Equivalent equations Explain why if a function u satisfies the equation $u(x) + 2\int_0^x u(t)\,dt = 10$, then it also satisfies the equation $u'(x) + 2u(x) = 0$. Is it true that if u satisfies the second equation, then it satisfies the first equation?

T **70. Area function properties** Consider the function $f(t) = t^2 - 5t + 4$ and the area function $A(x) = \int_0^x f(t)\,dt$.
a. Graph f on the interval $[0, 6]$.
b. Compute and graph A on the interval $[0, 6]$.
c. Show that the local extrema of A occur at the zeros of f.
d. Give a geometrical and analytical explanation for the observation in part (c).
e. Find the approximate zeros of A, other than 0, and call them x_1 and x_2, where $x_1 < x_2$.
f. Find b such that the area bounded by the graph of f and the t-axis on the interval $[0, t_1]$ equals the area bounded by the graph of f and the t-axis on the interval $[t_1, b]$.
g. If f is an integrable function and $A(x) = \int_a^x f(t)\,dt$, is it always true that the local extrema of A occur at the zeros of f? Explain.

71. Function defined by an integral
Let $f(x) = \int_0^x (t-1)^{15}(t-2)^9\,dt$.
a. Find the intervals on which f is increasing and the intervals on which f is decreasing.
b. Find the intervals on which f is concave up and the intervals on which f is concave down.
c. For what values of x does f have local minima? Local maxima?
d. Where are the inflection points of f?

72. Exponential inequalities Sketch a graph of $f(t) = e^t$ on an arbitrary interval $[a, b]$. Use the graph and compare areas of regions to prove that

$$e^{(a+b)/2} < \frac{e^b - e^a}{b-a} < \frac{e^a + e^b}{2}.$$

(*Source: Mathematics Magazine* 81, 5, Dec 2008)

Chapter 5 Guided Projects

Applications of the material in this chapter and related topics can be found in the following Guided Projects. For additional information, see the Preface.

- Limits of sums
- Distribution of wealth
- Symmetry in integrals

6

Applications of Integration

Chapter Preview Now that we have some basic techniques for evaluating integrals, we turn our attention to the uses of integration, which are virtually endless. We first illustrate the general rule that if the rate of change of a quantity is known, then integration can be used to determine the net change or the future value of that quantity over a certain time interval. Next, we explore some rich geometric applications of integration: computing the area of regions bounded by several curves, the volume and surface area of three-dimensional solids, and the length of curves. A variety of physical applications of integration include finding the work done by a variable force and computing the total force exerted by water behind a dam. All of these applications are unified by their use of the *slice-and-sum* strategy. We end this chapter by revisiting the logarithmic function, exploring the many applications of the exponential function, and introducing hyperbolic functions.

6.1 Velocity and Net Change

In previous chapters, we established the relationship between the position and velocity of an object moving along a line. With integration, we can now say much more about this relationship. Once we relate velocity and position through integration, we can make analogous observations about a variety of other practical problems, which include fluid flow, population growth, manufacturing costs, and production and consumption of natural resources. The ideas in this section come directly from the Fundamental Theorem of Calculus, and they are among the most powerful applications of calculus.

Velocity, Position, and Displacement

Suppose you are driving along a straight highway and your position relative to a reference point or origin is $s(t)$ for times $t \geq 0$. Your *displacement* over a time interval $[a, b]$ is the change in the position $s(b) - s(a)$ (Figure 6.1). If $s(b) > s(a)$, then your displacement is positive; when $s(b) < s(a)$, your displacement is negative.

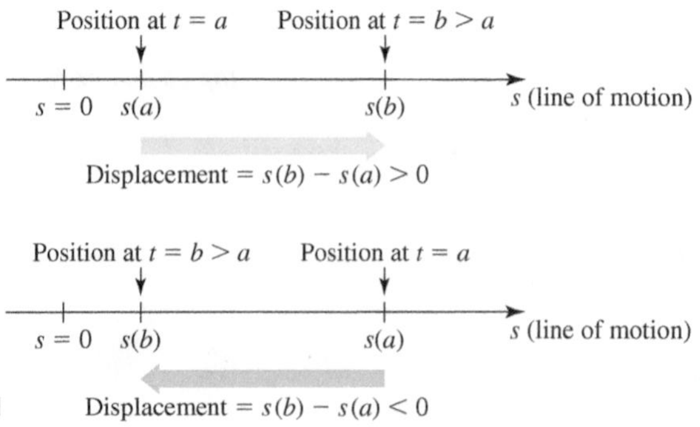

Figure 6.1

Now assume that $v(t)$ is the velocity of the object at a particular time t. Recall from Chapter 3 that $v(t) = s'(t)$, which means that s is an antiderivative of v. From the Fundamental Theorem of Calculus, it follows that

$$\int_a^b v(t)\,dt = \int_a^b s'(t)\,dt = s(b) - s(a) = \text{displacement}.$$

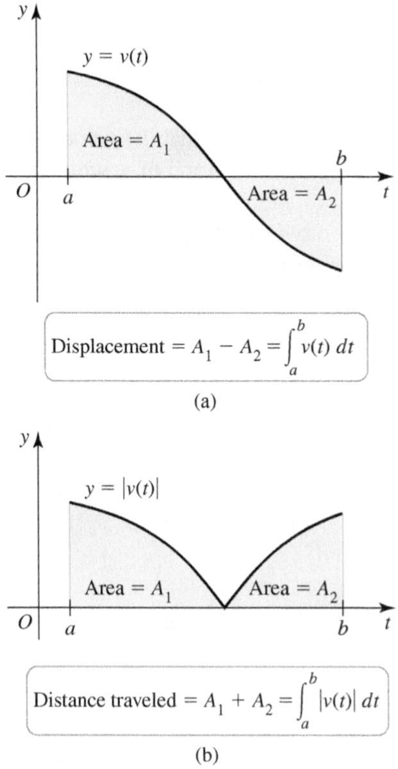

Figure 6.2

We see that the definite integral $\int_a^b v(t)\,dt$ is the displacement (change in position) between times $t = a$ and $t = b$. Equivalently, the displacement over the time interval $[a, b]$ is the net area under the velocity curve over $[a, b]$ (Figure 6.2a).

Not to be confused with the displacement is the *distance traveled* over a time interval, which is the total distance traveled by the object, independent of the direction of motion. If the velocity is positive, the object moves in the positive direction and the displacement equals the distance traveled. However, if the velocity changes sign, then the displacement and the distance traveled are not generally equal.

QUICK CHECK 1 A police officer leaves his station on a north-south freeway at 9 A.M., traveling north (the positive direction) for 40 mi between 9 A.M. and 10 A.M. From 10 A.M. to 11 A.M., he travels south to a point 20 mi south of the station. What are the distance traveled and the displacement between 9 A.M. and 11 A.M.? ◀

To compute the distance traveled, we need the magnitude, but not the sign, of the velocity. The magnitude of the velocity $|v(t)|$ is called the *speed*. The distance traveled over a small time interval dt is $|v(t)|\,dt$ (speed multiplied by elapsed time). Summing these distances, the distance traveled over the time interval $[a, b]$ is the integral of the speed; that is,

$$\text{distance traveled} = \int_a^b |v(t)|\,dt.$$

As shown in Figure 6.2b, integrating the speed produces the area (not net area) bounded by the velocity curve and the t-axis, which corresponds to the distance traveled. The distance traveled is always nonnegative.

DEFINITION Position, Velocity, Displacement, and Distance

1. The **position** of an object moving along a line at time t, denoted $s(t)$, is the location of the object relative to the origin.
2. The **velocity** of an object at time t is $v(t) = s'(t)$.
3. The **displacement** of the object between $t = a$ and $t = b > a$ is

$$s(b) - s(a) = \int_a^b v(t)\,dt.$$

4. The **distance traveled** by the object between $t = a$ and $t = b > a$ is

$$\int_a^b |v(t)|\,dt,$$

where $|v(t)|$ is the **speed** of the object at time t.

QUICK CHECK 2 Describe a possible motion of an object along a line for $0 \le t \le 5$ for which the displacement and the distance traveled are different. ◀

EXAMPLE 1 Displacement from velocity A jogger runs along a straight road with velocity (in mi/hr) $v(t) = 2t^2 - 8t + 6$, for $0 \le t \le 3$, where t is measured in hours.

a. Graph the velocity function over the interval $[0, 3]$. Determine when the jogger moves in the positive direction and when she moves in the negative direction.

b. Find the displacement of the jogger (in miles) on the time intervals $[0, 1]$, $[1, 3]$, and $[0, 3]$. Interpret these results.

c. Find the distance traveled over the interval $[0, 3]$.

SOLUTION

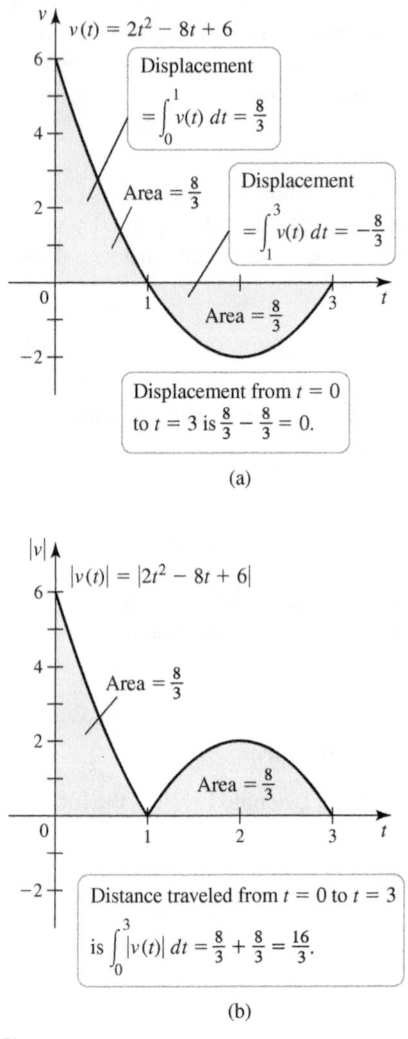

Figure 6.3

a. By solving $v(t) = 2t^2 - 8t + 6 = 2(t-1)(t-3) = 0$, we find that the velocity is zero at $t = 1$ and $t = 3$; these values are the t-intercepts of the graph of v, which is an upward-opening parabola with a v-intercept of 6 (Figure 6.3a). The velocity is positive on the interval $0 \le t < 1$, which means the jogger moves in the positive s direction. For $1 < t < 3$, the velocity is negative and the jogger moves in the negative s direction.

b. The displacement (in miles) over the interval $[0, 1]$ is

$$\begin{aligned} s(1) - s(0) &= \int_0^1 v(t)\,dt \\ &= \int_0^1 (2t^2 - 8t + 6)\,dt && \text{Substitute for } v. \\ &= \left(\frac{2}{3}t^3 - 4t^2 + 6t\right)\Bigg|_0^1 = \frac{8}{3}. && \text{Evaluate integral.} \end{aligned}$$

A similar calculation shows that the displacement over the interval $[1, 3]$ is

$$s(3) - s(1) = \int_1^3 v(t)\,dt = -\frac{8}{3}.$$

Over the interval $[0, 3]$, the displacement is $\frac{8}{3} + \left(-\frac{8}{3}\right) = 0$, which means the jogger returns to the starting point after three hours.

c. From part (b), we can deduce the total distance traveled by the jogger. On the interval $[0, 1]$, the distance traveled is $\frac{8}{3}$ mi; on the interval $[1, 3]$, the distance traveled is also $\frac{8}{3}$ mi. Therefore, the distance traveled on $[0, 3]$ is $\frac{16}{3}$ mi. Alternatively (Figure 6.3b), we can integrate the speed and get the same result:

$$\begin{aligned} \int_0^3 |v(t)|\,dt &= \int_0^1 (2t^2 - 8t + 6)\,dt + \int_1^3 (-(2t^2 - 8t + 6))\,dt && \text{Definition of } |v(t)| \\ &= \left(\frac{2}{3}t^3 - 4t^2 + 6t\right)\Bigg|_0^1 + \left(-\frac{2}{3}t^3 + 4t^2 - 6t\right)\Bigg|_1^3 && \text{Evaluate integrals.} \\ &= \frac{16}{3}. && \text{Simplify.} \end{aligned}$$

Related Exercises 7–14 ◄

Future Value of the Position Function

To find the displacement of an object, we do not need to know its initial position. For example, whether an object moves from $s = -20$ to $s = -10$ or from $s = 50$ to $s = 60$, its displacement is 10 units. What happens if we are interested in the actual *position* of the object at some future time?

Suppose we know the velocity of an object and its initial position $s(0)$. The goal is to find the position $s(t)$ at some future time $t \geq 0$. The Fundamental Theorem of Calculus gives us the answer directly. Because the position s is an antiderivative of the velocity v, we have

> Note that t is the independent variable of the position function. Therefore, another (dummy) variable, in this case x, must be used as the variable of integration.

$$\int_0^t v(x)\,dx = \int_0^t s'(x)\,dx = s(x)\Big|_0^t = s(t) - s(0).$$

Rearranging this expression leads to the following result.

> Theorem 6.1 is a consequence (actually a statement) of the Fundamental Theorem of Calculus.

THEOREM 6.1 Position from Velocity
Given the velocity $v(t)$ of an object moving along a line and its initial position $s(0)$, the position function of the object for future times $t \geq 0$ is

$$\underbrace{s(t)}_{\substack{\text{position}\\ \text{at } t}} = \underbrace{s(0)}_{\substack{\text{initial}\\ \text{position}}} + \underbrace{\int_0^t v(x)\,dx.}_{\substack{\text{displacement}\\ \text{over } [0,\,t]}}$$

Theorem 6.1 says that to find the position $s(t)$, we add the displacement over the interval $[0, t]$ to the initial position $s(0)$.

QUICK CHECK 3 Is the position $s(t)$ a number or a function? For fixed times $t = a$ and $t = b$, is the displacement $s(b) - s(a)$ a number or a function? ◄

There are two *equivalent* ways to determine the position function:

- Using antiderivatives (Section 4.9)
- Using Theorem 6.1

The latter method is usually more efficient, but either method produces the same result. The following example illustrates both approaches.

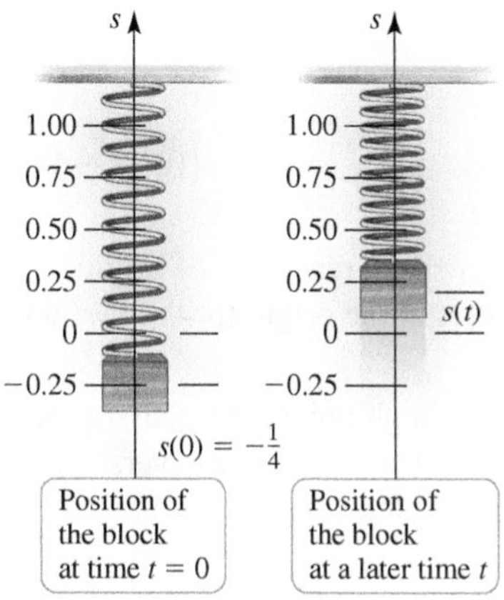

Figure 6.4

EXAMPLE 2 Position from velocity A block hangs at rest from a massless spring at the origin ($s = 0$). At $t = 0$, the block is pulled downward $\frac{1}{4}$ m to its initial position $s(0) = -\frac{1}{4}$ and released (Figure 6.4). Its velocity (in m/s) is given by $v(t) = \frac{1}{4}\sin t$, for $t \geq 0$. Assume that the upward direction is positive.

a. Find the position of the block, for $t \geq 0$.

b. Graph the position function, for $0 \leq t \leq 3\pi$.

c. When does the block move through the origin for the first time?

d. When does the block reach its highest point for the first time and what is its position at that time? When does the block return to its lowest point?

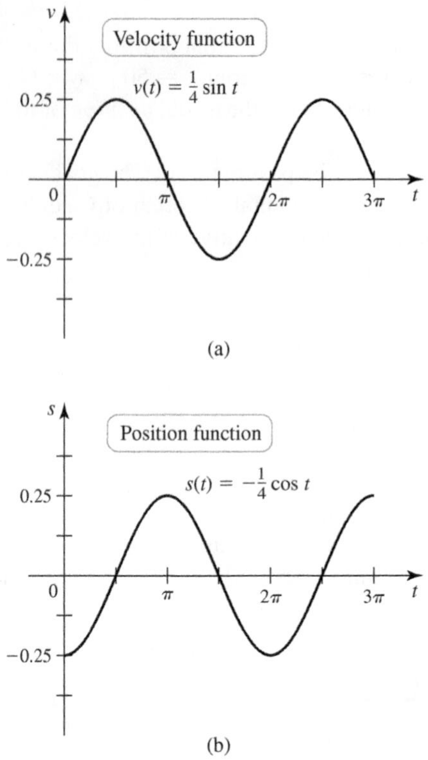

Figure 6.5

SOLUTION

a. The velocity function (Figure 6.5a) is positive for $0 < t < \pi$, which means the block moves in the positive (upward) direction. At $t = \pi$, the block comes to rest momentarily; for $\pi < t < 2\pi$, the block moves in the negative (downward) direction. We let $s(t)$ be the position at time $t \geq 0$ with the initial position $s(0) = -\frac{1}{4}$ m.

Method 1: Using antiderivatives Because the position is an antiderivative of the velocity, we have

$$s(t) = \int v(t)\,dt = \int \frac{1}{4}\sin t\,dt = -\frac{1}{4}\cos t + C.$$

To determine the arbitrary constant C, we substitute the initial condition $s(0) = -\frac{1}{4}$ into the expression for $s(t)$:

$$-\frac{1}{4} = -\frac{1}{4}\cos 0 + C.$$

Solving for C, we find that $C = 0$. Therefore, the position for any time $t \geq 0$ is

$$s(t) = -\frac{1}{4}\cos t.$$

Method 2: Using Theorem 6.1 Alternatively, we may use the relationship

$$s(t) = s(0) + \int_0^t v(x)\,dx.$$

Substituting $v(x) = \frac{1}{4}\sin x$ and $s(0) = -\frac{1}{4}$, the position function is

$$\begin{aligned} s(t) &= \underbrace{-\frac{1}{4}}_{s(0)} + \int_0^t \underbrace{\frac{1}{4}\sin x}_{v(x)}\,dx \\ &= -\frac{1}{4} - \left(\frac{1}{4}\cos x\right)\Big|_0^t && \text{Evaluate integral.} \\ &= -\frac{1}{4} - \frac{1}{4}(\cos t - 1) && \text{Simplify.} \\ &= -\frac{1}{4}\cos t. && \text{Simplify.} \end{aligned}$$

➤ It is worth repeating that to find the displacement, we need to know only the velocity. To find the position, we must know both the velocity and the initial position $s(0)$.

b. The graph of the position function is shown in Figure 6.5b. We see that $s(0) = -\frac{1}{4}$ m, as prescribed.

c. The block initially moves in the positive s direction (upward), reaching the origin ($s = 0$) when $s(t) = -\frac{1}{4}\cos t = 0$. So the block arrives at the origin for the first time when $t = \pi/2$.

d. The block moves in the positive direction and reaches its high point for the first time when $t = \pi$; the position at that moment is $s(\pi) = \frac{1}{4}$ m. The block then reverses direction and moves in the negative (downward) direction, reaching its low point at $t = 2\pi$. This motion repeats every 2π seconds.

Related Exercises 15–24 ◀

QUICK CHECK 4 Without doing further calculations, what are the displacement and distance traveled by the block in Example 2 over the interval $[0, 2\pi]$? ◀

➤ The terminal velocity of an object depends on its density, shape, size, and the medium through which it falls. Estimates for human beings in free fall in the lower atmosphere vary from 120 mi/hr (54 m/s) to 180 mi/hr (80 m/s).

EXAMPLE 3 **Skydiving** Suppose a skydiver leaps from a hovering helicopter and falls in a straight line. He reaches a terminal velocity of 80 m/s at $t = 0$ and falls for 19 seconds, at which time he opens his parachute. The velocity decreases linearly to 6 m/s over a two-second period and then remains constant until he reaches the ground at $t = 40$ s. The motion is described by the velocity function

$$v(t) = \begin{cases} 80 & \text{if } 0 \le t < 19 \\ 783 - 37t & \text{if } 19 \le t < 21 \\ 6 & \text{if } 21 \le t \le 40. \end{cases}$$

Determine the height above the ground from which the skydiver jumped.

SOLUTION We let the position of the skydiver increase *downward* with the origin ($s = 0$) corresponding to the position of the helicopter. The velocity is positive, so the distance traveled by the skydiver equals the displacement, which is

$$\int_0^{40} |v(t)|\, dt = \int_0^{19} 80\, dt + \int_{19}^{21} (783 - 37t)\, dt + \int_{21}^{40} 6\, dt$$

$$= 80t\Big|_0^{19} + \left(783t - \frac{37t^2}{2}\right)\Big|_{19}^{21} + 6t\Big|_{21}^{40} \qquad \text{Fundamental Theorem}$$

$$= 1720. \qquad \text{Evaluate and simplify.}$$

The skydiver jumped from 1720 m above the ground. Notice that the displacement of the skydiver is the area under the velocity curve (Figure 6.6).

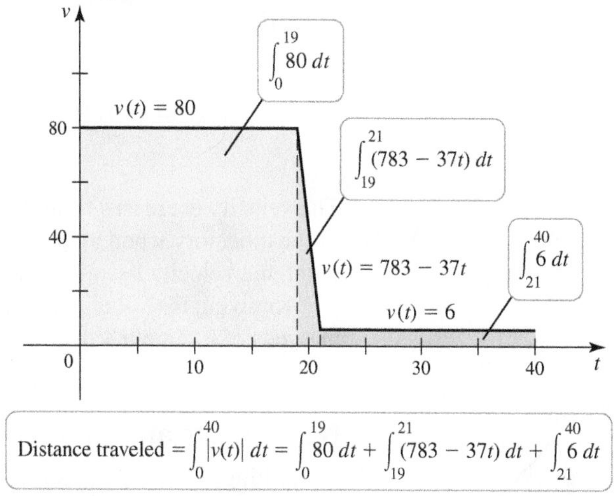

Figure 6.6

Related Exercises 25–26 ◀

QUICK CHECK 5 Suppose (unrealistically) in Example 3 that the velocity of the skydiver is 80 m/s, for $0 \le t < 20$, and then it changes instantaneously to 6 m/s, for $20 \le t \le 40$. Sketch the velocity function and, without integrating, find the distance the skydiver falls in 40 s. ◀

Acceleration

Because the acceleration of an object moving along a line is given by $a(t) = v'(t)$, the relationship between velocity and acceleration is the same as the relationship between position and velocity. Given the acceleration of an object, the change in velocity over an interval $[a, b]$ is

$$\text{change in velocity} = v(b) - v(a) = \int_a^b v'(t)\,dt = \int_a^b a(t)\,dt.$$

Furthermore, if we know the acceleration and initial velocity $v(0)$, then the velocity at future times can also be found.

➤ Theorem 6.2 is a consequence of the Fundamental Theorem of Calculus.

THEOREM 6.2 Velocity from Acceleration
Given the acceleration $a(t)$ of an object moving along a line and its initial velocity $v(0)$, the velocity of the object for future times $t \geq 0$ is

$$v(t) = v(0) + \int_0^t a(x)\,dx.$$

EXAMPLE 4 Motion in a gravitational field An artillery shell is fired directly upward with an initial velocity of 300 m/s from a point 30 m above the ground (Figure 6.7). Assume that only the force of gravity acts on the shell and it produces an acceleration of 9.8 m/s^2. Find the velocity of the shell while it is in the air.

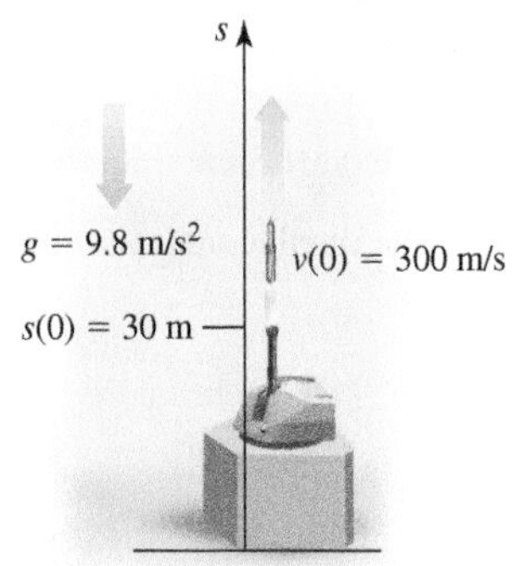

Figure 6.7

SOLUTION We let the positive direction be upward with the origin ($s = 0$) corresponding to the ground. The initial velocity of the shell is $v(0) = 300$ m/s. The acceleration due to gravity is downward; therefore, $a(t) = -9.8\text{ m/s}^2$. Integrating the acceleration, the velocity is

$$v(t) = \underbrace{v(0)}_{300\text{ m/s}} + \int_0^t \underbrace{a(x)}_{-9.8\text{ m/s}^2}\,dx = 300 + \int_0^t (-9.8)\,dx = 300 - 9.8t.$$

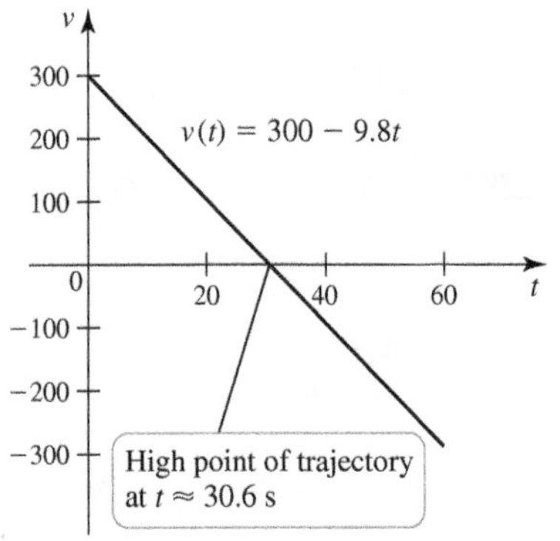

Figure 6.8

The velocity decreases from its initial value of 300 m/s, reaching zero at the high point of the trajectory when $v(t) = 300 - 9.8t = 0$, or at $t \approx 30.6$ s (Figure 6.8). At this point, the velocity becomes negative, and the shell begins its descent to Earth.

Knowing the velocity function, you could now find the position function using the methods of Example 3.

Related Exercises 27–37 ◀

Net Change and Future Value

Everything we have said about velocity, position, and displacement carries over to more general situations. Suppose you are interested in some quantity Q that changes over *time*; Q may represent the amount of water in a reservoir, the population of a cell culture, or the amount of a resource that is consumed or produced. If you are given the rate Q' at which Q changes, then integration allows you to calculate either the net change in the quantity Q or the future value of Q.

We argue just as we did for velocity and position: Because $Q(t)$ is an antiderivative of $Q'(t)$, the Fundamental Theorem of Calculus tells us that

$$\int_a^b Q'(t)\,dt = Q(b) - Q(a) = \text{net change in } Q \text{ over } [a, b].$$

➤ Note that the units in the integral are consistent. For example, if Q' has units of gallons/second, and t and x have units of seconds, then $Q'(x)\,dx$ has units of (gallons/second)(seconds) = gallons, which are the units of Q.

Geometrically, the net change in Q over the time interval $[a, b]$ is the net area under the graph of Q' over $[a, b]$. We interpret the product $Q'(t)\,dt$ as a change in Q over a small increment of time. Integrating $Q'(t)$ accumulates, or adds up, these small changes over the interval $[a, b]$. The result is the net change in Q between $t = a$ and $t = b$. We see that accumulating the rate of change of a quantity over the interval gives the net change in that quantity over the interval.

Alternatively, suppose we are given both the rate of change Q' and the initial value $Q(0)$. Integrating over the interval $[0, t]$, where $t \geq 0$, we have

$$\int_0^t Q'(x)\,dx = Q(t) - Q(0).$$

Rearranging this equation, we write the value of Q at any future time $t \geq 0$ as

$$\underbrace{Q(t)}_{\text{future value}} = \underbrace{Q(0)}_{\text{initial value}} + \underbrace{\int_0^t Q'(x)\,dx}_{\text{net change over } [0,t]}.$$

➤ At the risk of being repetitious, Theorem 6.3 is also a consequence of the Fundamental Theorem of Calculus. We assume that Q' is an integrable function.

THEOREM 6.3 Net Change and Future Value

Suppose a quantity Q changes over time at a known rate Q'. Then the **net change** in Q between $t = a$ and $t = b > a$ is

$$\underbrace{Q(b) - Q(a)}_{\text{net change in } Q} = \int_a^b Q'(t)\,dt.$$

Given the initial value $Q(0)$, the **future value** of Q at time $t \geq 0$ is

$$Q(t) = Q(0) + \int_0^t Q'(x)\,dx.$$

The correspondences between velocity–displacement problems and more general problems are shown in Table 6.1.

Table 6.1

Velocity–Displacement Problems	General Problems
Position $s(t)$	Quantity $Q(t)$ (such as volume or population)
Velocity: $s'(t) = v(t)$	Rate of change: $Q'(t)$
Displacement: $s(b) - s(a) = \int_a^b v(t)\,dt$	Net change: $Q(b) - Q(a) = \int_a^b Q'(t)\,dt$
Future position: $s(t) = s(0) + \int_0^t v(x)\,dx$	Future value of Q: $Q(t) = Q(0) + \int_0^t Q'(x)\,dx$

EXAMPLE 5 Cell growth A culture of cells in a lab has a population of 100 cells when nutrients are added at time $t = 0$. Suppose the population $N(t)$ (in cells/hr) increases at a rate given by

$$N'(t) = 90e^{-0.1t}.$$

Find $N(t)$, for $t \geq 0$.

➤ Although N is a positive integer (the number of cells), we treat it as a continuous variable in this example.

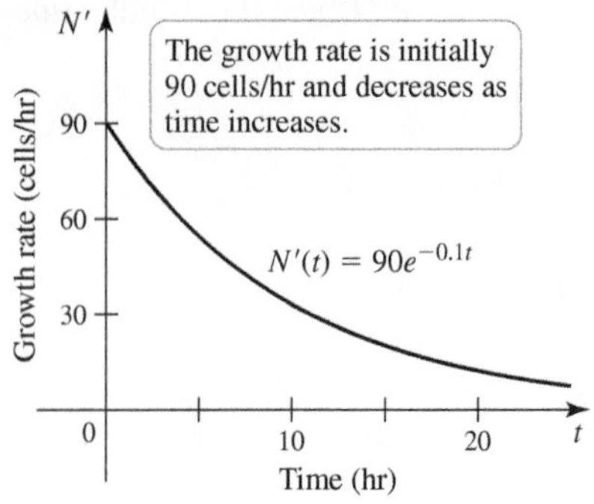

Figure 6.9

SOLUTION As shown in Figure 6.9, the growth rate is large when t is small (plenty of food and space) and decreases as t increases. Knowing that the initial population is $N(0) = 100$ cells, we can find the population $N(t)$ at any future time $t \geq 0$ using Theorem 6.3:

$$\begin{aligned} N(t) &= N(0) + \int_0^t N'(x)\,dx \\ &= \underbrace{100}_{N(0)} + \int_0^t \underbrace{90e^{-0.1x}}_{N'(x)}\,dx \\ &= 100 + \left[\left(\frac{90}{-0.1}\right)e^{-0.1x}\right]\Bigg|_0^t && \text{Fundamental Theorem} \\ &= 1000 - 900e^{-0.1t}. && \text{Simplify.} \end{aligned}$$

The graph of the population function (Figure 6.10) shows that the population increases, but at a decreasing rate. Note that the initial condition $N(0) = 100$ cells is satisfied and that the population size approaches 1000 cells as $t \to \infty$.

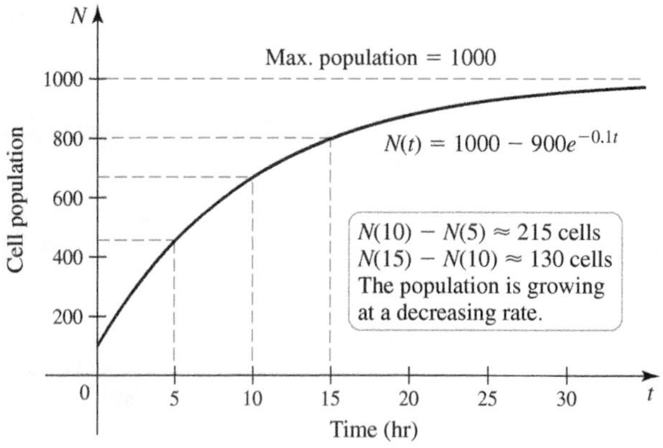

Figure 6.10

Related Exercises 38–44 ◀

EXAMPLE 6 **Production costs** A book publisher estimates that the marginal cost of a particular title (in dollars/book) is given by

$$C'(x) = 12 - 0.0002x,$$

where $0 \leq x \leq 50{,}000$ is the number of books printed. What is the cost of producing the 12,001st through the 15,000th book?

SOLUTION Recall from Section 3.6 that the cost function $C(x)$ is the cost required to produce x units of a product. The marginal cost $C'(x)$ is the approximate cost of producing one additional unit after x units have already been produced. The cost of producing books $x = 12{,}001$ through $x = 15{,}000$ is the cost of producing 15,000 books minus the cost of producing the first 12,000 books. Therefore, the cost in dollars of producing books 12,001 through 15,000 is

➤ Although x is a positive integer (the number of books produced), we treat it as a continuous variable in this example.

$$\begin{aligned} C(15{,}000) - C(12{,}000) &= \int_{12{,}000}^{15{,}000} C'(x)\,dx \\ &= \int_{12{,}000}^{15{,}000} (12 - 0.0002x)\,dx && \text{Substitute for } C'(x). \\ &= (12x - 0.0001x^2)\Big|_{12{,}000}^{15{,}000} && \text{Fundamental Theorem} \\ &= 27{,}900. && \text{Simplify.} \end{aligned}$$

Related Exercises 45–48 ◀

QUICK CHECK 6 Is the cost of increasing the production from 9000 books to 12,000 books in Example 6 more or less than the cost of increasing the production from 12,000 books to 15,000 books? Explain. ◀

SECTION 6.1 EXERCISES

Review Questions

1. Explain the meaning of position, displacement, and distance traveled as they apply to an object moving along a line.

2. Suppose the velocity of an object moving along a line is positive. Are displacement and distance traveled equal? Explain.

3. Given the velocity function v of an object moving along a line, explain how definite integrals can be used to find the displacement of the object.

4. Explain how to use definite integrals to find the net change in a quantity, given the rate of change of that quantity.

5. Given the rate of change of a quantity Q and its initial value $Q(0)$, explain how to find the value of Q at a future time $t \geq 0$.

6. What is the result of integrating a population growth rate between times $t = a$ and $t = b$, where $b > a$?

Basic Skills

7. **Displacement and distance from velocity** Consider the graph shown in the figure, which gives the velocity of an object moving along a line. Assume time is measured in hours and distance is measured in miles. The areas of three regions bounded by the velocity curve and the t-axis are also given.

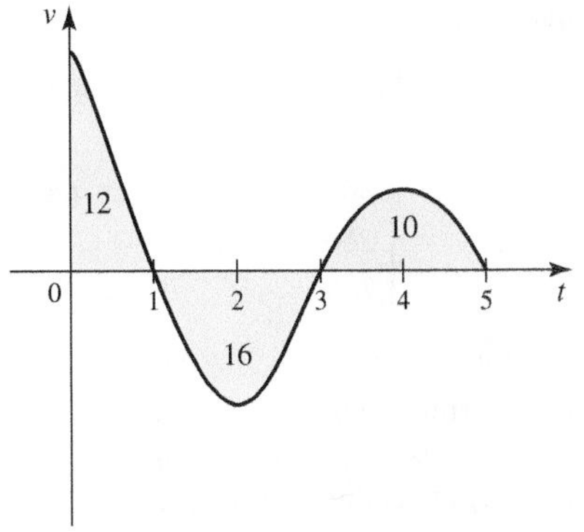

   a. On what intervals is the object moving in the positive direction?
   b. What is the displacement of the object over the interval $[0, 3]$?
   c. What is the total distance traveled by the object over the interval $[1, 5]$?
   d. What is the displacement of the object over the interval $[0, 5]$?
   e. Describe the position of the object relative to its initial position after 5 hours.

8. **Displacement and distance from velocity** Consider the velocity function shown below of an object moving along a line. Assume time is measured in seconds and distance is measured in meters. The areas of four regions bounded by the velocity curve and the t-axis are also given.

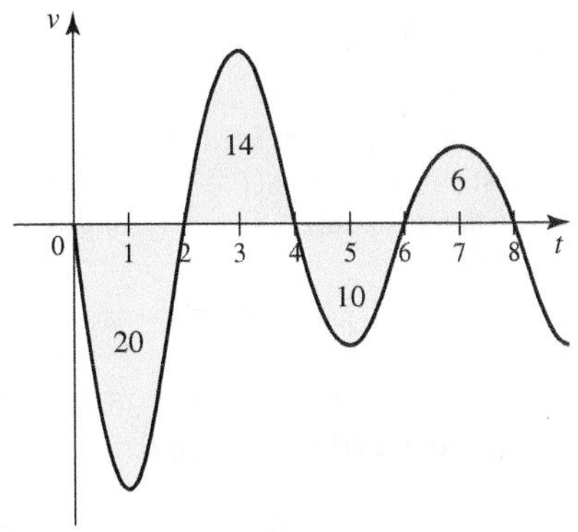

   a. On what intervals is the object moving in the negative direction?
   b. What is the displacement of the object over the interval $[2, 6]$?
   c. How far does the object travel over the interval $[0, 6]$?
   d. What is the displacement of the object over the interval $[0, 8]$?
   e. Describe the position of the object relative to its initial position after 8 hours.

T **9–14. Displacement from velocity** *Assume t is time measured in seconds and velocities have units of m/s.*

   a. *Graph the velocity function over the given interval. Then determine when the motion is in the positive direction and when it is in the negative direction.*
   b. *Find the displacement over the given interval.*
   c. *Find the distance traveled over the given interval.*

9. $v(t) = 6 - 2t$ on $0 \leq t \leq 6$

10. $v(t) = 10 \sin 2t$ on $0 \leq t \leq 2\pi$

11. $v(t) = t^2 - 6t + 8$ on $0 \leq t \leq 5$

12. $v(t) = -t^2 + 5t - 4$ on $0 \leq t \leq 5$

13. $v(t) = t^3 - 5t^2 + 6t$ on $0 \leq t \leq 5$

14. $v(t) = 50e^{-2t}$ on $0 \leq t \leq 4$

T **15–20. Position from velocity** *Consider an object moving along a line with the following velocities and initial positions.*

   a. *Graph the velocity function on the given interval and determine when the object is moving in the positive direction and when it is moving in the negative direction.*
   b. *Determine the position function, for $t \geq 0$, using both the antiderivative method and the Fundamental Theorem of Calculus (Theorem 6.1). Check for agreement between the two methods.*
   c. *Graph the position function on the given interval.*

15. $v(t) = \sin t$ on $[0, 2\pi]$; $s(0) = 1$

16. $v(t) = -t^3 + 3t^2 - 2t$ on $[0, 3]$; $s(0) = 4$

17. $v(t) = 6 - 2t$ on $[0, 5]$; $s(0) = 0$

18. $v(t) = 3 \sin \pi t$ on $[0, 4]$; $s(0) = 1$

19. $v(t) = 9 - t^2$ on $[0, 4]$; $s(0) = -2$

20. $v(t) = 1/(t + 1)$ on $[0, 8]$; $s(0) = -4$

T 21. **Oscillating motion** A mass hanging from a spring is set in motion, and its ensuing velocity is given by $v(t) = 2\pi \cos \pi t$, for $t \geq 0$. Assume that the positive direction is upward and that $s(0) = 0$.
   a. Determine the position function, for $t \geq 0$.
   b. Graph the position function on the interval $[0, 4]$.
   c. At what times does the mass reach its low point the first three times?
   d. At what times does the mass reach its high point the first three times?

22. **Cycling distance** A cyclist rides down a long straight road at a velocity (in m/min) given by $v(t) = 400 - 20t$, for $0 \leq t \leq 10$, where t is measured in minutes.
   a. How far does the cyclist travel in the first 5 min?
   b. How far does the cyclist travel in the first 10 min?
   c. How far has the cyclist traveled when her velocity is 250 m/min?

23. Flying into a headwind The velocity (in mi/hr) of an airplane flying into a headwind is given by $v(t) = 30(16 - t^2)$, for $0 \le t \le 3$. Assume that $s(0) = 0$ and t is measured in hours.

a. Determine and graph the position function, for $0 \le t \le 3$.
b. How far does the airplane travel in the first 2 hr?
c. How far has the airplane traveled at the instant its velocity reaches 400 mi/hr?

24. Day hike The velocity (in mi/hr) of a hiker walking along a straight trail is given by $v(t) = 3\sin^2(\pi t/2)$, for $0 \le t \le 4$. Assume that $s(0) = 0$ and t is measured in hours.

a. Determine and graph the position function, for $0 \le t \le 4$. (*Hint:* $\sin^2 t = \frac{1}{2}(1 - \cos 2t)$.)
b. What is the distance traveled by the hiker in the first 15 min of the hike?
c. What is the hiker's position at $t = 3$?

25. Piecewise velocity The velocity of a (fast) automobile on a straight highway is given by the function

$$v(t) = \begin{cases} 3t & \text{if } 0 \le t < 20 \\ 60 & \text{if } 20 \le t < 45 \\ 240 - 4t & \text{if } t \ge 45, \end{cases}$$

where t is measured in seconds and v has units of m/s.

a. Graph the velocity function, for $0 \le t \le 70$. When is the velocity a maximum? When is the velocity zero?
b. What is the distance traveled by the automobile in the first 30 s?
c. What is the distance traveled by the automobile in the first 60 s?
d. What is the position of the automobile when $t = 75$?

26. Probe speed A data collection probe is dropped from a stationary balloon, and it falls with a velocity (in m/s) given by $v(t) = 9.8t$, neglecting air resistance. After 10 s, a chute deploys and the probe immediately slows to a constant speed of 10 m/s, which it maintains until it enters the ocean.

a. Graph the velocity function.
b. How far does the probe fall in the first 30 s after it is released?
c. If the probe was released from an altitude of 3 km, when does it enter the ocean?

27–34. Position and velocity from acceleration *Find the position and velocity of an object moving along a straight line with the given acceleration, initial velocity, and initial position.*

27. $a(t) = -32, v(0) = 70, s(0) = 10$

28. $a(t) = -32, v(0) = 50, s(0) = 0$

29. $a(t) = -9.8, v(0) = 20, s(0) = 0$

30. $a(t) = e^{-t}, v(0) = 60, s(0) = 40$

31. $a(t) = -0.01t, v(0) = 10, s(0) = 0$

32. $a(t) = \dfrac{20}{(t + 2)^2}, v(0) = 20, s(0) = 10$

33. $a(t) = \cos 2t, v(0) = 5, s(0) = 7$

34. $a(t) = \dfrac{2t}{(t^2 + 1)^2}, v(0) = 0, s(0) = 0$

35. Acceleration A drag racer accelerates at $a(t) = 88$ ft/s². Assume that $v(0) = 0$, $s(0) = 0$, and t is measured in seconds.

a. Determine and graph the position function, for $t \ge 0$.
b. How far does the racer travel in the first 4 seconds?
c. At this rate, how long will it take the racer to travel $\frac{1}{4}$ mi?
d. How long does it take the racer to travel 300 ft?
e. How far has the racer traveled when it reaches a speed of 178 ft/s?

36. Deceleration A car slows down with an acceleration of $a(t) = -15$ ft/s². Assume that $v(0) = 60$ ft/s, $s(0) = 0$, and t is measured in seconds.

a. Determine and graph the position function, for $t \ge 0$.
b. How far does the car travel in the time it takes to come to rest?

37. Approaching a station At $t = 0$, a train approaching a station begins decelerating from a speed of 80 mi/hr according to the acceleration function $a(t) = -1280(1 + 8t)^{-3}$, where $t \ge 0$ is measured in hours. How far does the train travel between $t = 0$ and $t = 0.2$? Between $t = 0.2$ and $t = 0.4$? The units of acceleration are mi/hr².

38. Peak oil extraction The owners of an oil reserve begin extracting oil at time $t = 0$. Based on estimates of the reserves, suppose the projected extraction rate is given by $Q'(t) = 3t^2(40 - t)^2$, where $0 \le t \le 40$, Q is measured in millions of barrels, and t is measured in years.

a. When does the peak extraction rate occur?
b. How much oil is extracted in the first 10, 20, and 30 years?
c. What is the total amount of oil extracted in 40 years?
d. Is one-fourth of the total oil extracted in the first one-fourth of the extraction period? Explain.

39. Oil production An oil refinery produces oil at a variable rate given by

$$Q'(t) = \begin{cases} 800 & \text{if } 0 \le t < 30 \\ 2600 - 60t & \text{if } 30 \le t < 40 \\ 200 & \text{if } t \ge 40, \end{cases}$$

where t is measured in days and Q is measured in barrels.

a. How many barrels are produced in the first 35 days?
b. How many barrels are produced in the first 50 days?
c. Without using integration, determine the number of barrels produced over the interval [60, 80].

40–43. Population growth

40. Starting with an initial value of $P(0) = 55$, the population of a prairie dog community grows at a rate of $P'(t) = 20 - t/5$ (prairie dogs/month), for $0 \le t \le 200$, where t is measured in months.

a. What is the population 6 months later?
b. Find the population $P(t)$, for $0 \le t \le 200$.

41. When records were first kept ($t = 0$), the population of a rural town was 250 people. During the following years, the population grew at a rate of $P'(t) = 30(1 + \sqrt{t})$, where t is measured in years.

a. What is the population after 20 years?
b. Find the population $P(t)$ at any time $t \ge 0$.

42. The population of a community of foxes is observed to fluctuate on a 10-year cycle due to variations in the availability of prey. When population measurements began ($t = 0$), the population was 35 foxes. The growth rate in units of foxes/year was observed to be

$$P'(t) = 5 + 10 \sin \frac{\pi t}{5}.$$

a. What is the population 15 years later? 35 years later?
b. Find the population $P(t)$ at any time $t \ge 0$.

43. A culture of bacteria in a Petri dish has an initial population of 1500 cells and grows at a rate (in cells/day) of $N'(t) = 100e^{-0.25t}$. Assume t is measured in days.

a. What is the population after 20 days? After 40 days?
b. Find the population $N(t)$ at any time $t \geq 0$.

44. Flow rates in the Spokane River The daily discharge of the Spokane River as it flows through Spokane, Washington, in April and June is modeled by the functions

$$r_1(t) = 0.25t^2 + 37.46t + 722.47 \text{ (April)} \quad \text{and}$$
$$r_2(t) = 0.90t^2 - 69.06t + 2053.12 \text{ (June)},$$

where the discharge is measured in millions of cubic feet per day and $t = 1$ corresponds to the first day of the month (see figure).

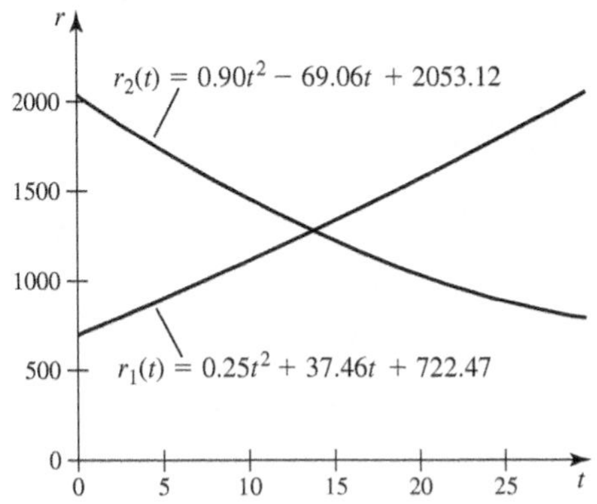

a. Determine the total amount of water that flows through Spokane in April (30 days).
b. Determine the total amount of water that flows through Spokane in June (30 days).
c. The Spokane River flows out of Lake Coeur d'Alene, which contains approximately 0.67 mi^3 of water. Determine the percentage of Lake Coeur d'Alene's volume that flows through Spokane in April and June.

45–48. Marginal cost *Consider the following marginal cost functions.*

a. Find the additional cost incurred in dollars when production is increased from 100 units to 150 units.
b. Find the additional cost incurred in dollars when production is increased from 500 units to 550 units.

45. $C'(x) = 2000 - 0.5x$ **46.** $C'(x) = 200 - 0.05x$

47. $C'(x) = 300 + 10x - 0.01x^2$

48. $C'(x) = 3000 - x - 0.001x^2$

Further Explorations

49. Explain why or why not Determine whether the following statements are true and give an explanation or counterexample.

a. The distance traveled by an object moving along a line is the same as the displacement of the object.
b. When the velocity is positive on an interval, the displacement and the distance traveled on that interval are equal.
c. Consider a tank that is filled and drained at a flow rate of $V'(t) = 1 - t^2/100$ (gal/min), for $t \geq 0$, where t is measured in minutes. It follows that the volume of water in the tank increases for 10 min and then decreases until the tank is empty.
d. A particular marginal cost function has the property that it is positive and decreasing. The cost of increasing production from A units to $2A$ units is greater than the cost of increasing production from $2A$ units to $3A$ units.

50–51. Velocity graphs *The figures show velocity functions for motion along a straight line. Assume the motion begins with an initial position of $s(0) = 0$. Determine the following:*

a. The displacement between $t = 0$ and $t = 5$
b. The distance traveled between $t = 0$ and $t = 5$
c. The position at $t = 5$
d. A piecewise function for $s(t)$

50.

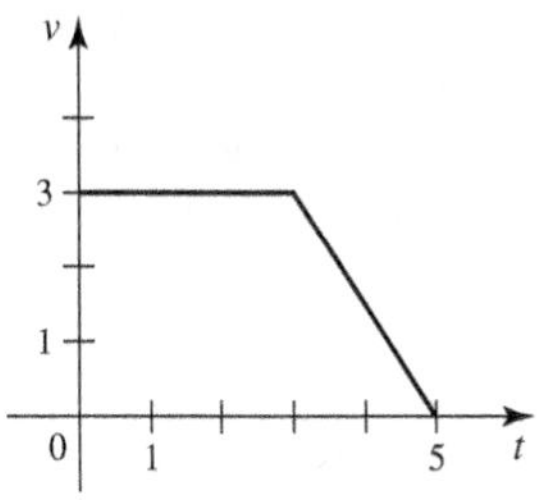

51.

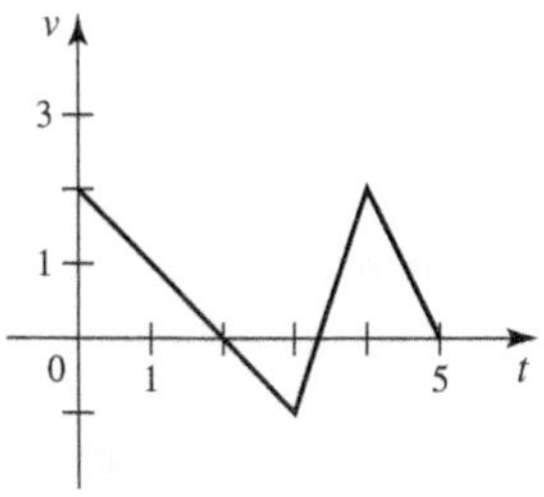

52–55. Equivalent constant velocity *Consider the following velocity functions. In each case, complete the sentence: The same distance could have been traveled over the given time period at a <u>constant</u> velocity of ________.*

52. $v(t) = 2t + 6$, for $0 \leq t \leq 8$

53. $v(t) = 1 - t^2/16$, for $0 \leq t \leq 4$

54. $v(t) = 2 \sin t$, for $0 \leq t \leq \pi$

55. $v(t) = t(25 - t^2)^{1/2}$, for $0 \leq t \leq 5$

56. Where do they meet? Kelly started at noon ($t = 0$) riding a bike from Niwot to Berthoud, a distance of 20 km, with velocity $v(t) = 15/(t + 1)^2$ (decreasing because of fatigue). Sandy started at noon ($t = 0$) riding a bike in the opposite direction from Berthoud to Niwot with velocity $u(t) = 20/(t + 1)^2$ (also decreasing because of fatigue). Assume distance is measured in kilometers and time is measured in hours.

a. Make a graph of Kelly's distance from Niwot as a function of time.
b. Make a graph of Sandy's distance from Berthoud as a function of time.
c. When do they meet? How far has each person traveled when they meet?
d. More generally, if the riders' speeds are $v(t) = A/(t + 1)^2$ and $u(t) = B/(t + 1)^2$ and the distance between the towns is D, what conditions on A, B, and D must be met to ensure that the riders will pass each other?
e. Looking ahead: With the velocity functions given in part (d), make a conjecture about the maximum distance each person can ride (given unlimited time).

57. Bike race Theo and Sasha start at the same place on a straight road, riding bikes with the following velocities (measured in mi/hr). Assume t is measured in hours.

Theo: $v_T(t) = 10$, for $t \geq 0$

Sasha: $v_S(t) = 15t$, for $0 \leq t \leq 1$ and $v_S(t) = 15$, for $t > 1$

a. Graph the velocity functions for both riders.
b. If the riders ride for 1 hr, who rides farther? Interpret your answer geometrically using the graphs of part (a).
c. If the riders ride for 2 hr, who rides farther? Interpret your answer geometrically using the graphs of part (a).

d. Which rider arrives first at the 10-, 15-, and 20-mile markers of the race? Interpret your answer geometrically using the graphs of part (a).

e. Suppose Sasha gives Theo a head start of 0.2 mi and the riders ride for 20 mi. Who wins the race?

f. Suppose Sasha gives Theo a head start of 0.2 hr and the riders ride for 20 mi. Who wins the race?

58. Two runners At noon ($t = 0$), Alicia starts running along a long straight road at 4 mi/hr. Her velocity decreases according to the function $v(t) = 4/(t + 1)$, for $t \geq 0$. At noon, Boris also starts running along the same road with a 2-mi head start on Alicia; his velocity is given by $u(t) = 2/(t + 1)$, for $t \geq 0$. Assume t is measured in hours.

a. Find the position functions for Alicia and Boris, where $s = 0$ corresponds to Alicia's starting point.

b. When, if ever, does Alicia overtake Boris?

59. Running in a wind A strong west wind blows across a circular running track. Abe and Bess start running at the south end of the track, and at the same time, Abe starts running clockwise and Bess starts running counterclockwise. Abe runs with a speed (in units of mi/hr) given by $u(\varphi) = 3 - 2\cos\varphi$ and Bess runs with a speed given by $v(\theta) = 3 + 2\cos\theta$, where φ and θ are the central angles of the runners.

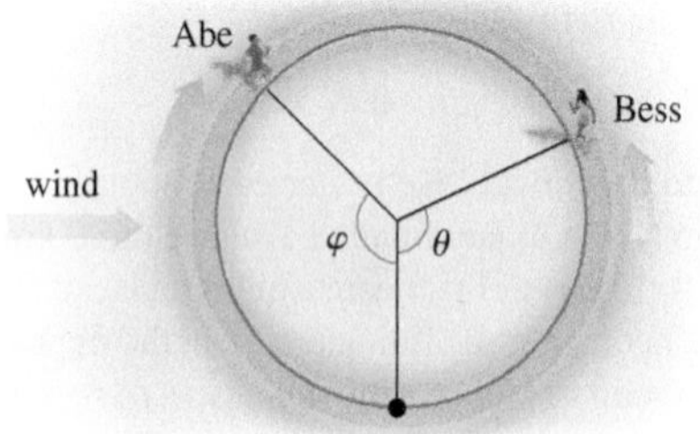

a. Graph the speed functions u and v, and explain why they describe the runners' speeds (in light of the wind).

b. Compute the average value of u and v with respect to the central angle.

c. Challenge: If the track has a radius of $\frac{1}{10}$ mi, how long does it take each runner to complete one lap and who wins the race?

Applications

60. Filling a tank A 2000-liter cistern is empty when water begins flowing into it (at $t = 0$) at a rate (in L/min) given by $Q'(t) = 3\sqrt{t}$, where t is measured in minutes.

a. How much water flows into the cistern in 1 hour?

b. Find and graph the function that gives the amount of water in the tank at any time $t \geq 0$.

c. When will the tank be full?

61. Depletion of natural resources Suppose that $r(t) = r_0 e^{-kt}$, with $k > 0$, is the rate at which a nation extracts oil, where $r_0 = 10^7$ barrels/yr is the current rate of extraction. Suppose also that the estimate of the total oil reserve is 2×10^9 barrels.

a. Find $Q(t)$, the total amount of oil extracted by the nation after t years.

b. Evaluate $\lim_{t \to \infty} Q(t)$ and explain the meaning of this limit.

c. Find the minimum decay constant k for which the total oil reserves will last forever.

d. Suppose $r_0 = 2 \times 10^7$ barrels/yr and the decay constant k is the minimum value found in part (c). How long will the total oil reserves last?

62. Snowplow problem With snow on the ground and falling at a constant rate, a snowplow began plowing down a long straight road at noon. The plow traveled twice as far in the first hour as it did in the second hour. At what time did the snow start falling? Assume the plowing rate is inversely proportional to the depth of the snow.

T **63. Filling a reservoir** A reservoir with a capacity of 2500 m^3 is filled with a single inflow pipe. The reservoir is empty when the inflow pipe is opened at $t = 0$. Letting $Q(t)$ be the amount of water in the reservoir at time t, the flow rate of water into the reservoir (in m^3/hr) oscillates on a 24-hr cycle (see figure) and is given by

$$Q'(t) = 20\left(1 + \cos\frac{\pi t}{12}\right).$$

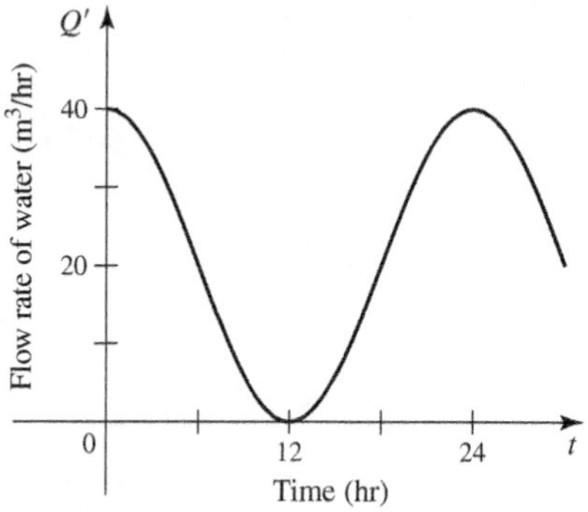

a. How much water flows into the reservoir in the first 2 hr?

b. Find and graph the function that gives the amount of water in the reservoir over the interval $[0, t]$, where $t \geq 0$.

c. When is the reservoir full?

64. Blood flow A typical human heart pumps 70 mL of blood with each stroke (stroke volume). Assuming a heart rate of 60 beats/min (1 beat/s), a reasonable model for the outflow rate of the heart is $V'(t) = 70(1 + \sin 2\pi t)$, where $V(t)$ is the amount of blood (in milliliters) pumped over the interval $[0, t]$, $V(0) = 0$, and t is measured in seconds.

a. Graph the outflow rate function.

b. Verify that the amount of blood pumped over a one-second interval is 70 mL.

c. Find the function that gives the total blood pumped between $t = 0$ and a future time $t > 0$.

d. What is the cardiac output over a period of 1 min? (Use calculus; then check your answer with algebra.)

65. Air flow in the lungs A simple model (with different parameters for different people) for the flow of air in and out of the lungs is

$$V'(t) = -\frac{\pi}{2}\sin\frac{\pi t}{2},$$

where $V(t)$ (measured in liters) is the volume of air in the lungs at time $t \geq 0$, t is measured in seconds, and $t = 0$ corresponds to a time at which the lungs are full and exhalation begins. Only a fraction of the air in the lungs in exchanged with each breath. The amount that is exchanged is called the *tidal volume*.

a. Find and graph the volume function V assuming that $V(0) = 6$ L.

b. What is the breathing rate in breaths/min?

c. What is the tidal volume and what is the total capacity of the lungs?

66. Oscillating growth rates Some species have growth rates that oscillate with an (approximately) constant period P. Consider the growth rate function

$$N'(t) = r + A \sin \frac{2\pi t}{P}$$

where A and r are constants with units of individuals/yr, and t is measured in years. A species becomes extinct if its population ever reaches 0 after $t = 0$.

a. Suppose $P = 10$, $A = 20$, and $r = 0$. If the initial population is $N(0) = 10$, does the population ever become extinct? Explain.

b. Suppose $P = 10$, $A = 20$, and $r = 0$. If the initial population is $N(0) = 100$, does the population ever become extinct? Explain.

c. Suppose $P = 10$, $A = 50$, and $r = 5$. If the initial population is $N(0) = 10$, does the population ever become extinct? Explain.

d. Suppose $P = 10$, $A = 50$, and $r = -5$. Find the initial population $N(0)$ needed to ensure that the population never becomes extinct.

67. Power and energy Power and energy are often used interchangeably, but they are quite different. **Energy** is what makes matter move or heat up and is measured in units of **joules** (J) or **Calories** (Cal), where 1 Cal = 4184 J. One hour of walking consumes roughly 10^6 J, or 250 Cal. On the other hand, **power** is the rate at which energy is used and is measured in **watts** (W; 1 W = 1 J/s). Other useful units of power are **kilowatts** (1 kW = 10^3 W) and **megawatts** (1 MW = 10^6 W). If energy is used at a rate of 1 kW for 1 hr, the total amount of energy used is 1 **kilowatt-hour** (kWh), which is 3.6×10^6 J.

Suppose the power function of a large city over a 24-hr period is given by

$$P(t) = E'(t) = 300 - 200 \sin \frac{\pi t}{12},$$

where P is measured in megawatts and $t = 0$ corresponds to 6:00 P.M. (see figure).

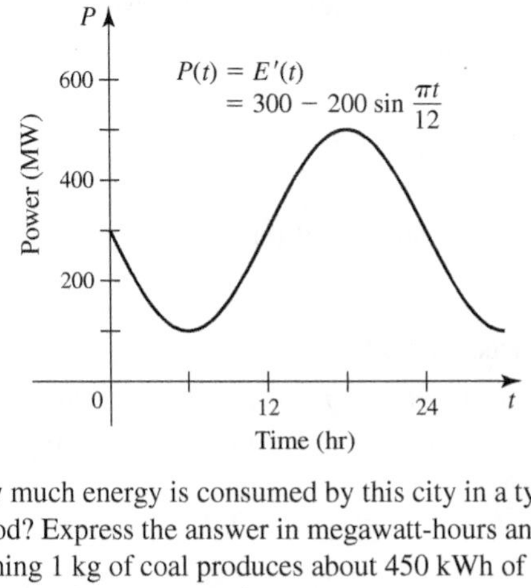

a. How much energy is consumed by this city in a typical 24-hr period? Express the answer in megawatt-hours and in joules.

b. Burning 1 kg of coal produces about 450 kWh of energy. How many kg of coal are required to meet the energy needs of the city for 1 day? For 1 year?

c. Fission of 1 g of uranium-235 (U-235) produces about 16,000 kWh of energy. How many grams of uranium are needed to meet the energy needs of the city for 1 day? For 1 year?

d. A typical wind turbine can generate electrical power at a rate of about 200 kW. Approximately how many wind turbines are needed to meet the average energy needs of the city?

68. Variable gravity At Earth's surface, the acceleration due to gravity is approximately $g = 9.8\ \text{m/s}^2$ (with local variations). However, the acceleration decreases with distance from the surface according to Newton's law of gravitation. At a distance of y meters from Earth's surface, the acceleration is given by

$$a(y) = -\frac{g}{(1 + y/R)^2},$$

where $R = 6.4 \times 10^6$ m is the radius of Earth.

a. Suppose a projectile is launched upward with an initial velocity of v_0 m/s. Let $v(t)$ be its velocity and $y(t)$ its height (in meters) above the surface t seconds after the launch. Neglecting forces such as air resistance, explain why $\frac{dv}{dt} = a(y)$ and $\frac{dy}{dt} = v(t)$.

b. Use the Chain Rule to show that $\frac{dv}{dt} = \frac{1}{2}\frac{d}{dy}(v^2)$.

c. Show that the equation of motion for the projectile is $\frac{1}{2}\frac{d}{dy}(v^2) = a(y)$, where $a(y)$ is given previously.

d. Integrate both sides of the equation in part (c) with respect to y using the fact that when $y = 0$, $v = v_0$. Show that

$$\frac{1}{2}(v^2 - v_0^2) = gR\left(\frac{1}{1 + y/R} - 1\right).$$

e. When the projectile reaches its maximum height, $v = 0$. Use this fact to determine that the maximum height is $y_{max} = \frac{Rv_0^2}{2gR - v_0^2}$.

f. Graph y_{max} as a function of v_0. What is the maximum height when v_0 = 500 m/s, 1500 m/s, and 5 km/s?

g. Show that the value of v_0 needed to put the projectile into orbit (called the escape velocity) is $\sqrt{2gR}$.

Additional Exercises

69–72. Another look at the Fundamental Theorem

69. Suppose that f and g have continuous derivatives on an interval $[a, b]$. Prove that if $f(a) = g(a)$ and $f(b) = g(b)$, then $\int_a^b f'(x)\,dx = \int_a^b g'(x)\,dx$.

70. Use Exercise 69 to prove that if two runners start and finish at the same time and place, then *regardless of the velocities at which they run*, their displacements are equal.

71. Use Exercise 69 to prove that if two trails start at the same place and finish at the same place, then *regardless of the ups and downs of the trails*, they have the same net change in elevation.

72. Without evaluating integrals, prove that

$$\int_0^2 \frac{d}{dx}(12 \sin \pi x^2)\,dx = \int_0^2 \frac{d}{dx}(x^{10}(2 - x)^3)\,dx.$$

QUICK CHECK ANSWERS

1. Displacement = −20 mi (20 mi south); distance traveled = 100 mi **2.** Suppose the object moves in the positive direction, for $0 \le t \le 3$, and then moves in the negative direction, for $3 < t \le 5$. **3.** A function; a number **4.** Displacement = 0; distance traveled = 1 **5.** 1720 m **6.** The production cost would increase more between 9000 and 12,000 books than between 12,000 and 15,000 books. Graph C' and look at the area under the curve.

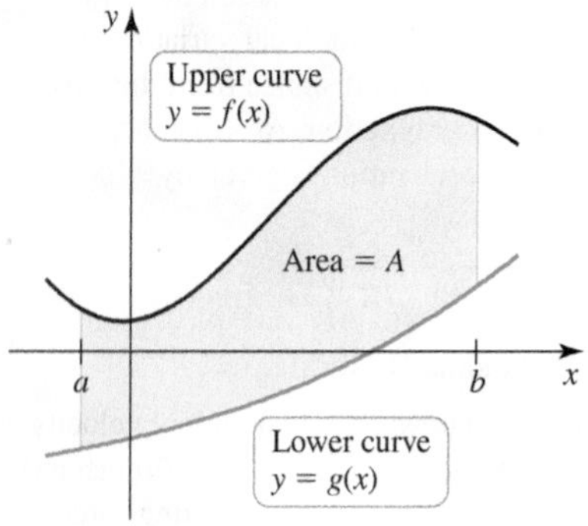

Figure 6.11

6.2 Regions Between Curves

In this section, the method for finding the area of a region bounded by a single curve is generalized to regions bounded by two or more curves. Consider two functions f and g continuous on an interval $[a, b]$ on which $f(x) \geq g(x)$ (Figure 6.11). The goal is to find the area A of the region bounded by the two curves and the vertical lines $x = a$ and $x = b$.

Once again, we rely on the *slice-and-sum* strategy (Section 5.2) for finding areas by Riemann sums. The interval $[a, b]$ is partitioned into n subintervals using uniformly spaced grid points separated by a distance $\Delta x = (b - a)/n$ (Figure 6.12). On each subinterval, we build a rectangle extending from the lower curve to the upper curve. On the kth subinterval, a point x_k^* is chosen, and the height of the corresponding rectangle is taken to be $f(x_k^*) - g(x_k^*)$. Therefore, the area of the kth rectangle is $(f(x_k^*) - g(x_k^*))\,\Delta x$ (Figure 6.13). Summing the areas of the n rectangles gives an approximation to the area of the region between the curves:

$$A \approx \sum_{k=1}^{n} (f(x_k^*) - g(x_k^*))\,\Delta x.$$

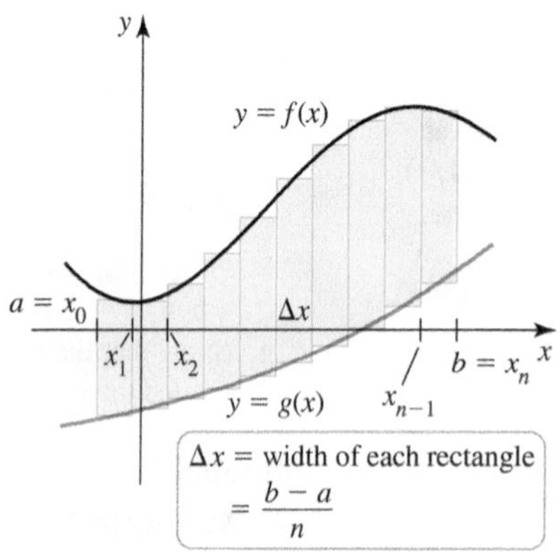

Figure 6.12

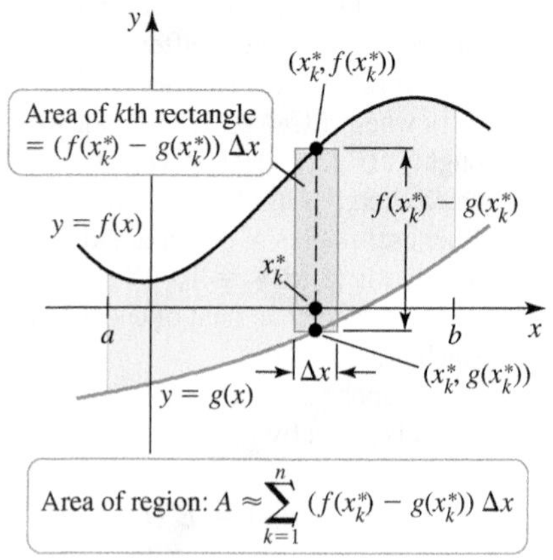

Figure 6.13

As the number of grid points increases, Δx approaches zero and these sums approach the area of the region between the curves; that is,

$$A = \lim_{n \to \infty} \sum_{k=1}^{n} (f(x_k^*) - g(x_k^*))\Delta x.$$

The limit of these Riemann sums is a definite integral of the function $f - g$.

➤ It is helpful to interpret the area formula: $f(x) - g(x)$ is the length of a rectangle and dx represents its width. We sum (integrate) the areas of the rectangles $(f(x) - g(x))\,dx$ to obtain the area of the region.

DEFINITION Area of a Region Between Two Curves

Suppose that f and g are continuous functions with $f(x) \geq g(x)$ on the interval $[a, b]$. The area of the region bounded by the graphs of f and g on $[a, b]$ is

$$A = \int_a^b (f(x) - g(x))\,dx.$$

QUICK CHECK 1 In the area formula for a region between two curves, verify that if the lower curve is $g(x) = 0$, the formula becomes the usual formula for the area of the region bounded by $y = f(x)$ and the x-axis. ◄

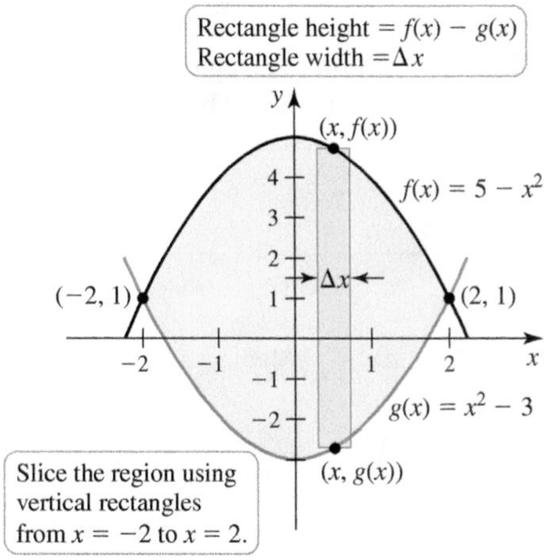

Figure 6.14

EXAMPLE 1 **Area between curves** Find the area of the region bounded by the graphs of $f(x) = 5 - x^2$ and $g(x) = x^2 - 3$ (Figure 6.14).

SOLUTION A key step in the solution of many area problems is finding the intersection points of the boundary curves, which often determine the limits of integration. The intersection points of these two curves satisfy the equation $5 - x^2 = x^2 - 3$. The solutions of this equation are $x = -2$ and $x = 2$, which become the lower and upper limits of integration, respectively. The graph of f is the upper curve and the graph of g is the lower curve on the interval $[-2, 2]$. Therefore, the area of the region is

$$\begin{aligned} A &= \int_{-2}^{2} \big(\underbrace{(5 - x^2)}_{f(x)} - \underbrace{(x^2 - 3)}_{g(x)}\big)\,dx && \text{Substitute for } f \text{ and } g. \\ &= 2\int_{0}^{2} (8 - 2x^2)\,dx && \text{Simplify and use symmetry.} \\ &= 2\left(8x - \frac{2}{3}x^3\right)\Big|_{0}^{2} && \text{Fundamental Theorem} \\ &= \frac{64}{3}. && \text{Simplify.} \end{aligned}$$

Notice how the symmetry of the problem simplifies the integration. Additionally, note that the area formula $A = \int_a^b (f(x) - g(x))\,dx$ is valid even if one or both curves lie below the x-axis, as long as $f(x) \geq g(x)$ on $[a, b]$.

Related Exercises 5–14 ◀

QUICK CHECK 2 Interpret the area formula when written in the form $A = \int_a^b f(x)\,dx - \int_a^b g(x)\,dx$, where $f(x) \geq g(x) \geq 0$ on $[a, b]$. ◀

EXAMPLE 2 **Compound region** Find the area of the region bounded by the graphs of $f(x) = -x^2 + 3x + 6$ and $g(x) = |2x|$ (Figure 6.15a).

SOLUTION The lower boundary of the region is bounded by two different branches of the absolute value function. In situations like this, the region is divided into two (or more) subregions whose areas are found independently and then summed; these subregions are labeled R_1 and R_2 (Figure 6.15b). By the definition of absolute value,

$$g(x) = |2x| = \begin{cases} 2x & \text{if } x \geq 0 \\ -2x & \text{if } x < 0. \end{cases}$$

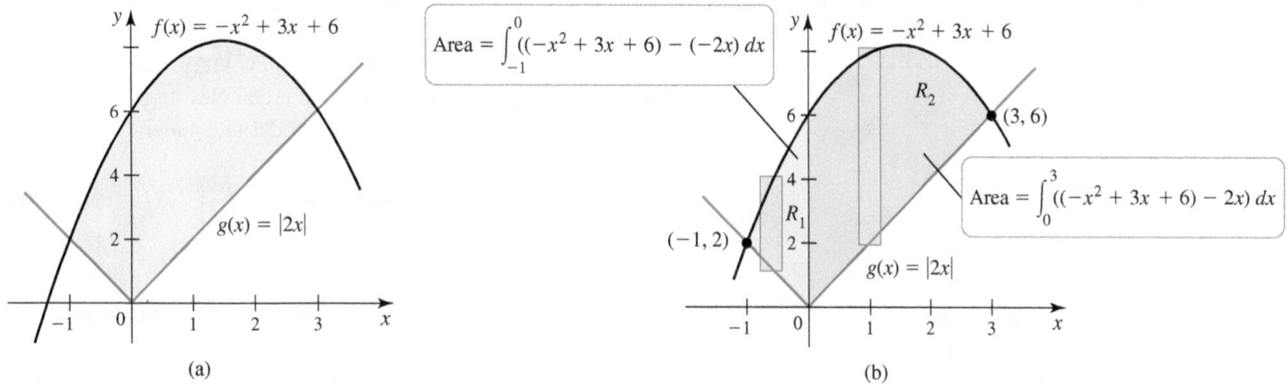

Figure 6.15

➤ The solution $x = 6$ corresponds to the intersection of the parabola $y = -x^2 + 3x + 6$ and the line $y = -2x$ in the fourth quadrant, not shown in Figure 6.15 because $g(x) = -2x$ only when $x < 0$.

The left intersection point of f and g satisfies $-2x = -x^2 + 3x + 6$, or $x^2 - 5x - 6 = 0$. Solving for x, we find that $(x + 1)(x - 6) = 0$, which implies $x = -1$ or $x = 6$; only the first solution is relevant. The right intersection point of f and g satisfies $2x = -x^2 + 3x + 6$; you should verify that the relevant solution in this case is $x = 3$.

Given these points of intersection, we see that the region R_1 is bounded by $y = -x^2 + 3x + 6$ and $y = -2x$ on the interval $[-1, 0]$. Similarly, region R_2 is bounded by $y = -x^2 + 3x + 6$ and $y = 2x$ on $[0, 3]$ (Figure 6.15b). Therefore,

$$A = \underbrace{\int_{-1}^{0} ((-x^2 + 3x + 6) - (-2x))\,dx}_{\text{area of region } R_1} + \underbrace{\int_{0}^{3} ((-x^2 + 3x + 6) - 2x)\,dx}_{\text{area of region } R_2}$$

$$= \int_{-1}^{0} (-x^2 + 5x + 6)\,dx + \int_{0}^{3} (-x^2 + x + 6)\,dx \qquad \text{Simplify.}$$

$$= \left(-\frac{x^3}{3} + \frac{5}{2}x^2 + 6x\right)\Bigg|_{-1}^{0} + \left(-\frac{x^3}{3} + \frac{1}{2}x^2 + 6x\right)\Bigg|_{0}^{3} \qquad \text{Fundamental Theorem}$$

$$= 0 - \left(\frac{1}{3} + \frac{5}{2} - 6\right) + \left(-9 + \frac{9}{2} + 18\right) - 0 = \frac{50}{3}. \qquad \text{Simplify.}$$

Related Exercises 15–22 ◀

Integrating with Respect to y

There are occasions when it is convenient to reverse the roles of x and y. Consider the regions shown in Figure 6.16 that are bounded by the graphs of $x = f(y)$ and $x = g(y)$, where $f(y) \ge g(y)$, for $c \le y \le d$ (which implies that the graph of f lies to the right of the graph of g). The lower and upper boundaries of the regions are $y = c$ and $y = d$, respectively.

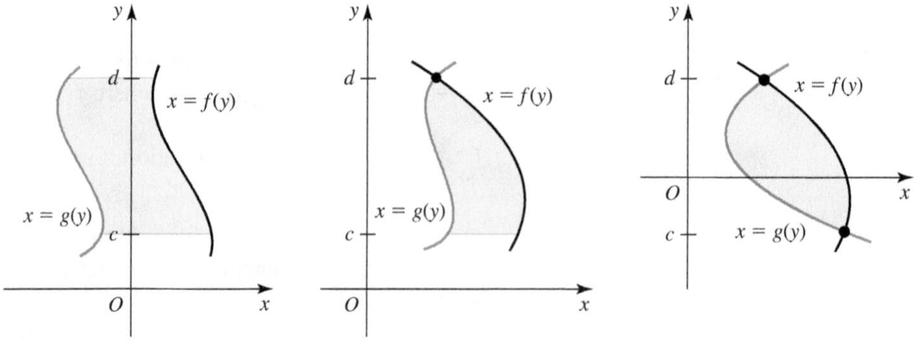

Figure 6.16

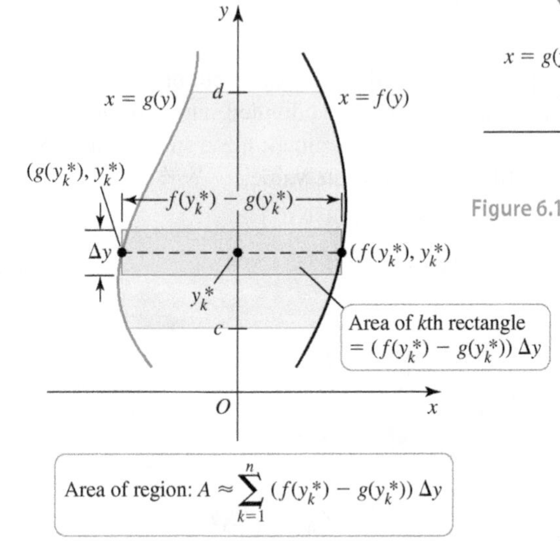

Figure 6.17

In cases such as these, we treat y as the independent variable and divide the interval $[c, d]$ into n subintervals of width $\Delta y = (d - c)/n$ (Figure 6.17). On the kth subinterval, a point y_k^* is selected, and we construct a rectangle that extends from the left curve to the right curve. The kth rectangle has length $f(y_k^*) - g(y_k^*)$, so the area of the kth rectangle is $(f(y_k^*) - g(y_k^*))\Delta y$. The area of the region is approximated by the sum of the areas of the rectangles. In the limit as $n \to \infty$ and $\Delta y \to 0$, the area of the region is given as the definite integral

$$A = \lim_{n\to\infty} \sum_{k=1}^{n} (f(y_k^*) - g(y_k^*))\Delta y = \int_c^d (f(y) - g(y))\,dy.$$

> **DEFINITION Area of a Region Between Two Curves with Respect to y**
>
> Suppose that f and g are continuous functions with $f(y) \ge g(y)$ on the interval $[c, d]$. The area of the region bounded by the graphs $x = f(y)$ and $x = g(y)$ on $[c, d]$ is
>
> $$A = \int_c^d (f(y) - g(y))\,dy.$$

➤ This area formula is analogous to the one given on page 412; it is now expressed with respect to the y-axis. In this case, $f(y) - g(y)$ is the length of a rectangle and dy represents its width. We sum (integrate) the areas of the rectangles $(f(y) - g(y))\,dy$ to obtain the area of the region.

EXAMPLE 3 **Integrating with respect to *y*** Find the area of the region R bounded by the graphs of $y = x^3$, $y = x + 6$, and the x-axis.

SOLUTION The area of this region could be found by integrating with respect to x. But this approach requires splitting the region into two pieces (Figure 6.18). Alternatively, we can view y as the independent variable, express the bounding curves as functions of y, and make horizontal slices parallel to the x-axis (Figure 6.19).

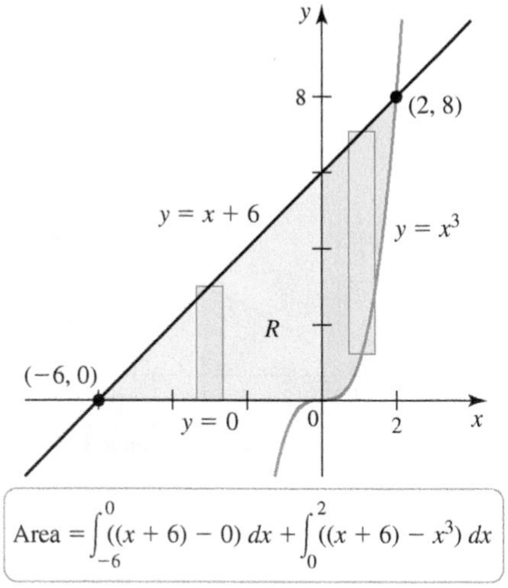

Figure 6.18

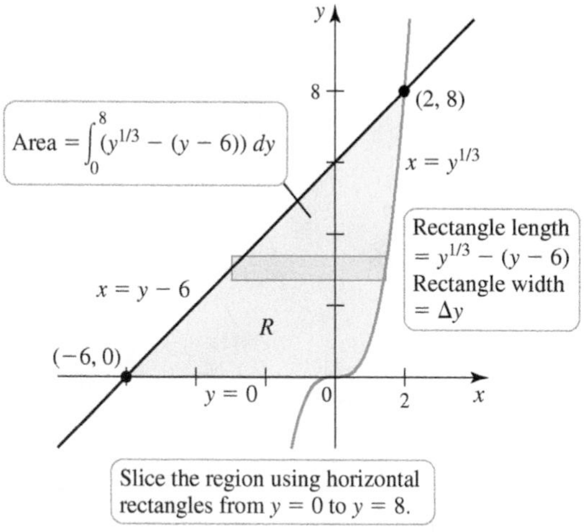

Figure 6.19

➤ You may use synthetic division or a root finder to factor the cubic polynomial in Example 3. Then the quadratic formula shows that the equation

$$y^2 - 10y + 27 = 0$$

has no real roots.

Solving for x in terms of y, the right curve $y = x^3$ becomes $x = f(y) = y^{1/3}$. The left curve $y = x + 6$ becomes $x = g(y) = y - 6$. The intersection point of the curves satisfies the equation $y^{1/3} = y - 6$, or $y = (y - 6)^3$. Expanding this equation gives the cubic equation

$$y^3 - 18y^2 + 107y - 216 = (y - 8)(y^2 - 10y + 27) = 0,$$

whose only real root is $y = 8$. As shown in Figure 6.19, the areas of the slices through the region are summed from $y = 0$ to $y = 8$. Therefore, the area of the region is given by

$$\int_0^8 (y^{1/3} - (y - 6))\,dy = \left(\frac{3}{4}y^{4/3} - \frac{y^2}{2} + 6y\right)\Bigg|_0^8 \qquad \text{Fundamental Theorem}$$

$$= \left(\frac{3}{4}\cdot 16 - 32 + 48\right) - 0 = 28. \qquad \text{Simplify.}$$

Related Exercises 23–32 ◀

QUICK CHECK 3 The region R is bounded by the curve $y = \sqrt{x}$, the line $y = x - 2$, and the x-axis. Express the area of R in terms of (a) integral(s) with respect to x and (b) integral(s) with respect to y. ◀

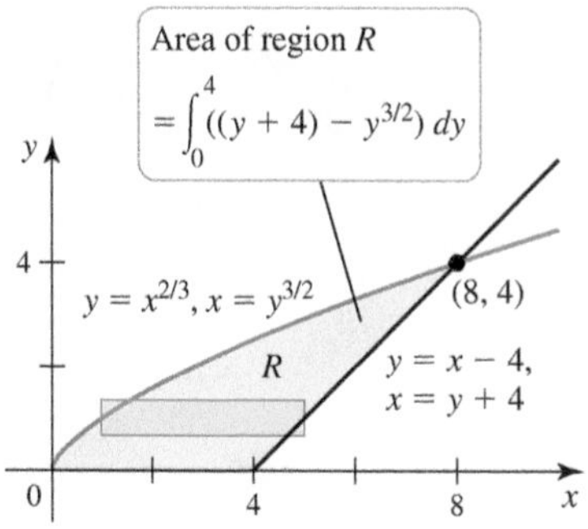

Figure 6.20

EXAMPLE 4 **Calculus and geometry** Find the area of the region R in the first quadrant bounded by the curves $y = x^{2/3}$ and $y = x - 4$ (Figure 6.20).

SOLUTION Slicing the region vertically and integrating with respect to x requires two integrals. Slicing the region horizontally requires a single integral with respect to y. The second approach appears to involve less work.

Slicing horizontally, the right bounding curve is $x = y + 4$ and the left bounding curve is $x = y^{3/2}$. The two curves intersect at $(8, 4)$, so the limits of integration are $y = 0$ and $y = 4$. The area of R is

$$\int_0^4 (\underbrace{(y + 4)}_{\text{right curve}} - \underbrace{y^{3/2}}_{\text{left curve}})\,dy = \left(\frac{y^2}{2} + 4y - \frac{2}{5}y^{5/2}\right)\Bigg|_0^4 = \frac{56}{5}.$$

➤ To find the point of intersection in Example 4, solve $y^{3/2} = y + 4$ by first squaring both sides of the equation.

Can this area be found using a different approach? Sometimes it helps to use geometry. Notice that the region R can be formed by taking the entire region under the curve $y = x^{2/3}$ on the interval $[0, 8]$ and then removing a triangle whose base is the interval $[4, 8]$ (Figure 6.21). The area of the region R_1 under the curve $y = x^{2/3}$ is

$$\int_0^8 x^{2/3}\,dx = \frac{3}{5}x^{5/3}\bigg|_0^8 = \frac{96}{5}.$$

The triangle R_2 has a base of length 4 and a height of 4, so its area is $\frac{1}{2}\cdot 4\cdot 4 = 8$. Therefore, the area of R is $\frac{96}{5} - 8 = \frac{56}{5}$, which agrees with the first calculation.

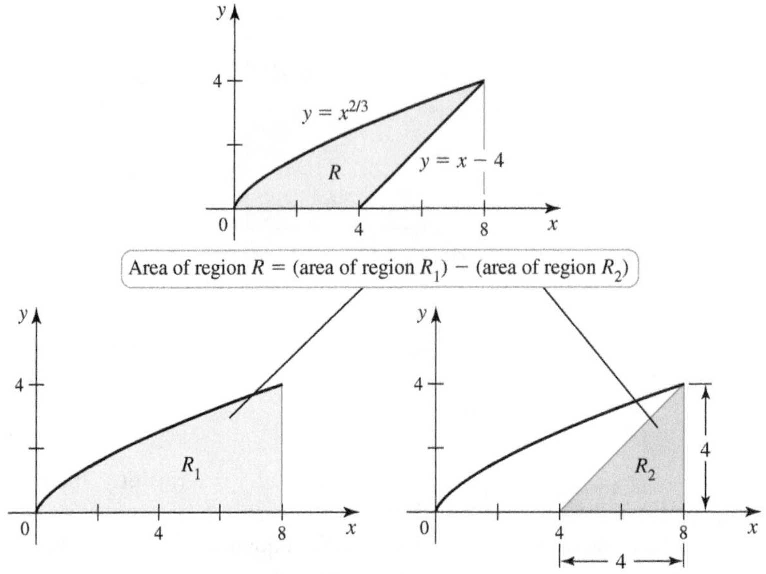

Figure 6.21

Related Exercises 33–38 ◄

QUICK CHECK 4 An alternative way to determine the area of the region in Example 3 (Figure 6.18) is to compute $18 + \int_0^2 (x + 6 - x^3)\,dx$. Why? ◄

SECTION 6.2 EXERCISES

Review Questions

1. Draw the graphs of two functions f and g that are continuous and intersect exactly twice on $(-\infty, \infty)$. Explain how to use integration to find the area of the region bounded by the two curves.

2. Draw the graphs of two functions f and g that are continuous and intersect exactly three times on $(-\infty, \infty)$. How is integration used to find the area of the region bounded by the two curves?

3. Make a sketch to show a case in which the area bounded by two curves is most easily found by integrating with respect to x.

4. Make a sketch to show a case in which the area bounded by two curves is most easily found by integrating with respect to y.

Basic Skills

5–8. Finding area *Determine the area of the shaded region in the following figures.*

5.

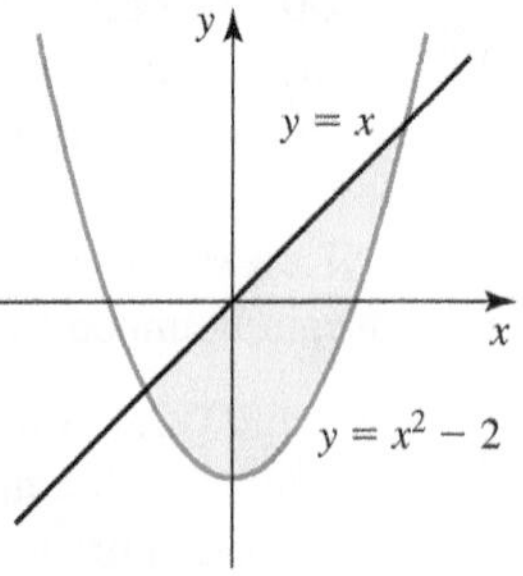

6.

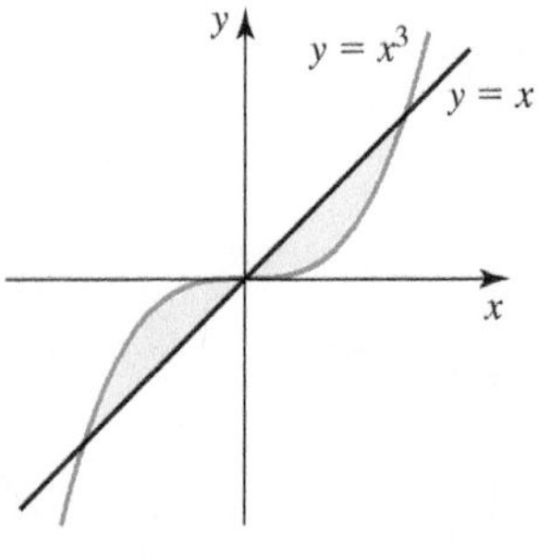

7.

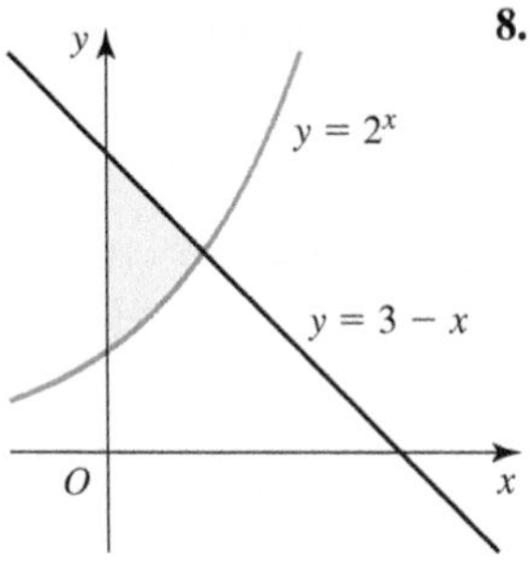

(*Hint:* Find the intersection point by inspection.)

8.

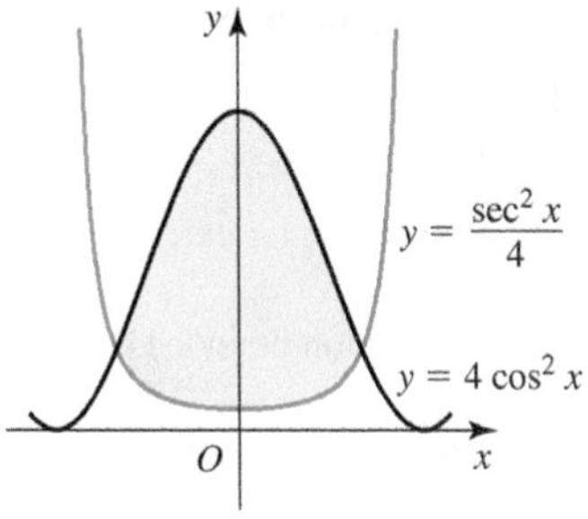

9–14. Regions between curves *Sketch the region and find its area.*

9. The region bounded by $y = 2(x + 1)$, $y = 3(x + 1)$, and $x = 4$

10. The region bounded by $y = \cos x$ and $y = \sin x$ between $x = \pi/4$ and $x = 5\pi/4$

11. The region bounded by $y = e^x$, $y = e^{-2x}$, and $x = \ln 4$

12. The region bounded by $y = 2x$ and $y = x^2 + 3x - 6$

13. The region bounded by $y = \dfrac{2}{1 + x^2}$ and $y = 1$

14. The region bounded by $y = 24\sqrt{x}$ and $y = 3x^2$

15–22. Compound regions *Sketch each region (if a figure is not given) and then find its total area.*

15. The region bounded by $y = \sin x$, $y = \cos x$, and the x-axis between $x = 0$ and $x = \pi/2$

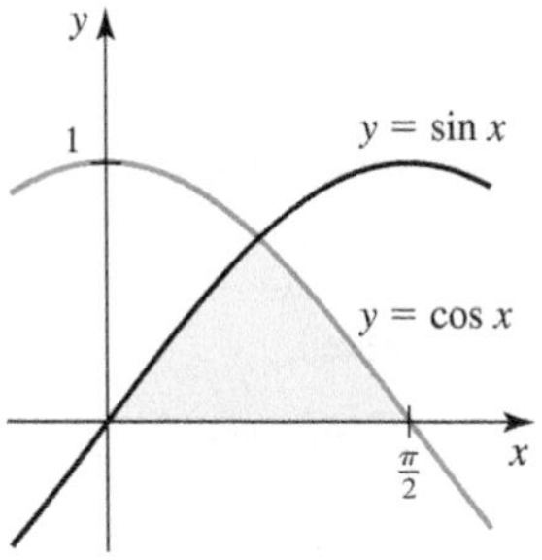

16. The regions between $y = \sin x$ and $y = \sin 2x$, for $0 \le x \le \pi$

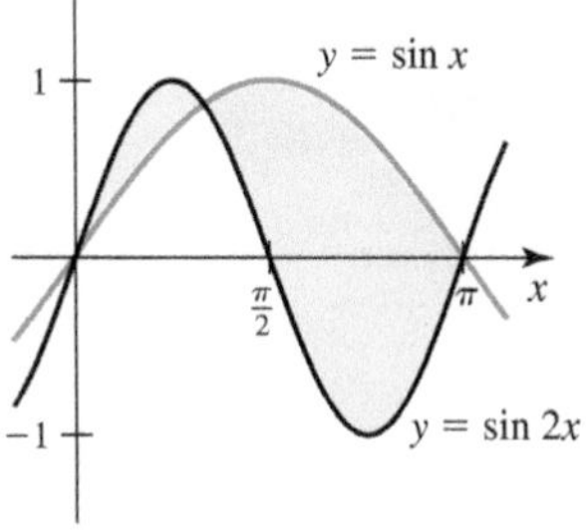

17. The region bounded by $y = x$, $y = 1/x$, $y = 0$, and $x = 2$

18. The regions in the first quadrant on the interval $[0, 2]$ bounded by $y = 4x - x^2$ and $y = 4x - 4$.

19. The region bounded by $y = 2 - |x|$ and $y = x^2$

20. The regions bounded by $y = x^3$ and $y = 9x$

21. The region bounded by $y = |x - 3|$ and $y = x/2$

22. The regions bounded by $y = x^2(3 - x)$ and $y = 12 - 4x$

23–26. Integrating with respect to y *Sketch each region (if a figure is not given) and find its area by integrating with respect to y.*

23. The region bounded by $y = \sqrt{\dfrac{x}{2} + 1}$, $y = \sqrt{1 - x}$, and $y = 0$.

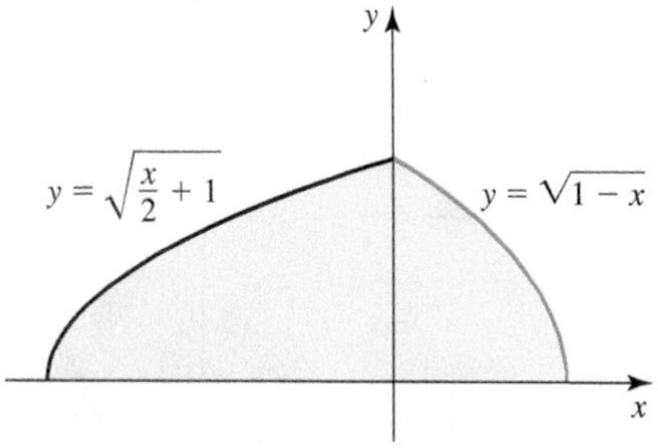

24. The region bounded by $x = \cos y$ and $x = -\sin 2y$

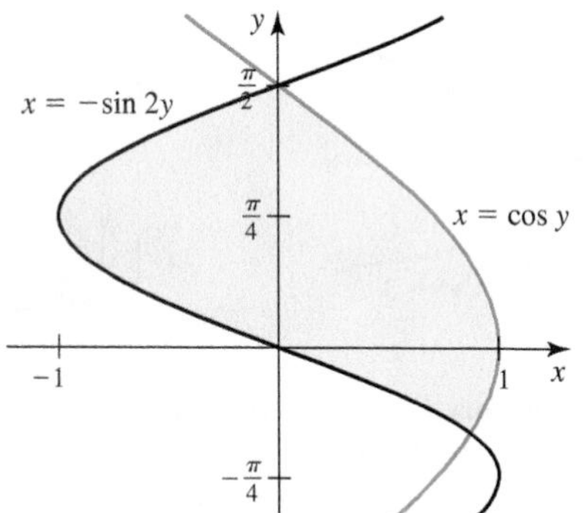

25. The region bounded by $x = y^2 - 3y + 12$ and $x = -2y^2 - 6y + 30$

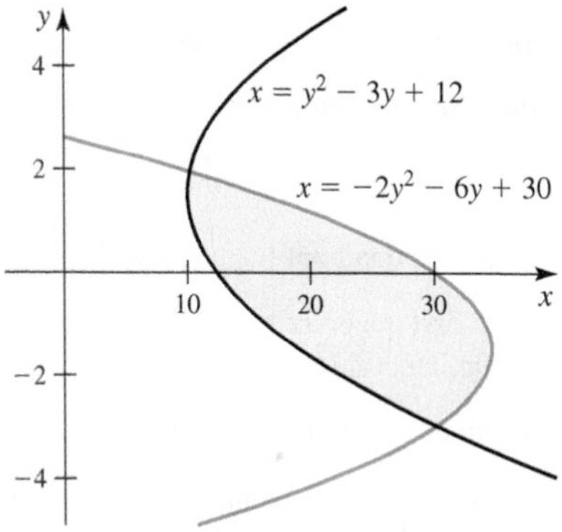

26. Both regions bounded by $x = y^3 - 4y^2 + 3y$ and $x = y^2 - y$

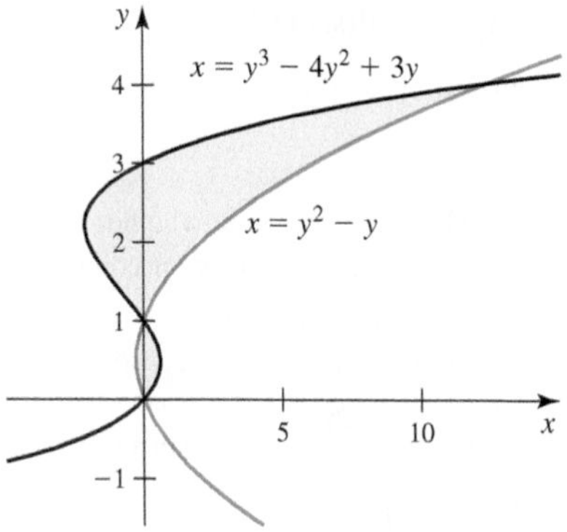

27–30. Two approaches *Express the area of the following shaded regions in terms of (a) one or more integrals with respect to x and (b) one or more integrals with respect to y. You do not need to evaluate the integrals.*

27.

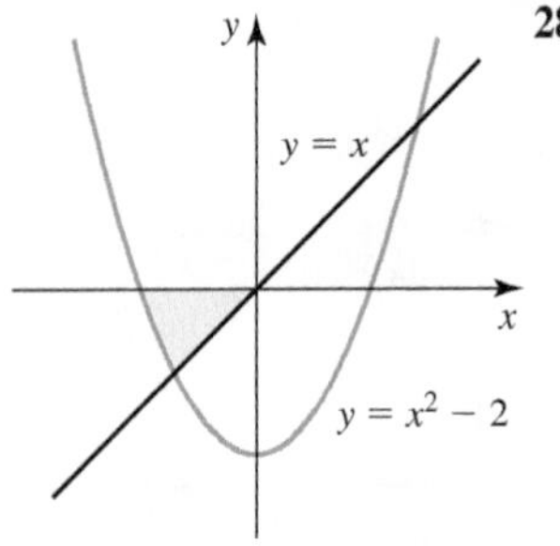

28.

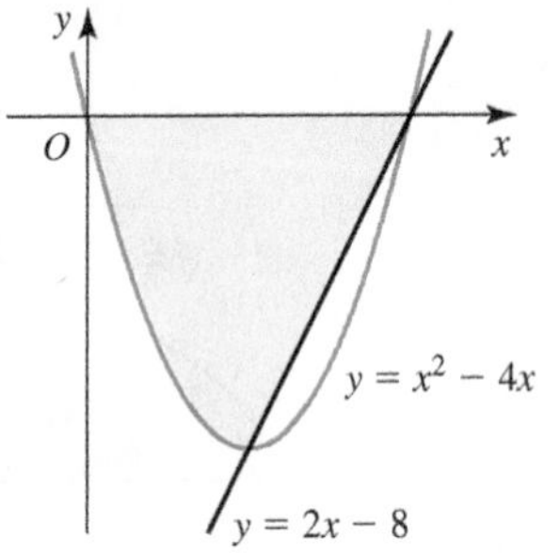

29.

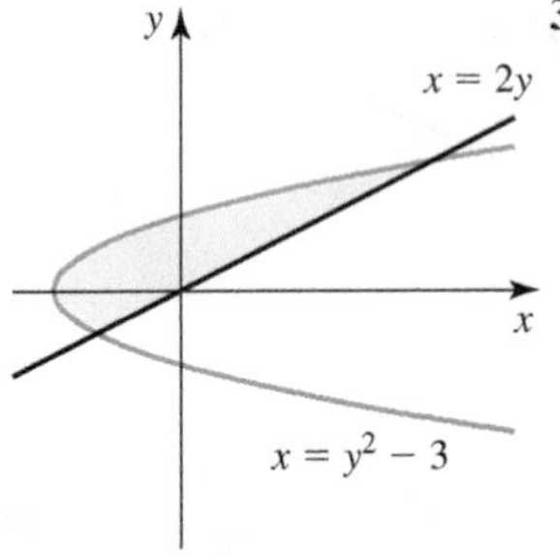

30.

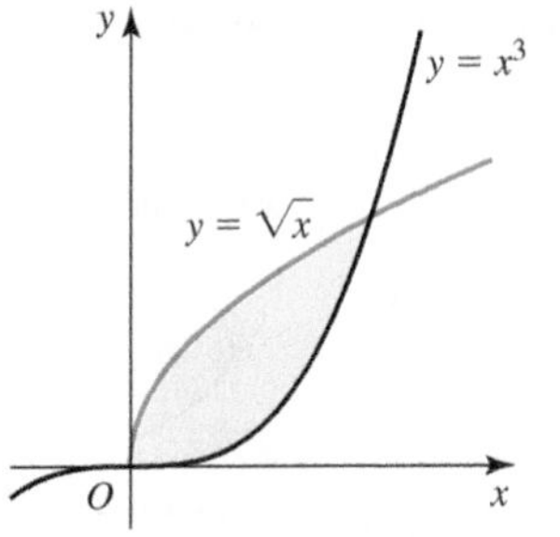

31–32. Two approaches *Find the area of the following regions by (a) integrating with respect to x and (b) integrating with respect to y. Be sure your results agree. Sketch the bounding curves and the region in question.*

31. The region bounded by $y = 2 - \frac{x}{2}$ and $x = 2y^2$

32. The region bounded by $x = 2 - y^2$ and $x = |y|$

33–38. Any method *Use any method (including geometry) to find the area of the following regions. In each case, sketch the bounding curves and the region in question.*

33. The region in the first quadrant bounded by $y = x^{2/3}$ and $y = 4$

34. The region in the first quadrant bounded by $y = 2$ and $y = 2 \sin x$ on the interval $[0, \pi/2]$

35. The region bounded by $y = e^x$, $y = 2e^{-x} + 1$, and $x = 0$

T **36.** The region below the line $y = 2$ and above the curve $y = \sec^2 x$ on the interval $[0, \pi/4]$

T **37.** The region between the line $y = x$ and the curve $y = 2x\sqrt{1 - x^2}$ in the first quadrant

38. The region bounded by $x = y^2 - 4$ and $y = x/3$

Further Explorations

39. Explain why or why not Determine whether the following statements are true and give an explanation or counterexample.

a. The area of the region bounded by $y = x$ and $x = y^2$ can be found only by integrating with respect to x.

b. The area of the region between $y = \sin x$ and $y = \cos x$ on the interval $[0, \pi/2]$ is $\int_0^{\pi/2} (\cos x - \sin x)\, dx$.

c. $\int_0^1 (x - x^2)\, dx = \int_0^1 (\sqrt{y} - y)\, dy$.

40–43. Regions between curves *Sketch the region and find its area.*

40. The region bounded by $y = \sin x$ and $y = x(x - \pi)$, for $0 \le x \le \pi$

41. The region bounded by $y = (x - 1)^2$ and $y = 7x - 19$

42. The region bounded by $y = 2$ and $y = \frac{1}{\sqrt{1 - x^2}}$

43. The region bounded by $y = x^2 - 2x + 1$ and $y = 5x - 9$

44–50. Either method *Use the most efficient strategy for computing the area of the following regions.*

44. The region bounded by $x = y(y - 1)$ and $x = -y(y - 1)$

45. The region bounded by $x = y(y - 1)$ and $y = x/3$

46. The region bounded by $y = x^3$, $y = -x^3$, and $3y - 7x - 10 = 0$

47. The region bounded by $y = \sqrt{x}$, $y = 2x - 15$, and $y = 0$

48. The region bounded by $y = x^2 - 4$, $4y - 5x - 5 = 0$, and $y = 0$, for $y \ge 0$

49. The region in the first quadrant bounded by $y = \frac{5}{2} - \frac{1}{x}$ and $y = x$

50. The region in the first quadrant bounded by $y = x^{-1}$, $y = 4x$, and $y = x/4$

51. Comparing areas Let $f(x) = x^p$ and $g(x) = x^{1/q}$, where $p > 1$ and $q > 1$ are positive integers. Let R_1 be the region in the first quadrant between $y = f(x)$ and $y = x$ and let R_2 be the region in the first quadrant between $y = g(x)$ and $y = x$.

a. Find the area of R_1 and R_2 when $p = q$, and determine which region has the greater area.

b. Find the area of R_1 and R_2 when $p > q$, and determine which region has the greater area.

c. Find the area of R_1 and R_2 when $p < q$, and determine which region has the greater area.

52–55. Complicated regions *Find the area of the regions shown in the following figures.*

52.

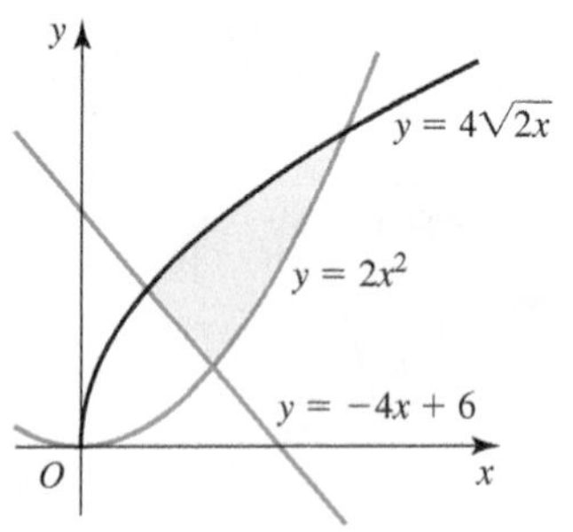

53.

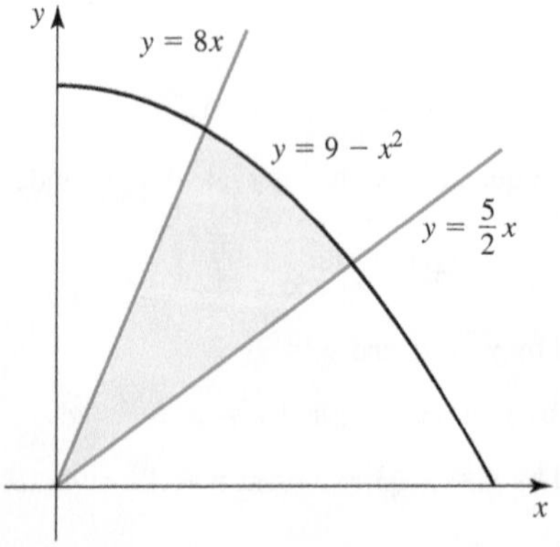

54.

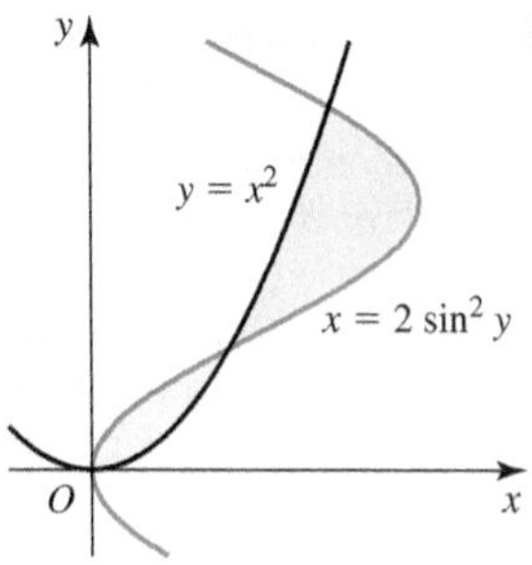

55.

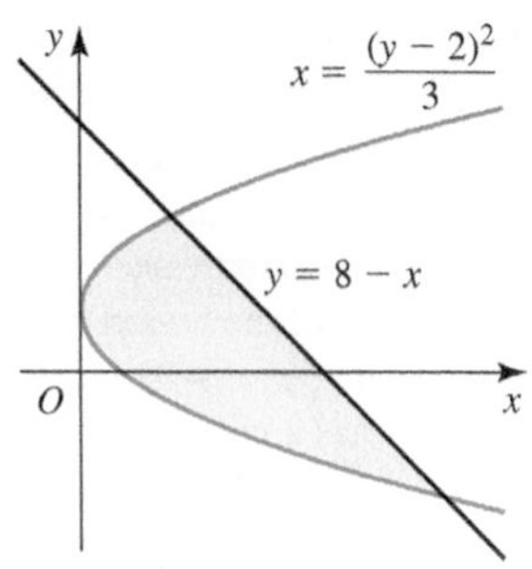

56–59. Roots and powers *Find the area of the following regions, expressing your results in terms of the positive integer $n \geq 2$.*

56. The region bounded by $f(x) = x$ and $g(x) = x^n$, for $x \geq 0$

57. The region bounded by $f(x) = x$ and $g(x) = x^{1/n}$, for $x \geq 0$

58. The region bounded by $f(x) = x^{1/n}$ and $g(x) = x^n$, for $x \geq 0$

59. Let A_n be the area of the region bounded by $f(x) = x^{1/n}$ and $g(x) = x^n$ on the interval $[0, 1]$, where n is a positive integer. Evaluate $\lim_{n\to\infty} A_n$ and interpret the result.

60–63. Bisecting regions *For each region R, find the horizontal line $y = k$ that divides R into two subregions of equal area.*

60. R is the region bounded by $y = 1 - x$, the x-axis, and the y-axis.

61. R is the region bounded by $y = 1 - |x - 1|$ and the x-axis.

62. R is the region bounded by $y = 4 - x^2$ and the x-axis.

63. R is the region bounded by $y = \sqrt{x}$ and $y = x$.

Applications

64. Geometric probability Suppose a dartboard occupies the square $\{(x, y): 0 \leq |x| \leq 1, 0 \leq |y| \leq 1\}$. A dart is thrown randomly at the board many times (meaning it is equally likely to land at any point in the square). What fraction of the dart throws land closer to the edge of the board than the center? Equivalently, what is the probability that the dart lands closer to the edge of the board than the center? Proceed as follows.

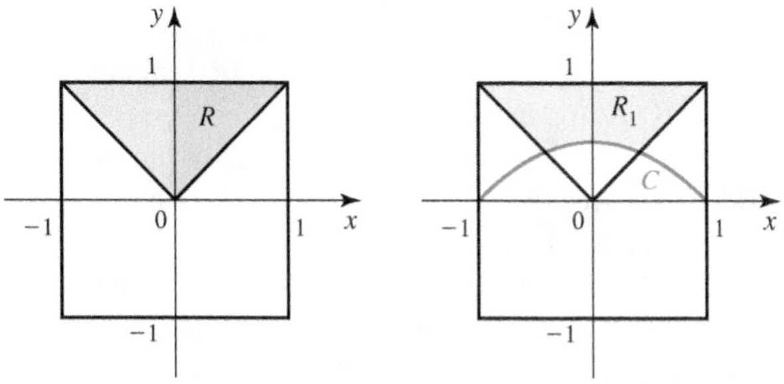

a. Argue that by symmetry, it is necessary to consider only one quarter of the board, say the region R: $\{(x, y): |x| \leq y \leq 1\}$.

b. Find the curve C in this region that is equidistant from the center of the board and the top edge of the board (see figure).

c. The probability that the dart lands closer to the edge of the board than the center is the ratio of the area of the region R_1 above C to the area of the entire region R. Compute this probability.

65. Lorenz curves and the Gini index A **Lorenz curve** is given by $y = L(x)$, where $0 \leq x \leq 1$ represents the lowest fraction of the population of a society in terms of wealth and $0 \leq y \leq 1$ represents the fraction of the total wealth that is owned by that fraction of the society. For example, the Lorenz curve in the figure shows that $L(0.5) = 0.2$, which means that the lowest 0.5 (50%) of the society owns 0.2 (20%) of the wealth. (See the Guided Project *Distribution of Wealth* for more on Lorenz curves.)

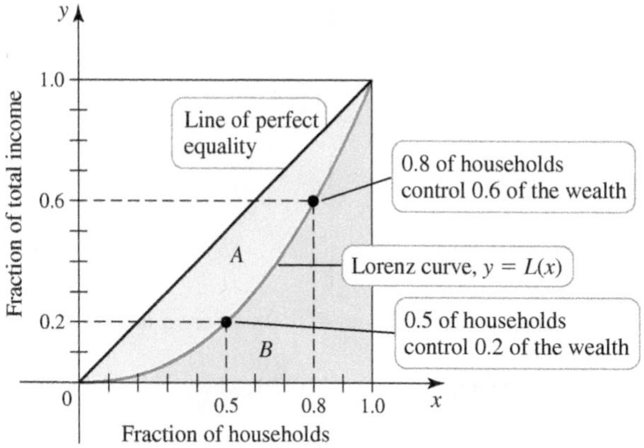

a. A Lorenz curve $y = L(x)$ is accompanied by the line $y = x$, called the **line of perfect equality**. Explain why this line is given this name.

b. Explain why a Lorenz curve satisfies the conditions $L(0) = 0$, $L(1) = 1$, $L(x) \leq x$, and $L'(x) \geq 0$ on $[0, 1]$.

c. Graph the Lorenz curves $L(x) = x^p$ corresponding to $p = 1.1, 1.5, 2, 3, 4$. Which value of p corresponds to the *most* equitable distribution of wealth (closest to the line of perfect equality)? Which value of p corresponds to the *least* equitable distribution of wealth? Explain.

d. The information in the Lorenz curve is often summarized in a single measure called the **Gini index**, which is defined as follows. Let A be the area of the region between $y = x$ and $y = L(x)$ (see figure) and let B be the area of the region between $y = L(x)$ and the x-axis. Then the Gini index is $G = \dfrac{A}{A + B}$. Show that $G = 2A = 1 - 2\displaystyle\int_0^1 L(x)\,dx$.

e. Compute the Gini index for the cases $L(x) = x^p$ and $p = 1.1, 1.5, 2, 3, 4$.

f. What is the smallest interval $[a, b]$ on which values of the Gini index lie for $L(x) = x^p$ with $p \geq 1$? Which endpoints of $[a, b]$ correspond to the least and most equitable distribution of wealth?

g. Consider the Lorenz curve described by $L(x) = 5x^2/6 + x/6$. Show that it satisfies the conditions $L(0) = 0$, $L(1) = 1$, and $L'(x) \geq 0$ on $[0, 1]$. Find the Gini index for this function.

Additional Exercises

66. Equal area properties for parabolas Consider the parabola $y = x^2$. Let P, Q, and R be points on the parabola with R between P and Q on the curve. Let ℓ_P, ℓ_Q, and ℓ_R be the lines tangent to the parabola at P, Q, and R, respectively (see figure). Let P' be the intersection point of ℓ_Q and ℓ_R, let Q' be the intersection point of ℓ_P and ℓ_R, and let R' be the intersection point of ℓ_P and ℓ_Q. Prove that Area $\Delta PQR = 2 \cdot$ Area $\Delta P'Q'R'$ in the following cases. (In fact, the property holds for any three points on any parabola.) (*Source: Mathematics Magazine* 81, 2, Apr 2008)

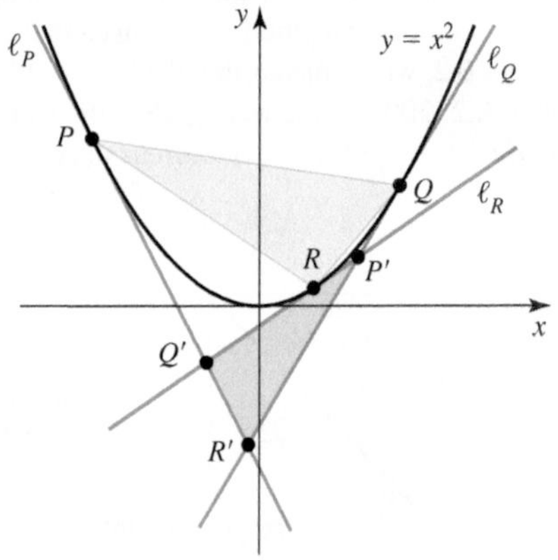

a. $P(-a, a^2)$, $Q(a, a^2)$, and $R(0, 0)$, where a is a positive real number

b. $P(-a, a^2)$, $Q(b, b^2)$, and $R(0, 0)$, where a and b are positive real numbers

c. $P(-a, a^2)$, $Q(b, b^2)$, and R is any point between P and Q on the curve

T **67. Minimum area** Graph the curves $y = (x + 1)(x - 2)$ and $y = ax + 1$ for various values of a. For what value of a is the area of the region between the two curves a minimum?

T **68. An area function** Graph the curves $y = a^2x^3$ and $y = \sqrt{x}$ for various values of $a > 0$. Note how the area $A(a)$ between the curves varies with a. Find and graph the area function $A(a)$. For what value of a is $A(a) = 16$?

69. Area of a curve defined implicitly Determine the area of the shaded region bounded by the curve $x^2 = y^4(1 - y^3)$ (see figure).

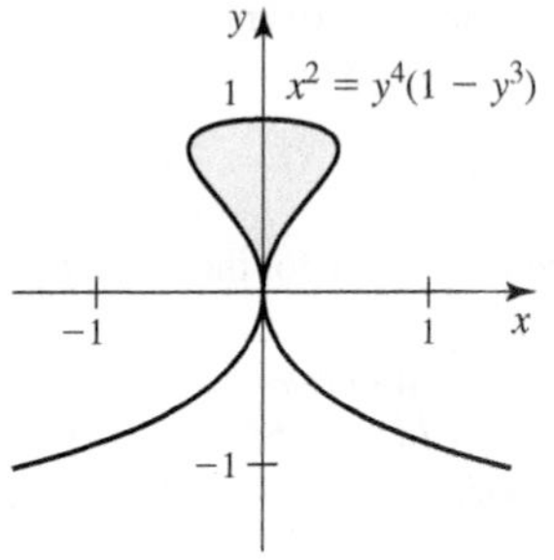

70. Rewrite first Find the area of the region bounded by the curve $x = \frac{1}{2y} - \sqrt{\frac{1}{4y^2} - 1}$ and the line $x = 1$ in the first quadrant. (*Hint:* Express y in terms of x.)

T **71. Area function for a cubic** Consider the cubic polynomial $f(x) = x(x - a)(x - b)$, where $0 \le a \le b$.

a. For a fixed value of b, find the function $F(a) = \int_0^b f(x)\,dx$. For what value of a (which depends on b) is $F(a) = 0$?

b. For a fixed value of b, find the function $A(a)$ that gives the area of the region bounded by the graph of f and the x-axis between $x = 0$ and $x = b$. Graph this function and show that it has a minimum at $a = b/2$. What is the maximum value of $A(a)$, and where does it occur (in terms of b)?

72. Differences of even functions Assume f and g are even, integrable functions on $[-a, a]$, where $a > 1$. Suppose $f(x) > g(x) > 0$ on $[-a, a]$ and the area bounded by the graphs of f and g on $[-a, a]$ is 10. What is the value of $\int_0^{\sqrt{a}} x(f(x^2) - g(x^2))\,dx$?

T **73. Roots and powers** Consider the functions $f(x) = x^n$ and $g(x) = x^{1/n}$, where $n \ge 2$ is a positive integer.

a. Graph f and g for $n = 2, 3,$ and 4, for $x \ge 0$.

b. Give a geometric interpretation of the area function $A_n(x) = \int_0^x (f(s) - g(s))\,ds$, for $n = 2, 3, 4, \ldots$ and $x > 0$.

c. Find the positive root of $A_n(x) = 0$ in terms of n. Does the root increase or decrease with n?

T **74. Shifting sines** Consider the functions $f(x) = a \sin 2x$ and $g(x) = (\sin x)/a$, where $a > 0$ is a real number.

a. Graph the two functions on the interval $[0, \pi/2]$, for $a = \frac{1}{2}, 1,$ and 2.

b. Show that the curves have an intersection point x^* (other than $x = 0$) on $[0, \pi/2]$ that satisfies $\cos x^* = 1/(2a^2)$, provided $a > 1/\sqrt{2}$.

c. Find the area of the region between the two curves on $[0, x^*]$ when $a = 1$.

d. Show that as $a \to 1/\sqrt{2}^+$, the area of the region between the two curves on $[0, x^*]$ approaches zero.

QUICK CHECK ANSWERS

1. If $g(x) = 0$ and $f(x) \ge 0$, then the area between the curves is $\int_a^b (f(x) - 0)\,dx = \int_a^b f(x)\,dx$, which is the area between $y = f(x)$ and the x-axis. **2.** $\int_a^b f(x)\,dx$ is the area of the region between the graph of f and the x-axis. $\int_a^b g(x)\,dx$ is the area of the region between the graph of g and the x-axis. The difference of the two integrals is the area of the region between the graphs of f and g. **3. a.** $\int_0^2 \sqrt{x}\,dx + \int_2^4 (\sqrt{x} - x + 2)\,dx$ **b.** $\int_0^2 (y + 2 - y^2)\,dy$ **4.** The area of the triangle to the left of the y-axis is 18. The area of the region to the right of the y-axis is given by the integral. ◀

6.3 Volume by Slicing

We have seen that integration is used to compute the area of two-dimensional regions bounded by curves. Integrals are also used to find the volume of three-dimensional regions (or solids). Once again, the slice-and-sum method is the key to solving these problems.

General Slicing Method

Consider a solid object that extends in the x-direction from $x = a$ to $x = b$. Imagine cutting through the solid, perpendicular to the x-axis at a particular point x, and suppose the area of the cross section created by the cut is given by a known integrable function A (Figure 6.22).

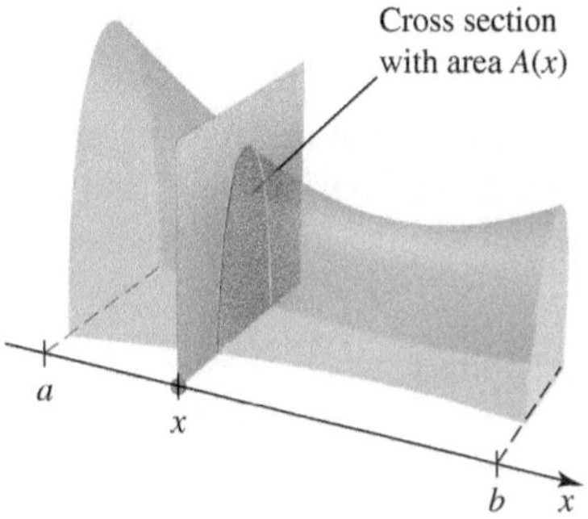

Figure 6.22

To find the volume of this solid, we first divide $[a, b]$ into n subintervals of length $\Delta x = (b - a)/n$. The endpoints of the subintervals are the grid points $x_0 = a, x_1, x_2, \ldots, x_n = b$. We now make vertical cuts through the solid perpendicular to the x-axis at each grid point, which produces n slices of thickness Δx. (Imagine cutting a loaf of bread to create n slices of equal width.) On each subinterval, an arbitrary point x_k^* is identified. The kth slice through the solid has a thickness Δx, and we take $A(x_k^*)$ as a representative cross-sectional area of the slice. Therefore, the volume of the kth slice is approximately $A(x_k^*)\Delta x$ (Figure 6.23). Summing the volumes of the slices, the approximate volume of the solid is

$$V \approx \sum_{k=1}^{n} A(x_k^*)\Delta x.$$

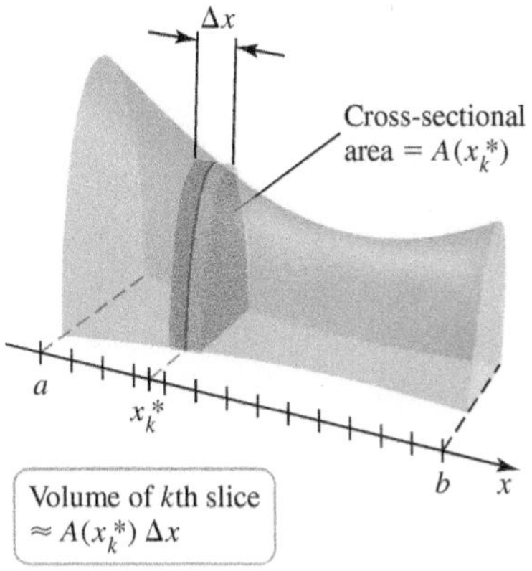

Figure 6.23

As the number of slices increases ($n \to \infty$) and the thickness of each slice goes to zero ($\Delta x \to 0$), the exact volume V is obtained in terms of a definite integral (Figure 6.24):

$$V = \lim_{n\to\infty} \sum_{k=1}^{n} A(x_k^*)\Delta x = \int_a^b A(x)\, dx.$$

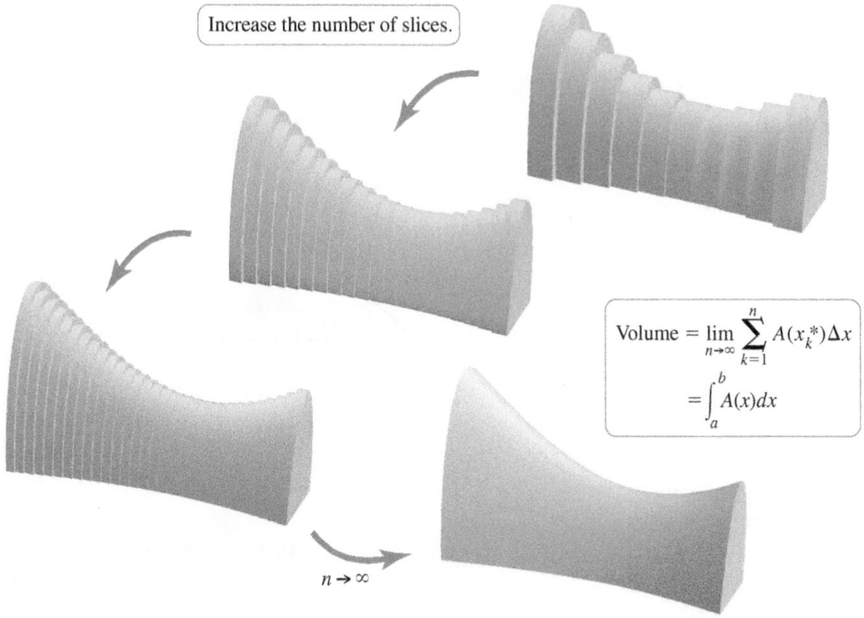

Figure 6.24

We summarize the important general slicing method, which is also the basis of other volume formulas to follow.

➤ The factors in this volume integral have meaning: $A(x)$ is the cross-sectional area of a slice and dx represents its thickness. Summing (integrating) the volumes of the slices $A(x)\,dx$ gives the volume of the solid.

General Slicing Method

Suppose a solid object extends from $x = a$ to $x = b$ and the cross section of the solid perpendicular to the x-axis has an area given by a function A that is integrable on $[a, b]$. The volume of the solid is

$$V = \int_a^b A(x)\, dx.$$

QUICK CHECK 1 Why is the volume, as given by the general slicing method, equal to the average value of the area function A on $[a, b]$ multiplied by $b - a$? ◀

EXAMPLE 1 Volume of a "parabolic cube" Let R be the region in the first quadrant bounded by the coordinate axes and the curve $y = 1 - x^2$. A solid has a base R, and cross sections through the solid perpendicular to the base and parallel to the y-axis are squares (Figure 6.25a). Find the volume of the solid.

SOLUTION Focus on a cross section through the solid at a point x, where $0 \le x \le 1$. That cross section is a square with sides of length $1 - x^2$. Therefore, the area of a typical cross section is $A(x) = (1 - x^2)^2$. Using the general slicing method, the volume of the solid is

$$\begin{aligned} V &= \int_0^1 A(x)\,dx && \text{General slicing method} \\ &= \int_0^1 (1 - x^2)^2\,dx && \text{Substitute for } A(x). \\ &= \int_0^1 (1 - 2x^2 + x^4)\,dx && \text{Expand integrand.} \\ &= \frac{8}{15}. && \text{Evaluate.} \end{aligned}$$

The actual solid with a square cross section is shown in Figure 6.25b.

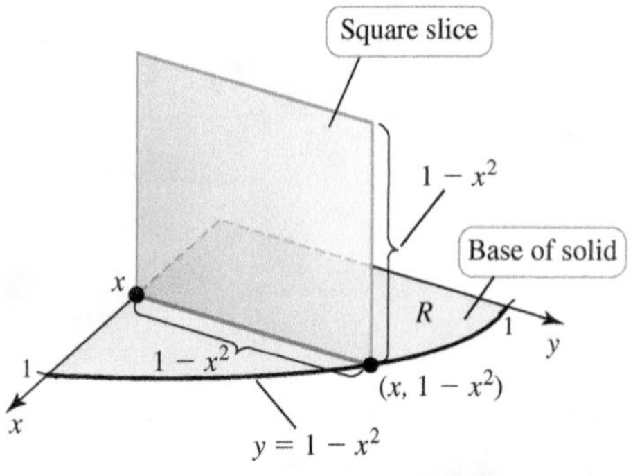

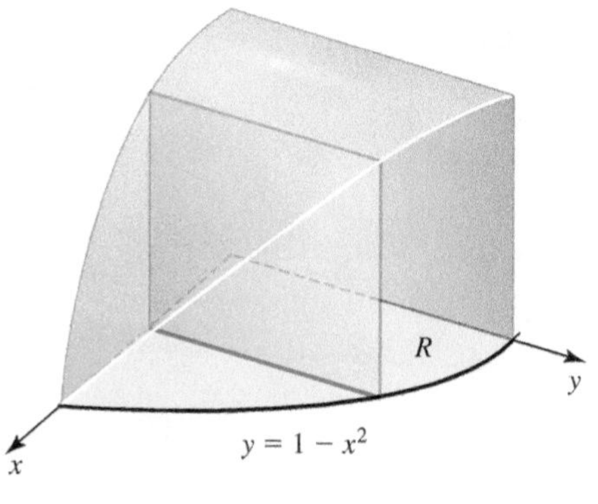

Figure 6.25

Related Exercises 7–16 ◀

EXAMPLE 2 Volume of a "parabolic hemisphere" A solid has a base that is bounded by the curves $y = x^2$ and $y = 2 - x^2$ in the xy-plane. Cross sections through the solid perpendicular to the base and parallel to the y-axis are semicircular disks. Find the volume of the solid.

SOLUTION Because a typical cross section perpendicular to the x-axis is a semicircular disk (Figure 6.26), the area of a cross section is $\frac{1}{2}\pi r^2$, where r is the radius of the cross section.

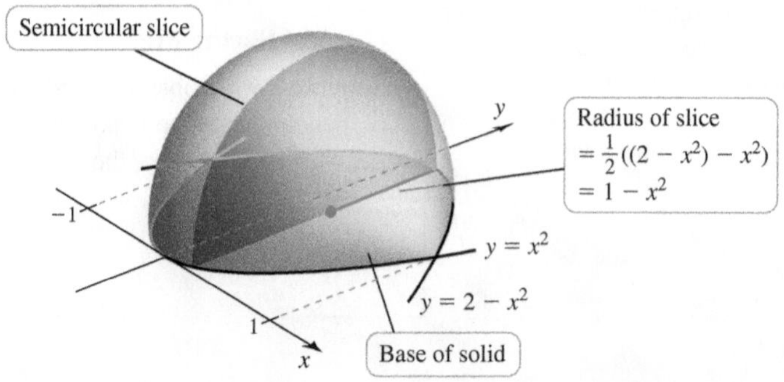

Figure 6.26

The key observation is that this radius is one-half of the distance between the upper bounding curve $y = 2 - x^2$ and the lower bounding curve $y = x^2$. So the radius at the point x is

$$r = \frac{1}{2}((2 - x^2) - x^2) = 1 - x^2.$$

This means that the area of the semicircular cross section at the point x is

$$A(x) = \frac{1}{2}\pi r^2 = \frac{\pi}{2}(1 - x^2)^2.$$

The intersection points of the two bounding curves satisfy $2 - x^2 = x^2$, which has solutions $x = \pm 1$. Therefore, the cross sections lie between $x = -1$ and $x = 1$. Integrating the cross-sectional areas, the volume of the solid is

$$\begin{aligned} V &= \int_{-1}^{1} A(x)\,dx && \text{General slicing method} \\ &= \int_{-1}^{1} \frac{\pi}{2}(1 - x^2)^2\,dx && \text{Substitute for } A(x). \\ &= \frac{\pi}{2}\int_{-1}^{1} (1 - 2x^2 + x^4)\,dx && \text{Expand integrand.} \\ &= \frac{8\pi}{15}. && \text{Evaluate.} \end{aligned}$$

Related Exercises 7–16 ◄

QUICK CHECK 2 In Example 2, what is the cross-sectional area function $A(x)$ if cross sections perpendicular to the base are squares rather than semicircles? ◄

The Disk Method

We now consider a specific type of solid known as a **solid of revolution**. Suppose f is a continuous function with $f(x) \geq 0$ on an interval $[a, b]$. Let R be the region bounded by the graph of f, the x-axis, and the lines $x = a$ and $x = b$ (Figure 6.27). Now revolve R around the x-axis. As R revolves once about the x-axis, it sweeps out a three-dimensional solid of revolution (Figure 6.28). The goal is to find the volume of this solid, and it may be done using the general slicing method.

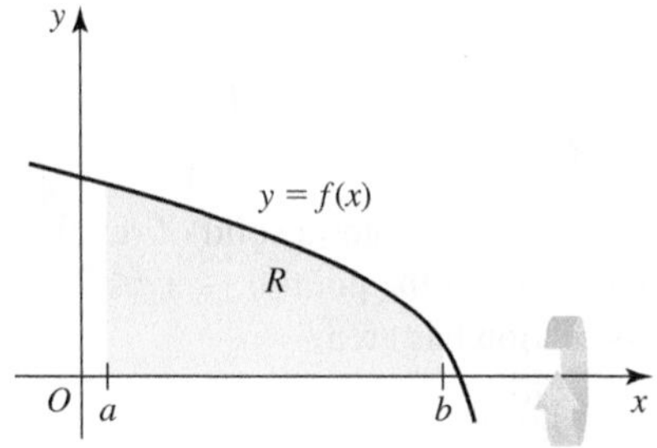

Figure 6.27

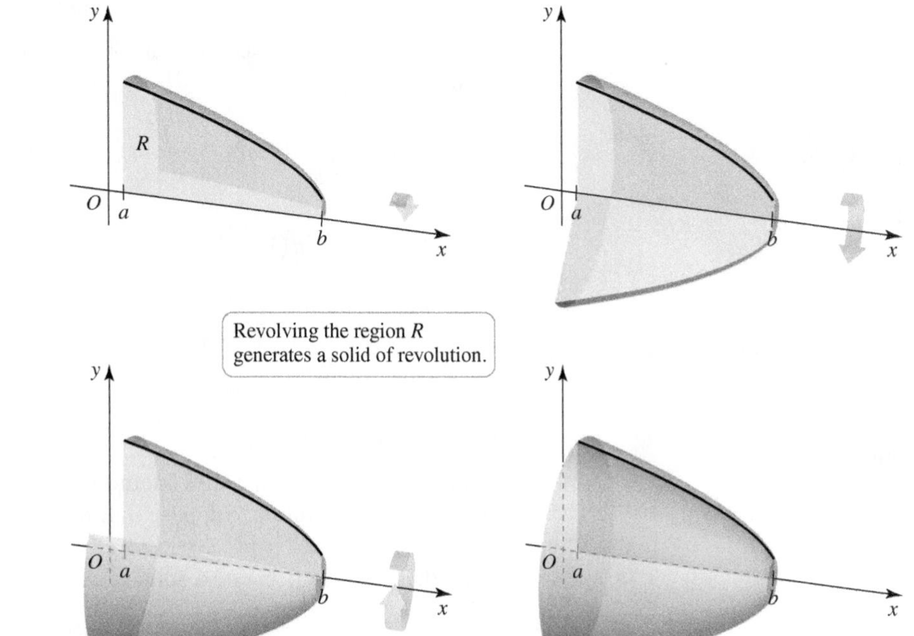

Figure 6.28

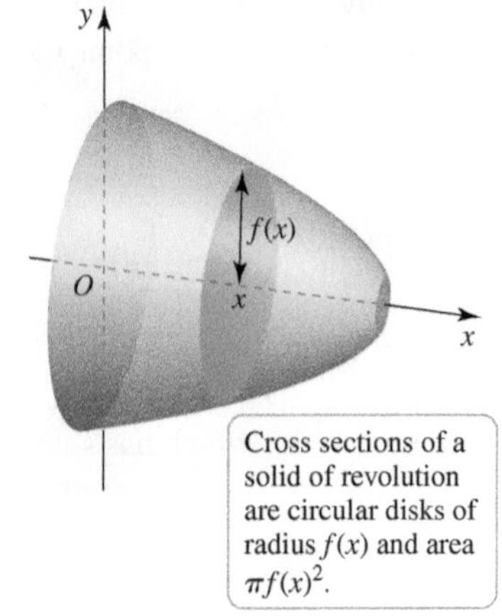

Figure 6.29

QUICK CHECK 3 What solid results when the region R is revolved about the x-axis if (a) R is a square with vertices $(0, 0)$, $(0, 2)$, $(2, 0)$, and $(2, 2)$, and (b) R is a triangle with vertices $(0, 0)$, $(0, 2)$, and $(2, 0)$? ◀

With a solid of revolution, the cross-sectional area function has a special form because all cross sections perpendicular to the x-axis are *circular disks* with radius $f(x)$ (Figure 6.29). Therefore, the cross section at the point x, where $a \le x \le b$, has area

$$A(x) = \pi(\text{radius})^2 = \pi f(x)^2.$$

By the general slicing method, the volume of the solid is

$$V = \int_a^b A(x)\,dx = \int_a^b \pi f(x)^2\,dx.$$

Because each slice through the solid is a circular disk, the resulting method is called the *disk method.*

Disk Method about the x-Axis

Let f be continuous with $f(x) \ge 0$ on the interval $[a, b]$. If the region R bounded by the graph of f, the x-axis, and the lines $x = a$ and $x = b$ is revolved about the x-axis, the volume of the resulting solid of revolution is

$$V = \int_a^b \pi f(x)^2\,dx.$$

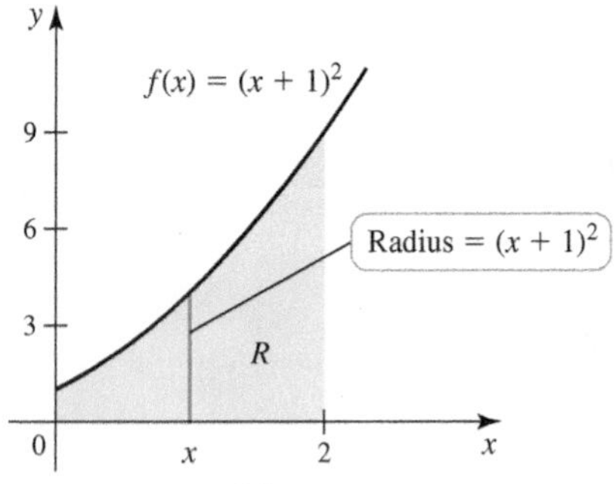

(a)

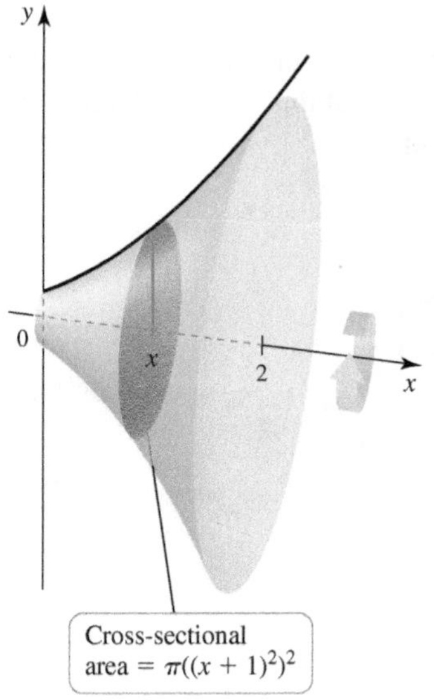

(b)

Figure 6.30

EXAMPLE 3 Disk method at work Let R be the region bounded by the curve $f(x) = (x + 1)^2$, the x-axis, and the lines $x = 0$ and $x = 2$ (Figure 6.30a). Find the volume of the solid of revolution obtained by revolving R about the x-axis.

SOLUTION When the region R is revolved about the x-axis, it generates a solid of revolution (Figure 6.30b). A cross section perpendicular to the x-axis at the point $0 \le x \le 2$ is a circular disk of radius $f(x)$. Therefore, a typical cross section has area

$$A(x) = \pi f(x)^2 = \pi((x + 1)^2)^2.$$

Integrating these cross-sectional areas between $x = 0$ and $x = 2$ gives the volume of the solid:

$$V = \int_0^2 A(x)\,dx = \int_0^2 \pi((x + 1)^2)^2\,dx \qquad \text{Substitute for } A(x).$$

$$= \int_0^2 \pi(x + 1)^4\,dx \qquad \text{Simplify.}$$

$$= \pi \frac{u^5}{5}\bigg|_1^3 = \frac{242\,\pi}{5}. \qquad \text{Let } u = x + 1 \text{ and evaluate.}$$

Related Exercises 17–26 ◀

Washer Method

A slight variation on the disk method enables us to compute the volume of more exotic solids of revolution. Suppose that R is the region bounded by the graphs of f and g between $x = a$ and $x = b$, where $f(x) \ge g(x) \ge 0$ (Figure 6.31). If R is revolved about the x-axis to generate a solid of revolution, the resulting solid generally has a hole through it.

Once again we apply the general slicing method. In this case, a cross section through the solid perpendicular to the x-axis is a circular *washer* with an outer radius of $R = f(x)$

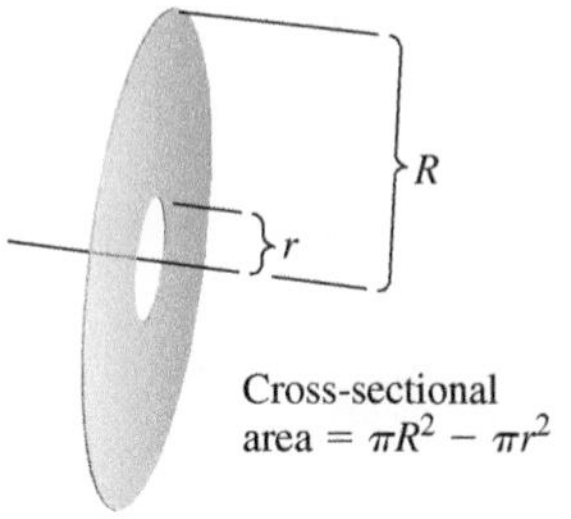

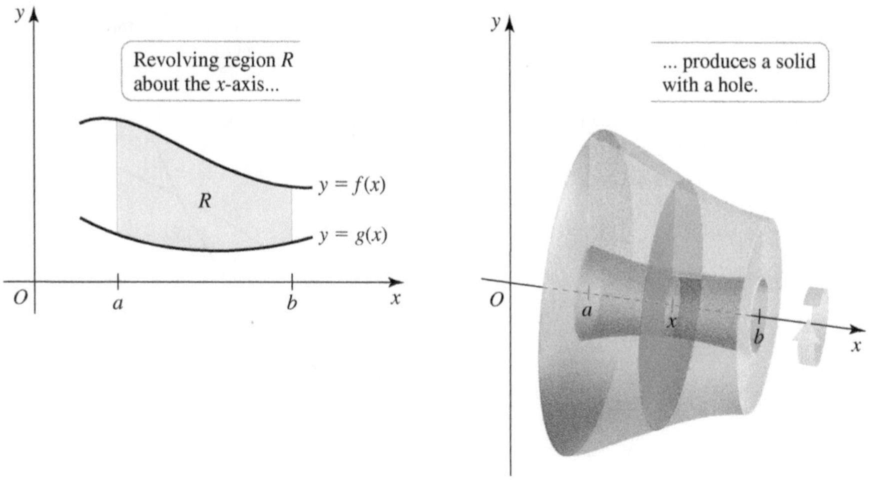

Figure 6.31

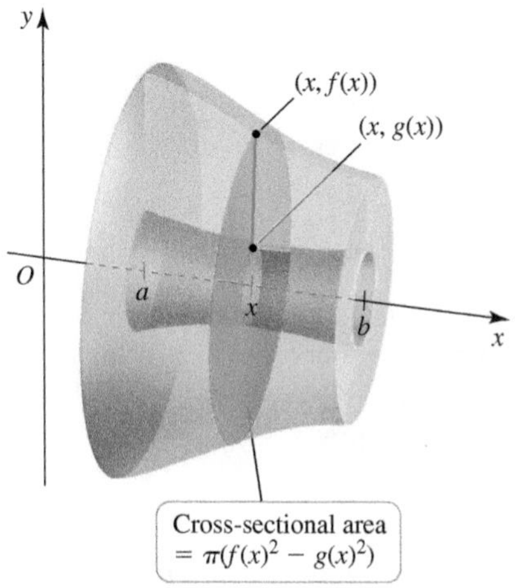

Figure 6.32

and an inner radius of $r = g(x)$, where $a \le x \le b$. The area of the cross section is the area of the entire disk minus the area of the hole, or

$$A(x) = \pi(R^2 - r^2) = \pi(f(x)^2 - g(x)^2)$$

(Figure 6.32). The general slicing method gives the area of the solid.

Washer Method about the *x*-Axis

Let f and g be continuous functions with $f(x) \ge g(x) \ge 0$ on $[a, b]$. Let R be the region bounded by $y = f(x)$, $y = g(x)$, and the lines $x = a$ and $x = b$. When R is revolved about the x-axis, the volume of the resulting solid of revolution is

$$V = \int_a^b \pi(f(x)^2 - g(x)^2)\,dx.$$

QUICK CHECK 4 Show that when $g(x) = 0$ in the washer method, the result is the disk method. ◀

EXAMPLE 4 Volume by the washer method The region R is bounded by the graphs of $f(x) = \sqrt{x}$ and $g(x) = x^2$ between $x = 0$ and $x = 1$. What is the volume of the solid that results when R is revolved about the x-axis?

SOLUTION The region R is bounded by the graphs of f and g with $f(x) \ge g(x)$ on $[0, 1]$, so the washer method is applicable (Figure 6.33). The area of a typical cross section at the point x is

$$A(x) = \pi(f(x)^2 - g(x)^2) = \pi((\sqrt{x})^2 - (x^2)^2) = \pi(x - x^4).$$

Therefore, the volume of the solid is

$$V = \int_0^1 \pi(x - x^4)\,dx \qquad \text{Washer method}$$

$$= \pi\left(\frac{x^2}{2} - \frac{x^5}{5}\right)\Bigg|_0^1 = \frac{3\pi}{10}. \qquad \text{Fundamental Theorem}$$

➤ The washer method is really two applications of the disk method. We compute the volume of the entire solid without the hole (by the disk method) and then subtract the volume of the hole (also computed by the disk method).

➤ Ignoring the factor of π, the integrand in the washer method integral is $f(x)^2 - g(x)^2$, which is not equal to $(f(x) - g(x))^2$.

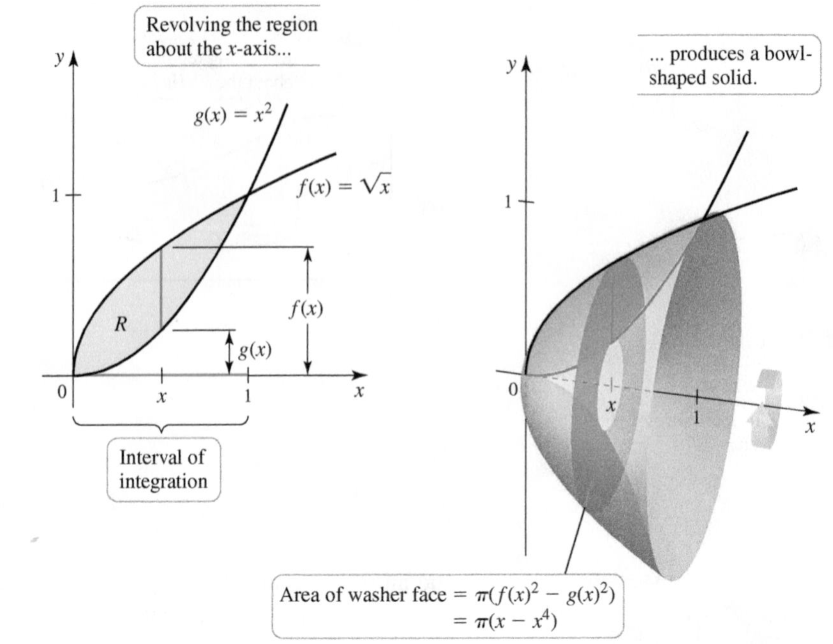

Figure 6.33

Related Exercises 27–34 ◀

QUICK CHECK 5 Suppose the region in Example 4 is revolved about the line $y = -1$ instead of the x-axis. (a) What is the inner radius of a typical washer? (b) What is the outer radius of a typical washer? ◀

Revolving about the y-Axis

Everything you learned about revolving regions about the x-axis applies to revolving regions about the y-axis. Consider a region R bounded by the curve $x = p(y)$ on the right, the curve $x = q(y)$ on the left, and the horizontal lines $y = c$ and $y = d$ (Figure 6.34a).

To find the volume of the solid generated when R is revolved about the y-axis, we use the general slicing method—now with respect to the y-axis (Figure 6.34b). The area of a typical cross section is $A(y) = \pi(p(y)^2 - q(y)^2)$, where $c \le y \le d$. As before, integrating these cross-sectional areas of the solid gives the volume.

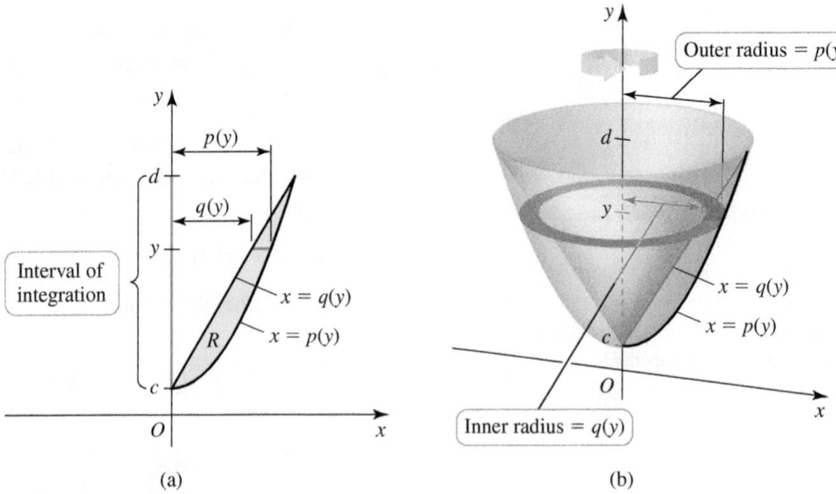

Figure 6.34

➤ The disk/washer method about the y-axis is the disk/washer method about the x-axis with x replaced with y.

Disk and Washer Methods about the y-Axis

Let p and q be continuous functions with $p(y) \geq q(y) \geq 0$ on $[c, d]$. Let R be the region bounded by $x = p(y)$, $x = q(y)$, and the lines $y = c$ and $y = d$. When R is revolved about the y-axis, the volume of the resulting solid of revolution is given by

$$V = \int_c^d \pi(p(y)^2 - q(y)^2)\, dy.$$

If $q(y) = 0$, the disk method results:

$$V = \int_c^d \pi p(y)^2\, dy.$$

EXAMPLE 5 **Which solid has greater volume?** Let R be the region in the first quadrant bounded by the graphs of $x = y^3$ and $x = 4y$. Which is greater, the volume of the solid generated when R is revolved about the x-axis or the y-axis?

SOLUTION Solving $y^3 = 4y$, or equivalently, $y(y^2 - 4) = 0$, we find that the bounding curves of R intersect at the points $(0, 0)$ and $(8, 2)$. When the region R (Figure 6.35a) is revolved about the y-axis, it generates a funnel with a curved inner surface (Figure 6.35b). Washer-shaped cross sections perpendicular to the y-axis extend from $y = 0$ to $y = 2$. The outer radius of the cross section at the point y is determined by the line $x = p(y) = 4y$. The inner radius of the cross section at the point y is determined by the curve $x = q(y) = y^3$. Applying the washer method, the volume of this solid is

$$V = \int_0^2 \pi(p(y)^2 - q(y)^2)\, dy \quad \text{Washer method}$$

$$= \int_0^2 \pi(16y^2 - y^6)\, dy \quad \text{Substitute for } p \text{ and } q.$$

$$= \pi\left(\frac{16}{3}y^3 - \frac{y^7}{7}\right)\Big|_0^2 \quad \text{Fundamental Theorem}$$

$$= \frac{512\pi}{21}. \quad \text{Evaluate.}$$

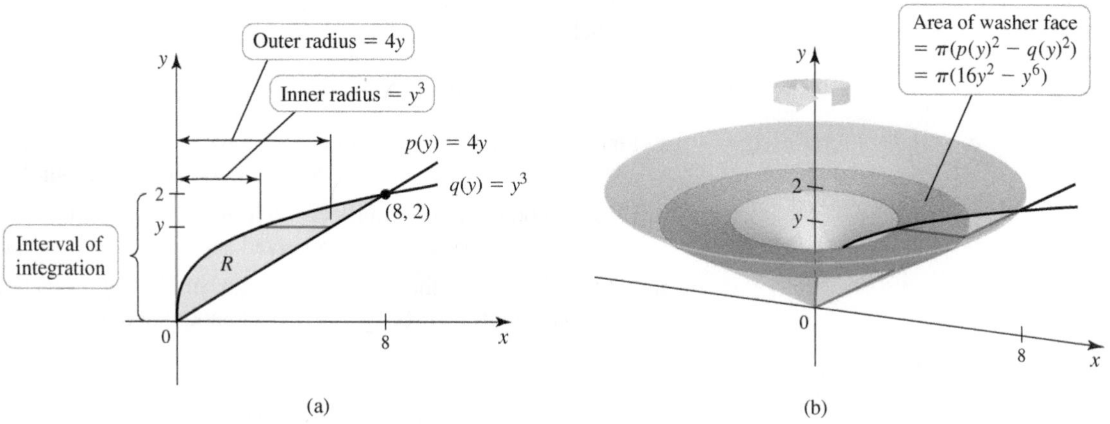

Figure 6.35

When the region R is revolved about the x-axis, it generates a different funnel (Figure 6.36). Vertical slices through the solid between $x = 0$ and $x = 8$ produce washers. The outer radius of the washer at the point x is determined by the curve $x = y^3$, or

$y = f(x) = x^{1/3}$. The inner radius is determined by $x = 4y$, or $y = g(x) = x/4$. The volume of the resulting solid is

$$
\begin{aligned}
V &= \int_0^8 \pi(f(x)^2 - g(x)^2)\,dx && \text{Washer method}\\
&= \int_0^8 \pi\left(x^{2/3} - \frac{x^2}{16}\right)dx && \text{Substitute for } f \text{ and } g.\\
&= \pi\left(\frac{3}{5}x^{5/3} - \frac{x^3}{48}\right)\Bigg|_0^8 && \text{Fundamental Theorem}\\
&= \frac{128\pi}{15}. && \text{Evaluate.}
\end{aligned}
$$

We see that revolving the region about the y-axis produces a solid of greater volume.

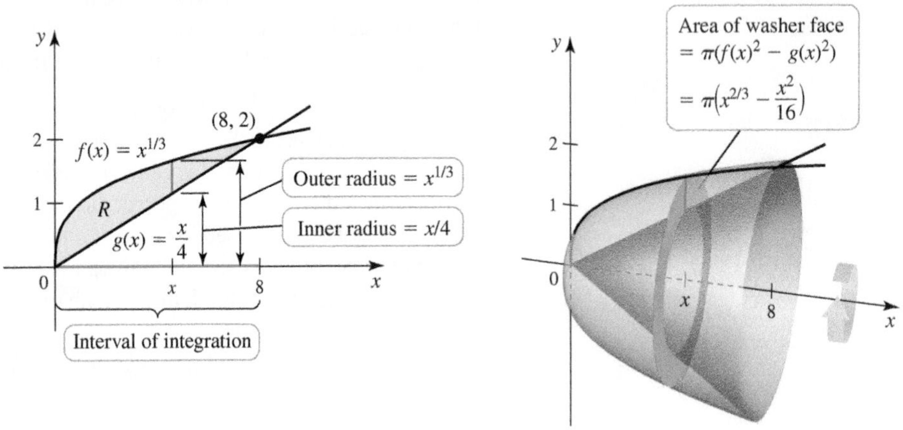

Figure 6.36

Related Exercises 35–44 ◄

QUICK CHECK 6 The region in the first quadrant bounded by $y = x$ and $y = x^3$ is revolved about the y-axis. Give the integral for the volume of the solid that is generated. ◄

The disk and washer methods may be generalized to handle situations in which a region R is revolved about a line parallel to one of the coordinate axes. The next example discusses three such cases.

EXAMPLE 6 Revolving about other lines Let $f(x) = \sqrt{x} + 1$ and $g(x) = x^2 + 1$.

a. Find the volume of the solid generated when the region R_1 bounded by the graph of f and the line $y = 2$ on the interval $[0, 1]$ is revolved about the line $y = 2$.

b. Find the volume of the solid generated when the region R_2 bounded by the graphs of f and g on the interval $[0, 1]$ is revolved about the line $y = -1$.

c. Find the volume of the solid generated when the region R_2 bounded by the graphs of f and g on the interval $[0, 1]$ is revolved about the line $x = 2$.

SOLUTION

a. Figure 6.37a shows the region R_1 and the axis of revolution. Applying the disk method, we see that a disk located at a point x has a radius of $2 - f(x) = 2 - (\sqrt{x} + 1) = 1 - \sqrt{x}$. Therefore, the volume of the solid generated when R_1 is revolved about $y = 2$ is

$$\int_0^1 \pi(1 - \sqrt{x})^2\,dx = \pi\int_0^1 (1 - 2\sqrt{x} + x)\,dx = \frac{\pi}{6}.$$

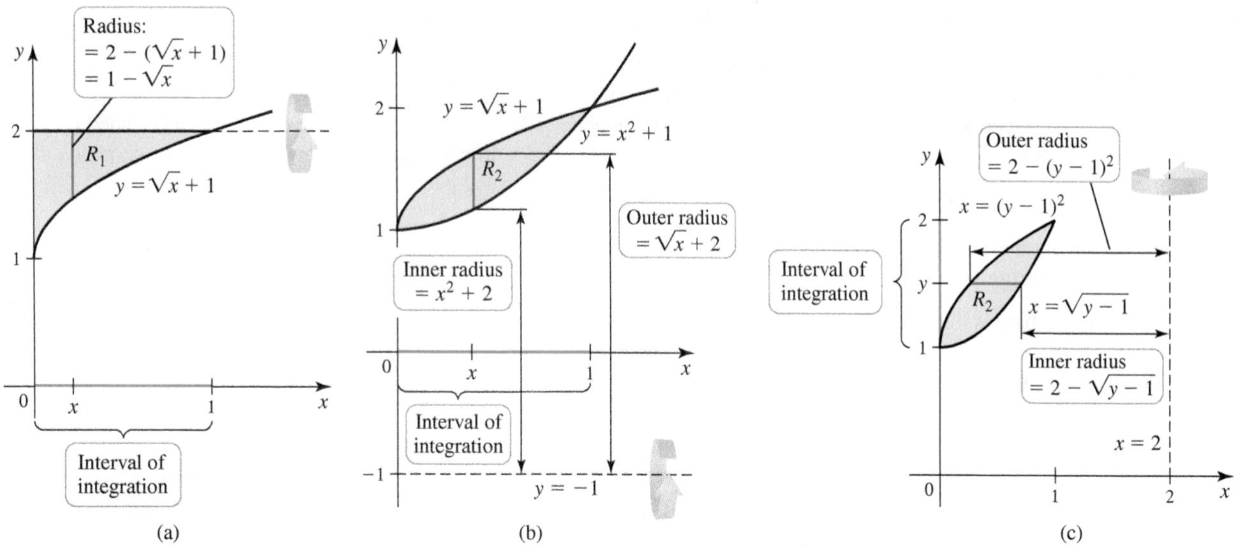

Figure 6.37

b. When the graph of f is revolved about $y = -1$, it sweeps out a solid of revolution whose radius at a point x is $f(x) + 1 = \sqrt{x} + 2$. Similarly, when the graph of g is revolved about $y = -1$, it sweeps out a solid of revolution whose radius at a point x is $g(x) + 1 = x^2 + 2$ (Figure 6.37b). Using the washer method, the volume of the solid generated when R_2 is revolved about $y = -1$ is

$$\int_0^1 \pi((\sqrt{x} + 2)^2 - (x^2 + 2)^2)\,dx$$

$$= \pi \int_0^1 (-x^4 - 4x^2 + x + 4\sqrt{x})\,dx$$

$$= \frac{49\pi}{30}.$$

c. When the region R_2 is revolved about the line $x = 2$, we use the washer method and integrate in the y-direction. First note that the graph of f is described by $y = \sqrt{x} + 1$, or equivalently, $x = (y - 1)^2$, for $y \geq 1$. Also, the graph of g is described by $y = x^2 + 1$, or equivalently, $x = \sqrt{y - 1}$ for $y \geq 1$ (Figure 6.37c). When the graph of f is revolved about the line $x = 2$, the radius of a typical disk at a point y is $2 - (y - 1)^2$. Similarly, when the graph of g is revolved about $x = 2$, the radius of a typical disk at a point y is $2 - \sqrt{y - 1}$. Finally, observe that the extent of the region R_2 in the y-direction is the interval $1 \leq y \leq 2$.

Applying the washer method, simplifying the integrand, and integrating powers of y, the volume of the solid of revolution is

$$\int_1^2 \pi\big((2 - (y - 1)^2)^2 - (2 - \sqrt{y - 1})^2\big)\,dy = \frac{31\pi}{30}.$$

Related Exercises 45–52 ◀

SECTION 6.3 EXERCISES

Review Questions

1. Suppose a cut is made through a solid object perpendicular to the x-axis at a particular point x. Explain the meaning of $A(x)$.

2. A solid has a circular base and cross sections perpendicular to the base are squares. What method should be used to find the volume of the solid?

3. The region bounded by the curves $y = 2x$ and $y = x^2$ is revolved about the x-axis. Give an integral for the volume of the solid that is generated.

4. The region bounded by the curves $y = 2x$ and $y = x^2$ is revolved about the y-axis. Give an integral for the volume of the solid that is generated.

5. Why is the disk method a special case of the general slicing method?

6. The region R bounded by the graph of $y = f(x) \geq 0$ and the x-axis on $[a, b]$ is revolved about the line $y = -2$ to form a solid of revolution whose cross sections are washers. What are the inner and outer radii of the washer at a point x in $[a, b]$?

Basic Skills

7–16. General slicing method *Use the general slicing method to find the volume of the following solids.*

7. The solid whose base is the region bounded by the curves $y = x^2$ and $y = 2 - x^2$, and whose cross sections through the solid perpendicular to the x-axis are squares

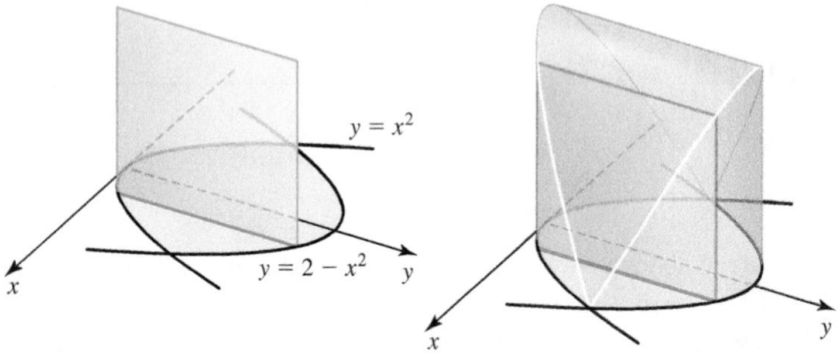

8. The solid whose base is the region bounded by the semicircle $y = \sqrt{1 - x^2}$ and the x-axis, and whose cross sections through the solid perpendicular to the x-axis are squares

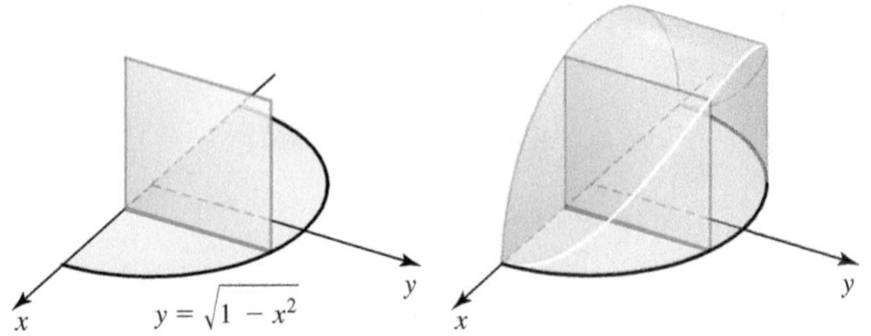

9. The solid whose base is the region bounded by the curve $y = \sqrt{\cos x}$ and the x-axis on $[-\pi/2, \pi/2]$, and whose cross sections through the solid perpendicular to the x-axis are isosceles right triangles with a horizontal leg in the xy-plane and a vertical leg above the x-axis

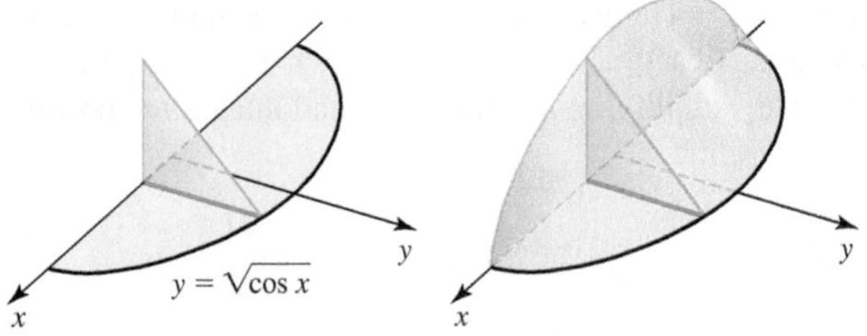

10. The solid with a circular base of radius 5 whose cross sections perpendicular to the base and parallel to the x-axis are equilateral triangles

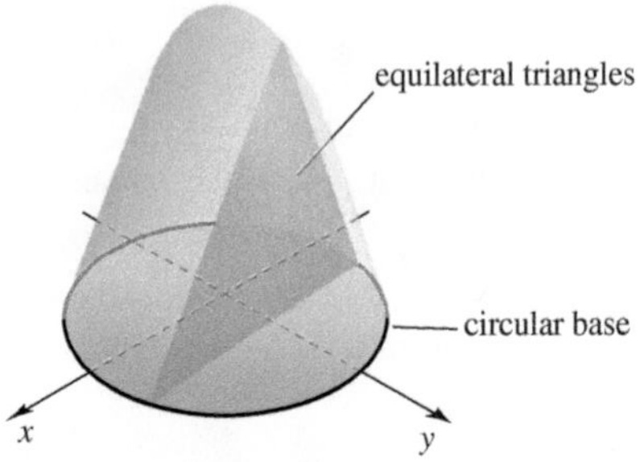

11. The solid with a semicircular base of radius 5 whose cross sections perpendicular to the base and parallel to the diameter are squares

12. The solid whose base is the region bounded by $y = x^2$ and the line $y = 1$, and whose cross sections perpendicular to the base and parallel to the x-axis are squares

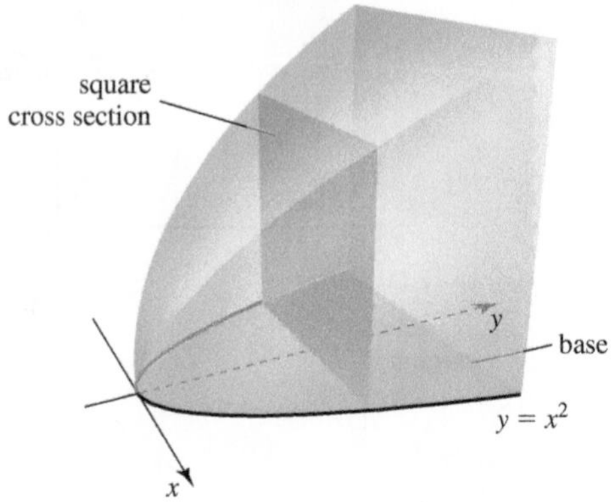

13. The solid whose base is the triangle with vertices $(0, 0)$, $(2, 0)$, and $(0, 2)$, and whose cross sections perpendicular to the base and parallel to the y-axis are semicircles

14. The pyramid with a square base 4 m on a side and a height of 2 m (Use calculus.)

15. The tetrahedron (pyramid with four triangular faces), all of whose edges have length 4

16. A circular cylinder of radius r and height h whose axis is at an angle of $\pi/4$ to the base

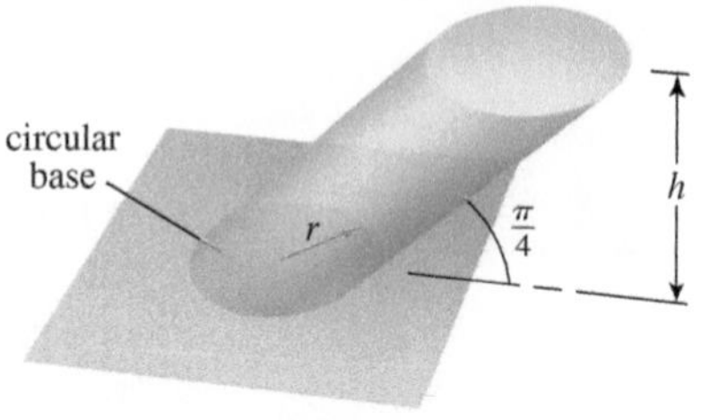

17–26. Disk method *Let R be the region bounded by the following curves. Use the disk method to find the volume of the solid generated when R is revolved about the x-axis.*

17. $y = 2x$, $y = 0$, $x = 3$ (Verify that your answer agrees with the volume formula for a cone.)

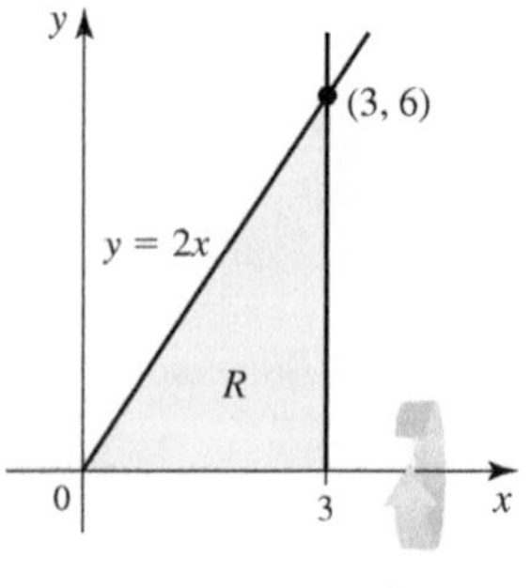

18. $y = 2 - 2x, y = 0, x = 0$ (Verify that your answer agrees with the volume formula for a cone.)

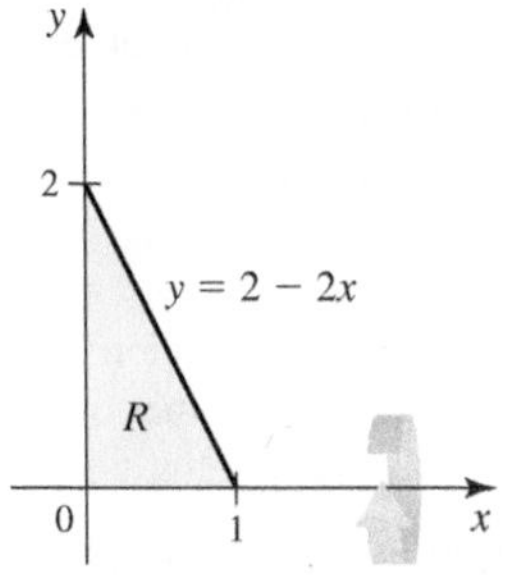

19. $y = e^{-x}, y = 0, x = 0, x = \ln 4$

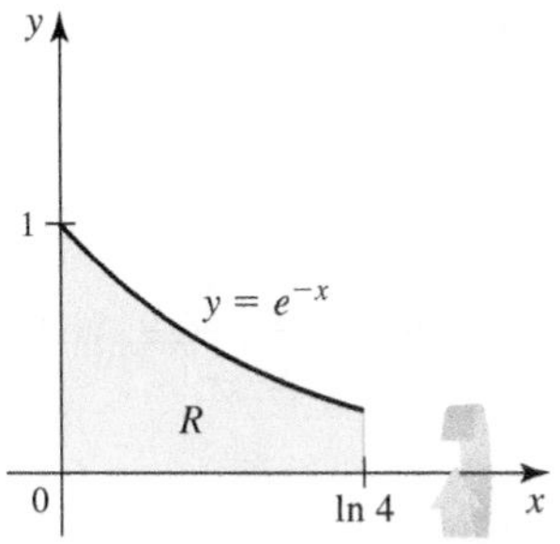

20. $y = \cos x$ on $[0, \pi/2], y = 0, x = 0$ (Recall that $\cos^2 x = \frac{1}{2}(1 + \cos 2x)$.)

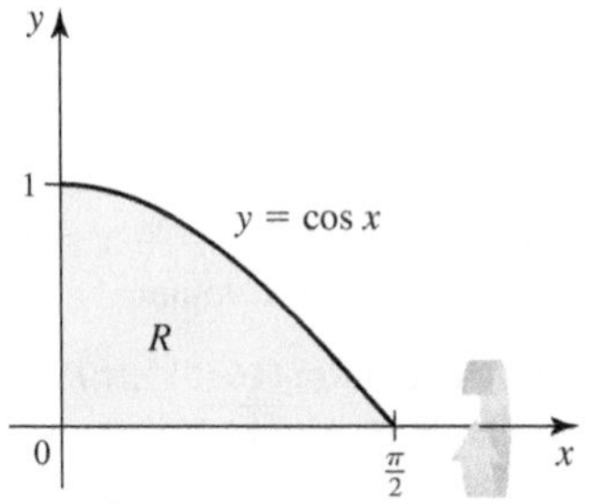

21. $y = \sin x$ on $[0, \pi], y = 0$ (Recall that $\sin^2 x = \frac{1}{2}(1 - \cos 2x)$.)

22. $y = \sqrt{25 - x^2}, y = 0$ (Verify that your answer agrees with the volume formula for a sphere.)

23. $y = \dfrac{1}{\sqrt[4]{1 - x^2}}, y = 0, x = 0$, and $x = \frac{1}{2}$

24. $y = \sec x, y = 0, x = 0$, and $x = \frac{\pi}{4}$

25. $y = \dfrac{1}{\sqrt{1 + x^2}}, y = 0, x = -1$, and $x = 1$

26. $y = \dfrac{1}{\sqrt[4]{1 - x^2}}, y = 0, x = -\frac{1}{2}$, and $x = \frac{1}{2}$

27–34. Washer method *Let R be the region bounded by the following curves. Use the washer method to find the volume of the solid generated when R is revolved about the x-axis.*

27. $y = x, y = 2\sqrt{x}$

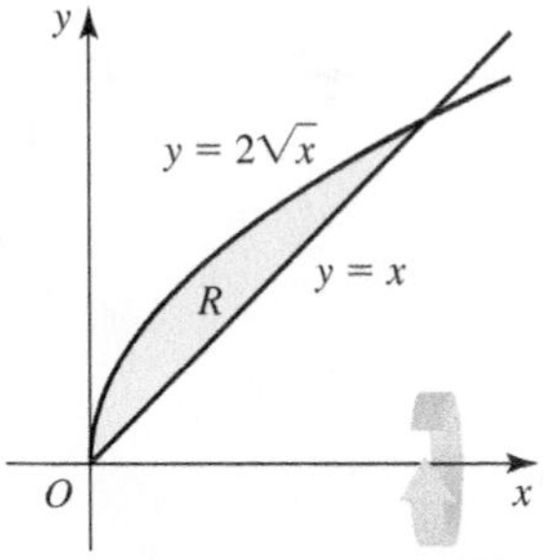

28. $y = x, y = \sqrt[4]{x}$

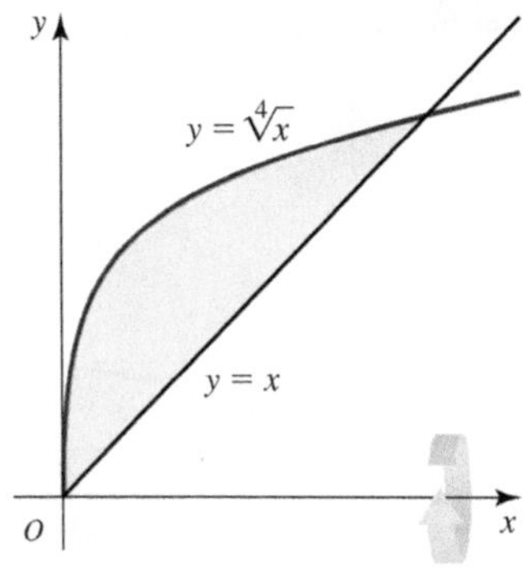

29. $y = e^{x/2}, y = e^{-x/2}, x = \ln 2, x = \ln 3$

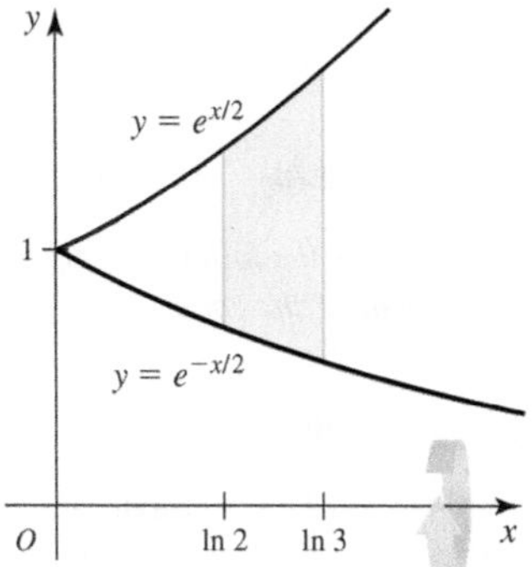

30. $y = x, y = x + 2, x = 0, x = 4$

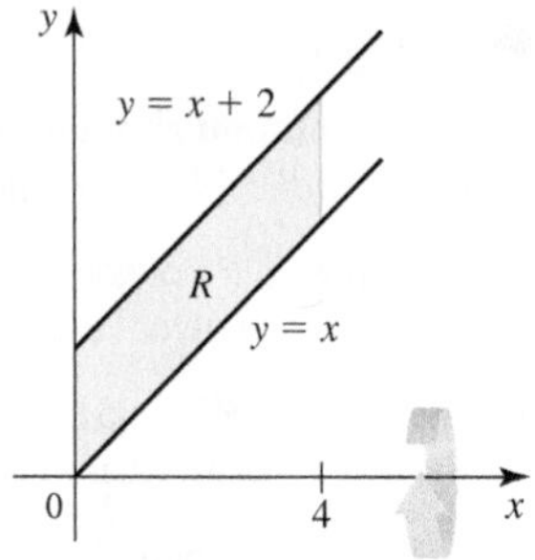

31. $y = x + 3, y = x^2 + 1$

32. $y = \sqrt{\sin x}, y = 1, x = 0$

33. $y = \sin x, y = \sqrt{\sin x}$, for $0 \le x \le \pi/2$

34. $y = |x|, y = 2 - x^2$

35–40. Disks / washers about the y-axis *Let R be the region bounded by the following curves. Use the disk or washer method to find the volume of the solid generated when R is revolved about the y-axis.*

35. $y = x, y = 2x, y = 6$

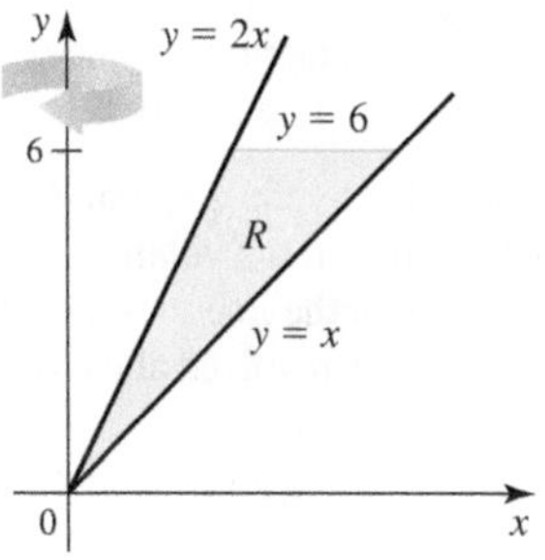

36. $y = 0, y = \ln x, y = 2, x = 0$

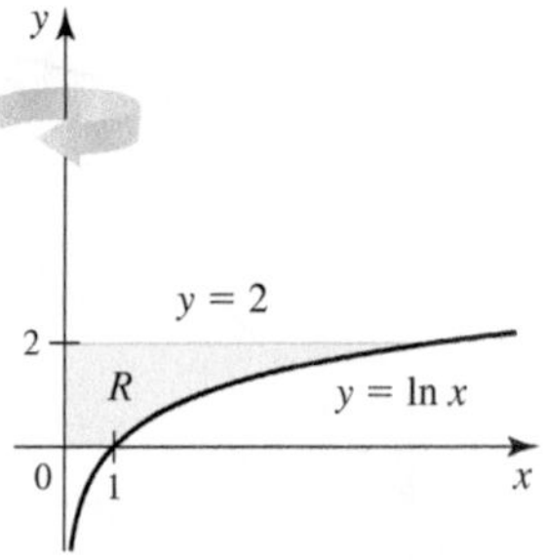

37. $y = x^3, y = 0, x = 2$

38. $y = \sqrt{x}, y = 0, x = 4$

39. $x = \sqrt{4 - y^2}, x = 0$

40. $y = \sin^{-1} x, x = 0, y = \pi/4$

41–44. Which is greater? *For the following regions R, determine which is greater—the volume of the solid generated when R is revolved about the x-axis or about the y-axis.*

41. R is bounded by $y = 2x$, the x-axis, and $x = 5$.

42. R is bounded by $y = 4 - 2x$, the x-axis, and the y-axis.

43. R is bounded by $y = 1 - x^3$, the x-axis, and the y-axis.

44. R is bounded by $y = x^2$ and $y = \sqrt{8x}$.

45–52. Revolution about other axes *Find the volume of the solid generated in the following situations.*

45. The region R bounded by the graphs of $x = 0, y = \sqrt{x}$, and $y = 1$ is revolved around the line $y = 1$.

46. The region R bounded by the graphs of $x = 0, y = \sqrt{x}$, and $y = 2$ is revolved around the line $x = 4$.

47. The region R bounded by the graph of $y = 2 \sin x$ and the x-axis on $[0, \pi]$ is revolved about the line $y = -2$.

48. The region R bounded by the graph of $y = \ln x$ and the y-axis on the interval $0 \le y \le 1$ is revolved about the line $x = -1$.

49. The region R bounded by the graphs of $y = \sin x$ and $y = 1 - \sin x$ on $\left[\frac{\pi}{6}, \frac{5\pi}{6}\right]$ is revolved about the line $y = -1$.

50. The region R in the first quadrant bounded by the graphs of $y = x$ and $y = 1 + \frac{x}{2}$ is revolved about the line $y = 3$.

51. The region R in the first quadrant bounded by the graphs of $y = 2 - x$ and $y = 2 - 2x$ is revolved about the line $x = 3$.

52. The region R is bounded by the graph of $f(x) = 2x(2 - x)$ and the x-axis. Which is greater, the volume of the solid generated when R is revolved about the line $y = 2$ or the volume of the solid generated when R is revolved about the line $y = 0$? Use integration to justify your answer.

Further Explorations

53. Explain why or why not Determine whether the following statements are true and give an explanation or counterexample.

a. A pyramid is a solid of revolution.

b. The volume of a hemisphere can be computed using the disk method.

c. Let R_1 be the region bounded by $y = \cos x$ and the x-axis on $[-\pi/2, \pi/2]$. Let R_2 be the region bounded by $y = \sin x$ and the x-axis on $[0, \pi]$. The volumes of the solids generated when R_1 and R_2 are revolved about the x-axis are equal.

54–60. Solids of revolution *Find the volume of the solid of revolution. Sketch the region in question.*

54. The region bounded by $y = (\ln x)/\sqrt{x}, y = 0$, and $x = 2$ revolved about the x-axis

55. The region bounded by $y = 1/\sqrt{x}, y = 0, x = 2$, and $x = 6$ revolved about the x-axis

56. The region bounded by $y = \dfrac{1}{\sqrt{x^2 + 1}}$ and $y = \dfrac{1}{\sqrt{2}}$ revolved about the x-axis

57. The region bounded by $y = e^x, y = 0, x = 0$, and $x = 2$ revolved about the x-axis

58. The region bounded by $y = e^{-x}, y = e^x, x = 0$, and $x = \ln 4$ revolved about the x-axis

59. The region bounded by $y = \ln x, y = \ln x^2$, and $y = \ln 8$ revolved about the y-axis

60. The region bounded by $y = e^{-x}, y = 0, x = 0$, and $x = p > 0$ revolved about the x-axis (Is the volume bounded as $p \to \infty$?)

61. Fermat's volume calculation (1636) Let R be the region bounded by the curve $y = \sqrt{x + a}$ (with $a > 0$), the y-axis, and the x-axis. Let S be the solid generated by rotating R about the y-axis. Let T be the inscribed cone that has the same circular base as S and height $\sqrt{a}$. Show that volume(S)/volume$(T) = \frac{8}{5}$.

62. Solid from a piecewise function Let

$$f(x) = \begin{cases} x & \text{if } 0 \le x \le 2 \\ 2x - 2 & \text{if } 2 < x \le 5 \\ -2x + 18 & \text{if } 5 < x \le 6. \end{cases}$$

Find the volume of the solid formed when the region bounded by the graph of f, the x-axis, and the line $x = 6$ is revolved about the x-axis.

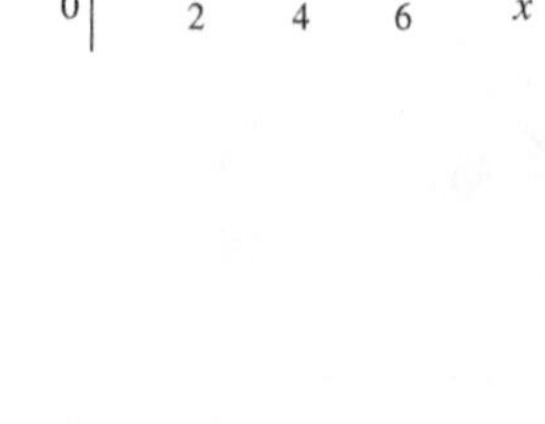

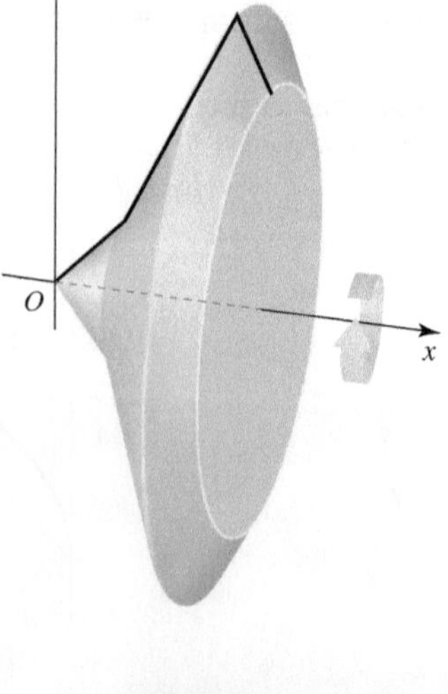

63. Solids from integrals Sketch a solid of revolution whose volume by the disk method is given by the following integrals. Indicate the function that generates the solid. Solutions are not unique.

a. $\int_0^{\pi} \pi \sin^2 x\, dx$

b. $\int_0^{2} \pi(x^2 + 2x + 1)\, dx$

Applications

64. Volume of a wooden object A solid wooden object turned on a lathe has a length of 50 cm and diameters (measured in cm) shown in the figure. (A lathe is a tool that spins and cuts a block of wood so that it has circular cross sections.) Use left Riemann sums with uniformly spaced grid points to estimate the volume of the object.

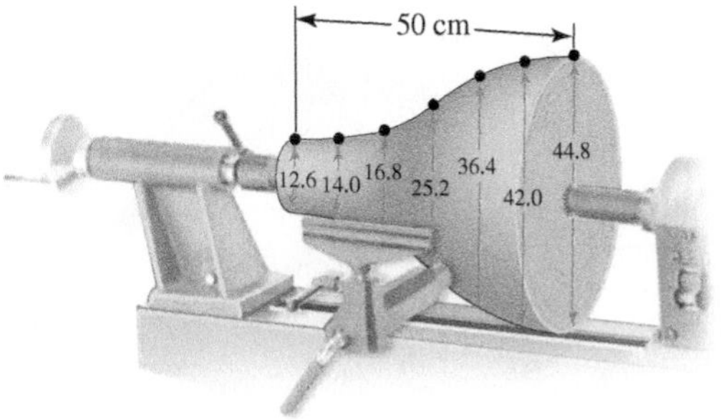

65. Cylinder, cone, hemisphere A right circular cylinder with height R and radius R has a volume of $V_C = \pi R^3$ (height = radius).

a. Find the volume of the cone that is inscribed in the cylinder with the same base as the cylinder and height R. Express the volume in terms of V_C.

b. Find the volume of the hemisphere that is inscribed in the cylinder with the same base as the cylinder. Express the volume in terms of V_C.

66. Water in a bowl A hemispherical bowl of radius 8 inches is filled to a depth of h inches, where $0 \le h \le 8$. Find the volume of water in the bowl as a function of h. (Check the special cases $h = 0$ and $h = 8$.)

67. A torus (doughnut) Find the volume of the torus formed when the circle of radius 2 centered at $(3, 0)$ is revolved about the y-axis. Use geometry to evaluate the integral.

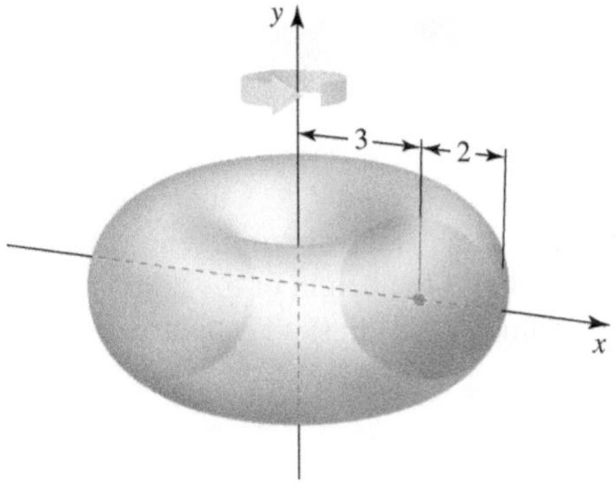

68. Which is greater? Let R be the region bounded by $y = x^2$ and $y = \sqrt{x}$. Use integration to determine which is greater, the volume of the solid generated when R is revolved about the x-axis or about the line $y = 1$.

Additional Exercises

69. Cavalieri's principle *Cavalieri's principle* states that if two solids of equal altitudes have the same cross-sectional areas at every height, then they have equal volumes (see figure).

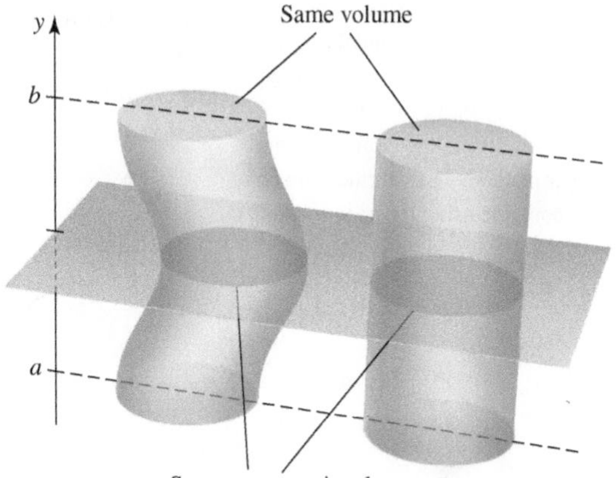

a. Use the theory of this section to justify Cavalieri's principle.

b. Find the radius of a circular cylinder of height 10 m that has the same volume as a box whose dimensions in meters are $2 \times 2 \times 10$.

70. Limiting volume Consider the region R in the first quadrant bounded by $y = x^{1/n}$ and $y = x^n$, where $n > 1$ is a positive number.

a. Find the volume $V(n)$ of the solid generated when R is revolved about the x-axis. Express your answer in terms of n.

b. Evaluate $\lim_{n\to\infty} V(n)$. Interpret this limit geometrically.

QUICK CHECK ANSWERS

1. The average value of A on $[a, b]$ is $\overline{A} = \dfrac{1}{b-a}\displaystyle\int_a^b A(x)\, dx.$ Therefore, $V = (b-a)\overline{A}$. **2.** $A(x) = (2 - 2x^2)^2$ **3. (a)** A cylinder with height 2 and radius 2; **(b)** a cone with height 2 and base radius 2 **4.** When $g(x) = 0$, the washer method $V = \int_a^b \pi(f(x)^2 - g(x)^2)\, dx$ reduces to the disk method $V = \int_a^b \pi(f(x)^2)\, dx$. **5. (a)** Inner radius $= x^2 + 1$ **(b)** outer radius $= \sqrt{x} + 1$; **6.** $\int_0^1 \pi(y^{2/3} - y^2)\, dy$ ◄

6.4 Volume by Shells

You can solve many challenging volume problems using the disk/washer method. There are, however, some volume problems that are difficult to solve with this method. For this reason, we extend our discussion of volume problems to the *shell method*, which—like the disk/washer method—is used to compute the volume of solids of revolution.

➤ Why another method? Suppose R is the region in the first quadrant bounded by the graph of $y = x^2 - x^3$ and the x-axis (Figure 6.38). When R is revolved about the y-axis, the resulting solid has a volume that is difficult to compute using the washer method. The volume is much easier to compute using the shell method.

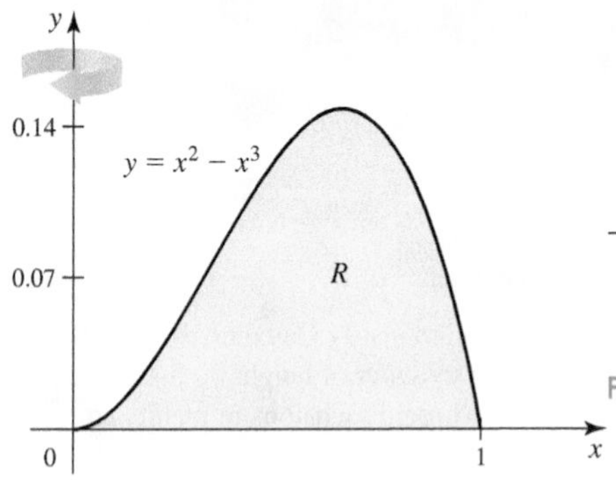

Figure 6.38

Cylindrical Shells

Let R be a region bounded by the graph of f, the x-axis, and the lines $x = a$ and $x = b$, where $0 \le a < b$ and $f(x) \ge 0$ on $[a, b]$. When R is revolved about the y-axis, a solid is generated (Figure 6.39) whose volume is computed with the slice-and-sum strategy.

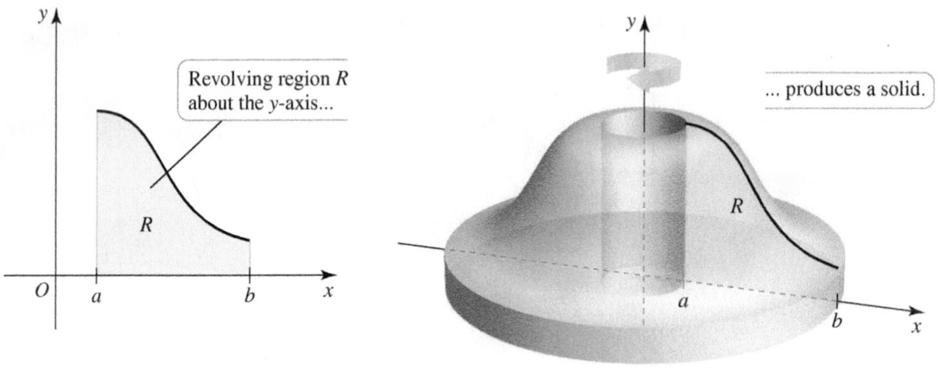

Figure 6.39

We divide $[a, b]$ into n subintervals of length $\Delta x = (b - a)/n$ and identify an arbitrary point x_k^* on the kth subinterval, for $k = 1, \dots, n$. Now observe the rectangle built on the kth subinterval with a height of $f(x_k^*)$ and a width Δx (Figure 6.40). As it revolves about the y-axis, this rectangle sweeps out a thin *cylindrical shell.*

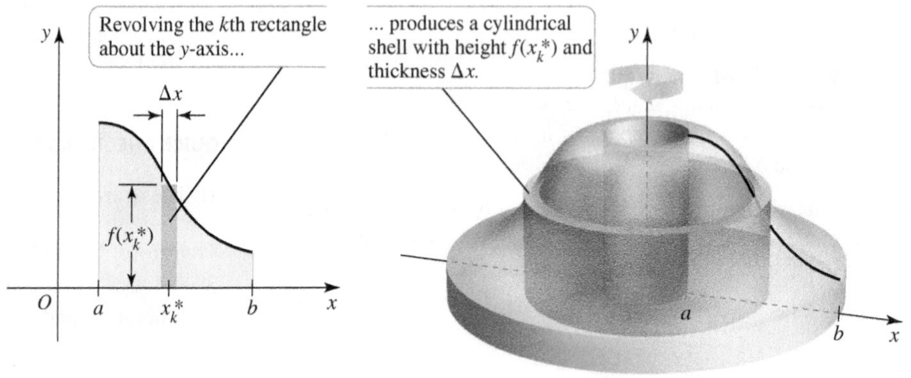

Figure 6.40

When the kth cylindrical shell is unwrapped (Figure 6.41), it approximates a thin rectangular slab. The approximate length of the slab is the circumference of a circle with radius x_k^*, which is $2\pi x_k^*$. The height of the slab is the height of the original rectangle $f(x_k^*)$ and its thickness is Δx; therefore, the volume of the kth shell is approximately

$$\underbrace{2\pi x_k^*}_{\text{length}} \cdot \underbrace{f(x_k^*)}_{\text{height}} \cdot \underbrace{\Delta x}_{\text{thickness}} = 2\pi x_k^* f(x_k^*)\,\Delta x.$$

Summing the volumes of the n cylindrical shells gives an approximation to the volume of the entire solid:

$$V \approx \sum_{k=1}^{n} 2\pi x_k^* f(x_k^*)\,\Delta x.$$

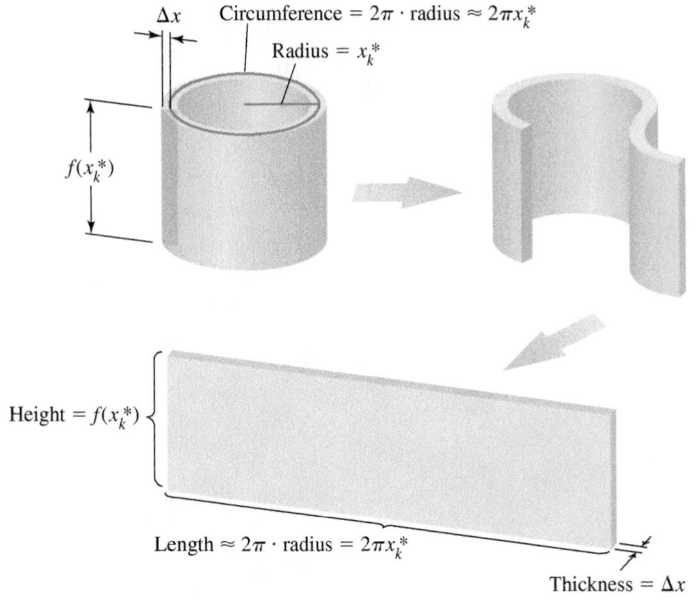

Figure 6.41

As n increases and as Δx approaches 0 (Figure 6.42), we obtain the exact volume of the solid as a definite integral:

$$V = \lim_{n\to\infty} \sum_{k=1}^{n} \underbrace{2\pi x_k^*}_{\text{shell circumference}} \overbrace{f(x_k^*)}^{\text{shell height}} \underbrace{\Delta x}_{\text{shell thickness}} = \int_a^b 2\pi x f(x)\,dx.$$

➤ Rather than memorizing, think of the meaning of the factors in this formula: $f(x)$ is the height of a single cylindrical shell, $2\pi x$ is the circumference of the shell, and dx corresponds to the thickness of a shell. Therefore, $2\pi x f(x)\,dx$ represents the volume of a single shell, and we sum the volumes from $x = a$ to $x = b$. Notice that the integrand for the shell method is the function $A(x)$ that gives the surface area of the shell of radius x, for $a \le x \le b$.

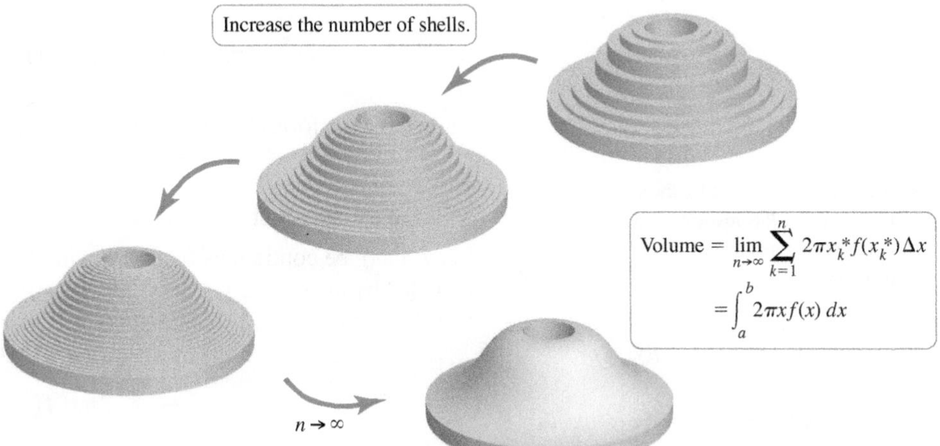

Figure 6.42

Before doing examples, we generalize this method as we did for the disk method. Suppose that the region R is bounded by two curves, $y = f(x)$ and $y = g(x)$, where $f(x) \ge g(x)$ on $[a, b]$ (Figure 6.43). What is the volume of the solid generated when R is revolved about the y-axis?

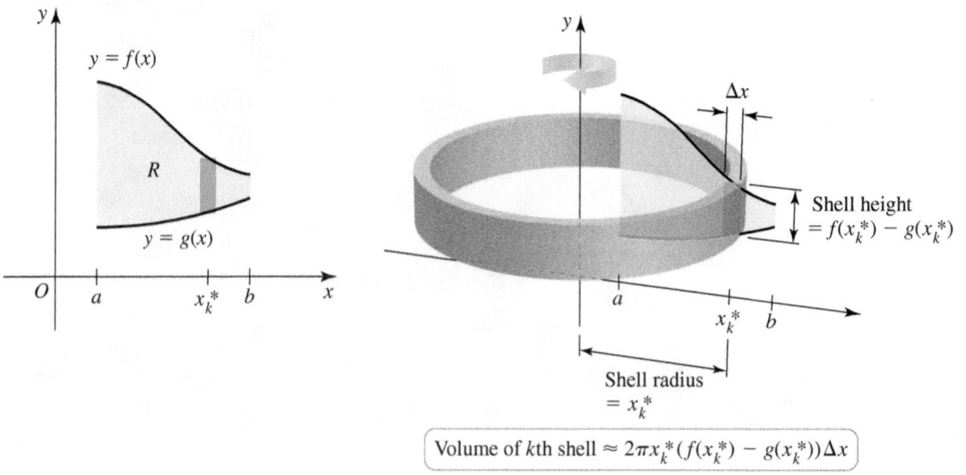

Figure 6.43

The situation is similar to the case we just considered. A typical rectangle in R sweeps out a cylindrical shell, but now the height of the kth shell is $f(x_k^*) - g(x_k^*)$, for $k = 1, \ldots, n$. As before, we take the radius of the kth shell to be x_k^*, which means the volume of the kth shell is approximated by $2\pi x_k^*(f(x_k^*) - g(x_k^*))\Delta x$ (Figure 6.43). Summing the volumes of all the shells gives an approximation to the volume of the entire solid:

$$V \approx \sum_{k=1}^{n} \underbrace{2\pi x_k^*}_{\text{shell circumference}} \underbrace{(f(x_k^*) - g(x_k^*))}_{\text{shell height}}\Delta x.$$

Taking the limit as $n \to \infty$ (which implies that $\Delta x \to 0$), the exact volume is the definite integral

$$V = \lim_{n\to\infty} \sum_{k=1}^{n} 2\pi x_k^*(f(x_k^*) - g(x_k^*))\Delta x = \int_a^b 2\pi x(f(x) - g(x))\,dx.$$

We now have the formula for the shell method.

➤ An analogous formula for the shell method when R is revolved about the x-axis is obtained by reversing the roles of x and y:

$$V = \int_c^d 2\pi y(p(y) - q(y))\,dy.$$

We assume R is bounded by the curves $x = p(y)$ and $x = q(y)$, where $p(y) \ge q(y)$ on $[c, d]$.

Volume by the Shell Method

Let f and g be continuous functions with $f(x) \ge g(x)$ on $[a, b]$. If R is the region bounded by the curves $y = f(x)$ and $y = g(x)$ between the lines $x = a$ and $x = b$, the volume of the solid generated when R is revolved about the y-axis is

$$V = \int_a^b 2\pi x(f(x) - g(x))\,dx.$$

EXAMPLE 1 **A sine bowl** Let R be the region bounded by the graph of $f(x) = \sin x^2$, the x-axis, and the vertical line $x = \sqrt{\pi/2}$ (Figure 6.44). Find the volume of the solid generated when R is revolved about the y-axis.

SOLUTION Revolving R about the y-axis produces a bowl-shaped region (Figure 6.45). The radius of a typical cylindrical shell is x and its height is $f(x) = \sin x^2$. Therefore, the volume by the shell method is

$$V = \int_a^b \underbrace{2\pi x}_{\text{shell circumference}} \underbrace{f(x)}_{\text{shell height}}\,dx = \int_0^{\sqrt{\pi/2}} 2\pi x \sin x^2\,dx.$$

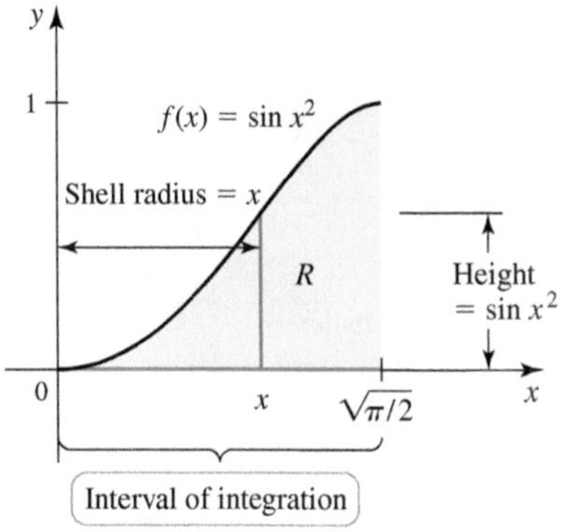

Figure 6.44

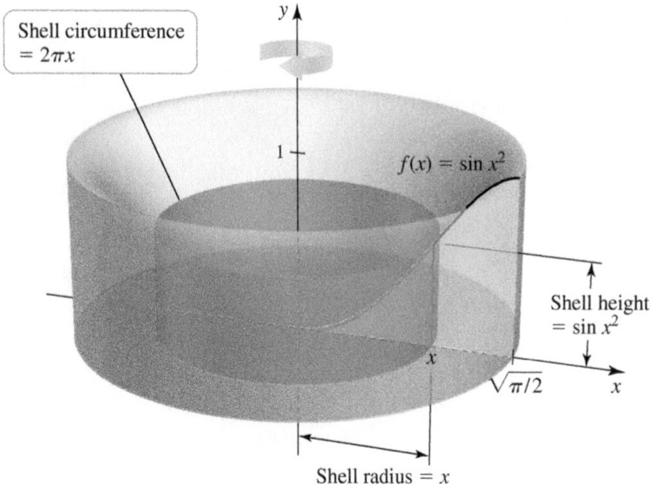

Figure 6.45

➤ When computing volumes using the shell method, it is best to sketch the region R in the xy-plane and draw a slice through the region that generates a typical shell.

Now we make the change of variables $u = x^2$, which means that $du = 2x\,dx$. The lower limit $x = 0$ becomes $u = 0$ and the upper limit $x = \sqrt{\pi/2}$ becomes $u = \pi/2$. The volume of the solid is

$$\begin{aligned} V &= \int_0^{\sqrt{\pi/2}} 2\pi x \sin x^2\, dx = \pi \int_0^{\pi/2} \sin u\, du && u = x^2,\ du = 2x\,dx \\ &= \pi(-\cos u)\Big|_0^{\pi/2} && \text{Fundamental Theorem} \\ &= \pi(0 - (-1)) = \pi. && \text{Simplify.} \end{aligned}$$

Related Exercises 5–14 ◄

QUICK CHECK 1 The triangle bounded by the x-axis, the line $y = 2x$, and the line $x = 1$ is revolved about the y-axis. Give an integral that equals the volume of the resulting solid using the shell method. ◄

EXAMPLE 2 Shells about the x-axis Let R be the region in the first quadrant bounded by the graph of $y = \sqrt{x - 2}$ and the line $y = 2$. Find the volume of the solid generated when R is revolved about the x-axis.

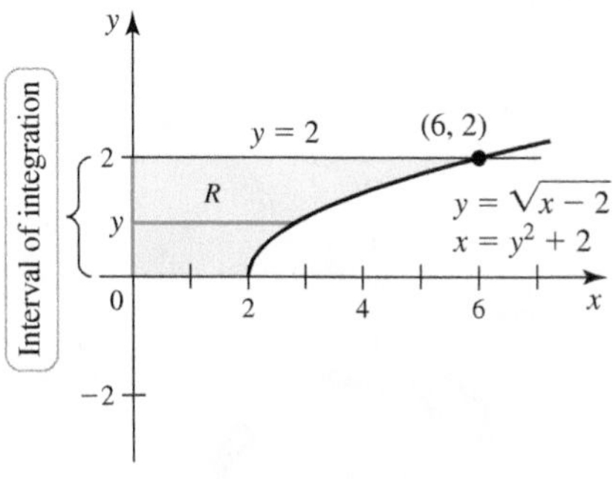

Figure 6.46

SOLUTION The revolution is about the x-axis, so the integration in the shell method is with respect to y. A typical shell runs parallel to the x-axis and has radius y, where $0 \le y \le 2$; the shells extend from the y-axis to the curve $y = \sqrt{x - 2}$ (Figure 6.46). Solving $y = \sqrt{x - 2}$ for x, we have $x = y^2 + 2$, which is the height of the shell at the point y (Figure 6.47). Integrating with respect to y, the volume of the solid is

$$V = \int_0^2 \underbrace{2\pi y}_{\substack{\text{shell} \\ \text{circumference}}} \underbrace{(y^2 + 2)}_{\substack{\text{shell} \\ \text{height}}} dy = 2\pi \int_0^2 (y^3 + 2y)\, dy = 16\pi.$$

➤ In Example 2, we could use the disk/washer method to compute the volume, but notice that this approach requires splitting the region into two subregions. A better approach is to use the shell method and integrate along the y-axis.

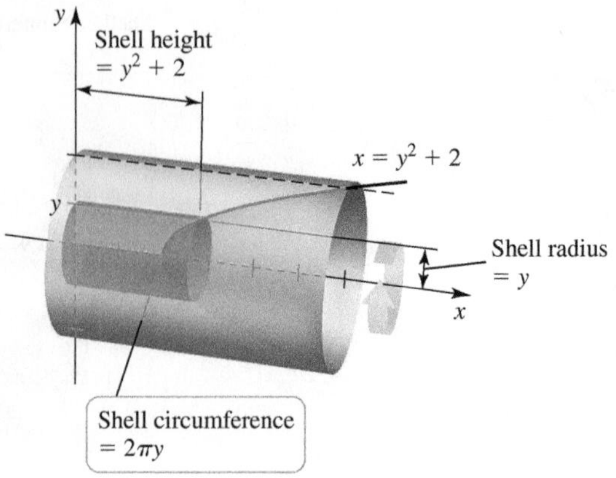

Figure 6.47

Related Exercises 15–26 ◀

EXAMPLE 3 **Volume of a drilled sphere** A cylindrical hole with radius r is drilled symmetrically through the center of a sphere with radius a, where $0 \le r \le a$. What is the volume of the remaining material?

SOLUTION The y-axis is chosen to coincide with the axis of the cylindrical hole. We let R be the region in the xy-plane bounded above by $f(x) = \sqrt{a^2 - x^2}$, the upper half of a circle of radius a, and bounded below by $g(x) = -\sqrt{a^2 - x^2}$, the lower half of a circle of radius a, for $r \le x \le a$ (Figure 6.48a). Slices are taken perpendicular to the x-axis from $x = r$ to $x = a$. When a slice is revolved about the y-axis, it sweeps out a cylindrical shell that is concentric with the hole through the sphere (Figure 6.48b). The radius of a typical shell is x and its height is $f(x) - g(x) = 2\sqrt{a^2 - x^2}$. Therefore, the volume of the material that remains in the sphere is

$$V = \int_r^a 2\pi x(2\sqrt{a^2 - x^2})\,dx$$

$$= -2\pi \int_{a^2-r^2}^{0} \sqrt{u}\,du \qquad u = a^2 - x^2,\ du = -2x\,dx$$

$$= 2\pi\left(\frac{2}{3}u^{3/2}\right)\Big|_0^{a^2-r^2} \qquad \text{Fundamental Theorem}$$

$$= \frac{4\pi}{3}(a^2 - r^2)^{3/2}. \qquad \text{Simplify.}$$

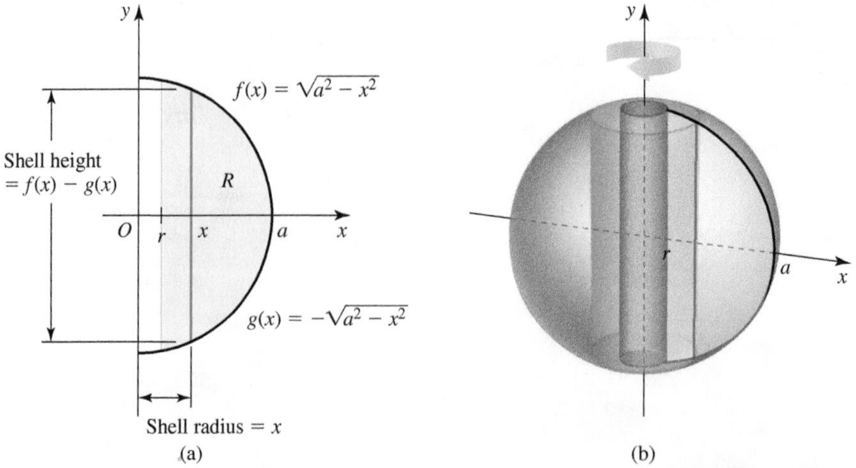

Figure 6.48

It is important to check the result by examining special cases. In the case that $r = a$ (the radius of the hole equals the radius of the sphere), our calculation gives a volume of 0, which is correct. In the case that $r = 0$ (no hole in the sphere), our calculation gives the correct volume of a sphere, $\frac{4}{3}\pi a^3$.

Related Exercises 27–32 ◂

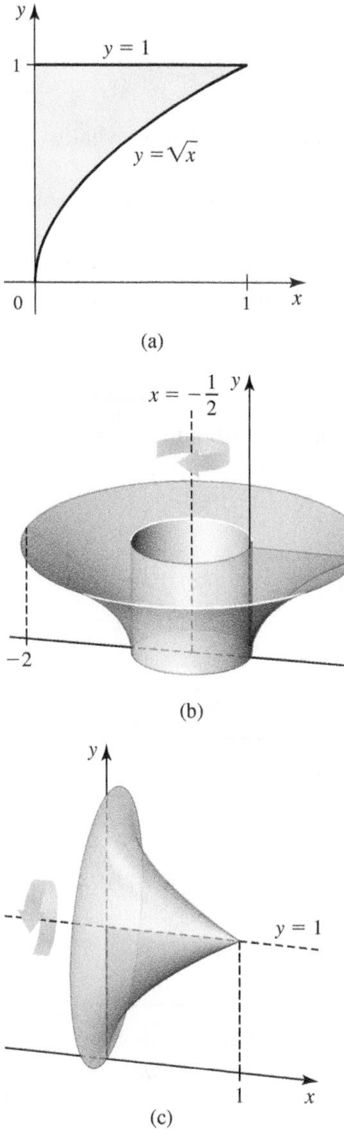

Figure 6.49

EXAMPLE 4 **Revolving about other lines** Let R be the region bounded by the curve $y = \sqrt{x}$, the line $y = 1$, and the y-axis (Figure 6.49a).

a. Use the shell method to find the volume of the solid generated when R is revolved about the line $x = -\frac{1}{2}$ (Figure 6.49b).

b. Use the disk/washer method to find the volume of the solid generated when R is revolved about the line $y = 1$ (Figure 6.49c).

SOLUTION

a. Using the shell method, we must imagine taking slices through R parallel to the y-axis. A typical slice through R at a point x, where $0 \le x \le 1$, has length $1 - \sqrt{x}$. When that slice is revolved about the line $x = -\frac{1}{2}$, it sweeps out a cylindrical shell with a radius of $x + \frac{1}{2}$ and a height of $1 - \sqrt{x}$ (Figure 6.50). A slight modification of the standard shell method gives the volume of the solid:

$$\int_0^1 \underbrace{2\pi\left(x + \frac{1}{2}\right)}_{\text{shell circumference}} \underbrace{(1 - \sqrt{x})}_{\text{shell height}}\, dx = 2\pi \int_0^1 \left(x - x^{3/2} + \frac{1}{2} - \frac{x^{1/2}}{2}\right) dx \quad \text{Expand integrand.}$$

$$= 2\pi\left(\frac{1}{2}x^2 - \frac{2}{5}x^{5/2} + \frac{1}{2}x - \frac{1}{3}x^{3/2}\right)\Big|_0^1 = \frac{8\pi}{15}. \quad \text{Evaluate integral.}$$

➤ If we instead revolved about the y-axis ($x = 0$), the radius of the shell would be x. Because we are revolving about the line $x = -\frac{1}{2}$, the radius of the shell is $x + \frac{1}{2}$.

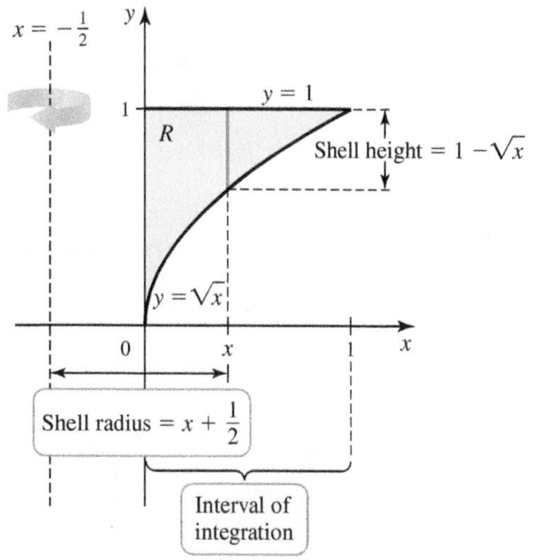

Figure 6.50

➤ The disk/washer method can also be used for part (a), and the shell method can also be used for part (b).

b. Using the disk/washer method, we take slices through R parallel to the y-axis. Consider a typical slice at a point x, where $0 \le x \le 1$. Its length, now measured with respect to the line $y = 1$, is $1 - \sqrt{x}$. When that slice is revolved about the line $y = 1$, it sweeps out a disk of radius $1 - \sqrt{x}$ (Figure 6.51). By the disk/washer method, the volume of the solid is

$$\int_0^1 \pi \underbrace{(1 - \sqrt{x})^2}_{\text{radius of disk}}\, dx = \pi \int_0^1 (1 - 2\sqrt{x} + x)\, dx \quad \text{Expand integrand.}$$

$$= \pi\left(x - \frac{4}{3}x^{3/2} + \frac{1}{2}x^2\right)\Big|_0^1 \quad \text{Evaluate integral.}$$

$$= \frac{\pi}{6}.$$

Related Exercises 33–40 ◂

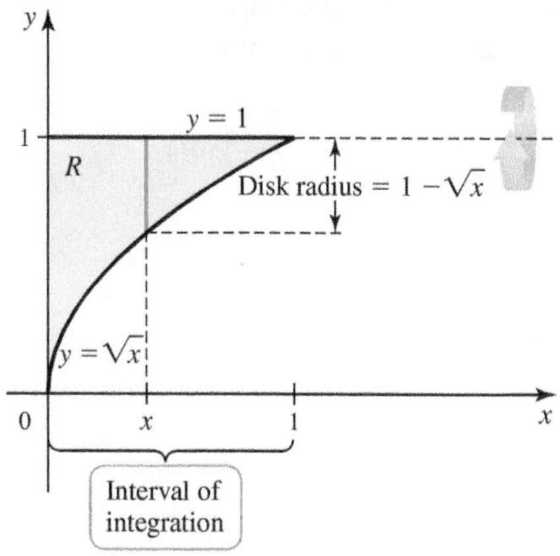

Figure 6.51

QUICK CHECK 2 Write the volume integral in Example 4b in the case that R is revolved about the line $y = -5$. ◄

Restoring Order

After working with slices, disks, washers, and shells, you may feel somewhat overwhelmed. How do you choose a method, and which method is best?

Notice that the disk method is just a special case of the washer method. So for solids of revolution, the choice is between the washer method and the shell method. In *principle*, either method can be used. In *practice*, one method usually produces an integral that is easier to evaluate than the other method. The following table summarizes these methods.

<table>
<tr><th colspan="2">SUMMARY **Disk/Washer and Shell Methods**</th></tr>
<tr><td>

Integration with respect to x

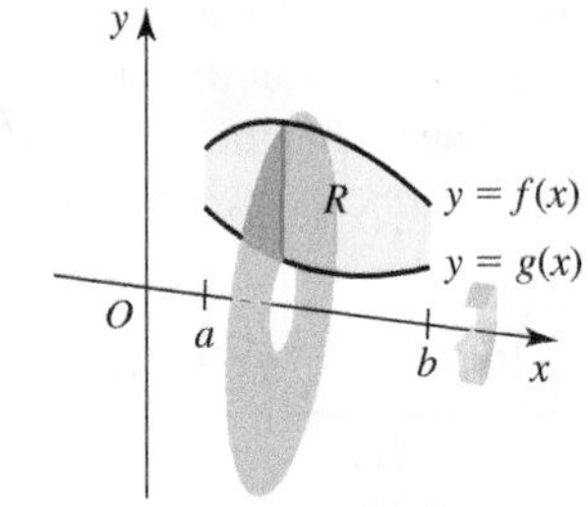

</td><td>

Disk/washer method about the x-axis
Disks/washers are *perpendicular* to the x-axis.

$$\int_a^b \pi(f(x)^2 - g(x)^2)\,dx$$

</td></tr>
<tr><td>

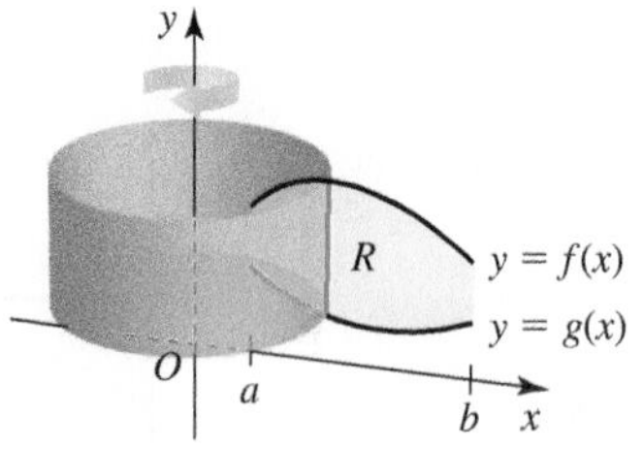

</td><td>

Shell method about the y-axis
Shells are *parallel* to the y-axis.

$$\int_a^b 2\pi x(f(x) - g(x))\,dx$$

</td></tr>
<tr><td>

Integration with respect to y

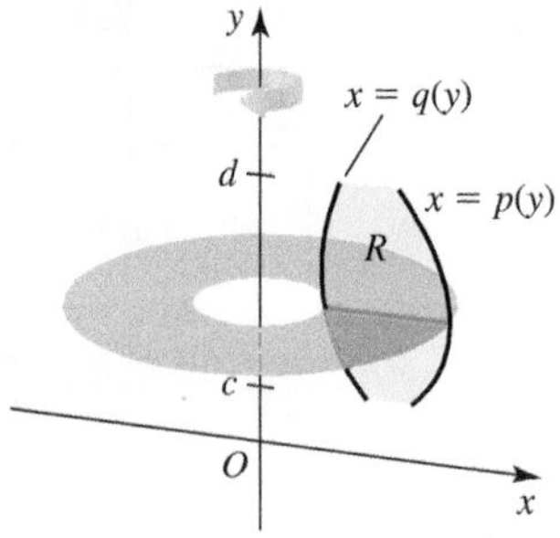

</td><td>

Disk/washer method about the y-axis
Disks/washers are *perpendicular* to the y-axis.

$$\int_c^d \pi(p(y)^2 - q(y)^2)\,dy$$

</td></tr>
<tr><td>

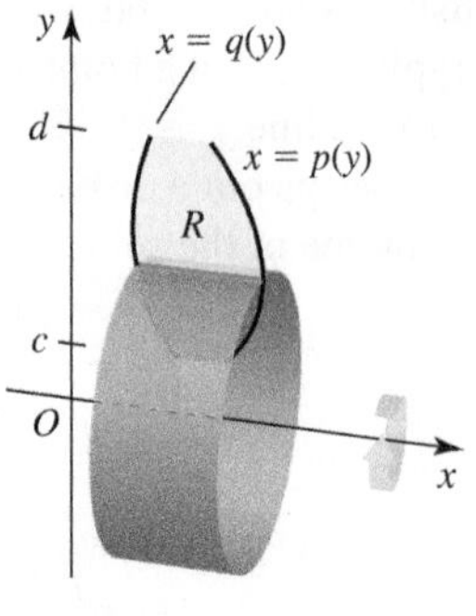

</td><td>

Shell method about the x-axis
Shells are *parallel* to the x-axis.

$$\int_c^d 2\pi y(p(y) - q(y))\,dy$$

</td></tr>
</table>

The following example shows that while two methods may be used on the same problem, one of them may be preferable.

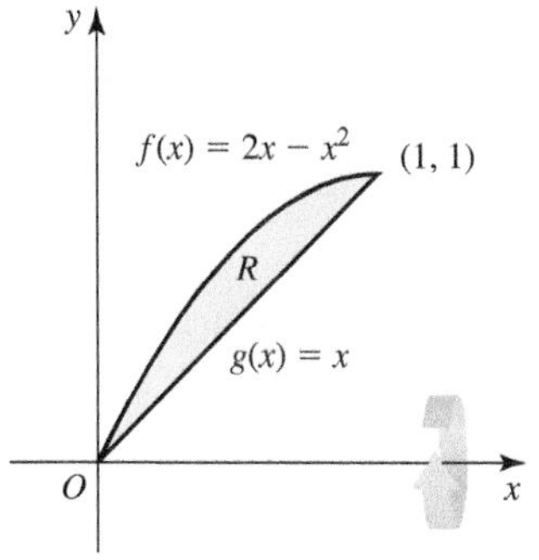

Figure 6.52

EXAMPLE 5 Volume by which method? The region R is bounded by the graphs of $f(x) = 2x - x^2$ and $g(x) = x$ on the interval $[0, 1]$ (Figure 6.52). Use the washer method and the shell method to find the volume of the solid formed when R is revolved about the x-axis.

SOLUTION Solving $f(x) = g(x)$, we find that the curves intersect at the points $(0, 0)$ and $(1, 1)$. Using the washer method, the upper bounding curve is the graph of f, the lower bounding curve is the graph of g, and a typical washer is perpendicular to the x-axis (Figure 6.53). Therefore, the volume is

$$V = \int_0^1 \pi((2x - x^2)^2 - x^2)\,dx \quad \text{Washer method}$$

$$= \pi \int_0^1 (x^4 - 4x^3 + 3x^2)\,dx \quad \text{Expand integrand.}$$

$$= \pi\left(\frac{x^5}{5} - x^4 + x^3\right)\Bigg|_0^1 = \frac{\pi}{5}. \quad \text{Evaluate integral.}$$

➤ To solve $y = 2x - x^2$ for x, write the equation as $x^2 - 2x + y = 0$ and complete the square or use the quadratic formula.

The shell method requires expressing the bounding curves in the form $x = p(y)$ for the right curve and $x = q(y)$ for the left curve. The right curve is $x = y$. Solving $y = 2x - x^2$ for x, we find that $x = 1 - \sqrt{1 - y}$ describes the left curve. A typical shell is parallel to the x-axis (Figure 6.54). Therefore, the volume is

$$V = \int_0^1 2\pi y\,(\underbrace{y}_{p(y)} - \underbrace{(1 - \sqrt{1 - y})}_{q(y)})\,dy.$$

This integral equals $\frac{\pi}{5}$, but it is more difficult to evaluate than the integral required by the washer method. In this case, the washer method is preferable. Of course, the shell method may be preferable for other problems.

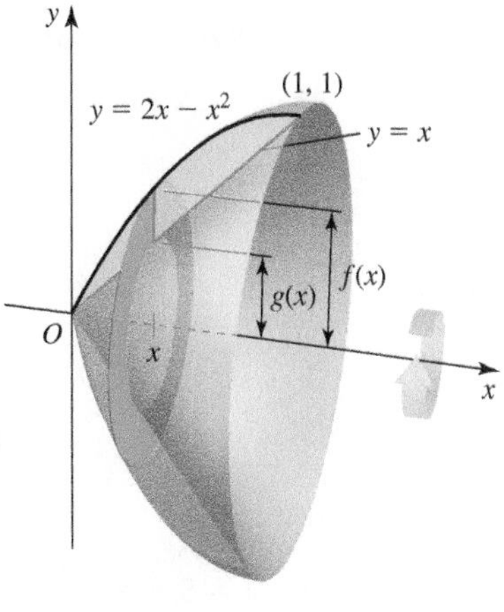

(Outer radius)^2 = $(2x - x^2)^2$
(Inner radius)^2 = x^2

Figure 6.53

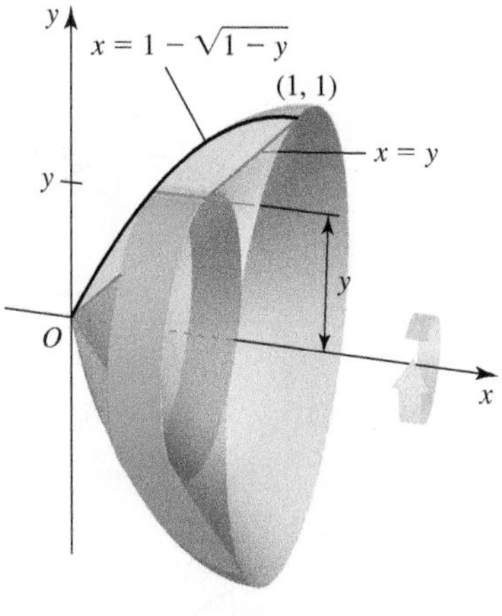

Shell height = $y - (1 - \sqrt{1 - y})$
Shell radius = y

Figure 6.54

Related Exercises 41–48 ◀

QUICK CHECK 3 Suppose the region in Example 5 is revolved about the y-axis. Which method (washer or shell) leads to an easier integral? ◀

SECTION 6.4 EXERCISES

Review Questions

1. Assume f and g are continuous with $f(x) \geq g(x)$ on $[a, b]$. The region bounded by the graphs of f and g and the lines $x = a$ and $x = b$ is revolved about the y-axis. Write the integral given by the shell method that equals the volume of the resulting solid.

2. Fill in the blanks: A region R is revolved about the y-axis. The volume of the resulting solid could (in principle) be found using the disk/washer method and integrating with respect to ________ or using the shell method and integrating with respect to ________.

3. Fill in the blanks: A region R is revolved about the x-axis. The volume of the resulting solid could (in principle) be found using the disk/washer method and integrating with respect to ________ or using the shell method and integrating with respect to ________.

4. Are shell method integrals easier to evaluate than washer method integrals? Explain.

Basic Skills

5–14. Shell method *Let R be the region bounded by the following curves. Use the shell method to find the volume of the solid generated when R is revolved about the y-axis.*

5. $y = x - x^2, y = 0$

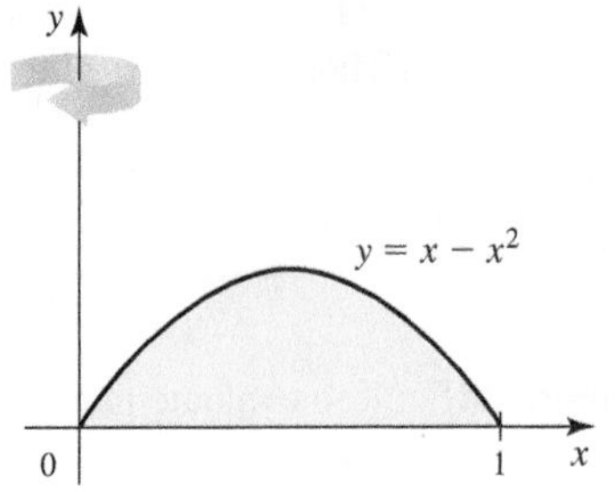

6. $y = -x^2 + 4x + 2, y = x^2 - 6x + 10$

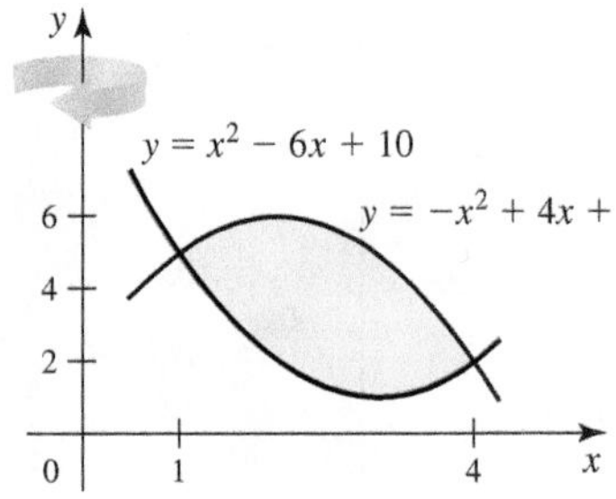

7. $y = (1 + x^2)^{-1}, y = 0, x = 0$, and $x = 2$

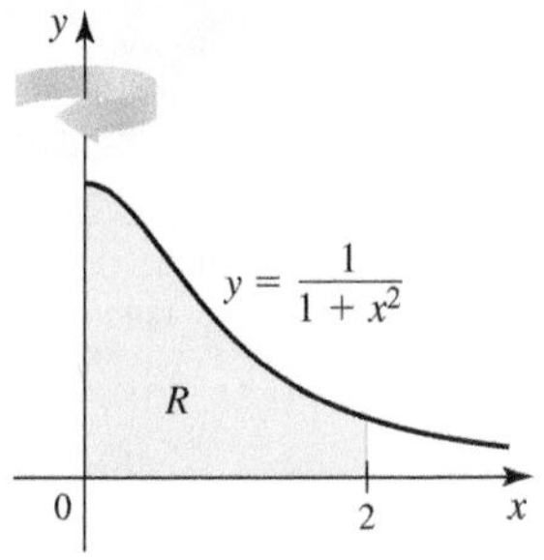

8. $y = 6 - x, y = 0, x = 2$, and $x = 4$

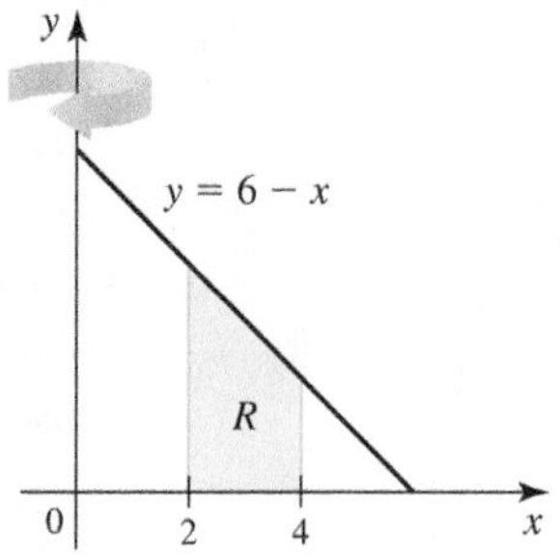

9. $y = 3x, y = 3$, and $x = 0$ (Use integration and check your answer using the volume formula for a cone.)

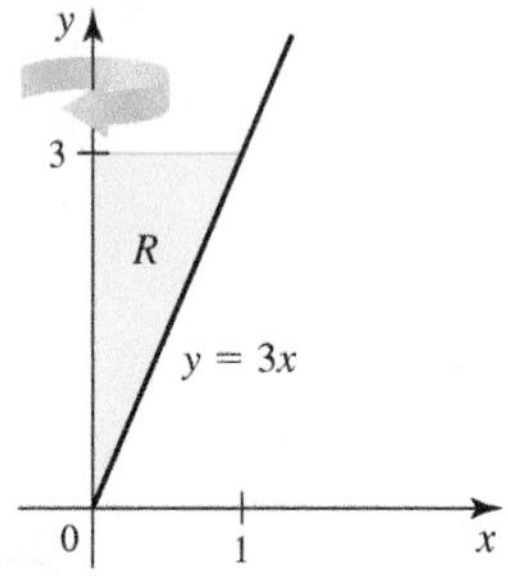

10. $y = 1 - x^2, x = 0$, and $y = 0$, in the first quadrant

11. $y = x^3 - x^8 + 1, y = 1$

12. $y = \sqrt{x}, y = 0$, and $x = 1$

13. $y = \cos x^2, y = 0$, for $0 \leq x \leq \sqrt{\pi/2}$

14. $y = \sqrt{4 - 2x^2}, y = 0$, and $x = 0$, in the first quadrant

15–26. Shell method *Let R be the region bounded by the following curves. Use the shell method to find the volume of the solid generated when R is revolved about the x-axis.*

15. $y = \sqrt{x}, y = 0$, and $x = 4$

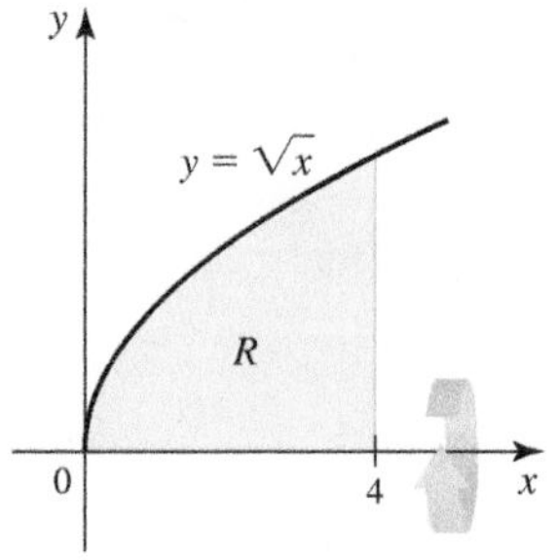

16. $y = 8, y = 2x + 2, x = 0$, and $x = 2$

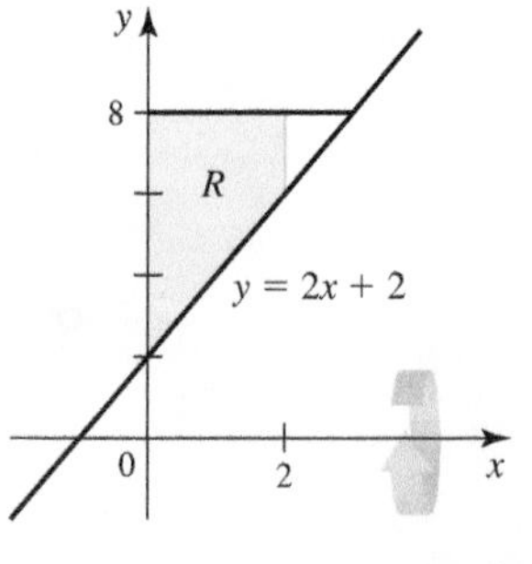

17. $y = 4 - x, y = 2$, and $x = 0$

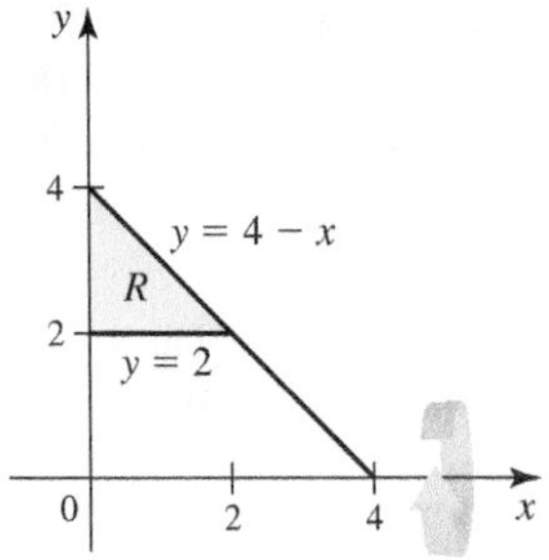

18. $x = \dfrac{4}{y + y^3}, x = \dfrac{1}{\sqrt{3}}$, and $y = 1$

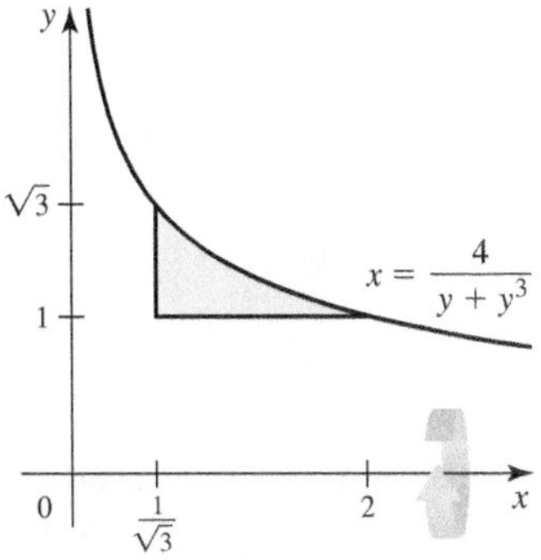

19. $y = x, y = 2 - x$, and $y = 0$

20. $x = y^2, x = 4$, and $y = 0$

21. $x = y^2, x = 0$, and $y = 3$

22. $y = x^3, y = 1$, and $x = 0$

23. $y = 2x^{-3/2}, y = 2, y = 16$, and $x = 0$

24. $y = \sqrt{\sin^{-1} x}, y = \sqrt{\pi/2}$, and $x = 0$

25. $y = \sqrt{\cos^{-1} x}$, in the first quadrant

26. $y = \sqrt{50 - 2x^2}$, in the first quadrant

27–32. Shell method *Use the shell method to find the volume of the following solids.*

27. A right circular cone of radius 3 and height 8

28. The solid formed when a hole of radius 2 is drilled symmetrically along the axis of a right circular cylinder of height 6 and radius 4

29. The solid formed when a hole of radius 3 is drilled symmetrically along the axis of a right circular cone of radius 6 and height 9

30. The solid formed when a hole of radius 3 is drilled symmetrically through the center of a sphere of radius 6

31. The *ellipsoid* formed when that part of the ellipse $x^2 + 2y^2 = 4$ with $x \geq 0$ is revolved about the y-axis

32. A hole of radius $r \leq R$ is drilled symmetrically along the axis of a bullet. The bullet is formed by revolving the parabola $y = 6\left(1 - \dfrac{x^2}{R^2}\right)$ about the y-axis, where $0 \leq x \leq R$.

33–36. Shell method about other lines *Let R be the region bounded by $y = x^2, x = 1$, and $y = 0$. Use the shell method to find the volume of the solid generated when R is revolved about the following lines.*

33. $x = -2$ **34.** $x = 1$ **35.** $y = -2$ **36.** $y = 2$

37–40. Different axes of revolution *Use either the washer or shell method to find the volume of the solid that is generated when the region in the first quadrant bounded by $y = x^2, y = 1$, and $x = 0$ is revolved about the following lines.*

37. $y = -2$ **38.** $x = -1$ **39.** $y = 6$ **40.** $x = 2$

41–48. Washers vs. shells *Let R be the region bounded by the following curves. Let S be the solid generated when R is revolved about the given axis. If possible, find the volume of S by both the disk/washer and shell methods. Check that your results agree and state which method is easier to apply.*

41. $y = x, y = x^{1/3}$ in the first quadrant; revolved about the x-axis

42. $y = x^2, y = 2 - x$, and $x = 0$ in the first quadrant; revolved about the y-axis

43. $y = 1/(x + 1), y = 1 - x/3$; revolved about the x-axis

44. $y = (x - 2)^3 - 2, x = 0$, and $y = 25$; revolved about the y-axis

45. $y = \sqrt{\ln x}, y = \sqrt{\ln x^2}$, and $y = 1$; revolved about the x-axis

46. $y = 6/(x + 3), y = 2 - x$; revolved about the x-axis

47. $y = x - x^4, y = 0$; revolved about the x-axis

48. $y = x - x^4, y = 0$; revolved about the y-axis

Further Explorations

49. Explain why or why not Determine whether the following statements are true and give an explanation or counterexample.

a. When using the shell method, the axis of the cylindrical shells is parallel to the axis of revolution.

b. If a region is revolved about the y-axis, then the shell method must be used.

c. If a region is revolved about the x-axis, then in principle, it is possible to use the disk/washer method and integrate with respect to x or the shell method and integrate with respect to y.

50–54. Solids of revolution *Find the volume of the following solids of revolution. Sketch the region in question.*

T **50.** The region bounded by $y = (\ln x)/x^2, y = 0$, and $x = 3$ revolved about the y-axis

51. The region bounded by $y = 1/x^2, y = 0, x = 2$, and $x = 8$ revolved about the y-axis

T **52.** The region bounded by $y = 1/(x^2 + 1), y = 0, x = 1$, and $x = 4$ revolved about the y-axis

T **53.** The region bounded by $y = e^x/x, y = 0, x = 1$, and $x = 2$ revolved about the y-axis

T **54.** The region bounded by $y^2 = \ln x, y^2 = \ln x^3$, and $y = 2$ revolved about the x-axis

55–62. Choose your method *Find the volume of the following solids using the method of your choice.*

55. The solid formed when the region bounded by $y = x^2$ and $y = 2 - x^2$ is revolved about the x-axis

56. The solid formed when the region bounded by $y = \sin x$ and $y = 1 - \sin x$ between $x = \pi/6$ and $x = 5\pi/6$ is revolved about the x-axis

57. The solid formed when the region bounded by $y = x, y = 2x + 2$, $x = 2$, and $x = 6$ is revolved about the y-axis

58. The solid formed when the region bounded by $y = x^3$, the x-axis, and $x = 2$ is revolved about the x-axis

59. The solid whose base is the region bounded by $y = x^2$ and the line $y = 1$, and whose cross sections perpendicular to the base and parallel to the x-axis are semicircles

60. The solid formed when the region bounded by $y = 2$, $y = 2x + 2$, and $x = 6$ is revolved about the y-axis

61. The solid whose base is the square with vertices $(1, 0)$, $(0, 1)$, $(-1, 0)$, and $(0, -1)$, and whose cross sections perpendicular to the base and perpendicular to the x-axis are semicircles

62. The solid formed when the region bounded by $y = \sqrt{x}$, the x-axis, and $x = 4$ is revolved about the x-axis

T **63. Equal volumes** Consider the region R bounded by the curves $y = ax^2 + 1$, $y = 0$, $x = 0$, and $x = 1$, for $a \geq -1$. Let S_1 and S_2 be solids generated when R is revolved about the x- and y-axes, respectively.

a. Find V_1 and V_2, the volumes of S_1 and S_2, as functions of a.
b. What are the values of $a \geq -1$ for which $V_1(a) = V_2(a)$?

64. A hemisphere by three methods Let R be the region in the first quadrant bounded by the circle $x^2 + y^2 = r^2$ and the coordinate axes. Find the volume of a hemisphere of radius r in the following ways.

a. Revolve R about the x-axis and use the disk method.
b. Revolve R about the x-axis and use the shell method.
c. Assume the base of the hemisphere is in the xy-plane and use the general slicing method with slices perpendicular to the xy-plane and parallel to the x-axis.

65. A cone by two methods Verify that the volume of a right circular cone with a base radius of r and a height of h is $\pi r^2 h/3$. Use the region bounded by the line $y = rx/h$, the x-axis, and the line $x = h$, where the region is rotated about the x-axis. Then (a) use the disk method and integrate with respect to x, and (b) use the shell method and integrate with respect to y.

66. A spherical cap by three methods Consider the cap of thickness h that has been sliced from a sphere of radius r (see figure). Verify that the volume of the cap is $\pi h^2 (3r - h)/3$ using (a) the washer method, (b) the shell method, and (c) the general slicing method. Check for consistency among the three methods and check the special cases $h = r$ and $h = 0$.

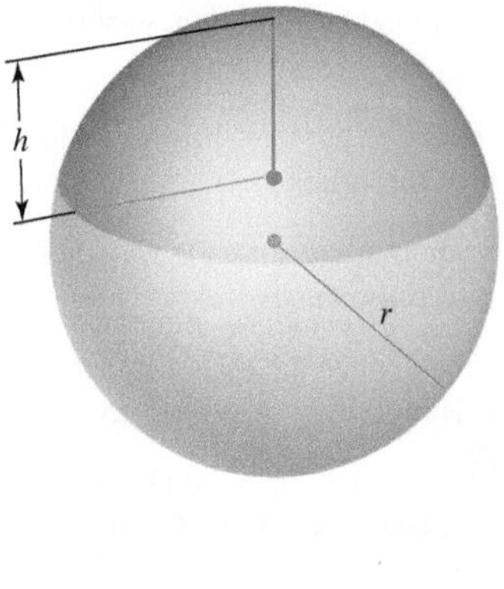

Applications

67. Water in a bowl A hemispherical bowl of radius 8 inches is filled to a depth of h inches, where $0 \leq h \leq 8$ ($h = 0$ corresponds to an empty bowl). Use the shell method to find the volume of water in the bowl as a function of h. (Check the special cases $h = 0$ and $h = 8$.)

68. Wedge from a tree Imagine a cylindrical tree of radius a. A wedge is cut from the tree by making two cuts: one in a horizontal plane P perpendicular to the axis of the cylinder and one that makes an angle θ with P, intersecting P along a diameter of the tree (see figure). What is the volume of the wedge?

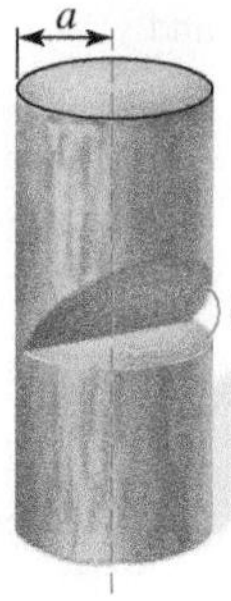

T **69. A torus (doughnut)** Find the volume of the torus formed when a circle of radius 2 centered at $(3, 0)$ is revolved about the y-axis. Use the shell method. You may need a computer algebra system or table of integrals to evaluate the integral.

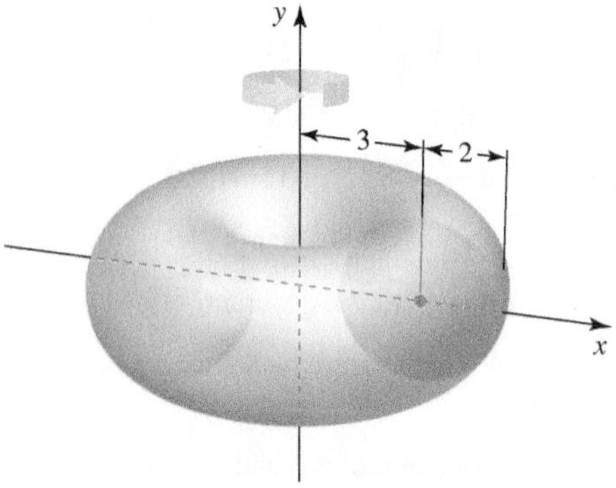

Additional Exercises

70. Different axes of revolution Suppose R is the region bounded by $y = f(x)$ and $y = g(x)$ on the interval $[a, b]$, where $f(x) \geq g(x)$.

a. Show that if R is revolved about the vertical line $x = x_0$, where $x_0 < a$, then by the shell method, the volume of the resulting solid is $V = \int_a^b 2\pi(x - x_0)(f(x) - g(x))\,dx$.
b. How is this formula changed if $x_0 > b$?

71. Different axes of revolution Suppose R is the region bounded by $y = f(x)$ and $y = g(x)$ on the interval $[a, b]$, where $f(x) \geq g(x) \geq 0$.

a. Show that if R is revolved about the horizontal line $y = y_0$ that lies below R, then by the washer method, the volume of the resulting solid is

$$V = \int_a^b \pi((f(x) - y_0)^2 - (g(x) - y_0)^2)\,dx.$$

b. How is this formula changed if the line $y = y_0$ lies above R?

72. Ellipsoids An ellipse centered at the origin is described by the equation $x^2/a^2 + y^2/b^2 = 1$. If an ellipse R is revolved about either axis, the resulting solid is an *ellipsoid*.

a. Find the volume of the ellipsoid generated when R is revolved about the x-axis (in terms of a and b).

b. Find the volume of the ellipsoid generated when R is revolved about the y-axis (in terms of a and b).

c. Should the results of parts (a) and (b) agree? Explain.

73. Change of variables Suppose $f(x) > 0$ for all x and $\int_0^4 f(x)\,dx = 10$. Let R be the region in the first quadrant bounded by the coordinate axes, $y = f(x^2)$, and $x = 2$. Find the volume of the solid generated by revolving R about the y-axis.

74. Equal integrals Without evaluating integrals, explain the following equalities. (*Hint:* Draw pictures.)

a. $\pi \int_0^4 (8 - 2x)^2\,dx = 2\pi \int_0^8 y\left(4 - \frac{y}{2}\right) dy$

b. $\int_0^2 (25 - (x^2 + 1)^2)\,dx = 2\int_1^5 y\sqrt{y - 1}\,dy$

75. Volumes without calculus Solve the following problems with *and* without calculus. A good picture helps.

a. A cube with side length r is inscribed in a sphere, which is inscribed in a right circular cone, which is inscribed in a right circular cylinder. The side length (slant height) of the cone is equal to its diameter. What is the volume of the cylinder?

b. A cube is inscribed in a right circular cone with a radius of 1 and a height of 3. What is the volume of the cube?

c. A cylindrical hole 10 in long is drilled symmetrically through the center of a sphere. How much material is left in the sphere? (Enough information *is* given.)

QUICK CHECK ANSWERS

1. $\int_0^1 2\pi x(2x)\,dx$ **2.** $V = \int_0^1 \pi(36 - (\sqrt{x} + 5)^2)\,dx$ **3.** The shell method is easier. ◄

6.5 Length of Curves

The space station orbits Earth in an elliptical path. How far does it travel in one orbit? A baseball slugger launches a home run into the upper deck and the sportscaster claims it landed 480 feet from home plate. But how far did the ball actually travel along its flight path? These questions deal with the length of trajectories or, more generally, with *arc length*. As you will see, their answers can be found by integration.

There are two common ways to formulate problems about arc length: The curve may be given explicitly in the form $y = f(x)$ or it may be defined *parametrically*. In this section, we deal with the first case. Parametric curves are introduced in Section 10.1, and the associated arc length problem is discussed in Section 11.8.

Arc Length for $y = f(x)$

Suppose a curve is given by $y = f(x)$, where f is a function with a continuous first derivative on the interval $[a, b]$. The goal is to determine how far you would travel if you walked along the curve from $(a, f(a))$ to $(b, f(b))$. This distance is the arc length, which we denote L.

As shown in Figure 6.55, we divide $[a, b]$ into n subintervals of length $\Delta x = (b - a)/n$, where x_k is the right endpoint of the kth subinterval, for $k = 1, \ldots, n$. Joining the corresponding points on the curve by line segments, we obtain a polygonal line with n line segments. If n is large and Δx is small, the length of the polygonal line is a good approximation to the length of the actual curve. The strategy is to find the length of the polygonal line and then let n increase, while Δx goes to zero, to get the exact length of the curve.

➤ More generally, we may choose any point in the kth subinterval and Δx may vary from one subinterval to the next. Using right endpoints, as we do here, simplifies the discussion and leads to the same result.

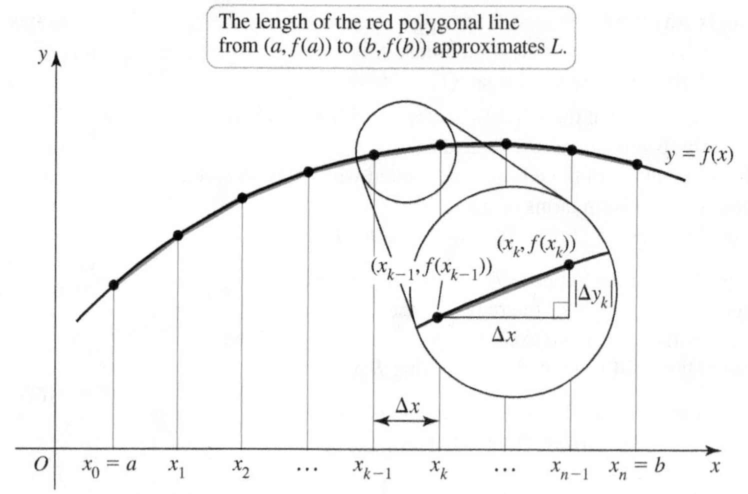

Figure 6.55

Consider the kth subinterval $[x_{k-1}, x_k]$ and the line segment between the points $(x_{k-1}, f(x_{k-1}))$ and $(x_k, f(x_k))$. We let the change in the y-coordinate between these points be

$$\Delta y_k = f(x_k) - f(x_{k-1}).$$

➤ Notice that Δx is the same for each subinterval, but Δy_k depends on the subinterval.

The kth line segment is the hypotenuse of a right triangle with sides of length Δx and $|\Delta y_k| = |f(x_k) - f(x_{k-1})|$. The length of each line segment is

$$\sqrt{(\Delta x)^2 + |\Delta y_k|^2}, \quad \text{for} \quad k = 1, 2, \ldots, n.$$

Summing these lengths, we obtain the length of the polygonal line, which approximates the length L of the curve:

$$L \approx \sum_{k=1}^{n} \sqrt{(\Delta x)^2 + |\Delta y_k|^2}.$$

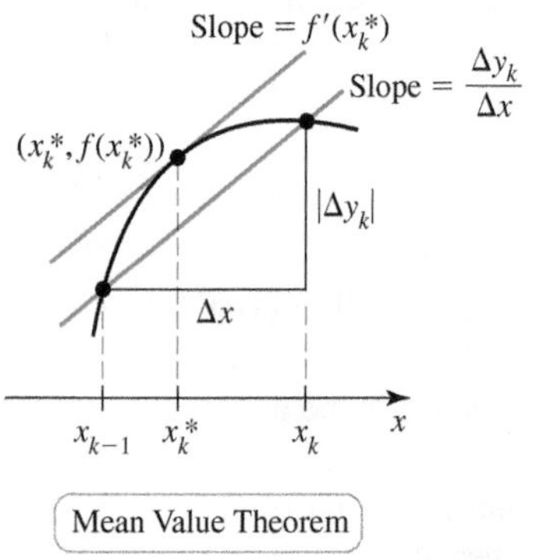

In previous applications of the integral, we would, at this point, take the limit as $n \to \infty$ and $\Delta x \to 0$ to obtain a definite integral. However, because of the presence of the Δy_k term, we must complete one additional step before taking a limit. Notice that the slope of the line segment on the kth subinterval is $\Delta y_k / \Delta x$ (rise over run). By the Mean Value Theorem (see the margin figure and Section 4.6), this slope equals $f'(x_k^*)$ for some point x_k^* on the kth subinterval. Therefore,

$$\begin{aligned} L &\approx \sum_{k=1}^{n} \sqrt{(\Delta x)^2 + |\Delta y_k|^2} \\ &= \sum_{k=1}^{n} \sqrt{(\Delta x)^2 \left(1 + \left(\frac{\Delta y_k}{\Delta x}\right)^2\right)} && \text{Factor out } (\Delta x)^2. \\ &= \sum_{k=1}^{n} \sqrt{1 + \left(\frac{\Delta y_k}{\Delta x}\right)^2}\, \Delta x && \text{Bring } \Delta x \text{ out of the square root.} \\ &= \sum_{k=1}^{n} \sqrt{1 + f'(x_k^*)^2}\, \Delta x. && \text{Mean Value Theorem} \end{aligned}$$

Now we have a Riemann sum. As n increases and as Δx approaches zero, the sum approaches a definite integral, which is also the exact length of the curve. We have

$$L = \lim_{n \to \infty} \sum_{k=1}^{n} \sqrt{1 + f'(x_k^*)^2}\, \Delta x = \int_a^b \sqrt{1 + f'(x)^2}\, dx.$$

➤ Note that $1 + f'(x)^2$ is positive, so the square root in the integrand is defined whenever f' exists. To ensure that $\sqrt{1 + f'(x)^2}$ is integrable on $[a, b]$, we require that f' be continuous.

DEFINITION Arc Length for $y = f(x)$

Let f have a continuous first derivative on the interval $[a, b]$. The length of the curve from $(a, f(a))$ to $(b, f(b))$ is

$$L = \int_a^b \sqrt{1 + f'(x)^2}\, dx.$$

QUICK CHECK 1 What does the arc length formula give for the length of the line $y = x$ between $x = 0$ and $x = a$, where $a \geq 0$? ◄

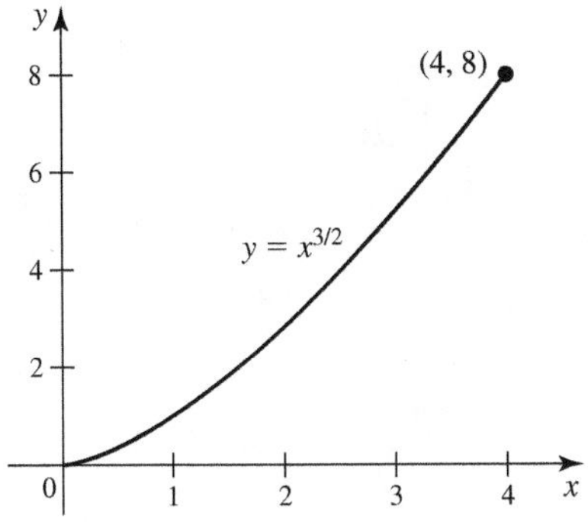

Figure 6.56

EXAMPLE 1 Arc length Find the length of the curve $f(x) = x^{3/2}$ between $x = 0$ and $x = 4$ (Figure 6.56).

SOLUTION Notice that $f'(x) = \frac{3}{2}x^{1/2}$, which is continuous on the interval $[0, 4]$. Using the arc length formula, we have

$$\begin{aligned}
L &= \int_a^b \sqrt{1 + f'(x)^2}\, dx = \int_0^4 \sqrt{1 + \left(\frac{3}{2}x^{1/2}\right)^2}\, dx && \text{Substitute for } f'(x).\\
&= \int_0^4 \sqrt{1 + \frac{9}{4}x}\, dx && \text{Simplify.}\\
&= \frac{4}{9}\int_1^{10} \sqrt{u}\, du && u = 1 + \frac{9x}{4},\ du = \frac{9}{4}dx\\
&= \frac{4}{9}\left(\frac{2}{3}u^{3/2}\right)\Bigg|_1^{10} && \text{Fundamental Theorem}\\
&= \frac{8}{27}(10^{3/2} - 1). && \text{Simplify.}
\end{aligned}$$

The length of the curve is $\frac{8}{27}(10^{3/2} - 1) \approx 9.1$ units.

Related Exercises 3–16 ◄

EXAMPLE 2 Arc length of an exponential curve Find the length of the curve $f(x) = 2e^x + \frac{1}{8}e^{-x}$ on the interval $[0, \ln 2]$.

SOLUTION We first calculate $f'(x) = 2e^x - \frac{1}{8}e^{-x}$ and $f'(x)^2 = 4e^{2x} - \frac{1}{2} + \frac{1}{64}e^{-2x}$. The length of the curve on the interval $[0, \ln 2]$ is

$$\begin{aligned}
L &= \int_0^{\ln 2} \sqrt{1 + f'(x)^2}\, dx = \int_0^{\ln 2} \sqrt{1 + \left(4e^{2x} - \tfrac{1}{2} + \tfrac{1}{64}e^{-2x}\right)}\, dx\\
&= \int_0^{\ln 2} \sqrt{4e^{2x} + \tfrac{1}{2} + \tfrac{1}{64}e^{-2x}}\, dx && \text{Simplify.}\\
&= \int_0^{\ln 2} \sqrt{\left(2e^x + \tfrac{1}{8}e^{-x}\right)^2}\, dx && \text{Factor.}\\
&= \int_0^{\ln 2} \left(2e^x + \tfrac{1}{8}e^{-x}\right) dx && \text{Simplify.}\\
&= \left(2e^x - \tfrac{1}{8}e^{-x}\right)\Big|_0^{\ln 2} = \frac{33}{16}. && \text{Evaluate the integral.}
\end{aligned}$$

Related Exercises 3–16 ◄

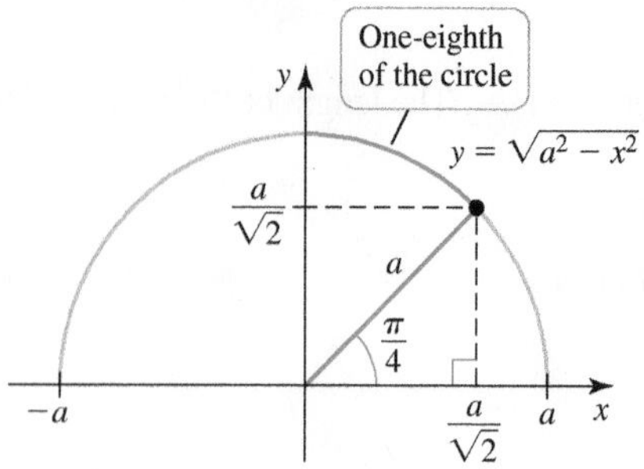

Figure 6.57

EXAMPLE 3 **Circumference of a circle** Confirm that the circumference of a circle of radius a is $2\pi a$.

SOLUTION The upper half of a circle of radius a centered at $(0, 0)$ is given by the function $f(x) = \sqrt{a^2 - x^2}$ for $|x| \le a$ (Figure 6.57). So we might consider using the arc length formula on the interval $[-a, a]$ to find the length of a semicircle. However, the circle has vertical tangent lines at $x = \pm a$ and $f'(\pm a)$ is undefined, which prevents us from using the arc length formula. An alternative approach is to use symmetry and avoid the points $x = \pm a$. For example, let's compute the length of one-eighth of the circle on the interval $[0, a/\sqrt{2}]$ (Figure 6.57).

We first determine that $f'(x) = -\dfrac{x}{\sqrt{a^2 - x^2}}$, which is continuous on $[0, a/\sqrt{2}]$. The length of one-eighth of the circle is

$$\begin{aligned}
\int_0^{a/\sqrt{2}} \sqrt{1 + f'(x)^2}\, dx &= \int_0^{a/\sqrt{2}} \sqrt{1 + \left(-\frac{x}{\sqrt{a^2 - x^2}}\right)^2}\, dx \\
&= \int_0^{a/\sqrt{2}} \sqrt{\frac{a^2}{a^2 - x^2}}\, dx && \text{Simplify.} \\
&= a \int_0^{a/\sqrt{2}} \frac{dx}{\sqrt{a^2 - x^2}} && \text{Simplify; } a > 0. \\
&= a \sin^{-1} \frac{x}{a}\Big|_0^{a/\sqrt{2}} && \text{Integrate.} \\
&= a\left(\sin^{-1} \frac{1}{\sqrt{2}} - 0\right) && \text{Evaluate.} \\
&= \frac{\pi a}{4}. && \text{Simplify.}
\end{aligned}$$

➤ The arc length integral for the semicircle on $[-a, a]$ is an example of an *improper integral*, a topic considered in Section 7.8.

It follows that the circumference of the full circle is $8(\pi a/4) = 2\pi a$ units.

Related Exercises 3–16 ◀

EXAMPLE 4 **Looking ahead** Consider the segment of the parabola $f(x) = x^2$ on the interval $[0, 2]$.

a. Write the integral for the length of the curve.

b. Use a calculator to evaluate the integral.

SOLUTION

a. Noting that $f'(x) = 2x$, the arc length integral is

$$\int_0^2 \sqrt{1 + f'(x)^2}\, dx = \int_0^2 \sqrt{1 + 4x^2}\, dx.$$

b. Using integration techniques presented so far, this integral cannot be evaluated (the required method is given in Section 7.4). This is typical of arc length integrals—even simple functions can lead to arc length integrals that are difficult to evaluate analytically. Without an analytical method, we may use numerical integration to *approximate* the value of a definite integral (Section 7.7). Many calculators have built-in functions for this purpose. For this integral, the approximate arc length is

$$\int_0^2 \sqrt{1 + 4x^2}\, dx \approx 4.647.$$

Related Exercises 17–26 ◀

➤ When relying on technology, it is a good idea to check whether an answer is plausible. In Example 4, we found that the arc length of $y = x^2$ on $[0, 2]$ is approximately 4.647. The straight-line distance between $(0, 0)$ and $(2, 4)$ is $\sqrt{20} \approx 4.472$, so our answer is reasonable.

Arc Length for $x = g(y)$

Sometimes it is advantageous to describe a curve as a function of y—that is, $x = g(y)$. The arc length formula in this case is derived exactly as in the case of $y = f(x)$, switching the roles of x and y. The result is the following arc length formula.

QUICK CHECK 2 What does the arc length formula give for the length of the line $x = y$ between $y = c$ and $y = d$, where $d \geq c$? Is the result consistent with the result given by the Pythagorean theorem? ◄

> DEFINITION **Arc Length for $x = g(y)$**
>
> Let $x = g(y)$ have a continuous first derivative on the interval $[c, d]$. The length of the curve from $(g(c), c)$ to $(g(d), d)$ is
>
> $$L = \int_c^d \sqrt{1 + g'(y)^2}\, dy.$$

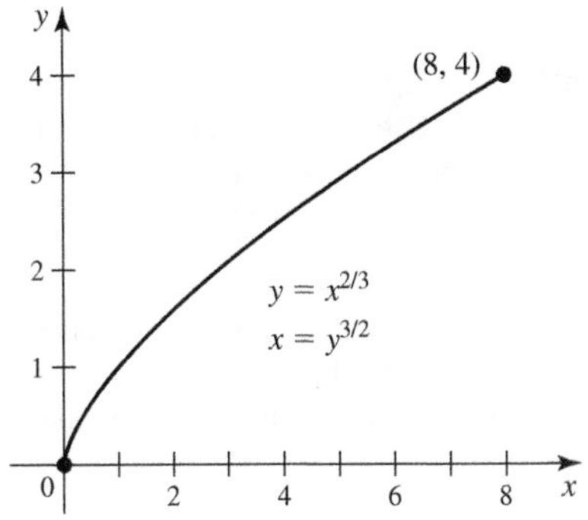

Figure 6.58

EXAMPLE 5 **Arc length** Find the length of the curve $y = f(x) = x^{2/3}$ between $x = 0$ and $x = 8$ (Figure 6.58).

SOLUTION The derivative of $f(x) = x^{2/3}$ is $f'(x) = \frac{2}{3}x^{-1/3}$, which is undefined at $x = 0$. Therefore, the arc length formula with respect to x cannot be used, yet the curve certainly appears to have a well-defined length.

The key is to describe the curve with y as the independent variable. Solving $y = x^{2/3}$ for x, we have $x = g(y) = \pm y^{3/2}$. Notice that when $x = 8$, $y = 8^{2/3} = 4$, which says that we should use the positive branch of $\pm y^{3/2}$. Therefore, finding the length of the curve $y = f(x) = x^{2/3}$ from $x = 0$ to $x = 8$ is equivalent to finding the length of the curve $x = g(y) = y^{3/2}$ from $y = 0$ to $y = 4$. This is precisely the problem solved in Example 1. The arc length is $\frac{8}{27}(10^{3/2} - 1) \approx 9.1$ units.

Related Exercises 27–30 ◄

QUICK CHECK 3 Write the integral for the length of the curve $x = \sin y$ on the interval $0 \leq y \leq \pi$. ◄

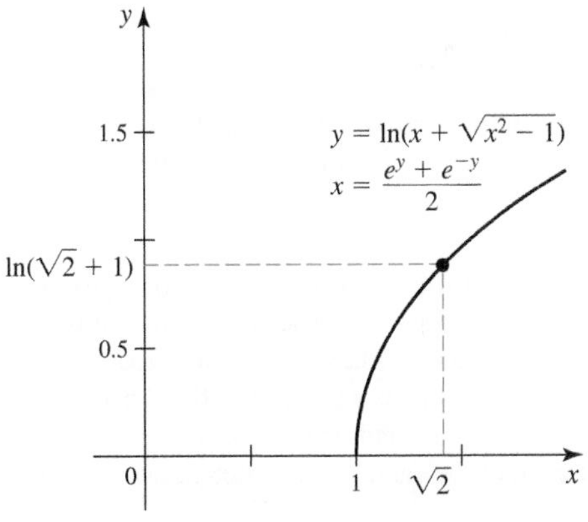

Figure 6.59

➤ The function $\frac{1}{2}(e^y + e^{-y})$ is the **hyperbolic cosine**, denoted $\cosh y$. The function $\frac{1}{2}(e^y - e^{-y})$ is the **hyperbolic sine**, denoted $\sinh y$. See Section 6.10.

EXAMPLE 6 **Ingenuity required** Find the length of the curve $y = f(x) = \ln(x + \sqrt{x^2 - 1})$ on the interval $[1, \sqrt{2}]$ (Figure 6.59).

SOLUTION Calculating f' shows that the graph of f has a vertical tangent line at $x = 1$. Therefore, the integrand in the arc length integral is undefined at $x = 1$. An alternative strategy is to express the function in the form $x = g(y)$ and evaluate the arc length integral with respect to y. Noting that $x \geq 1$ and $y \geq 0$, we solve $y = \ln(x + \sqrt{x^2 - 1})$ for x in the following steps:

$$e^y = x + \sqrt{x^2 - 1} \quad \text{Exponentiate both sides.}$$

$$e^y - x = \sqrt{x^2 - 1} \quad \text{Subtract } x \text{ from both sides.}$$

$$e^{2y} - 2e^y x = -1 \quad \text{Square both sides and cancel } x^2.$$

$$x = \frac{e^{2y} + 1}{2e^y} = \frac{e^y + e^{-y}}{2}. \quad \text{Solve for } x.$$

We conclude that the given curve is also described by the function $x = g(y) = \dfrac{e^y + e^{-y}}{2}$. The interval $1 \leq x \leq \sqrt{2}$ corresponds to the interval $0 \leq y \leq \ln(\sqrt{2} + 1)$ (Figure 6.59). Note that $g'(y) = \dfrac{e^y - e^{-y}}{2}$ is continuous on $[0, \ln(\sqrt{2} + 1)]$. The arc length is

$$\int_0^{\ln(\sqrt{2}+1)} \sqrt{1 + g'(y)^2}\, dy = \int_0^{\ln(\sqrt{2}+1)} \sqrt{1 + \left(\frac{e^y - e^{-y}}{2}\right)^2}\, dy \quad \text{Substitute for } g'(y).$$

$$= \frac{1}{2}\int_0^{\ln(\sqrt{2}+1)} (e^y + e^{-y})\, dy \quad \text{Expand and simplify.}$$

$$= \frac{1}{2}(e^y - e^{-y})\Big|_0^{\ln(\sqrt{2}+1)} = 1. \quad \text{Fundamental Theorem}$$

Related Exercises 27–30 ◄

SECTION 6.5 EXERCISES

Review Questions

1. Explain the steps required to find the length of a curve $y = f(x)$ between $x = a$ and $x = b$.

2. Explain the steps required to find the length of a curve $x = g(y)$ between $y = c$ and $y = d$.

Basic Skills

3–6. Setting up arc length integrals *Write and simplify, but do not evaluate, an integral with respect to x that gives the length of the following curves on the given interval.*

3. $y = x^3 + 2$ on $[-2, 5]$
4. $y = 2\cos 3x$ on $[-\pi, \pi]$
5. $y = e^{-2x}$ on $[0, 2]$
6. $y = \ln x$ on $[1, 10]$

7–16. Arc length calculations *Find the arc length of the following curves on the given interval by integrating with respect to x.*

7. $y = 2x + 1$ on $[1, 5]$ (Use calculus.)
8. $y = 4 - 3x$ on $[-3, 2]$ (Use calculus.)
9. $y = -8x - 3$ on $[-2, 6]$ (Use calculus.)
10. $y = \frac{1}{2}(e^x + e^{-x})$ on $[-\ln 2, \ln 2]$
11. $y = \frac{1}{3}x^{3/2}$ on $[0, 60]$
12. $y = 3\ln x - \frac{x^2}{24}$ on $[1, 6]$
13. $y = \frac{(x^2 + 2)^{3/2}}{3}$ on $[0, 1]$
14. $y = \frac{x^{3/2}}{3} - x^{1/2}$ on $[4, 16]$
15. $y = \frac{x^4}{4} + \frac{1}{8x^2}$ on $[1, 2]$
16. $y = \frac{2}{3}x^{3/2} - \frac{1}{2}x^{1/2}$ on $[1, 9]$

T 17–26. Arc length by calculator

a. Write and simplify the integral that gives the arc length of the following curves on the given interval.

b. If necessary, use technology to evaluate or approximate the integral.

17. $y = x^2$ on $[-1, 1]$
18. $y = \sin x$ on $[0, \pi]$
19. $y = \ln x$ on $[1, 4]$
20. $y = \frac{x^3}{3}$ on $[-1, 1]$
21. $y = \sqrt{x - 2}$ on $[3, 4]$
22. $y = \frac{8}{x^2}$ on $[1, 4]$
23. $y = \cos 2x$ on $[0, \pi]$
24. $y = 4x - x^2$ on $[0, 4]$
25. $y = \frac{1}{x}$ on $[1, 10]$
26. $y = \frac{1}{x^2 + 1}$ on $[-5, 5]$

27–30. Arc length calculations with respect to y *Find the arc length of the following curves by integrating with respect to y.*

27. $x = 2y - 4$, for $-3 \le y \le 4$ (Use calculus.)
28. $y = \ln(x - \sqrt{x^2 - 1})$, for $1 \le x \le \sqrt{2}$
29. $x = \frac{y^4}{4} + \frac{1}{8y^2}$, for $1 \le y \le 2$
30. $x = 2e^{\sqrt{2}y} + \frac{1}{16}e^{-\sqrt{2}y}$, for $0 \le y \le \frac{\ln 2}{\sqrt{2}}$

Further Explorations

31. **Explain why or why not** Determine whether the following statements are true and give an explanation or counterexample.

   a. $\int_a^b \sqrt{1 + f'(x)^2}\,dx = \int_a^b (1 + f'(x))\,dx.$

   b. Assuming f' is continuous on the interval $[a, b]$, the length of the curve $y = f(x)$ on $[a, b]$ is the area under the curve $y = \sqrt{1 + f'(x)^2}$ on $[a, b]$.

   c. Arc length may be negative if $f(x) < 0$ on part of the interval in question.

32. **Arc length for a line** Consider the segment of the line $y = mx + c$ on the interval $[a, b]$. Use the arc length formula to show that the length of the line segment is $(b - a)\sqrt{1 + m^2}$. Verify this result by computing the length of the line segment using the distance formula.

33. **Functions from arc length** What differentiable functions have an arc length on the interval $[a, b]$ given by the following integrals? Note that the answers are not unique. Give a family of functions that satisfy the conditions.

   a. $\int_a^b \sqrt{1 + 16x^4}\,dx$ b. $\int_a^b \sqrt{1 + 36\cos^2 2x}\,dx$

34. **Function from arc length** Find a curve that passes through the point $(1, 5)$ and has an arc length on the interval $[2, 6]$ given by $\int_2^6 \sqrt{1 + 16x^{-6}}\,dx$.

T 35. **Cosine vs. parabola** Which curve has the greater length on the interval $[-1, 1]$, $y = 1 - x^2$ or $y = \cos(\pi x/2)$?

36. **Function defined as an integral** Write the integral that gives the length of the curve $y = f(x) = \int_0^x \sin t\,dt$ on the interval $[0, \pi]$.

Applications

T 37. **Golden Gate cables** The profile of the cables on a suspension bridge may be modeled by a parabola. The central span of the Golden Gate Bridge (see figure) is 1280 m long and 152 m high. The parabola $y = 0.00037x^2$ gives a good fit to the shape of the cables, where $|x| \le 640$, and x and y are measured in meters. Approximate the length of the cables that stretch between the tops of the two towers.

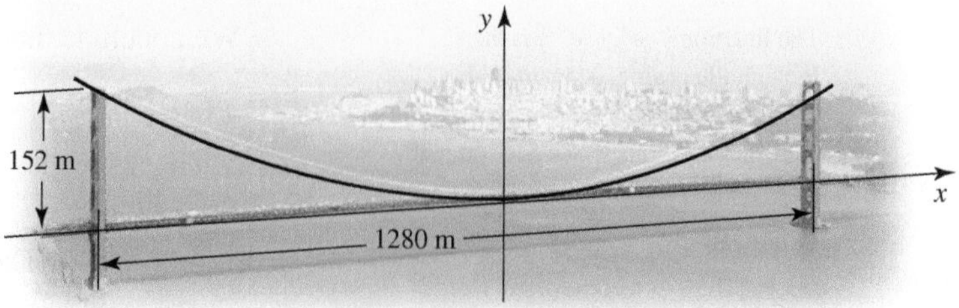

T 38. **Gateway Arch** The shape of the Gateway Arch in St. Louis (with a height and a base length of 630 ft) is modeled by the function $y = -630\cosh(x/239.2) + 1260$, where $|x| \le 315$, and x and y are measured in feet (see figure). The function $\cosh x$ is the **hyperbolic cosine**, defined by $\cosh x = \frac{e^x + e^{-x}}{2}$ (see Section 6.10

for more on hyperbolic functions). Estimate the length of the Gateway Arch.

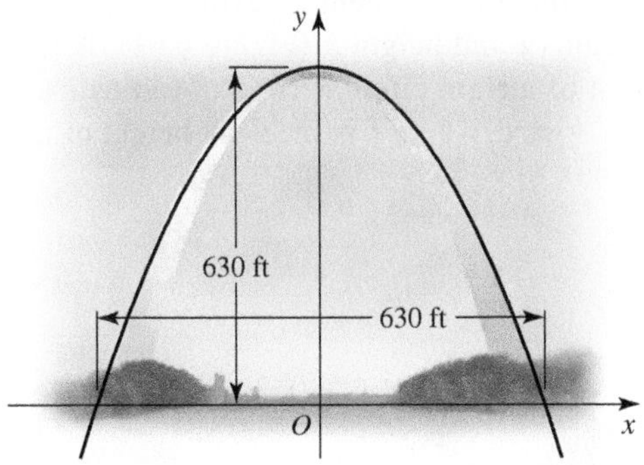

Additional Exercises

39. Lengths of related curves Suppose the graph of f on the interval $[a, b]$ has length L, where f' is continuous on $[a, b]$. Evaluate the following integrals in terms of L.

a. $\int_{a/2}^{b/2} \sqrt{1 + f'(2x)^2}\, dx$ **b.** $\int_{a/c}^{b/c} \sqrt{1 + f'(cx)^2}\, dx$ if $c \neq 0$

40. Lengths of symmetric curves Suppose a curve is described by $y = f(x)$ on the interval $[-b, b]$, where f' is continuous on $[-b, b]$. Show that if f is symmetric about the origin (f is odd) *or* f is symmetric about the y-axis (f is even), then the length of the curve $y = f(x)$ from $x = -b$ to $x = b$ is twice the length of the curve from $x = 0$ to $x = b$. Use a geometric argument and prove it using integration.

41. A family of exponential functions

a. Show that the arc length integral for the function $f(x) = Ae^{ax} + \frac{1}{4Aa^2}e^{-ax}$, where $a > 0$ and $A > 0$, may be integrated using methods you already know.

b. Verify that the arc length of the curve $y = f(x)$ on the interval $[0, \ln 2]$ is

$$A(2^a - 1) - \frac{1}{4a^2 A}(2^{-a} - 1).$$

T **42. Bernoulli's "parabolas"** Johann Bernoulli (1667–1748) evaluated the arc length of curves of the form $y = x^{(2n+1)/2n}$, where n is a positive integer, on the interval $[0, a]$.

a. Write the arc length integral.

b. Make the change of variables $u^2 = 1 + \left(\frac{2n + 1}{2n}\right)^2 x^{1/n}$ to obtain a new integral with respect to u.

c. Use the Binomial Theorem to expand this integrand and evaluate the integral.

d. The case $n = 1$ ($y = x^{3/2}$) was done in Example 1. With $a = 1$, compute the arc length in the cases $n = 2$ and $n = 3$. Does the arc length increase or decrease with n?

e. Graph the arc length of the curves for $a = 1$ as a function of n.

QUICK CHECK ANSWERS

1. $\sqrt{2}a$ (The length of the line segment joining the points) **2.** $\sqrt{2}(d - c)$ (The length of the line segment joining the points) **3.** $L = \int_0^\pi \sqrt{1 + \cos^2 y}\, dy$ ◀

6.6 Surface Area

In Sections 6.3 and 6.4, we introduced solids of revolution and presented methods for computing the volume of such solids. We now consider a related problem: computing the *area* of the surface of a solid of revolution. Surface area calculations are important in aerodynamics (computing the lift on an airplane wing) and biology (computing transport rates across cell membranes), to name just two applications. Here is an interesting observation: A surface area problem is "between" a volume problem (which is three-dimensional) and an arc length problem (which is one-dimensional). For this reason, you will see ideas that appear in both volume and arc length calculations as we develop the surface area integral.

Some Preliminary Calculations

Consider a curve $y = f(x)$ on an interval $[a, b]$, where f is a nonnegative function with a continuous first derivative on $[a, b]$. Now imagine revolving the curve about the x-axis to generate a *surface of revolution* (Figure 6.60). Our objective is to find the area of this surface.

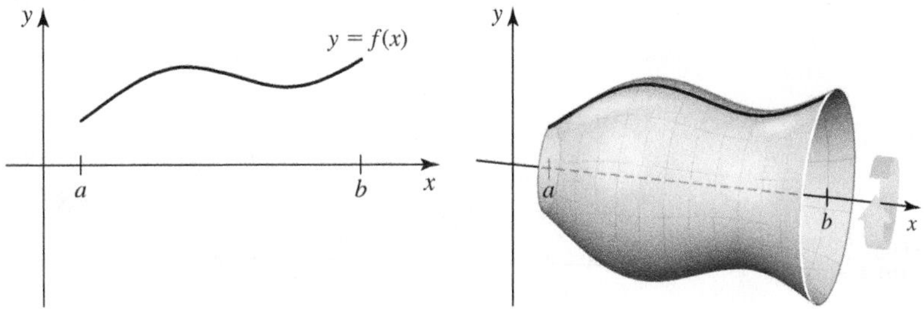

Figure 6.60

➤ One way to derive the formula for the surface area of a cone (not including the base) is to cut the cone on a line from its base to its vertex. When the cone is unfolded, it forms a sector of a circular disk of radius ℓ with a curved edge of length $2\pi r$. This sector is a fraction $\frac{2\pi r}{2\pi\ell} = \frac{r}{\ell}$ of a full circular disk of radius ℓ. So the area of the sector, which is also the surface area of the cone, is $\pi\ell^2 \cdot \frac{r}{\ell} = \pi r\ell$.

Curved edge length = $2\pi r$

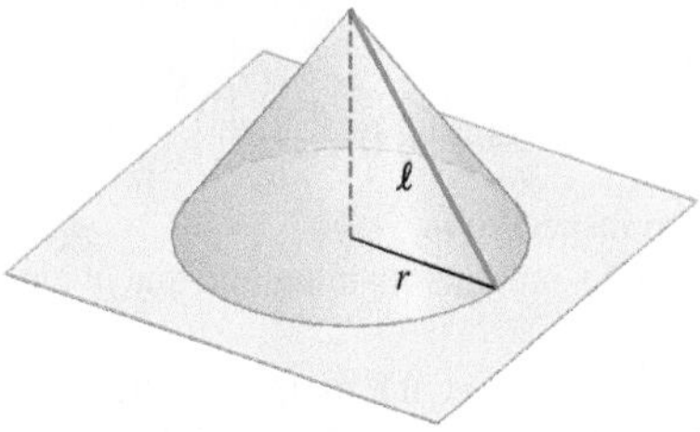

Curved edge length = $2\pi r$

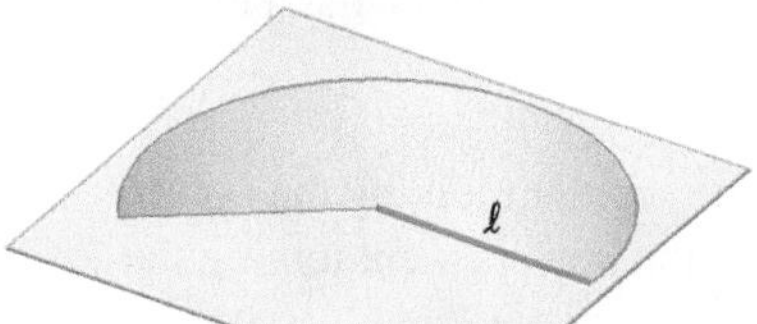

Before tackling this problem, we consider a preliminary problem upon which we build a general surface area formula. First consider the graph of $f(x) = rx/h$ on the interval $[0, h]$, where $h > 0$ and $r > 0$. When this line segment is revolved about the x-axis, it generates the surface of a cone of radius r and height h (Figure 6.61). A formula from geometry states that the surface area of a right circular cone of radius r and height h (excluding the base) is $\pi r\sqrt{r^2 + h^2} = \pi r\ell$, where ℓ is the slant height of the cone (the length of the slanted "edge" of the cone).

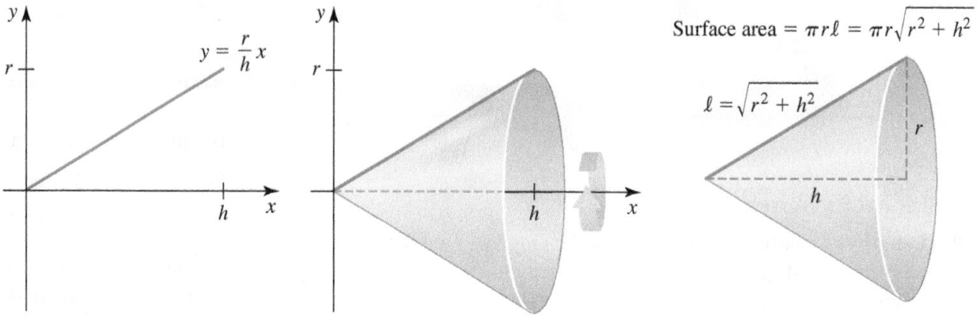

Figure 6.61

QUICK CHECK 1 Which is greater, the surface area of a cone of height 10 and radius 20 or the surface area of a cone of height 20 and radius 10 (excluding the bases)? ◄

With this result, we can solve a preliminary problem that will be useful. Consider the linear function $f(x) = cx$ on the interval $[a, b]$, where $0 < a < b$ and $c > 0$. When this line segment is revolved about the x-axis, it generates a *frustum of a cone* (a cone whose top has been sliced off). The goal is to find S, the surface area of the frustum. Figure 6.62 shows that S is the difference between the surface area S_b of the cone that extends over the interval $[0, b]$ and the surface area S_a of the cone that extends over the interval $[0, a]$.

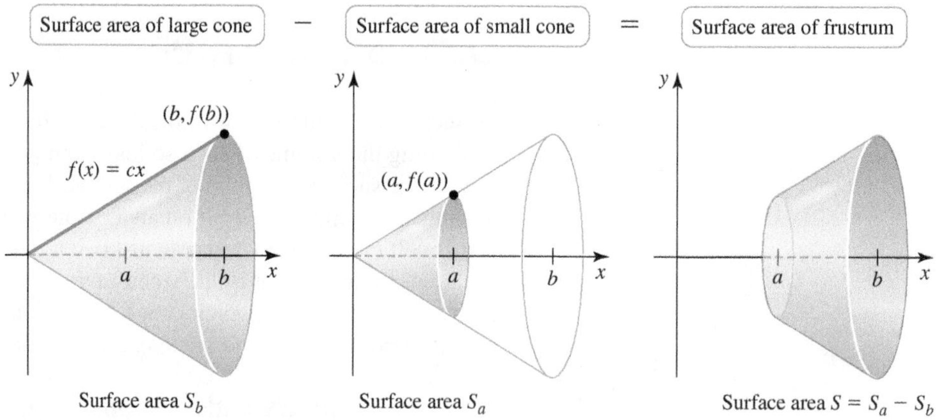

Figure 6.62

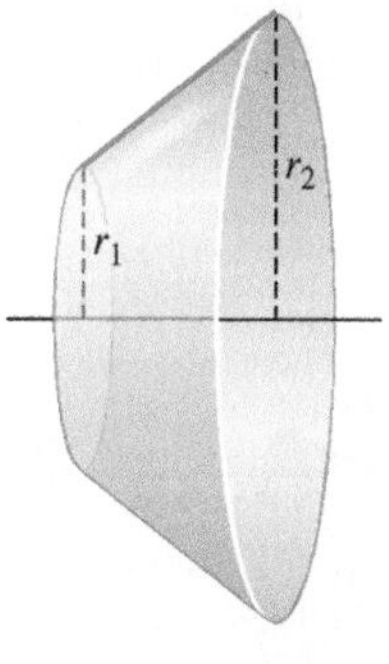

Surface area of frustrum:
$S = \pi(f(b) + f(a))\ell$
$= \pi(r_2 + r_1)\ell$

Notice that the radius of the cone on $[0, b]$ is $r = f(b) = cb$, and its height is $h = b$. Therefore, this cone has surface area

$$S_b = \pi r\sqrt{r^2 + h^2} = \pi(bc)\sqrt{(bc)^2 + b^2} = \pi b^2 c\sqrt{c^2 + 1}.$$

Similarly, the cone on $[0, a]$ has radius $r = f(a) = ca$ and height $h = a$, so its surface area is

$$S_a = \pi(ac)\sqrt{(ac)^2 + a^2} = \pi a^2 c\sqrt{c^2 + 1}.$$

The difference of the surface areas $S_b - S_a$ is the surface area S of the frustum on $[a, b]$:

$$S = S_b - S_a = \pi b^2 c\sqrt{c^2 + 1} - \pi a^2 c\sqrt{c^2 + 1}$$
$$= \pi c(b^2 - a^2)\sqrt{c^2 + 1}.$$

A slightly different form of this surface area formula will be useful. Observe that the line segment from $(a, f(a))$ to $(b, f(b))$ (which is the slant height of the frustum in Figure 6.62) has length

$$\ell = \sqrt{(b - a)^2 + (bc - ac)^2} = (b - a)\sqrt{c^2 + 1}.$$

Therefore, the surface area of the frustum can also be written

$$\begin{aligned} S &= \pi c(b^2 - a^2)\sqrt{c^2 + 1} \\ &= \pi c(b + a)(b - a)\sqrt{c^2 + 1} && \text{Factor } b^2 - a^2. \\ &= \pi\Big(\underbrace{cb}_{f(b)} + \underbrace{ca}_{f(a)}\Big)\underbrace{(b - a)\sqrt{c^2 + 1}}_{\ell} && \text{Expand } c(b + a). \\ &= \pi(f(b) + f(a))\ell. \end{aligned}$$

This result can be generalized to *any* linear function $g(x) = cx + d$ that is positive on the interval $[a, b]$. That is, the surface area of the frustum generated by revolving the line segment between $(a, g(a))$ and $(b, g(b))$ about the x-axis is given by $\pi(g(b) + g(a))\ell$ (Exercise 36).

QUICK CHECK 2 What is the surface area of the frustum of a cone generated when the graph of $f(x) = 3x$ on the interval $[2, 5]$ is revolved about the x-axis? ◀

Surface Area Formula

With the surface area formula for a frustum of a cone, we now derive a general area formula for a surface of revolution. We assume the surface is generated by revolving the graph of a positive, differentiable function f on the interval $[a, b]$ about the x-axis. We begin by subdividing the interval $[a, b]$ into n subintervals of equal length $\Delta x = \frac{b - a}{n}$. The grid points in this partition are

$$x_0 = a, x_1, x_2, \ldots, x_{n-1}, x_n = b.$$

Now consider the kth subinterval $[x_{k-1}, x_k]$ and the line segment between the points $(x_{k-1}, f(x_{k-1}))$ and $(x_k, f(x_k))$ (Figure 6.63). We let the change in the y-coordinates between these points be $\Delta y_k = f(x_k) - f(x_{k-1})$.

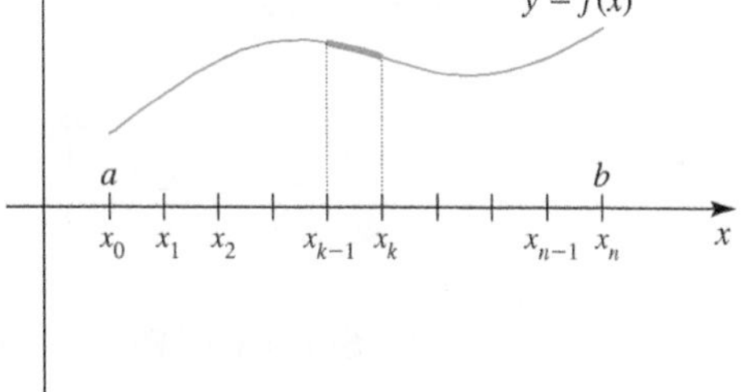

Figure 6.63

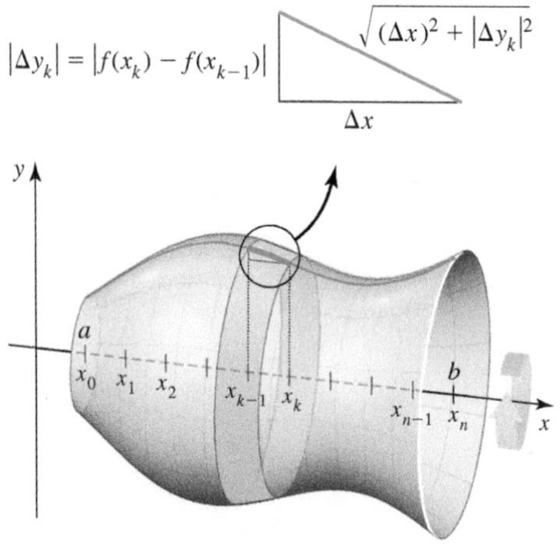

Figure 6.64

When this line segment is revolved about the x-axis, it generates a frustum of a cone (Figure 6.64). The slant height of this frustum is the length of the hypotenuse of a right triangle whose sides have lengths Δx and $|\Delta y_k|$. Therefore, the slant height of the kth frustum is

$$\sqrt{(\Delta x)^2 + |\Delta y_k|^2} = \sqrt{(\Delta x)^2 + (\Delta y_k)^2}$$

and its surface area is

$$S_k = \pi(f(x_k) + f(x_{k-1}))\sqrt{(\Delta x)^2 + (\Delta y_k)^2}.$$

It follows that the area S of the entire surface of revolution is approximately the sum of the surface areas of the individual frustums S_k, for $k = 1, \ldots, n$; that is,

$$S \approx \sum_{k=1}^{n} S_k = \sum_{k=1}^{n} \pi(f(x_k) + f(x_{k-1}))\sqrt{(\Delta x)^2 + (\Delta y_k)^2}.$$

➤ Notice that f is assumed to be differentiable on $[a, b]$; therefore, it satisfies the conditions of the Mean Value Theorem. Recall that a similar argument was used to derive the arc length formula in Section 6.5.

We would like to identify this sum as a Riemann sum. However, one more step is required to put it in the correct form. We apply the Mean Value Theorem on the kth subinterval $[x_{k-1}, x_k]$ and observe that

$$\frac{f(x_k) - f(x_{k-1})}{\Delta x} = f'(x_k^*),$$

for some number x_k^* in the interval (x_{k-1}, x_k), for $k = 1, \ldots, n$. It follows that $\Delta y_k = f(x_k) - f(x_{k-1}) = f'(x_k^*)\Delta x$.

We now replace Δy_k with $f'(x_k^*)\Delta x$ in the expression for the approximate surface area. The result is

$$\begin{aligned} S \approx \sum_{k=1}^{n} S_k &= \sum_{k=1}^{n} \pi(f(x_k) + f(x_{k-1}))\sqrt{(\Delta x)^2 + (\Delta y_k)^2} \\ &= \sum_{k=1}^{n} \pi(f(x_k) + f(x_{k-1}))\sqrt{(\Delta x)^2(1 + f'(x_k^*)^2)} && \text{Mean Value Theorem} \\ &= \sum_{k=1}^{n} \pi(f(x_k) + f(x_{k-1}))\sqrt{1 + f'(x_k^*)^2}\,\Delta x. && \text{Factor out } \Delta x. \end{aligned}$$

When Δx is small, we have $x_{k-1} \approx x_k \approx x_k^*$, and by the continuity of f, it follows that $f(x_{k-1}) \approx f(x_k) \approx f(x_k^*)$, for $k = 1, \ldots, n$. These observations allow us to write

$$\begin{aligned} S &\approx \sum_{k=1}^{n} \pi(f(x_k^*) + f(x_k^*))\sqrt{1 + f'(x_k^*)^2}\,\Delta x \\ &= \sum_{k=1}^{n} 2\pi f(x_k^*)\sqrt{1 + f'(x_k^*)^2}\,\Delta x. \end{aligned}$$

This approximation to S, which has the form of a Riemann sum, improves as the number of subintervals increases and as the length of the subintervals approaches 0. Specifically, as $n \to \infty$ and as $\Delta x \to 0$, we obtain an integral for the surface area:

$$\begin{aligned} S &= \lim_{n\to\infty} \sum_{k=1}^{n} 2\pi f(x_k^*)\sqrt{1 + f'(x_k^*)^2}\,\Delta x \\ &= \int_a^b 2\pi f(x)\sqrt{1 + f'(x)^2}\,dx. \end{aligned}$$

DEFINITION Area of a Surface of Revolution

Let f be a nonnegative function with a continuous first derivative on the interval $[a, b]$. The area of the surface generated when the graph of f on the interval $[a, b]$ is revolved about the x-axis is

$$S = \int_a^b 2\pi f(x)\sqrt{1 + f'(x)^2}\,dx.$$

QUICK CHECK 3 Let $f(x) = c$, where $c > 0$. What surface is generated when the graph of f on $[a, b]$ is revolved about the x-axis? Without using calculus, what is the area of the surface? ◀

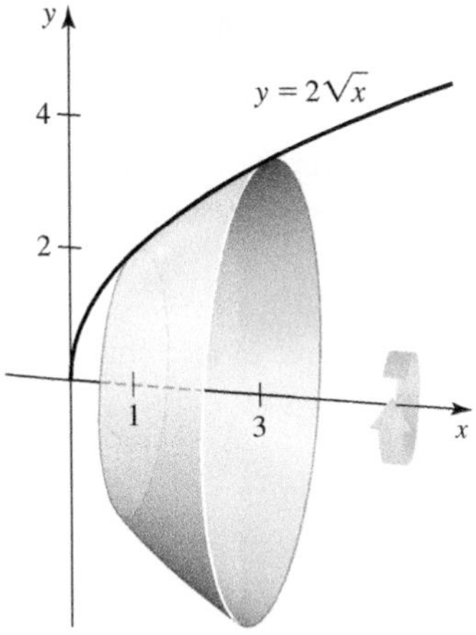

Figure 6.65

EXAMPLE 1 Using the surface area formula The graph of $f(x) = 2\sqrt{x}$ on the interval $[1, 3]$ is revolved about the x-axis. What is the area of the surface generated (Figure 6.65)?

SOLUTION Noting that $f'(x) = \frac{1}{\sqrt{x}}$, the surface area formula gives

$$\begin{aligned} S &= \int_a^b 2\pi f(x)\sqrt{1 + f'(x)^2}\,dx \\ &= 2\pi \int_1^3 2\sqrt{x}\sqrt{1 + \frac{1}{x}}\,dx && \text{Substitute for } f \text{ and } f'. \\ &= 4\pi \int_1^3 \sqrt{x + 1}\,dx && \text{Simplify.} \\ &= \frac{8\pi}{3}(x + 1)^{3/2}\Big|_1^3 = \frac{16\pi}{3}(4 - \sqrt{2}). && \text{Integrate and simplify.} \end{aligned}$$

Related Exercises 5–14 ◄

EXAMPLE 2 Surface area of a spherical cap A spherical cap is produced when a sphere of radius a is sliced by a horizontal plane that is a vertical distance h below the north pole of the sphere, where $0 \le h \le 2a$ (Figure 6.66a). We take the spherical cap to be that part of the sphere above the plane, so that h is the depth of the cap. Show that the area of a spherical cap of depth h cut from a sphere of radius a is $2\pi ah$.

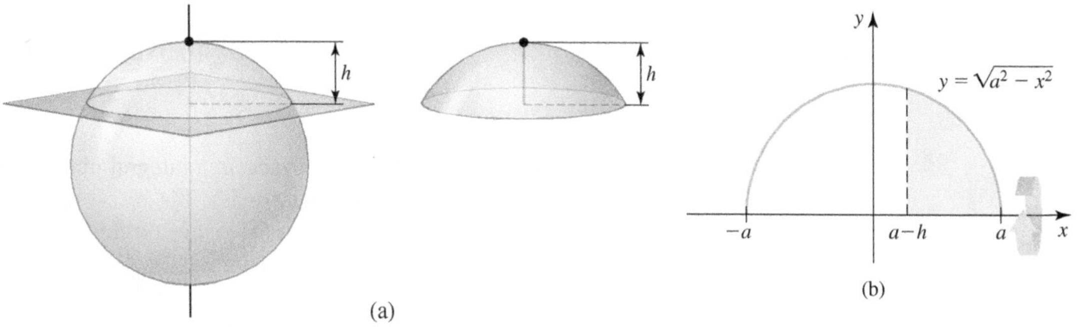

Figure 6.66

SOLUTION To generate the spherical surface, we revolve the curve $f(x) = \sqrt{a^2 - x^2}$ on the interval $[-a, a]$ about the x-axis (Figure 6.66b). The spherical cap of height h corresponds to that part of the sphere on the interval $[a - h, a]$, for $0 \le h \le 2a$. Noting that $f'(x) = -x(a^2 - x^2)^{-1/2}$, the surface area of the spherical cap of height h is

➤ Notice that f is not differentiable at $\pm a$. Nevertheless, in this case, the surface area integral can be evaluated using methods you know.

$$\begin{aligned} S &= \int_a^b 2\pi f(x)\sqrt{1 + f'(x)^2}\,dx \\ &= 2\pi \int_{a-h}^a \sqrt{a^2 - x^2}\sqrt{1 + (-x(a^2 - x^2)^{-1/2})^2}\,dx && \text{Substitute for } f \text{ and } f'. \\ &= 2\pi \int_{a-h}^a \sqrt{a^2 - x^2}\sqrt{\frac{a^2}{a^2 - x^2}}\,dx && \text{Simplify.} \\ &= 2\pi \int_{a-h}^a a\,dx = 2\pi ah. && \text{Simplify and integrate.} \end{aligned}$$

➤ The surface area of a sphere of radius a is $4\pi a^2$.

It is worthwhile to check this result with three special cases. With $h = 2a$, we have a complete sphere, so $S = 4\pi a^2$. The case $h = a$ corresponds to a hemispherical cap, so $S = (4\pi a^2)/2 = 2\pi a^2$. The case $h = 0$ corresponds to no spherical cap, so $S = 0$.

Related Exercises 5–14 ◄

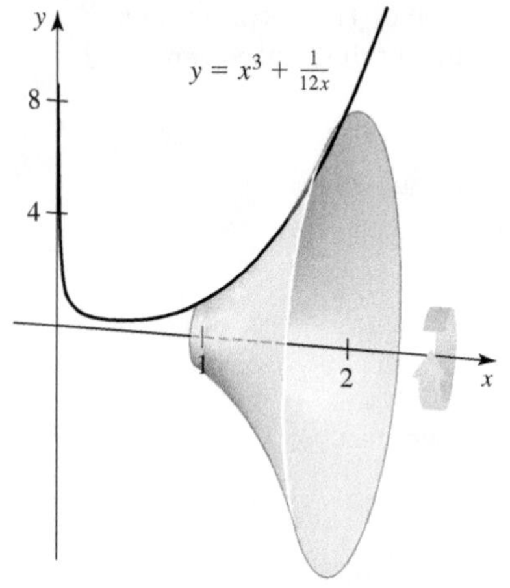

Figure 6.67

EXAMPLE 3 Painting a funnel The curved surface of a funnel is generated by revolving the graph of $y = f(x) = x^3 + \dfrac{1}{12x}$ on the interval $[1, 2]$ about the x-axis (Figure 6.67). Approximately what volume of paint is needed to cover the outside of the funnel with a layer of paint 0.05 cm thick? Assume that x and y are measured in centimeters.

SOLUTION Note that $f'(x) = 3x^2 - \dfrac{1}{12x^2}$. Therefore, the surface area of the funnel in cm^2 is

$$\begin{aligned} S &= \int_a^b 2\pi f(x)\sqrt{1 + f'(x)^2}\,dx \\ &= 2\pi \int_1^2 \left(x^3 + \frac{1}{12x}\right)\sqrt{1 + \left(3x^2 - \frac{1}{12x^2}\right)^2}\,dx && \text{Substitute for } f \text{ and } f'. \\ &= 2\pi \int_1^2 \left(x^3 + \frac{1}{12x}\right)\sqrt{\left(3x^2 + \frac{1}{12x^2}\right)^2}\,dx && \text{Expand and factor under square root.} \\ &= 2\pi \int_1^2 \left(x^3 + \frac{1}{12x}\right)\left(3x^2 + \frac{1}{12x^2}\right)dx && \text{Simplify.} \\ &= \frac{12{,}289}{192}\pi. && \text{Evaluate integral.} \end{aligned}$$

Because the paint layer is 0.05 cm thick, the approximate volume of paint needed is

$$\left(\frac{12{,}289\pi}{192}\,\text{cm}^2\right)(0.05\text{ cm}) \approx 10.1\text{ cm}^3.$$

Related Exercises 15–16 ◄

The derivation that led to the surface area integral may be used when a curve is revolved about the y-axis (rather than the x-axis). The result is the same integral with x replaced with y. For example, if the curve $x = g(y)$ on the interval $[c, d]$ is revolved about the y-axis, the area of the surface generated is

$$S = \int_c^d 2\pi g(y)\sqrt{1 + g'(y)^2}\,dy.$$

To use this integral, we must first describe the given curve as a differentiable function of y.

EXAMPLE 4 Change of perspective Consider the function $y = \ln\left(\dfrac{x + \sqrt{x^2 - 1}}{2}\right)$. Find the area of the surface generated when the part of the curve between the points $\left(\frac{5}{4}, 0\right)$ and $\left(\frac{17}{8}, \ln 2\right)$ is revolved about the y-axis (Figure 6.68).

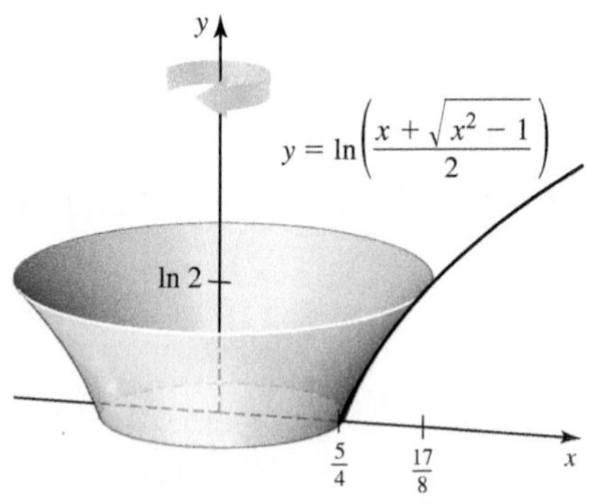

Figure 6.68

SOLUTION We solve for x in terms of y in the following steps:

$$\begin{aligned} y &= \ln\left(\frac{x + \sqrt{x^2 - 1}}{2}\right) \\ e^y &= \frac{x + \sqrt{x^2 - 1}}{2} && \text{Exponentiate both sides.} \\ 2e^y - x &= \sqrt{x^2 - 1} && \text{Rearrange terms.} \\ 4e^{2y} - 4xe^y + x^2 &= x^2 - 1 && \text{Square both sides.} \\ x = g(y) &= e^y + \frac{1}{4}e^{-y}. && \text{Solve for } x. \end{aligned}$$

Note that $g'(y) = e^y - \frac{1}{4}e^{-y}$ and that the interval of integration on the y-axis is $[0, \ln 2]$. The area of the surface is

$$S = \int_c^d 2\pi g(y)\sqrt{1 + g'(y)^2}\,dy$$

$$= 2\pi \int_0^{\ln 2} \left(e^y + \frac{1}{4}e^{-y}\right)\sqrt{1 + \left(e^y - \frac{1}{4}e^{-y}\right)^2}\,dy \quad \text{Substitute for } g \text{ and } g'.$$

$$= 2\pi \int_0^{\ln 2} \left(e^y + \frac{1}{4}e^{-y}\right)\sqrt{\left(e^y + \frac{1}{4}e^{-y}\right)^2}\,dy \quad \text{Expand and factor.}$$

$$= 2\pi \int_0^{\ln 2} \left(e^y + \frac{1}{4}e^{-y}\right)^2 dy \quad \text{Simplify.}$$

$$= 2\pi \int_0^{\ln 2} \left(e^{2y} + \frac{1}{2} + \frac{1}{16}e^{-2y}\right) dy \quad \text{Expand.}$$

$$= \pi\left(\frac{195}{64} + \ln 2\right). \quad \text{Integrate.}$$

Related Exercises 17–20 ◀

SECTION 6.6 EXERCISES

Review Questions

1. What is the area of the curved surface of a right circular cone of radius 3 and height 4?

2. A frustum of a cone is generated by revolving the graph of $y = 4x$ on the interval $[2, 6]$ about the x-axis. What is the area of the surface of the frustum?

3. Suppose f is positive and differentiable on $[a, b]$. The curve $y = f(x)$ on $[a, b]$ is revolved about the x-axis. Explain how to find the area of the surface that is generated.

4. Suppose g is positive and differentiable on $[c, d]$. The curve $x = g(y)$ on $[c, d]$ is revolved about the y-axis. Explain how to find the area of the surface that is generated.

Basic Skills

5–14. Computing surface areas *Find the area of the surface generated when the given curve is revolved about the x-axis.*

5. $y = 3x + 4$ on $[0, 6]$

6. $y = 12 - 3x$ on $[1, 3]$

7. $y = 8\sqrt{x}$ on $[9, 20]$

8. $y = x^3$ on $[0, 1]$

9. $y = x^{3/2} - \dfrac{x^{1/2}}{3}$ on $[1, 2]$

10. $y = \sqrt{4x + 6}$ on $[0, 5]$

11. $y = \dfrac{1}{4}(e^{2x} + e^{-2x})$ on $[-2, 2]$

12. $y = \dfrac{x^4}{8} + \dfrac{1}{4x^2}$ on $[1, 2]$

13. $y = \dfrac{x^3}{3} + \dfrac{1}{4x}$ on $\left[\dfrac{1}{2}, 2\right]$

14. $y = \sqrt{5x - x^2}$ on $[1, 4]$

15–16. Painting surfaces *A 1.5-mm layer of paint is applied to one side of the following surfaces. Find the approximate volume of paint needed. Assume that x and y are measured in meters.*

15. The spherical zone generated when the curve $y = \sqrt{8x - x^2}$ on the interval $[1, 7]$ is revolved about the x-axis

16. The spherical zone generated when the upper portion of the circle $x^2 + y^2 = 100$ on the interval $[-8, 8]$ is revolved about the x-axis

17–20. Revolving about the y-axis *Find the area of the surface generated when the given curve is revolved about the y-axis.*

17. $y = (3x)^{1/3}$, for $0 \le x \le \dfrac{8}{3}$

18. $y = \dfrac{x^2}{4}$, for $2 \le x \le 4$

19. The part of the curve $y = 4x - 1$ between the points $(1, 3)$ and $(4, 15)$

20. The part of the curve $y = \frac{1}{2}\ln\left(2x + \sqrt{4x^2 - 1}\right)$ between the points $\left(\frac{1}{2}, 0\right)$ and $\left(\frac{17}{16}, \ln 2\right)$

Further Explorations

21. **Explain why or why not** Determine whether the following statements are true and give an explanation or counterexample.

    a. If the curve $y = f(x)$ on the interval $[a, b]$ is revolved about the y-axis, the area of the surface generated is
    $$\int_{f(a)}^{f(b)} 2\pi f(y)\sqrt{1 + f'(y)^2}\,dy.$$

    b. If f is not one-to-one on the interval $[a, b]$, then the area of the surface generated when the graph of f on $[a, b]$ is revolved about the x-axis is not defined.

c. Let $f(x) = 12x^2$. The area of the surface generated when the graph of f on $[-4, 4]$ is revolved about the x-axis is twice the area of the surface generated when the graph of f on $[0, 4]$ is revolved about the x-axis.

d. Let $f(x) = 12x^2$. The area of the surface generated when the graph of f on $[-4, 4]$ is revolved about the y-axis is twice the area of the surface generated when the graph of f on $[0, 4]$ is revolved about the y-axis.

22–25. Surface area calculations *Use the method of your choice to determine the area of the surface generated when the following curves are revolved about the indicated axis.*

22. $x = \sqrt{12y - y^2}$, for $2 \le y \le 10$; about the y-axis

23. $x = 4y^{3/2} - \dfrac{y^{1/2}}{12}$, for $1 \le y \le 4$; about the y-axis

24. $y = 1 + \sqrt{1 - x^2}$ between the points $(1, 1)$ and $\left(\dfrac{\sqrt{3}}{2}, \dfrac{3}{2}\right)$; about the y-axis

25. $y = 9x^{2/3} - \dfrac{x^{4/3}}{32}$, for $1 \le x \le 8$; about the x-axis

26–29. Surface area using technology *Consider the following curves on the given intervals.*

a. *Write the integral that gives the area of the surface generated when the curve is revolved about the x-axis.*

b. *Use a calculator or software to approximate the surface area.*

26. $y = x^5$ on $[0, 1]$

27. $y = \cos x$ on $\left[0, \dfrac{\pi}{2}\right]$

28. $y = \ln x^2$ on $[1, \sqrt{e}]$

29. $y = \tan x$ on $\left[0, \dfrac{\pi}{4}\right]$

30. Cones and cylinders The volume of a cone of radius r and height h is one-third the volume of a cylinder with the same radius and height. Does the surface area of a cone of radius r and height h equal one-third the surface area of a cylinder with the same radius and height? If not, find the correct relationship. Exclude the bases of the cone and cylinder.

31. Revolving an astroid Consider the upper half of the astroid described by $x^{2/3} + y^{2/3} = a^{2/3}$, where $a > 0$ and $|x| \le a$. Find the area of the surface generated when this curve is revolved about the x-axis. Use symmetry. Note that the function describing the curve is not differentiable at 0. However, the surface area integral can be evaluated using methods you know.

Applications

32. Surface area of a torus When the circle $x^2 + (y - a)^2 = r^2$ on the interval $[-r, r]$ is revolved about the x-axis, the result is the surface of a torus, where $0 < r < a$. Show that the surface area of the torus is $S = 4\pi^2 ar$.

33. Zones of a sphere Suppose a sphere of radius r is sliced by two horizontal planes h units apart (see figure). Show that the surface area of the resulting zone on the sphere is $2\pi rh$, independent of the location of the cutting planes.

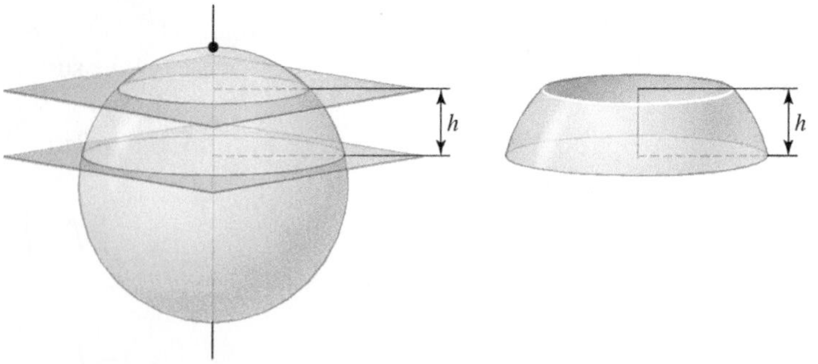

34. Surface area of an ellipsoid If the top half of the ellipse $\dfrac{x^2}{a^2} + \dfrac{y^2}{b^2} = 1$ is revolved about the x-axis, the result is an *ellipsoid* whose axis along the x-axis has length $2a$, whose axis along the y-axis has length $2b$, and whose axis perpendicular to the xy-plane has length $2b$. We assume that $0 < b < a$ (see figure). Use the following steps to find the surface area S of this ellipsoid.

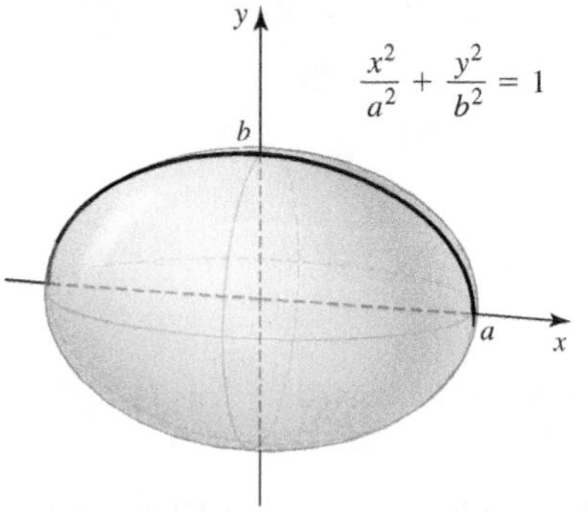

a. Use the surface area formula to show that
$$S = \frac{4\pi b}{a}\int_0^a \sqrt{a^2 - c^2x^2}\,dx, \text{ where } c^2 = 1 - \frac{b^2}{a^2}.$$

b. Use the change of variables $u = cx$ to show that
$$S = \frac{4\pi b}{\sqrt{a^2 - b^2}}\int_0^{\sqrt{a^2-b^2}} \sqrt{a^2 - u^2}\,du.$$

c. A table of integrals shows that
$$\int \sqrt{a^2 - u^2}\,du = \frac{1}{2}\left(u\sqrt{a^2 - u^2} + a^2 \sin^{-1}\frac{u}{a}\right) + C.$$
Use this fact to show that the surface area of the ellipsoid is
$$S = 2\pi b\left(b + \frac{a^2}{\sqrt{a^2 - b^2}}\sin^{-1}\frac{\sqrt{a^2 - b^2}}{a}\right).$$

d. If a and b have units of length (say, meters), what are the units of S according to this formula?

e. Use part (a) to show that if $a = b$, then $S = 4\pi a^2$, which is the surface area of a sphere of radius a.

35. Surface-area-to-volume ratio (SAV) In the design of solid objects (both artificial and natural), the ratio of the surface area to the volume of the object is important. Animals typically generate heat at a rate proportional to their volume and lose heat at a rate proportional to their surface area. Therefore, animals with a low SAV ratio tend to retain heat, whereas animals with a high SAV ratio (such as children and hummingbirds) lose heat relatively quickly.

a. What is the SAV ratio of a cube with side lengths a?

b. What is the SAV ratio of a ball with radius a?

c. Use the result of Exercise 34 to find the SAV ratio of an ellipsoid whose long axis has length $2a\sqrt[3]{4}$, for $a \geq 1$, and whose other two axes have half the length of the long axis. (This scaling is used so that, for a given value of a, the volumes of the ellipsoid and the ball of radius a are equal.) The volume of a general ellipsoid is $V = \frac{4\pi}{3}ABC$, where the axes have lengths $2A$, $2B$, and $2C$.

d. Graph the SAV ratio of the ball of radius $a \geq 1$ as a function of a (part (b)) and graph the SAV ratio of the ellipsoid described in (part (c)) on the same set of axes. Which object has the smaller SAV ratio?

e. Among all ellipsoids of a fixed volume, which one would you choose for the shape of an animal if the goal is to minimize heat loss?

Additional Exercises

36. Surface area of a frustum Show that the surface area of the frustum of a cone generated by revolving the line segment between $(a, g(a))$ and $(b, g(b))$ about the x-axis is $\pi(g(b) + g(a))\ell$, for any linear function $g(x) = cx + d$ that is positive on the interval $[a, b]$, where ℓ is the slant height of the frustum.

37. Scaling surface area Let f be a nonnegative function with a continuous first derivative on $[a, b]$ and suppose that $g(x) = cf(x)$ and $h(x) = f(cx)$, where $c > 0$. When the curve $y = f(x)$ on $[a, b]$ is revolved about the x-axis, the area of the resulting surface is A. Evaluate the following integrals in terms of A and c.

a. $\displaystyle\int_a^b 2\pi g(x)\sqrt{c^2 + g'(x)^2}\,dx$ **b.** $\displaystyle\int_{a/c}^{b/c} 2\pi h(x)\sqrt{c^2 + h'(x)^2}\,dx$

38. Surface plus cylinder Suppose f is a nonnegative function with a continuous first derivative on $[a, b]$. Let L equal the length of the graph of f on $[a, b]$ and let S be the area of the surface generated by revolving the graph of f on $[a, b]$ about the x-axis. For a positive constant C, assume the curve $y = f(x) + C$ is revolved about the x-axis. Show that the area of the resulting surface equals the sum of S and the surface area of a right circular cylinder of radius C and height L.

QUICK CHECK ANSWERS

1. The surface area of the first cone $(200\sqrt{5}\pi)$ is twice as great as the surface area of the second cone $(100\sqrt{5}\pi)$. **2.** The surface area is $63\sqrt{10}\pi$. **3.** The surface is a cylinder of radius c and height $b - a$. The area of the curved surface is $2\pi c(b - a)$. ◄

6.7 Physical Applications

We continue this chapter on applications of integration with several problems from physics and engineering. The physical themes in these problems are mass, work, force, and pressure. The common mathematical theme is the use of the slice-and-sum strategy, which always leads to a definite integral.

Density and Mass

Density is the concentration of mass in an object and is usually measured in units of mass per volume (for example, g/cm^3). An object with *uniform* density satisfies the basic relationship

$$\text{mass} = \text{density} \cdot \text{volume}.$$

➤ In Chapter 13, we return to mass calculations for two- and three-dimensional objects (plates and solids).

When the density of an object *varies*, this formula no longer holds, and we must appeal to calculus.

In this section, we introduce mass calculations for thin objects that can be viewed as line segments (such as wires or thin bars). The bar shown in Figure 6.69 has a density ρ that varies along its length. For one-dimensional objects, we use *linear density* with units of mass per length (for example, g/cm). What is the mass of such an object?

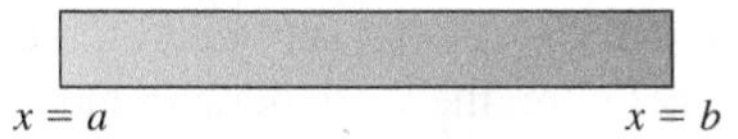

Figure 6.69

QUICK CHECK 1 In Figure 6.69, suppose $a = 0$, $b = 3$, and the density of the rod in g/cm is $\rho(x) = (4 - x)$. (a) Where is the rod lightest and heaviest? (b) What is the density at the middle of the bar? ◄

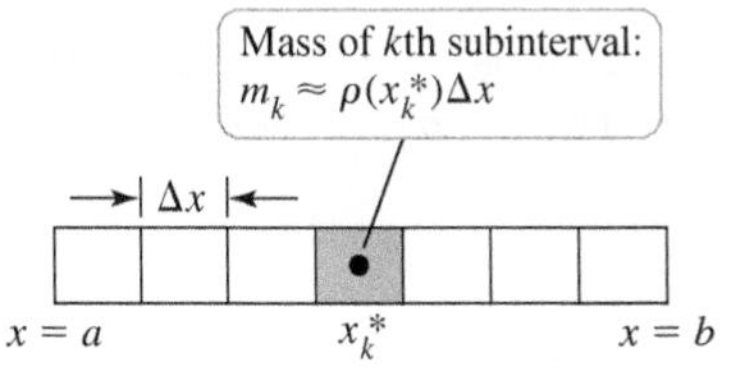

Figure 6.70

We begin by dividing the bar, represented by the interval $a \leq x \leq b$, into n subintervals of equal length $\Delta x = (b - a)/n$ (Figure 6.70). Let x_k^* be any point in the kth subinterval, for $k = 1, \ldots, n$. The mass of the kth segment of the bar m_k is approximately the density at x_k^* multiplied by the length of the interval, or $m_k \approx \rho(x_k^*)\Delta x$. So the approximate mass of the entire bar is

$$\sum_{k=1}^{n} m_k \approx \sum_{k=1}^{n} \underbrace{\rho(x_k^*)\Delta x}_{m_k}.$$

The exact mass is obtained by taking the limit as $n \to \infty$ and as $\Delta x \to 0$, which produces a definite integral.

➤ Note that the units of the integral work out as they should: ρ has units of mass per length and dx has units of length, so $\rho(x)\,dx$ has units of mass.

➤ Another interpretation of the mass integral is that mass equals the average value of the density multiplied by the length of the bar $b - a$.

DEFINITION Mass of a One-Dimensional Object

Suppose a thin bar or wire is represented by the interval $a \le x \le b$ with a density function ρ (with units of mass per length). The **mass** of the object is

$$m = \int_a^b \rho(x)\,dx.$$

EXAMPLE 1 Mass from variable density A thin 2-m bar, represented by the interval $0 \le x \le 2$, is made of an alloy whose density in units of kg/m is given by $\rho(x) = (1 + x^2)$. What is the mass of the bar?

SOLUTION The mass of the bar in kilograms is

$$m = \int_a^b \rho(x)\,dx = \int_0^2 (1 + x^2)\,dx = \left(x + \frac{x^3}{3}\right)\Big|_0^2 = \frac{14}{3}.$$

Related Exercises 9–16 ◀

QUICK CHECK 2 A thin bar occupies the interval $0 \le x \le 2$ and has a density in kg/m of $\rho(x) = (1 + x^2)$. Using the minimum value of the density, what is a lower bound for the mass of the object? Using the maximum value of the density, what is an upper bound for the mass of the object? ◀

Work

Work can be described as the change in energy when a force causes a displacement of an object. When you carry a basket of laundry up a flight of stairs or push a stalled car, you apply a force that results in the displacement of an object, and work is done. If a *constant* force F displaces an object a distance d in the direction of the force, the work done is the force multiplied by the distance:

$$\text{work} = \text{force} \cdot \text{distance}.$$

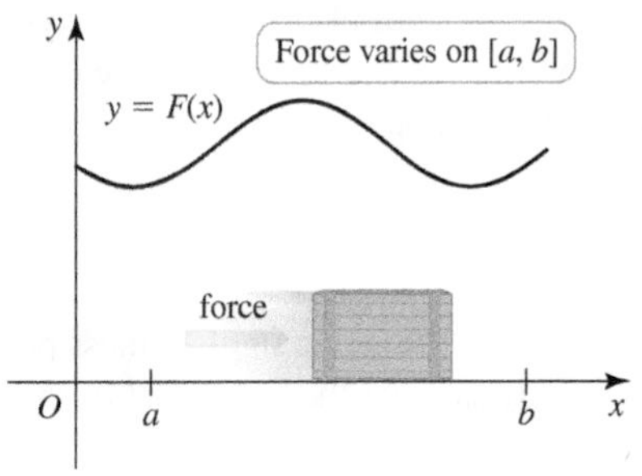

Figure 6.71

It is easiest to use metric units for force and work. A newton (N) is the force required to give a 1-kg mass an acceleration of 1 m/s². A joule (J) is 1 newton-meter (N-m), the work done by a 1-N force over a distance of 1 m.

Calculus enters the picture with *variable* forces. Suppose an object is moved along the x-axis by a variable force F that is directed along the x-axis (Figure 6.71). How much work is done in moving the object between $x = a$ and $x = b$? Once again, we use the slice-and-sum strategy.

The interval $[a, b]$ is divided into n subintervals of equal length $\Delta x = (b - a)/n$. We let x_k^* be any point in the kth subinterval, for $k = 1, \ldots, n$. On that subinterval, the force is approximately constant with a value of $F(x_k^*)$. Therefore, the work done in moving the object across the kth subinterval is approximately $F(x_k^*)\Delta x$ (force · distance). Summing the work done over each of the n subintervals, the total work over the interval $[a, b]$ is approximately

$$W \approx \sum_{k=1}^{n} F(x_k^*)\Delta x.$$

This approximation becomes exact when we take the limit as $n \to \infty$ and $\Delta x \to 0$. The total work done is the integral of the force over the interval $[a, b]$ (or, equivalently, the net area under the force curve in Figure 6.71).

QUICK CHECK 3 Explain why the sum of the work over n subintervals is only an approximation of the total work. ◂

DEFINITION Work

The work done by a variable force F moving an object along a line from $x = a$ to $x = b$ in the direction of the force is

$$W = \int_a^b F(x)\, dx.$$

An application of force and work that is easy to visualize is the stretching and compression of a spring. Suppose an object is attached to a spring on a frictionless horizontal surface; the object slides back and forth under the influence of the spring. We say that the spring is at *equilibrium* when it is neither compressed nor stretched. It is convenient to let x be the position of the object, where $x = 0$ is the equilibrium position (Figure 6.72).

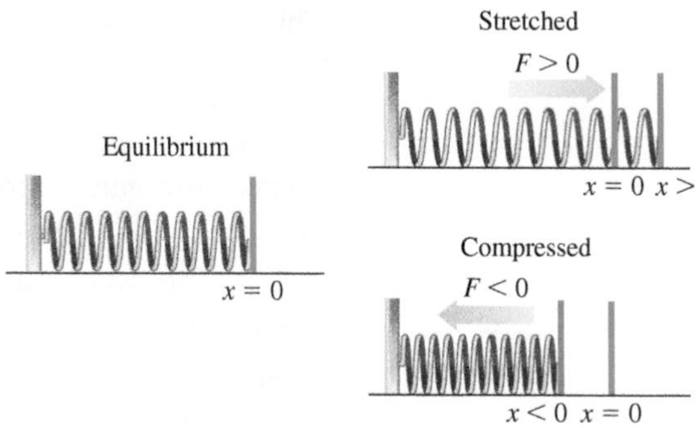

Figure 6.72

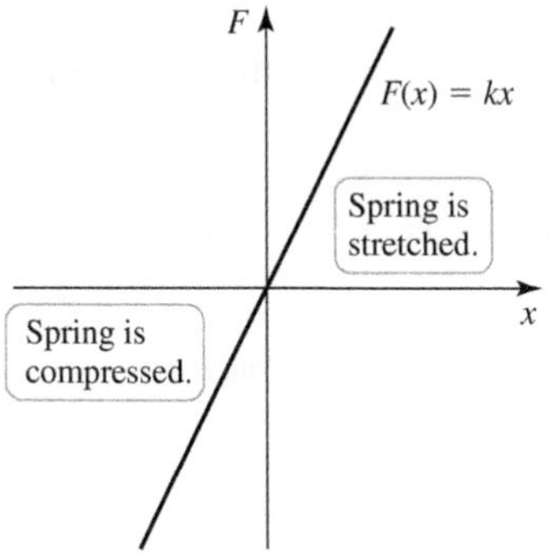

Figure 6.73

According to **Hooke's law**, the force required to keep the spring in a compressed or stretched position x units from the equilibrium position is $F(x) = kx$, where the positive spring constant k measures the stiffness of the spring. Note that to stretch the spring to a position $x > 0$, a force $F > 0$ (in the positive direction) is required. To compress the spring to a position $x < 0$, a force $F < 0$ (in the negative direction) is required (Figure 6.73). In other words, the force required to displace the spring is always in the direction of the displacement.

EXAMPLE 2 **Compressing a spring** Suppose a force of 10 N is required to stretch a spring 0.1 m from its equilibrium position and hold it in that position.

a. Assuming that the spring obeys Hooke's law, find the spring constant k.

b. How much work is needed to *compress* the spring 0.5 m from its equilibrium position?

c. How much work is needed to *stretch* the spring 0.25 m from its equilibrium position?

d. How much additional work is required to stretch the spring 0.25 m if it has already been stretched 0.1 m from its equilibrium position?

SOLUTION

➤ Hooke's law was proposed by the English scientist Robert Hooke (1635–1703), who also coined the biological term *cell*. Hooke's law works well for springs made of many common materials. However, some springs obey more complicated spring laws (see Exercise 51).

a. The fact that a force of 10 N is required to keep the spring stretched at $x = 0.1$ m means (by Hooke's law) that $F(0.1) = k(0.1\text{ m}) = 10\text{ N}$. Solving for the spring constant, we find that $k = 100\text{ N/m}$. Therefore, Hooke's law for this spring is $F(x) = 100x$.

b. The work in joules required to compress the spring from $x = 0$ to $x = -0.5$ is

$$W = \int_a^b F(x)\, dx = \int_0^{-0.5} 100x\, dx = 50x^2 \Big|_0^{-0.5} = 12.5.$$

➤ Notice again that the units in the integral are consistent. If F has units of N and x has units of m, then W has units of $F\,dx$, or N-m, which are the units of work (1 N-m = 1 J).

c. The work in joules required to stretch the spring from $x = 0$ to $x = 0.25$ is

$$W = \int_a^b F(x)\,dx = \int_0^{0.25} 100x\,dx = 50x^2\Big|_0^{0.25} = 3.125.$$

d. The work in joules required to stretch the spring from $x = 0.1$ to $x = 0.35$ is

$$W = \int_a^b F(x)\,dx = \int_{0.1}^{0.35} 100x\,dx = 50x^2\Big|_{0.1}^{0.35} = 5.625.$$

QUICK CHECK 4 In Example 2, explain why more work is needed in part (d) than in part (c), even though the displacement is the same. ◄

Comparing parts (c) and (d), we see that more work is required to stretch the spring 0.25 m starting at $x = 0.1$ than starting at $x = 0$. *Related Exercises 17–26* ◄

Lifting Problems Another common work problem arises when the motion is vertical and the force is the gravitational force. The gravitational force exerted on an object with mass m is $F = mg$, where $g \approx 9.8\text{ m/s}^2$ is the acceleration due to gravity near the surface of Earth. The work in joules required to lift an object of mass m a vertical distance of y meters is

$$\text{work} = \text{force} \cdot \text{distance} = mgy.$$

This type of problem becomes interesting when the object being lifted is a body of water, a rope, or a chain. In these situations, different parts of the object are lifted different distances—so integration is necessary. Here is a typical situation and the strategy used.

Suppose a fluid such as water is pumped out of a tank to a height h above the bottom of the tank. How much work is required, assuming the tank is full of water? Three key observations lead to the solution.

- Water from different levels of the tank is lifted different vertical distances, requiring different amounts of work.
- Two equal volumes of water from the same horizontal plane are lifted the same distance and require the same amount of work.
- A volume V of water has mass ρV, where $\rho = 1\text{ g/cm}^3 = 1000\text{ kg/m}^3$ is the density of water.

➤ The choice of a coordinate system is somewhat arbitrary and may depend on the geometry of the problem. You can let the y-axis point upward or downward, and there are usually several logical choices for the location of $y = 0$. You should experiment with different coordinate systems.

To solve this problem, we let the y-axis point upward with $y = 0$ at the bottom of the tank. The body of water that must be lifted extends from $y = 0$ to $y = b$ (which *may* be the top of the tank). The level to which the water must be raised is $y = h$, where $h \geq b$ (Figure 6.74). We now slice the water into n horizontal layers, each having thickness Δy.

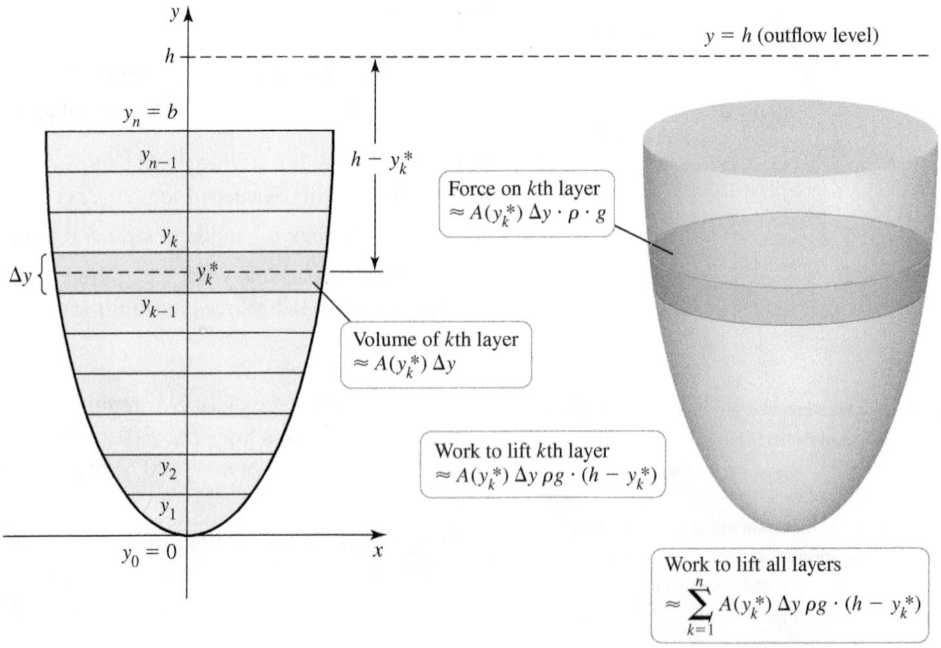

Figure 6.74

The kth layer occupying the interval $[y_{k-1}, y_k]$, for $k = 1, \ldots, n$, is approximately y_k^* units above the bottom of the tank, where y_k^* is any point in $[y_{k-1}, y_k]$.

The cross-sectional area of the kth layer at y_k^*, denoted $A(y_k^*)$, is determined by the shape of the tank; the solution depends on being able to find A for all values of y. Because the volume of the kth layer is approximately $A(y_k^*)\Delta y$, the force on the kth layer (its weight) is

$$F_k = mg \approx \overbrace{\underbrace{A(y_k^*)\Delta y}_{\text{volume}} \cdot \underbrace{\rho}_{\text{density}}}^{\text{mass}} \cdot\, g.$$

To reach the level $y = h$, the kth layer is lifted an approximate distance $(h - y_k^*)$ (Figure 6.74). So the work in lifting the kth layer to a height h is approximately

$$W_k = \underbrace{A(y_k^*)\Delta y \rho g}_{\text{force}} \cdot \underbrace{(h - y_k^*)}_{\text{distance}}.$$

Summing the work required to lift all the layers to a height h, the total work is

$$W \approx \sum_{k=1}^{n} W_k = \sum_{k=1}^{n} A(y_k^*)\rho g(h - y_k^*)\Delta y.$$

This approximation becomes more accurate as the width of the layers Δy tends to zero and the number of layers tends to infinity. In this limit, we obtain a definite integral from $y = 0$ to $y = b$. The total work required to empty the tank is

$$W = \lim_{n\to\infty} \sum_{k=1}^{n} A(y_k^*)\rho g(h - y_k^*)\Delta y = \int_0^b \rho g A(y)(h - y)\, dy.$$

This derivation assumes that the *bottom* of the tank is at $y = 0$, in which case the distance that the slice at level y must be lifted is $D(y) = h - y$. If you choose a different location for the origin, the function D will be different. Here is a general procedure for any choice of origin.

PROCEDURE Solving Lifting Problems

1. Draw a y-axis in the vertical direction (parallel to gravity) and choose a convenient origin. Assume the interval $[a, b]$ corresponds to the vertical extent of the fluid.
2. For $a \le y \le b$, find the cross-sectional area $A(y)$ of the horizontal slices and the distance $D(y)$ the slices must be lifted.
3. The work required to lift the water is

$$W = \int_a^b \rho g A(y) D(y)\, dy.$$

We now use this procedure to solve two pumping problems.

EXAMPLE 3 Pumping water How much work is needed to pump all the water out of a cylindrical tank with a height of 10 m and a radius of 5 m? The water is pumped to an outflow pipe 15 m above the bottom of the tank.

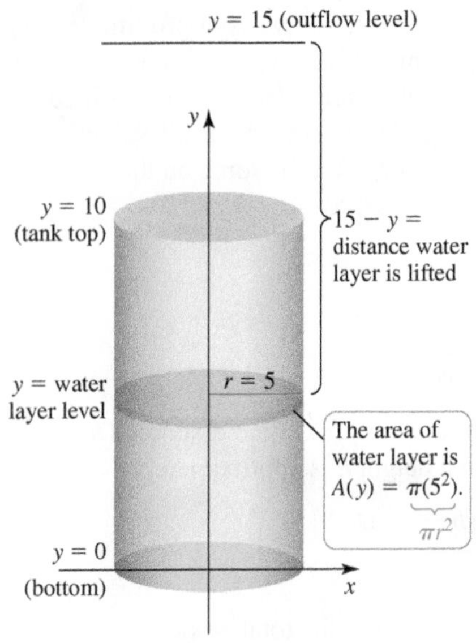

Figure 6.75

SOLUTION Figure 6.75 shows the cylindrical tank filled to capacity and the outflow 15 m above the bottom of the tank. We let $y = 0$ represent the bottom of the tank and $y = 10$ represent the top of the tank. In this case, all horizontal slices are circular disks of radius $r = 5$ m. Therefore, for $0 \le y \le 10$, the cross-sectional area is

$$A(y) = \pi r^2 = \pi 5^2 = 25\pi.$$

Note that the water is pumped to a level $h = 15$ m above the bottom of the tank, so the lifting distance is $D(y) = 15 - y$. The resulting work integral is

$$W = \int_0^{10} \rho g \underbrace{A(y)}_{25\pi} \underbrace{D(y)}_{15-y} \, dy = 25\pi\rho g \int_0^{10} (15 - y) \, dy.$$

Substituting $\rho = 1000 \text{ kg/m}^3$ and $g = 9.8 \text{ m/s}^2$, the total work in joules is

$$\begin{aligned} W &= 25\pi\rho g \int_0^{10} (15 - y) \, dy \\ &= 25\pi \underbrace{(1000)}_{\rho} \underbrace{(9.8)}_{g} \left(15y - \frac{1}{2}y^2\right)\Bigg|_0^{10} \\ &\approx 7.7 \times 10^7. \end{aligned}$$

➤ Recall that $g \approx 9.8 \text{ m/s}^2$. You should verify that the units are consistent in this calculation: The units of ρ, g, $A(y)$, $D(y)$, and dy are kg/m^3, m/s^2, m^2, m, and m, respectively. The resulting units of W are $\text{kg m}^2/\text{s}^2$, or J. A more convenient unit for large amounts of work and energy is the kilowatt-hour, which is 3.6 million joules.

The work required to pump the water out of the tank is approximately 77 million joules.

Related Exercises 27–37 ◀

QUICK CHECK 5 In the previous example, how would the integral change if the outflow pipe were at the top of the tank? ◀

EXAMPLE 4 **Pumping gasoline** A cylindrical tank with a length of 10 m and a radius of 5 m is on its side and half-full of gasoline (Figure 6.76). How much work is required to empty the tank through an outlet pipe at the top of the tank? (The density of gasoline is $\rho \approx 737 \text{ kg/m}^3$.)

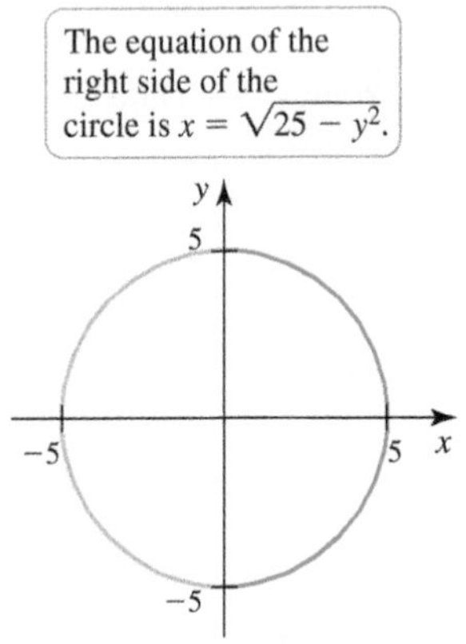

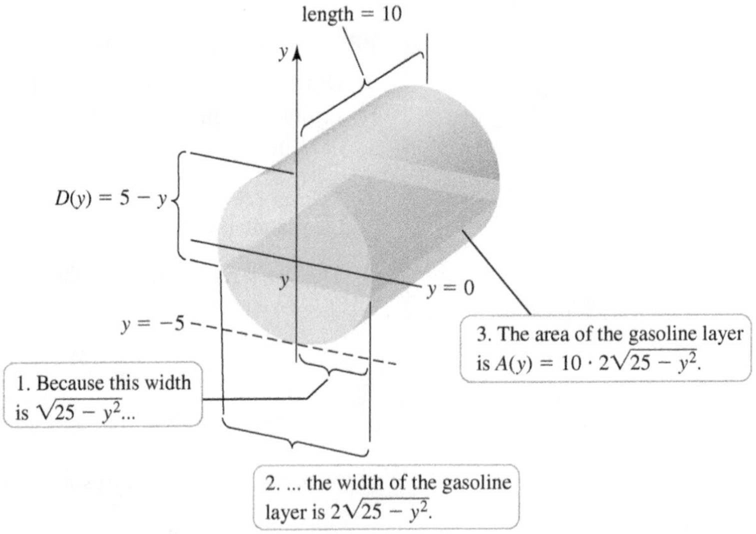

Figure 6.76

➤ Again, there are several choices for the location of the origin. The location in this example makes $A(y)$ easy to compute.

SOLUTION In this problem, we choose a different origin by letting $y = 0$ and $y = -5$ correspond to the center and the bottom of the tank, respectively. For $-5 \le y \le 0$, a horizontal layer of gasoline located at a depth y is a rectangle with a length of 10 and width of $2\sqrt{25 - y^2}$ (Figure 6.76). Therefore, the cross-sectional area of the layer at depth y is

$$A(y) = 20\sqrt{25 - y^2}.$$

The distance the layer at level y must be lifted to reach the top of the tank is $D(y) = 5 - y$, where $5 \le D(y) \le 10$. The resulting work integral is

$$W = \underbrace{737}_{\rho}\underbrace{(9.8)}_{g}\int_{-5}^{0} \underbrace{20\sqrt{25 - y^2}}_{A(y)}\,\underbrace{(5 - y)}_{D(y)}\,dy = 144{,}452\int_{-5}^{0}\sqrt{25 - y^2}\,(5 - y)\,dy.$$

This integral is evaluated by splitting the integrand into two pieces and recognizing that one piece is the area of a quarter circle of radius 5:

$$\int_{-5}^{0}\sqrt{25 - y^2}\,(5 - y)\,dy = 5\underbrace{\int_{-5}^{0}\sqrt{25 - y^2}\,dy}_{\text{area of quarter circle}} - \underbrace{\int_{-5}^{0} y\sqrt{25 - y^2}\,dy}_{\text{let } u = 25 - y^2;\ du = -2y\,dy}$$

$$= 5\cdot\frac{25\pi}{4} + \frac{1}{2}\int_{0}^{25}\sqrt{u}\,du$$

$$= \frac{125\pi}{4} + \frac{1}{3}u^{3/2}\Big|_{0}^{25} = \frac{375\pi + 500}{12}.$$

Multiplying this result by $20\,\rho g = 144{,}452$, we find that the work required is approximately 20.2 million joules. *Related Exercises 27–37* ◀

Force and Pressure

Another application of integration deals with the force exerted on a surface by a body of water. Again, we need a few physical principles.

Pressure is a force per unit area, measured in units such as newtons per square meter (N/m^2). For example, the pressure of the atmosphere on the surface of Earth is about $14\ \text{lb/in}^2$ (approximately 100 kilopascals, or $10^5\ \text{N/m}^2$). As another example, if you stood on the bottom of a swimming pool, you would feel pressure due to the weight (force) of the column of water above your head. If your head is flat and has surface area $A\ \text{m}^2$ and it is h meters below the surface, then the column of water above your head has volume $Ah\ \text{m}^3$. That column of water exerts a force (its weight)

$$F = \text{mass}\cdot\text{acceleration} = \underbrace{\text{volume}\cdot\text{density}}_{\text{mass}}\cdot g = Ah\rho g,$$

where ρ is the density of water and g is the acceleration due to gravity. Therefore, the pressure on your head is the force divided by the surface area of your head:

$$\text{pressure} = \frac{\text{force}}{A} = \frac{Ah\rho g}{A} = \rho g h.$$

This pressure is called **hydrostatic pressure** (meaning the pressure of *water at rest*), and it has the following important property: *It has the same magnitude in all directions.* Specifically, the hydrostatic pressure on a vertical wall of the swimming pool at a depth h is also $\rho g h$. This is the only fact needed to find the total force on vertical walls such as dams. We assume that the water completely covers the face of the dam.

The first step in finding the force on the face of the dam is to introduce a coordinate system. We choose a y-axis pointing upward with $y = 0$ corresponding to the base of the dam and $y = a$ corresponding to the top of the dam (Figure 6.77). Because the pressure varies with depth (y-direction), the dam is sliced horizontally into n strips of equal thickness Δy. The kth strip corresponds to the interval $[y_{k-1}, y_k]$, and we let y_k^* be any point in that interval. The depth of that strip is approximately $h = a - y_k^*$, so the hydrostatic pressure on that strip is approximately $\rho g(a - y_k^*)$.

The crux of any dam problem is finding the width of the strips as a function of y, which we denote $w(y)$. Each dam has its own width function; however, once the width function is known, the solution follows directly. The approximate area of the kth strip is

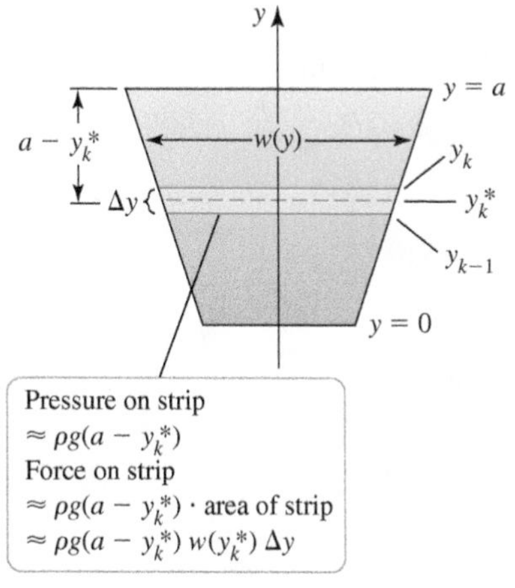

Figure 6.77

its width multiplied by its thickness, or $w(y_k^*)\Delta y$. The force on the kth strip (which is the area of the strip multiplied by the pressure) is approximately

$$F_k = \underbrace{\rho g(a - y_k^*)}_{\text{pressure}}\underbrace{w(y_k^*)\Delta y}_{\text{area of strip}}.$$

Summing the forces over the n strips, the total force is

$$F \approx \sum_{k=1}^{n} F_k = \sum_{k=1}^{n} \rho g(a - y_k^*)w(y_k^*)\Delta y.$$

To find the exact force, we let the thickness of the strips tend to zero and the number of strips tend to infinity, which produces a definite integral. The limits of integration correspond to the base ($y = 0$) and top ($y = a$) of the dam. Therefore, the total force on the dam is

$$F = \lim_{n\to\infty} \sum_{k=1}^{n} \rho g(a - y_k^*)w(y_k^*)\Delta y = \int_0^a \rho g(a - y)w(y)\,dy.$$

➤ We have chosen $y = 0$ to be the base of the dam. Depending on the geometry of the problem, it may be more convenient (less computation) to let $y = 0$ be at the top of the dam. Experiment with different choices.

PROCEDURE Solving Force Problems

1. Draw a y-axis on the face of the dam in the vertical direction and choose a convenient origin (often taken to be the base of the dam).
2. Find the width function $w(y)$ for each value of y on the face of the dam.
3. If the base of the dam is at $y = 0$ and the top of the dam is at $y = a$, then the total force on the dam is

$$F = \int_0^a \rho g\underbrace{(b - y)}_{\text{depth}}\underbrace{w(y)}_{\text{width}}\,dy.$$

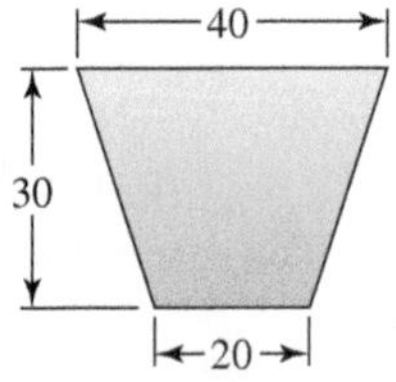

Figure 6.78

EXAMPLE 5 Force on a dam A large vertical dam in the shape of a symmetric trapezoid has a height of 30 m, a width of 20 m at its base, and a width of 40 m at the top (Figure 6.78). What is the total force on the face of the dam when the reservoir is full?

SOLUTION We place the origin at the center of the base of the dam (Figure 6.79). The right slanted edge of the dam is a segment of the line that passes through the points $(10, 0)$ and $(20, 30)$. An equation of that line is

$$y - 0 = \frac{30}{10}(x - 10) \quad\text{or}\quad y = 3x - 30 \quad\text{or}\quad x = \frac{1}{3}(y + 30).$$

Notice that at a depth of y, where $0 \le y \le 30$, the width of the dam is

$$w(y) = 2x = \frac{2}{3}(y + 30).$$

➤ You should check the width function: $w(0) = 20$ (the width of the dam at its base) and $w(30) = 40$ (the width of the dam at its top).

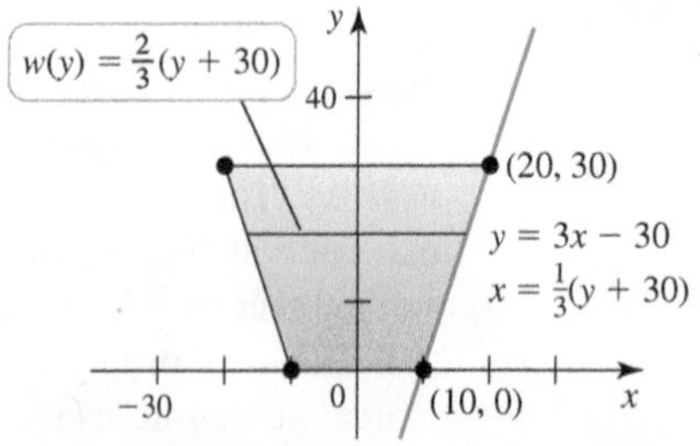

Figure 6.79

Using $\rho = 1000 \text{ kg/m}^3$ and $g = 9.8 \text{ m/s}^2$, the total force on the dam (in newtons) is

$$\begin{aligned} F &= \int_0^a \rho g(a - y)w(y)\,dy && \text{Force integral} \\ &= \rho g \int_0^{30} \underbrace{(30 - y)}_{a-y} \underbrace{\frac{2}{3}(y + 30)}_{w(y)}\,dy && \text{Substitute.} \\ &= \frac{2}{3}\rho g \int_0^{30} (900 - y^2)\,dy && \text{Simplify.} \\ &= \frac{2}{3}\rho g\left(900y - \frac{y^3}{3}\right)\Big|_0^{30} && \text{Fundamental Theorem} \\ &\approx 1.18 \times 10^8. \end{aligned}$$

The force of 1.18×10^8 N on the dam amounts to about 26 million pounds, or 13,000 tons.

Related Exercises 38–48 ◄

SECTION 6.7 EXERCISES

Review Questions

1. Suppose a 1-m cylindrical bar has a constant density of 1 g/cm for its left half and a constant density 2 g/cm for its right half. What is its mass?

2. Explain how to find the mass of a one-dimensional object with a variable density ρ.

3. How much work is required to move an object from $x = 0$ to $x = 5$ (measured in meters) in the presence of a constant force of 5 N acting along the x-axis?

4. Why is integration used to find the work done by a variable force?

5. Why is integration used to find the work required to pump water out of a tank?

6. Why is integration used to find the total force on the face of a dam?

7. What is the pressure on a horizontal surface with an area of 2 m^2 that is 4 m underwater?

8. Explain why you integrate in the vertical direction (parallel to the acceleration due to gravity) rather than the horizontal direction to find the force on the face of a dam.

Basic Skills

9–16. Mass of one-dimensional objects *Find the mass of the following thin bars with the given density function.*

9. $\rho(x) = 1 + \sin x$; for $0 \le x \le \pi$

10. $\rho(x) = 1 + x^3$; for $0 \le x \le 1$

11. $\rho(x) = 2 - x/2$; for $0 \le x \le 2$

12. $\rho(x) = 5e^{-2x}$; for $0 \le x \le 4$

13. $\rho(x) = x\sqrt{2 - x^2}$; for $0 \le x \le 1$

14. $\rho(x) = \begin{cases} 1 & \text{if } 0 \le x \le 2 \\ 2 & \text{if } 2 < x \le 3 \end{cases}$

15. $\rho(x) = \begin{cases} 1 & \text{if } 0 \le x \le 2 \\ 1 + x & \text{if } 2 < x \le 4 \end{cases}$

16. $\rho(x) = \begin{cases} x^2 & \text{if } 0 \le x \le 1 \\ x(2 - x) & \text{if } 1 < x \le 2 \end{cases}$

17. Work from force How much work is required to move an object from $x = 0$ to $x = 3$ (measured in meters) in the presence of a force (in N) given by $F(x) = 2x$ acting along the x-axis?

18. Work from force How much work is required to move an object from $x = 1$ to $x = 3$ (measured in meters) in the presence of a force (in N) given by $F(x) = 2/x^2$ acting along the x-axis?

19. Compressing and stretching a spring Suppose a force of 30 N is required to stretch and hold a spring 0.2 m from its equilibrium position.

a. Assuming the spring obeys Hooke's law, find the spring constant k.

b. How much work is required to compress the spring 0.4 m from its equilibrium position?

c. How much work is required to stretch the spring 0.3 m from its equilibrium position?

d. How much additional work is required to stretch the spring 0.2 m if it has already been stretched 0.2 m from its equilibrium position?

20. Compressing and stretching a spring Suppose a force of 15 N is required to stretch and hold a spring 0.25 m from its equilibrium position.

a. Assuming the spring obeys Hooke's law, find the spring constant k.

b. How much work is required to compress the spring 0.2 m from its equilibrium position?

c. How much additional work is required to stretch the spring 0.3 m if it has already been stretched 0.25 m from its equilibrium position?

21. Work done by a spring A spring on a horizontal surface can be stretched and held 0.5 m from its equilibrium position with a force of 50 N.

a. How much work is done in stretching the spring 1.5 m from its equilibrium position?
b. How much work is done in compressing the spring 0.5 m from its equilibrium position?

22. Shock absorber A heavy-duty shock absorber is compressed 2 cm from its equilibrium position by a mass of 500 kg. How much work is required to compress the shock absorber 4 cm from its equilibrium position? (A mass of 500 kg exerts a force (in newtons) of $500\,g$, where $g \approx 9.8\ \mathrm{m/s^2}$.)

23. Calculating work for different springs Calculate the work required to stretch the following springs 0.5 m from their equilibrium positions. Assume Hooke's law is obeyed.

a. A spring that requires a force of 50 N to be stretched 0.2 m from its equilibrium position
b. A spring that requires 50 J of work to be stretched 0.2 m from its equilibrium position

24. Calculating work for different springs Calculate the work required to stretch the following springs 0.4 m from their equilibrium positions. Assume Hooke's law is obeyed.

a. A spring that requires a force of 50 N to be stretched 0.1 m from its equilibrium position
b. A spring that requires 2 J of work to be stretched 0.1 m from its equilibrium position

25. Calculating work for different springs Calculate the work required to stretch the following springs 1.25 m from their equilibrium positions. Assume Hooke's law is obeyed.

a. A spring that requires 100 J of work to be stretched 0.5 m from its equilibrium position
b. A spring that requires a force of 250 N to be stretched 0.5 m from its equilibrium

26. Work function A spring has a restoring force given by $F(x) = 25x$. Let $W(x)$ be the work required to stretch the spring from its equilibrium position ($x = 0$) to a variable distance x. Find and graph the work function. Compare the work required to stretch the spring x units from equilibrium to the work required to compress the spring x units from equilibrium.

27. Emptying a swimming pool A swimming pool has the shape of a box with a base that measures 25 m by 15 m and a uniform depth of 2.5 m. How much work is required to pump the water out of the pool when it is full?

28. Emptying a cylindrical tank A cylindrical water tank has height 8 m and radius 2 m (see figure).

a. If the tank is full of water, how much work is required to pump the water to the level of the top of the tank and out of the tank?
b. Is it true that it takes half as much work to pump the water out of the tank when it is half full as when it is full? Explain.

29. Emptying a half-full cylindrical tank Suppose the water tank in Exercise 28 is half full of water. Determine the work required to empty the tank by pumping the water to a level 2 m above the top of the tank.

30. Emptying a partially filled swimming pool If the water in the swimming pool in Exercise 27 is 2 m deep, then how much work is required to pump all the water to a level 3 m above the bottom of the pool?

31. Emptying a conical tank A water tank is shaped like an inverted cone with height 6 m and base radius 1.5 m (see figure).

a. If the tank is full, how much work is required to pump the water to the level of the top of the tank and out of the tank?
b. Is it true that it takes half as much work to pump the water out of the tank when it is filled to half its depth as when it is full? Explain.

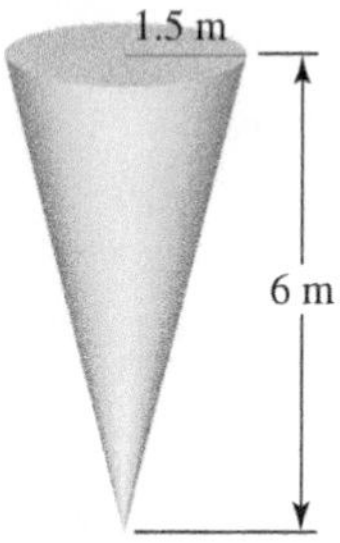

32. Emptying a real swimming pool A swimming pool is 20 m long and 10 m wide, with a bottom that slopes uniformly from a depth of 1 m at one end to a depth of 2 m at the other end (see figure). Assuming the pool is full, how much work is required to pump the water to a level 0.2 m above the top of the pool?

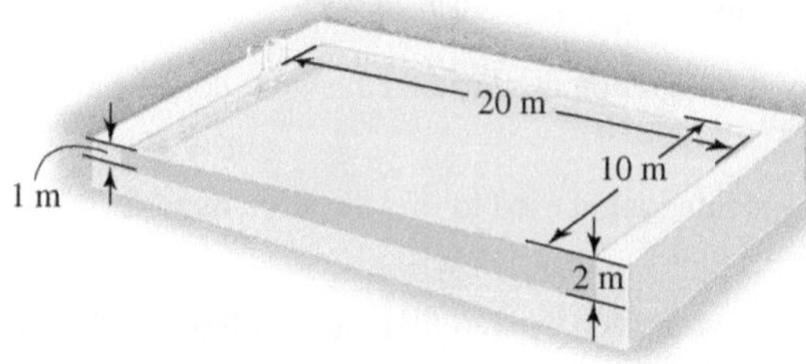

33. Filling a spherical tank A spherical water tank with an inner radius of 8 m has its lowest point 2 m above the ground. It is filled by a pipe that feeds the tank at its lowest point (see figure).

a. Neglecting the volume of the inflow pipe, how much work is required to fill the tank if it is initially empty?
b. Now assume that the inflow pipe feeds the tank at the top of the tank. Neglecting the volume of the inflow pipe, how much work is required to fill the tank if it is initially empty?

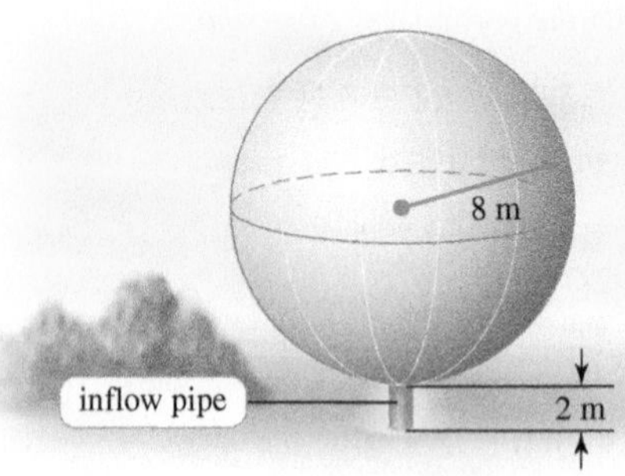

34. **Emptying a water trough** A water trough has a semicircular cross section with a radius of 0.25 m and a length of 3 m (see figure).

 a. How much work is required to pump the water out of the trough when it is full?
 b. If the length is doubled, is the required work doubled? Explain.
 c. If the radius is doubled, is the required work doubled? Explain.

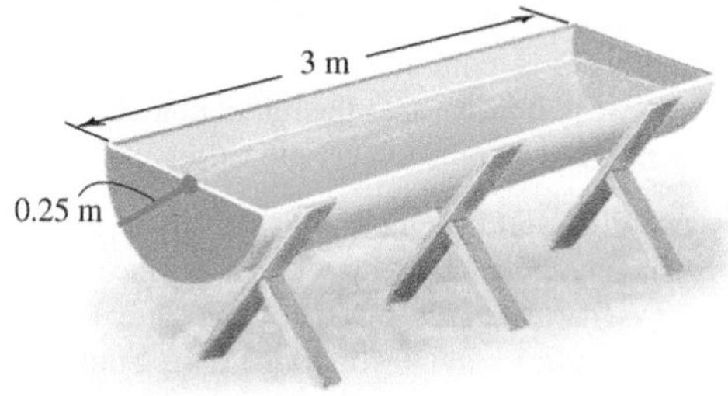

35. **Emptying a water trough** A cattle trough has a trapezoidal cross section with a height of 1 m and horizontal sides of length $\frac{1}{2}$ m and 1 m. Assume the length of the trough is 10 m (see figure).

 a. How much work is required to pump the water out of the trough (to the level of the top of the trough) when it is full?
 b. If the length is doubled, is the required work doubled? Explain.

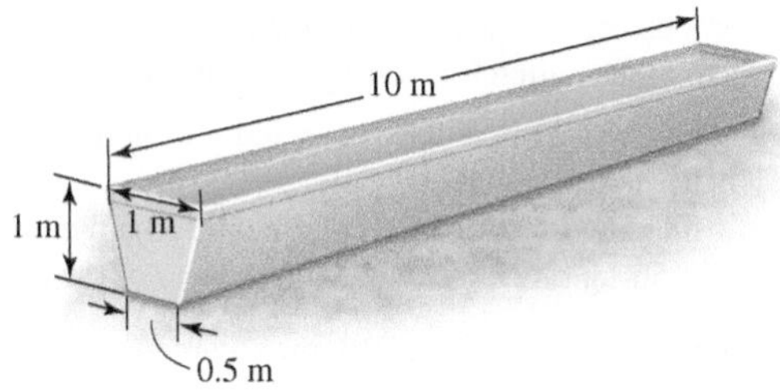

36. **Pumping water** Suppose the tank in Example 4 is full of water (rather than half full of gas). Determine the work required to pump all the water to an outlet pipe 15 m above the bottom of the tank.

37. **Emptying a conical tank** An inverted cone is 2 m high and has a base radius of $\frac{1}{2}$ m. If the tank is full, how much work is required to pump the water to a level 1 m above the top of the tank?

38–41. Force on dams *The following figures show the shape and dimensions of small dams. Assuming the water level is at the top of the dam, find the total force on the face of the dam.*

38.

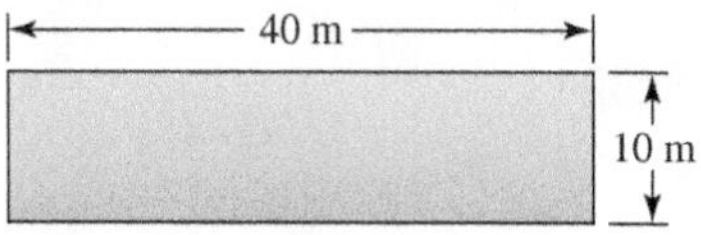

39.

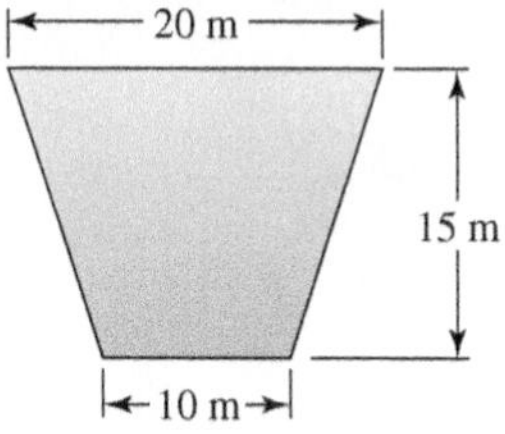

40.

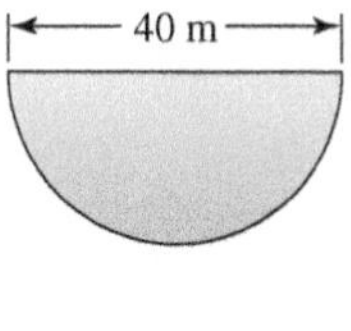

41.

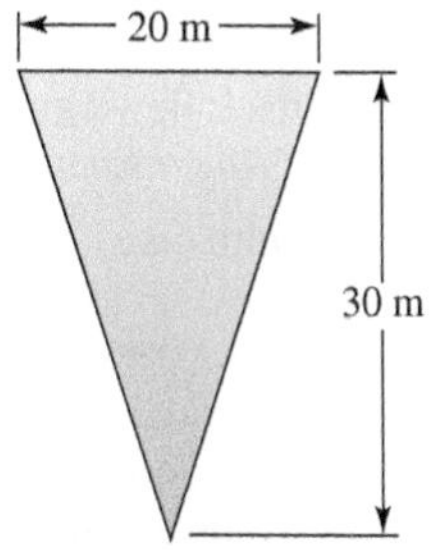

42. **Parabolic dam** The lower edge of a dam is defined by the parabola $y = x^2/16$ (see figure). Use a coordinate system with $y = 0$ at the bottom of the dam to determine the total force on the dam. Lengths are measured in meters. Assume the water level is at the top of the dam.

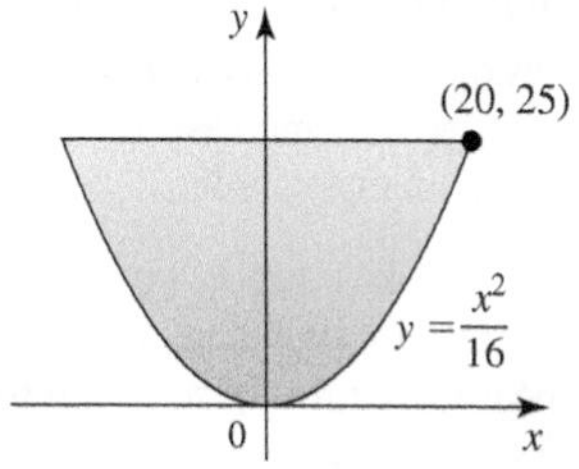

43. **Orientation and force** A plate shaped like an isosceles triangle with a height of 1 m is placed on a vertical wall 1 m below the surface of a pool filled with water (see figure). Compute the force on the plate.

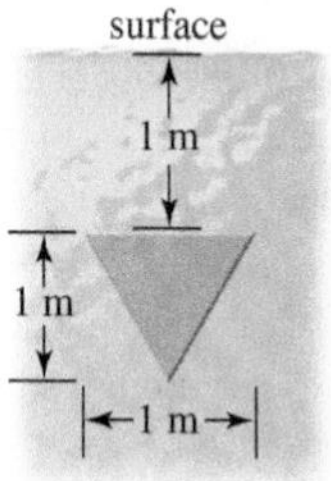

44. **Force on the end of a tank** Determine the force on a circular end of the tank in Figure 6.76 if the tank is full of gasoline. The density of gasoline is $\rho = 737\ \text{kg/m}^3$.

45. **Force on a building** A large building shaped like a box is 50 m high with a face that is 80 m wide. A strong wind blows directly at the face of the building, exerting a pressure of $150\ \text{N/m}^2$ at the ground and increasing with height according to $P(y) = 150 + 2y$, where y is the height above the ground. Calculate the total force on the building, which is a measure of the resistance that must be included in the design of the building.

46–48. Force on a window *A diving pool that is 4 m deep and full of water has a viewing window on one of its vertical walls. Find the force on the following windows.*

46. The window is a square, 0.5 m on a side, with the lower edge of the window on the bottom of the pool.

47. The window is a square, 0.5 m on a side, with the lower edge of the window 1 m from the bottom of the pool.

48. The window is a circle, with a radius of 0.5 m, tangent to the bottom of the pool.

Further Explorations

49. Explain why or why not Determine whether the following statements are true and give an explanation or counterexample.

a. The mass of a thin wire is the length of the wire times its average density over its length.
b. The work required to stretch a linear spring (that obeys Hooke's law) 100 cm from equilibrium is the same as the work required to compress it 100 cm from equilibrium.
c. The work required to lift a 10-kg object vertically 10 m is the same as the work required to lift a 20-kg object vertically 5 m.
d. The total force on a 10-ft² region on the (horizontal) floor of a pool is the same as the total force on a 10-ft² region on a (vertical) wall of the pool.

50. Mass of two bars Two bars of length L have densities $\rho_1(x) = 4e^{-x}$ and $\rho_2(x) = 6e^{-2x}$, for $0 \le x \le L$.

a. For what values of L is bar 1 heavier than bar 2?
b. As the lengths of the bars increase, do their masses increase without bound? Explain.

51. A nonlinear spring Hooke's law is applicable to idealized (linear) springs that are not stretched or compressed too far. Consider a nonlinear spring whose restoring force is given by $F(x) = 16x - 0.1x^3$, for $|x| \le 7$.

a. Graph the restoring force and interpret it.
b. How much work is done in stretching the spring from its equilibrium position ($x = 0$) to $x = 1.5$?
c. How much work is done in compressing the spring from its equilibrium position ($x = 0$) to $x = -2$?

52. A vertical spring A 10-kg mass is attached to a spring that hangs vertically and is stretched 2 m from the equilibrium position of the spring. Assume a linear spring with $F(x) = kx$.

a. How much work is required to compress the spring and lift the mass 0.5 m?
b. How much work is required to stretch the spring and lower the mass 0.5 m?

53. Drinking juice A glass has circular cross sections that taper (linearly) from a radius of 5 cm at the top of the glass to a radius of 4 cm at the bottom. The glass is 15 cm high and full of orange juice. How much work is required to drink all the juice through a straw if your mouth is 5 cm above the top of the glass? Assume the density of orange juice equals the density of water.

54. Upper and lower half A cylinder with height 8 m and radius 3 m is filled with water and must be emptied through an outlet pipe 2 m above the top of the cylinder.

a. Compute the work required to empty the water in the top half of the tank.
b. Compute the work required to empty the (equal amount of) water in the lower half of the tank.
c. Interpret the results of parts (a) and (b).

Applications

55. Work in a gravitational field For large distances from the surface of Earth, the gravitational force is given by $F(x) = GMm/(x + R)^2$, where $G = 6.7 \times 10^{-11}$ N-m²/kg² is the gravitational constant, $M = 6 \times 10^{24}$ kg is the mass of Earth, m is the mass of the object in the gravitational field, $R = 6.378 \times 10^6$ m is the radius of Earth, and $x \ge 0$ is the distance above the surface of Earth (in meters).

a. How much work is required to launch a rocket with a mass of 500 kg in a vertical flight path to a height of 2500 km (from Earth's surface)?
b. Find the work required to launch the rocket to a height of x kilometers, for $x > 0$.
c. How much work is required to reach outer space ($x \to \infty$)?
d. Equate the work in part (c) to the initial kinetic energy of the rocket, $\frac{1}{2}mv^2$, to compute the escape velocity of the rocket.

56. Work by two different integrals A rigid body with a mass of 2 kg moves along a line due to a force that produces a position function $x(t) = 4t^2$, where x is measured in meters and t is measured in seconds. Find the work done during the first 5 s in two ways.

a. Note that $x''(t) = 8$; then use Newton's second law ($F = ma = mx''(t)$) to evaluate the work integral $W = \int_{x_0}^{x_f} F(x)\,dx$, where x_0 and x_f are the initial and final positions, respectively.
b. Change variables in the work integral and integrate with respect to t. Be sure your answer agrees with part (a).

57. Winding a chain A 30-m-long chain hangs vertically from a cylinder attached to a winch. Assume there is no friction in the system and the chain has a density of 5 kg/m.

a. How much work is required to wind the entire chain onto the cylinder using the winch?
b. How much work is required to wind the chain onto the cylinder if a 50-kg block is attached to the end of the chain?

58. Coiling a rope A 60-m-long, 9.4-mm-diameter rope hangs free from a ledge. The density of the rope is 55 g/m. How much work is needed to pull the entire rope to the ledge?

59. Lifting a pendulum A body of mass m is suspended by a rod of length L that pivots without friction (see figure). The mass is slowly lifted along a circular arc to a height h.

a. Assuming that the only force acting on the mass is the gravitational force, show that the component of this force acting along the arc of motion is $F = mg \sin\theta$.
b. Noting that an element of length along the path of the pendulum is $ds = L\,d\theta$, evaluate an integral in θ to show that the work done in lifting the mass to a height h is mgh.

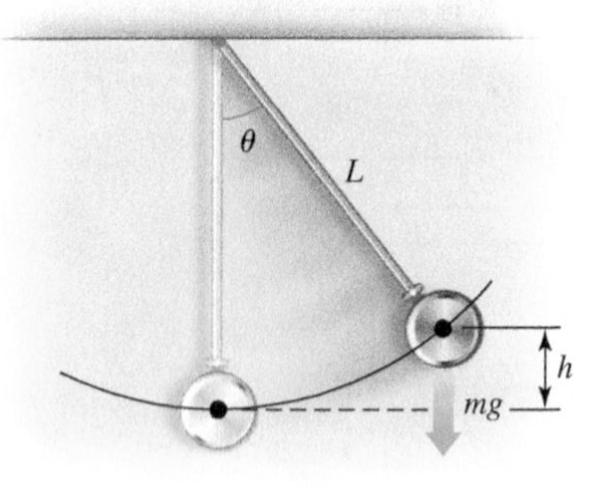

60. Orientation and force A plate shaped like an equilateral triangle 1 m on a side is placed on a vertical wall 1 m below the surface of a pool filled with water. On which plate in the figure is the force greater? Try to anticipate the answer and then compute the force on each plate.

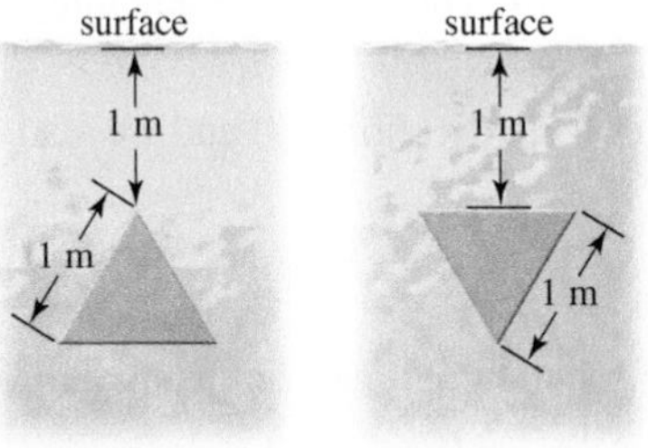

61. Orientation and force A square plate 1 m on a side is placed on a vertical wall 1 m below the surface of a pool filled with water. On which plate in the figure is the force greater? Try to anticipate the answer and then compute the force on each plate.

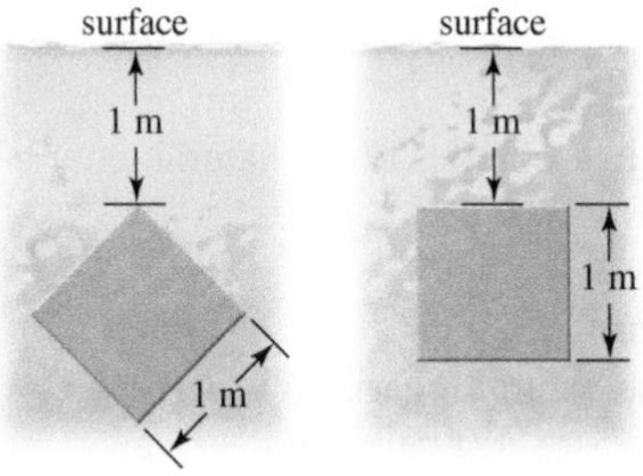

62. A calorie-free milkshake? Suppose a cylindrical glass with a diameter of $\frac{1}{12}$ m and a height of $\frac{1}{10}$ m is filled to the brim with a 400-Cal milkshake. If you have a straw that is 1.1 m long (so the top of the straw is 1 m above the top of the glass), do you burn off all the calories in the milkshake in drinking it? Assume that the density of the milkshake is $1\ \text{g/cm}^3$ (1 Cal = 4184 J).

63. Critical depth A large tank has a plastic window on one wall that is designed to withstand a force of 90,000 N. The square window is 2 m on a side, and its lower edge is 1 m from the bottom of the tank.

a. If the tank is filled to a depth of 4 m, will the window withstand the resulting force?

b. What is the maximum depth to which the tank can be filled without the window failing?

64. Buoyancy Archimedes' principle says that the buoyant force exerted on an object that is (partially or totally) submerged in water is equal to the weight of the water displaced by the object (see figure). Let $\rho_w = 1\ \text{g/cm}^3 = 1000\ \text{kg/m}^3$ be the density of water and let ρ be the density of an object in water. Let $f = \rho/\rho_w$. If $0 < f \le 1$, then the object floats with a fraction f of its volume submerged; if $f > 1$, then the object sinks.

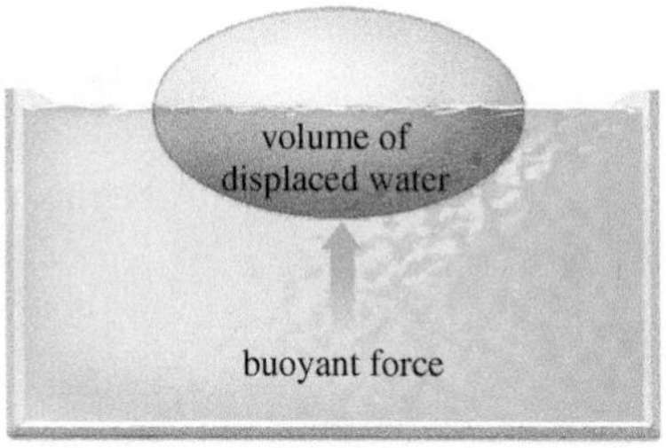

Consider a cubical box with sides 2 m long floating in water with one-half of its volume submerged ($\rho = \rho_w/2$). Find the force required to fully submerge the box (so its top surface is at the water level).

(See the Guided Project *Buoyancy and Archimedes' Principle* for further explorations of buoyancy problems.)

QUICK CHECK ANSWERS

1. a. The bar is heaviest at the left end and lightest at the right end. **b.** $\rho = 2.5\ \text{g/cm}$. **2.** Minimum mass = 2 kg; maximum mass = 10 kg **3.** We assume that the force is constant over each subinterval, when, in fact, it varies over each subinterval. **4.** The restoring force of the spring increases as the spring is stretched ($f(x) = 100x$). Greater restoring forces are encountered on the interval $[0.1, 0.35]$ than on the interval $[0, 0.25]$. **5.** The factor $(15 - y)$ in the integral is replaced with $(10 - y)$. ◀

6.8 Logarithmic and Exponential Functions Revisited

Earlier in the text, we made several claims about exponential and logarithmic functions, but we did not prove them. (For example, these functions are continuous and differentiable on their domains.) Our objective in this section is to place these important functions on a solid foundation by presenting a more rigorous development of their properties.

Before embarking on this program, we offer a roadmap to help guide you through the section. We carry out the following four steps.

1. We first define the natural logarithm function in terms of an integral, and then derive the properties of $\ln x$ directly from this new definition.

2. The natural exponential function e^x is introduced as the inverse of $\ln x$, and the properties of e^x are developed by appealing to this inverse relationship. We also present derivative and integral formulas associated with these functions.
3. Next, we define the general exponential function b^x in terms of e^x, and the general logarithmic function $\log_b x$ in terms of $\ln x$. The derivative and integral results stated in Section 3.9 follow immediately.
4. Finally, we revisit the General Power Rule (Section 3.9) and we also derive a limit that can be used to approximate e.

Step 1: The Natural Logarithm

Our aim is to develop the properties of the natural logarithm using definite integrals. It all begins with the following definition.

DEFINITION The Natural Logarithm

The **natural logarithm** of a number $x > 0$, is $\ln x = \displaystyle\int_1^x \frac{1}{t}\,dt.$

All the familiar geometric and algebraic properties of the natural logarithmic function follow directly from this new integral definition.

Properties of the Natural Logarithm

Domain, range, and sign Because the natural logarithm is defined as a definite integral, its value is the net area under the curve $y = 1/t$ between $t = 1$ and $t = x$. The integrand is undefined at $t = 0$, so the domain of $\ln x$ is $(0, \infty)$. On the interval $(1, \infty)$, $\ln x$ is positive because the net area of the region under the curve is positive (Figure 6.80a). On $(0, 1)$, we have $\displaystyle\int_1^x \frac{1}{t}\,dt = -\int_x^1 \frac{1}{t}\,dt$, which implies $\ln x$ is negative (Figure 6.80b). As expected, when $x = 1$, we have $\ln 1 = \displaystyle\int_1^1 \frac{1}{t}\,dt = 0$. The net area interpretation of $\ln x$ also implies that the range of $\ln x$ is $(-\infty, \infty)$ (see Exercise 72 for an outline of a proof).

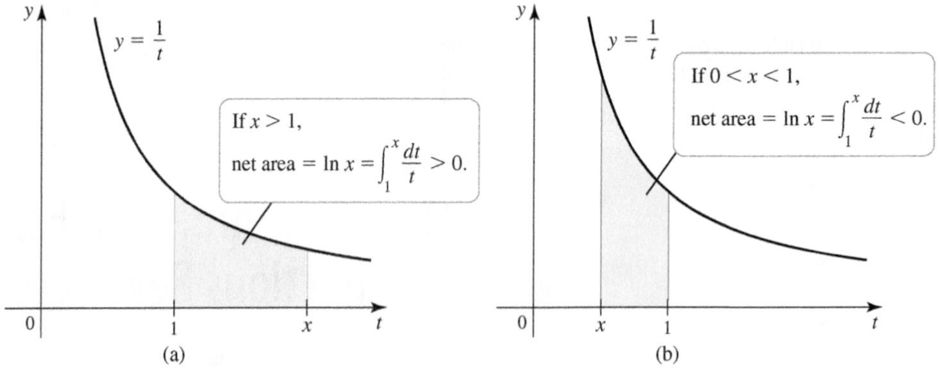

Figure 6.80

Derivative The derivative of the natural logarithm follows immediately from its definition and the Fundamental Theorem of Calculus:

$$\frac{d}{dx}(\ln x) = \frac{d}{dx}\int_1^x \frac{dt}{t} = \frac{1}{x}, \text{ for } x > 0.$$

➤ By the Fundamental Theorem of Calculus,

$$\frac{d}{dx}\int_a^x f(t)\,dt = f(x).$$

We have two important consequences.

- Because its derivative is defined for $x > 0$, $\ln x$ is a differentiable function for $x > 0$, which means it is continuous on its domain (Theorem 3.1).
- Because $1/x > 0$ for $x > 0$, $\ln x$ is strictly increasing and one-to-one on its domain; therefore, it has a well-defined inverse.

The Chain Rule allows us to extend the derivative property to all nonzero real numbers (Exercise 70). By differentiating $\ln(-x)$ for $x < 0$, we find that

$$\frac{d}{dx}(\ln|x|) = \frac{1}{x}, \quad \text{for } x \neq 0.$$

QUICK CHECK 1 What is the domain of $\ln|x|$? ◄

More generally, by the Chain Rule,

$$\frac{d}{dx}(\ln|u(x)|) = \frac{1}{u(x)}u'(x) = \frac{u'(x)}{u(x)}.$$

Graph of $\ln x$ As noted before, $\ln x$ is continuous and strictly increasing for $x > 0$. The second derivative, $\frac{d^2}{dx^2}(\ln x) = -\frac{1}{x^2}$, is negative for $x > 0$, which implies the graph of $\ln x$ is concave down for $x > 0$. As demonstrated in Exercise 72,

$$\lim_{x\to\infty} \ln x = \infty, \quad \text{and} \quad \lim_{x\to 0^+} \ln x = -\infty.$$

This information, coupled with the fact that $\ln 1 = 0$, gives the graph of $y = \ln x$ (Figure 6.81).

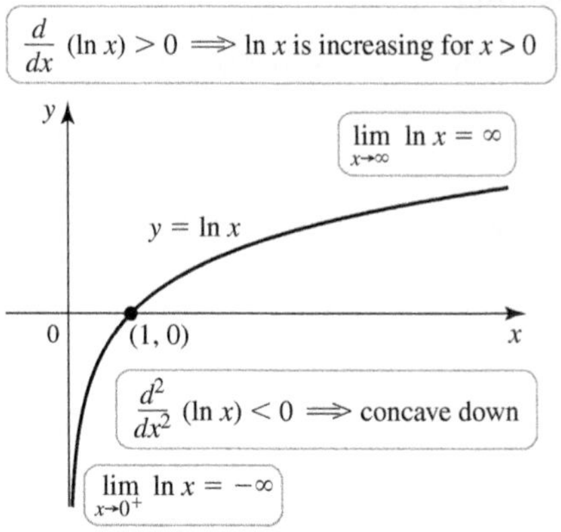

Figure 6.81

Logarithm of a product The familiar logarithm property

$$\ln xy = \ln x + \ln y, \quad \text{for } x > 0, \quad y > 0,$$

may be proved using the integral definition:

$$\begin{aligned} \ln xy &= \int_1^{xy} \frac{dt}{t} && \text{Definition of } \ln xy \\ &= \int_1^{x} \frac{dt}{t} + \int_x^{xy} \frac{dt}{t} && \text{Additive property of integrals} \\ &= \int_1^{x} \frac{dt}{t} + \int_1^{y} \frac{du}{u} && \text{Substitute } u = t/x \text{ in second integral.} \\ &= \ln x + \ln y. && \text{Definition of } \ln \end{aligned}$$

Logarithm of a quotient Assuming $x > 0$ and $y > 0$, the product property and a bit of algebra give

$$\ln x = \ln\left(y \cdot \frac{x}{y}\right) = \ln y + \ln\frac{x}{y}.$$

Solving for $\ln(x/y)$, we have

$$\ln\frac{x}{y} = \ln x - \ln y,$$

which is the quotient property for logarithms.

Logarithm of a power Assuming $x > 0$ and p is rational, we have

$$\ln x^p = \int_1^{x^p} \frac{dt}{t} \quad \text{Definition of } \ln x^p$$

$$= p\int_1^{x} \frac{du}{u} \quad \text{Let } t = u^p;\ dt = pu^{p-1}du.$$

$$= p \ln x. \quad \text{By definition, } \ln x = \int_1^x \frac{du}{u}.$$

This argument relies on the Power Rule ($dt = pu^{p-1}\,du$), which we proved only for rational exponents. Later in this section, we prove that $\ln x^p = p \ln x$, for all real values of p.

Integrals Because $\frac{d}{dx}(\ln |x|) = \frac{1}{x}$, we have

$$\int \frac{1}{x}\,dx = \ln |x| + C.$$

We have shown that the familiar properties of $\ln x$ follow from its new integral definition.

THEOREM 6.4 Properties of the Natural Logarithm

1. The domain and range of $\ln x$ are $(0, \infty)$ and $(-\infty, \infty)$, respectively.
2. $\ln xy = \ln x + \ln y$, for $x > 0$ and $y > 0$
3. $\ln (x/y) = \ln x - \ln y$, for $x > 0$ and $y > 0$
4. $\ln x^p = p \ln x$, for $x > 0$ and p a rational number
5. $\frac{d}{dx}(\ln |x|) = \frac{1}{x}$, for $x \neq 0$
6. $\frac{d}{dx}(\ln |u(x)|) = \frac{u'(x)}{u(x)}$, for $u(x) \neq 0$
7. $\int \frac{1}{x}\,dx = \ln |x| + C$

EXAMPLE 1 Integrals with ln *x* Evaluate $\int_0^4 \frac{x}{x^2 + 9}\,dx$.

SOLUTION

$$\int_0^4 \frac{x}{x^2+9}\,dx = \frac{1}{2}\int_9^{25} \frac{du}{u} \quad \text{Let } u = x^2 + 9;\ du = 2x\,dx.$$

$$= \frac{1}{2} \ln |u| \Big|_9^{25} \quad \text{Fundamental Theorem}$$

$$= \frac{1}{2}(\ln 25 - \ln 9) \quad \text{Evaluate.}$$

$$= \ln \frac{5}{3} \quad \text{Properties of logarithms}$$

Related Exercises 7–20 ◀

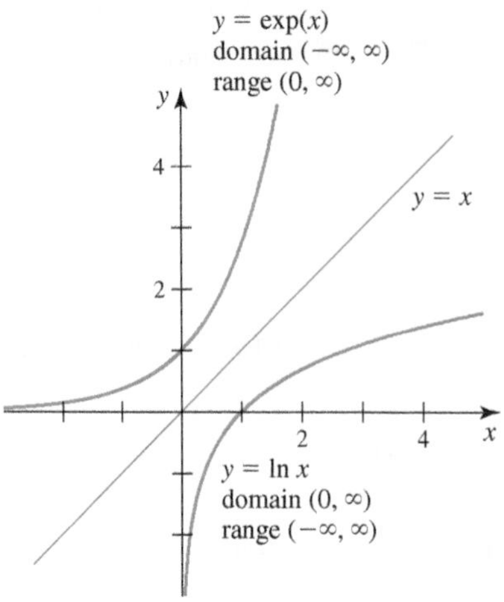

Figure 6.82

Step 2: The Exponential Function

We have established that $f(x) = \ln x$ is a continuous, increasing function on the interval $(0, \infty)$. Therefore, it is one-to-one and its inverse function exists on $(0, \infty)$. We denote the inverse function $f^{-1}(x) = \exp(x)$. Its graph is obtained by reflecting the graph of $f(x) = \ln x$ about the line $y = x$ (Figure 6.82). The domain of $\exp(x)$ is $(-\infty, \infty)$ because the range of $\ln x$ is $(-\infty, \infty)$, and the range of $\exp(x)$ is $(0, \infty)$ because the domain of $\ln x$ is $(0, \infty)$.

The usual relationships between a function and its inverse also hold:

- $y = \exp(x)$ if and only if $x = \ln y$;
- $\exp(\ln x) = x$, for $x > 0$, and $\ln(\exp(x)) = x$, for all x.

We now appeal to the properties of $\ln x$ and use the inverse relations between $\ln x$ and $\exp(x)$ to show that $\exp(x)$ satisfies the expected properties of any exponential function. For example, if $x_1 = \ln y_1$ and $x_2 = \ln y_2$, then it follows that $y_1 = \exp(x_1)$, $y_2 = \exp(x_2)$, and

$$\begin{aligned}
\exp(x_1 + x_2) &= \exp(\underbrace{\ln y_1 + \ln y_2}_{\ln y_1 y_2}) && \text{Substitute } x_1 = \ln y_1, x_2 = \ln y_2. \\
&= \exp(\ln y_1 y_2) && \text{Properties of logarithms} \\
&= y_1 y_2 && \text{Inverse property of } \exp(x) \text{ and } \ln x \\
&= \exp(x_1)\exp(x_2). && y_1 = \exp(x_1), y_2 = \exp(x_2)
\end{aligned}$$

Therefore, $\exp(x)$ satisfies the property of exponential functions $b^{x_1 + x_2} = b^{x_1}b^{x_2}$. Similar arguments show that $\exp(x)$ satisfies other characteristic properties of exponential functions (Exercise 71):

$$\begin{aligned}
\exp(0) &= 1, \\
\exp(x_1 - x_2) &= \frac{\exp(x_1)}{\exp(x_2)}, \quad \text{and} \\
(\exp(x))^p &= \exp(px), \text{ for rational numbers } p.
\end{aligned}$$

Suspecting that $\exp(x)$ is an exponential function, the next task is to identify its base. Let's consider the real number $\exp(1)$, and with a bit of forethought, call it e. The inverse relationship between $\ln x$ and $\exp(x)$ implies that

$$\text{if } e = \exp(1), \text{ then } \quad \ln e = \ln(\exp(1)) = 1.$$

Using the fact that $\ln e = 1$ and the integral definition of $\ln x$, we now formally define e.

> **DEFINITION The Number e**
>
> The number e is the real number that satisfies $\ln e = \displaystyle\int_1^e \frac{dt}{t} = 1.$

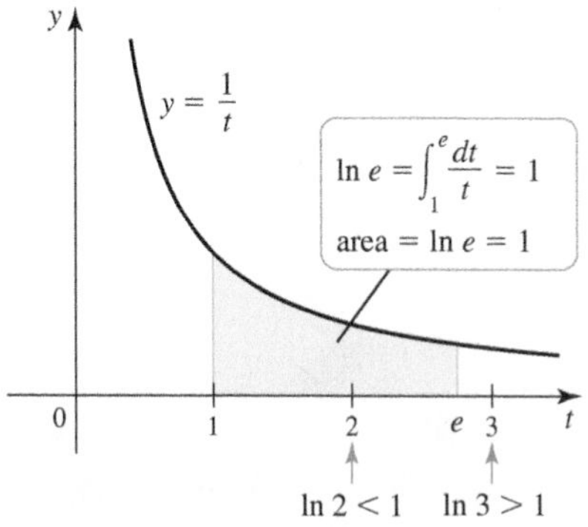

Figure 6.83

➤ We give a limit definition that provides a good approximation to e at the end of this section.

The number e has the property that the area of the region bounded by the graph of $y = \dfrac{1}{t}$ and the t-axis on the interval $[1, e]$ is 1 (Figure 6.83). Note that $\ln 2 < 1$ and $\ln 3 > 1$ (Exercise 73). Because $\ln x$ is continuous on its domain, the Intermediate Value Theorem ensures that there is a number e with $2 < e < 3$ such that $\ln e = 1$.

We can now show that indeed $\exp(x)$ is the exponential function e^x. Assume that p is a rational number and note that $e^p > 0$. By property 4 of Theorem 6.4 we have

$$\ln e^p = p \underbrace{\ln e}_{1} = p.$$

Using the inverse relationship between $\ln x$ and $\exp(x)$, we also know that

$$\ln \exp(p) = p.$$

Equating these two expressions for p, we conclude that $\ln e^p = \ln \exp(p)$. Because $\ln x$ is a one-to-one function, it follows that

$$e^p = \exp(p), \text{ for rational numbers } p,$$

and we conclude that $\exp(x)$ is the exponential function with base e.

We already know how to evaluate e^x when x is rational. For example, $e^3 = e \cdot e \cdot e$, $e^{-2} = \dfrac{1}{e \cdot e}$, and $e^{1/2} = \sqrt{e}$. But how do we evaluate e^x when x is irrational? We proceed as follows. The function $x = \ln y$ is defined for $y > 0$ and its range is all real numbers. Therefore, the domain of its inverse $y = \exp(x)$ is all real numbers; that is, $\exp(x)$ is defined for all real numbers. We now define e^x to be $\exp(x)$ when x is irrational.

DEFINITION The Exponential Function

For any real number x, $y = e^x = \exp(x)$, where $x = \ln y$.

We may now dispense with the notation $\exp(x)$ and use e^x as the inverse of $\ln x$. The usual inverse relationships between e^x and $\ln x$ hold, and the properties of $\exp(x)$ can now be written for e^x.

THEOREM 6.5 Properties of e^x

The exponential function e^x satisfies the following properties, all of which result from the integral definition of $\ln x$. Let x and y be real numbers.

1. $e^{x+y} = e^x e^y$

2. $e^{x-y} = e^x / e^y$

3. $(e^x)^p = e^{xp}$, where p is a rational number

4. $\ln(e^x) = x$

5. $e^{\ln x} = x$, for $x > 0$

➤ The restriction on p in property 3 will be lifted shortly.

QUICK CHECK 2 Simplify $e^{\ln 2x}$, $\ln(e^{2x})$, $e^{2 \ln x}$, and $\ln(2e^x)$. ◄

Derivatives and Integrals

By Theorem 3.23 (derivatives of inverse functions), the derivative of the exponential function exists for all x. To compute $\dfrac{d}{dx}(e^x)$, we observe that $\ln(e^x) = x$ and then differentiate both sides with respect to x:

$$\frac{d}{dx}(\ln e^x) = \underbrace{\frac{d}{dx}(x)}_{1}$$

$$\frac{1}{e^x}\frac{d}{dx}(e^x) = 1 \qquad \frac{d}{dx}(\ln u(x)) = \frac{u'(x)}{u(x)} \text{ (Chain Rule)}$$

$$\frac{d}{dx}(e^x) = e^x. \qquad \text{Solve for } \frac{d}{dx}(e^x).$$

QUICK CHECK 3 What is the slope of the curve $y = e^x$ at $x = \ln 2$? What is the area of the region bounded by the graph of $y = e^x$ and the x-axis between $x = 0$ and $x = \ln 2$? ◀

Once again, we obtain the remarkable result that the exponential function is its own derivative. It follows that e^x is its own antiderivative up to a constant; that is,

$$\int e^x\,dx = e^x + C.$$

Extending these results using the Chain Rule, we have the following theorem.

> **THEOREM 6.6 Derivative and Integral of the Exponential Function**
> For real numbers x,
>
> $$\frac{d}{dx}\left(e^{u(x)}\right) = e^{u(x)}u'(x) \quad \text{and} \quad \int e^x\,dx = e^x + C.$$

EXAMPLE 2 Integrals with e^x Evaluate $\displaystyle\int \frac{e^x}{1 + e^x}\,dx.$

SOLUTION The change of variables $u = 1 + e^x$ implies $du = e^x\,dx$:

$$\int \underbrace{\frac{1}{1 + e^x}}_{u}\,\underbrace{e^x\,dx}_{du} = \int \frac{1}{u}\,du \qquad u = 1 + e^x,\ du = e^x\,dx$$

$$= \ln|u| + C \qquad \text{Antiderivative of } u^{-1}$$

$$= \ln\left(1 + e^x\right) + C. \qquad \text{Replace } u \text{ with } 1 + e^x.$$

Note that the absolute value may be removed from $\ln|u|$ because $1 + e^x > 0$, for all x.

Related Exercises 21–26 ◀

Step 3: General Logarithmic and Exponential Functions

We now turn to exponential and logarithmic functions with a general positive base b. The first step is to define the exponential function b^x for positive bases with $b \neq 1$ and for all real numbers x. We use property 3 of Theorem 6.5 and the fact that $b = e^{\ln b}$. If x is a rational number, then

$$b^x = (\underbrace{e^{\ln b}}_{b})^x = e^{x \ln b};$$

this important relationship expresses b^x in terms of e^x. Because e^x is defined for all real x, we use this relationship to define b^x for all real x.

> **DEFINITION Exponential Functions with General Bases**
> Let b be a positive real number with $b \neq 1$. Then for all real x,
>
> $$b^x = e^{x \ln b}.$$

This definition fills the gap in property 4 of Theorem 6.4 ($\ln x^p = p \ln x$). We use the definition of b^x to write

$$x^p = e^{p \ln x}, \text{ for } x > 0 \text{ and } p \text{ real}.$$

Taking the natural logarithm of both sides and using the inverse relationship between e^x and $\ln x$, we find that

$$\ln x^p = \ln e^{p \ln x} = p \ln x, \text{ for } x > 0 \text{ and } p \text{ real}.$$

➤ Knowing that $\ln x^p = p \ln x$ for real p, we can also extend property 3 of Theorem 6.5 to real numbers. For real x and y, we take the natural logarithm of both sides of $z = (e^x)^y$, which gives $\ln z = y \ln e^x = xy$, or $z = e^{xy}$. Therefore, $(e^x)^y = e^{xy}$.

In this way, we extend property 4 of Theorem 6.4 to real powers.

Just as b^x is defined in terms of e^x, logarithms with base $b > 1$ and $b \neq 1$ may be expressed in terms of $\ln x$. All that is needed is the change of base formula (Section 1.3)

$$\log_b x = \frac{\ln x}{\ln b}.$$

Theorems 3.18 and 3.20 give us the derivative results for exponential and logarithmic functions with a general base $b > 0$. Extending those results with the Chain Rule, we have the following derivatives and integrals.

> **SUMMARY Derivatives and Integrals with Other Bases**
>
> Let $b > 0$ and $b \neq 1$. Then
>
> $$\frac{d}{dx}(\log_b |u(x)|) = \frac{u'(x)}{u(x)\ln b}, \text{ for } u(x) \neq 0 \text{ and } \frac{d}{dx}(b^{u(x)}) = (\ln b)b^{u(x)}u'(x).$$
>
> For $b > 0$ and $b \neq 1$, $\displaystyle\int b^x\,dx = \frac{1}{\ln b}b^x + C.$

QUICK CHECK 4 Verify that the derivative and integral results for a general base b reduce to the expected results when $b = e$. ◄

EXAMPLE 3 Integrals involving exponentials with other bases Evaluate the following integrals.

a. $\displaystyle\int x\,3^{x^2}\,dx$ **b.** $\displaystyle\int_1^4 \frac{6^{-\sqrt{x}}}{\sqrt{x}}\,dx$

SOLUTION

a.
$$\begin{aligned}\int x\,3^{x^2}\,dx &= \frac{1}{2}\int 3^u\,du && u = x^2,\ du = 2x\,dx\\ &= \frac{1}{2}\frac{1}{\ln 3}3^u + C && \text{Integrate.}\\ &= \frac{1}{2\ln 3}3^{x^2} + C && \text{Substitute } u = x^2.\end{aligned}$$

b.
$$\begin{aligned}\int_1^4 \frac{6^{-\sqrt{x}}}{\sqrt{x}}\,dx &= -2\int_{-1}^{-2} 6^u\,du && u = -\sqrt{x},\ du = -\frac{1}{2\sqrt{x}}dx\\ &= -\frac{2}{\ln 6}6^u\Big|_{-1}^{-2} && \text{Fundamental Theorem}\\ &= \frac{5}{18\ln 6} && \text{Simplify.}\end{aligned}$$

Related Exercises 27–32 ◄

Step 4: General Power Rule

With the identity $x^p = e^{p\ln x}$, we can state and prove the final version of the Power Rule. In Chapter 3, we showed that

$$\frac{d}{dx}(x^p) = px^{p-1}$$

when p is a rational number. This result is extended to all real values of p by differentiating $x^p = e^{p\ln x}$:

$$\begin{aligned}\frac{d}{dx}(x^p) &= \frac{d}{dx}(e^{p\ln x}) && x^p = e^{p\ln x}\\ &= \underbrace{e^{p\ln x}}_{x^p}\frac{p}{x} && \text{Chain Rule}\\ &= x^p\frac{p}{x} && e^{p\ln x} = x^p\\ &= px^{p-1}. && \text{Simplify.}\end{aligned}$$

> **THEOREM 6.7 General Power Rule**
> For any real number p,
> $$\frac{d}{dx}(x^p) = px^{p-1} \quad \text{and} \quad \frac{d}{dx}(u(x)^p) = pu(x)^{p-1}u'(x).$$

EXAMPLE 4 Derivative of a tower function Evaluate the derivative of $f(x) = x^{2x}$.

SOLUTION We use the inverse relationship $e^{\ln x} = x$ to write $x^{2x} = e^{\ln(x^{2x})} = e^{2x \ln x}$. It follows that

$$\begin{aligned}
\frac{d}{dx}(x^{2x}) &= \frac{d}{dx}(e^{2x \ln x}) \\
&= \underbrace{e^{2x \ln x}}_{x^{2x}} \frac{d}{dx}(2x \ln x) && \frac{d}{dx}(e^{u(x)}) = e^{u(x)}u'(x) \\
&= x^{2x}\left(2 \ln x + 2x \cdot \frac{1}{x}\right) && \text{Product Rule} \\
&= 2x^{2x}(1 + \ln x). && \text{Simplify.}
\end{aligned}$$

Related Exercises 33–40 ◀

Computing e

We have shown that the number e serves as a base for both $\ln x$ and e^x, but how do we approximate its value? Recall that the derivative of $\ln x$ at $x = 1$ is 1. By the definition of the derivative, it follows that

$$\begin{aligned}
1 = \frac{d}{dx}(\ln x)\bigg|_{x=1} &= \lim_{h \to 0} \frac{\ln(1 + h) - \ln 1}{h} && \text{Derivative of } \ln x \text{ at } x = 1 \\
&= \lim_{h \to 0} \frac{\ln(1 + h)}{h} && \ln 1 = 0 \\
&= \lim_{h \to 0} \ln(1 + h)^{1/h}. && p \ln x = \ln x^p
\end{aligned}$$

➤ Because $\frac{d}{dx}(\ln x) = \frac{1}{x}$, $\frac{d}{dx}(\ln x)\Big|_{x=1} = \frac{1}{1} = 1.$

➤ We rely on Theorem 2.12 of Section 2.6 here. If f is continuous at $g(a)$ and $\lim_{x \to a} g(x)$ exists, then $\lim_{x \to a} f(g(x)) = f(\lim_{x \to a} g(x))$.

The natural logarithm is continuous for $x > 0$, so it is permissible to interchange the order of $\lim_{h \to 0}$ and the evaluation of $\ln(1 + h)^{1/h}$. The result is that

$$\ln\underbrace{\left(\lim_{h \to 0}(1 + h)^{1/h}\right)}_{e} = 1.$$

Observe that the limit within the brackets is e because $\ln e = 1$ and only one number satisfies this equation. Therefore, we have isolated e as a limit:

$$e = \lim_{h \to 0}(1 + h)^{1/h}.$$

It is evident from Table 6.2 that $(1 + h)^{1/h} \to 2.718282\ldots$ as $h \to 0$. The value of this limit is e, and it has been computed to millions of digits. A better approximation,

$$e \approx 2.718281828459045,$$

is obtained by methods introduced in Chapter 9.

Table 6.2

h	$(1 + h)^{1/h}$	h	$(1 + h)^{1/h}$
10^{-1}	2.593742	-10^{-1}	2.867972
10^{-2}	2.704814	-10^{-2}	2.731999
10^{-3}	2.716924	-10^{-3}	2.719642
10^{-4}	2.718146	-10^{-4}	2.718418
10^{-5}	2.718268	-10^{-5}	2.718295
10^{-6}	2.718280	-10^{-6}	2.718283
10^{-7}	2.718282	-10^{-7}	2.718282

SECTION 6.8 EXERCISES

Review Questions

1. What are the domain and range of $\ln x$?

2. Give a geometrical interpretation of the function $\ln x = \int_1^x \frac{dt}{t}$.

3. Evaluate $\int 4^x\,dx$.

4. What is the inverse function of $\ln x$, and what are its domain and range?

5. Express 3^x, x^π, and $x^{\sin x}$ using the base e.

6. Evaluate $\frac{d}{dx}(3^x)$.

Basic Skills

7–12. Derivatives with ln *x* *Evaluate the following derivatives.*

7. $\frac{d}{dx}(x \ln x^3)\Big|_{x=1}$

8. $\frac{d}{dx}(\ln(\ln x))$

9. $\frac{d}{dx}(\sin(\ln x))$

10. $\frac{d}{dx}(\ln(\cos^2 x))$

11. $\frac{d}{dx}((\ln 2x)^{-5})$

12. $\frac{d}{dx}(\ln^3(3x^2+2))$

13–20. Integrals with ln *x* *Evaluate the following integrals. Include absolute values only when needed.*

13. $\int_0^3 \frac{2x-1}{x+1}\,dx$

14. $\int \tan 10x\,dx$

15. $\int_e^{e^2} \frac{dx}{x \ln^3 x}$

16. $\int_0^{\pi/2} \frac{\sin x}{1+\cos x}\,dx$

17. $\int \frac{e^{2x}}{4+e^{2x}}\,dx$

18. $\int \frac{dx}{x \ln x \ln(\ln x)}$

19. $\int_{e^2}^{e^3} \frac{dx}{x \ln x \ln^2(\ln x)}$

20. $\int_0^1 \frac{y \ln^4(y^2+1)}{y^2+1}\,dy$

21–26. Integrals with e^x *Evaluate the following integrals.*

21. $\int_0^2 4xe^{-x^2/2}\,dx$

22. $\int \frac{e^{\sin x}}{\sec x}\,dx$

23. $\int \frac{e^{\sqrt{x}}}{\sqrt{x}}\,dx$

24. $\int_{-2}^{2} \frac{e^{z/2}}{e^{z/2}+1}\,dz$

25. $\int \frac{e^x+e^{-x}}{e^x-e^{-x}}\,dx$

26. $\int_{\ln 2}^{\ln 3} \frac{e^x+e^{-x}}{e^{2x}-2+e^{-2x}}\,dx$

27–32. Integrals with general bases *Evaluate the following integrals.*

27. $\int_{-1}^{1} 10^x\,dx$

28. $\int_0^{\pi/2} 4^{\sin x}\cos x\,dx$

29. $\int_1^2 (1+\ln x)x^x\,dx$

30. $\int_{1/3}^{1/2} \frac{10^{1/p}}{p^2}\,dp$

31. $\int x^2\,6^{x^3+8}\,dx$

32. $\int \frac{4^{\cot x}}{\sin^2 x}\,dx$

33–40. Derivatives *Evaluate the derivatives of the following functions.*

33. $f(x) = (2x)^{4x}$

34. $f(x) = x^\pi$

35. $h(x) = 2^{(x^2)}$

36. $h(t) = (\sin t)^{\sqrt{t}}$

37. $H(x) = (x+1)^{2x}$

38. $p(x) = x^{-\ln x}$

39. $G(y) = y^{\sin y}$

40. $Q(t) = t^{1/t}$

Further Explorations

41. **Explain why or why not** Determine whether the following statements are true and give an explanation or counterexample. Assume $x > 0$ and $y > 0$.
    a. $\ln xy = \ln x + \ln y$.
    b. $\ln 0 = 1$.
    c. $\ln(x+y) = \ln x + \ln y$.
    d. $2^x = e^{2\ln x}$.
    e. The area under the curve $y = 1/x$ and the x-axis on the interval $[1, e]$ is 1.

42. **Logarithm properties** Use the integral definition of the natural logarithm to prove that $\ln(x/y) = \ln x - \ln y$.

T 43–46. Calculator limits *Use a calculator to make a table similar to Table 6.2 to approximate the following limits. Confirm your result with l'Hôpital's Rule.*

43. $\lim_{h\to 0}(1+2h)^{1/h}$

44. $\lim_{h\to 0}(1+3h)^{2/h}$

45. $\lim_{x\to 0}\frac{2^x-1}{x}$

46. $\lim_{x\to 0}\frac{\ln(1+x)}{x}$

47. **Zero net area** Consider the function $f(x) = \frac{1-x}{x}$.
    a. Are there numbers $0 < a < 1$ such that $\int_{1-a}^{1+a} f(x)\,dx = 0$?
    b. Are there numbers $a > 1$ such that $\int_{1/a}^{a} f(x)\,dx = 0$?

T 48. **Behavior at the origin** Using calculus and accurate sketches, explain how the graphs of $f(x) = x^p \ln x$ differ as $x \to 0^+$ for $p = \frac{1}{2}$, 1, and 2.

49. **Average value** What is the average value of $f(x) = 1/x$ on the interval $[1, p]$ for $p > 1$? What is the average value of f as $p \to \infty$?

50–57. Miscellaneous derivatives *Compute the following derivatives using the method of your choice.*

50. $\frac{d}{dx}(x^{2x})$

51. $\frac{d}{dx}(e^{-10x^2})$

52. $\frac{d}{dx}(x^{\tan x})$

53. $\frac{d}{dx}\left(\left(\frac{1}{x}\right)^x\right)$

54. $\frac{d}{dx}(x^e + e^x)$

55. $\frac{d}{dx}\left(1 + \frac{4}{x}\right)^x$

56. $\frac{d}{dx}(x^{(x^{10})})$

57. $\frac{d}{dx}(\cos(x^{2\sin x}))$

58–68. Miscellaneous integrals *Evaluate the following integrals.*

58. $\int 7^{2x}\,dx$

59. $\int 3^{-2x}\,dx$

60. $\int_0^5 5^{5x}\,dx$

61. $\int x^2 10^{x^3}\,dx$

62. $\int_0^{\pi} 2^{\sin x}\cos x\,dx$

63. $\int_1^{2e} \frac{3^{\ln x}}{x}\,dx$

64. $\int \frac{\sin(\ln x)}{4x}\,dx$

65. $\int_1^{e^2} \frac{(\ln x)^5}{x}\,dx$

66. $\int \frac{\ln^2 x + 2\ln x - 1}{x}\,dx$

67. $\int_0^{\ln 2} \frac{e^{3x} - e^{-3x}}{e^{3x} + e^{-3x}}\,dx$

68. $\int_0^1 \frac{16^x}{4^{2x}}\,dx$

Applications

69. Probability as an integral Two points P and Q are chosen randomly, one on each of two adjacent sides of a unit square (see figure). What is the probability that the area of the triangle formed by the sides of the square and the line segment PQ is less than one-fourth the area of the square? Begin by showing that x and y must satisfy $xy < \frac{1}{2}$ in order for the area condition to be met. Then argue that the required probability is $\frac{1}{2} + \int_{1/2}^{1} \frac{dx}{2x}$ and evaluate the integral.

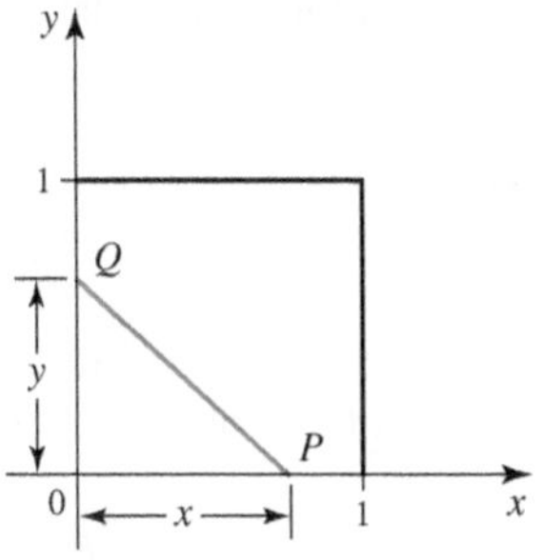

Additional Exercises

70. Derivative of ln |x| Differentiate $\ln x$ for $x > 0$ and differentiate $\ln(-x)$ for $x < 0$ to conclude that $\frac{d}{dx}(\ln|x|) = \frac{1}{x}$.

71. Properties of e^x Use the inverse relations between $\ln x$ and e^x $(\exp(x))$, and the properties of $\ln x$ to prove the following properties.

a. $\exp(0) = 1$

b. $\exp(x - y) = \frac{\exp(x)}{\exp(y)}$

c. $(\exp(x))^p = \exp(px)$, p rational

72. ln x is unbounded Use the following argument to show that $\lim_{x\to\infty} \ln x = \infty$ and $\lim_{x\to 0^+} \ln x = -\infty$.

a. Make a sketch of the function $f(x) = 1/x$ on the interval $[1, 2]$. Explain why the area of the region bounded by $y = f(x)$ and the x-axis on $[1, 2]$ is $\ln 2$.

b. Construct a rectangle over the interval $[1, 2]$ with height $\frac{1}{2}$. Explain why $\ln 2 > \frac{1}{2}$.

c. Show that $\ln 2^n > n/2$ and $\ln 2^{-n} < -n/2$.

d. Conclude that $\lim_{x\to\infty} \ln x = \infty$ and $\lim_{x\to 0^+} \ln x = -\infty$.

73. Bounds on *e* Use a left Riemann sum with at least $n = 2$ subintervals of equal length to approximate $\ln 2 = \int_1^2 \frac{dt}{t}$ and show that $\ln 2 < 1$. Use a right Riemann sum with $n = 7$ subintervals of equal length to approximate $\ln 3 = \int_1^3 \frac{dt}{t}$ and show that $\ln 3 > 1$.

74. Alternative proof of product property Assume that $y > 0$ is fixed and that $x > 0$. Show that $\frac{d}{dx}(\ln xy) = \frac{d}{dx}(\ln x)$. Recall that if two functions have the same derivative, then they differ by an additive constant. Set $x = 1$ to evaluate the constant and prove that $\ln xy = \ln x + \ln y$.

75. Harmonic sum In Chapter 8, we will encounter the harmonic sum $1 + \frac{1}{2} + \frac{1}{3} + \cdots + \frac{1}{n}$. Use a left Riemann sum to approximate $\int_1^{n+1} \frac{dx}{x}$ (with unit spacing between the grid points) to show that $1 + \frac{1}{2} + \frac{1}{3} + \cdots + \frac{1}{n} > \ln(n + 1)$. Use this fact to conclude that $\lim_{n\to\infty}\left(1 + \frac{1}{2} + \frac{1}{3} + \cdots + \frac{1}{n}\right)$ does not exist.

QUICK CHECK ANSWERS

1. $\{x: x \neq 0\}$ **2.** $2x, 2x, x^2, \ln 2 + x$ **3.** Slope $= 2$; area $= 1$ **4.** Note that when $b = e$, we have $\ln b = 1$. ◄

6.9 Exponential Models

The uses of exponential functions are wide-ranging. In this section, you will see them applied to problems in finance, medicine, ecology, biology, economics, pharmacokinetics, anthropology, and physics.

Exponential Growth

Exponential growth functions have the form $y(t) = Ce^{kt}$, where C is a constant and the *rate constant* k is positive (Figure 6.84). If we start with this function and take its derivative, we find that

$$y'(t) = \frac{d}{dt}(Ce^{kt}) = C \cdot ke^{kt} = k(\underbrace{Ce^{kt}}_{y});$$

that is, $y'(t) = ky$. Here is the first insight about exponential functions: *Their rate of change is proportional to their value.* If y represents a population, then $y'(t)$ is the **growth rate** with units such as people/month or cells/hr. We see that the larger the population, the faster its growth.

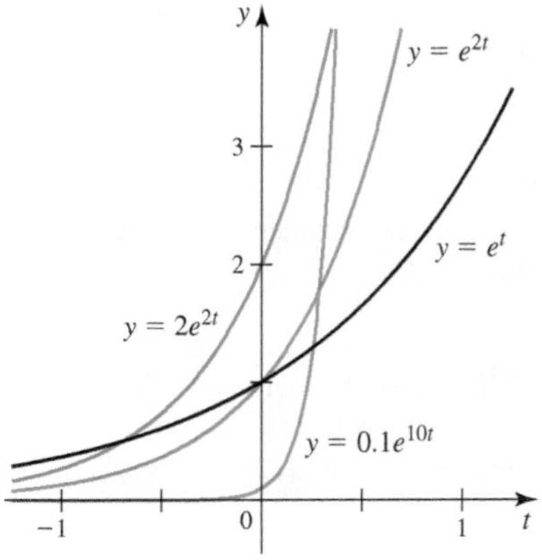

Figure 6.84

➤ The derivative $\frac{dy}{dt}$ is the *absolute* growth rate but is usually simply called the *growth rate*.

➤ A consumer price index that increases at a constant rate of 4% per year increases exponentially. A currency that is devalued at a constant rate of 3% per month decreases exponentially. By contrast, linear growth is characterized by constant absolute growth rates, such as 500 people per year or \$400 per month.

Another way to talk about growth rates is to use the **relative growth rate**, which is the growth rate divided by the current value of that quantity, or $y'(t)/y(t)$. For example, if y is a population, the relative growth rate is the fraction or percentage by which the population grows each unit of time. Examples of relative growth rates are 5% *per year* or *a factor of* 1.2 *per month*. Therefore, when the equation $y'(t) = ky$ is written in the form $y'(t)/y = k$, it has another interpretation. It says *a quantity that grows exponentially has a constant relative growth rate*. Constant relative or percentage change is the hallmark of exponential growth.

EXAMPLE 1 Linear versus exponential growth Suppose the population of the town of Pine is given by $P(t) = 1500 + 125t$, while the population of the town of Spruce is given by $S(t) = 1500e^{0.1t}$, where $t \geq 0$ is measured in years. Find the growth rate and the relative growth rate of each town.

SOLUTION Note that Pine grows according to a linear function, while Spruce grows exponentially (Figure 6.85). The growth rate of Pine is $\frac{dP}{dt} = 125$ people/year, which is constant for all times. The growth rate of Spruce is

$$\frac{dS}{dt} = 0.1(\underbrace{1500e^{0.1t}}_{S(t)}) = 0.1S(t),$$

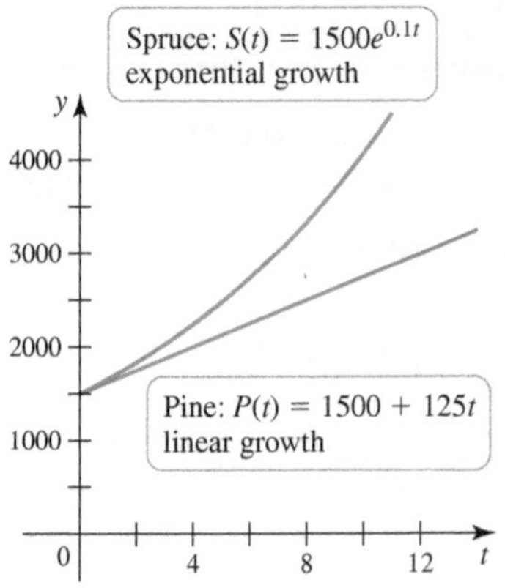

Figure 6.85

showing that the growth rate is proportional to the population. The relative growth rate of Pine is $\frac{1}{P}\frac{dP}{dt} = \frac{125}{1500 + 125t}$, which decreases in time. The relative growth rate of Spruce is

$$\frac{1}{S}\frac{dS}{dt} = \frac{0.1 \cdot 1500e^{0.1t}}{1500e^{0.1t}} = 0.1,$$

which is constant for all times. In summary, the linear population function has a *constant absolute growth rate* and the exponential population function has a *constant relative growth rate*.

Related Exercises 9–10 ◀

QUICK CHECK 1 Population A increases at a constant rate of 4%/yr. Population B increases at a constant rate of 500 people/yr. Which population exhibits exponential growth? What kind of growth is exhibited by the other population? ◀

The rate constant k in $y(t) = Ce^{kt}$ determines the growth rate of the exponential function. We adopt the convention that $k > 0$; then it is clear that $y(t) = Ce^{kt}$ describes exponential growth and $y(t) = Ce^{-kt}$ describes exponential decay, to be discussed shortly. For problems that involve time, the units of k are time^{-1}; for example, if t is measured in months, the units of k are month^{-1}. In this way, the exponent kt is dimensionless (without units).

➤ The unit time^{-1} is read *per unit time*. For example, month^{-1} is read *per month*.

Unless there is good reason to do otherwise, it is customary to take $t = 0$ as the reference point for time. Notice that with $y(t) = Ce^{kt}$, we have $y(0) = C$. Therefore, C has a simple meaning: It is the **initial value** of the quantity of interest, which we denote y_0. In the examples that follow, two pieces of information are typically given: the initial value and clues for determining the rate constant k. The initial value and the rate constant determine an exponential growth function completely.

Exponential Growth Functions

Exponential growth is described by functions of the form $y(t) = y_0 e^{kt}$. The initial value of y at $t = 0$ is $y(0) = y_0$, and the **rate constant** $k > 0$ determines the rate of growth. Exponential growth is characterized by a constant relative growth rate.

Because exponential growth is characterized by a constant relative growth rate, the time required for a quantity to double (a 100% increase) is constant. Therefore, one way to describe an exponentially growing quantity is to give its *doubling time*. To compute the time it takes the function $y(t) = y_0 e^{kt}$ to double in value, say from y_0 to $2y_0$, we find the value of t that satisfies

➤ Note that the initial value y_0 appears on both sides of this equation. It may be canceled, meaning that the doubling time is independent of the initial condition: *The doubling time is constant for all t.*

$$y(t) = 2y_0 \quad \text{or} \quad y_0 e^{kt} = 2y_0.$$

Canceling y_0 from the equation $y_0 e^{kt} = 2y_0$ leaves the equation $e^{kt} = 2$. Taking logarithms of both sides, we have $\ln e^{kt} = \ln 2$, or $kt = \ln 2$, which has the solution $t = \frac{\ln 2}{k}$. We denote this doubling time T_2 so that $T_2 = \frac{\ln 2}{k}$. If y increases exponentially, the time it takes to double from 100 to 200 is the same as the time it takes to double from 1000 to 2000.

DEFINITION **Doubling Time**

The quantity described by the function $y(t) = y_0 e^{kt}$, for $k > 0$, has a constant **doubling time** of $T_2 = \frac{\ln 2}{k}$, with the same units as t.

QUICK CHECK 2 Verify that the time needed for $y(t) = y_0 e^{kt}$ to double from y_0 to $2y_0$ is the same as the time needed to double from $2y_0$ to $4y_0$. ◄

➤ **World population**

1804	1 billion
1927	2 billion
1960	3 billion
1974	4 billion
1987	5 billion
1999	6 billion
2011	7 billion
2050	9 billion (proj.)

EXAMPLE 2 **World population** Human population growth rates vary geographically and fluctuate over time. The overall growth rate for world population peaked at an annual rate of 2.1% per year in the 1960s. Assume a world population of 6.0 billion in 1999 ($t = 0$) and 6.9 billion in 2009 ($t = 10$).

a. Find an exponential growth function for the world population that fits the two data points.

b. Find the doubling time for the world population using the model in part (a).

c. Find the (absolute) growth rate $y'(t)$ and graph it, for $0 \le t \le 50$.

d. How fast was the population growing in 2014 ($t = 15$)?

➤ It is a common mistake to assume that if the annual growth rate is 1.4% per year, then $k = 1.4\% = 0.014\ \text{year}^{-1}$. The rate constant k must be calculated, as it is in Example 2, to give $k = 0.013976$. For larger growth rates, the difference between k and the actual growth rate is greater.

SOLUTION

a. Let $y(t)$ be world population measured in billions of people t years after 1999. We use the growth function $y(t) = y_0 e^{kt}$, where y_0 and k must be determined. The initial value is $y_0 = 6$ (billion). To determine the rate constant k, we use the fact that $y(10) = 6.9$. Substituting $t = 10$ into the growth function with $y_0 = 6$ implies

$$y(10) = 6e^{10k} = 6.9.$$

Solving for k yields the rate constant $k = \dfrac{\ln(6.9/6)}{10} \approx 0.013976 \approx 0.014\ \text{year}^{-1}$.

Therefore, the growth function is

$$y(t) = 6e^{0.014t}.$$

b. The doubling time of the population is

$$T_2 = \frac{\ln 2}{k} \approx \frac{\ln 2}{0.014} \approx 50 \text{ years}.$$

c. Working with the growth function $y(t) = 6e^{0.014t}$, we find that

$$y'(t) = 6(0.014)e^{0.014t} = 0.084e^{0.014t},$$

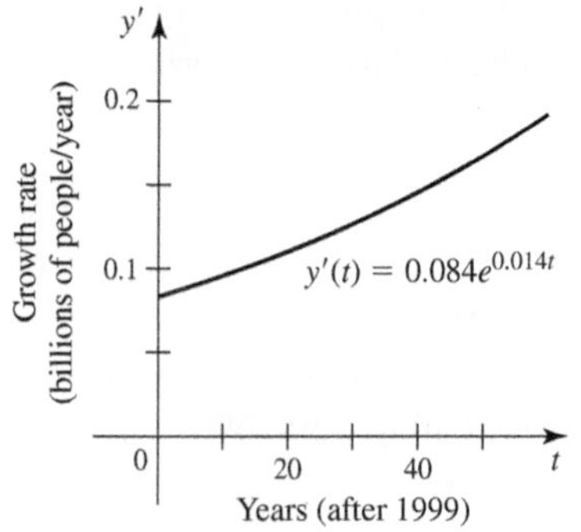

Figure 6.86

which has units of *billions of people/year*. As shown in Figure 6.86 the growth rate itself increases exponentially.

➤ Converted to a daily rate (dividing by 365), the world population in 2014 increased at a rate of roughly 284,000 people per day.

d. In 2014 ($t = 15$), the growth rate was

$$y'(15) = 0.084e^{(0.014)(15)} \approx 0.104 \text{ billion people/year},$$

or roughly 104 million people/year.

Related Exercises 11–20 ◀

QUICK CHECK 3 Assume $y(t) = 100e^{0.05t}$. By (exactly) what percentage does y increase when t increases by 1 unit? ◀

➤ The concept of continuous compounding was introduced in Exercise 109 of Section 4.7.

A Financial Model Exponential functions are used in many financial applications, several of which are explored in the exercises. For now, consider a simple savings account in which an initial deposit earns interest that is reinvested in the account. Interest payments are made on a regular basis (for example, annually, monthly, daily), or interest may be compounded continuously. In all cases, the balance in the account increases exponentially at a rate that can be determined from the advertised **annual percentage yield** (or **APY**) of the account. Assuming that no additional deposits are made, the balance in the account is given by the exponential growth function $y(t) = y_0 e^{kt}$, where y_0 is the initial deposit, t is measured in years, and k is determined by the annual percentage yield.

EXAMPLE 3 **Compounding** The APY of a savings account is the percentage increase in the balance over the course of a year. Suppose you deposit \$500 in a savings account that has an APY of 6.18% per year. Assume that the interest rate remains constant and that no additional deposits or withdrawals are made. How long will it take the balance to reach \$2500?

➤ If the balance increases by 6.18% in one year, it increases by a factor of 1.0618 in one year.

SOLUTION Because the balance grows by a fixed percentage every year, it grows exponentially. Letting $y(t)$ be the balance t years after the initial deposit of $y_0 = \$500$, we have $y(t) = y_0 e^{kt}$, where the rate constant k must be determined. Note that if the initial balance is y_0, one year later the balance is 6.18% more, or

$$y(1) = 1.0618\, y_0 = y_0 e^k.$$

Solving for k, we find that the rate constant is

$$k = \ln 1.0618 \approx 0.060\ \text{yr}^{-1}.$$

Therefore, the balance at any time $t \geq 0$ is $y(t) = 500e^{0.060t}$. To determine the time required for the balance to reach \$2500, we solve the equation

$$y(t) = 500e^{0.060t} = 2500.$$

Dividing by 500 and taking the natural logarithm of both sides yields

$$0.060t = \ln 5.$$

The balance reaches \$2500 in $t = (\ln 5)/0.060 \approx 26.8$ yr.

Related Exercises 11–20 ◀

Resource Consumption Among the many resources that people use, energy is certainly one of the most important. The basic unit of energy is the **joule** (J), roughly the energy needed to lift a 0.1-kg object (say an orange) 1 m. The *rate* at which energy is consumed is called **power**. The basic unit of power is the **watt** (W), where $1\text{ W} = 1\text{ J/s}$. If you turn on a 100-W lightbulb for 1 min, the bulb consumes energy at a rate of 100 J/s, and it uses a total of $100\text{ J/s} \cdot 60\text{ s} = 6000\text{ J}$ of energy.

A more useful measure of energy for large quantities is the **kilowatt-hour** (kWh). A kilowatt is 1000 W or 1000 J/s. So if you consume energy at the rate of 1 kW for 1 hr (3600 s), you use a total of $1000\text{ J/s} \cdot 3600\text{ s} = 3.6 \times 10^6\text{ J}$, which is 1 kWh. A person running for one hour consumes roughly 1 kWh of energy. A typical house uses on the order of 1000 kWh of energy in a month.

Assume that the total energy used (by a person, machine, or city) is given by the function $E(t)$. Because the power $P(t)$ is the rate at which energy is used, we have $P(t) = E'(t)$. Using the ideas of Section 6.1, the total amount of energy used between the times $t = a$ and $t = b$ is

$$\text{total energy used} = \int_a^b E'(t)\,dt = \int_a^b P(t)\,dt.$$

We see that energy is the area under the power curve. With this background, we can investigate a situation in which the rate of energy consumption increases exponentially.

EXAMPLE 4 Energy consumption At the beginning of 2010, the rate of energy consumption for the city of Denver was 7000 megawatts (MW), where $1\text{ MW} = 10^6\text{ W}$. That rate is expected to increase at an annual growth rate of 2% per year.

a. Find the function that gives the power or rate of energy consumption for all times after the beginning of 2010.

b. Find the total amount of energy used during 2014.

c. Find the function that gives the total (cumulative) amount of energy used by the city between 2010 and any time $t \geq 0$.

➤ In one year, the power function increases by 2% or by a factor of 1.02.

SOLUTION

a. Let $t \geq 0$ be the number of years after the beginning of 2010 and let $P(t)$ be the power function that gives the rate of energy consumption at time t. Because P increases at a constant rate of 2% per year, it increases exponentially. Therefore, $P(t) = P_0 e^{kt}$, where $P_0 = 7000$ MW. We determine k as before by setting $t = 1$; after one year the power is

$$P(1) = P_0 e^k = 1.02P_0.$$

Canceling P_0 and solving for k, we find that $k = \ln 1.02 \approx 0.0198$. Therefore, the power function (Figure 6.87) is

$$P(t) = 7000e^{0.0198t}, \quad \text{for } t \geq 0.$$

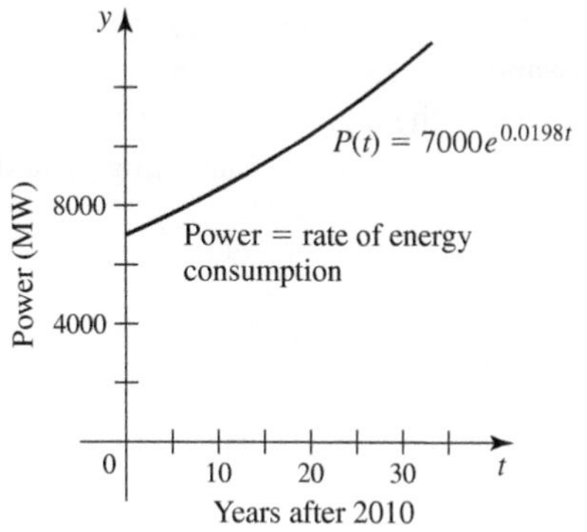

Figure 6.87

b. The entire year 2014 corresponds to the interval $4 \le t \le 5$. Substituting $P(t) = 7000e^{0.0198t}$, the total energy used in 2014 was

$$\int_4^5 P(t)\,dt = \int_4^5 7000e^{0.0198t}\,dt \quad \text{Substitute for } P(t).$$

$$= \frac{7000}{0.0198}e^{0.0198t}\Big|_4^5 \quad \text{Fundamental Theorem}$$

$$\approx 7652. \quad \text{Evaluate.}$$

Because the units of P are MW and t is measured in years, the units of energy are MW-yr. To convert to MWh, we multiply by 8760 hr/yr to get the total energy of about 6.7×10^7 MWh (or 6.7×10^{10} kWh).

c. The total energy used between $t = 0$ and any future time t is given by the future value formula (Section 6.1):

$$E(t) = E(0) + \int_0^t E'(s)\,ds = E(0) + \int_0^t P(s)\,ds.$$

Assuming $t = 0$ corresponds to the beginning of 2010, we take $E(0) = 0$. Substituting again for the power function P, the total energy (in MW-yr) at time t is

$$E(t) = E(0) + \int_0^t P(s)\,ds$$

$$= 0 + \int_0^t 7000e^{0.0198s}\,ds \quad \text{Substitute for } P(s) \text{ and } E(0).$$

$$= \frac{7000}{0.0198}e^{0.0198s}\Big|_0^t \quad \text{Fundamental Theorem}$$

$$\approx 353{,}535(e^{0.0198t} - 1). \quad \text{Evaluate.}$$

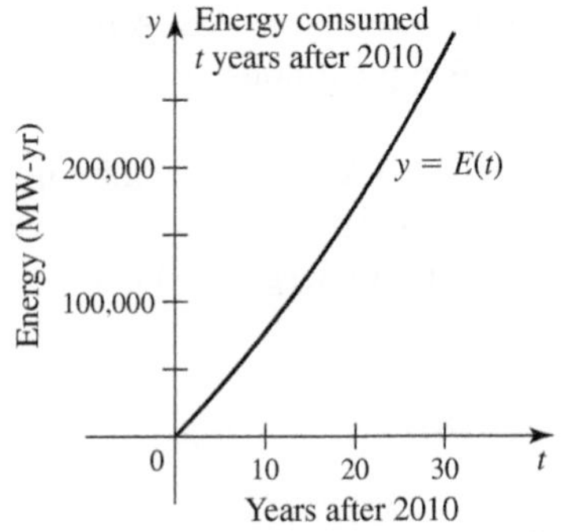

Figure 6.88

As shown in Figure 6.88, when the rate of energy consumption increases exponentially, the total amount of energy consumed also increases exponentially.

Related Exercises 11–20 ◀

Exponential Decay

Everything you have learned about exponential growth carries over directly to exponential decay. A function that decreases exponentially has the form $y(t) = y_0e^{-kt}$, where $y_0 = y(0)$ is the initial value and $k > 0$ is the rate constant.

Exponential decay is characterized by a constant relative decay rate and by a constant *half-life*. For example, radioactive plutonium has a half-life of 24,000 years. An initial sample of 1 mg decays to 0.5 mg after 24,000 years and to 0.25 mg after 48,000 years. To compute the half-life, we determine the time required for the quantity $y(t) = y_0e^{-kt}$ to reach one-half of its current value; that is, we solve $y_0e^{-kt} = y_0/2$ for t. Canceling y_0 and taking logarithms of both sides, we find that

$$e^{-kt} = \frac{1}{2} \quad \Rightarrow \quad -kt = \ln\frac{1}{2} = -\ln 2 \quad \Rightarrow \quad t = \frac{\ln 2}{k}.$$

QUICK CHECK 4 If a quantity decreases by a factor of 8 every 30 years, what is its half-life? ◀

The half-life is given by the same formula as the doubling time.

> **Exponential Decay Functions**
>
> Exponential decay is described by functions of the form $y(t) = y_0e^{-kt}$. The initial value of y is $y(0) = y_0$, and the rate constant $k > 0$ determines the rate of decay. Exponential decay is characterized by a constant relative decay rate. The constant **half-life** is $T_{1/2} = \frac{\ln 2}{k}$, with the same units as t.

Radiometric Dating A powerful method for estimating the age of ancient objects (for example, fossils, bones, meteorites, and cave paintings) relies on the radioactive decay of certain elements. A common version of radiometric dating uses the carbon isotope C-14, which is present in all living matter. When a living organism dies, it ceases to replace C-14, and the C-14 that is present decays with a half-life of about $T_{1/2} = 5730$ years. Comparing the C-14 in a living organism to the amount in a dead sample provides an estimate of its age.

EXAMPLE 5 **Radiometric dating** Researchers determine that a fossilized bone has 30% of the C-14 of a live bone. Estimate the age of the bone. Assume a half-life for C-14 of 5730 years.

SOLUTION The exponential decay function $y(t) = y_0 e^{-kt}$ represents the amount of C-14 in the bone t years after its owner died. By the half-life formula, $T_{1/2} = (\ln 2)/k$. Substituting $T_{1/2} = 5730$ yr, the rate constant is

$$k = \frac{\ln 2}{T_{1/2}} = \frac{\ln 2}{5730\text{ yr}} \approx 0.000121\text{ yr}^{-1}.$$

Assume that the amount of C-14 in a living bone is y_0. Over t years, the amount of C-14 in the fossilized bone decays to 30% of its initial value, or $0.3y_0$. Using the decay function, we have

$$0.3y_0 = y_0 e^{-0.000121t}.$$

Solving for t, the age of the bone (in years) is

$$t = \frac{\ln 0.3}{-0.000121} \approx 9950.$$

Related Exercises 21–26 ◀

Pharmacokinetics Pharmacokinetics describes the processes by which drugs are assimilated by the body. The elimination of most drugs from the body may be modeled by an exponential decay function with a known half-life (alcohol is a notable exception). The simplest models assume that an entire drug dose is immediately absorbed into the blood. This assumption is a bit of an idealization; more refined mathematical models account for the absorption process.

➤ **Half-lives of common drugs**

Penicillin	1 hr
Amoxicillin	1 hr
Nicotine	2 hr
Morphine	3 hr
Tetracycline	9 hr
Digitalis	33 hr
Phenobarbitol	2–6 days

EXAMPLE 6 **Pharmacokinetics** An exponential decay function $y(t) = y_0 e^{-kt}$ models the amount of drug in the blood t hr after an initial dose of $y_0 = 100$ mg is administered. Assume the half-life of the drug is 16 hours.

a. Find the exponential decay function that governs the amount of drug in the blood.

b. How much time is required for the drug to reach 1% of the initial dose (1 mg)?

c. If a second 100-mg dose is given 12 hr after the first dose, how much time is required for the drug level to reach 1 mg?

SOLUTION

a. Knowing that the half-life is 16 hr, the rate constant is

$$k = \frac{\ln 2}{T_{1/2}} = \frac{\ln 2}{16\text{ hr}} \approx 0.0433\text{ hr}^{-1}.$$

Therefore, the decay function is $y(t) = 100e^{-0.0433t}$.

b. The time required for the drug to reach 1 mg is the solution of

$$100e^{-0.0433t} = 1.$$

Solving for t, we have

$$t = \frac{\ln 0.01}{-0.0433\text{ hr}^{-1}} \approx 106\text{ hr}.$$

It takes more than 4 days for the drug to be reduced to 1% of the initial dose.

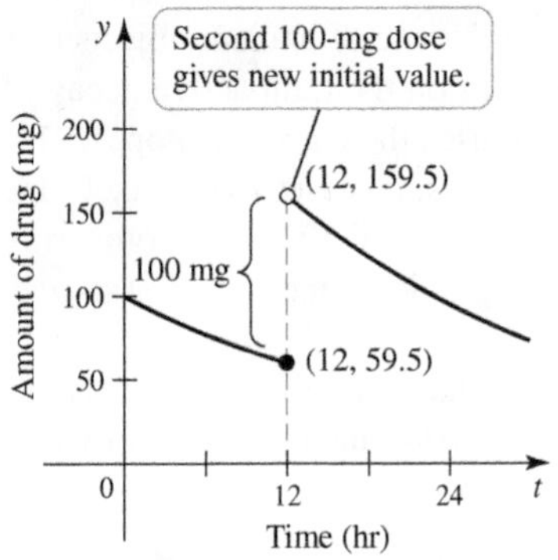

Figure 6.89

c. Using the exponential decay function of part (a), the amount of drug in the blood after 12 hr is

$$y(12) = 100e^{-0.0433 \cdot 12} \approx 59.5 \text{ mg}.$$

The second 100-mg dose given after 12 hr increases the amount of drug (assuming instantaneous absorption) to 159.5 mg. This amount becomes the new initial value for another exponential decay process (Figure 6.89). Measuring t from the time of the second dose, the amount of drug in the blood is

$$y(t) = 159.5e^{-0.0433t}.$$

The amount of drug reaches 1 mg when

$$y(t) = 159.5e^{-0.0433t} = 1,$$

which implies that

$$t = \frac{-\ln 159.5}{-0.0433 \text{ hr}^{-1}} = 117.1 \text{ hr}.$$

Approximately 117 hr after the second dose (or 129 hr after the first dose), the amount of drug reaches 1 mg.

Related Exercises 27–30 ◄

SECTION 6.9 EXERCISES

Review Questions

1. In terms of relative growth rate, what is the defining property of exponential growth?
2. Give two pieces of information that may be used to formulate an exponential growth or decay function.
3. Explain the meaning of doubling time.
4. Explain the meaning of half-life.
5. How are the rate constant and the doubling time related?
6. How are the rate constant and the half-life related?
7. Give two examples of processes that are modeled by exponential growth.
8. Give two examples of processes that are modeled by exponential decay.

Basic Skills

9–10. Absolute and relative growth rates *Two functions f and g are given. Show that the growth rate of the linear function is constant and the relative growth rate of the exponential function is constant.*

9. $f(t) = 100 + 10.5t,\ g(t) = 100e^{t/10}$
10. $f(t) = 2200 + 400t,\ g(t) = 400 \cdot 2^{t/20}$

11–16. Designing exponential growth functions *Devise the exponential growth function that fits the given data; then answer the accompanying questions. Be sure to identify the reference point ($t = 0$) and units of time.*

11. **Population** The population of a town with a 2010 population of 90,000 grows at a rate of 2.4%/yr. In what year will the population double its initial value (to 180,000)?
12. **Population** The population of Clark County, Nevada, was 2 million in 2013. Assuming an annual growth rate of 4.5%/yr, what will the county population be in 2020?
13. **Population** The current population of a town is 50,000 and is growing exponentially. If the population is projected to be 55,000 in 10 years, then what will be the population 20 years from now?
14. **Savings account** How long will it take an initial deposit of $1500 to increase in value to $2500 in a saving account with an APY of 3.1%? Assume the interest rate remains constant and no additional deposits or withdrawals are made.
15. **Rising costs** Between 2005 and 2010, the average rate of inflation was about 3%/yr (as measured by the Consumer Price Index). If a cart of groceries cost $100 in 2005, what will it cost in 2018, assuming the rate of inflation remains constant?
16. **Cell growth** The number of cells in a tumor doubles every 6 weeks starting with 8 cells. After how many weeks does the tumor have 1500 cells?
17. **Projection sensitivity** According to the 2010 census, the U.S. population was 309 million with an estimated growth rate of 0.8%/yr.
    - **a.** Based on these figures, find the doubling time and project the population in 2050.
    - **b.** Suppose the actual growth rate is just 0.2 percentage point lower than 0.8%/yr (0.6%). What are the resulting doubling time and projected 2050 population? Repeat these calculations assuming the growth rate is 0.2 percentage point higher than 0.8%/yr.
    - **c.** Comment on the sensitivity of these projections to the growth rate.
18. **Energy consumption** On the first day of the year ($t = 0$), a city uses electricity at a rate of 2000 MW. That rate is projected to increase at a rate of 1.3% per year.
    - **a.** Based on these figures, find an exponential growth function for the power (rate of electricity use) for the city.
    - **b.** Find the total energy (in MW-yr) used by the city over four full years beginning at $t = 0$.
    - **c.** Find a function that gives the total energy used (in MW-yr) between $t = 0$ and any future time $t > 0$.

19. **Population of Texas** Texas had the largest increase in population of any state in the United States from 2000 to 2010. During that decade, Texas grew from 20.9 million in 2000 to 25.1 million in 2010. Use an exponential growth model to predict the population of Texas in 2025.

20. **Oil consumption** Starting in 2010 ($t = 0$), the rate at which oil is consumed by a small country increases at a rate of 1.5%/yr, starting with an initial rate of 1.2 million barrels/yr.
    - **a.** How much oil is consumed over the course of the year 2010 (between $t = 0$ and $t = 1$)?
    - **b.** Find the function that gives the amount of oil consumed between $t = 0$ and any future time t.
    - **c.** How many years after 2010 will the amount of oil consumed since 2010 reach 10 million barrels?

21–25. Designing exponential decay functions *Devise an exponential decay function that fits the following data; then answer the accompanying questions. Be sure to identify the reference point* ($t = 0$) *and units of time.*

21. **Crime rate** The homicide rate decreases at a rate of 3%/yr in a city that had 800 homicides/yr in 2010. At this rate, when will the homicide rate reach 600 homicides/yr?

22. **Drug metabolism** A drug is eliminated from the body at a rate of 15%/hr. After how many hours does the amount of drug reach 10% of the initial dose?

23. **Valium metabolism** The drug Valium is eliminated from the bloodstream with a half-life of 36 hr. Suppose that a patient receives an initial dose of 20 mg of Valium at midnight. How much Valium is in the patient's blood at noon the next day? When will the Valium concentration reach 10% of its initial level?

24. **China's population** China's one-child policy was implemented with a goal of reducing China's population to 700 million by 2050 (from 1.2 billion in 2000). Suppose China's population declines at a rate of 0.5%/yr. Will this rate of decline be sufficient to meet the goal?

25. **Population of Michigan** The population of Michigan decreased from 9.94 million in 2000 to 9.88 million in 2010. Use an exponential model to predict the population in 2020. Explain why an exponential (decay) model might not be an appropriate long-term model of the population of Michigan.

26. **Depreciation of equipment** A large die-casting machine used to make automobile engine blocks is purchased for \$2.5 million. For tax purposes, the value of the machine can be depreciated by 6.8% of its current value each year.
    - **a.** What is the value of the machine after 10 years?
    - **b.** After how many years is the value of the machine 10% of its original value?

27. **Atmospheric pressure** The pressure of Earth's atmosphere at sea level is approximately 1000 millibars and decreases exponentially with elevation. At an elevation of 30,000 ft (approximately the altitude of Mt. Everest), the pressure is one-third the sea-level pressure. At what elevation is the pressure half the sea-level pressure? At what elevation is it 1% of the sea-level pressure?

28. **Carbon dating** The half-life of C-14 is about 5730 yr.
    - **a.** Archaeologists find a piece of cloth painted with organic dyes. Analysis of the dye in the cloth shows that only 77% of the C-14 originally in the dye remains. When was the cloth painted?
    - **b.** A well-preserved piece of wood found at an archaeological site has 6.2% of the C-14 that it had when it was alive. Estimate when the wood was cut.

29. **Uranium dating** Uranium-238 (U-238) has a half-life of 4.5 billion years. Geologists find a rock containing a mixture of U-238 and lead, and determine that 85% of the original U-238 remains; the other 15% has decayed into lead. How old is the rock?

30. **Radioiodine treatment** Roughly 12,000 Americans are diagnosed with thyroid cancer every year, which accounts for 1% of all cancer cases. It occurs in women three times as frequently as in men. Fortunately, thyroid cancer can be treated successfully in many cases with radioactive iodine, or I-131. This unstable form of iodine has a half-life of 8 days and is given in small doses measured in millicuries.
    - **a.** Suppose a patient is given an initial dose of 100 millicuries. Find the function that gives the amount of I-131 in the body after $t \geq 0$ days.
    - **b.** How long does it take the amount of I-131 to reach 10% of the initial dose?
    - **c.** Finding the initial dose to give a particular patient is a critical calculation. How does the time to reach 10% of the initial dose change if the initial dose is increased by 5%?

Further Explorations

31. **Explain why or why not** Determine whether the following statements are true and give an explanation or counterexample.
    - **a.** A quantity that increases at 6%/yr obeys the growth function $y(t) = y_0 e^{0.06t}$.
    - **b.** If a quantity increases by 10%/yr, it increases by 30% over 3 years.
    - **c.** A quantity decreases by one-third every month. Therefore, it decreases exponentially.
    - **d.** If the rate constant of an exponential growth function is increased, its doubling time is decreased.
    - **e.** If a quantity increases exponentially, the time required to increase by a factor of 10 remains constant for all time.

32. **Tripling time** A quantity increases according to the exponential function $y(t) = y_0 e^{kt}$. What is the tripling time for the quantity? What is the time required for the quantity to increase p-fold?

33. **Constant doubling time** Prove that the doubling time for an exponentially increasing quantity is constant for all time.

34. **Overtaking** City A has a current population of 500,000 people and grows at a rate of 3%/yr. City B has a current population of 300,000 and grows at a rate of 5%/yr.
    - **a.** When will the cities have the same population?
    - **b.** Suppose City C has a current population of $y_0 < 500{,}000$ and a growth rate of $p > 3\%$/yr. What is the relationship between y_0 and p such that the Cities A and C have the same population in 10 years?

T 35. **A slowing race** Starting at the same time and place, Abe and Bob race, running at velocities $u(t) = 4/(t + 1)$ mi/hr and $v(t) = 4e^{-t/2}$ mi/hr, respectively, for $t \geq 0$.
    - **a.** Who is ahead after $t = 5$ hr? After $t = 10$ hr?
    - **b.** Find and graph the position functions of both runners. Which runner can run only a finite distance in an unlimited amount of time?

Applications

36. **Law of 70** Bankers use the law of 70, which says that if an account increases at a fixed rate of $p\%/\text{yr}$, its doubling time is approximately $70/p$. Explain why and when this statement is true.

37. **Compounded inflation** The U.S. government reports the rate of inflation (as measured by the Consumer Price Index) both monthly and annually. Suppose that for a particular month, the *monthly* rate of inflation is reported as 0.8%. Assuming that this rate remains constant, what is the corresponding *annual* rate of inflation? Is the annual rate 12 times the monthly rate? Explain.

38. **Acceleration, velocity, position** Suppose the acceleration of an object moving along a line is given by $a(t) = -kv(t)$, where k is a positive constant and v is the object's velocity. Assume that the initial velocity and position are given by $v(0) = 10$ and $s(0) = 0$, respectively.
    a. Use $a(t) = v'(t)$ to find the velocity of the object as a function of time.
    b. Use $v(t) = s'(t)$ to find the position of the object as a function of time.
    c. Use the fact that $dv/dt = (dv/ds)(ds/dt)$ (by the Chain Rule) to find the velocity as a function of position.

T 39. **Air resistance** (adapted from Putnam Exam, 1939) An object moves in a straight line, acted on by air resistance, which is proportional to its velocity; this means its acceleration is $a(t) = -kv(t)$. The velocity of the object decreases from 1000 ft/s to 900 ft/s over a distance of 1200 ft. Approximate the time required for this deceleration to occur. (Exercise 38 may be useful.)

T 40. **A running model** A model for the startup of a runner in a short race results in the velocity function $v(t) = a(1 - e^{-t/c})$, where a and c are positive constants and v has units of m/s. (*Source: A Theory of Competitive Running*, Joe Keller, *Physics Today* 26, Sep 1973)
    a. Graph the velocity function for $a = 12$ and $c = 2$. What is the runner's maximum velocity?
    b. Using the velocity in part (a) and assuming $s(0) = 0$, find the position function $s(t)$, for $t \geq 0$.
    c. Graph the position function and estimate the time required to run 100 m.

41. **Tumor growth** Suppose the cells of a tumor are idealized as spheres each with a radius of 5 μm (micrometers). The number of cells has a doubling time of 35 days. Approximately how long will it take a single cell to grow into a multi-celled spherical tumor with a volume of 0.5 cm^3 (1 cm = 10,000 μm)? Assume that the tumor spheres are tightly packed.

42. **Carbon emissions in China and the United States** The burning of fossil fuels releases greenhouse gases (roughly 60% carbon dioxide) into the atmosphere. In 2010, the United States released approximately 5.8 billion metric tons of carbon dioxide (Environmental Protection Agency estimate), while China released approximately 8.2 billion metric tons (U.S. Department of Energy estimate). Reasonable estimates of the growth rate in carbon dioxide emissions are 4% per year for the United States and 9% per year for China. In 2010, the U.S. population was 309 million, growing at a rate of 0.7% per year, and the population of China was 1.3 billion, growing at a rate of 0.5% per year.
    a. Find exponential growth functions for the amount of carbon dioxide released by the United States and China. Let $t = 0$ correspond to 2010.
    b. According to the models in part (a), when will Chinese emissions double those of the United States?
    c. What was the amount of carbon dioxide released by the United States and China *per capita* in 2010?
    d. Find exponential growth functions for the per capita amount of carbon dioxide released by the United States and China. Let $t = 0$ correspond to 2010.
    e. Use the models of part (d) to determine the year in which per capita emissions in the two countries are equal.

43. **A revenue model** The owner of a clothing store understands that the demand for shirts decreases with the price. In fact, she has developed a model that predicts that at a price of $\$x$ per shirt, she can sell $D(x) = 40e^{-x/50}$ shirts in a day. It follows that the revenue (total money taken in) in a day is $R(x) = xD(x)$ ($\$x/\text{shirt} \cdot D(x)$ shirts). What price should the owner charge to maximize revenue?

Additional Exercises

44. **Geometric means** A quantity grows exponentially according to $y(t) = y_0e^{kt}$. What is the relationship between m, n, and p such that $y(p) = \sqrt{y(m)y(n)}$?

45. **Equivalent growth functions** The same exponential growth function can be written in the forms $y(t) = y_0e^{kt}$, $y(t) = y_0(1 + r)^t$, and $y(t) = y_0 2^{t/T_2}$. Write k as a function of r, r as a function of T_2, and T_2 as a function of k.

46. **General relative growth rates** Define the relative growth rate of the function f over the time interval T to be the relative change in f over an interval of length T:
$$R_T = \frac{f(t + T) - f(t)}{f(t)}.$$
Show that for the exponential function $y(t) = y_0e^{kt}$, the relative growth rate R_T is constant for any T; that is, choose any T and show that R_T is constant for all t.

QUICK CHECK ANSWERS

1. Population A grows exponentially; population B grows linearly. **3.** The function $100e^{0.05t}$ increases by a factor of 1.0513, or by 5.13%, in 1 unit of time. **4.** 10 years ◄

6.10 Hyperbolic Functions

In this section, we introduce a new family of functions called the *hyperbolic* functions, which are closely related to both trigonometric functions and exponential functions. Hyperbolic functions find widespread use in applied problems in fluid dynamics, projectile motion, architecture, and electrical engineering, to name just a few areas. Hyperbolic functions are also important in the development of many theoretical results in mathematics.

Relationship Between Trigonometric and Hyperbolic Functions

The trigonometric functions defined in Chapter 1 are based on relationships involving a circle—for this reason, trigonometric functions are also known as *circular* functions. Specifically, $\cos t$ and $\sin t$ are equal to the x- and y-coordinates, respectively, of the point $P(x, y)$ on the unit circle that corresponds to an angle of t radians (Figure 6.90). We can also regard t as the length of the arc from $(1, 0)$ to the point $P(x, y)$.

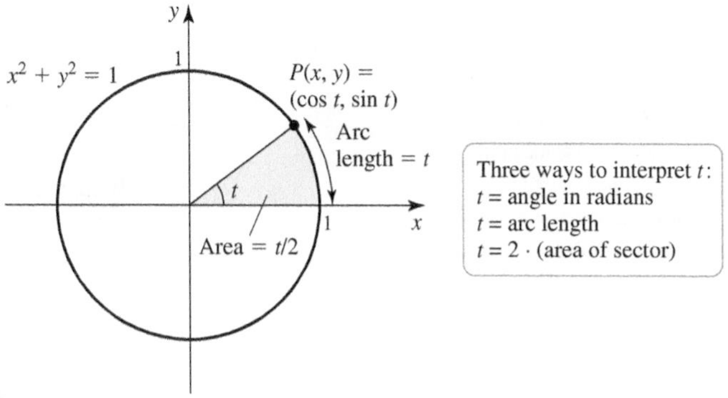

Figure 6.90

There is yet another way to interpret the number t, and it is this third interpretation that links the trigonometric and hyperbolic functions. Observe that t is twice the area of the circular sector in Figure 6.90. The functions $\cos t$ and $\sin t$ are still defined as the x- and y-coordinates of the point P, but now we associate P with a sector whose area is one-half of t.

➤ Recall that the area of a circular sector of radius r and angle θ is $A = \frac{1}{2}r^2\theta$. With $r = 1$ and $\theta = t$, we have $A = \frac{1}{2}t$, which implies $t = 2A$.

The *hyperbolic cosine* and *hyperbolic sine* are defined in an analogous fashion using the hyperbola $x^2 - y^2 = 1$ instead of the circle $x^2 + y^2 = 1$. Consider the region bounded by the x-axis, the right branch of the unit hyperbola $x^2 - y^2 = 1$, and a line segment from the origin to a point $P(x, y)$ on the hyperbola (Figure 6.91); let t equal twice the area of this region.

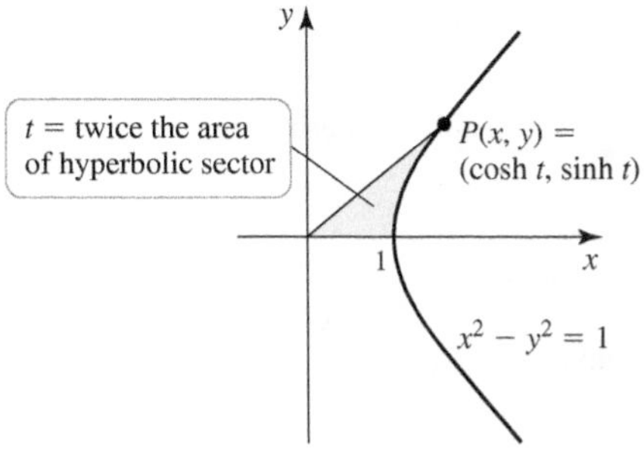

Figure 6.91

The hyperbolic cosine of t, denoted $\cosh t$, is the x-coordinate of P and the hyperbolic sine of t, denoted $\sinh t$, is the y-coordinate of P. Expressing x and y in terms of t leads to the standard definitions of the hyperbolic functions. We accomplish this task by writing t, which is an area, as an integral that depends on the coordinates of P. In Exercise 112, we ask you to carry out the calculations to show that

$$x = \cosh t = \frac{e^t + e^{-t}}{2} \quad \text{and} \quad y = \sinh t = \frac{e^t - e^{-t}}{2}.$$

Everything that follows in this section is based on these two definitions.

Definitions, Identities, and Graphs of the Hyperbolic Functions

Once the hyperbolic cosine and hyperbolic sine are defined, the four remaining hyperbolic functions follow in a manner analogous to the trigonometric functions.

➤ There is no universally accepted pronunciation of the names of the hyperbolic functions. In the United States, *cohsh x* (long *oh* sound) and *sinch x* are common choices for cosh x and sinh x. The pronunciations *tanch x*, *cotanch x*, *seech x* or *sech x*, and *coseech x* or *cosech x* are used for the other functions. International pronunciations vary as well.

DEFINITION Hyperbolic Functions

Hyperbolic cosine

$$\cosh x = \frac{e^x + e^{-x}}{2}$$

Hyperbolic sine

$$\sinh x = \frac{e^x - e^{-x}}{2}$$

Hyperbolic tangent

$$\tanh x = \frac{\sinh x}{\cosh x} = \frac{e^x - e^{-x}}{e^x + e^{-x}}$$

Hyperbolic cotangent

$$\coth x = \frac{\cosh x}{\sinh x} = \frac{e^x + e^{-x}}{e^x - e^{-x}}$$

Hyperbolic secant

$$\operatorname{sech} x = \frac{1}{\cosh x} = \frac{2}{e^x + e^{-x}}$$

Hyperbolic cosecant

$$\operatorname{csch} x = \frac{1}{\sinh x} = \frac{2}{e^x - e^{-x}}$$

The hyperbolic functions satisfy many important identities. Let's begin with the fundamental identity for hyperbolic functions, which is analogous to the familiar trigonometric identity $\cos^2 x + \sin^2 x = 1$:

$$\cosh^2 x - \sinh^2 x = 1.$$

➤ The fundamental identity for hyperbolic functions can also be understood in terms of the geometric definition of the hyperbolic functions. Because the point $P(\cosh t, \sinh t)$ is on the hyperbola $x^2 - y^2 = 1$, the coordinates of P satisfy the equation of the hyperbola, which leads immediately to

$$\cosh^2 t - \sinh^2 t = 1.$$

This identity is verified by appealing to the definitions:

$$\cosh^2 x - \sinh^2 x = \left(\frac{e^x + e^{-x}}{2}\right)^2 - \left(\frac{e^x - e^{-x}}{2}\right)^2 \quad \text{Definition of cosh } x \text{ and sinh } x$$

$$= \frac{e^{2x} + 2 + e^{-2x} - (e^{2x} - 2 + e^{-2x})}{4} \quad \text{Expand and combine fractions.}$$

$$= \frac{4}{4} = 1. \quad \text{Simplify.}$$

EXAMPLE 1 Deriving hyperbolic identities

a. Use the fundamental identity $\cosh^2 x - \sinh^2 x = 1$ to prove that $1 - \tanh^2 x = \operatorname{sech}^2 x$.

b. Derive the identity $\sinh 2x = 2 \sinh x \cosh x$.

SOLUTION

a. Dividing both sides of the fundamental identity $\cosh^2 x - \sinh^2 x = 1$ by $\cosh^2 x$ leads to the desired result:

$$\cosh^2 x - \sinh^2 x = 1 \quad \text{Fundamental identity}$$

$$\frac{\cosh^2 x}{\cosh^2 x} - \underbrace{\frac{\sinh^2 x}{\cosh^2 x}}_{\tanh^2 x} = \underbrace{\frac{1}{\cosh^2 x}}_{\operatorname{sech}^2 x} \quad \text{Divide both sides by } \cosh^2 x.$$

$$1 - \tanh^2 x = \operatorname{sech}^2 x. \quad \text{Identify functions.}$$

b. Using the definition of the hyperbolic sine, we have

$$\sinh 2x = \frac{e^{2x} - e^{-2x}}{2} \quad \text{Definition of sinh}$$

$$= \frac{(e^x - e^{-x})(e^x + e^{-x})}{2} \quad \text{Factor; difference of perfect squares}$$

$$= 2 \sinh x \cosh x. \quad \text{Identify functions.}$$

Related Exercises 11–18 ◄

The identities in Example 1 are just two of many useful hyperbolic identities, some of which we list next.

Hyperbolic Identities

$\cosh^2 x - \sinh^2 x = 1$ $\qquad$ $\cosh(-x) = \cosh x$

$1 - \tanh^2 x = \operatorname{sech}^2 x$ $\qquad$ $\sinh(-x) = -\sinh x$

$\coth^2 x - 1 = \operatorname{csch}^2 x$ $\qquad$ $\tanh(-x) = -\tanh x$

$\cosh(x + y) = \cosh x \cosh y + \sinh x \sinh y$

$\sinh(x + y) = \sinh x \cosh y + \cosh x \sinh y$

$\cosh 2x = \cosh^2 x + \sinh^2 x$ $\qquad$ $\sinh 2x = 2 \sinh x \cosh x$

$\cosh^2 x = \dfrac{\cosh 2x + 1}{2}$ $\qquad$ $\sinh^2 x = \dfrac{\cosh 2x - 1}{2}$

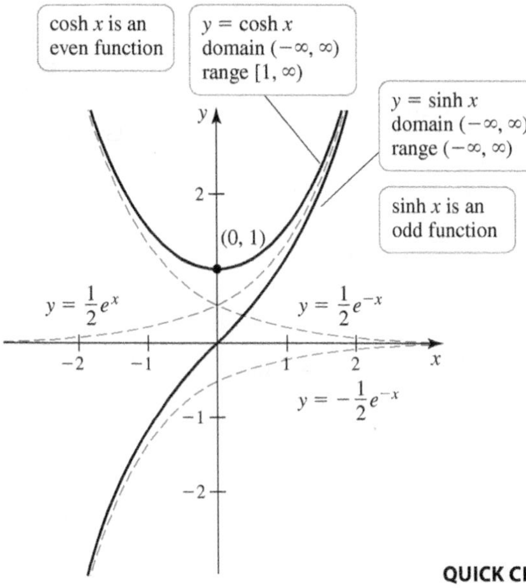

Figure 6.92

Graphs of the hyperbolic functions are relatively easy to produce because they are based on the familiar graphs of e^x and e^{-x}. Recall that $\lim_{x\to\infty} e^{-x} = 0$ and that $\lim_{x\to-\infty} e^x = 0$. With these facts in mind, we see that the graph of $\cosh x$ (Figure 6.92) approaches the graph of $y = \frac{1}{2}e^x$ as $x \to \infty$ because $\cosh x = \frac{e^x + e^{-x}}{2} \approx \frac{e^x}{2}$ for large values of x. A similar argument shows that as $x \to -\infty$, $\cosh x$ approaches $y = \frac{1}{2}e^{-x}$. Note also that $\cosh x$ is an even function:

$$\cosh(-x) = \frac{e^{-x} + e^{-(-x)}}{2} = \frac{e^x + e^{-x}}{2} = \cosh x.$$

Finally, $\cosh 0 = \frac{e^0 + e^0}{2} = 1$, so its y-intercept is $(0, 1)$. The behavior of $\sinh x$, an odd function also shown in Figure 6.92, can be explained in much the same way.

QUICK CHECK 1 Use the definition of the hyperbolic sine to show that $\sinh x$ is an odd function. ◀

The graphs of the other four hyperbolic functions are shown in Figure 6.93. As a consequence of their definitions, we see that the domain of $\cosh x$, $\sinh x$, $\tanh x$, and $\operatorname{sech} x$ is $(-\infty, \infty)$, whereas the domain of $\coth x$ and $\operatorname{csch} x$ is the set of all real numbers excluding 0.

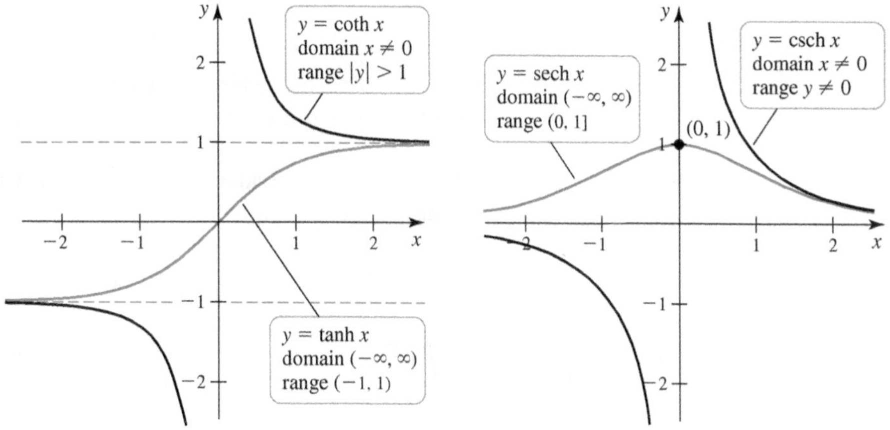

Figure 6.93

QUICK CHECK 2 Explain why the graph of $\tanh x$ has the horizontal asymptotes $y = 1$ and $y = -1$. ◀

Derivatives and Integrals of Hyperbolic Functions

Because the hyperbolic functions are defined in terms of e^x and e^{-x}, computing their derivatives is straightforward. The derivatives of the hyperbolic functions are given in Theorem 6.8—reversing these formulas produces corresponding integral formulas.

➤ The identities, derivative formulas, and integral formulas for the hyperbolic functions are similar to the corresponding formulas for the trigonometric functions, which makes them easy to remember. However, be aware of some subtle differences in the signs associated with these formulas. For instance,

$$d/dx(\cos x) = -\sin x,$$

whereas

$$d/dx(\cosh x) = \sinh x.$$

THEOREM 6.8 Derivative and Integral Formulas

1. $\frac{d}{dx}(\cosh x) = \sinh x \quad \Rightarrow \quad \int \sinh x \, dx = \cosh x + C$
2. $\frac{d}{dx}(\sinh x) = \cosh x \quad \Rightarrow \quad \int \cosh x \, dx = \sinh x + C$
3. $\frac{d}{dx}(\tanh x) = \operatorname{sech}^2 x \quad \Rightarrow \quad \int \operatorname{sech}^2 x \, dx = \tanh x + C$
4. $\frac{d}{dx}(\coth x) = -\operatorname{csch}^2 x \quad \Rightarrow \quad \int \operatorname{csch}^2 x \, dx = -\coth x + C$
5. $\frac{d}{dx}(\operatorname{sech} x) = -\operatorname{sech} x \tanh x \quad \Rightarrow \quad \int \operatorname{sech} x \tanh x \, dx = -\operatorname{sech} x + C$
6. $\frac{d}{dx}(\operatorname{csch} x) = -\operatorname{csch} x \coth x \quad \Rightarrow \quad \int \operatorname{csch} x \coth x \, dx = -\operatorname{csch} x + C$

Proof: Using the definitions of $\cosh x$ and $\sinh x$, we have

$$\frac{d}{dx}(\cosh x) = \frac{d}{dx}\left(\frac{e^x + e^{-x}}{2}\right) = \frac{e^x - e^{-x}}{2} = \sinh x \quad \text{and}$$

$$\frac{d}{dx}(\sinh x) = \frac{d}{dx}\left(\frac{e^x - e^{-x}}{2}\right) = \frac{e^x + e^{-x}}{2} = \cosh x.$$

To prove formula (3), we begin with $\tanh x = \sinh x/\cosh x$ and then apply the Quotient Rule:

$$\begin{aligned}
\frac{d}{dx}(\tanh x) &= \frac{d}{dx}\left(\frac{\sinh x}{\cosh x}\right) && \text{Definition of } \tanh x \\
&= \frac{\cosh x(\cosh x) - \sinh x(\sinh x)}{\cosh^2 x} && \text{Quotient Rule} \\
&= \frac{1}{\cosh^2 x} && \cosh^2 x - \sinh^2 x = 1 \\
&= \operatorname{sech}^2 x. && \operatorname{sech} x = 1/\cosh x
\end{aligned}$$

The proofs of the remaining derivative formulas are assigned in Exercises 19–21. The integral formulas are a direct consequence of their corresponding derivative formulas. ◀

EXAMPLE 2 Derivatives and integrals of hyperbolic functions Evaluate the following derivatives and integrals.

a. $\frac{d}{dx}(\operatorname{sech} 3x)$ **b.** $\frac{d^2}{dx^2}(\operatorname{sech} 3x)$

c. $\int \frac{\operatorname{csch}^2 \sqrt{x}}{\sqrt{x}} \, dx$ **d.** $\int_0^{\ln 3} \sinh^3 x \cosh x \, dx$

SOLUTION

a. Combining formula (5) of Theorem 6.8 with the Chain Rule gives

$$\frac{d}{dx}(\text{sech } 3x) = -3 \text{ sech } 3x \tanh 3x.$$

b. Applying the Product Rule and Chain Rule to the result of part (a), we have

$$\begin{aligned}
\frac{d^2}{dx^2}(\text{sech } 3x) &= \frac{d}{dx}(-3 \text{ sech } 3x \tanh 3x) \\
&= \underbrace{\frac{d}{dx}(-3 \text{ sech } 3x)}_{9 \text{ sech } 3x \tanh 3x} \cdot \tanh 3x + (-3 \text{ sech } 3x) \cdot \underbrace{\frac{d}{dx}(\tanh 3x)}_{3 \text{ sech}^2 3x} && \text{Product Rule} \\
&= 9 \text{ sech } 3x \tanh^2 3x - 9 \text{ sech}^3 3x && \text{Chain Rule} \\
&= 9 \text{ sech } 3x(\tanh^2 3x - \text{sech}^2 3x). && \text{Simplify.}
\end{aligned}$$

c. The integrand suggests the substitution $u = \sqrt{x}$:

$$\begin{aligned}
\int \frac{\text{csch}^2 \sqrt{x}}{\sqrt{x}}\, dx &= 2 \int \text{csch}^2 u\, du && \text{Let } u = \sqrt{x};\ du = \frac{1}{2\sqrt{x}}\, dx. \\
&= -2 \coth u + C && \text{Formula (4), Theorem 6.8} \\
&= -2 \coth \sqrt{x} + C. && u = \sqrt{x}
\end{aligned}$$

d. The derivative formula $d/dx(\sinh x) = \cosh x$ suggests the substitution $u = \sinh x$:

$$\int_0^{\ln 3} \sinh^3 x \cosh x\, dx = \int_0^{4/3} u^3\, du. \qquad \text{Let } u = \sinh x;\ du = \cosh x\, dx.$$

The new limits of integration are determined by the calculations

$$x = 0 \quad \Rightarrow \quad u = \sinh 0 = 0 \quad \text{and}$$

$$x = \ln 3 \quad \Rightarrow \quad u = \sinh(\ln 3) = \frac{e^{\ln 3} - e^{-\ln 3}}{2} = \frac{3 - 1/3}{2} = \frac{4}{3}.$$

We now evaluate the integral in the variable u:

$$\begin{aligned}
\int_0^{4/3} u^3\, du &= \frac{1}{4} u^4 \Big|_0^{4/3} \\
&= \frac{1}{4}\left(\left(\frac{4}{3}\right)^4 - 0^4\right) = \frac{64}{81}.
\end{aligned}$$

Related Exercises 19–40 ◂

QUICK CHECK 3 Find both the derivative and indefinite integral of $f(x) = 4 \cosh 2x$. ◂

Theorem 6.9 presents integral formulas for the four hyperbolic functions not covered in Theorem 6.8.

THEOREM 6.9 Integrals of Hyperbolic Functions

1. $\int \tanh x\, dx = \ln \cosh x + C$

2. $\int \coth x\, dx = \ln|\sinh x| + C$

3. $\int \text{sech } x\, dx = \tan^{-1}(\sinh x) + C$

4. $\int \text{csch } x\, dx = \ln|\tanh(x/2)| + C$

Proof: Formula (1) is derived by first writing $\tanh x$ in terms of $\sinh x$ and $\cosh x$:

$$\int \tanh x\,dx = \int \frac{\sinh x}{\cosh x}\,dx \qquad \text{Definition of } \tanh x$$

$$= \int \frac{1}{u}\,du \qquad \text{Let } u = \cosh x;\ du = \sinh x\,dx.$$

$$= \ln|u| + C \qquad \text{Evaluate integral.}$$

$$= \ln \cosh x + C. \qquad u = \cosh x > 0$$

Formula (2) is derived in a similar fashion (Exercise 44). The more challenging proofs of formulas (3) and (4) are considered in Exercises 107 and 108. ◄

EXAMPLE 3 Integrals involving hyperbolic functions Determine the indefinite integral $\int x \coth (x^2)\,dx$.

SOLUTION The integrand suggests the substitution $u = x^2$:

$$\int x \coth x^2\,dx = \frac{1}{2}\int \coth u\,du. \qquad \text{Let } u = x^2;\ du = 2x\,dx.$$

$$= \frac{1}{2}\ln|\sinh u| + C \qquad \text{Evaluate integral; use Theorem 6.9.}$$

$$= \frac{1}{2}\ln(\sinh x^2) + C. \qquad u = x^2;\ \sinh x^2 \geq 0$$

Related Exercises 41–44 ◄

QUICK CHECK 4 Determine the indefinite integral $\int \operatorname{csch} 2x\,dx$. ◄

Inverse Hyperbolic Functions

At present, we don't have the tools for evaluating an integral such as $\int \frac{dx}{\sqrt{x^2+4}}$. By studying inverse hyperbolic functions, we can discover new integration formulas. Inverse hyperbolic functions are also useful for solving equations involving hyperbolic functions.

Figures 6.92 and 6.93 show that the functions $\sinh x$, $\tanh x$, $\coth x$, and $\operatorname{csch} x$ are all one-to-one on their respective domains. This observation implies that each of these functions has a well-defined inverse. However, the function $y = \cosh x$ is not one-to-one on $(-\infty, \infty)$, so its inverse, denoted $y = \cosh^{-1} x$, exists only if we restrict the domain of $\cosh x$. Specifically, when $y = \cosh x$ is restricted to the interval $[0, \infty)$, it is one-to-one, and its inverse is defined as follows:

$$y = \cosh^{-1} x \quad \text{if and only if} \quad x = \cosh y, \ \text{for } x \geq 1 \text{ and } 0 \leq y < \infty.$$

Figure 6.94a shows the graph of $y = \cosh^{-1} x$, obtained by reflecting the graph of $y = \cosh x$ on $[0, \infty)$ over the line $y = x$. The definitions and graphs of the other five inverse hyperbolic functions are also shown in Figure 6.94. Notice that the domain of $y = \operatorname{sech} x$ (Figure 6.94d) must be restricted to $[0, \infty)$ to ensure the existence of its inverse.

Because hyperbolic functions are defined in terms of exponential functions, we can find explicit formulas for their inverses in terms of logarithms. For example, let's start with the definition of the inverse hyperbolic sine. For all real x and y, we have

$$y = \sinh^{-1} x \quad \Leftrightarrow \quad x = \sinh y.$$

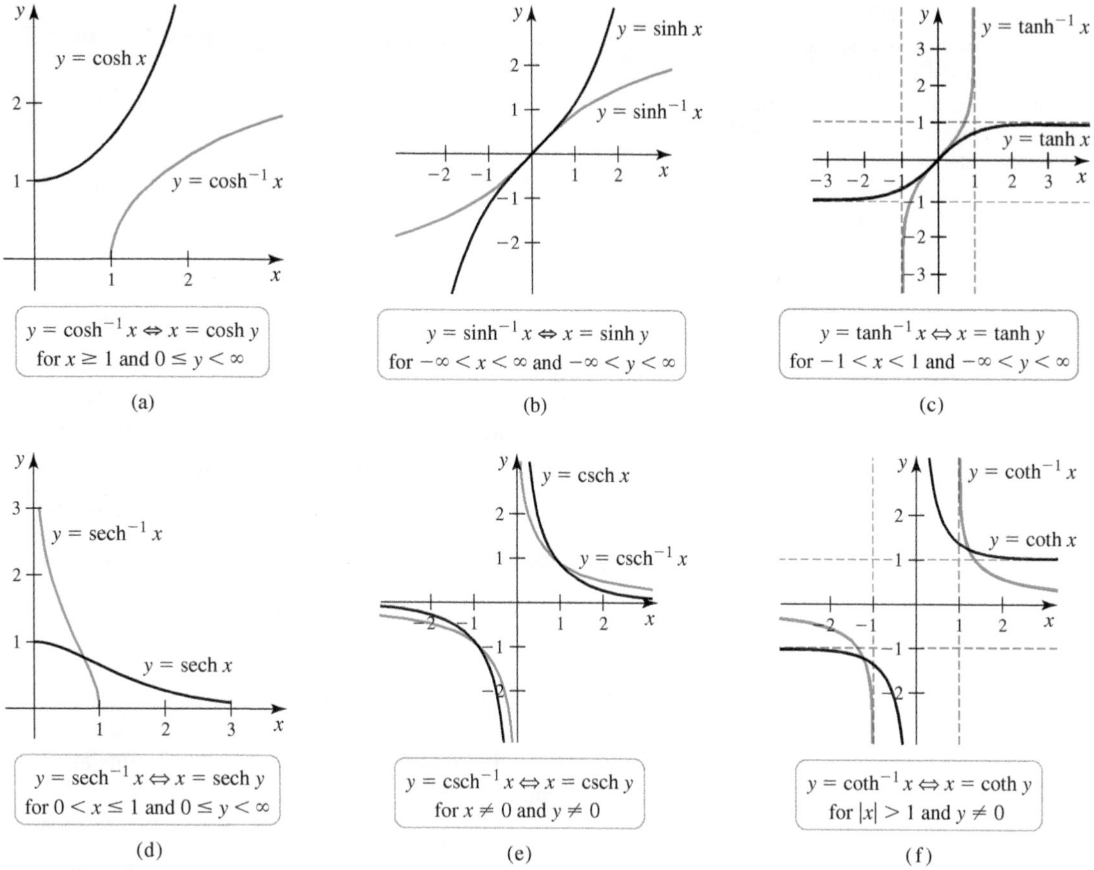

Figure 6.94

Following the procedure outlined in Section 1.3, we solve

$$x = \sinh y = \frac{e^y - e^{-y}}{2}$$

for y to give a formula for $\sinh^{-1} x$:

$$x = \frac{e^y - e^{-y}}{2} \quad \Rightarrow \quad e^y - 2x - e^{-y} = 0 \qquad \text{Rearrange equation.}$$

$$\Rightarrow \quad (e^y)^2 - 2xe^y - 1 = 0. \qquad \text{Multiply by } e^y.$$

At this stage, we recognize a quadratic equation in e^y and solve for e^y using the quadratic formula, with $a = 1$, $b = -2x$, and $c = -1$:

$$e^y = \frac{2x \pm \sqrt{4x^2 + 4}}{2} = x \pm \sqrt{x^2 + 1} = \underbrace{x + \sqrt{x^2 + 1}}_{\text{choose positive root}}.$$

Because $e^y > 0$ and $\sqrt{x^2 + 1} > x$, the positive root must be chosen. We now solve for y by taking the natural logarithm of both sides:

$$e^y = x + \sqrt{x^2 + 1} \quad \Rightarrow \quad y = \ln(x + \sqrt{x^2 + 1}).$$

Therefore, the formula we seek is $\sinh^{-1} x = \ln(x + \sqrt{x^2 + 1})$.

A similar procedure can be carried out for the other inverse hyperbolic functions (Exercise 110). Theorem 6.10 lists the results of these calculations.

➤ Most calculators allow for the direct evaluation of the hyperbolic sine, cosine, and tangent, along with their inverses, but are not programmed to evaluate $\operatorname{sech}^{-1} x$, $\operatorname{csch}^{-1} x$, and $\coth^{-1} x$. The formulas in Theorem 6.10 are useful for evaluating these functions on a calculator.

THEOREM 6.10 Inverses of the Hyperbolic Functions Expressed as Logarithms

$$\cosh^{-1} x = \ln\left(x + \sqrt{x^2 - 1}\right)\ (x \ge 1) \qquad \operatorname{sech}^{-1} x = \cosh^{-1}\frac{1}{x}\ (0 < x \le 1)$$

$$\sinh^{-1} x = \ln\left(x + \sqrt{x^2 + 1}\right) \qquad \operatorname{csch}^{-1} x = \sinh^{-1}\frac{1}{x}\ (x \ne 0)$$

$$\tanh^{-1} x = \frac{1}{2}\ln\left(\frac{1 + x}{1 - x}\right)\ (|x| < 1) \qquad \coth^{-1} x = \tanh^{-1}\frac{1}{x}\ (|x| > 1)$$

Notice that the formulas in Theorem 6.10 for the inverse hyperbolic secant, cosecant, and cotangent are given in terms of the inverses of their corresponding reciprocal functions. Justification for these formulas follows from the definitions of the inverse functions. For example, from the definition of $\operatorname{csch}^{-1} x$, we have

$$y = \operatorname{csch}^{-1} x \quad \Leftrightarrow \quad x = \operatorname{csch} y \quad \Leftrightarrow \quad 1/x = \sinh y.$$

Applying the inverse hyperbolic sine to both sides of $1/x = \sinh y$ yields

$$\sinh^{-1}(1/x) = \underbrace{\sinh^{-1}(\sinh y)}_{y} \quad \text{or} \quad y = \operatorname{csch}^{-1} x = \sinh^{-1}(1/x).$$

Similar derivations yield the other two formulas.

EXAMPLE 4 Points of intersection Find the points at which the curves $y = \cosh x$ and $y = \frac{5}{3}$ intersect (Figure 6.95).

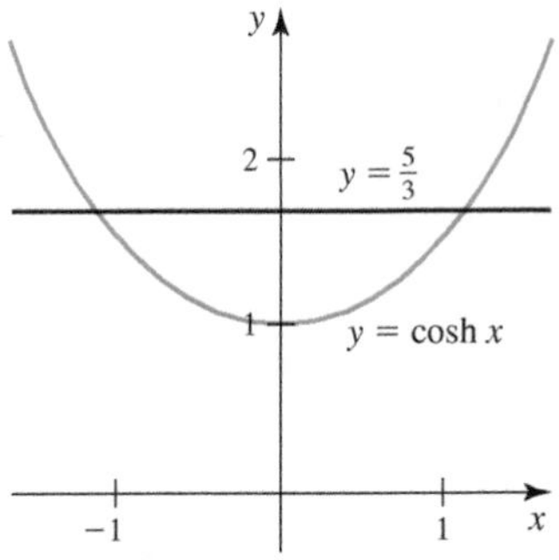

Figure 6.95

SOLUTION The x-coordinates of the points of intersection satisfy the equation $\cosh x = \frac{5}{3}$, which is solved by applying $\cosh^{-1}$ to both sides of the equation. However, evaluating $\cosh^{-1}(\cosh x)$ requires care—in Exercise 105, you are asked to show that $\cosh^{-1}(\cosh x) = |x|$. With this fact, the points of intersection can be found:

$$\begin{aligned} \cosh x &= \tfrac{5}{3} && \text{Set equations equal to one another.}\\ \cosh^{-1}(\cosh x) &= \cosh^{-1}\tfrac{5}{3} && \text{Apply } \cosh^{-1} \text{ to both sides.}\\ |x| &= \ln\left(\tfrac{5}{3} + \sqrt{\left(\tfrac{5}{3}\right)^2 - 1}\right) && \text{Simplify; use Theorem 6.10.}\\ x &= \pm\ln 3. && \text{Simplify.} \end{aligned}$$

The points of intersection lie on the line $y = \frac{5}{3}$, so the points are $\left(-\ln 3, \frac{5}{3}\right)$ and $\left(\ln 3, \frac{5}{3}\right)$.

Related Exercises 45–46 ◄

QUICK CHECK 5 Use the results of Example 4 to write an integral for the area of the region bounded by $y = \cosh x$ and $y = \frac{5}{3}$ (Figure 6.95) and then evaluate the integral. ◄

Derivatives of the Inverse Hyperbolic Functions and Related Integral Formulas

The derivatives of the inverse hyperbolic functions can be computed directly from the logarithmic formulas given in Theorem 6.10. However, it is more efficient to use the definitions in Figure 6.94.

Recall that the inverse hyperbolic sine is defined by

$$y = \sinh^{-1} x \quad \Leftrightarrow \quad x = \sinh y.$$

We differentiate both sides of $x = \sinh y$ with respect to x and solve for dy/dx:

$$\begin{aligned} x &= \sinh y && y = \sinh^{-1} x \ \Leftrightarrow\ x = \sinh y\\ 1 &= (\cosh y)\frac{dy}{dx} && \text{Use implicit differentiation.}\\ \frac{dy}{dx} &= \frac{1}{\cosh y} && \text{Solve for } dy/dx.\\ \frac{dy}{dx} &= \frac{1}{\pm\sqrt{\sinh^2 y + 1}} && \cosh^2 y - \sinh^2 y = 1\\ \frac{dy}{dx} &= \frac{1}{\sqrt{x^2 + 1}}. && x = \sinh y \end{aligned}$$

In the last step, the positive root is chosen because $\cosh y > 0$ for all y.

The derivatives of the other inverse hyperbolic functions, listed in Theorem 6.11, are derived in a similar way (Exercise 106).

THEOREM 6.11 Derivatives of the Inverse Hyperbolic Functions

$$\frac{d}{dx}(\cosh^{-1} x) = \frac{1}{\sqrt{x^2 - 1}} \quad (x > 1) \qquad \frac{d}{dx}(\sinh^{-1} x) = \frac{1}{\sqrt{x^2 + 1}}$$

$$\frac{d}{dx}(\tanh^{-1} x) = \frac{1}{1 - x^2} \quad (|x| < 1) \qquad \frac{d}{dx}(\coth^{-1} x) = \frac{1}{1 - x^2} \quad (|x| > 1)$$

$$\frac{d}{dx}(\operatorname{sech}^{-1} x) = -\frac{1}{x\sqrt{1 - x^2}} \quad (0 < x < 1) \qquad \frac{d}{dx}(\operatorname{csch}^{-1} x) = -\frac{1}{|x|\sqrt{1 + x^2}} \quad (x \neq 0)$$

The restrictions associated with the formulas in Theorem 6.11 are a direct consequence of the domains of the inverse functions (Figure 6.94). Note that the derivative of both $\tanh^{-1} x$ and $\coth^{-1} x$ is $1/(1 - x^2)$, although this result is valid on different domains ($|x| < 1$ for $\tanh^{-1} x$ and $|x| > 1$ for $\coth^{-1} x$). These facts have a bearing on formula (3) in the next theorem, which is a reversal of the derivative formulas in Theorem 6.11. Here we list integral results, where a is a positive constant; each formula can be verified by differentiation.

➤ The integrals in Theorem 6.12 appear again in Chapter 7 in terms of logarithms and with fewer restrictions on the variable of integration.

THEOREM 6.12 Integral Formulas

1. $\displaystyle\int \frac{dx}{\sqrt{x^2 - a^2}} = \cosh^{-1}\frac{x}{a} + C, \text{ for } x > a$

2. $\displaystyle\int \frac{dx}{\sqrt{x^2 + a^2}} = \sinh^{-1}\frac{x}{a} + C, \text{ for all } x$

3. $\displaystyle\int \frac{dx}{a^2 - x^2} = \begin{cases} \dfrac{1}{a}\tanh^{-1}\dfrac{x}{a} + C, \text{ for } |x| < a \\ \dfrac{1}{a}\coth^{-1}\dfrac{x}{a} + C, \text{ for } |x| > a \end{cases}$

4. $\displaystyle\int \frac{dx}{x\sqrt{a^2 - x^2}} = -\frac{1}{a}\operatorname{sech}^{-1}\frac{x}{a} + C, \text{ for } 0 < x < a$

5. $\displaystyle\int \frac{dx}{x\sqrt{a^2 + x^2}} = -\frac{1}{a}\operatorname{csch}^{-1}\frac{|x|}{a} + C, \text{ for } x \neq 0$

EXAMPLE 5 Derivatives of inverse hyperbolic functions Compute dy/dx for each function.

a. $y = \tanh^{-1} 3x$ **b.** $y = x^2 \sinh^{-1} x$

SOLUTION

a. Using the Chain Rule, we have

$$\frac{dy}{dx} = \frac{d}{dx}(\tanh^{-1} 3x) = \frac{1}{1 - (3x)^2}\cdot 3 = \frac{3}{1 - 9x^2}.$$

➤ The function $3/(1 - 9x^2)$ in the solution to Example 5a is defined for all $x \neq \pm 1/3$. However, the derivative formula $dy/dx = 3/(1 - 9x^2)$ is valid only on $-1/3 < x < 1/3$ because $\tanh^{-1} 3x$ is defined only on $-1/3 < x < 1/3$. The result of computing $d/dx(\coth^{-1} 3x)$ is the same, but valid on $(-\infty, -1/3) \cup (1/3, \infty)$.

b. $$\frac{dy}{dx} = 2x \sinh^{-1} x + x^2 \cdot \frac{1}{\sqrt{x^2 + 1}} \qquad \text{Product Rule; Theorem 6.11}$$

$$= x\left(\frac{2\sqrt{x^2 + 1}\cdot \sinh^{-1} x + x}{\sqrt{x^2 + 1}}\right) \qquad \text{Simplify.}$$

Related Exercises 47–52 ◀

EXAMPLE 6 Integral computations

a. Compute the area of the region bounded by $y = 1/\sqrt{x^2 + 16}$ over the interval $[0, 3]$.

b. Evaluate $\int_9^{25} \frac{dx}{\sqrt{x}(4 - x)}$.

SOLUTION

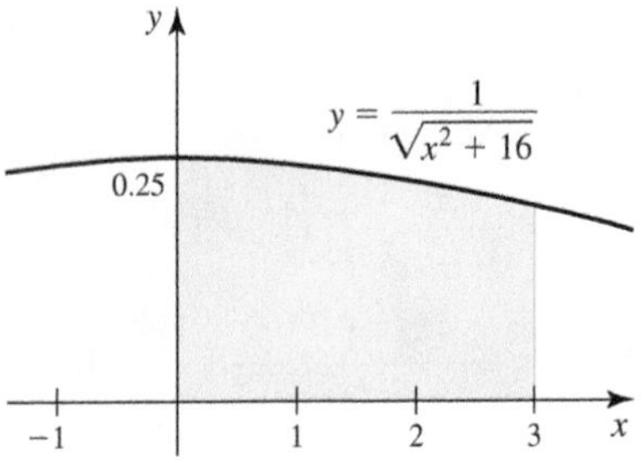

Figure 6.96

a. The region in question is shown in Figure 6.96, and its area is given by $\int_0^3 \frac{dx}{\sqrt{x^2 + 16}}$. Using formula (2) in Theorem 6.12 with $a = 4$, we have

$$\int_0^3 \frac{dx}{\sqrt{x^2 + 16}} = \sinh^{-1} \frac{x}{4}\bigg|_0^3 \quad \text{Theorem 6.12}$$

$$= \sinh^{-1} \frac{3}{4} - \sinh^{-1} 0 \quad \text{Evaluate.}$$

$$= \sinh^{-1} \frac{3}{4}. \quad \sinh^{-1} 0 = 0$$

A calculator gives an approximate result of $\sinh^{-1}(3/4) \approx 0.693$. The exact result can be written in terms of logarithms using Theorem 6.10:

$$\sinh^{-1}(3/4) = \ln(3/4 + \sqrt{(3/4)^2 + 1}) = \ln 2.$$

b. The integral doesn't match any of the formulas in Theorem 6.12, so we use the substitution $u = \sqrt{x}$:

$$\int_9^{25} \frac{dx}{\sqrt{x}(4 - x)} = 2\int_3^5 \frac{du}{4 - u^2}. \quad \text{Let } u = \sqrt{x};\ du = \frac{dx}{2\sqrt{x}}.$$

The new integral now matches formula (3), with $a = 2$. We conclude that

$$2\int_3^5 \frac{du}{4 - u^2} = 2 \cdot \frac{1}{2} \coth^{-1} \frac{u}{2}\bigg|_3^5 \quad \int \frac{dx}{a^2 - x^2} = \frac{1}{a}\coth^{-1}\frac{x}{a} + C$$

$$= \coth^{-1} \frac{5}{2} - \coth^{-1} \frac{3}{2}. \quad \text{Evaluate.}$$

The antiderivative involving $\coth^{-1} x$ was chosen because the interval of integration $(3 \le u \le 5)$ satisfies $|u| > a = 2$. Theorem 6.10 is used to express the result in numerical form in case your calculator cannot evaluate $\coth^{-1} x$:

$$\coth^{-1} \frac{5}{2} - \coth^{-1} \frac{3}{2} = \tanh^{-1} \frac{2}{5} - \tanh^{-1} \frac{2}{3} \approx -0.381.$$

Related Exercises 53–64 ◀

QUICK CHECK 6 Evaluate $\int_0^1 \frac{du}{4 - u^2}$. ◀

Applications of Hyperbolic Functions

This section concludes with a brief look at two applied problems associated with hyperbolic functions. Additional applications are presented in the exercises.

The Catenary When a free-hanging rope or flexible cable supporting only its own weight is attached to two points of equal height, it takes the shape of a curve known as a *catenary*. You can see catenaries in telephone wires, ropes strung across chasms for Tyrolean traverses (Example 7), and spider webs.

The equation for a general catenary is $y = a\cosh(x/a)$, where $a \neq 0$ is a real number. When $a < 0$, the curve is called an inverted catenary, sometimes used in the design of arches. Figure 6.97 illustrates catenaries for several values of a.

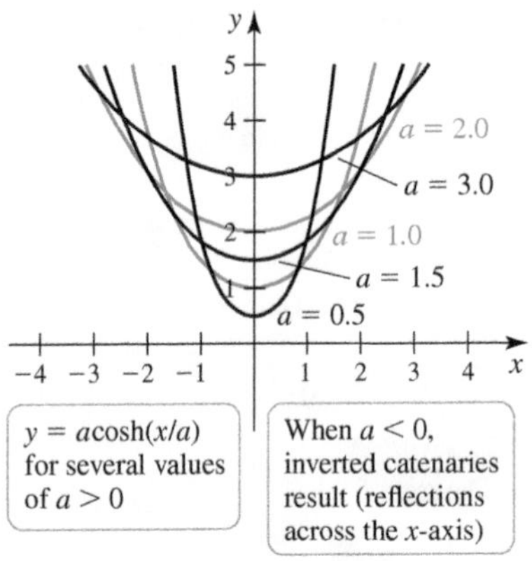

Figure 6.97

➤ A Tyrolean traverse is used to pass over difficult terrain, such as a chasm between two cliffs or a raging river. A rope is strung between two anchor points, the climber clips onto the rope and then traverses the gap by pulling on the rope.

EXAMPLE 7 Length of a catenary A climber anchors a rope at two points of equal height, separated by a distance of 100 ft, in order to perform a *Tyrolean traverse.* The rope follows the catenary $f(x) = 200\cosh(x/200)$ over the interval $[-50, 50]$ (Figure 6.98). Find the length of the rope between the two anchor points.

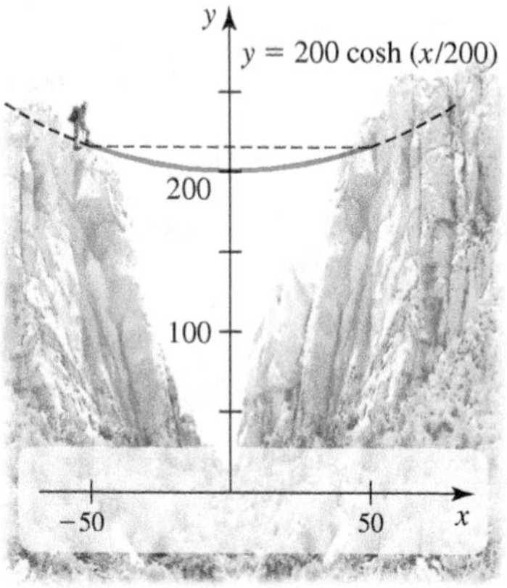

Figure 6.98

SOLUTION Recall from Section 6.5 that the arc length of the curve $y = f(x)$ over the interval $[a, b]$ is $L = \int_a^b \sqrt{1 + f'(x)^2}\,dx$. Also note that

$$f'(x) = 200\sinh\left(\frac{x}{200}\right)\cdot\frac{1}{200} = \sinh\frac{x}{200}.$$

➤ Using the principles of vector analysis introduced in Chapter 11, the tension in the rope and the forces acting upon the anchors in Example 7 can be computed. This is crucial information for anyone setting up a Tyrolean traverse; the *sag angle* (Exercise 68) figures into these calculations. Similar calculations are important for catenary lifelines used in construction and for rigging camera shots in Hollywood movies.

Therefore, the length of the rope is

$$\begin{aligned}
L &= \int_{-50}^{50} \sqrt{1 + \sinh^2\left(\frac{x}{200}\right)}\,dx && \text{Arc length formula}\\
&= 2\int_0^{50} \sqrt{1 + \sinh^2\left(\frac{x}{200}\right)}\,dx && \text{Use symmetry.}\\
&= 400\int_0^{1/4} \sqrt{1 + \sinh^2 u}\,du && \text{Let } u = \frac{x}{200}.\\
&= 400\int_0^{1/4} \cosh u\,du && 1 + \sinh^2 u = \cosh^2 u\\
&= 400 \sinh u\Big|_0^{1/4} && \text{Evaluate integral.}\\
&= 400\left(\sinh\frac{1}{4} - \sinh 0\right) && \text{Simplify.}\\
&\approx 101 \text{ ft.} && \text{Evaluate.}
\end{aligned}$$

Related Exercises 65–68 ◀

Velocity of a Wave To describe the characteristics of a traveling wave, researchers formulate a *wave equation* that reflects the known (or hypothesized) properties of the wave and that often takes the form of a differential equation (Section 7.9). Solving a wave equation produces additional information about the wave, and it turns out that hyperbolic functions may arise naturally in this context.

EXAMPLE 8 Velocity of an ocean wave The velocity v (in meters/second) of an idealized surface wave traveling on the ocean is modeled by the equation

$$v = \sqrt{\frac{g\lambda}{2\pi}\tanh\left(\frac{2\pi d}{\lambda}\right)},$$

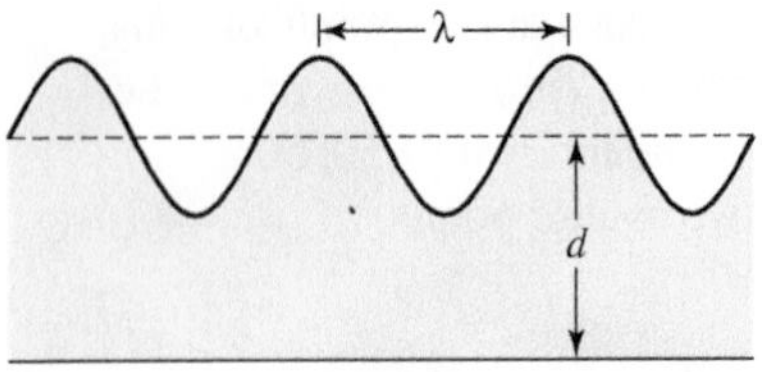

Figure 6.99

➤ In fluid dynamics, *water depth* is often discussed in terms of the depth-to-wavelength ratio d/λ, not the actual depth of the water. Three classifications are generally used:

shallow water: $d/\lambda < 0.05$

intermediate depth: $0.05 < d/\lambda < 0.5$

deep water: $d/\lambda > 0.5$

where $g = 9.8\ \text{m/s}^2$ is the acceleration due to gravity, λ is the wavelength measured in meters from crest to crest, and d is the depth of the undisturbed water, also measured in meters (Figure 6.99).

a. A sea kayaker observes several waves that pass beneath her kayak, and she estimates that $\lambda = 12$ m and $v = 4$ m/s. How deep is the water in which she is kayaking?

b. The *deep-water* equation for wave velocity is $v = \sqrt{\frac{g\lambda}{2\pi}}$, which is an approximation to the velocity formula given above. Waves are said to be in deep water if the depth-to-wavelength ratio d/λ is greater than $\frac{1}{2}$. Explain why $v = \sqrt{\frac{g\lambda}{2\pi}}$ is a good approximation when $d/\lambda > \frac{1}{2}$.

SOLUTION

a. We substitute $\lambda = 12$ and $v = 4$ into the velocity equation and solve for d.

$$4 = \sqrt{\frac{g \cdot 12}{2\pi}\tanh\left(\frac{2\pi d}{12}\right)} \quad \Rightarrow \quad 16 = \frac{6g}{\pi}\tanh\left(\frac{\pi d}{6}\right) \qquad \text{Square both sides.}$$

$$\Rightarrow \quad \frac{8\pi}{3g} = \tanh\left(\frac{\pi d}{6}\right) \qquad \text{Multiply by } \frac{\pi}{6g}.$$

In order to extract d from the argument of tanh, we apply $\tanh^{-1}$ to both sides of the equation and then use the property $\tanh^{-1}(\tanh x) = x$, for all x.

$$\tanh^{-1}\left(\frac{8\pi}{3g}\right) = \tanh^{-1}\left(\tanh\left(\frac{\pi d}{6}\right)\right) \qquad \text{Apply } \tanh^{-1} \text{ to both sides.}$$

$$\tanh^{-1}\left(\frac{8\pi}{29.4}\right) = \frac{\pi d}{6} \qquad \text{Simplify; } 3g = 29.4.$$

$$d = \frac{6}{\pi}\tanh^{-1}\left(\frac{8\pi}{29.4}\right) \approx 2.4 \text{ m} \qquad \text{Solve for } d.$$

Therefore, the kayaker is in water that is about 2.4 m deep.

b. Recall that $y = \tanh x$ is an increasing function $(dy/dx = \operatorname{sech}^2 x > 0)$ whose values approach 1 as $x \to \infty$. Also notice that when $\frac{d}{\lambda} = \frac{1}{2}$, $\tanh\left(\frac{2\pi d}{\lambda}\right) = \tanh \pi \approx 0.996$, which is nearly equal to 1. These facts imply that whenever $\frac{d}{\lambda} > \frac{1}{2}$, we can replace $\tanh\left(\frac{2\pi d}{\lambda}\right)$ with 1 in the velocity formula, resulting in the deep-water velocity function $v = \sqrt{\frac{g\lambda}{2\pi}}$.

Related Exercises 69–72 ◄

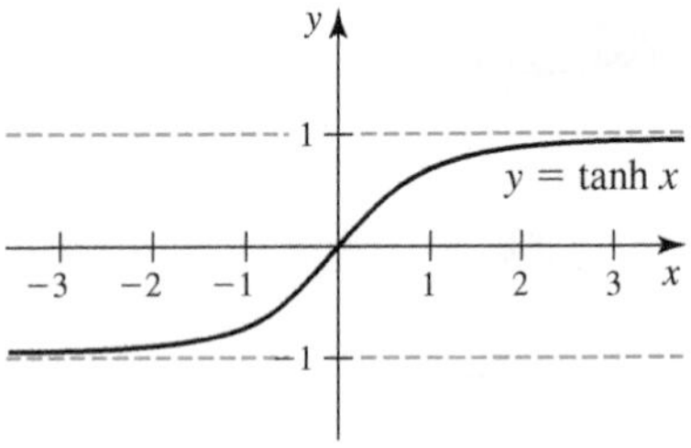

QUICK CHECK 7 Explain why longer waves travel faster than shorter waves in deep water. ◄

SECTION 6.10 EXERCISES

Review Questions

1. State the definition of the hyperbolic cosine and hyperbolic sine functions.

2. Sketch the graphs of $y = \cosh x$, $y = \sinh x$, and $y = \tanh x$ (include asymptotes), and state whether each function is even, odd, or neither.

3. What is the fundamental identity for hyperbolic functions?

4. How are the derivative formulas for the hyperbolic functions and the trigonometric functions alike? How are they different?

5. Express $\sinh^{-1} x$ in terms of logarithms.

6. What is the domain of $\operatorname{sech}^{-1} x$? How is $\operatorname{sech}^{-1} x$ defined in terms of the inverse hyperbolic cosine?

7. A calculator has a built-in $\sinh^{-1} x$ function, but no $\operatorname{csch}^{-1} x$ function. How do you evaluate $\operatorname{csch}^{-1} 5$ on such a calculator?

8. On what interval is the formula $d/dx(\tanh^{-1} x) = 1/(x^2 - 1)$ valid?

9. When evaluating the definite integral $\int_6^8 \frac{dx}{16 - x^2}$, why must you choose the antiderivative $\frac{1}{4}\coth^{-1}\frac{x}{4}$ rather than $\frac{1}{4}\tanh^{-1}\frac{x}{4}$?

10. How does the graph of the catenary $y = a\cosh(x/a)$ change as $a > 0$ increases?

Basic Skills

11–15. Verifying identities *Verify each identity using the definitions of the hyperbolic functions.*

11. $\tanh x = \frac{e^{2x} - 1}{e^{2x} + 1}$

12. $\tanh(-x) = -\tanh x$

13. $\cosh 2x = \cosh^2 x + \sinh^2 x$ (*Hint:* Begin with the right side of the equation.)

14. $2\sinh(\ln(\sec x)) = \sin x \tan x$

15. $\cosh x + \sinh x = e^x$

16–18. Verifying identities *Use the given identity to verify the related identity.*

16. Use the fundamental identity $\cosh^2 x - \sinh^2 x = 1$ to verify the identity $\coth^2 x - 1 = \operatorname{csch}^2 x$.

17. Use the identity $\cosh 2x = \cosh^2 x + \sinh^2 x$ to verify the identities $\cosh^2 x = \frac{\cosh 2x + 1}{2}$ and $\sinh^2 x = \frac{\cosh 2x - 1}{2}$.

18. Use the identity $\cosh(x + y) = \cosh x \cosh y + \sinh x \sinh y$ to verify the identity $\cosh 2x = \cosh^2 x + \sinh^2 x$.

19–21. Derivative formulas *Derive the following derivative formulas given that $d/dx(\cosh x) = \sinh x$ and $d/dx(\sinh x) = \cosh x$.*

19. $d/dx(\coth x) = -\operatorname{csch}^2 x$

20. $d/dx(\operatorname{sech} x) = -\operatorname{sech} x \tanh x$

21. $d/dx(\operatorname{csch} x) = -\operatorname{csch} x \coth x$

22–30. Derivatives *Compute dy/dx for the following functions.*

22. $y = \sinh 4x$

23. $y = \cosh^2 x$

24. $y = -\sinh^3 4x$

25. $y = \tanh^2 x$

26. $y = \sqrt{\coth 3x}$

27. $y = \ln \operatorname{sech} 2x$

28. $y = x \tanh x$

29. $y = x^2 \cosh^2 3x$

30. $y = x/\operatorname{csch} x$

31–36. Indefinite integrals *Determine each indefinite integral.*

31. $\int \cosh 2x\,dx$

32. $\int \operatorname{sech}^2 x \tanh x\,dx$

33. $\int \frac{\sinh x}{1 + \cosh x}\,dx$

34. $\int \coth^2 x \operatorname{csch}^2 x\,dx$

35. $\int \tanh^2 x\,dx$ (*Hint:* Use an identity.)

36. $\int \sinh^2 x\,dx$ (*Hint:* Use an identity.)

37–40. Definite integrals *Evaluate each definite integral.*

37. $\int_0^1 \cosh^3 3x \sinh 3x\,dx$

38. $\int_0^4 \frac{\operatorname{sech}^2 \sqrt{x}}{\sqrt{x}}\,dx$

39. $\int_0^{\ln 2} \tanh x\,dx$

40. $\int_{\ln 2}^{\ln 3} \operatorname{csch} y\,dy$

41–42. Two ways *Evaluate the following integrals two ways.*

a. *Simplify the integrand first and then integrate.*
b. *Change variables (let $u = \ln x$), integrate, and then simplify your answer. Verify that both methods give the same answer.*

41. $\int \frac{\sinh(\ln x)}{x}\,dx$

42. $\int_1^{\sqrt{3}} \frac{\operatorname{sech}(\ln x)}{x}\,dx$

T 43. **Visual approximation**

a. Use a graphing utility to sketch the graph of $y = \coth x$ and then explain why $\int_5^{10} \coth x\,dx \approx 5$.
b. Evaluate $\int_5^{10} \coth x\,dx$ analytically and use a calculator to arrive at a decimal approximation to the answer. How large is the error in the approximation in part (a)?

44. **Integral proof** Prove the formula $\int \coth x\,dx = \ln|\sinh x| + C$ of Theorem 6.9.

45–46. Points of intersection and area

a. *Sketch the graphs of the functions f and g and find the x-coordinate of the points at which they intersect.*
b. *Compute the area of the region described.*

45. $f(x) = \operatorname{sech} x$, $g(x) = \tanh x$; the region bounded by the graphs of f, g, and the y-axis

46. $f(x) = \sinh x$, $g(x) = \tanh x$; the region bounded by the graphs of f, g, and $x = \ln 3$

47–52. Derivatives *Find the derivatives of the following functions.*

47. $f(x) = \cosh^{-1} 4x$

48. $f(t) = 2\tanh^{-1}\sqrt{t}$

49. $f(v) = \sinh^{-1} v^2$

50. $f(x) = \operatorname{csch}^{-1}(2/x)$

51. $f(x) = x\sinh^{-1} x - \sqrt{x^2 + 1}$

52. $f(u) = \sinh^{-1}(\tan u)$

53–58. Indefinite integrals *Determine the following indefinite integrals.*

53. $\int \frac{dx}{8 - x^2}$, $x > 2\sqrt{2}$

54. $\int \frac{dx}{\sqrt{x^2 - 16}}$

55. $\int \frac{e^x}{36 - e^{2x}}\,dx$, $x < \ln 6$

56. $\int \frac{dx}{x\sqrt{16 + x^2}}$

57. $\int \frac{dx}{x\sqrt{4 - x^8}}$

58. $\int \frac{dx}{x\sqrt{1 + x^4}}$

59–64. Definite integrals *Evaluate the following definite integrals. Use Theorem 6.10 to express your answer in terms of logarithms.*

59. $\int_1^{e^2} \frac{dx}{x\sqrt{\ln^2 x + 1}}$

60. $\int_5^{3\sqrt{5}} \frac{dx}{\sqrt{x^2 - 9}}$

61. $\int_{-2}^{2} \frac{dt}{t^2 - 9}$

62. $\int_{1/6}^{1/4} \frac{dt}{t\sqrt{1 - 4t^2}}$

63. $\int_{1/8}^{1} \frac{dx}{x\sqrt{1 + x^{2/3}}}$

64. $\int_{\ln 5}^{\ln 9} \frac{\cosh x}{4 - \sinh^2 x}\,dx$

65. **Catenary arch** The portion of the curve $y = \frac{17}{15} - \cosh x$ that lies above the x-axis forms a catenary arch. Find the average height of the arch above the x-axis.

66. **Length of a catenary** Show that the arc length of the catenary $y = \cosh x$ over the interval $[0, a]$ is $L = \sinh a$.

67. **Power lines** A power line is attached at the same height to two utility poles that are separated by a distance of 100 ft; the power line follows the curve $f(x) = a\cosh(x/a)$. Use the following steps to find the value of a that produces a sag of 10 ft midway between the poles. Use a coordinate system that places the poles at $x = \pm 50$.

a. Show that a satisfies the equation $\cosh(50/a) - 1 = 10/a$.
b. Let $t = 10/a$, confirm that the equation in part (a) reduces to $\cosh 5t - 1 = t$, and solve for t using a graphing utility. Report your answer accurate to two decimal places.
c. Use your answer in part (b) to find a and then compute the length of the power line.

68. **Sag angle** Imagine a climber clipping onto the rope described in Example 7 and pulling himself to the rope's midpoint. Because the rope is supporting the weight of the climber, it no longer takes the shape of the catenary $y = 200\cosh(x/200)$. Instead, the rope (nearly) forms two sides of an isosceles triangle. Compute the *sag angle* θ illustrated in the figure, assuming that the rope does not stretch when weighted. Recall from Example 7 that the length of the rope is 101 ft.

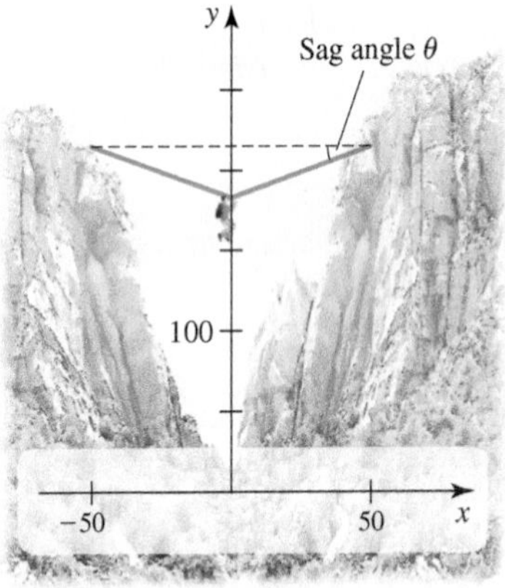

69. **Wavelength** The velocity of a surface wave on the ocean is given by $v = \sqrt{\frac{g\lambda}{2\pi}\tanh\left(\frac{2\pi d}{\lambda}\right)}$ (Example 8). Use a graphing utility or root finder to approximate the wavelength λ of an ocean wave traveling at $v = 7$ m/s in water that is $d = 10$ m deep.

70. **Wave velocity** Use Exercise 69 to do the following calculations.

a. Find the velocity of a wave where $\lambda = 50$ m and $d = 20$ m.
b. Determine the depth of the water if a wave with $\lambda = 15$ m is traveling at $v = 4.5$ m/s.

71. **Shallow-water velocity equation**

a. Confirm that the linear approximation to $f(x) = \tanh x$ at $a = 0$ is $L(x) = x$.
b. Recall that the velocity of a surface wave on the ocean is $v = \sqrt{\frac{g\lambda}{2\pi}\tanh\frac{2\pi d}{\lambda}}$. In fluid dynamics, *shallow water* refers to water where the depth-to-wavelength ratio $d/\lambda < 0.05$. Use your answer to part (a) to explain why the shallow water velocity equation is $v = \sqrt{gd}$.
c. Use the shallow-water velocity equation to explain why waves tend to slow down as they approach the shore.

72. **Tsunamis** A tsunami is an ocean wave often caused by earthquakes on the ocean floor; these waves typically have long wavelengths, ranging between 150 to 1000 km. Imagine a tsunami traveling across the Pacific Ocean, which is the deepest ocean in the world, with an average depth of about 4000 m. Explain why the *shallow-water velocity equation* (Exercise 71) applies to tsunamis even though the actual depth of the water is large. What does the shallow-water equation say about the speed of a tsunami in the Pacific Ocean (use $d = 4000$ m)?

Further Explorations

73. **Explain why or why not** Determine whether the following statements are true and give an explanation or counterexample.

a. $\frac{d}{dx}(\sinh \ln 3) = \frac{\cosh \ln 3}{3}$.
b. $\frac{d}{dx}(\sinh x) = \cosh x$ and $\frac{d}{dx}(\cosh x) = -\sinh x$.
c. Differentiating the velocity equation for an ocean wave $v = \sqrt{\frac{g\lambda}{2\pi}\tanh\left(\frac{2\pi d}{\lambda}\right)}$ results in the acceleration of the wave.
d. $\ln(1 + \sqrt{2}) = -\ln(-1 + \sqrt{2})$.
e. $\int_0^1 \frac{dx}{4 - x^2} = \frac{1}{2}\left(\coth^{-1}\frac{1}{2} - \coth^{-1} 0\right)$.

74. **Evaluating hyperbolic functions** Use a calculator to evaluate each expression or state that the value does not exist. Report answers accurate to four decimal places.

a. $\coth 4$ **b.** $\tanh^{-1} 2$ **c.** $\operatorname{csch}^{-1} 5$ **d.** $\operatorname{csch} x\big|_{1/2}^{2}$
e. $\ln\left|\tanh\left(\frac{x}{2}\right)\right|\Big|_1^{10}$ **f.** $\tan^{-1}(\sinh x)\Big|_{-3}^{3}$ **g.** $\frac{1}{4}\coth^{-1}\frac{x}{4}\Big|_{20}^{36}$

75. **Evaluating hyperbolic functions** Evaluate each expression without using a calculator or state that the value does not exist. Simplify answers to the extent possible.

a. $\cosh 0$ **b.** $\tanh 0$ **c.** $\operatorname{csch} 0$ **d.** $\operatorname{sech}(\sinh 0)$
e. $\coth(\ln 5)$ **f.** $\sinh(2\ln 3)$ **g.** $\cosh^2 1$ **h.** $\operatorname{sech}^{-1}(\ln 3)$
i. $\cosh^{-1}(17/8)$ **j.** $\sinh^{-1}\left(\frac{e^2 - 1}{2e}\right)$

76. **Confirming a graph** The graph of $f(x) = \sinh x$ is shown in Figure 6.92. Use calculus to find the intervals of increase and decrease for f, and find the intervals on which f is concave up and concave down to confirm that the graph is correct.

77. **Critical points** Find the critical points of the function $f(x) = \sinh^2 x \cosh x$.

78. **Critical points**

a. Show that the critical points of $f(x) = \frac{\cosh x}{x}$ satisfy $x = \coth x$.
b. Use a root finder to approximate the critical points of f.

79. **Points of inflection** Find the x-coordinate of the point(s) of inflection of $f(x) = \tanh^2 x$.

80. **Points of inflection** Find the x-coordinate of the point(s) of inflection of $f(x) = \operatorname{sech} x$. Report exact answers in terms of logarithms (use Theorem 6.10).

81. **Area of region** Find the area of the region bounded by $y = \operatorname{sech} x$, $x = 1$, and the unit circle.

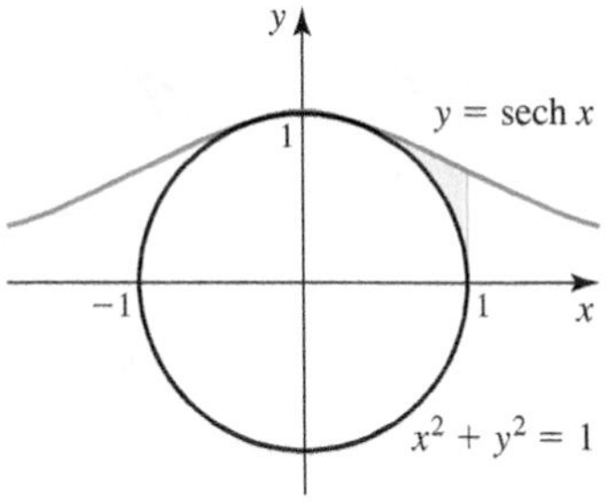

82. **Solid of revolution** Compute the volume of the solid of revolution that results when the region in Exercise 81 is revolved about the x-axis.

83. **L'Hôpital loophole** Explain why l'Hôpital's Rule fails when applied to the limit $\lim_{x\to\infty} \frac{\sinh x}{\cosh x}$ and then find the limit another way.

84–87. Limits *Use l'Hôpital's Rule to evaluate the following limits.*

84. $\lim_{x\to\infty} \frac{1 - \coth x}{1 - \tanh x}$

85. $\lim_{x\to 0} \frac{\tanh^{-1} x}{\tan(\pi x/2)}$

86. $\lim_{x\to 1^-} \frac{\tanh^{-1} x}{\tan(\pi x/2)}$

87. $\lim_{x\to 0^+} (\tanh x)^x$

T 88. **Slant asymptote** The linear function $\ell(x) = mx + b$, for finite $m \neq 0$, is a slant asymptote of $f(x)$ if $\lim_{x\to\infty} (f(x) - \ell(x)) = 0$.

a. Use a graphing utility to make a sketch that shows $\ell(x) = x$ is a slant asymptote of $f(x) = x \tanh x$. Does f have any other slant asymptotes?
b. Provide an intuitive argument showing that $f(x) = x \tanh x$ behaves like $\ell(x) = x$ as x gets large.
c. Prove that $\ell(x) = x$ is a slant asymptote of f by confirming $\lim_{x\to\infty} (x \tanh x - x) = 0$.

89–92. Additional integrals *Evaluate the following integrals.*

89. $\int \frac{\cosh z}{\sinh^2 z}\, dz$

90. $\int \frac{\cos\theta}{9 - \sin^2\theta}\, d\theta$

91. $\int_{5/12}^{3/4} \frac{\sinh^{-1} x}{\sqrt{x^2 + 1}}\, dx$

92. $\int_{25}^{225} \frac{dx}{\sqrt{x^2 + 25x}}$ (*Hint:* $\sqrt{x^2 + 25x} = \sqrt{x}\sqrt{x + 25}$.)

Applications

93. **Kiln design** Find the volume interior to the inverted catenary kiln (an oven used to fire pottery) shown in the figure.

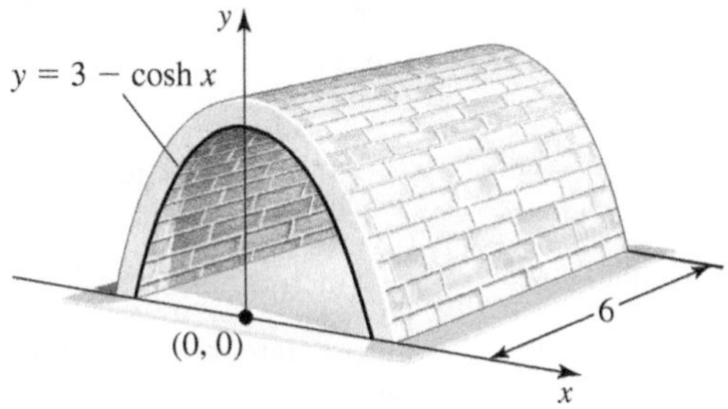

T 94. **Newton's method** Use Newton's method to find all local extreme values of $f(x) = x \operatorname{sech} x$.

95. **Falling body** When an object falling from rest encounters air resistance proportional to the square of its velocity, the distance it falls (in meters) after t seconds is given by $d(t) = \frac{m}{k} \ln\left(\cosh\left(\sqrt{\frac{kg}{m}}\, t\right)\right)$, where m is the mass of the object in kilograms, $g = 9.8\ \text{m/s}^2$ is the acceleration due to gravity, and k is a physical constant.

a. A BASE jumper ($m = 75$ kg) leaps from a tall cliff and performs a ten-second delay (she free-falls for 10 s and then opens her chute). How far does she fall in 10 s? Assume $k = 0.2$.
b. How long does it take her to fall the first 100 m? The second 100 m? What is her average velocity over each of these intervals?

96. **Velocity of falling body** Refer to Exercise 95, which gives the position function for a falling body. Use $m = 75$ kg and $k = 0.2$.

a. Confirm that the base jumper's velocity t seconds after jumping is $v(t) = d'(t) = \sqrt{\frac{mg}{k}} \tanh\left(\sqrt{\frac{kg}{m}}\, t\right)$.
b. How fast is the BASE jumper falling at the end of a 10 s delay?
c. How long does it take the BASE jumper to reach a speed of 45 m/s (roughly 100 mi/hr)?

97. **Terminal velocity** Refer to Exercises 95 and 96.

a. Compute a jumper's *terminal velocity*, which is defined as $\lim_{t\to\infty} v(t) = \lim_{t\to\infty} \sqrt{\frac{mg}{k}} \tanh\left(\sqrt{\frac{kg}{m}}\, t\right)$.
b. Find the terminal velocity for the jumper in Exercise 96 ($m = 75$ kg and $k = 0.2$).
c. How long does it take any falling object to reach a speed equal to 95% of its terminal velocity? Leave your answer in terms of k, g, and m.
d. How tall must a cliff be so that the BASE jumper ($m = 75$ kg and $k = 0.2$) reaches 95% of terminal velocity? Assume that the jumper needs at least 300 m at the end of free fall to deploy the chute and land safely.

98. **Acceleration of a falling body**

a. Find the acceleration $a(t) = v'(t)$ of a falling body whose velocity is given in part (a) of Exercise 96.
b. Compute $\lim_{t\to\infty} a(t)$. Explain your answer as it relates to terminal velocity (Exercise 97).

99. **Differential equations** Hyperbolic functions are useful in solving differential equations (Section 7.9). Show that the functions $y = A \sinh kx$ and $y = B \cosh kx$, where A, B, and k are constants, satisfy the equation $y''(x) - k^2 y(x) = 0$.

100. **Surface area of a catenoid** When the catenary $y = a \cosh(x/a)$ is revolved about the x-axis, it sweeps out a surface of revolution called a *catenoid*. Find the area of the surface generated when $y = \cosh x$ on $[-\ln 2, \ln 2]$ is rotated around the x-axis.

Additional Exercises

101–104. Verifying identities *Verify the following identities.*

101. $\sinh(\cosh^{-1} x) = \sqrt{x^2 - 1}$, for $x \geq 1$

102. $\cosh(\sinh^{-1} x) = \sqrt{x^2 + 1}$, for all x

103. $\cosh(x + y) = \cosh x \cosh y + \sinh x \sinh y$

104. $\sinh(x + y) = \sinh x \cosh y + \cosh x \sinh y$

105. Inverse identity Show that $\cosh^{-1}(\cosh x) = |x|$ by using the formula $\cosh^{-1} t = \ln(t + \sqrt{t^2 - 1})$ and by considering the cases $x \geq 0$ and $x < 0$.

106. Theorem 6.11

a. The definition of the inverse hyperbolic cosine is $y = \cosh^{-1} x \Leftrightarrow x = \cosh y$, for $x \geq 1, 0 \leq y < \infty$. Use implicit differentiation to show that $\frac{d}{dx}(\cosh^{-1} x) = 1/\sqrt{x^2 - 1}$.

b. Differentiate $\sinh^{-1} x = \ln(x + \sqrt{x^2 + 1})$ to show that $\frac{d}{dx}(\sinh^{-1} x) = 1/\sqrt{x^2 + 1}$.

107. Many formulas There are several ways to express the indefinite integral of sech x.

a. Show that $\int \operatorname{sech} x\, dx = \tan^{-1}(\sinh x) + C$ (Theorem 6.9). (*Hint:* Write $\operatorname{sech} x = \frac{1}{\cosh x} = \frac{\cosh x}{\cosh^2 x} = \frac{\cosh x}{1 + \sinh^2 x}$ and then make a change of variables.)

b. Show that $\int \operatorname{sech} x\, dx = \sin^{-1}(\tanh x) + C$. (*Hint:* Show that $\operatorname{sech} x = \frac{\operatorname{sech}^2 x}{\sqrt{1 - \tanh^2 x}}$ and then make a change of variables.)

c. Verify that $\int \operatorname{sech} x\, dx = 2\tan^{-1} e^x + C$ by proving $\frac{d}{dx}(2\tan^{-1} e^x) = \operatorname{sech} x$.

108. Integral formula Carry out the following steps to derive the formula $\int \operatorname{csch} x\, dx = \ln|\tanh(x/2)| + C$ (Theorem 6.9).

a. Change variables with the substitution $u = x/2$ to show that
$$\int \operatorname{csch} x dx = \int \frac{2du}{\sinh 2u}.$$

b. Use the identity for $\sinh 2u$ to show that $\frac{2}{\sinh 2u} = \frac{\operatorname{sech}^2 u}{\tanh u}$.

c. Change variables again to determine $\int \frac{\operatorname{sech}^2 u}{\tanh u} du$ and then express your answer in terms of x.

109. Arc length Use the result of Exercise 108 to find the arc length of $f(x) = \ln|\tanh(x/2)|$ on $[\ln 2, \ln 8]$.

110. Inverse hyperbolic tangent Recall that the inverse hyperbolic tangent is defined as $y = \tanh^{-1} x \Leftrightarrow x = \tanh y$, for $-1 < x < 1$ and all real y. Solve $x = \tanh y$ for y to express the formula for $\tanh^{-1} x$ in terms of logarithms.

111. Integral family Use the substitution $u = x^r$ to show that
$$\int \frac{dx}{x\sqrt{1 - x^{2r}}} = -\frac{1}{r}\operatorname{sech}^{-1} x^r + C, \text{ for } r > 0 \text{ and } 0 < x < 1.$$

112. Definitions of hyperbolic sine and cosine Complete the following steps to prove that when the x- and y-coordinates of a point on the hyperbola $x^2 - y^2 = 1$ are defined as $\cosh t$ and $\sinh t$, respectively, where t is twice the area of the shaded region in the figure, x and y can be expressed as
$$x = \cosh t = \frac{e^t + e^{-t}}{2} \text{ and } y = \sinh t = \frac{e^t - e^{-t}}{2}.$$

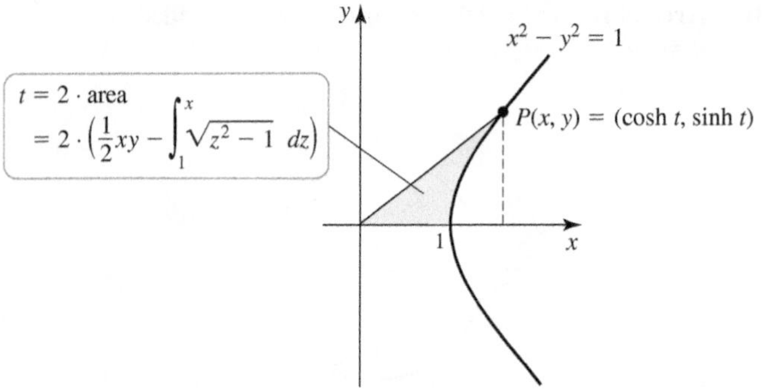

a. Explain why twice the area of the shaded region is given by
$$t = 2 \cdot \left(\frac{1}{2}xy - \int_1^x \sqrt{z^2 - 1}\, dz\right) = x\sqrt{x^2 - 1} - 2\int_1^x \sqrt{z^2 - 1}\, dz.$$

b. In Chapter 7, the formula for the integral in part (a) is derived:
$$\int \sqrt{z^2 - 1}\, dz = \frac{z}{2}\sqrt{z^2 - 1} - \frac{1}{2}\ln|z + \sqrt{z^2 - 1}| + C.$$
Evaluate this integral on the interval $[1, x]$, explain why the absolute value can be dropped, and combine the result with part (a) to show that
$$t = \ln(x + \sqrt{x^2 - 1}).$$

c. Solve the final result from part (b) for x to show that
$$x = \frac{e^t + e^{-t}}{2}.$$

d. Use the fact that $y = \sqrt{x^2 - 1}$ in combination with part (c) to show that $y = \frac{e^t - e^{-t}}{2}$.

QUICK CHECK ANSWERS

1. $\sinh(-x) = \frac{e^{-x} - e^{-(-x)}}{2} = -\frac{e^x - e^{-x}}{2} = -\sinh x$

2. Because $\tanh x = \frac{e^x - e^{-x}}{e^x + e^{-x}}$ and $\lim_{x\to\infty} e^{-x} = 0$, $\tanh x \approx \frac{e^x}{e^x} = 1$ for large x, which implies that $y = 1$ is a horizontal asymptote. A similar argument shows that $\tanh x \to -1$ as $x \to -\infty$, which means that $y = -1$ is also a horizontal asymptote. **3.** $\frac{d}{dx}(4\cosh 2x) = 8\sinh 2x$; $\int 4\cosh 2x\, dx = 2\sinh 2x + C$ **4.** $\frac{1}{2}\ln|\tanh x| + C$

5. Area $= 2\int_0^{\ln 3}\left(\frac{5}{3} - \cosh x\right)dx = \frac{2}{3}(5\ln 3 - 4) \approx 0.995$

6. $\int_0^1 \frac{du}{4 - u^2} = \frac{1}{2}\tanh^{-1}\frac{1}{2} \approx 0.275$ **7.** The deep-water velocity formula is $v = \sqrt{\frac{g\lambda}{2\pi}}$, which is an increasing function of the wavelength λ. Therefore, larger values of λ correspond with faster waves.◄

CHAPTER 6 REVIEW EXERCISES

1. **Explain why or why not** Determine whether the following statements are true and give an explanation or counterexample.
   a. A region R is revolved about the y-axis to generate a solid S. To find the volume of S, you could use either the disk/washer method and integrate with respect to y or the shell method and integrate with respect to x.
   b. Given only the velocity of an object moving on a line, it is possible to find its displacement, but not its position.
   c. If water flows into a tank at a constant rate (for example, 6 gal/min), the volume of water in the tank increases according to a linear function of time.
   d. The variable $y = t + 1$ doubles in value whenever t increases by 1 unit.
   e. The function $y = Ae^{0.1t}$ increases by 10% when t increases by 1 unit.
   f. $\ln xy = (\ln x)(\ln y)$.
   g. $\sinh(\ln x) = \frac{x^2 - 1}{2x}$.

2. **Displacement from velocity** The velocity of an object moving along a line is given by $v(t) = 20 \cos \pi t$ (in ft/s). What is the displacement of the object after 1.5 s?

3. **Position, displacement, and distance** A projectile is launched vertically from the ground at $t = 0$, and its velocity in flight (in m/s) is given by $v(t) = 20 - 10t$. Find the position, displacement, and distance traveled after t seconds, for $0 \le t \le 4$.

4. **Deceleration** At $t = 0$, a car begins decelerating from a velocity of 80 ft/s at a constant rate of 5 ft/s^2. Find its position function assuming $s(0) = 0$.

5. **An oscillator** The acceleration of an object moving along a line is given by $a(t) = 2 \sin\left(\frac{\pi t}{4}\right)$. The initial velocity and position are $v(0) = -\frac{8}{\pi}$ and $s(0) = 0$.
   a. Find the velocity and position for $t \ge 0$.
   b. What are the minimum and maximum values of s?
   c. Find the average velocity and average position over the interval $[0, 8]$.

6. **A race** Starting at the same point on a straight road, Anna and Benny begin running with velocities (in mi/hr) given by $v_A(t) = 2t + 1$ and $v_B(t) = 4 - t$, respectively.
   a. Graph the velocity functions, for $0 \le t \le 4$.
   b. If the runners run for 1 hr, who runs farther? Interpret your conclusion geometrically using the graph in part (a).
   c. If the runners run for 6 mi, who wins the race? Interpret your conclusion geometrically using the graph in part (a).

7. **Fuel consumption** A small plane in flight consumes fuel at a rate (in gal/min) given by

$$R'(t) = \begin{cases} 4t^{1/3} & \text{if } 0 \le t \le 8 \text{ (take-off)} \\ 2 & \text{if } t > 8 \text{ (cruising).} \end{cases}$$

   a. Find a function R that gives the total fuel consumed, for $0 \le t \le 8$.
   b. Find a function R that gives the total fuel consumed, for $t \ge 0$.
   c. If the fuel tank capacity is 150 gal, when does the fuel run out?

8. **Variable flow rate** Water flows out of a tank at a rate (in m^3/hr) given by $V'(t) = 15/(t + 1)$. If the tank initially holds 75 m^3 of water, when will the tank be empty?

T 9. **Decreasing velocity** A projectile is fired upward, and its velocity in m/s is given by $v(t) = 200e^{-t/10}$, for $t \ge 0$.
   a. Graph the velocity function for $t \ge 0$.
   b. When does the velocity reach 50 m/s?
   c. Find and graph the position function for the projectile for $t \ge 0$, assuming $s(0) = 0$.
   d. Given unlimited time, can the projectile travel 2500 m? If so, at what time does the distance traveled equal 2500 m?

T 10. **Decreasing velocity** A projectile is fired upward, and its velocity (in m/s) is given by $v(t) = \frac{200}{\sqrt{t + 1}}$, for $t \ge 0$.
   a. Graph the velocity function for $t \ge 0$.
   b. Find and graph the position function for the projectile, for $t \ge 0$, assuming $s(0) = 0$.
   c. Given unlimited time, can the projectile travel 2500 m? If so, at what time does the distance traveled equal 2500 m?

11. **An exponential bike ride** Tom and Sue took a bike ride, both starting at the same time and position. Tom started riding at 20 mi/hr, and his velocity decreased according to the function $v(t) = 20e^{-2t}$ for $t \ge 0$. Sue started riding at 15 mi/hr, and her velocity decreased according to the function $u(t) = 15e^{-t}$ for $t \ge 0$.
   a. Find and graph the position functions of Tom and Sue.
   b. Find the times at which the riders had the same position at the same time.
   c. Who ultimately took the lead and remained in the lead?

T **12–19. Areas of regions** *Use any method to find the area of the region described.*

12. The region in the first quadrant bounded by $y = x^p$ and $y = \sqrt[p]{x}$, where $p = 100$ and $p = 1000$

13. The region in the first quadrant bounded by $y = 4x$ and $y = x\sqrt{25 - x^2}$

14. The regions R_1 and R_2 (separately) shown in the figure, which are formed by the graphs of $y = 16 - x^2$ and $y = 5x - 8$

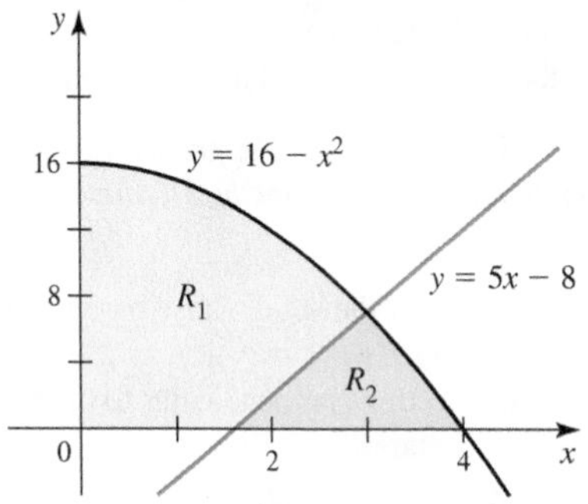

15. The regions R_1, R_2, and R_3 (separately) shown in the figure, which are formed by the graphs of $y = 2\sqrt{x}$, $y = 3 - x$, and $y = x(x - 3)$ (First find the intersection points by inspection.)

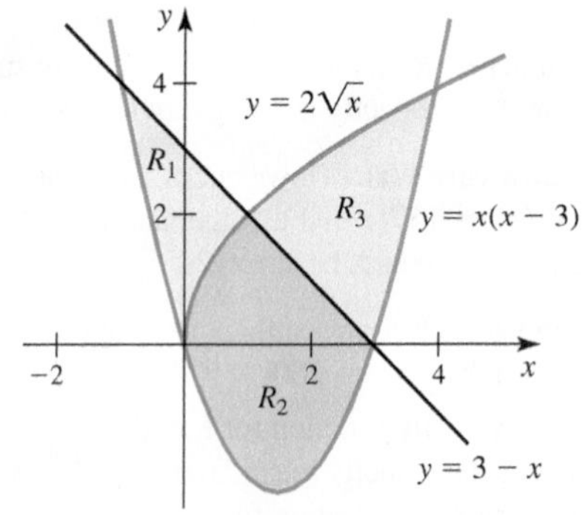

16. The region between $y = \sin x$ and $y = x$ on the interval $[0, 2\pi]$

17. The region bounded by $y = x^2$, $y = 2x^2 - 4x$, and $y = 0$

18. The region in the first quadrant bounded by the curve $\sqrt{x} + \sqrt{y} = 1$

19. The region in the first quadrant bounded by $y = x/6$ and $y = 1 - |x/2 - 1|$

20. An area function Let $R(x)$ be the area of the shaded region between the graphs of $y = f(t)$ and $y = g(t)$ on the interval $[a, x]$ (see figure).

a. Sketch a plausible graph of R, for $a \le x \le c$.
b. Give expressions for $R(x)$ and $R'(x)$, for $a \le x \le c$.

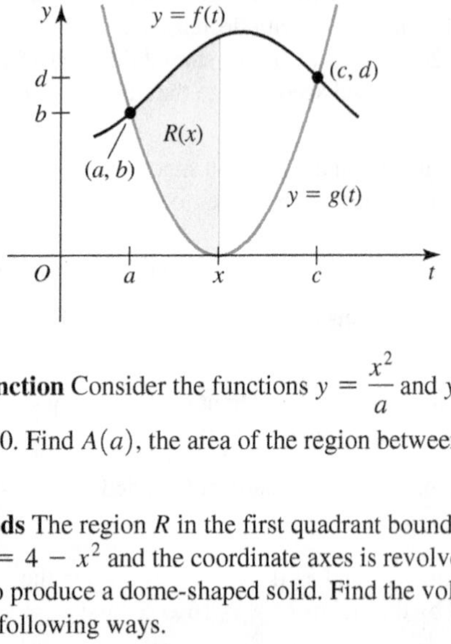

21. An area function Consider the functions $y = \dfrac{x^2}{a}$ and $y = \sqrt{\dfrac{x}{a}}$, where $a > 0$. Find $A(a)$, the area of the region between the curves.

22. Two methods The region R in the first quadrant bounded by the parabola $y = 4 - x^2$ and the coordinate axes is revolved about the y-axis to produce a dome-shaped solid. Find the volume of the solid in the following ways.

a. Apply the disk method and integrate with respect to y.
b. Apply the shell method and integrate with respect to x.

23–35. Volumes of solids *Choose the general slicing method, the disk/washer method, or the shell method to answer the following questions.*

23. What is the volume of the solid whose base is the region in the first quadrant bounded by $y = \sqrt{x}$, $y = 2 - x$, and the x-axis, and whose cross sections perpendicular to the base and parallel to the y-axis are squares?

24. What is the volume of the solid whose base is the region in the first quadrant bounded by $y = \sqrt{x}$, $y = 2 - x$, and the x-axis, and whose cross sections perpendicular to the base and parallel to the y-axis are semicircles?

25. What is the volume of the solid whose base is the region in the first quadrant bounded by $y = \sqrt{x}$, $y = 2 - x$, and the y-axis, and whose cross sections perpendicular to the base and parallel to the x-axis are square?

26. The region bounded by the curves $y = -x^2 + 2x + 2$ and $y = 2x^2 - 4x + 2$ is revolved about the x-axis. What is the volume of the solid that is generated?

27. The region bounded by the curves $y = 1 + \sqrt{x}$, $y = 1 - \sqrt{x}$, and the line $x = 1$ is revolved about the y-axis. Find the volume of the resulting solid by (a) integrating with respect to x and (b) integrating with respect to y. Be sure your answers agree.

28. The region bounded by the curves $y = 2e^{-x}$, $y = e^x$, and the y-axis is revolved about the x-axis. What is the volume of the solid that is generated?

29. The region bounded by the graphs of $x = 0$, $x = \sqrt{\ln y}$, and $x = \sqrt{2 - \ln y}$ in the first quadrant is revolved about the y-axis. What is the volume of the resulting solid?

30. The region bounded by the curves $y = \sec x$ and $y = 2$, for $0 \le x \le \frac{\pi}{3}$, is revolved around the x-axis. What is the volume of the solid that is generated?

31. The region bounded by $y = (1 - x^2)^{-1/2}$ and the x-axis over the interval $[0, \sqrt{3}/2]$ is revolved around the y-axis. What is the volume of the solid that is generated?

32. The region bounded by the graph of $y = 4 - x^2$ and the x-axis on the interval $[-2, 2]$ is revolved about the line $x = -2$. What is the volume of the solid that is generated?

33. The region bounded by the graphs of $y = (x - 2)^2$ and $y = 4$ is revolved about the line $y = 4$. What is the volume of the resulting solid?

34. The region bounded by the graphs of $y = 6x$ and $y = x^2 + 5$ is revolved about the line $y = -1$ and the line $x = -1$. Find the volumes of the resulting solids. Which one is greater?

35. The region bounded by the graphs of $y = 2x$, $y = 6 - x$, and $y = 0$ is revolved about the line $y = -2$ and the line $x = -2$. Find the volumes of the resulting solids. Which one is greater?

36. Area and volume The region R is bounded by the curves $x = y^2 + 2$, $y = x - 4$, and $y = 0$ (see figure).

a. Write a single integral that gives the area of R.
b. Write a single integral that gives the volume of the solid generated when R is revolved about the x-axis.
c. Write a single integral that gives the volume of the solid generated when R is revolved about the y-axis.
d. Suppose S is a solid whose base is R and whose cross sections perpendicular to R and parallel to the x-axis are semicircles. Write a single integral that gives the volume of S.

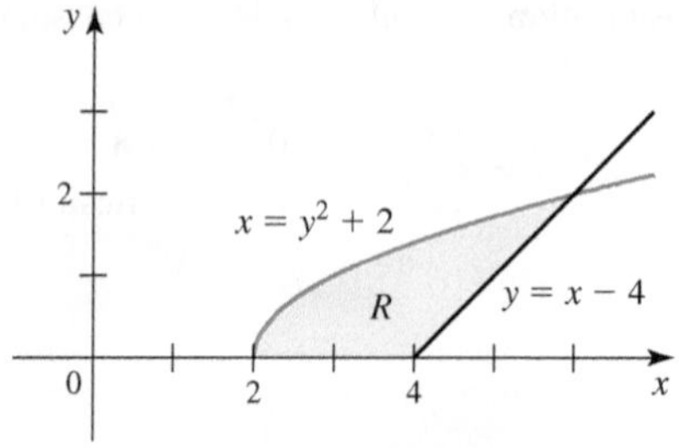

37. **Comparing volumes** Let R be the region bounded by $y = 1/x^p$ and the x-axis on the interval $[1, a]$, where $p > 0$ and $a > 1$ (see figure). Let V_x and V_y be the volumes of the solids generated when R is revolved about the x- and y-axes, respectively.
   a. With $a = 2$ and $p = 1$, which is greater, V_x or V_y?
   b. With $a = 4$ and $p = 3$, which is greater, V_x or V_y?
   c. Find a general expression for V_x in terms of a and p. Note that $p = \frac{1}{2}$ is a special case. What is V_x when $p = \frac{1}{2}$?
   d. Find a general expression for V_y in terms of a and p. Note that $p = 2$ is a special case. What is V_y when $p = 2$?
   e. Explain how parts (c) and (d) demonstrate that
   $$\lim_{h \to 0} \frac{a^h - 1}{h} = \ln a.$$
   f. Find any values of a and p for which $V_x > V_y$.

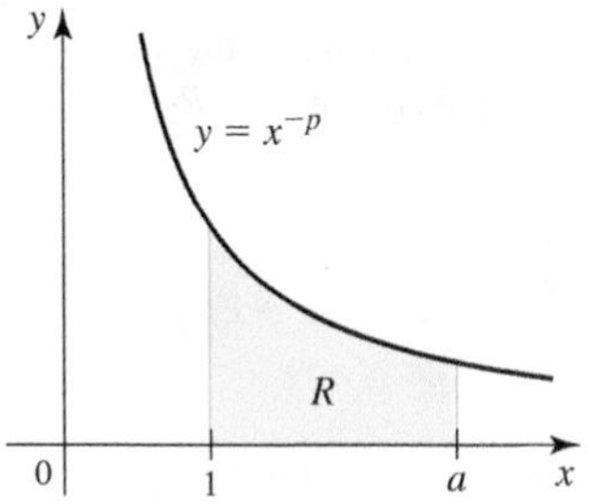

38. **Multiple regions** Determine the area of the region bounded by the curves $x = y^2$ and $x = (2 - y^2)^2$ (see figure).

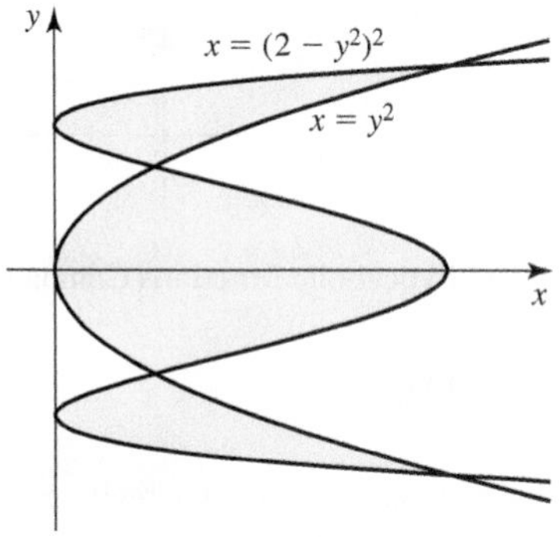

39. **Comparing volumes** Let R be the region bounded by the graph of $f(x) = cx(1 - x)$ and the x-axis on $[0, 1]$. Find the positive value of c such that the volume of the solid generated by revolving R about the x-axis equals the volume of the solid generated by revolving R about the y-axis.

40–45. Arc length *Find the length of the following curves.*

40. $y = 2x + 4$ on the interval $[-2, 2]$ (Use calculus.)

41. $y = \cosh^{-1} x$ on the interval $[\sqrt{2}, \sqrt{5}]$

42. $y = x^3/6 + 1/(2x)$ on the interval $[1, 2]$

43. $y = x^{1/2} - x^{3/2}/3$ on the interval $[1, 3]$

44. $y = x^3/3 + x^2 + x + 1/(4x + 4)$ on the interval $[0, 4]$

45. $y = \ln x$ between $x = 1$ and $x = b > 1$ given that
   $$\int \frac{\sqrt{x^2 + a^2}}{x}\,dx = \sqrt{x^2 + a^2} - a \ln\left(\frac{a + \sqrt{x^2 + a^2}}{x}\right) + C.$$
   Use any means to approximate the value of b for which the curve has length 2.

46. **Surface area and volume** Let $f(x) = \frac{1}{3}x^3$ and let R be the region bounded by the graph of f and the x-axis on the interval $[0, 2]$.
   a. Find the area of the surface generated when the graph of f on $[0, 2]$ is revolved about the x-axis.
   b. Find the volume of the solid generated when R is revolved about the y-axis.
   c. Find the volume of the solid generated when R is revolved about the x-axis.

47. **Surface area and volume** Let $f(x) = \sqrt{3x - x^2}$ and let R be the region bounded by the graph of f and the x-axis on the interval $[0, 3]$.
   a. Find the area of the surface generated when the graph of f on $[0, 3]$ is revolved about the x-axis.
   b. Find the volume of the solid generated when R is revolved about the x-axis.

48. **Surface area of a cone** Find the surface area of a cone (excluding the base) with radius 4 and height 8 using integration and a surface area integral.

49. **Surface area and more** Let $f(x) = \dfrac{x^4}{2} + \dfrac{1}{16x^2}$ and let R be the region bounded by the graph of f and the x-axis on the interval $[1, 2]$.
   a. Find the area of the surface generated when the graph of f on $[1, 2]$ is revolved about the x-axis.
   b. Find the length of the curve $y = f(x)$ on $[1, 2]$.
   c. Find the volume of the solid generated when R is revolved about the y-axis.
   d. Find the volume of the solid generated when R is revolved about the x-axis.

50–52. Variable density in one dimension *Find the mass of the following thin bars.*

50. A bar on the interval $0 \le x \le 9$ with a density (in g/cm) given by $\rho(x) = 3 + 2\sqrt{x}$

51. A 3-m bar with a density (in g/m) of $\rho(x) = 150e^{-x/3}$, for $0 \le x \le 3$

52. A bar on the interval $0 \le x \le 6$ with a density
   $$\rho(x) = \begin{cases} 1 & \text{if } 0 \le x < 2 \\ 2 & \text{if } 2 \le x < 4 \\ 4 & \text{if } 4 \le x \le 6. \end{cases}$$

53. **Spring work**
   a. It takes 50 J of work to stretch a spring 0.2 m from its equilibrium position. How much work is needed to stretch it an additional 0.5 m?
   b. It takes 50 N of force to stretch a spring 0.2 m from its equilibrium position. How much work is needed to stretch it an additional 0.5 m?

54. **Pumping water** A cylindrical water tank has a height of 6 m and a radius of 4 m. How much work is required to empty the full tank by pumping the water to an outflow pipe at the top of the tank?

55. **Force on a dam** Find the total force on the face of a semicircular dam with a radius of 20 m when its reservoir is full of water. The diameter of the semicircle is the top of the dam.

56–63. Integrals *Evaluate the following integrals.*

56. $\displaystyle\int \frac{e^x}{4e^x + 6}\,dx$

57. $\displaystyle\int_{e^2}^{e^8} \frac{dx}{x \ln x}$

58. $\displaystyle\int_1^4 \frac{10^{\sqrt{x}}}{\sqrt{x}}\,dx$

59. $\displaystyle\int \frac{x + 4}{x^2 + 8x + 25}\,dx$

60. $\displaystyle\int_{\ln 2}^{\ln 3} \coth s\,ds$

61. $\displaystyle\int \frac{dx}{\sqrt{x^2 - 9}}, x > 3$

62. $\displaystyle\int \frac{e^x}{\sqrt{e^{2x} + 4}}\,dx$

63. $\displaystyle\int_0^1 \frac{x^2}{9 - x^6}\,dx$

64. Radioactive decay The mass of radioactive material in a sample has decreased by 30% since the decay began. Assuming a half-life of 1500 years, how long ago did the decay begin?

65. Population growth Growing from an initial population of 150,000 at a constant annual growth rate of 4%/yr, how long will it take a city to reach a population of 1 million?

66. Savings account A savings account advertises an annual percentage yield (APY) of 5.4%, which means that the balance in the account increases at an annual growth rate of 5.4%/yr.

a. Find the balance in the account for $t \geq 0$ with an initial deposit of \$1500, assuming the APY remains fixed and no additional deposits or withdrawals are made.

b. What is the doubling time of the balance?

c. After how many years does the balance reach \$5000?

67–68. Curve sketching *Use the graphing techniques of Section 4.3 to graph the following functions on their domains. Identify local extreme points, inflection points, concavity, and end behavior. Use a graphing utility only to check your work.*

67. $f(x) = e^x(x^2 - x)$

68. $f(x) = \ln x - \ln^2 x$

T **69. Log-normal probability distribution** A commonly used distribution in probability and statistics is the log-normal distribution. (If the logarithm of a variable has a normal distribution, then the variable itself has a log-normal distribution.) The distribution function is

$$f(x) = \frac{1}{x\sigma\sqrt{2\pi}} e^{-\ln^2 x/(2\sigma^2)}, \quad \text{for } x > 0,$$

where $\ln x$ has zero mean and standard deviation $\sigma > 0$.

a. Graph f for $\sigma = \frac{1}{2}$, 1, and 2. Based on your graphs, does $\displaystyle\lim_{x \to 0^+} f(x)$ appear to exist?

b. Evaluate $\displaystyle\lim_{x \to 0^+} f(x)$. (*Hint:* Let $x = e^y$.)

c. Show that f has a single local maximum at $x^* = e^{-\sigma^2}$.

d. Evaluate $f(x^*)$ and express the result as a function of σ.

e. For what value of $\sigma > 0$ in part (d) does $f(x^*)$ have a minimum?

70. Equal area property for parabolas Let $f(x) = ax^2 + bx + c$ be an arbitrary quadratic function and choose two points $x = p$ and $x = q$. Let L_1 be the line tangent to the graph of f at the point $(p, f(p))$ and let L_2 be the line tangent to the graph at the point $(q, f(q))$. Let $x = s$ be the vertical line through the intersection point of L_1 and L_2. Finally, let R_1 be the region bounded by $y = f(x)$, L_1, and the vertical line $x = s$, and let R_2 be the region bounded by $y = f(x)$, L_2, and the vertical line $x = s$. Prove that the area of R_1 equals the area of R_2.

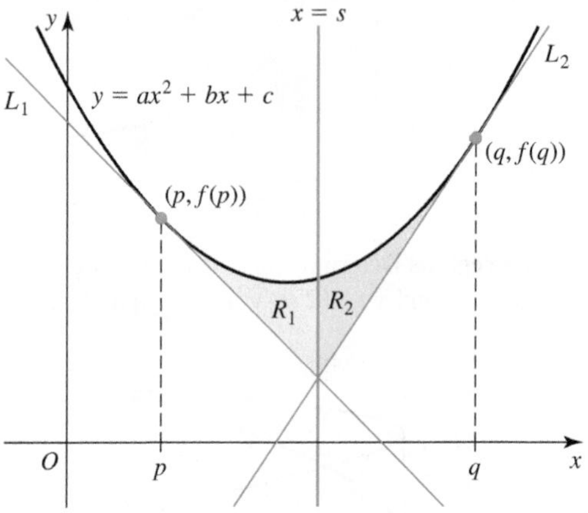

71. Derivatives of hyperbolic functions Compute the following derivatives.

a. $d^6/dx^6(\cosh x)$

b. $d/dx(x \operatorname{sech} x)$

72. Area of region Find the area of the region bounded by the curves $f(x) = 8 \operatorname{sech}^2 x$ and $g(x) = \cosh x$.

73. Linear approximation Find the linear approximation to $f(x) = \cosh x$ at $a = \ln 3$ and then use it to approximate the value of $\cosh 1$.

74. Limit Evaluate $\displaystyle\lim_{x \to \infty} (\tanh x)^x$.

Chapter 6 Guided Projects

Applications of the material in this chapter and related topics can be found in the following Guided Projects. For additional information, see the Preface.

- Means and tangent lines
- Landing an airliner
- Geometric probability
- Mathematics of the CD player
- Designing a water clock
- Buoyancy and Archimedes' principle
- Dipstick problems
- Hyperbolic functions
- Optimizing fuel use
- Inverse sine from geometry

A

Appendix

The goal of this appendix is to establish the essential notation, terminology, and algebraic skills that are used throughout the book.

Algebra

EXAMPLE 1 Algebra review

a. Evaluate $(-32)^{2/5}$.

b. Simplify $\dfrac{1}{x-2} - \dfrac{1}{x+2}$.

c. Solve the equation $\dfrac{x^4 - 5x^2 + 4}{x - 1} = 0$.

SOLUTION

a. Recall that $(-32)^{2/5} = ((-32)^{1/5})^2$. Because $(-32)^{1/5} = \sqrt[5]{-32} = -2$, we have $(-32)^{2/5} = (-2)^2 = 4$.

Another option is to write $(-32)^{2/5} = ((-32)^2)^{1/5} = 1024^{1/5} = 4$.

b. Finding a common denominator and simplifying leads to

$$\frac{1}{x-2} - \frac{1}{x+2} = \frac{(x+2)-(x-2)}{(x-2)(x+2)} = \frac{4}{x^2-4}.$$

c. Notice that $x = 1$ cannot be a solution of the equation because the left side of the equation is undefined at $x = 1$. Because $x - 1 \neq 0$, both sides of the equation can be multiplied by $x - 1$ to produce $x^4 - 5x^2 + 4 = 0$. After factoring, this equation becomes $(x^2 - 4)(x^2 - 1) = 0$, which implies $x^2 - 4 = (x-2)(x+2) = 0$ or $x^2 - 1 = (x-1)(x+1) = 0$. The roots of $x^2 - 4 = 0$ are $x = \pm 2$, and the roots of $x^2 - 1 = 0$ are $x = \pm 1$. Excluding $x = 1$, the roots of the original equation are $x = -1$ and $x = \pm 2$.

Related Exercises 15–26 ◀

Sets of Real Numbers

Figure A.1 shows the notation for **open intervals**, **closed intervals**, and various **bounded** and **unbounded intervals**. Notice that either interval notation or set notation may be used.

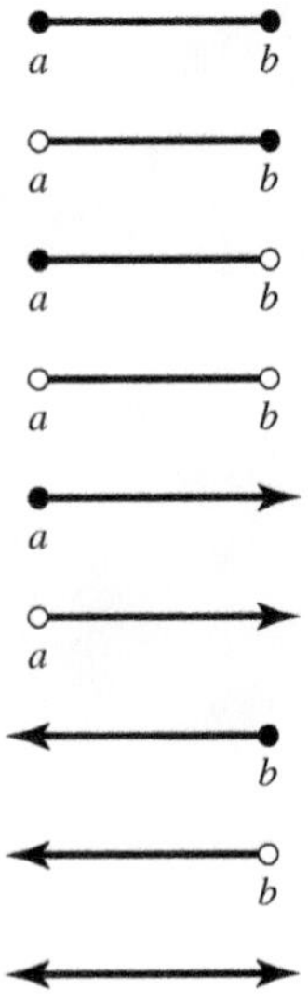

$[a, b] = \{x: a \le x \le b\}$	Closed, bounded interval
$(a, b] = \{x: a < x \le b\}$	Bounded interval
$[a, b) = \{x: a \le x < b\}$	Bounded interval
$(a, b) = \{x: a < x < b\}$	Open, bounded interval
$[a, \infty) = \{x: x \ge a\}$	Unbounded interval
$(a, \infty) = \{x: x > a\}$	Unbounded interval
$(-\infty, b] = \{x: x \le b\}$	Unbounded interval
$(-\infty, b) = \{x: x < b\}$	Unbounded interval
$(-\infty, \infty) = \{x: -\infty < x < \infty\}$	Unbounded interval

Figure A.1

EXAMPLE 2 **Solving inequalities** Solve the following inequalities.

a. $-x^2 + 5x - 6 < 0$ **b.** $\dfrac{x^2 - x - 2}{x - 3} \le 0$

SOLUTION

a. We multiply by -1, reverse the inequality, and then factor:

$$x^2 - 5x + 6 > 0 \quad \text{Multiply by } -1.$$
$$(x - 2)(x - 3) > 0. \quad \text{Factor.}$$

The roots of the corresponding equation $(x - 2)(x - 3) = 0$ are $x = 2$ and $x = 3$. These roots partition the number line (Figure A.2) into three intervals: $(-\infty, 2)$, $(2, 3)$, and $(3, \infty)$. On each interval, the product $(x - 2)(x - 3)$ does not change sign. To determine the sign of the product on a given interval, a **test value** x is selected and the sign of $(x - 2)(x - 3)$ is determined at x.

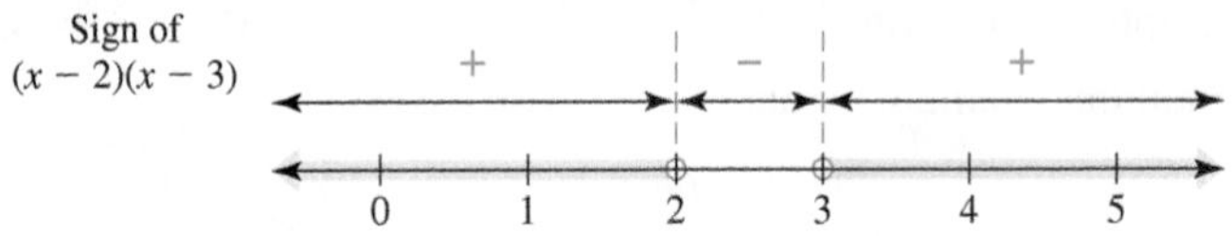

Figure A.2

A convenient choice for x in $(-\infty, 2)$ is $x = 0$. At this test value,

$$(x - 2)(x - 3) = (-2)(-3) > 0.$$

Using a test value of $x = 2.5$ in the interval $(2, 3)$, we have

$$(x - 2)(x - 3) = (0.5)(-0.5) < 0.$$

A test value of $x = 4$ in $(3, \infty)$ gives

$$(x - 2)(x - 3) = (2)(1) > 0.$$

Therefore, $(x - 2)(x - 3) > 0$ on $(-\infty, 2)$ and $(3, \infty)$. We conclude that the inequality $-x^2 + 5x - 6 < 0$ is satisfied for all x in either $(-\infty, 2)$ or $(3, \infty)$ (Figure A.2).

➤ The set of numbers $\{x: x \text{ is in } (-\infty, 2) \text{ or } (3, \infty)\}$ may also be expressed using the union symbol:

$$(-\infty, 2) \cup (3, \infty).$$

b. The expression $\frac{x^2 - x - 2}{x - 3}$ can change sign only at points where the numerator or denominator of $\frac{x^2 - x - 2}{x - 3}$ equals 0. Because

$$\frac{x^2 - x - 2}{x - 3} = \frac{(x + 1)(x - 2)}{x - 3},$$

the numerator is 0 when $x = -1$ or $x = 2$, and the denominator is 0 at $x = 3$. Therefore, we examine the sign of $\frac{(x + 1)(x - 2)}{x - 3}$ on the intervals $(-\infty, -1)$, $(-1, 2)$, $(2, 3)$, and $(3, \infty)$.

Test Value	$x + 1$	$x - 2$	$x - 3$	Result
-2	$-$	$-$	$-$	$-$
0	$+$	$-$	$-$	$+$
2.5	$+$	$+$	$-$	$-$
4	$+$	$+$	$+$	$+$

Using test values on these intervals, we see that $\frac{(x + 1)(x - 2)}{x - 3} < 0$ on $(-\infty, -1)$ and $(2, 3)$. Furthermore, the expression is 0 when $x = -1$ and $x = 2$. Therefore, $\frac{x^2 - x - 2}{x - 3} \le 0$ for all values of x in either $(-\infty, -1]$ or $[2, 3)$ (Figure A.3).

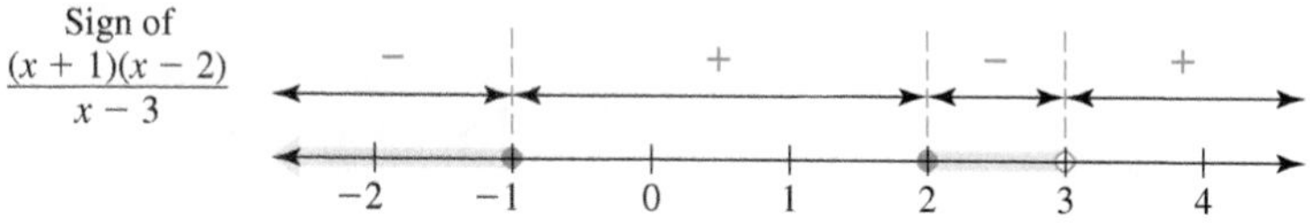

Figure A.3

Related Exercises 27–30

Absolute Value

The **absolute value** of a real number x, denoted $|x|$, is the distance between x and the origin on the number line (Figure A.4). More generally, $|x - y|$ is the distance between the points x and y on the number line. The absolute value has the following definition and properties.

> The absolute value is useful in simplifying square roots. Because $\sqrt{a}$ is nonnegative, we have $\sqrt{a^2} = |a|$. For example, $\sqrt{3^2} = 3$ and $\sqrt{(-3)^2} = \sqrt{9} = 3$. Note that the solutions of $x^2 = 9$ are $|x| = 3$ or $x = \pm 3$.

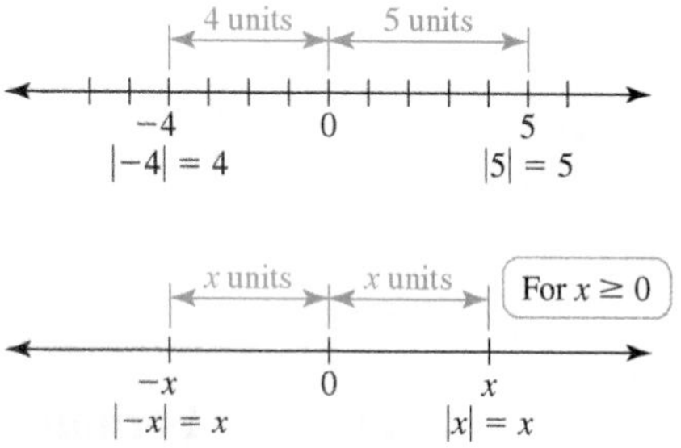

Figure A.4

> Property 6 is called the **triangle inequality**.

Definition and Properties of the Absolute Value

The absolute value of a real number x is defined as

$$|x| = \begin{cases} x & \text{if } x \ge 0 \\ -x & \text{if } x < 0. \end{cases}$$

Let a be a positive real number.

1. $|x| = a \Leftrightarrow x = \pm a$
2. $|x| < a \Leftrightarrow -a < x < a$
3. $|x| > a \Leftrightarrow x > a$ or $x < -a$
4. $|x| \le a \Leftrightarrow -a \le x \le a$
5. $|x| \ge a \Leftrightarrow x \ge a$ or $x \le -a$
6. $|x + y| \le |x| + |y|$

EXAMPLE 3 **Inequalities with absolute values** Solve the following inequalities. Then sketch the solution on the number line and express it in interval notation.

a. $|x - 2| < 3$ **b.** $|2x - 6| \geq 10$

SOLUTION

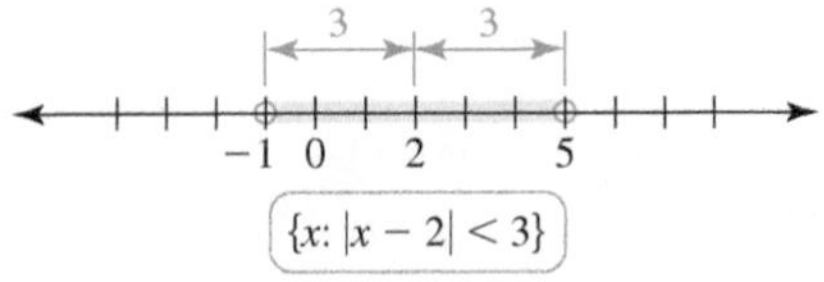

Figure A.5

a. Using property 2 of the absolute value, $|x - 2| < 3$ is written as

$$-3 < x - 2 < 3.$$

Adding 2 to each term of these inequalities results in $-1 < x < 5$ (Figure A.5). This set of numbers is written as $(-1, 5)$ in interval notation.

b. Using property 5, the inequality $|2x - 6| \geq 10$ implies that

$$2x - 6 \geq 10 \quad \text{or} \quad 2x - 6 \leq -10.$$

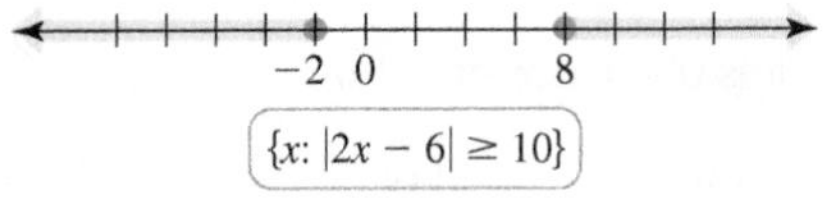

Figure A.6

We add 6 to both sides of the first inequality to obtain $2x \geq 16$, which implies $x \geq 8$. Similarly, the second inequality yields $x \leq -2$ (Figure A.6). In interval notation, the solution is $(-\infty, -2]$ or $[8, \infty)$.

Related Exercises 31–34 ◀

Cartesian Coordinate System

The conventions of the **Cartesian coordinate system** or ***xy*-coordinate system** are illustrated in Figure A.7. The set of real numbers is often denoted $\mathbb{R}$. The set of all ordered pairs of real numbers, which comprise the *xy*-plane, is often denoted $\mathbb{R}^2$.

➤ The familiar (x, y) coordinate system is named after René Descartes (1596–1650). However, it was introduced independently and simultaneously by Pierre de Fermat (1601–1665).

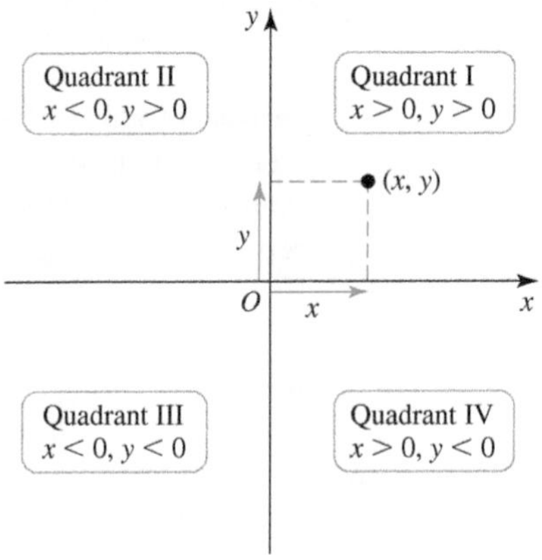

Figure A.7

Distance Formula and Circles

By the Pythagorean theorem (Figure A.8), we have the following formula for the distance between two points $P_1(x_1, y_1)$ and $P_2(x_2, y_2)$.

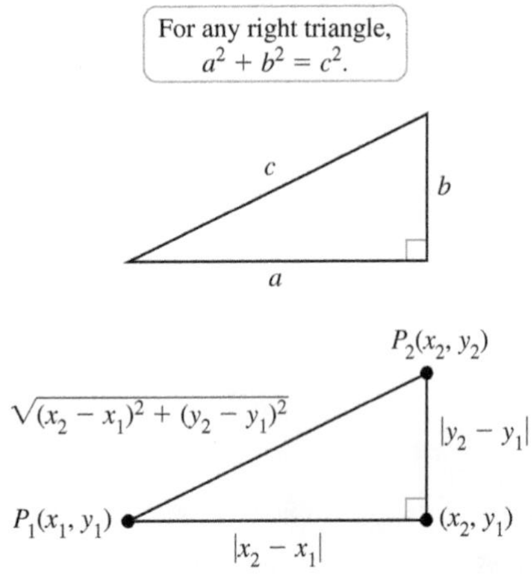

Figure A.8

> **Distance Formula**
>
> The distance between the points $P_1(x_1, y_1)$ and $P_2(x_2, y_2)$ is
>
> $$|P_1P_2| = \sqrt{(x_2 - x_1)^2 + (y_2 - y_1)^2}.$$

A **circle** is the set of points in the plane whose distance from a fixed point (the **center**) is constant (the **radius**). This definition leads to the following equations that describe a circle.

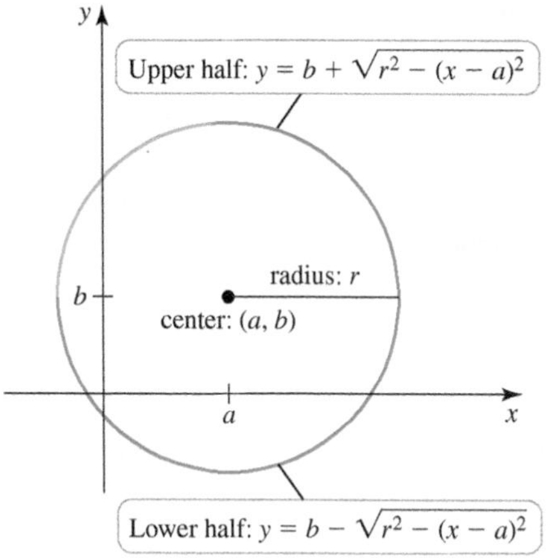

Figure A.9

Equation of a Circle

The equation of a circle centered at (a, b) with radius r is

$$(x-a)^2 + (y-b)^2 = r^2.$$

Solving for y, the equations of the upper and lower halves of the circle (Figure A.9) are

$$y = b + \sqrt{r^2 - (x-a)^2} \quad \text{Upper half of the circle}$$
$$y = b - \sqrt{r^2 - (x-a)^2}. \quad \text{Lower half of the circle}$$

EXAMPLE 4 Sets involving circles

a. Find the equation of the circle with center $(2, 4)$ passing through $(-2, 1)$.

b. Describe the set of points satisfying $x^2 + y^2 - 4x - 6y < 12$.

SOLUTION

a. The radius of the circle equals the length of the line segment between the center $(2, 4)$ and the point on the circle $(-2, 1)$, which is

$$\sqrt{(2-(-2))^2 + (4-1)^2} = 5.$$

Therefore, the equation of the circle is

$$(x-2)^2 + (y-4)^2 = 25.$$

b. To put this inequality in a recognizable form, we complete the square on the left side of the inequality:

$$\begin{aligned} x^2 + y^2 - 4x - 6y &= \underbrace{x^2 - 4x + 4 - 4}_{\text{Add and subtract the square of half the coefficient of } x} + \underbrace{y^2 - 6y + 9 - 9}_{\text{Add and subtract the square of half the coefficient of } y} \\ &= \underbrace{x^2 - 4x + 4}_{(x-2)^2} + \underbrace{y^2 - 6y + 9}_{(y-3)^2} - 4 - 9 \\ &= (x-2)^2 + (y-3)^2 - 13. \end{aligned}$$

➤ Recall that the procedure shown here for completing the square works when the coefficient on the quadratic term is 1. When the coefficient is not 1, it must be factored out before completing the square.

Therefore, the original inequality becomes

$$(x-2)^2 + (y-3)^2 - 13 < 12, \quad \text{or} \quad (x-2)^2 + (y-3)^2 < 25.$$

This inequality describes those points that lie within the circle centered at $(2, 3)$ with radius 5 (Figure A.10). Note that a dashed curve is used to indicate that the circle itself is not part of the solution.

➤ A **circle** is the set of all points whose distance from a fixed point is a constant. A **disk** is the set of all points within and possibly on a circle.

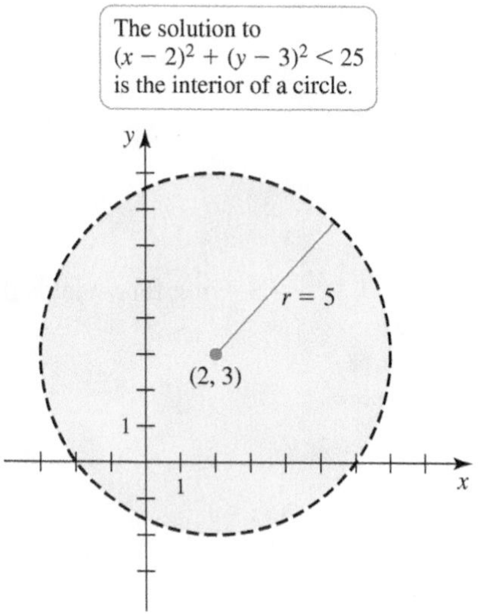

Figure A.10

Related Exercises 35–36 ◄

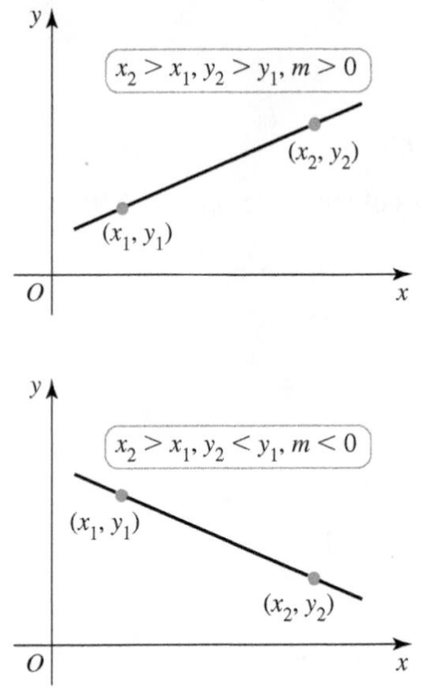

Figure A.11

Equations of Lines

The **slope** m of the line passing through the points $P_1(x_1, y_1)$ and $P_2(x_2, y_2)$ is the *rise over run* (Figure A.11), computed as

$$m = \frac{\text{change in vertical coordinate}}{\text{change in horizontal coordinate}} = \frac{y_2 - y_1}{x_2 - x_1}.$$

Equations of a Line

Point-slope form The equation of the line with slope m passing through the point (x_1, y_1) is $y - y_1 = m(x - x_1)$.

Slope-intercept form The equation of the line with slope m and y-intercept $(0, b)$ is $y = mx + b$ (Figure A.12a).

General linear equation The equation $Ax + By + C = 0$ describes a line in the plane, provided A and B are not both zero.

Vertical and horizontal lines The vertical line that passes through $(a, 0)$ has an equation $x = a$; its slope is undefined. The horizontal line through $(0, b)$ has an equation $y = b$, with slope equal to 0 (Figure A.12b).

➤ Given a particular line, we often talk about *the* equation of a line. But the equation of a specific line is not unique. Having found one equation, we can multiply it by any nonzero constant to produce another equation of the same line.

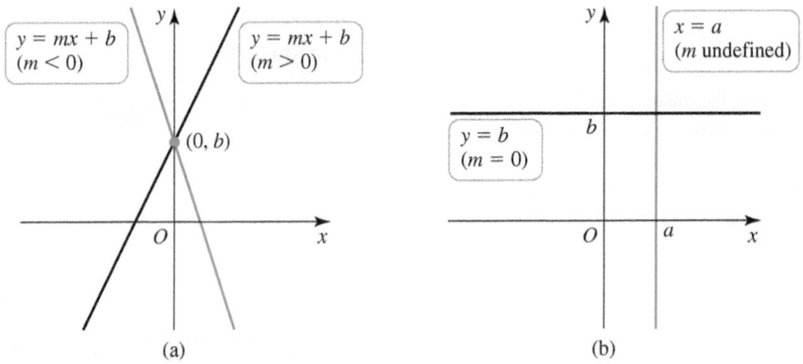

Figure A.12

EXAMPLE 5 Working with linear equations Find an equation of the line passing through the points $(1, -2)$ and $(-4, 5)$.

SOLUTION The slope of the line through the points $(1, -2)$ and $(-4, 5)$ is

$$m = \frac{5 - (-2)}{-4 - 1} = \frac{7}{-5} = -\frac{7}{5}.$$

Using the point $(1, -2)$, the point-slope form of the equation is

$$y - (-2) = -\frac{7}{5}(x - 1).$$

➤ Because both points $(1, -2)$ and $(-4, 5)$ lie on the line and must satisfy the equation of the line, either point can be used to determine an equation of the line.

Solving for y yields the slope-intercept form of the equation:

$$y = -\frac{7}{5}x - \frac{3}{5}.$$

Related Exercises 37–40 ◀

Parallel and Perpendicular Lines

Two lines in the plane may have either of two special relationships to each other: They may be parallel or perpendicular.

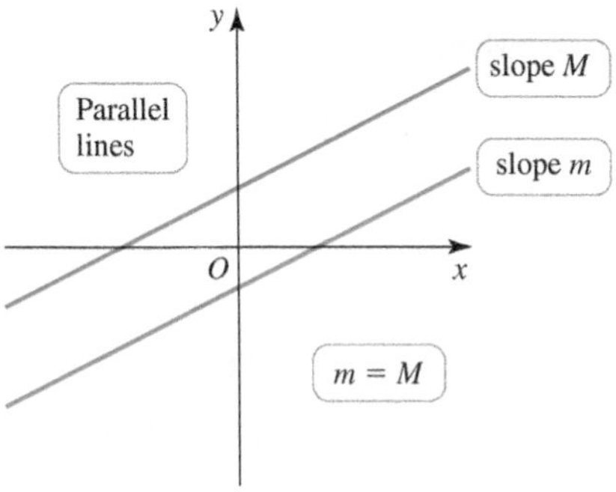

Parallel Lines

Two distinct nonvertical lines are **parallel** if they have the same slope; that is, the lines with equations $y = mx + b$ and $y = Mx + B$ are parallel if and only if $m = M$. Two distinct vertical lines are parallel.

EXAMPLE 6 **Parallel lines** Find an equation of the line parallel to $3x - 6y + 12 = 0$ that intersects the x-axis at $(4, 0)$.

SOLUTION Solving the equation $3x - 6y + 12 = 0$ for y, we have

$$y = \frac{1}{2}x + 2.$$

This line has a slope of $\frac{1}{2}$ and any line parallel to it has a slope of $\frac{1}{2}$. Therefore, the line that passes through $(4, 0)$ with slope $\frac{1}{2}$ has the point-slope equation $y - 0 = \frac{1}{2}(x - 4)$. After simplifying, an equation of the line is

$$y = \frac{1}{2}x - 2.$$

Notice that the slopes of the two lines are the same; only the y-intercepts differ.

Related Exercises 41–42 ◀

➤ The slopes of perpendicular lines are *negative reciprocals* of each other.

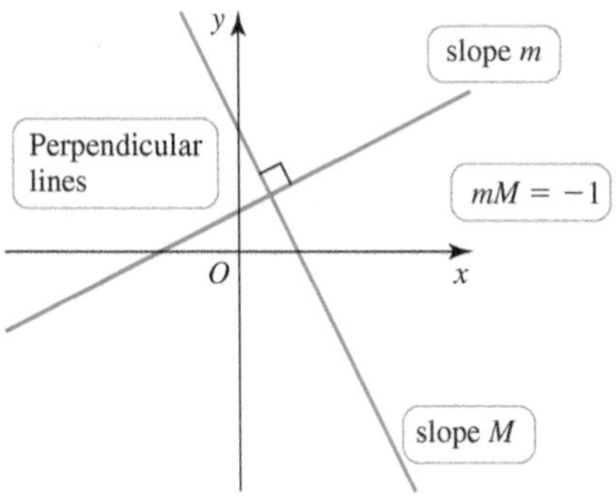

Perpendicular Lines

Two lines with slopes $m \neq 0$ and $M \neq 0$ are **perpendicular** if and only if $mM = -1$, or equivalently, $m = -1/M$.

EXAMPLE 7 **Perpendicular lines** Find an equation of the line passing through the point $(-2, 5)$ perpendicular to the line ℓ: $4x - 2y + 7 = 0$.

SOLUTION The equation of ℓ can be written $y = 2x + \frac{7}{2}$, which reveals that its slope is 2. Therefore, the slope of any line perpendicular to ℓ is $-\frac{1}{2}$. The line with slope $-\frac{1}{2}$ passing through the point $(-2, 5)$ is

$$y - 5 = -\frac{1}{2}(x + 2), \quad \text{or} \quad y = -\frac{x}{2} + 4.$$

Related Exercises 43–44 ◀

APPENDIX A EXERCISES

Review Questions

1. State the meaning of $\{x: -4 < x \leq 10\}$. Express the set $\{x: -4 < x \leq 10\}$ using interval notation and draw it on a number line.
2. Write the interval $(-\infty, 2)$ in set notation and draw it on a number line.
3. Give the definition of $|x|$.
4. Write the inequality $|x - 2| \leq 3$ without absolute value symbols.
5. Write the inequality $|2x - 4| \geq 3$ without absolute value symbols.
6. Write an equation of the set of all points that are a distance 5 units from the point $(2, 3)$.
7. Explain how to find the distance between two points whose coordinates are known.
8. Sketch the set of points $\{(x, y): x^2 + (y - 2)^2 > 16\}$.
9. Give an equation of the upper half of the circle centered at the origin with radius 6.
10. What are the possible solution sets of the equation $x^2 + y^2 + Cx + Dy + E = 0$?
11. Give an equation of the line with slope m that passes through the point $(4, -2)$.

12. Give an equation of the line with slope m and y-intercept $(0, 6)$.

13. What is the relationship between the slopes of two parallel lines?

14. What is the relationship between the slopes of two perpendicular lines?

Basic Skills

15–20. Algebra review *Simplify or evaluate the following expressions without a calculator.*

15. $(1/8)^{-2/3}$

16. $\sqrt[3]{-125} + \sqrt{1/25}$

17. $(u + v)^2 - (u - v)^2$

18. $\dfrac{(a + h)^2 - a^2}{h}$

19. $\dfrac{1}{x + h} - \dfrac{1}{x}$

20. $\dfrac{2}{x + 3} - \dfrac{2}{x - 3}$

21–26. Algebra review

21. Factor $y^2 - y^{-2}$.

22. Solve $x^3 - 9x = 0$.

23. Solve $u^4 - 11u^2 + 18 = 0$.

24. Solve $4^x - 6(2^x) = -8$.

25. Simplify $\dfrac{(x + h)^3 - x^3}{h}$, for $h \neq 0$.

26. Rewrite $\dfrac{\sqrt{x + h} - \sqrt{x}}{h}$, where $h \neq 0$, without square roots in the numerator.

27–30. Solving inequalities *Solve the following inequalities and draw the solution on a number line.*

27. $x^2 - 6x + 5 < 0$

28. $\dfrac{x + 1}{x + 2} < 6$

29. $\dfrac{x^2 - 9x + 20}{x - 6} \leq 0$

30. $x\sqrt{x - 1} > 0$

31–34. Inequalities with absolute values *Solve the following inequalities. Then draw the solution on a number line and express it using interval notation.*

31. $|3x - 4| > 8$

32. $1 \leq |x| \leq 10$

33. $3 < |2x - 1| < 5$

34. $2 < |\frac{x}{2} - 5| < 6$

35–36. Circle calculations *Solve the following problems.*

35. Find the equation of the lower half of the circle with center $(-1, 2)$ and radius 3.

36. Describe the set of points that satisfy $x^2 + y^2 + 6x + 8y \geq 25$.

37–40. Working with linear equations *Find an equation of the line ℓ that satisfies the given condition. Then draw the graph of ℓ.*

37. ℓ has slope $5/3$ and y-intercept $(0, 4)$.

38. ℓ has undefined slope and passes through $(0, 5)$.

39. ℓ has y-intercept $(0, -4)$ and x-intercept $(5, 0)$.

40. ℓ is parallel to the x-axis and passes through the point $(2, 3)$.

41–42. Parallel lines *Find an equation of the following lines and draw their graphs.*

41. The line with y-intercept $(0, 12)$ parallel to the line $x + 2y = 8$

42. The line with x-intercept $(-6, 0)$ parallel to the line $2x - 5 = 0$

43–44. Perpendicular lines *Find an equation of the following lines.*

43. The line passing through $(3, -6)$ perpendicular to the line $y = -3x + 2$

44. The perpendicular bisector of the line joining the points $(-9, 2)$ and $(3, -5)$

Further Explorations

45. **Explain why or why not** State whether the following statements are true and give an explanation or counterexample.
   a. $\sqrt{16} = \pm 4$.
   b. $\sqrt{4^2} = \sqrt{(-4)^2}$.
   c. There are two real numbers that satisfy the condition $|x| = -2$.
   d. $|\pi^2 - 9| < 0$.
   e. The point $(1, 1)$ is inside the circle of radius 1 centered at the origin.
   f. $\sqrt{x^4} = x^2$ for all real numbers x.
   g. $\sqrt{a^2} < \sqrt{b^2}$ implies $a < b$ for all real numbers a and b.

46–48. Intervals to sets *Express the following intervals in set notation. Use absolute value notation when possible.*

46. $(-\infty, 12)$

47. $(-\infty, -2]$ or $[4, \infty)$

48. $(2, 3]$ or $[4, 5)$

49–50. Sets in the plane *Graph each set in the xy-plane.*

49. $\{(x, y): |x - y| = 0\}$

50. $\{(x, y): |x| = |y|\}$

B

Appendix

Proofs of Selected Theorems

THEOREM 2.3 Limit Laws

Assume $\lim_{x \to a} f(x)$ and $\lim_{x \to a} g(x)$ exist. The following properties hold, where c is a real number, and $m > 0$ and $n > 0$ are integers.

1. **Sum** $\lim_{x \to a} (f(x) + g(x)) = \lim_{x \to a} f(x) + \lim_{x \to a} g(x)$
2. **Difference** $\lim_{x \to a} (f(x) - g(x)) = \lim_{x \to a} f(x) - \lim_{x \to a} g(x)$
3. **Constant multiple** $\lim_{x \to a} (cf(x)) = c \lim_{x \to a} f(x)$
4. **Product** $\lim_{x \to a} (f(x)g(x)) = (\lim_{x \to a} f(x))(\lim_{x \to a} g(x))$
5. **Quotient** $\lim_{x \to a} \dfrac{f(x)}{g(x)} = \dfrac{\lim_{x \to a} f(x)}{\lim_{x \to a} g(x)}$, provided $\lim_{x \to a} g(x) \neq 0$
6. **Power** $\lim_{x \to a} (f(x))^n = (\lim_{x \to a} f(x))^n$
7. **Fractional power** $\lim_{x \to a} (f(x))^{n/m} = (\lim_{x \to a} f(x))^{n/m}$, provided $f(x) \geq 0$, for x near a, if m is even and n/m is reduced to lowest terms

Proof: The proof of Law 1 is given in Example 5 of Section 2.7. The proof of Law 2 is analogous to that of Law 1; the triangle inequality in the form $|x - y| \leq |x| + |y|$ is used. The proof of Law 3 is outlined in Exercise 26 of Section 2.7. The proofs of Laws 4 and 5 are given below. The proof of Law 6 involves the repeated use of Law 4. The proof of Law 7 is given in advanced texts. ◀

Proof of Product Law: Let $L = \lim_{x \to a} f(x)$ and $M = \lim_{x \to a} g(x)$. Using the definition of a limit, the goal is to show that given any $\varepsilon > 0$, it is possible to specify a $\delta > 0$ such that $|f(x)g(x) - LM| < \varepsilon$ whenever $0 < |x - a| < \delta$. Notice that

$$\begin{aligned}
|f(x)g(x) - LM| &= |f(x)g(x) - Lg(x) + Lg(x) - LM| && \text{Add and subtract } Lg(x). \\
&= |(f(x) - L)g(x) + (g(x) - M)L| && \text{Group terms.} \\
&\leq |(f(x) - L)g(x)| + |(g(x) - M)L| && \text{Triangle inequality} \\
&= |f(x) - L||g(x)| + |g(x) - M||L|. && |xy| = |x||y|
\end{aligned}$$

➤ Real numbers x and y obey the triangle inequality $|x + y| \le |x| + |y|$.

We now use the definition of the limits of f and g, and note that L and M are fixed real numbers. Given $\varepsilon > 0$, there exist $\delta_1 > 0$ and $\delta_2 > 0$ such that

$$|f(x) - L| < \frac{\varepsilon}{2(|M| + 1)} \quad \text{and} \quad |g(x) - M| < \frac{\varepsilon}{2(|L| + 1)}$$

➤ $|g(x) - M| < 1$ implies that $g(x)$ is less than 1 unit from M. Therefore, whether $g(x)$ and M are positive or negative, $|g(x)| < |M| + 1$.

whenever $0 < |x - a| < \delta_1$ and $0 < |x - a| < \delta_2$, respectively. Furthermore, by the definition of the limit of g, there exits a $\delta_3 > 0$ such that $|g(x) - M| < 1$ whenever $0 < |x - a| < \delta_3$. It follows that $|g(x)| < |M| + 1$ whenever $0 < |x - a| < \delta_3$. Now take δ to be the minimum of δ_1, δ_2, and δ_3. Then for $0 < |x - a| < \delta$, we have

$$|f(x)g(x) - LM| \le \underbrace{|f(x) - L|}_{<\frac{\varepsilon}{2(|M|+1)}}\underbrace{|g(x)|}_{<(|M|+1)} + \underbrace{|g(x) - M|}_{<\frac{\varepsilon}{2(|L|+1)}}|L|$$

$$< \frac{\varepsilon}{2} + \frac{\varepsilon}{2}\underbrace{\frac{|L|}{|L| + 1}}_{<1} < \frac{\varepsilon}{2} + \frac{\varepsilon}{2} = \varepsilon.$$

It follows that $\lim_{x \to a} [f(x)g(x)] = LM$. ◄

Proof of Quotient Law: We first prove that if $\lim_{x \to a} g(x) = M$ exists, where $M \ne 0$, then $\lim_{x \to a} \frac{1}{g(x)} = \frac{1}{M}$. The Quotient Law then follows when we replace g with $1/g$ in the Product Law. Therefore, the goal is to show that given any $\varepsilon > 0$, it is possible to specify a $\delta > 0$ such that $\left|\frac{1}{g(x)} - \frac{1}{M}\right| < \varepsilon$ whenever $0 < |x - a| < \delta$. First note that $M \ne 0$ and $g(x)$ can be made arbitrarily close to M. For this reason, there exists a $\delta_1 > 0$ such that $|g(x)| > |M|/2$, or equivalently, $1/|g(x)| < 2/|M|$, whenever $0 < |x - a| < \delta_1$. Furthermore, using the definition of the limit of g, given any $\varepsilon > 0$, there exists a $\delta_2 > 0$ such that $|g(x) - M| < \frac{\varepsilon|M|^2}{2}$ whenever $0 < |x - a| < \delta_2$. Now take δ to be the minimum of δ_1 and δ_2. Then for $0 < |x - a| < \delta$, we have

➤ Note that if $|g(x)| > |M|/2$, then $1/|g(x)| < 2/|M|$.

$$\left|\frac{1}{g(x)} - \frac{1}{M}\right| = \left|\frac{M - g(x)}{Mg(x)}\right| \quad \text{Common denominator}$$

$$= \frac{1}{|M|}\underbrace{\frac{1}{|g(x)|}}_{<\frac{2}{|M|}}\underbrace{|g(x) - M|}_{<\frac{\varepsilon|M|^2}{2}} \quad \text{Rewrite.}$$

$$< \frac{1}{|M|}\frac{2}{|M|}\frac{\varepsilon|M|^2}{2} = \varepsilon. \quad \text{Simplify.}$$

By the definition of a limit, we have $\lim_{x \to a} \frac{1}{g(x)} = \frac{1}{M}$. The proof can be completed by applying the Product Law with g replaced with $1/g$. ◄

THEOREM 8.14 Ratio Test

Let Σa_k be an infinite series with positive terms and let $r = \lim_{k \to \infty} \frac{a_{k+1}}{a_k}$.

1. If $0 \le r < 1$, the series converges.
2. If $r > 1$ (including $r = \infty$), the series diverges.
3. If $r = 1$, the test is inconclusive.

Proof: We consider three cases: $0 \le r < 1$, $r > 1$, and $r = 1$.

1. Assume $0 \le r < 1$ and choose a number R such that $r < R < 1$. Because the sequence $\left\{\frac{a_{k+1}}{a_k}\right\}$ converges to a number r less than R, eventually all the terms in the tail of the sequence $\left\{\frac{a_{k+1}}{a_k}\right\}$ are less than R. That is, there is a positive integer N such that $\frac{a_{k+1}}{a_k} < R$, for all $k > N$. Multiplying both sides of this inequality by $\frac{a_k}{R^{k+1}}$, we have $\frac{a_{k+1}}{R^{k+1}} < \frac{a_k}{R^k}$, for all $k > N$. So the sequence $\left\{\frac{a_k}{R^k}\right\}_{k=N+1}^{\infty}$ is decreasing and it follows that $\frac{a_k}{R^k} < \frac{a_{N+1}}{R^{N+1}}$, for all $k \ge N + 1$. By letting $c = \frac{a_{N+1}}{R^{N+1}}$, we have $0 < a_k \le cR^k$, for all $k \ge N + 1$. Let S_n represent the nth partial sum of $\sum_{k=N+1}^{\infty} a_k$; note that the partial sums of this series are bounded by a convergent geometric series:

$$\begin{aligned} S_n &= a_{N+1} + a_{N+2} + \cdots + a_{N+n} \\ &\le cR^{N+1} + cR^{N+2} + \cdots + cR^{N+n} \\ &< cR^{N+1} + cR^{N+2} + \cdots + cR^{N+n} + \cdots \\ &= \frac{cR^{N+1}}{1 - R}. \end{aligned}$$

   Because the sequence $\{S_n\}$ is increasing (each partial sum in the sequence consists of positive terms) and is bounded above by $\frac{cR^{N+1}}{1 - R}$, it converges by the Bounded Monotonic Sequences Theorem (Theorem 8.5). Therefore, $\sum_{k=N+1}^{\infty} a_k$ converges and we conclude that $\sum_{k=1}^{\infty} a_k$ converges (Theorem 8.13).

2. If $r > 1$, there is a positive integer N for which $\frac{a_{k+1}}{a_k} > 1$, or equivalently $a_{k+1} > a_k$, for all $k > N$. So every term in the sequence $\{a_k\}_{k=N+1}^{\infty}$ is greater than or equal to the positive number a_{N+1}, which implies that $\lim_{n\to\infty} a_n \ne 0$. Therefore, the series $\sum_{k=N+1}^{\infty} a_k$ diverges by the Divergence Test, and we conclude that $\sum_{k=1}^{\infty} a_k$ diverges (Theorem 8.13).

3. In the case that $r = 1$, the series $\sum_{k=1}^{\infty} a_k$ may or may not converge. For example, both the divergent harmonic series $\sum_{k=1}^{\infty} \frac{1}{k}$ and the convergent p-series $\sum_{k=1}^{\infty} \frac{1}{k^2}$ produce a value of $r = 1$. ◄

> **THEOREM 8.15 Root Test**
> Let $\sum a_k$ be an infinite series with nonnegative terms and let $\rho = \lim_{k\to\infty} \sqrt[k]{a_k}$.
>
> 1. If $0 \le \rho < 1$, the series converges.
> 2. If $\rho > 1$ (including $\rho = \infty$), the series diverges.
> 3. If $\rho = 1$, the test is inconclusive.

Proof: We consider three cases: $0 \le \rho < 1$, $\rho > 1$, and $\rho = 1$.

1. Assume $0 \le \rho < 1$ and choose a number R such that $\rho < R < 1$. Because the sequence $\{\sqrt[k]{a_k}\}$ converges to a number less than R, there is a positive integer N such that

$\sqrt[k]{a_k} < R$, or equivalently $a_k < R^k$, for all $k > N$. Let S_n represent the nth partial sum of $\sum_{k=N+1}^{\infty} a_k$; note that the partial sums of this series are bounded by a convergent geometric series:

$$\begin{aligned} S_n &= a_{N+1} + a_{N+2} + \cdots + a_{N+n} \\ &\le R^{N+1} + R^{N+2} + \cdots + R^{N+n} \\ &< R^{N+1} + R^{N+2} + \cdots + R^{N+n} + \cdots \\ &= \frac{R^{N+1}}{1 - R}. \end{aligned}$$

Because the sequence $\{S_n\}$ is increasing (each partial sum in the sequence consists of positive terms) and is bounded above by $\frac{R^{N+1}}{1 - R}$, it converges by the Bounded Monotonic Sequences Theorem (Theorem 8.5). Therefore, $\sum_{k=N+1}^{\infty} a_k$ converges and we conclude that $\sum_{k=1}^{\infty} a_k$ converges (Theorem 8.13).

2. If $\rho > 1$, there is an integer N for which $\sqrt[k]{a_k} > 1$, or equivalently $a_k > 1$, for all $k > N$. So every term in the sequence $\{a_k\}_{k=N+1}^{\infty}$ is greater than or equal to 1, which implies that $\lim_{n\to\infty} a_n \ne 0$. Therefore, the series $\sum_{k=N+1}^{\infty} a_k$ diverges by the Divergence Test, and we conclude that $\sum_{k=1}^{\infty} a_k$ diverges (Theorem 8.13).

3. If $\rho = 1$, the series $\sum_{k=1}^{\infty} a_k$ may or may not converge. For example, both the divergent harmonic series $\sum_{k=1}^{\infty} \frac{1}{k}$ and the convergent p-series $\sum_{k=1}^{\infty} \frac{1}{k^2}$ produce a value of $\rho = 1$. ◄

THEOREM 9.3 Convergence of Power Series

A power series $\sum_{k=0}^{\infty} c_k(x - a)^k$ centered at a converges in one of three ways.

1. The series converges for all x, in which case the interval of convergence is $(-\infty, \infty)$ and the radius of convergence is $R = \infty$.
2. There is a real number $R > 0$ such that the series converges for $|x - a| < R$ and diverges for $|x - a| > R$, in which case the radius of convergence is R.
3. The series converges only at a, in which case the radius of convergence is $R = 0$.

Proof: Without loss of generality, we take $a = 0$. (If $a \ne 0$, the following argument may be shifted so it is centered at $x = a$.) The proof hinges on a preliminary result:

If $\sum_{k=0}^{\infty} c_k x^k$ converges for $x = b \ne 0$, then it converges absolutely, for $|x| < |b|$. If $\sum_{k=0}^{\infty} c_k x^k$ diverges for $x = d$, then it diverges, for $|x| > |d|$.

To prove these facts, assume that $\sum_{k=0}^{\infty} c_k b^k$ converges, which implies that $\lim_{k\to\infty} c_k b^k = 0$. Then there exists a real number $M > 0$ such that $|c_k b^k| < M$, for $k = 0, 1, 2, 3, \ldots$. It follows that

$$\sum_{k=0}^{\infty} |c_k x^k| = \sum_{k=0}^{\infty} \underbrace{|c_k b^k|}_{< M} \left|\frac{x}{b}\right|^k < M \sum_{k=0}^{\infty} \left|\frac{x}{b}\right|^k.$$

If $|x| < |b|$, then $|x/b| < 1$ and $\sum_{k=0}^{\infty} \left|\frac{x}{b}\right|^k$ is a convergent geometric series. Therefore, $\sum_{k=0}^{\infty} |c_k x^k|$ converges by the comparison test, which implies that $\sum_{k=0}^{\infty} c_k x^k$ converges absolutely for $|x| < |b|$. The second half of the preliminary result is proved by supposing the series diverges at $x = d$. The series cannot converge at a point x_0 with $|x_0| > |d|$ because by the preceding argument, it would converge for $|x| < |x_0|$, which includes $x = d$. Therefore, the series diverges for $|x| > |d|$.

Now we may deal with the three cases in the theorem. Let S be the set of real numbers for which the series converges, which always includes 0. If $S = \{0\}$, then we have Case 3. If S consists of all real numbers, then we have Case 1. For Case 2, assume that $d \neq 0$ is a point at which the series diverges. By the preliminary result, the series diverges for $|x| > |d|$. Therefore, if x is in S, then $|x| < |d|$, which implies that S is bounded. By the Least Upper Bound Property for real numbers, S has a least upper bound R, such that $x \leq R$, for all x in S. If $|x| > R$, then x is not in S and the series diverges. If $|x| < R$, then x is not the least upper bound of S and there exists a number b in S with $|x| < b \leq R$. Because the series converges at $x = b$, by the preliminary result, $\sum_{k=0}^{\infty} |c_k x^k|$ converges for $|x| < |b|$. Therefore, the series $\sum_{k=0}^{\infty} c_k x^k$ converges absolutely for $|x| < R$ and diverges for $|x| > R$. ◄

➤ The Least Upper Bound Property for real numbers states that if a nonempty set S is bounded (that is, there exists a number M, called an *upper bound*, such that $x \leq M$ for all x in S), then S has a *least upper bound* L, which is the smallest of the upper bounds.

THEOREM 10.3 Eccentricity-Directrix Theorem

Let ℓ be a line, F a point not on ℓ, and $e > 0$ a real number. Let C be the set of points P in a plane with the property that $\frac{|PF|}{|PL|} = e$, where $|PL|$ is the perpendicular distance from P to ℓ.

1. If $e = 1$, C is a **parabola**.
2. If $0 < e < 1$, C is an **ellipse**.
3. If $e > 1$, C is a **hyperbola**.

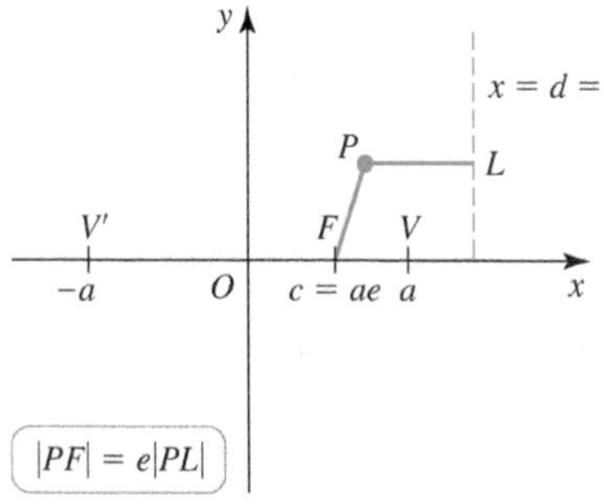

Figure B.1

Proof: If $e = 1$, then the defining property becomes $|PF| = |PL|$, which is the standard definition of a parabola (Section 11.4). We prove the result for ellipses $(0 < e < 1)$; a small modification handles the case of hyperbolas $(e > 1)$.

Let E be the curve whose points satisfy $|PF| = e\,|PL|$; the goal is to show that E is an ellipse. There are two points on the x-axis (the *vertices*), call them V and V', that satisfy $|VF| = e|VL|$ and $|V'F| = e|V'L|$. We choose the origin such that V and V' have coordinates $(a, 0)$ and $(-a, 0)$, respectively (Figure B.1). We locate the point F (a *focus*) at $(c, 0)$ and let ℓ (a *directrix*) be the line $x = d$, where $c > 0$ and $d > 0$. These choices place the center of E at the origin. Notice that we have four parameters (a, c, d, and e) that must be related.

Because the vertex $V(a, 0)$ is on E, it satisfies the defining property $|PF| = e\,|PL|$, with $P = V$. This condition implies that $a - c = e(d - a)$. Because the vertex $V'(-a, 0)$ is on the curve E, it also satisfies the defining property $|PF| = e\,|PL|$, with $P = V'$. This condition implies that $a + c = e(d + a)$. Solving these two equations for c and d, we find that $c = ae$ and $d = a/e$. To summarize, the parameters a, c, d, and e are related by the equations

$$c = ae \quad \text{and} \quad a = de.$$

Because $e < 1$, it follows that $c < a < d$.

We now use the property $|PF| = e\,|PL|$ with an arbitrary point $P(x, y)$ on the curve E. Figure B.1 shows the geometry with the focus $(c, 0) = (ae, 0)$ and the directrix $x = d = a/e$. The condition $|PF| = e\,|PL|$ becomes

$$\sqrt{(x - ae)^2 + y^2} = e\left(\frac{a}{e} - x\right).$$

The goal is to find the simplest possible relationship between x and y. Squaring both sides and collecting terms, we have

$$(1 - e^2)x^2 + y^2 = a^2(1 - e^2).$$

Dividing through by $a^2(1 - e^2)$ gives the equation of the standard ellipse:

$$\frac{x^2}{a^2} + \frac{y^2}{a^2(1 - e^2)} = \frac{x^2}{a^2} + \frac{y^2}{b^2} = 1, \quad \text{where} \quad b^2 = a^2(1 - e^2).$$

This is the equation of an ellipse centered at the origin with vertices and foci on the x-axis.

The preceding proof is now applied with $e > 1$. The argument for ellipses with $0 < e < 1$ led to the equation

$$\frac{x^2}{a^2} + \frac{y^2}{a^2(1 - e^2)} = 1.$$

With $e > 1$, we have $1 - e^2 < 0$, so we write $(1 - e^2) = -(e^2 - 1)$. The resulting equation describes a hyperbola centered at the origin with the foci on the x-axis:

$$\frac{x^2}{a^2} - \frac{y^2}{b^2} = 1, \quad \text{where} \quad b^2 = a^2(e^2 - 1).$$

◀

THEOREM 12.3 Continuity of Composite Functions
If $u = g(x, y)$ is continuous at (a, b) and $z = f(u)$ is continuous at $g(a, b)$, then the composite function $z = f(g(x, y))$ is continuous at (a, b).

Proof: Let P and P_0 represent the points (x, y) and (a, b), respectively. Let $u = g(P)$ and $u_0 = g(P_0)$. The continuity of f at u_0 means that $\lim_{u \to u_0} f(u) = f(u_0)$. This limit implies that given any $\varepsilon > 0$, there exists a $\delta^* > 0$ such that

$$|f(u) - f(u_0)| < \varepsilon \quad \text{whenever} \quad 0 < |u - u_0| < \delta^*.$$

The continuity of g at P_0 means that $\lim_{P \to P_0} g(P) = g(P_0)$. Letting $|P - P_0|$ denote the distance between P and P_0, this limit implies that given any $\delta^* > 0$, there exists a $\delta > 0$ such that

$$|g(P) - g(P_0)| = |u - u_0| < \delta^* \quad \text{whenever} \quad 0 < |P - P_0| < \delta.$$

We now combine these two statements. Given any $\varepsilon > 0$, there exists a $\delta > 0$ such that

$$|f(g(P)) - f(g(P_0))| = |f(u) - f(u_0)| < \varepsilon \quad \text{whenever} \quad 0 < |P - P_0| < \delta.$$

Therefore, $\lim_{(x,y) \to (a,b)} f(g(x, y)) = f(g(a, b))$ and $z = f(g(x, y))$ is continuous at (a, b).

◀

THEOREM 12.5 Conditions for Differentiability
Suppose the function f has partial derivatives f_x and f_y defined in a region containing (a, b), with f_x and f_y continuous at (a, b). Then f is differentiable at (a, b).

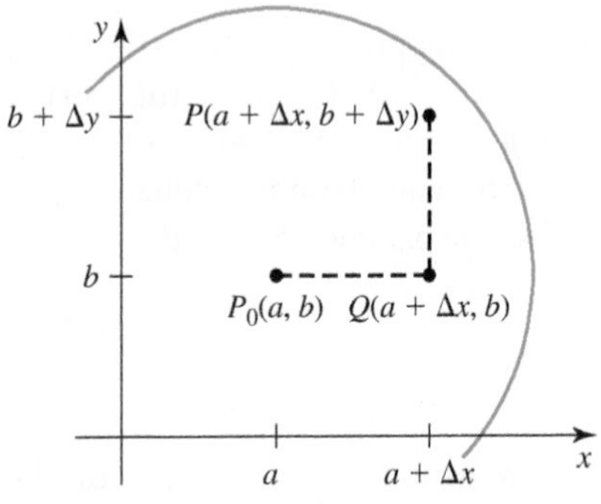

Figure B.2

Proof: Figure B.2 shows a region on which the conditions of the theorem are satisfied containing the points $P_0(a, b)$, $Q(a + \Delta x, b)$, and $P(a + \Delta x, b + \Delta y)$. By the definition of differentiability of f at P_0, we must show that

$$\Delta z = f(P) - f(P_0) = f_x(a, b)\Delta x + f_y(a, b)\Delta y + \varepsilon_1 \Delta x + \varepsilon_2 \Delta y,$$

where ε_1 and ε_2 depend only on $a, b, \Delta x$, and Δy, with $(\varepsilon_1, \varepsilon_2) \to (0, 0)$ as $(\Delta x, \Delta y) \to (0, 0)$. We can view the change Δz taking place in two stages:

- $\Delta z_1 = f(a + \Delta x, b) - f(a, b)$ is the change in z as (x, y) moves from P_0 to Q.
- $\Delta z_2 = f(a + \Delta x, b + \Delta y) - f(a + \Delta x, b)$ is the change in z as (x, y) moves from Q to P.

Applying the Mean Value Theorem to the first variable and noting that f is differentiable with respect to x, we have

$$\Delta z_1 = f(a + \Delta x, b) - f(a, b) = f_x(c, b)\Delta x,$$

where c lies in the interval $(a, a + \Delta x)$. Similarly, applying the Mean Value Theorem to the second variable and noting that f is differentiable with respect to y, we have

$$\Delta z_2 = f(a + \Delta x, b + \Delta y) - f(a + \Delta x, b) = f_y(a + \Delta x, d)\Delta y,$$

where d lies in the interval $(b, b + \Delta y)$. We now express Δz as the sum of Δz_1 and Δz_2:

$$\begin{aligned}
\Delta z &= \Delta z_1 + \Delta z_2 \\
&= f_x(c, b)\Delta x + f_y(a + \Delta x, d)\Delta y \\
&= (\underbrace{f_x(c, b) - f_x(a, b)}_{\varepsilon_1} + f_x(a, b))\Delta x && \text{Add and subtract } f_x(a, b). \\
&\quad + (\underbrace{f_y(a + \Delta x, d) - f_y(a, b)}_{\varepsilon_2} + f_y(a, b))\Delta y && \text{Add and subtract } f_y(a, b). \\
&= (f_x(a, b) + \varepsilon_1)\Delta x + (f_y(a, b) + \varepsilon_2)\Delta y.
\end{aligned}$$

Note that as $\Delta x \to 0$ and $\Delta y \to 0$, we have $c \to a$ and $d \to b$. Because f_x and f_y are continuous at (a, b), it follows that as $\Delta x \to 0$ and $\Delta y \to 0$,

$$\varepsilon_1 = f_x(c, b) - f_x(a, b) \to 0 \quad \text{and} \quad \varepsilon_2 = f_y(a + \Delta x, d) - f_y(a, b) \to 0.$$

Therefore, the condition for differentiability of f at (a, b) has been proved. ◀

THEOREM 12.7 Chain Rule (One Independent Variable)
Let $z = f(x, y)$ be a differentiable function of x and y on its domain, where x and y are differentiable functions of t on an interval I. Then

$$\frac{dz}{dt} = \frac{\partial f}{\partial x}\frac{dx}{dt} + \frac{\partial f}{\partial y}\frac{dy}{dt}.$$

Proof: Assume $(a, b) = (x(t), y(t))$ is in the domain of f, where t is in I. Let $\Delta x = x(t + \Delta t) - x(t)$ and $\Delta y = y(t + \Delta t) - y(t)$. Because f is differentiable at (a, b), we know (Section 13.4) that

$$\Delta z = \frac{\partial f}{\partial x}(a, b)\Delta x + \frac{\partial f}{\partial y}(a, b)\Delta y + \varepsilon_1\Delta x + \varepsilon_2\Delta y,$$

where $(\varepsilon_1, \varepsilon_2) \to (0, 0)$ as $(\Delta x, \Delta y) \to (0, 0)$. Dividing this equation by Δt gives

$$\frac{\Delta z}{\Delta t} = \frac{\partial f}{\partial x}\frac{\Delta x}{\Delta t} + \frac{\partial f}{\partial y}\frac{\Delta y}{\Delta t} + \varepsilon_1\frac{\Delta x}{\Delta t} + \varepsilon_2\frac{\Delta y}{\Delta t}.$$

As $\Delta t \to 0$, several things occur. First, because $x = g(t)$ and $y = h(t)$ are differentiable on I, $\frac{\Delta x}{\Delta t}$ and $\frac{\Delta y}{\Delta t}$ approach $\frac{dx}{dt}$ and $\frac{dy}{dt}$, respectively. Similarly, $\frac{\Delta z}{\Delta t}$ approaches $\frac{dz}{dt}$ as $\Delta t \to 0$. The fact that x and y are continuous on I (because they are differentiable there) means that $\Delta x \to 0$ and $\Delta y \to 0$ as $\Delta t \to 0$. Therefore, because $(\varepsilon_1, \varepsilon_2) \to (0, 0)$ as $(\Delta x, \Delta y) \to (0, 0)$, it follows that $(\varepsilon_1, \varepsilon_2) \to (0, 0)$ as $\Delta t \to 0$. Letting $\Delta t \to 0$, we have

$$\underbrace{\lim_{\Delta t \to 0} \frac{\Delta z}{\Delta t}}_{\frac{dz}{dt}} = \frac{\partial f}{\partial x} \underbrace{\lim_{\Delta t \to 0} \frac{\Delta x}{\Delta t}}_{\frac{dx}{dt}} + \frac{\partial f}{\partial y} \underbrace{\lim_{\Delta t \to 0} \frac{\Delta y}{\Delta t}}_{\frac{dy}{dt}} + \lim_{\Delta t \to 0} \underbrace{\varepsilon_1}_{\to 0} \underbrace{\frac{\Delta x}{\Delta t}}_{\to \frac{dx}{dt}} + \lim_{\Delta t \to 0} \underbrace{\varepsilon_2}_{\to 0} \underbrace{\frac{\Delta y}{\Delta t}}_{\to \frac{dy}{dt}}$$

or

$$\frac{dz}{dt} = \frac{\partial f}{\partial x}\frac{dx}{dt} + \frac{\partial f}{\partial y}\frac{dy}{dt}.$$

THEOREM 12.14 Second Derivative Test

Suppose that the second partial derivatives of f are continuous throughout an open disk centered at the point (a, b) where $f_x(a, b) = f_y(a, b) = 0$. Let $D(x, y) = f_{xx}(x, y) f_{yy}(x, y) - (f_{xy}(x, y))^2$.

1. If $D(a, b) > 0$ and $f_{xx}(a, b) < 0$, then f has a local maximum value at (a, b).
2. If $D(a, b) > 0$ and $f_{xx}(a, b) > 0$, then f has a local minimum value at (a, b).
3. If $D(a, b) < 0$, then f has a saddle point at (a, b).
4. If $D(a, b) = 0$, then the test is inconclusive.

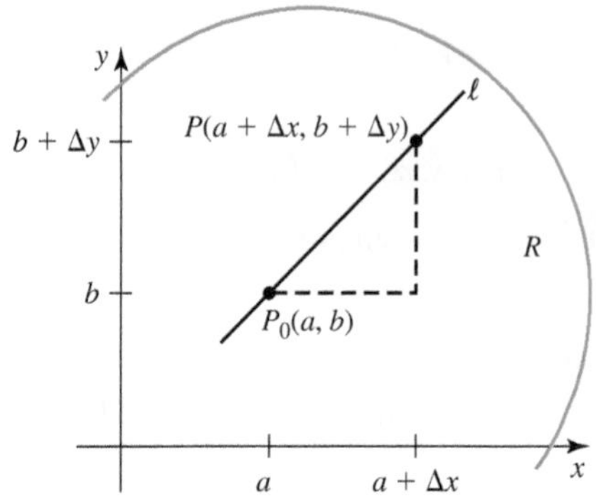

Figure B.3

Proof: The proof relies on a two-variable version of Taylor's Theorem, which we prove first. Figure B.3 shows the open disk R on which the conditions of Theorem 12.14 are satisfied; it contains the points $P_0(a, b)$ and $P(a + \Delta x, b + \Delta y)$. The line ℓ through $P_0 P$ has a parametric description

$$\langle x(t), y(t) \rangle = \langle a + t\Delta x, b + t\Delta y \rangle,$$

where $t = 0$ corresponds to P_0 and $t = 1$ corresponds to P.

We now let $F(t) = f(a + t\Delta x, b + t\Delta y)$ be the value of f along that part of ℓ that lies in R. By the Chain Rule, we have

$$F'(t) = f_x \underbrace{x'(t)}_{\Delta x} + f_y \underbrace{y'(t)}_{\Delta y} = f_x\,\Delta x + f_y\,\Delta y.$$

Differentiating again with respect to t (f_x and f_y are differentiable), we use $f_{xy} = f_{yx}$ to obtain

$$\begin{aligned} F''(t) &= \frac{\partial F'}{\partial x} \underbrace{x'(t)}_{\Delta x} + \frac{\partial F'}{\partial y} \underbrace{y'(t)}_{\Delta y} \\ &= \frac{\partial}{\partial x}(f_x\,\Delta x + f_y\,\Delta y)\Delta x + \frac{\partial}{\partial y}(f_x\,\Delta x + f_y\,\Delta y)\Delta y \\ &= f_{xx}\,\Delta x^2 + 2 f_{xy}\,\Delta x \Delta y + f_{yy}\,\Delta y^2. \end{aligned}$$

Noting that F meets the conditions of Taylor's Theorem for one variable with $n = 1$, we write

$$F(t) = F(0) + F'(0)(t - 0) + \frac{1}{2}F''(c)(t - 0)^2,$$

where c is between 0 and t. Setting $t = 1$, it follows that

$$F(1) = F(0) + F'(0) + \frac{1}{2}F''(c), \qquad (1)$$

where $0 < c < 1$. Recalling that $F(t) = f(a + t\Delta x, b + t\Delta y)$ and invoking the condition $f_x(a, b) = f_y(a, b) = 0$, we have

$$\begin{aligned} F(1) &= f(a + \Delta x, b + \Delta y) \\ &= f(a, b) + \underbrace{f_x(a, b)\Delta x + f_y(a, b)\Delta y}_{F'(0)=0} \\ &\quad + \frac{1}{2}(f_{xx}\Delta x^2 + 2f_{xy}\Delta x\Delta y + f_{yy}\Delta y^2)\Big|_{(a+c\Delta x,\, b+c\Delta y)} \\ &= f(a, b) + \frac{1}{2}\underbrace{(f_{xx}\Delta x^2 + 2f_{xy}\Delta x\Delta y + f_{yy}\Delta y^2)\Big|_{(a+c\Delta x,\, b+c\Delta y)}}_{H(c)} \\ &= f(a, b) + \frac{1}{2}H(c). \end{aligned}$$

The existence and type of extreme point at (a, b) is determined by the sign of $f(a + \Delta x, b + \Delta y) - f(a, b)$ (for example, if $f(a + \Delta x, b + \Delta y) - f(a, b) \geq 0$ for all Δx and Δy near 0, then f has a local minimum at (a, b)). Note that $f(a + \Delta x, b + \Delta y) - f(a, b)$ has the same sign as the quantity we have denoted $H(c)$. Assuming $H(0) \neq 0$, for Δx and Δy sufficiently small and nonzero, the sign of $H(c)$ is the same as the sign of

$$H(0) = f_{xx}(a, b)\Delta x^2 + 2f_{xy}(a, b)\Delta x\Delta y + f_{yy}(a, b)\Delta y^2$$

(because the second partial derivatives are continuous at (a, b) and $(a + c\Delta x, b + c\Delta y)$ can be made arbitrarily close to (a, b)). Multiplying both sides of the previous expression by f_{xx} and rearranging terms leads to

$$\begin{aligned} f_{xx}H(0) &= f_{xx}^2\Delta x^2 + 2f_{xy}f_{xx}\Delta x\Delta y + f_{yy}f_{xx}\Delta y^2 \\ &= \underbrace{(f_{xx}\Delta x + f_{xy}\Delta y)^2}_{\geq 0} + \underbrace{(f_{xx}f_{yy} - f_{xy}^2)}_{D}\Delta y^2, \end{aligned}$$

where all derivatives are evaluated at (a, b). Recall that the signs of $H(0)$ and $f(a + \Delta x, b + \Delta y) - f(a, b)$ are the same. Letting $D(a, b) = (f_{xx}f_{yy} - f_{xy}^2)\big|_{(a, b)}$, we reach the following conclusions:

- If $D(a, b) > 0$ and $f_{xx}(a, b) < 0$, then $H(0) < 0$ (for Δx and Δy sufficiently close to 0) and $f(a + \Delta x, b + \Delta y) - f(a, b) < 0$. Therefore, f has a local maximum value at (a, b).
- If $D(a, b) > 0$ and $f_{xx}(a, b) > 0$, then $H(0) > 0$ (for Δx and Δy sufficiently close to 0) and $f(a + \Delta x, b + \Delta y) - f(a, b) > 0$. Therefore, f has a local minimum value at (a, b).
- If $D(a, b) < 0$, then $H(0) > 0$ for some small nonzero values of Δx and Δy (implying $f(a + \Delta x, b + \Delta y) > f(a, b)$), *and* $H(0) < 0$ for other small nonzero values of Δx and Δy (implying $f(a + \Delta x, b + \Delta y) < f(a, b)$). (The relative sizes of $(f_{xx}\Delta x + f_{xy}\Delta y)^2$ and $(f_{xx}f_{yy} - f_{xy}^2)\Delta y^2$ can be adjusted by varying Δx and Δy.) Therefore, f has a saddle point at (a, b).
- If $D(a, b) = 0$, then $H(0)$ may be zero, in which case the sign of $H(c)$ cannot be determined. Therefore, the test is inconclusive. ◀

Answers

CHAPTER 1

Section 1.1 Exercises, pp. 9–12

1. A function is a rule that assigns to each value of the independent variable in the domain a unique value of the dependent variable in the range. **3.** A graph is that of a function provided no vertical line intersects the graph at more than one point. **5.** The first statement **7.** 2; −2
9. $f(-x) = f(x)$

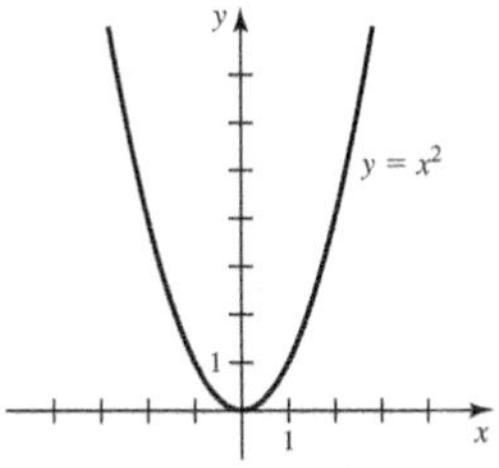

11. B **13.** $D = \mathbb{R}, R = [-10, \infty)$ **15.** $D = [-2, 2], R = [0, 2]$ **17.** $D = \mathbb{R}, R = \mathbb{R}$ **19.** $D = [-3, 3]; R = [0, 27]$ **21.** The independent variable is t; the dependent variable is d; $D = [0, 8]$. **23.** The independent variable is h; the dependent variable is V; $D = [0, 50]$.
25. 96 **27.** $1/z^3$ **29.** $1/(y^3 - 3)$ **31.** $(u^2 - 4)^3$ **33.** $\dfrac{x - 3}{10 - 3x}$
35. x **37.** $g(x) = x^3 - 5, f(x) = x^{10}; D = \mathbb{R}$
39. $g(x) = x^4 + 2, f(x) = \sqrt{x}; D = \mathbb{R}$
41. $(f \circ g)(x) = |x^2 - 4|; D = \mathbb{R}$
43. $(f \circ G)(x) = \dfrac{1}{|x - 2|}; D = \{x: x \neq 2\}$
45. $(G \circ g \circ f)(x) = \dfrac{1}{x^2 - 6}; D = \{x: x \neq \sqrt{6}, -\sqrt{6}\}$
47. $x^4 - 8x^2 + 12$ **49.** $f(x) = x - 3$ **51.** $f(x) = x^2$
53. $f(x) = x^2$ **55. a.** 4 **b.** 1 **c.** 3 **d.** 3 **e.** 8 **f.** 1 **57.** $2x + h$
59. $-\dfrac{2}{x(x + h)}$ **61.** $\dfrac{1}{(x + h + 1)(x + 1)}$ **63.** $x^2 + ax + a^2 - 2$
65. $\dfrac{4(x + a)}{a^2 x^2}$ **67. a.**

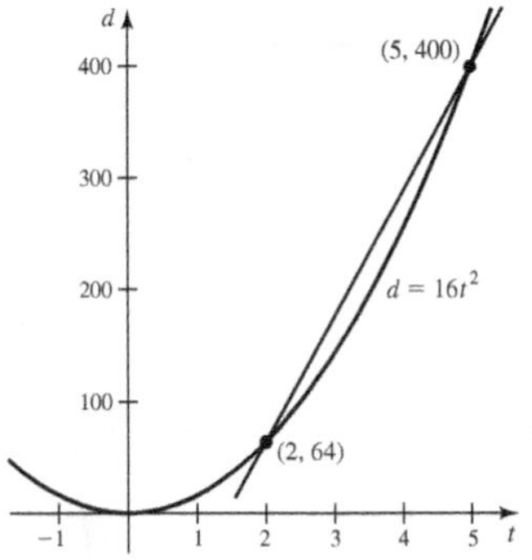

b. $m_{\text{sec}} = 112$ ft/s; the object falls at an average rate of 112 ft/s.
69. a.

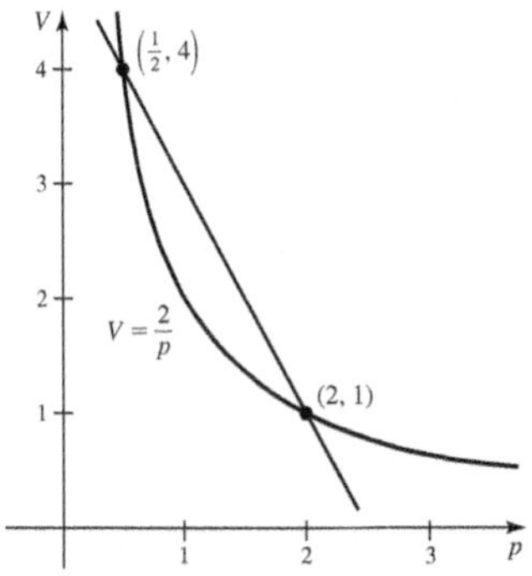

b. $m_{\text{sec}} = -2$ cm^3/atmosphere; the volume decreases at an average rate of 2 cm^3/atmosphere over the interval $0.5 \leq p \leq 2$.

71. y-axis **73.** No symmetry **75.** x-axis, y-axis, origin **77.** Origin **79.** A is even, B is odd, and C is even. **81. a.** True **b.** False **c.** True **d.** False **e.** False **f.** True **g.** True **h.** False **i.** True
83.

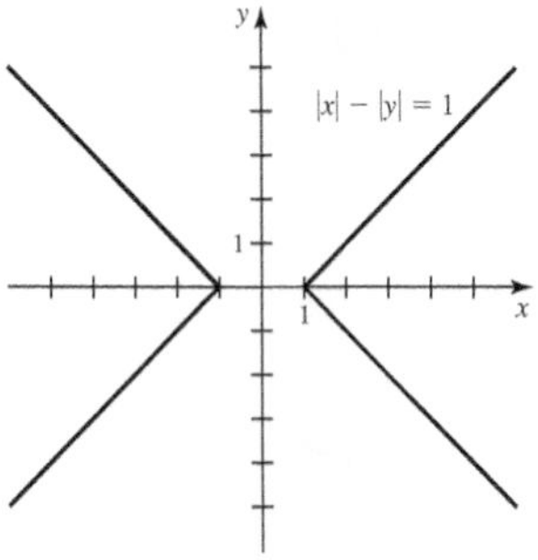

85. $f(x) = 3x - 2$ or $f(x) = -3x + 4$ **87.** $f(x) = x^2 - 6$
89. $\dfrac{1}{\sqrt{x + h} + \sqrt{x}}; \dfrac{1}{\sqrt{x} + \sqrt{a}}$
91. $\dfrac{3}{\sqrt{x}(x + h) + x\sqrt{x + h}}; \dfrac{3}{x\sqrt{a} + a\sqrt{x}}$
93. a. $[0, 3 + \sqrt{14}]$
b.

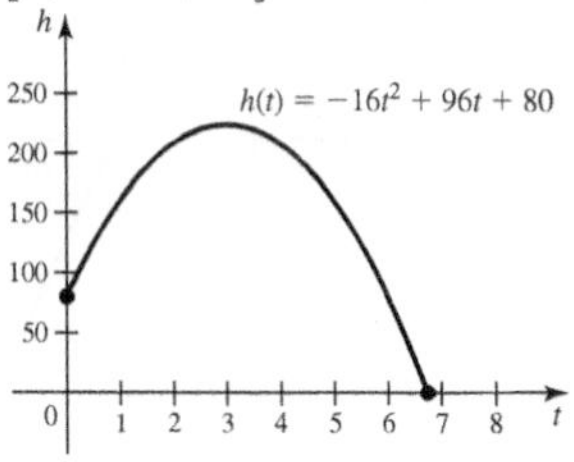

At time $t = 3$, the maximum height is 224 ft.

95. None **97.** Symmetry about the origin **99.** y-axis **101.** y-axis **103. a.** 4 **b.** 1 **c.** 3 **d.** −2 **e.** −1 **f.** 7

Section 1.2 Exercises, pp. 21–26

1. A formula, a graph, a table, words **3.** $\mathbb{R}$ except points at which the denominator is zero
5.

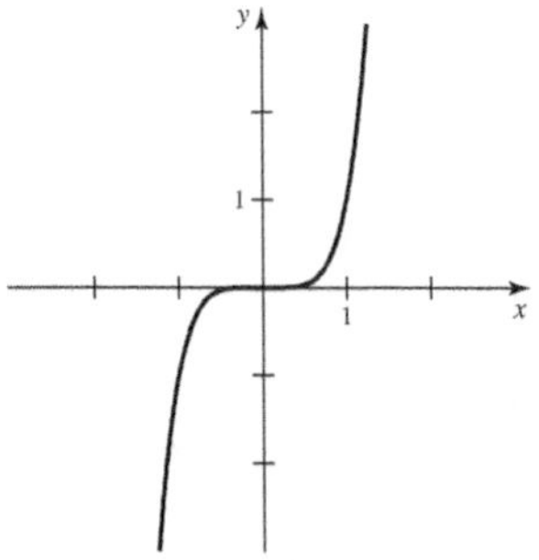

7. Shift the graph to the left 2 units. **9.** Compress the graph horizontally by a factor of 3. **11.** $y = -\frac{2}{3}x - 1$
13. $y = 2x + 1$

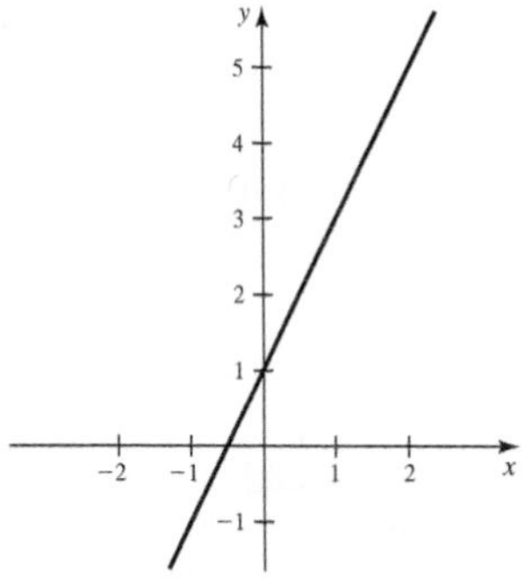

15. $d = -3p/50 + 27$; $D = [0, 450]$

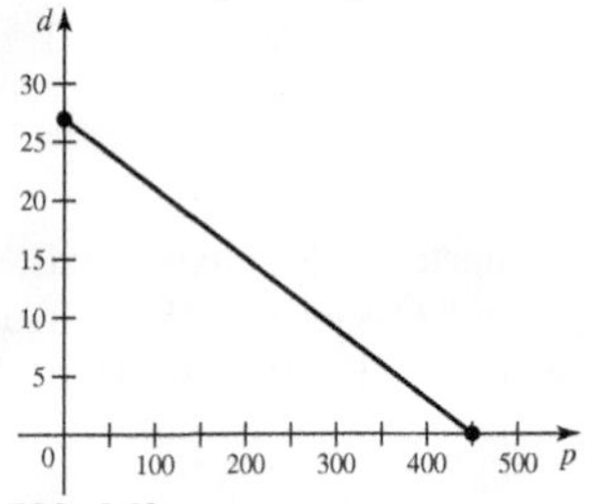

17. $p(t) = 24t + 500$; 860

19. $y = \begin{cases} x + 3 & \text{if } x < 0 \\ -\frac{1}{2}x + 3 & \text{if } x \geq 0 \end{cases}$

21. $c(t) = \begin{cases} 0.05t & \text{if } 0 \leq t \leq 60 \\ 1.2 + 0.03t & \text{if } 60 < t \leq 120 \end{cases}$

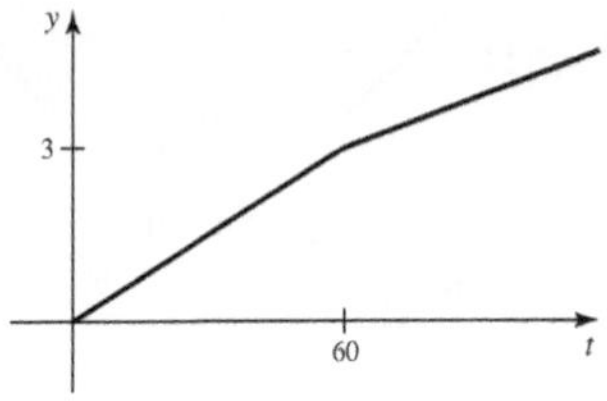

23.

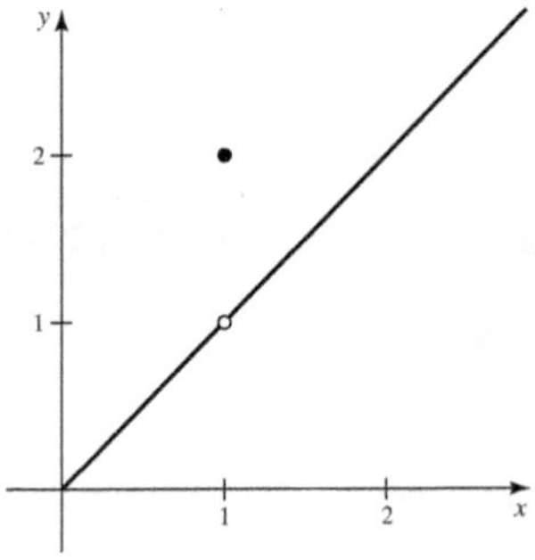

25.

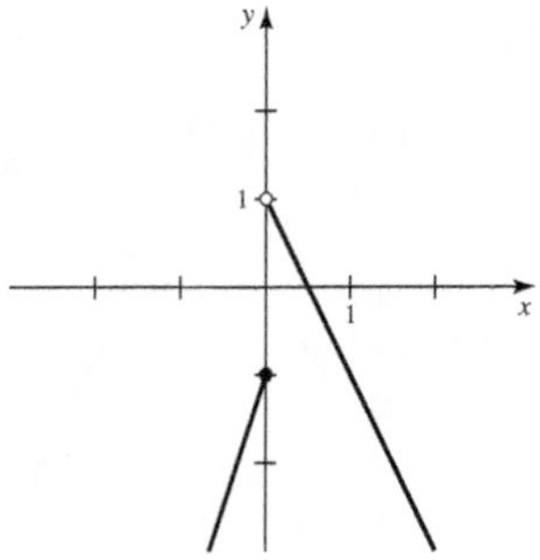

27.

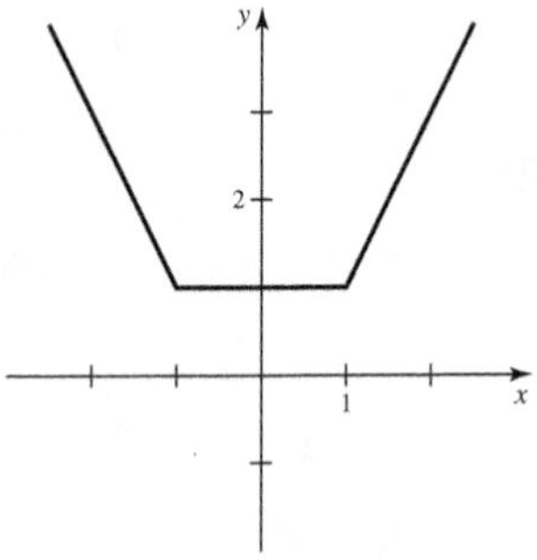

29. a.

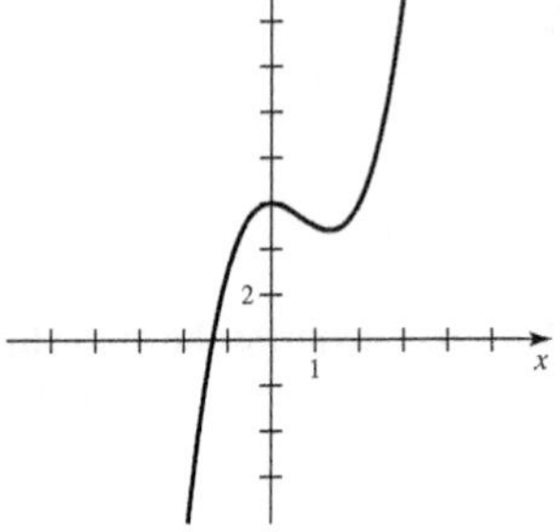

b. $D = \mathbb{R}$

c. One peak near $x = 0$; one valley near $x = 4/3$; x-intercept approx. $(-1.3, 0)$, y-intercept $(0, 6)$

31. a.

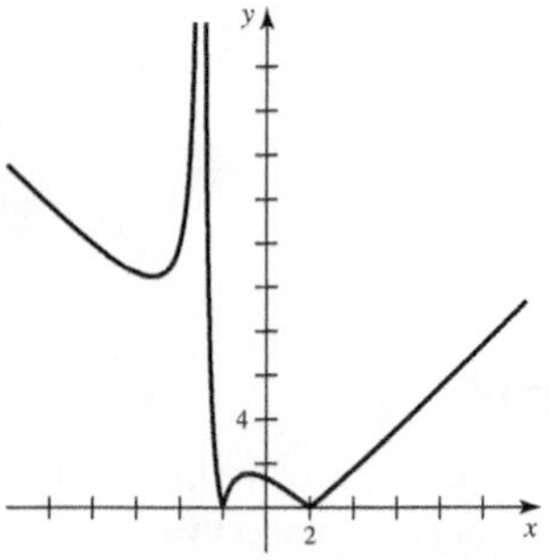

b. $D = \{x: x \neq -3\}$ **c.** Undefined at $x = -3$; a valley near $x = -5.2$; x-intercepts (and valleys) at $(-2, 0)$ and $(2, 0)$; a peak near $x = -0.8$; y-intercept $(0, \frac{4}{3})$

33. a.

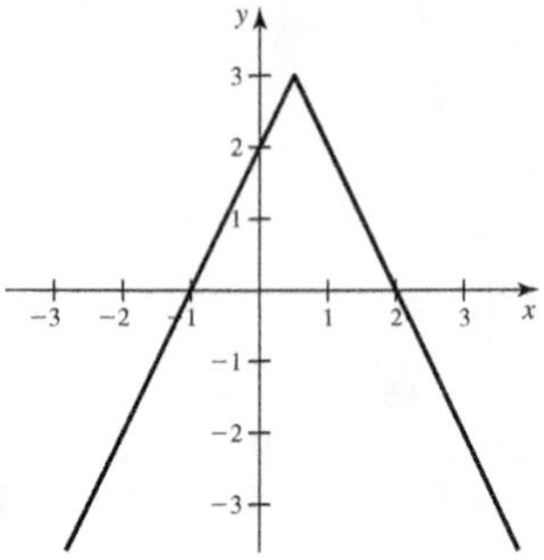

b. $D = (-\infty, \infty)$ **c.** One peak at $x = \frac{1}{2}$; x-intercepts $(-1, 0)$ and $(2, 0)$; y-intercept $(0, 2)$ **35.** $s(x) = 2$

37. $s(x) = \begin{cases} 1 & \text{if } x < 0 \\ -\frac{1}{2} & \text{if } x > 0 \end{cases}$

39. a. 12 **b.** 36 **c.** $A(x) = 6x$ **41. a.** 12 **b.** 21

c. $A(x) = \begin{cases} 8x - x^2 & \text{if } 0 \leq x \leq 3 \\ 2x + 9 & \text{if } x > 3 \end{cases}$

43. $f(x) = |x - 2| + 3$; $g(x) = -|x + 2| - 1$

45. a. Shift 3 units to the right.

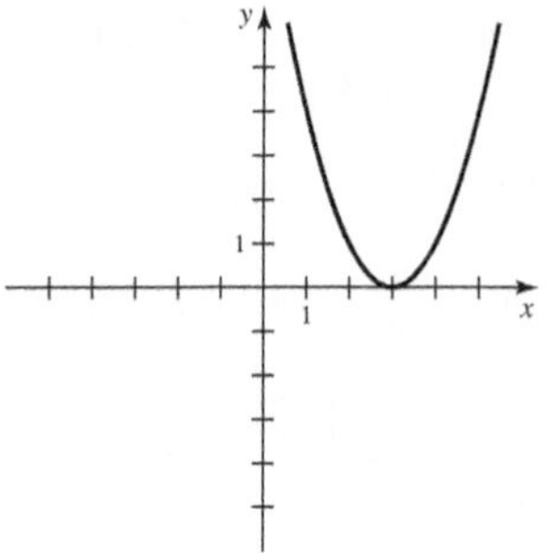

b. Horizontal scaling by a factor of 2, then shift 2 units to the right.

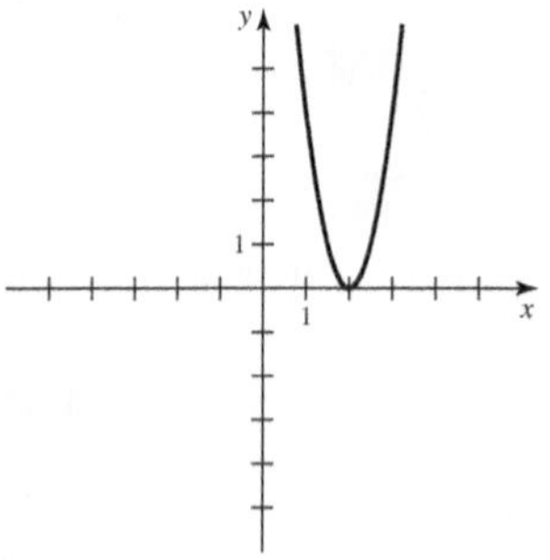

c. Shift to the right 2 units, vertical scaling by a factor of 3 and flip, shift up 4 units.

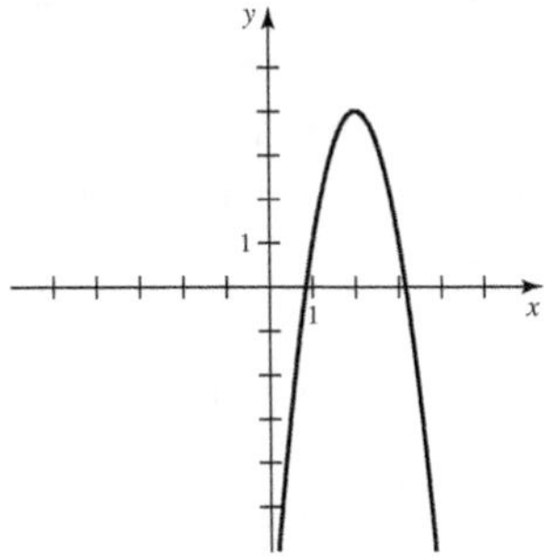

d. Horizontal scaling by a factor of $\frac{1}{3}$, horizontal shift right 2 units, vertical scaling by a factor of 6, vertical shift up 1 unit

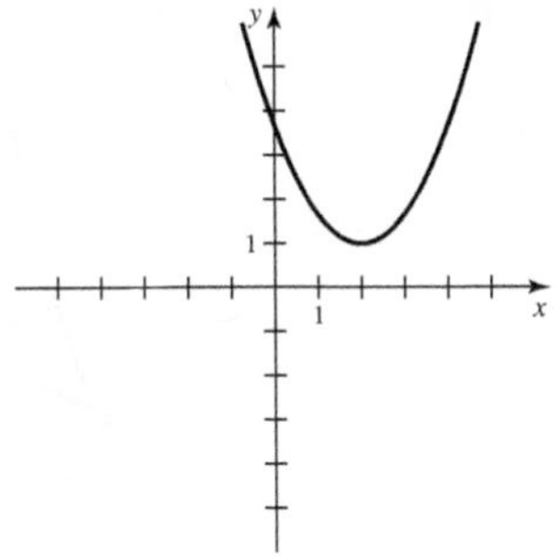

47. Shift the graph of $y = x^2$ right 2 units and up 1 unit.

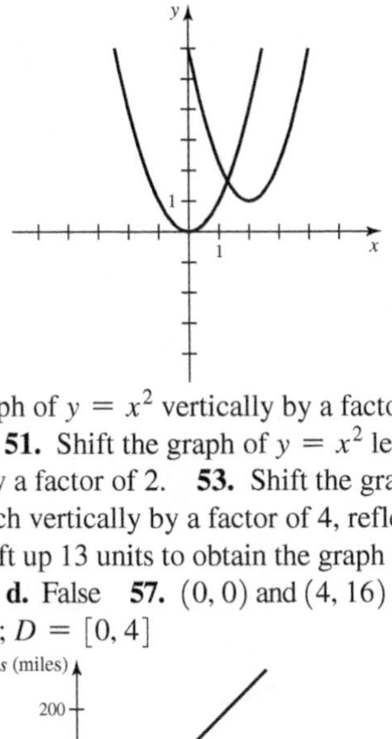

49. Stretch the graph of $y = x^2$ vertically by a factor of 3 and reflect across the x-axis. **51.** Shift the graph of $y = x^2$ left 3 units and stretch vertically by a factor of 2. **53.** Shift the graph of $y = x^2$ to the left $\frac{1}{2}$ unit, stretch vertically by a factor of 4, reflect across the x-axis, and then shift up 13 units to obtain the graph of h. **55. a.** True **b.** False **c.** True **d.** False **57.** $(0, 0)$ and $(4, 16)$ **59.** $y = \sqrt{x} - 1$ **61.** $s(t) = 30\sqrt{5}t$; $D = [0, 4]$

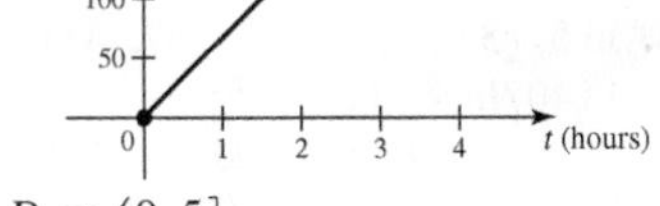

63. $y = 3200/x$; $D = (0, 5]$

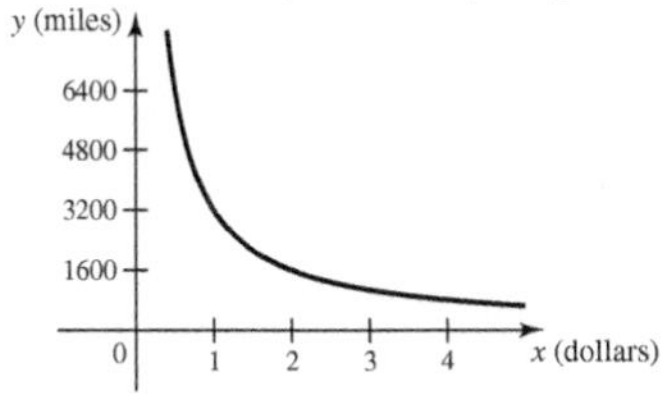

65.

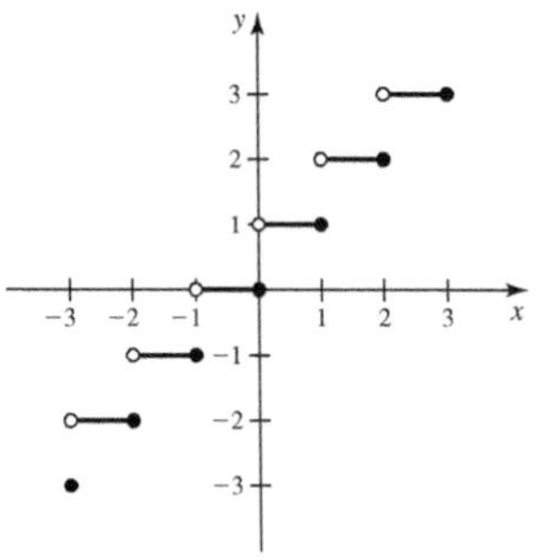

67.

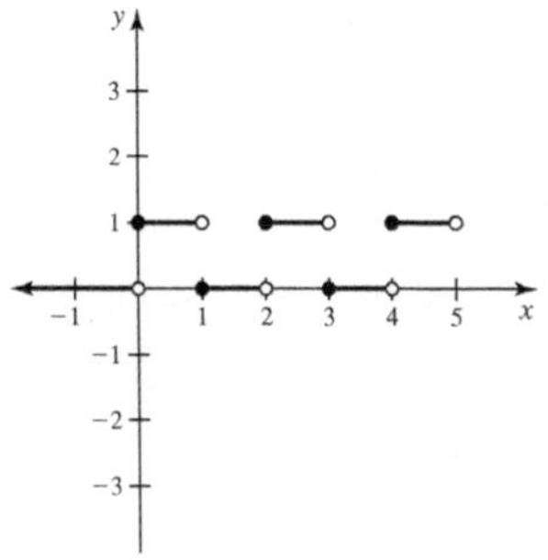

69.

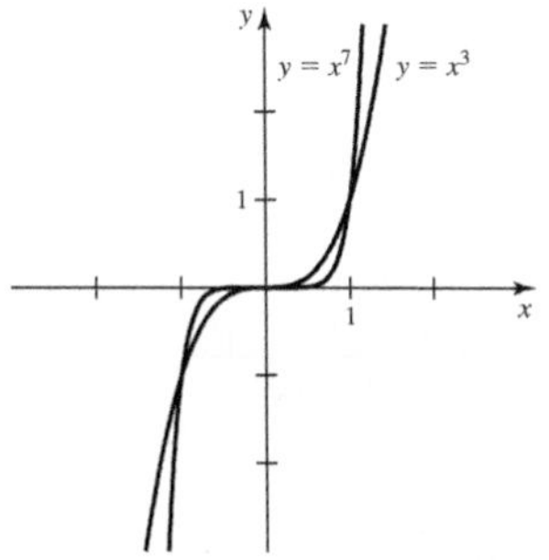

71. a. A, D, F, I **b.** E **c.** B, H **d.** I **e.** A

73. a.

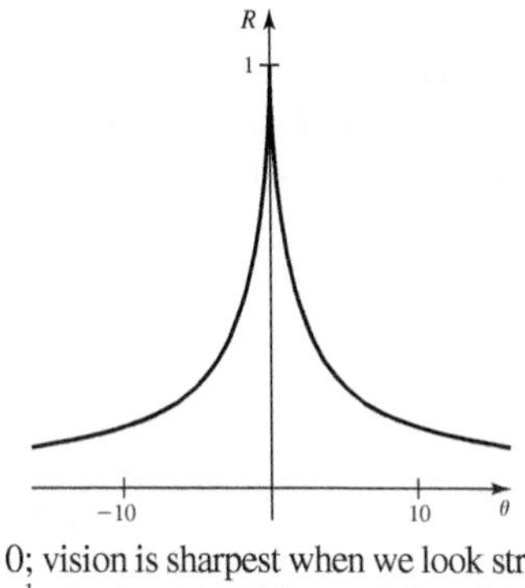

b. $\theta = 0$; vision is sharpest when we look straight ahead. **c.** $|\theta| \le 0.19°$ (less than $\frac{1}{5}$ of a degree) **75. a.** $p(t) = 328.3t + 1875$ **b.** 4830 **77. a.** $f(m) = 350m + 1200$ **b.** Buy **79.** $0 \le h \le 2$

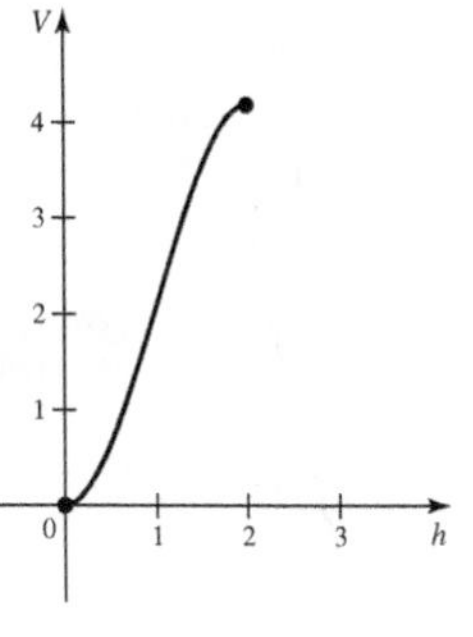

81. a. $S(x) = x^2 + \dfrac{500}{x}$ **b.** Approximately 6.3 ft

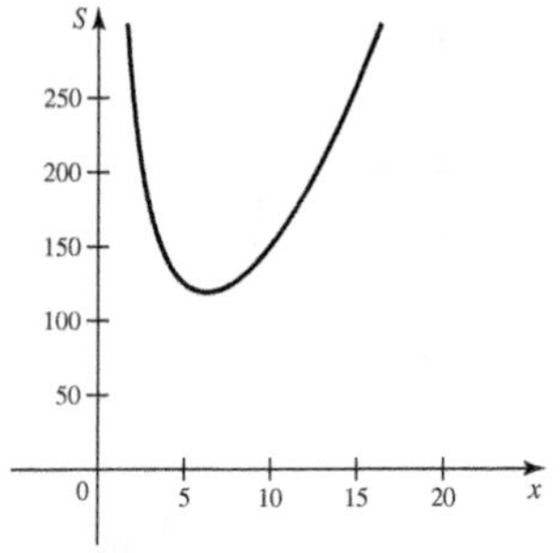

85. a.

n	1	2	3	4	5
$f(n)$	1	2	6	24	120

b.

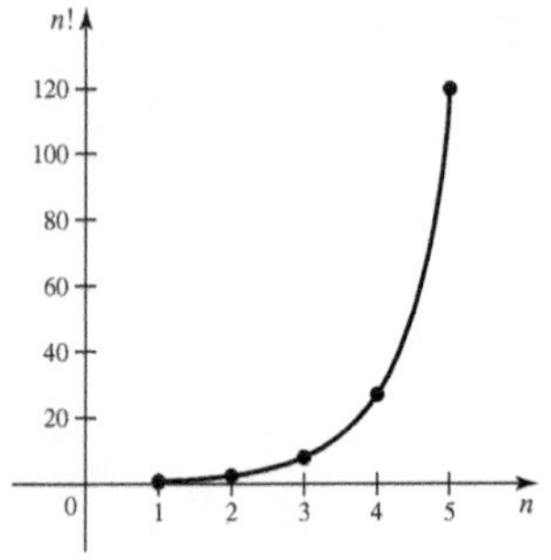

c. 10

87. a.

n	1	2	3	4	5	6	7	8	9	10
$T(n)$	1	5	14	30	55	91	140	204	285	385

b. $D = \{n: n \text{ is a positive integer}\}$ **c.** 14

Section 1.3 Exercises, pp. 35–38

1. $D = \mathbb{R}$; $R = (0, \infty)$ **3.** If a function f is not one-to-one, then there are domain values, x_1 and x_2, such that $x_1 \neq x_2$ but $f(x_1) = f(x_2)$. If f^{-1} exists, by definition, $f^{-1}(f(x_1)) = x_1$ and $f^{-1}(f(x_2)) = x_2$ so that f^{-1} assigns two different range values to the single domain value of $f(x_1)$.

5.

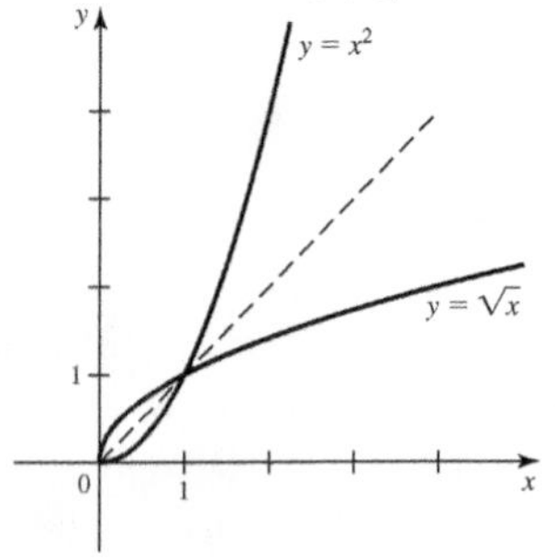

7. The expression $\log_b x$ represents the power to which b must be raised to obtain x. **9.** $D = (0, \infty)$; $R = \mathbb{R}$

11. $(-\infty, -1], [-1, 1], [1, \infty)$

13.

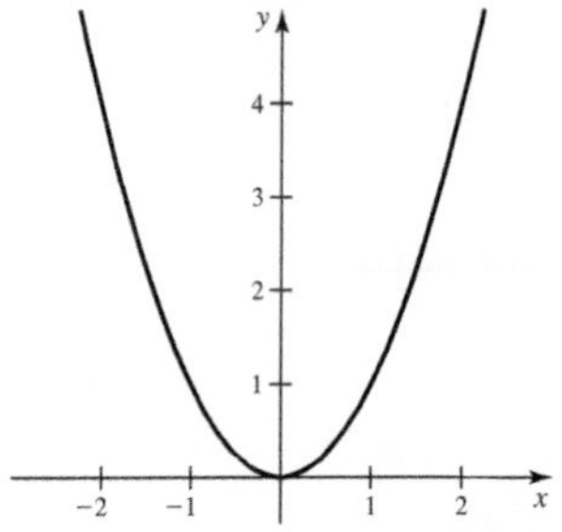

15. $(-\infty, \infty)$ **17.** $(-\infty, 5), (5, \infty)$ **19.** $(-\infty, 0), (0, \infty)$

21. a. $f^{-1}(x) = \frac{1}{2}x$ **23. a.** $f^{-1}(x) = -\frac{1}{4}x + \frac{3}{2}$

25. a. $f^{-1}(x) = \frac{1}{3}x - \frac{5}{3}$ **27. a.** $f^{-1}(x) = x^2 - 2, x \geq 0$

29. a. $f_1(x) = \sqrt{1 - x^2};\quad 0 \leq x \leq 1$

$f_2(x) = \sqrt{1 - x^2};\quad -1 \leq x \leq 0$

$f_3(x) = -\sqrt{1 - x^2};\quad -1 \leq x \leq 0$

$f_4(x) = -\sqrt{1 - x^2};\quad 0 \leq x \leq 1$

b. $f_1^{-1}(x) = \sqrt{1 - x^2};\quad 0 \leq x \leq 1$

$f_2^{-1}(x) = -\sqrt{1 - x^2};\quad 0 \leq x \leq 1$

$f_3^{-1}(x) = -\sqrt{1 - x^2};\quad -1 \leq x \leq 0$

$f_4^{-1}(x) = \sqrt{1 - x^2};\quad -1 \leq x \leq 0$

31. $f^{-1}(x) = -\dfrac{1}{4}x + 2$

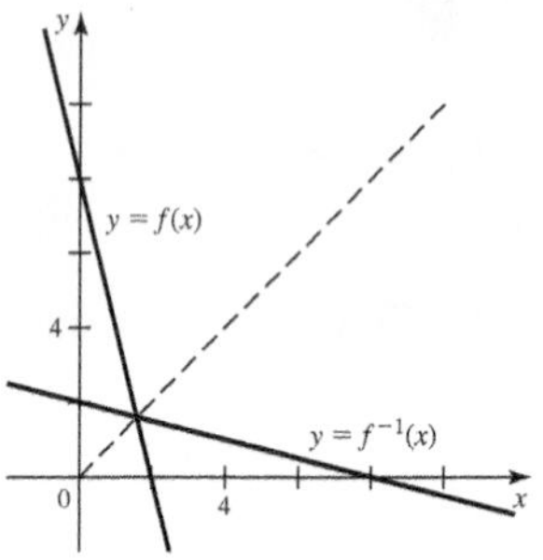

33. $f^{-1}(x) = x^2, x \geq 0$

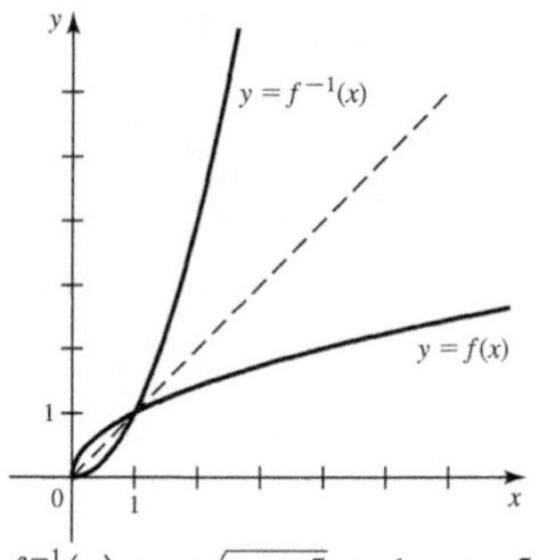

35. $f^{-1}(x) = \sqrt[4]{x - 4}, x \geq 4$

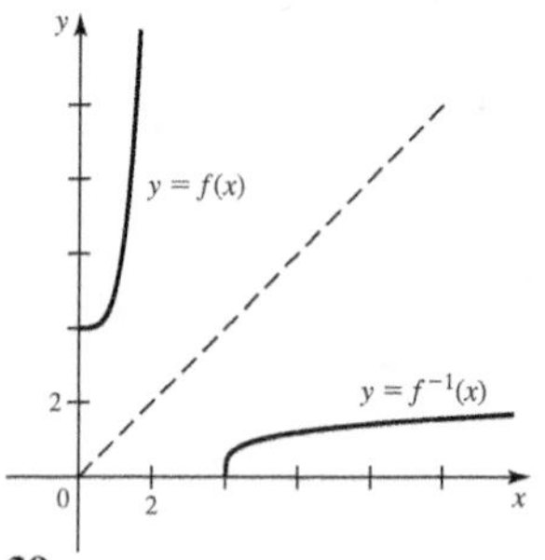

37. $f^{-1}(x) = \sqrt{x - 5} + 1, x \geq 5$

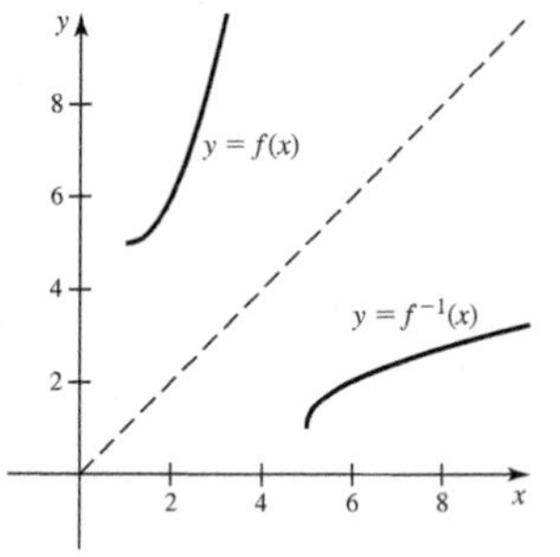

39.

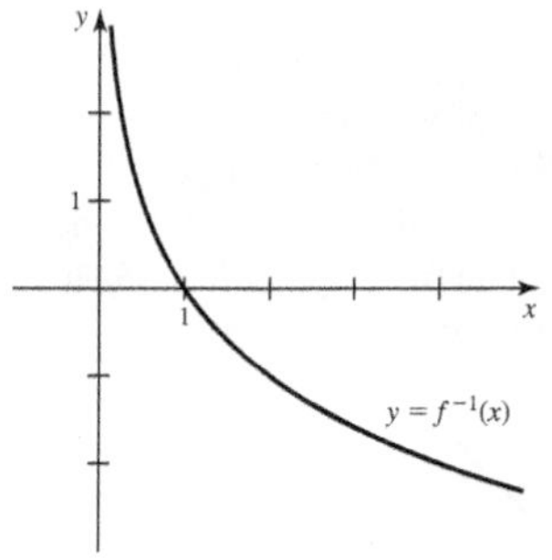

41. 1000 **43.** 2 **45.** $1/e$ **47.** -0.2 **49.** 1.19 **51.** $-0.09\overline{6}$

53. $\ln 21/\ln 7$ **55.** $\ln 5/(3 \ln 3) + 5/3$ **57.** 451 years

59. $\ln 15/\ln 2$ **61.** $\ln 40/\ln 4$ **63.** $e^{x \ln 2}$

65. $\log_5 |x| / \log_5 e$ **67.** e **69. a.** False **b.** False **c.** False **d.** True **e.** False **f.** False **g.** True **71.** A is $y = \log_2 x$; B is $y = \log_4 x$; C is $y = \log_{10} x$.

73.

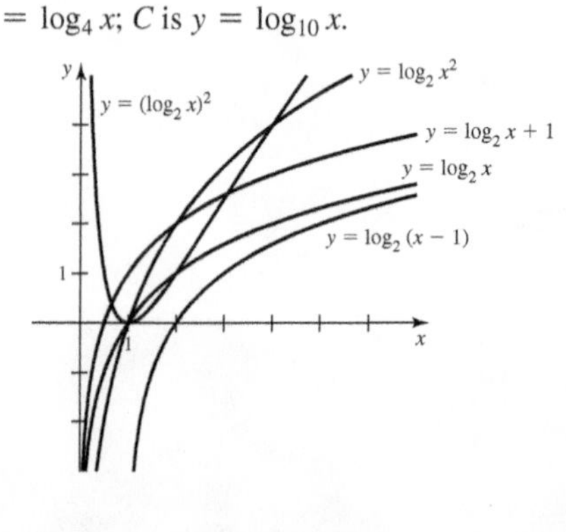

75. $f^{-1}(x) = \sqrt[3]{x} - 1, D = \mathbb{R}$
77. $f_1^{-1}(x) = \sqrt{2/x - 2}, D_1 = (0, 1]; f_2^{-1}(x) = -\sqrt{2/x - 2}$, $D_2 = (0, 1]$ **79. b.** $\dfrac{p(t + 12)}{p(t)} = 2$ **c.** 38,400 **d.** 19.0 hr **e.** 72.7 hr **81. a.** No **b.** $f^{-1}(h) = 2 - \dfrac{1}{4}\sqrt{64 - h}$ **c.** $f^{-1}(h) = 2 + \dfrac{1}{4}\sqrt{64 - h}$ **d.** 0.542 s **e.** 3.837 s
83. Let $y = \log_b x$. Then $b^y = x$ and $(1/b)^y = 1/x$. Therefore, $y = -\log_{1/b} x$. Thus, $\log_{1/b} x = -y = -\log_b x$.
87. a.

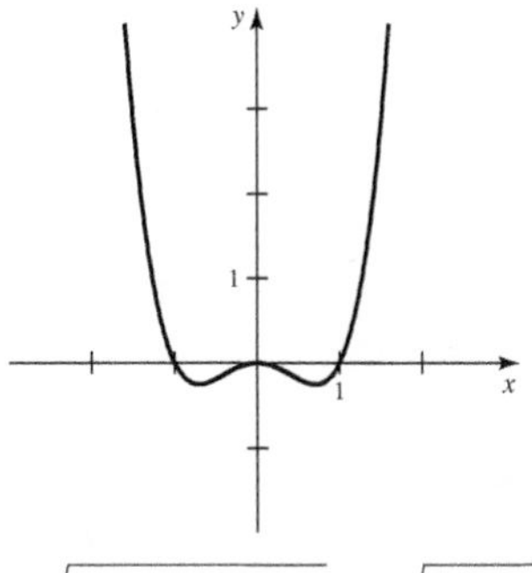

f is one-to-one on the intervals $(-\infty, -1/\sqrt{2}], [-1/\sqrt{2}, 0], [0, 1/\sqrt{2}], [1/\sqrt{2}, \infty)$

b. $x = \sqrt{\dfrac{1 \pm \sqrt{4y + 1}}{2}}, -\sqrt{\dfrac{1 \pm \sqrt{4y + 1}}{2}}$

Section 1.4 Exercises, pp. 47–51

1. $\sin\theta = \text{opp}/\text{hyp}; \cos\theta = \text{adj}/\text{hyp}; \tan\theta = \text{opp}/\text{adj}$; $\cot\theta = \text{adj}/\text{opp}; \sec\theta = \text{hyp}/\text{adj}; \csc\theta = \text{hyp}/\text{opp}$
3. The radian measure of an angle θ is the length s of an arc on the unit circle associated with θ. **5.** $\sin^2\theta + \cos^2\theta = 1$, $1 + \cot^2\theta = \csc^2\theta, \tan^2\theta + 1 = \sec^2\theta$
7. $\{x: x$ is an odd multiple of $\pi/2\}$ **9.** Sine is not one-to-one on its domain. **11.** Yes; no **13.** Vertical asymptotes at $x = \pi/2$ and $x = -\pi/2$ **15.** $-\frac{1}{2}$ **17.** 1 **19.** $-1/\sqrt{3}$
21. $1/\sqrt{3}$ **23.** 1 **25.** -1 **27.** Undefined
29. $\sec\theta = \dfrac{r}{x} = \dfrac{1}{x/r} = \dfrac{1}{\cos\theta}$ **31.** Dividing both sides of $\cos^2\theta + \sin^2\theta = 1$ by $\cos^2\theta$ gives $1 + \tan^2\theta = \sec^2\theta$.
33. Because $\cos(\pi/2 - \theta) = \sin\theta$, for all θ, $1/\cos(\pi/2 - \theta) = 1/\sin\theta$, excluding integer multiples of π, and $\sec(\pi/2 - \theta) = \csc\theta$. **35.** $\dfrac{\sqrt{2 + \sqrt{3}}}{2}$ or $\dfrac{\sqrt{6} + \sqrt{2}}{4}$
37. $\pi/4 + n\pi, n = 0, \pm 1, \pm 2, \ldots$
39. $\pi/6, 5\pi/6, 7\pi/6, 11\pi/6$
41. $\pi/4 + 2n\pi, 3\pi/4 + 2n\pi, n = 0, \pm 1, \pm 2, \ldots$
43. $\pi/12, 5\pi/12, 3\pi/4, 13\pi/12, 17\pi/12, 7\pi/4$
45. $0, \pi/2, \pi, 3\pi/2$ **47.** $\pi/2$ **49.** $\pi/4$ **51.** $\pi/3$ **53.** $2\pi/3$
55. -1 **57.** $\sqrt{1 - x^2}$ **59.** $\dfrac{\sqrt{4 - x^2}}{2}$ **61.** $2x\sqrt{1 - x^2}$
63. $\cos^{-1} x + \cos^{-1}(-x) = \theta + (\pi - \theta) = \pi$

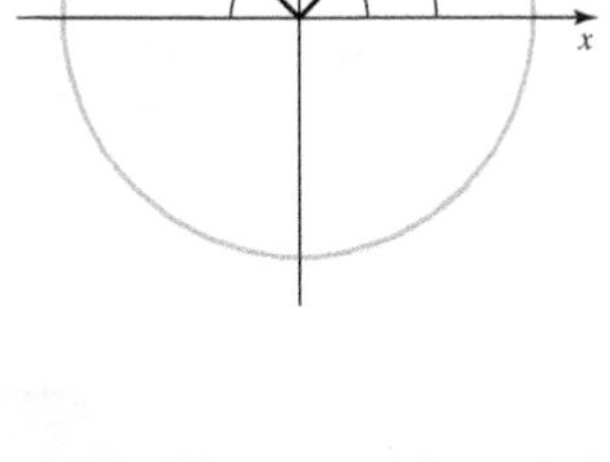

65. The functions are equal. **67.** $\pi/3$ **69.** $\pi/3$ **71.** $\pi/4$
73. $\pi/2 - 2$ **75.** $\dfrac{1}{\sqrt{x^2 + 1}}$ **77.** $1/x$ **79.** $x/\sqrt{x^2 + 16}$
81. $\sin^{-1}\dfrac{x}{6} = \tan^{-1}\left(\dfrac{x}{\sqrt{36 - x^2}}\right) = \sec^{-1}\left(\dfrac{6}{\sqrt{36 - x^2}}\right)$
83. a. False **b.** False **c.** False **d.** False **e.** True **f.** False **g.** True **h.** False **85.** $\sin\theta = \frac{12}{13}; \tan\theta = \frac{12}{5}; \sec\theta = \frac{13}{5}$; $\csc\theta = \frac{13}{12}; \cot\theta = \frac{5}{12}$ **87.** $\sin\theta = \frac{12}{13}; \cos\theta = \frac{5}{13}; \tan\theta = \frac{12}{5}$; $\sec\theta = \frac{13}{5}; \cot\theta = \frac{5}{12}$ **89.** Amp $= 3$; period $= 6\pi$
91. Amp $= 3.6$; period $= 48$ **93.** Stretch the graph of $y = \cos x$ horizontally by a factor of 3, stretch vertically by a factor of 2, and reflect across the x-axis.

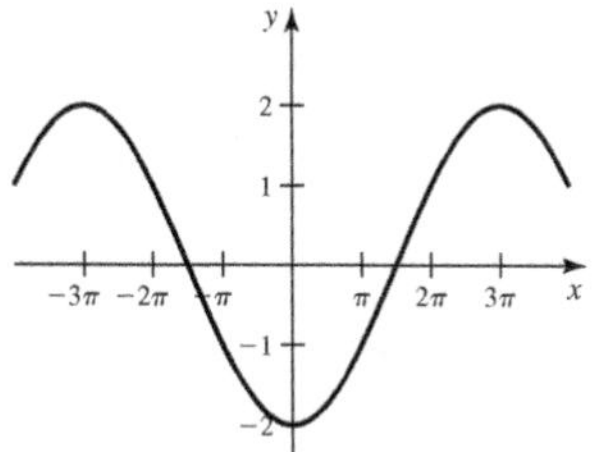

95. Stretch the graph of $y = \cos x$ horizontally by a factor of $24/\pi$; then stretch it vertically by a factor of 3.6 and shift it up 2 units.

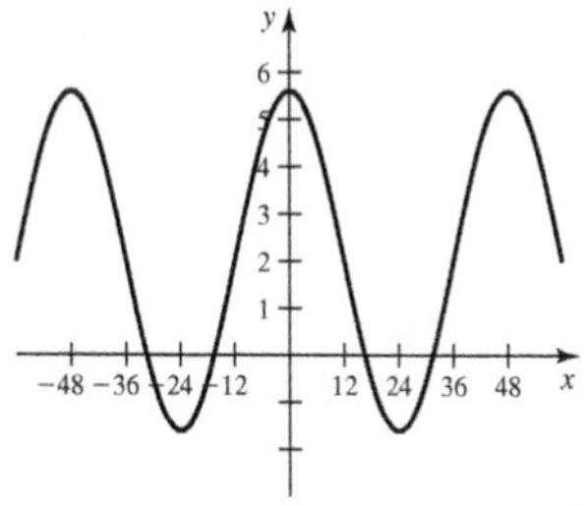

97. $y = 3\sin(\pi x/12 - 3\pi/4) + 13$ **99.** About 6 ft
101. $d(t) = 10\cos(4\pi t/3)$ **103.** h
105. $s(t) = 117.5 - 87.5\sin\left(\dfrac{\pi}{182.5}(t - 95)\right)$
$S(t) = 844.5 + 87.5\sin\left(\dfrac{\pi}{182.5}(t - 67)\right)$

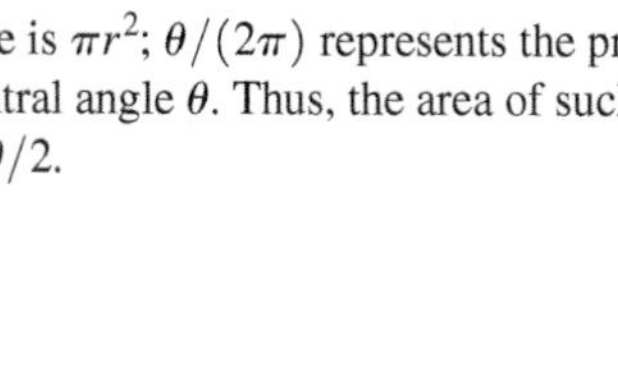

107. Area of circle is πr^2; $\theta/(2\pi)$ represents the proportion of area swept out by a central angle θ. Thus, the area of such a sector is $(\theta/2\pi)\pi r^2 = r^2\theta/2$.

Chapter 1 Review Exercises, pp. 51–53

1. a. True **b.** False **c.** False **d.** True **e.** False **f.** False **g.** True

3. a.

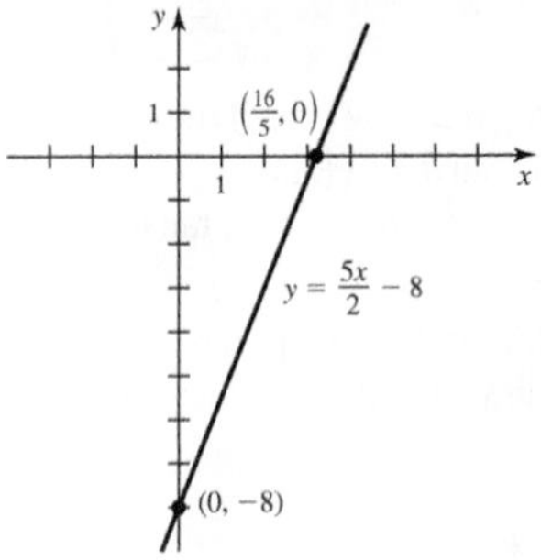

b.

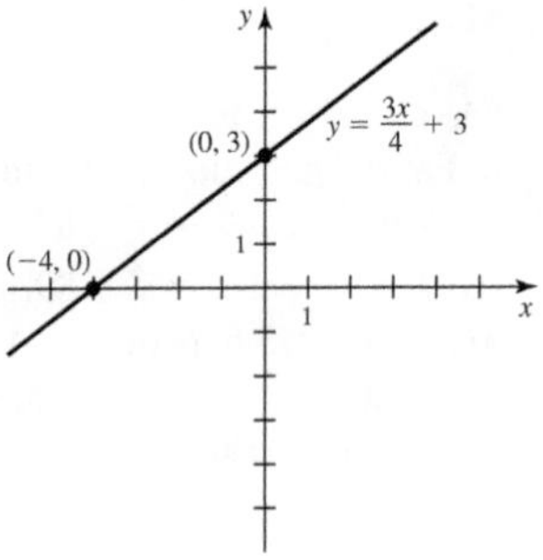

c.

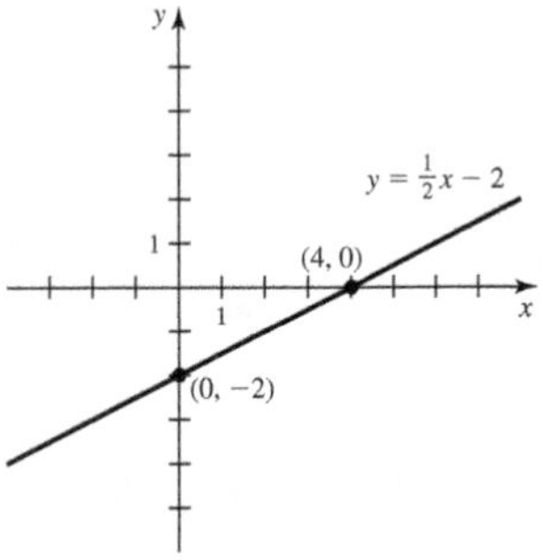

5. $f(x) = \begin{cases} 0 & \text{if } x \geq 0 \\ 4x & \text{if } x < 0 \end{cases}$

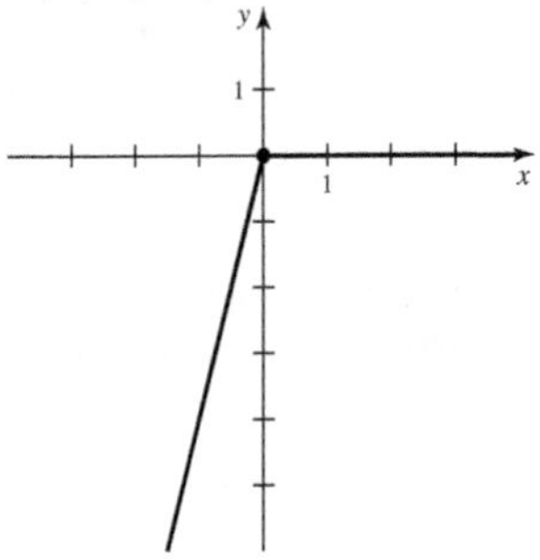

7. a.

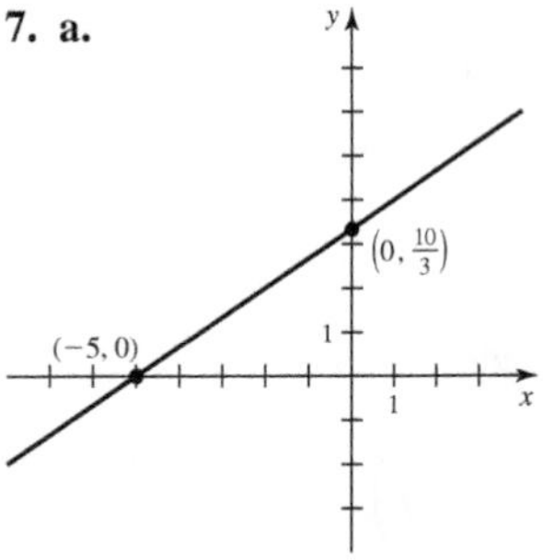

b.

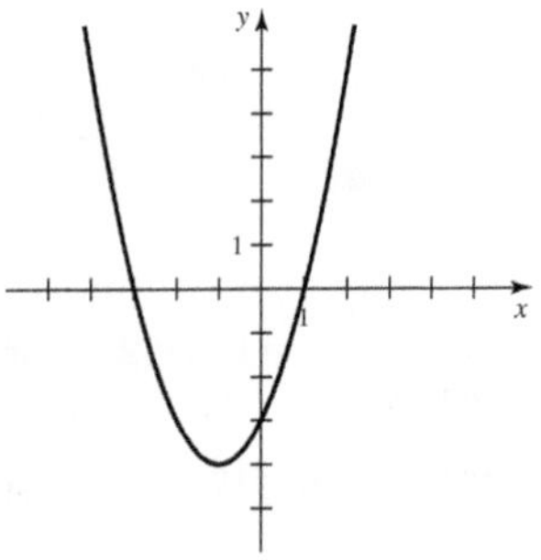

c.

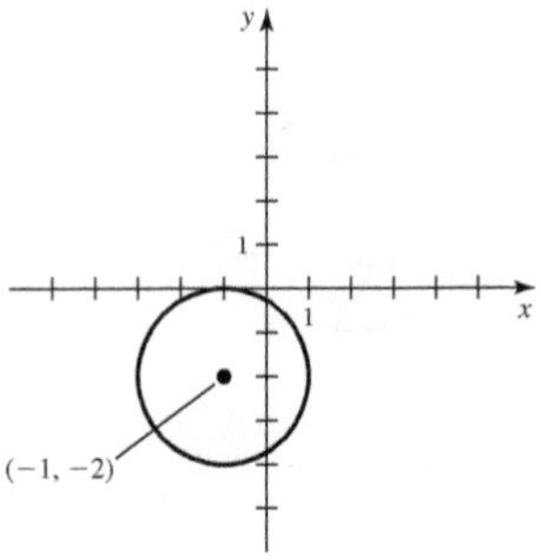

d.

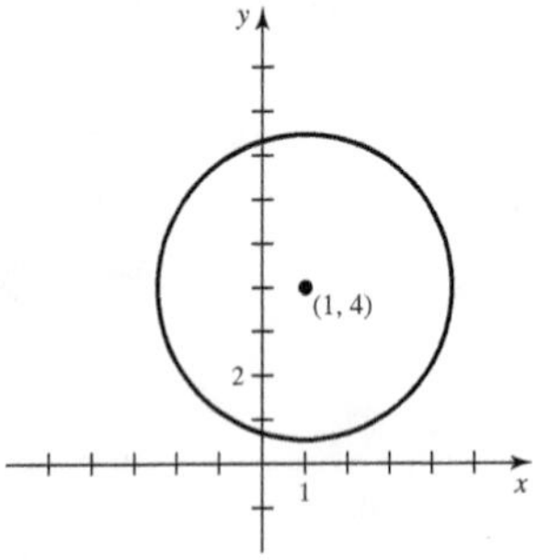

9. $D_f = \mathbb{R}, R_f = \mathbb{R}; D_g = [0, \infty), R_g = [0, \infty)$

11. $B = -\dfrac{1}{500}a + 212$

13. a.

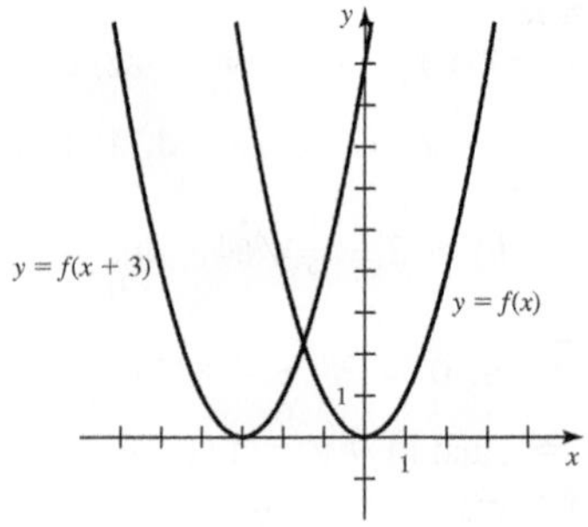

b.

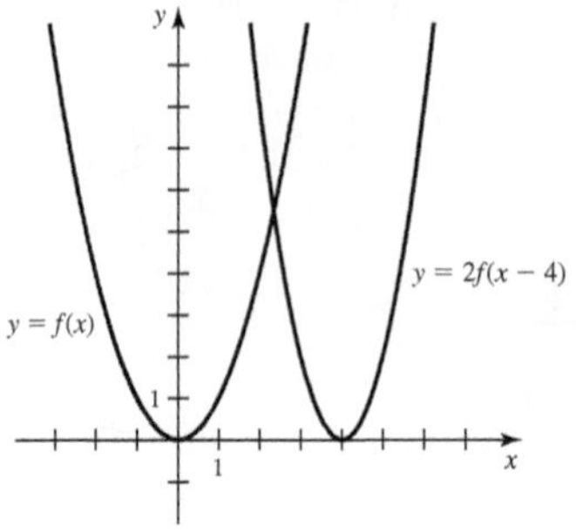

c.

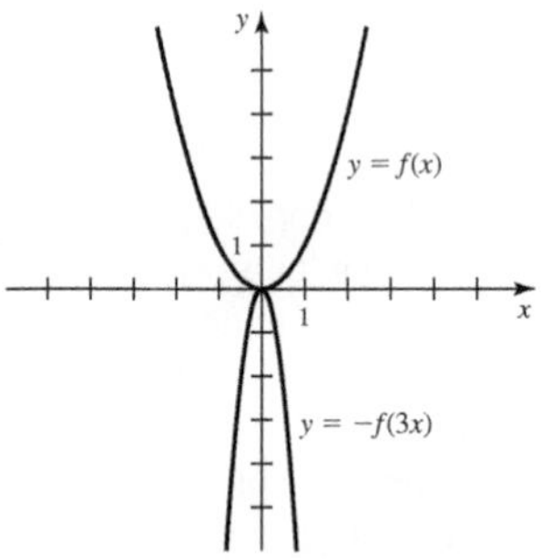

d.

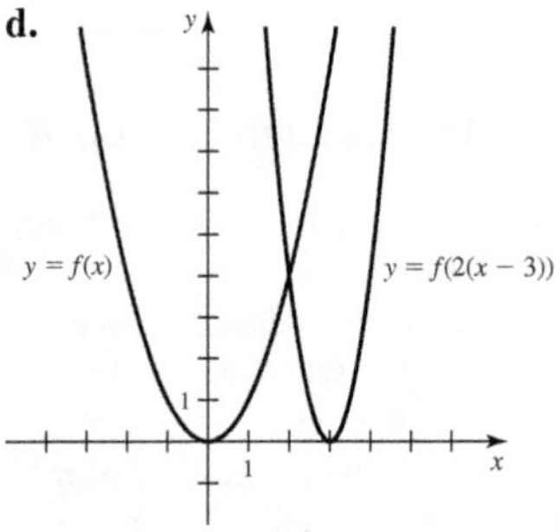

15. a. 1 **b.** $\sqrt{x^3}$ **c.** $\sin^3 \sqrt{x}$ **d.** $\mathbb{R}$ **e.** $[-1, 1]$
17. $2x + h - 2; x + a - 2$ **19.** $3x^2 + 3xh + h^2; x^2 + ax + a^2$
21. a. y-axis **b.** y-axis **c.** x-axis, y-axis, origin **23.** $x = 2$; base does not matter **25.** $(-\infty, 0], [0, 2]$, and $[2, \infty)$
27. $f^{-1}(x) = 2 + \sqrt{x - 1}$

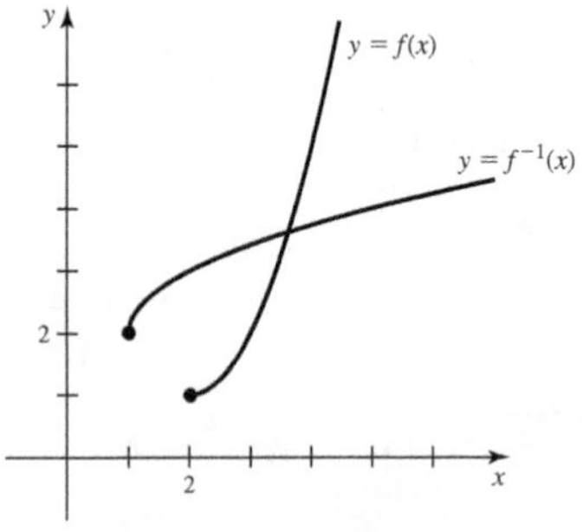

29. a. $3\pi/4$ **b.** 144° **c.** $40\pi/3$ **31. a.** $f(t) = -2\cos\dfrac{\pi t}{3}$ **b.** $f(t) = 5\sin\dfrac{\pi t}{12} + 15$ **33. a.** F **b.** E **c.** D **d.** B **e.** C **f.** A **35.** $(7\pi/6, -1/2); (11\pi/6, -1/2)$ **37.** $\pi/6$ **39.** $-\pi/2$ **41.** x **43.** $\cos\theta = \frac{5}{13}; \tan\theta = \frac{12}{5}; \cot\theta = \frac{5}{12}; \sec\theta = \frac{13}{5}; \csc\theta = \frac{13}{12}$ **45.** $\dfrac{\sqrt{4 - x^2}}{2}$ **47.** $\pi/2 - \theta$ **49.** 0
51. $1 - 2x^2$

CHAPTER 2

Section 2.1 Exercises, pp. 59–60

1. $\dfrac{s(b) - s(a)}{b - a}$ **3.** $\dfrac{f(b) - f(a)}{b - a}$ **5.** The instantaneous velocity at $t = a$ is the slope of the line tangent to the position curve at $t = a$. **7.** 20 **9. a.** 48 **b.** 64 **c.** 80 **d.** $16(6 - h)$ **11. a.** 36 **b.** 44 **c.** 52 **d.** 60 **13.** $m_{\text{sec}} = 60$; the slope is the average velocity of the object over the interval $[0.5, 2]$.

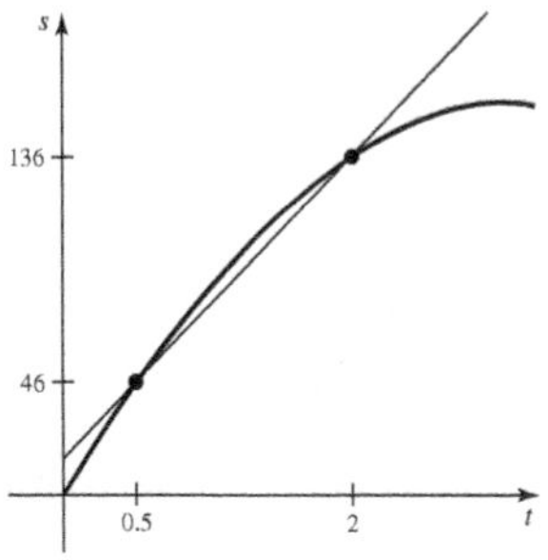

15.

Time interval	Average velocity
[1, 2]	80
[1, 1.5]	88
[1, 1.1]	94.4
[1, 1.01]	95.84
[1, 1.001]	95.984
$v_{\text{inst}} = 96$	

17. 47.84, 47.984, 47.9984; instantaneous velocity appears to be 48

19.

Time interval	Average velocity
[2, 3]	20
[2.9, 3]	5.60
[2.99, 3]	4.16
[2.999, 3]	4.016
[2.9999, 3]	4.002
$v_{\text{inst}} = 4$	

21.

Time interval	Average velocity
[3, 3.5]	−24
[3, 3.1]	−17.6
[3, 3.01]	−16.16
[3, 3.001]	−16.016
[3, 3.0001]	−16.002
$v_{\text{inst}} = -16$	

23.

Time interval	Average velocity
[0, 1]	36.372
[0, 0.5]	67.318
[0, 0.1]	79.468
[0, 0.01]	79.995
[0, 0.001]	80.000
$v_{\text{inst}} = 80$	

25.

Interval	Slope of secant line
[1, 2]	6
[1.5, 2]	7
[1.9, 2]	7.8
[1.99, 2]	7.98
[1.999, 2]	7.998
$m_{\tan} = 8$	

27.

Interval	Slope of secant line
[0, 1]	1.718
[0, 0.5]	1.297
[0, 0.1]	1.052
[0, 0.01]	1.005
[0, 0.001]	1.001
$m_{\tan} = 1$	

29. a.

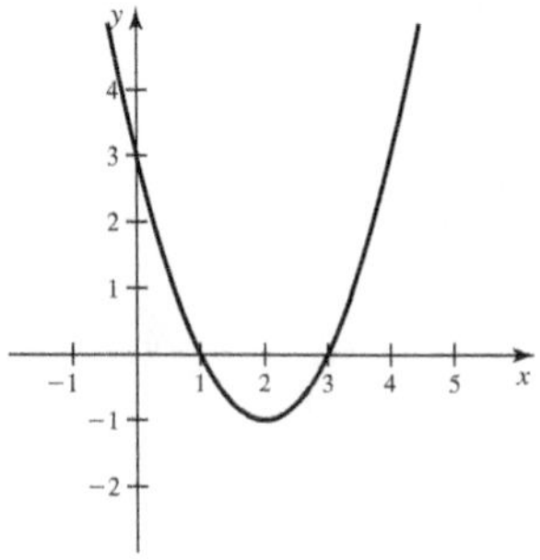

b. $(2, -1)$

c.

Interval	Slope of secant line
[2, 2.5]	0.5
[2, 2.1]	0.1
[2, 2.01]	0.01
[2, 2.001]	0.001
[2, 2.0001]	0.0001
$m_{\tan} = 0$	

31. a.

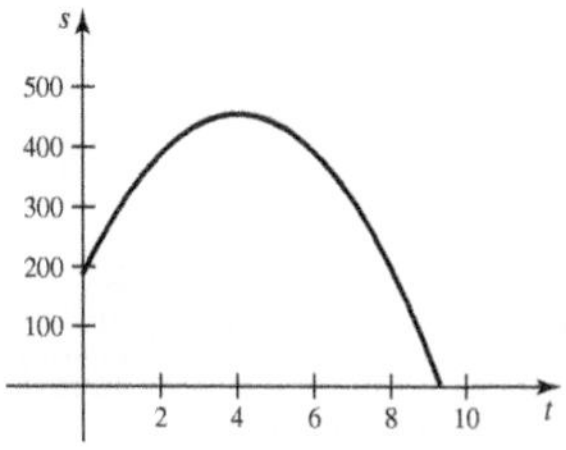

b. $t = 4$

c.

Interval	Average velocity
[4, 4.5]	−8
[4, 4.1]	−1.6
[4, 4.01]	−0.16
[4, 4.001]	−0.016
[4, 4.0001]	−0.0016
$v_{\text{inst}} = 0$	

d. $0 \le t < 4$ **e.** $4 < t \le 9$ **33.** 0.6366, 0.9589, 0.9996, 1

Section 2.2 Exercises, pp. 65–68

1. As x approaches a from either side, the values of $f(x)$ approach L.
3. As x approaches a from the right, the values of $f(x)$ approach L.
5. $L = M$ **7. a.** 5 **b.** 3 **c.** Does not exist **d.** 1 **e.** 2
9. a. -1 **b.** 1 **c.** 2 **d.** 2
11. a.

x	$f(x)$	x	$f(x)$
1.9	3.9	2.1	4.1
1.99	3.99	2.01	4.01
1.999	3.999	2.001	4.001
1.9999	3.9999	2.0001	4.0001

b. 4

13. a.

t	$g(t)$	t	$g(t)$
8.9	5.983287	9.1	6.016621
8.99	5.998333	9.01	6.001666
8.999	5.999833	9.001	6.000167

b. 6

15. From the graph and table, the limit appears to be 0.

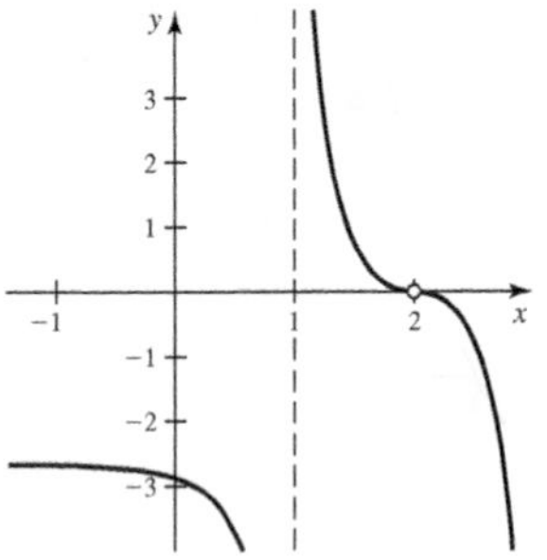

x	1.99	1.999	1.9999	2.0001	2.001	2.01
$f(x)$	0.0021715	0.00014476	0.000010857	−0.000010857	−0.00014476	−0.0021715

17. From the graph and table, the limit appears to be 2.

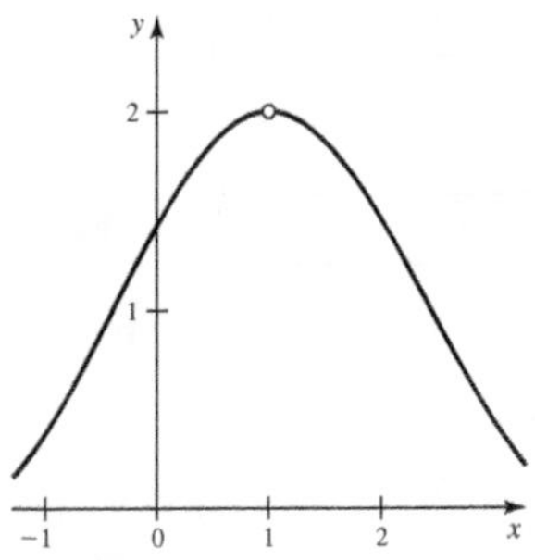

x	0.9	0.99	0.999	1.001	1.01	1.1
$f(x)$	1.993342	1.999933	1.999999	1.999999	1.999933	1.993342

19. $\lim_{x\to5^+} f(x) = 10$; $\lim_{x\to5^-} f(x) = 10$; $\lim_{x\to5} f(x) = 10$

21. a. 0 **b.** 1 **c.** 0 **d.** Does not exist; $\lim_{x\to1^-} f(x) \neq \lim_{x\to1^+} f(x)$

23. a. 3 **b.** 2 **c.** 2 **d.** 2 **e.** 2 **f.** 4 **g.** 1 **h.** Does not exist **i.** 3 **j.** 3 **k.** 3 **l.** 3

25. a.

x	$\sin(1/x)$
$2/\pi$	1
$2/(3\pi)$	−1
$2/(5\pi)$	1
$2/(7\pi)$	−1
$2/(9\pi)$	1
$2/(11\pi)$	−1

The value alternates between 1 and -1.

b. The function alternates between 1 and -1 infinitely many times on the interval $(0, h)$ no matter how small $h > 0$ becomes. **c.** Does not exist. **27. a.** False **b.** False **c.** False **d.** False **e.** True

29.

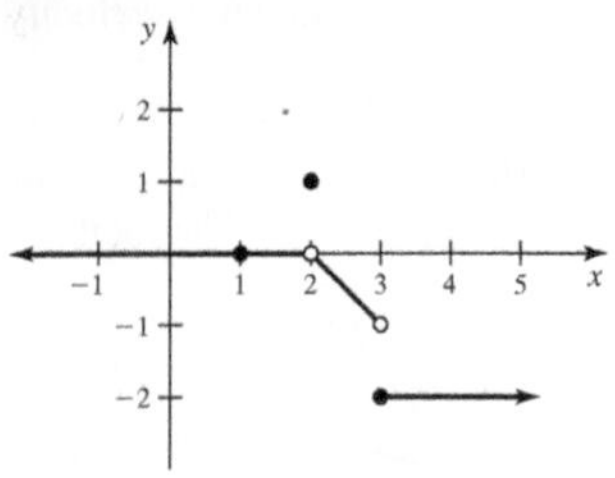

31.

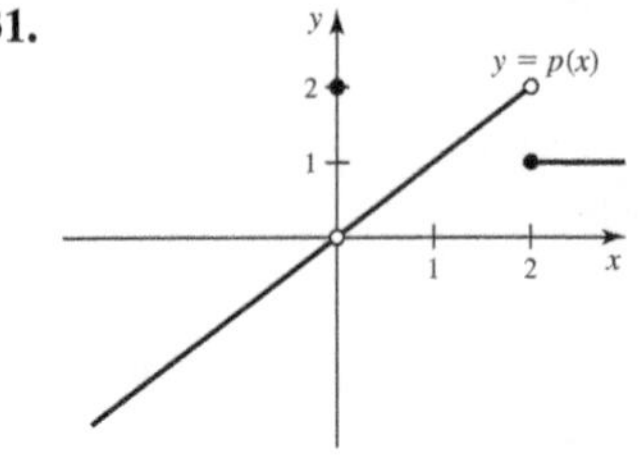

33. Approximately 403.4 **35.** 1 **37. a.** $-2, -1, 1, 2$ **b.** 2, 2, 2
c. $\lim_{x\to a^-} \lfloor x \rfloor = a - 1$ and $\lim_{x\to a^+} \lfloor x \rfloor = a$, if a is an integer
d. $\lim_{x\to a^-} \lfloor x \rfloor = \lfloor a \rfloor$ and $\lim_{x\to a^+} \lfloor x \rfloor = \lfloor a \rfloor$, if a is not an integer
e. Limit exists provided a is not an integer **39.** 0 **41.** 16

43. a.

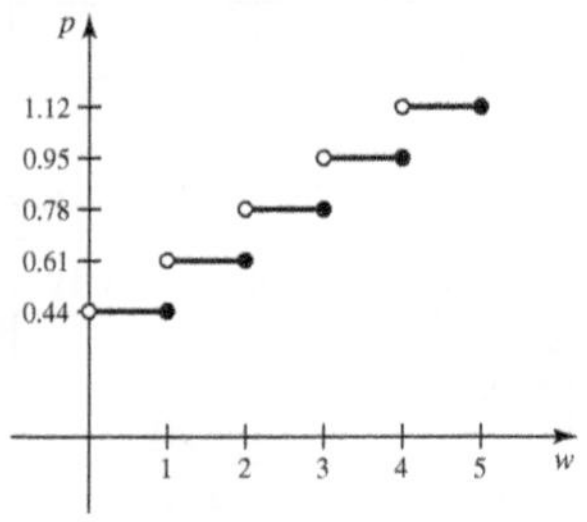

b. \$0.95

c. $\lim_{x\to1^+} f(w) = 0.61$ is the cost of a letter that weighs just over 1 oz; $\lim_{x\to1^-} f(w) = 0.44$ is the cost of a letter that weighs just under 1 oz.
d. No; $\lim_{x\to4^+} f(w) \neq \lim_{x\to4^-} f(w)$ **45. a.** 8 **b.** 5 **47. a.** 2; 3; 4 **b.** p **49.** $\frac{p}{q}$

Section 2.3 Exercises, pp. 76–79

1. $\lim_{x\to a} f(x) = f(a)$ **3.** Those values of a for which the denominator is not zero **5.** $\frac{x^2 - 7x + 12}{x - 3} = x - 4$, for $x \neq 3$ **7.** 20 **9.** 4
11. 5 **13.** -45 **15.** 4 **17.** 32; Constant Multiple Law **19.** 5; Difference Law **21.** 12; Quotient and Product Laws **23.** 32; Power Law **25.** 8 **27.** 3 **29.** 3 **31.** -5 **33. a.** 2 **b.** 0 **c.** Does not exist **35. a.** 0 **b.** $\sqrt{x - 2}$ is undefined for $x < 2$.
37. $\lim_{x\to0^-} |x| = \lim_{x\to0^-} (-x) = 0$ and $\lim_{x\to0^+} |x| = \lim_{x\to0^+} x = 0$ **39.** 2
41. -8 **43.** -1 **45.** -12 **47.** $\frac{1}{6}$ **49.** $2\sqrt{a}$ **51.** $\frac{1}{8}$

53. a.

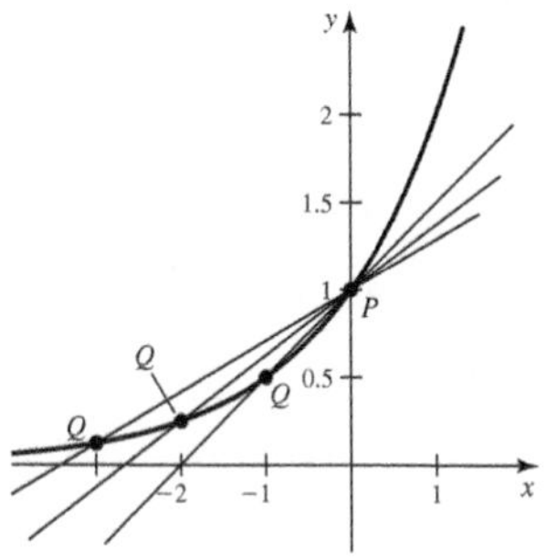

b. $\frac{2^x - 1}{x}$

c.

x	$\frac{2^x - 1}{x}$
−1	0.5
−0.1	0.6697
−0.01	0.6908
−0.001	0.6929
−0.0001	0.6931
−0.00001	0.6931
Limit ≈ 0.693	

55. a. Because $\left|\sin\frac{1}{x}\right| \le 1$ for all $x \ne 0$, we have that

$$|x|\left|\sin\frac{1}{x}\right| \le |x|.$$

That is, $\left|x\sin\frac{1}{x}\right| \le |x|$, so that $-|x| \le x\sin\frac{1}{x} \le |x|$ for all $x \ne 0$.

b.

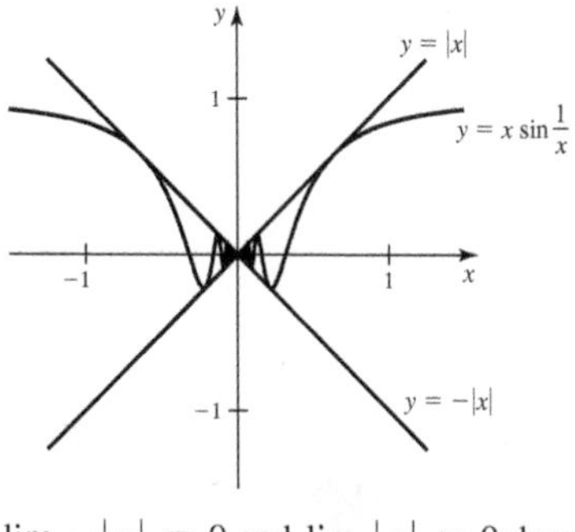

c. $\lim_{x\to 0} -|x| = 0$ and $\lim_{x\to 0} |x| = 0$; by part (a) and the Squeeze Theorem, $\lim_{x\to 0} x\sin\frac{1}{x} = 0$

57. a.

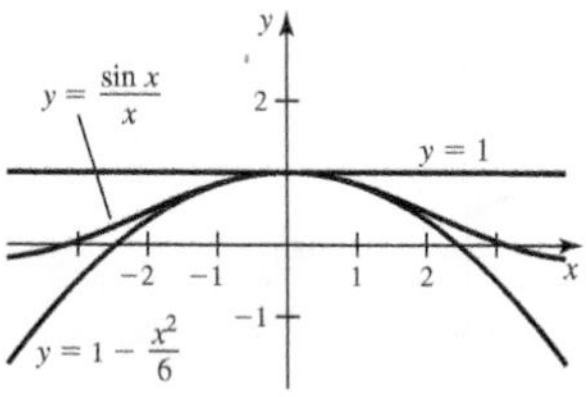

b. $\lim_{x\to 0}\frac{\sin x}{x} = 1$ **59. a.** False **b.** False **c.** False **d.** False **e.** False **61.** 8 **63.** 5 **65.** 10 **67.** −3 **69.** $a = -13$; $\lim_{x\to -1} g(x) = 6$ **71.** 6 **73.** $5a^4$ **75.** $\frac{1}{3}$ **77.** 2 **79.** −54

81. $f(x) = x - 1$, $g(x) = \frac{5}{x - 1}$ **83.** $b = 2$ and $c = -8$; yes

85. $\lim_{S\to 0^+} r(S) = 0$; the radius of the cylinder approaches 0 as the surface area of the cylinder approaches 0. **87.** 0.0435 N/C **89.** 6; 4

Section 2.4 Exercises, pp. 85–88

1. $\lim_{x\to a^+} f(x) = -\infty$ means that as x approaches a from the right, the values of $f(x)$ are negative and become arbitrarily large in magnitude. **3.** A vertical asymptote for a function f is a vertical line $x = a$ where one (or more) of the following is true:

$$\lim_{x\to a^-} f(x) = \pm\infty;\ \lim_{x\to a^+} f(x) = \pm\infty.$$

5. $-\infty$ **7.** ∞ **9. a.** ∞ **b.** ∞ **c.** ∞ **d.** ∞ **e.** $-\infty$ **f.** Does not exist **11. a.** $-\infty$ **b.** $-\infty$ **c.** $-\infty$ **d.** ∞ **e.** $-\infty$ **f.** Does not exist **13. a.** ∞ **b.** $-\infty$ **c.** $-\infty$ **d.** ∞

15.

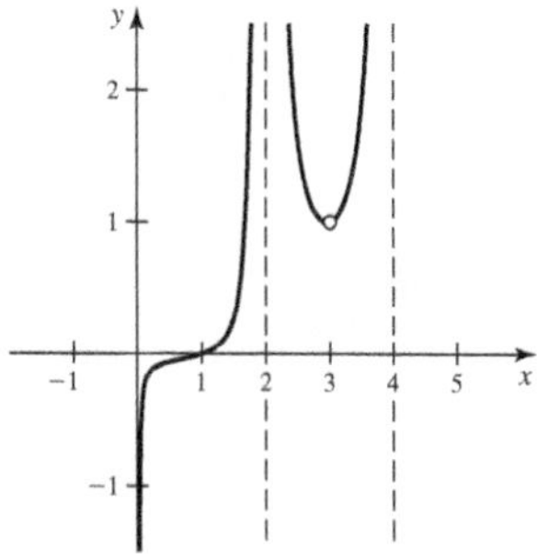

17. a. ∞ **b.** $-\infty$ **c.** Does not exist **19. a.** $-\infty$ **b.** $-\infty$ **c.** $-\infty$ **21. a.** ∞ **b.** $-\infty$ **c.** Does not exist **23. a.** $-\infty$ **b.** $-\infty$ **c.** $-\infty$ **25.** −5 **27.** ∞ **29. a.** 1/10 **b.** $-\infty$ **c.** ∞; vertical asymptote: $x = -5$ **31.** $x = 3$; $\lim_{x\to 3^+} f(x) = -\infty$; $\lim_{x\to 3^-} f(x) = \infty$; $\lim_{x\to 3} f(x)$ does not exist **33.** $x = 0$ and $x = 2$; $\lim_{x\to 0^+} f(x) = \infty$; $\lim_{x\to 0^-} f(x) = -\infty$; $\lim_{x\to 0} f(x)$ does not exist; $\lim_{x\to 2^+} f(x) = \infty$; $\lim_{x\to 2^-} f(x) = \infty$; $\lim_{x\to 2} f(x) = \infty$ **35.** ∞ **37.** $-\infty$ **39. a.** $-\infty$ **b.** ∞ **c.** $-\infty$ **d.** ∞ **41. a.** False **b.** True **c.** False **43.** $f(x) = \frac{1}{x - 6}$ **45.** $x = 0$ **47.** $x = -1$ **49.** $\theta = 10k + 5$, for any integer k **51.** $x = 0$ **53. a.** $a = 4$ or $a = 3$ **b.** Either $a > 4$ or $a < 3$ **c.** $3 < a < 4$ **55. a.** $\frac{1}{\sqrt[3]{h}}$, regardless of the sign of h **b.** $\lim_{h\to 0^+}\frac{1}{\sqrt[3]{h}} = \infty$; $\lim_{h\to 0^-}\frac{1}{\sqrt[3]{h}} = -\infty$; the tangent line at (0, 0) is vertical.

Section 2.5 Exercises, pp. 96–98

1. As $x < 0$ becomes arbitrarily large in magnitude, the corresponding values of f approach 10. **3.** 0 **5.** $\lim_{x\to\infty} f(x) = -\infty$; $\lim_{x\to -\infty} f(x) = \infty$ **7.** ∞; 0; 0 **9.** 3 **11.** 0 **13.** 0 **15.** ∞ **17.** 0 **19.** ∞ **21.** $-\infty$ **23.** 0 **25.** $\lim_{x\to\infty} f(x) = \lim_{x\to -\infty} f(x) = \frac{1}{5}$; $y = \frac{1}{5}$

27. $\lim_{x\to\infty} f(x) = 2$; $\lim_{x\to -\infty} f(x) = 2$; $y = 2$

29. $\lim_{x\to\infty} f(x) = \lim_{x\to -\infty} f(x) = 0$; $y = 0$

31. $\lim_{x\to\infty} f(x) = \lim_{x\to -\infty} f(x) = 0$; $y = 0$ **33.** $\lim_{x\to\infty} f(x) = \infty$; $\lim_{x\to -\infty} f(x) = -\infty$; none **35. a.** $y = x - 6$ **b.** $x = -6$

c.

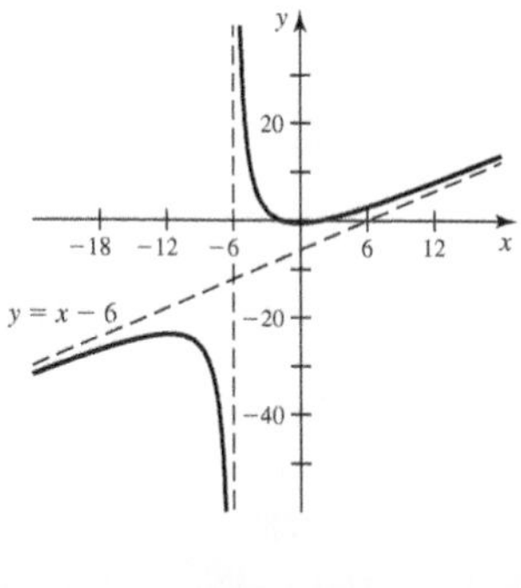

37. a. $y = \frac{1}{3}x - \frac{4}{9}$ **b.** $x = \frac{2}{3}$

c.

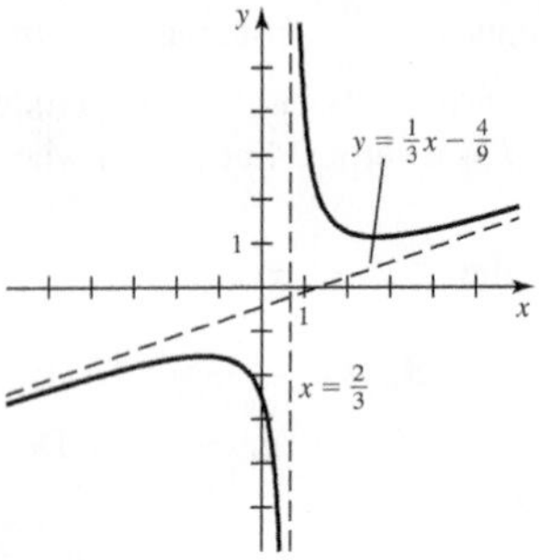

39. a. $y = 4x + 4$ **b.** No vertical asymptote

c.

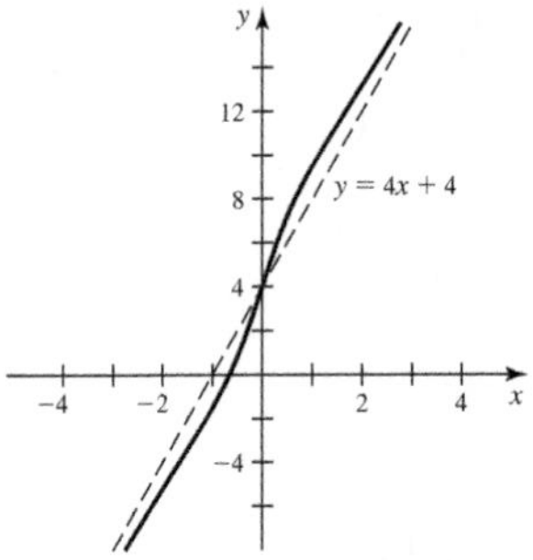

41. $\lim_{x\to\infty} f(x) = \frac{2}{3}$; $\lim_{x\to-\infty} f(x) = -2$; $y = \frac{2}{3}$; $y = -2$

43. $\lim_{x\to\infty} f(x) = \lim_{x\to-\infty} f(x) = \dfrac{1}{4+\sqrt{3}}$; $y = \dfrac{1}{4+\sqrt{3}}$

45. $\lim_{x\to\infty} (-3e^{-x}) = 0$; $\lim_{x\to-\infty} (-3e^{-x}) = -\infty$

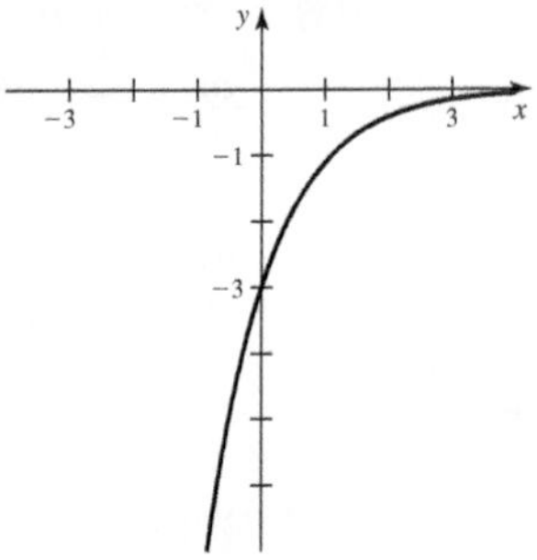

47. $\lim_{x\to\infty} (1 - \ln x) = -\infty$; $\lim_{x\to0^+} (1 - \ln x) = \infty$

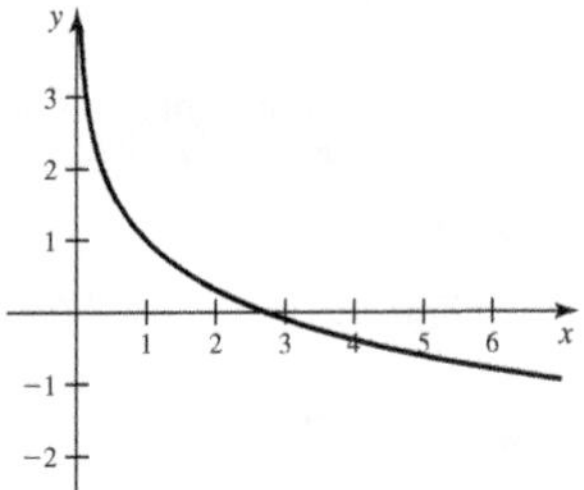

49. $\lim_{x\to\infty} \sin x$ does not exist; $\lim_{x\to-\infty} \sin x$ does not exist

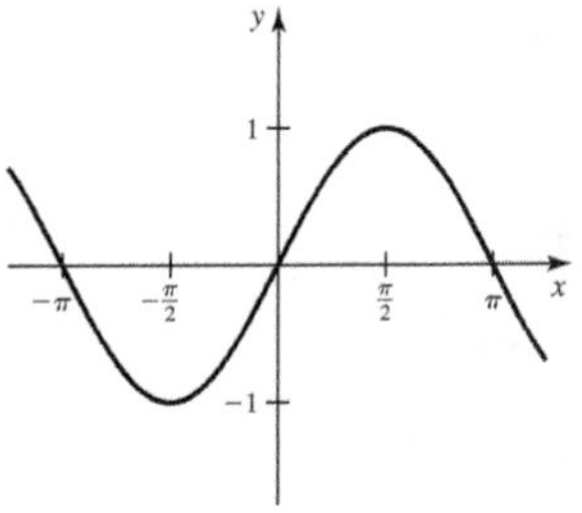

51. a. False **b.** False **c.** True

53. a. $\lim_{x\to\infty} f(x) = 2$; $\lim_{x\to-\infty} f(x) = 2$; $y = 2$

b. $x = 0$; $\lim_{x\to0^+} f(x) = \infty$; $\lim_{x\to0^-} f(x) = -\infty$

55. a. $\lim_{x\to\infty} f(x) = 3$; $\lim_{x\to-\infty} f(x) = 3$; $y = 3$

b. $x = -3$ and $x = 4$; $\lim_{x\to-3^-} f(x) = \infty$; $\lim_{x\to-3^+} f(x) = -\infty$; $\lim_{x\to4^-} f(x) = -\infty$; $\lim_{x\to4^+} f(x) = \infty$

57. a. $\lim_{x\to\infty} f(x) = 1$; $\lim_{x\to-\infty} f(x) = 1$; $y = 1$

b. $x = 0$; $\lim_{x\to0^+} f(x) = \infty$; $\lim_{x\to0^-} f(x) = -\infty$

59. a. $\lim_{x\to\infty} f(x) = 1$; $\lim_{x\to-\infty} f(x) = -1$; $y = 1$ and $y = -1$

b. No vertical asymptote **61. a.** $\lim_{x\to\infty} f(x) = 0$; $\lim_{x\to-\infty} f(x) = 0$; $y = 0$ **b.** No vertical asymptote **63. a.** $\dfrac{\pi}{2}$ **b.** $\dfrac{\pi}{2}$

65. a. $\lim_{x\to\infty} \sinh x = \infty$; $\lim_{x\to-\infty} \sinh x = -\infty$

b. $\sinh 0 = 0$

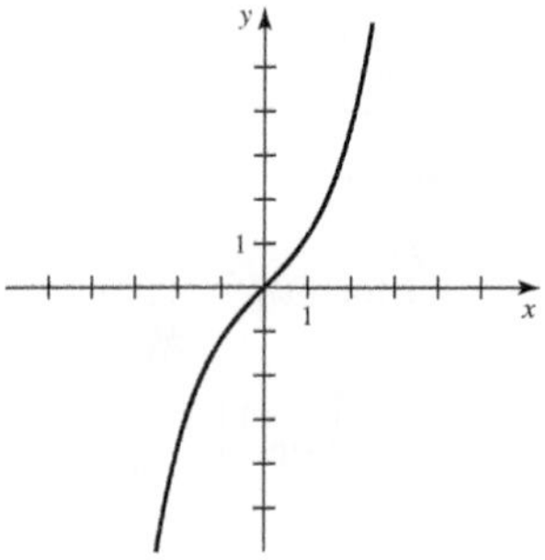

67.

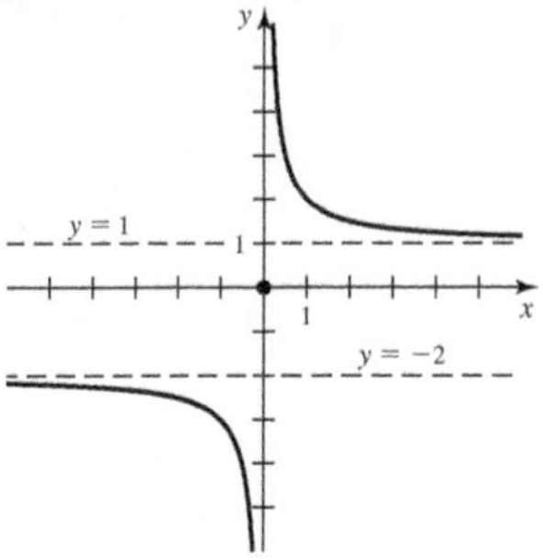

69. $x = 0$; $y = 2$ **71.** 3500 **73.** No steady state **75.** 2 **77.** 1

79. 0 **81. a.** No; f has a horizontal asymptote if $m = n$ and it has a slant asymptote if $m = n + 1$. **b.** Yes; $f(x) = x^4/\sqrt{x^6 + 1}$

83. $\lim_{x\to\infty} f(x) = 0$; $\lim_{x\to-\infty} f(x) = \infty$; $y = 0$

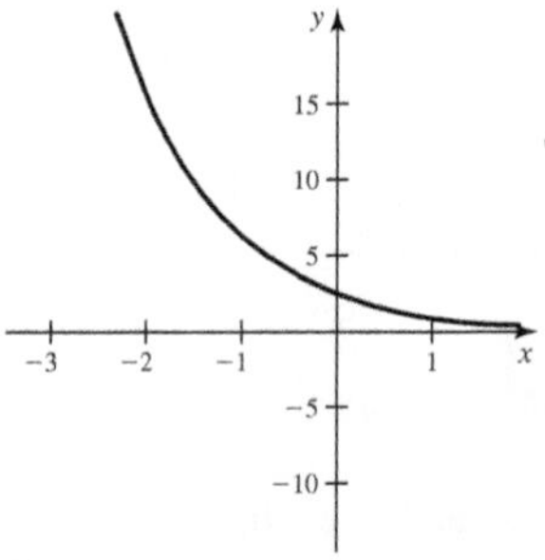

85. $x = \pm 3$, $x = -\frac{1}{2}\ln 2 \approx -0.347$

Section 2.6 Exercises, pp. 108–112

1. a, c **3.** A function is continuous on an interval if it is continuous at each point of the interval. If the interval contains endpoints, then the function must be right- or left-continuous at those points.
5. a. $\lim_{x \to a^-} f(x) = f(a)$ **b.** $\lim_{x \to a^+} f(x) = f(a)$
7. $\{x: x \neq 0\}, \{x: x \neq 0\}$ **9.** $a = 2$, item 3; $a = 3$, item 2; $a = 1$, item 1 **11.** $a = 1$, item 1; $a = 2$, item 2; $a = 3$, item 1
13. Yes; $\lim_{x \to 5} f(x) = f(5)$. **15.** No; $f(1)$ is undefined. **17.** No; $\lim_{x \to 1} f(x) = 2$ but $f(1) = 3$. **19.** No; $f(4)$ is undefined.
21. $(-\infty, \infty)$ **23.** $(-\infty, -3), (-3, 3), (3, \infty)$
25. $(-\infty, -2), (-2, 2), (2, \infty)$ **27.** 1 **29.** 16 **31.** $2\sqrt{6}$
33. ln 2 **35.** $[0, 1), (1, 2), (2, 3], (3, 4]$
37. $[0, 1), (1, 2), [2, 3), (3, 5]$ **39. a.** $\lim_{x \to 1} f(x)$ does not exist.
b. Continuous from the right **c.** $(-\infty, 1), [1, \infty)$
41. $(-\infty, -2\sqrt{2}]; [2\sqrt{2}, \infty)$ **43.** $(-\infty, \infty)$ **45.** $(-\infty, \infty)$ **47.** 3
49. 4 **51.** $(n\pi, (n + 1)\pi)$, where n is an integer; $\sqrt{2}$; $-\infty$
53. $\left(\frac{n\pi}{2}, \left(\frac{n}{2} + 1\right)\frac{\pi}{2}\right)$, where n is an odd integer; ∞; $\sqrt{3} - 2$
55. $(-\infty, 0), (0, \infty)$; ∞; $-\infty$
57. a. A is continuous on $[0, 0.08]$, and 7000 is between $A(0) = 5000$ and $A(0.08) = 11{,}098.20$. By the Intermediate Value Theorem, there is at least one c in $(0, 0.08)$ such that $A(c) = 7000$.
b. $c \approx 0.034$ or 3.4%

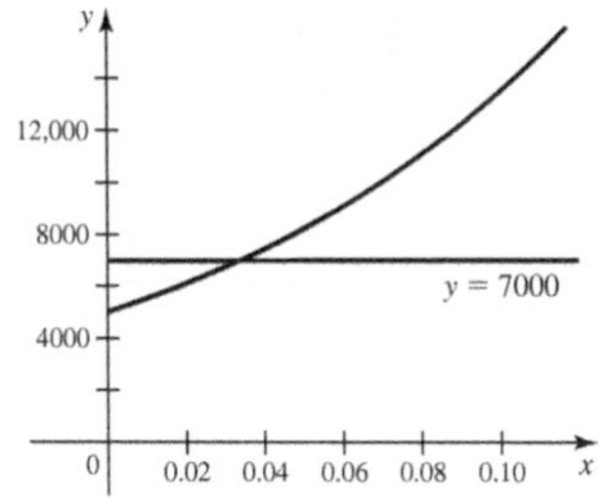

59. b. $x \approx 0.835$ **61. b.** $x \approx -0.285$; $x \approx 0.778$; $x \approx 4.507$
63. b. -0.567 **65. a.** True **b.** True **c.** False **d.** False
67. $(-\infty, \infty)$ **69.** $[0, 16), (16, \infty)$ **71.** 1 **73.** 2 **75.** $-\frac{1}{2}$
77. 0 **79.** $-\infty$
81. The vertical line segments should not appear.

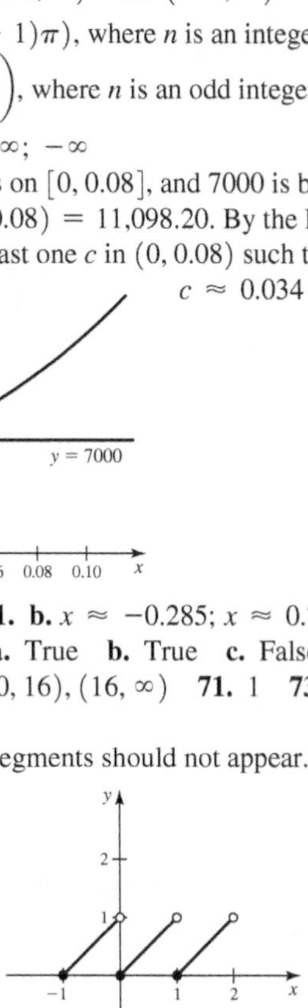

83. a, b.

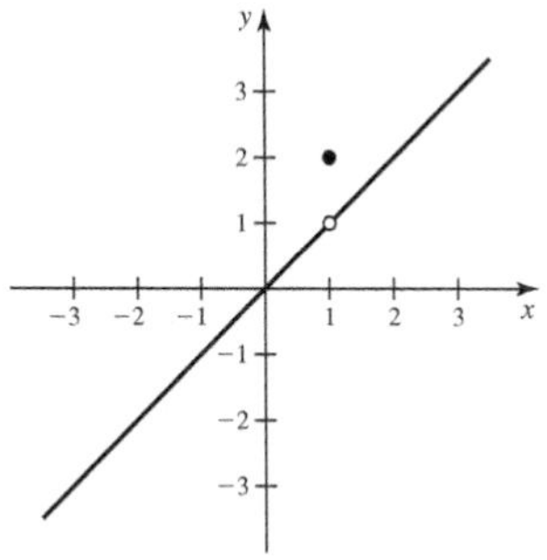

85. a. 2 **b.** 8 **c.** No; $\lim_{x \to 1^-} g(x) = 2$ and $\lim_{x \to 1^+} g(x) = 8$.

87. $\lim_{x \to 0} f(x) = 6$, $\lim_{x \to -\infty} f(x) = 10$, and $\lim_{x \to \infty} f(x) = 2$; no vertical asymptote; $y = 2$ and $y = 10$ are the horizontal asymptotes.

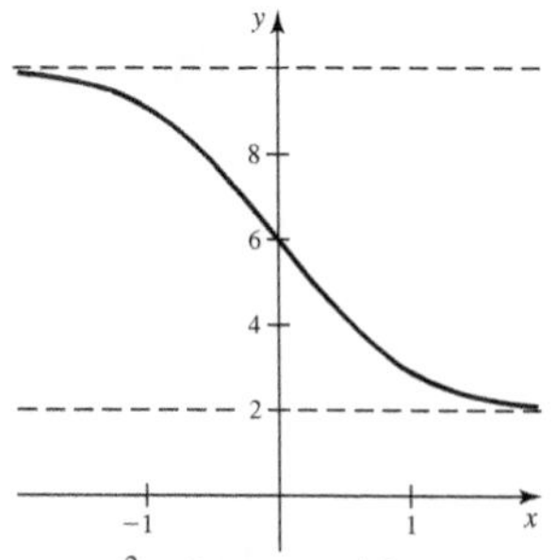

89. $x_1 = \frac{1}{7}$; $x_2 = \frac{1}{2}$; $x_3 = \frac{3}{5}$ **91. a.** $A(r)$ is continuous on $[0.01, 0.10]$ and $A(0.01) = 2615.55$, while $A(0.10) = 3984.36$. Therefore, $A(0.01) < 3500 < A(0.10)$. By the Intermediate Value Theorem, there exists c in $(0.01, 0.10)$ such that $A(c) = 3500$. Therefore, c is the desired interest rate. **b.** $r \approx 7.28\%$ **93.** Yes. Imagine there is a clone of the monk who walks down the path at the same time the monk walks up the path. The monk and his clone must cross paths at some time between dawn and dusk. **95.** No; f cannot be made continuous at $x = a$ by redefining $f(a)$. **97.** $\lim_{x \to 2} f(x) = -3$; define $f(2)$ to be -3. **99. a.** Yes **b.** No
101. $a = 0$ removable discontinuity; $a = 1$ infinite discontinuity
103. a. For example, $f(x) = 1/(x - 1)$, $g(x) = x + 1$
b. For continuity, g must be continuous at 0 and f must be continuous at $g(0)$.

Section 2.7 Exercises, pp. 120–123

1. 1 **3.** c **5.** Given any $\varepsilon > 0$ there exists a $\delta > 0$ such that $|f(x) - L| < \varepsilon$ whenever $0 < |x - a| < \delta$. **7.** $0 < \delta \leq 2$
9. a. $\delta = 1$ **b.** $\delta = \frac{1}{2}$ **11. a.** $\delta = 2$ **b.** $\delta = \frac{1}{2}$
13. a. $0 < \delta \leq 1$ **b.** $0 < \delta \leq 0.79$
15. a. $0 < \delta \leq 1$ **b.** $0 < \delta \leq \frac{1}{2}$ **c.** $0 < \delta \leq \varepsilon$
17. a. $0 < \delta \leq 1$ **b.** $0 < \delta \leq \frac{1}{2}$ **c.** $0 < \delta \leq \frac{\varepsilon}{2}$
19. $\delta = \varepsilon/8$ **21.** $\delta = \varepsilon$ **23.** $\delta = \sqrt{\varepsilon}$ **27. a.** Use any $\delta > 0$
b. $\delta = \varepsilon$ **29.** $\delta = 1/\sqrt{N}$ **31.** $\delta = 1/\sqrt{N - 1}$ **33. a.** False
b. False **c.** True **d.** True **35.** $\delta = \min\{1, 6\varepsilon\}$
37. $\delta = \min\{1/20, \varepsilon/200\}$ **39.** For $x > a$, $|x - a| = x - a$.
41. a. $\delta = \varepsilon/2$ **b.** $\delta = \varepsilon/3$ **c.** Because $\lim_{x \to 0^+} f(x) = \lim_{x \to 0^-} f(x) = -4$, $\lim_{x \to 0} f(x) = -4$. **43.** $\delta = \varepsilon^2$
45. a. For each $N > 0$ there exists $\delta > 0$ such that $f(x) > N$ whenever $0 < x - a < \delta$. **b.** For each $N < 0$ there exists $\delta > 0$ such that $f(x) < N$ whenever $0 < a - x < \delta$. **c.** For each $N > 0$ there exists $\delta > 0$ such that $f(x) > N$ whenever $0 < a - x < \delta$. **47.** $\delta = 1/N$ **49.** $\delta = (-10/M)^{1/4}$
51. $N = 1/\varepsilon$ **53.** $N = M - 1$

Chapter 2 Review Exercises, pp. 123–125

1. a. False **b.** False **c.** False **d.** True **e.** False **f.** False
g. False **h.** True **3.** $x = -1$; $\lim_{x \to -1} f(x)$ does not exist; $x = 1$; $\lim_{x \to 1} f(x) \neq f(1)$; $x = 3$; $f(3)$ is undefined. **5. a.** 1.414 **b.** $\sqrt{2}$
7.

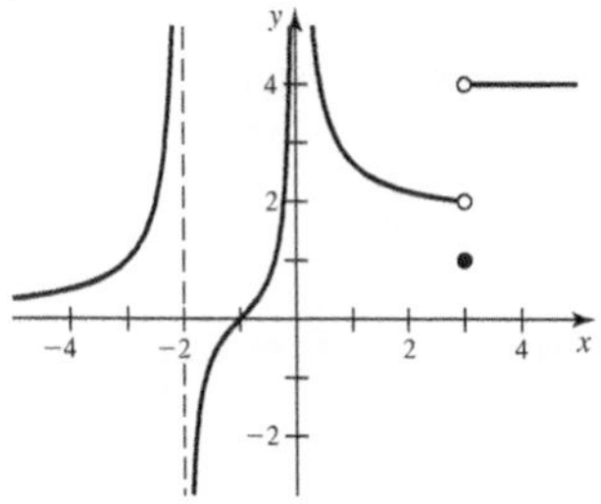

9. $\sqrt{11}$ **11.** 2 **13.** $\frac{1}{3}$ **15.** $-\frac{1}{16}$ **17.** 108 **19.** $\frac{1}{108}$ **21.** 0
23. a.

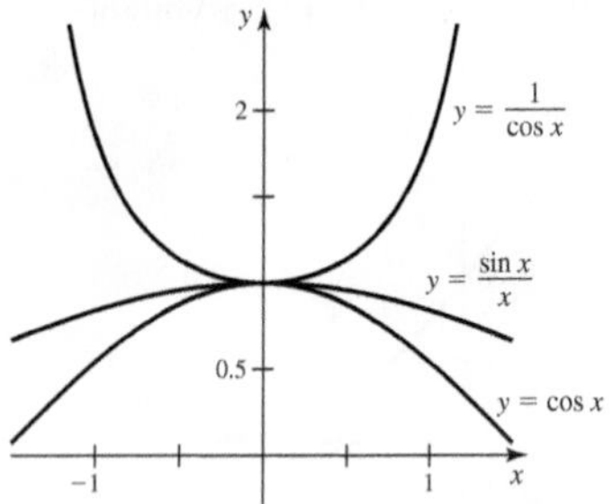

b. $\lim\limits_{x\to 0} \cos x \le \lim\limits_{x\to 0} \dfrac{\sin x}{x} \le \lim\limits_{x\to 0} \dfrac{1}{\cos x}$;

$$1 \le \lim_{x\to 0} \frac{\sin x}{x} \le 1;$$

$$\lim_{x\to 0} \frac{\sin x}{x} = 1$$

25. $-\infty$ **27.** ∞ **29.** $-\infty$ **31.** $\frac{1}{2}$ **33.** ∞
35. $3\pi/2 + 2$ **37.** $\lim\limits_{x\to\infty} f(x) = -4$; $\lim\limits_{x\to-\infty} f(x) = -4$
39. $\lim\limits_{x\to\infty} f(x) = 1$; $\lim\limits_{x\to-\infty} f(x) = -\infty$ **41.** Horizontal asymptotes at $y = 2/\pi$ and $y = -2/\pi$; vertical asymptote at $x = 0$
43. a. ∞; $-\infty$ **b.** $y = \dfrac{3x}{4} + \dfrac{5}{16}$ is the slant asymptote.
45. a. $-\infty$; ∞ **b.** $y = -x - 2$ is the slant asymptote. **47.** No; $f(5)$ does not exist. **49.** No; $\lim\limits_{x\to 3^-} h(x)$ does not exist, which implies $\lim\limits_{x\to 3} h(x)$ does not exist. **51.** $(-\infty, -\sqrt{5}]$ and $[\sqrt{5}, \infty)$; left-continuous at $-\sqrt{5}$ and right-continuous at $\sqrt{5}$ **53.** $(-\infty, -5)$, $(-5, 0)$, $(0, 5)$, and $(5, \infty)$ **55.** $a = 3, b = 0$
57.

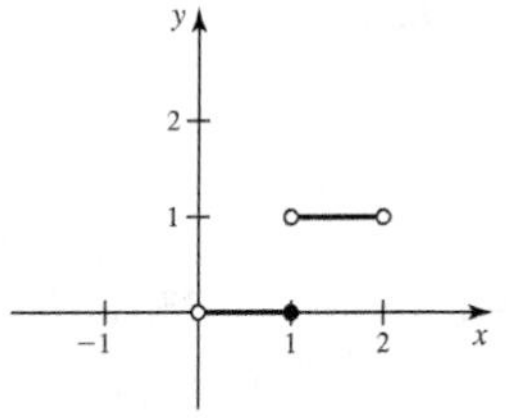

59. a. $m(0) < 30 < m(5)$ and $m(5) > 30 > m(15)$. **b.** $m = 30$ when $t \approx 2.4$ and $t \approx 10.8$. **c.** No; the maximum amount is approximately $m(5.5) \approx 38.5$. **61.** $\delta = \varepsilon$ **63.** $\delta = 1/\sqrt[4]{N}$

CHAPTER 3

Section 3.1 Exercises, pp. 133–135

1. Given the point $(a, f(a))$ and any point $(x, f(x))$ near $(a, f(a))$, the slope of the secant line joining these points is $\dfrac{f(x) - f(a)}{x - a}$. The limit of this quotient as x approaches a is the slope of the tangent line at the point. **3.** The average rate of change over the interval $[a, x]$ is $\dfrac{f(x) - f(a)}{x - a}$. The value of $\lim\limits_{x\to a} \dfrac{f(x) - f(a)}{x - a}$ is the slope of the tangent line; it is also the limit of average rates of change, which is the instantaneous rate of change at $x = a$. **5.** $f'(a)$ is the slope of the tangent line at $(a, f(a))$ or the instantaneous rate of change of f at a. **7.** $\dfrac{dy}{dx}$ is the limit of $\dfrac{\Delta y}{\Delta x}$ and is the rate of change of y with respect to x.

9. a. 6 **b.** $y = 6x - 14$
c.

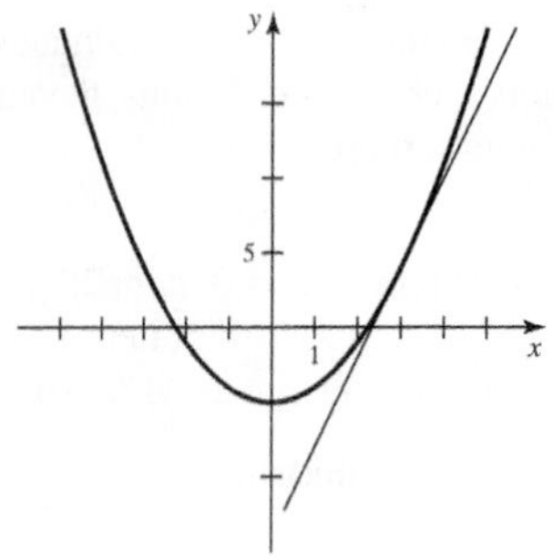

11. a. -5 **b.** $y = -5x + 1$
c.

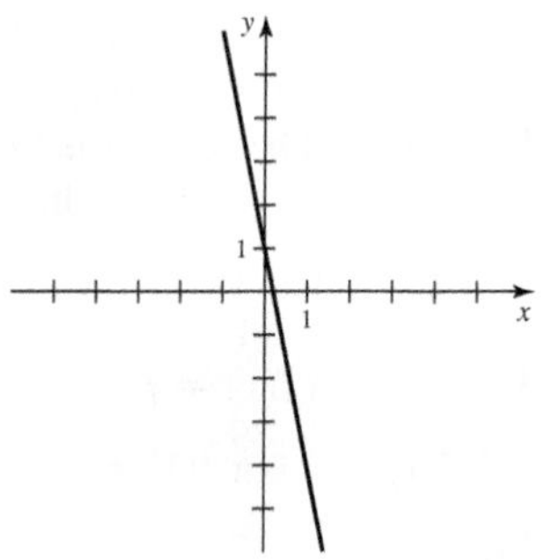

13. a. -1 **b.** $y = -x - 2$
c.

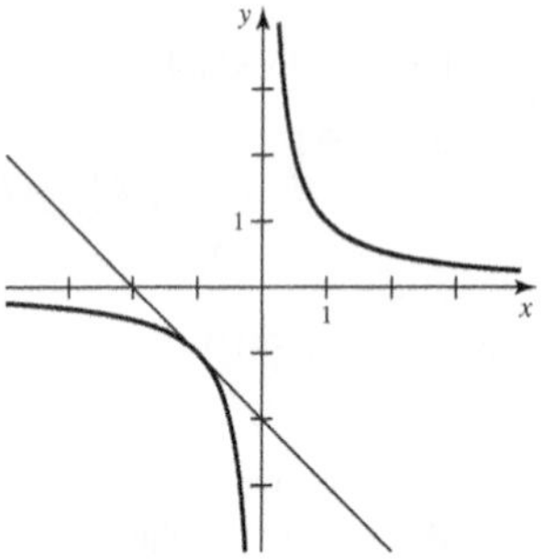

15. a. 2 **b.** $y = 2x + 1$

17. a. -7 **b.** $y = -7x$ **19. a.** 4 **b.** $y = 4x - 8$ **21. a.** 3 **b.** $y = 3x - 2$ **23. a.** $\frac{2}{25}$ **b.** $y = \frac{2}{25}x + \frac{7}{25}$ **25. a.** $\frac{1}{4}$ **b.** $y = \frac{1}{4}x + \frac{7}{4}$ **27. a.** $f'(-3) = 8$ **b.** $y = 8x$
29. a. $f'(-2) = -14$ **b.** $y = -14x - 16$ **31. a.** $f'(\frac{1}{4}) = -4$ **b.** $y = -4x + 3$ **33. a.** $\frac{1}{3}$ **b.** $y = \frac{1}{3}x + \frac{5}{3}$ **35. a.** $-\frac{1}{100}$ **b.** $y = -\frac{x}{100} + \frac{3}{20}$ **37. a.** $f'(x) = 6x + 2$ **b.** $y = 8x - 13$
c.

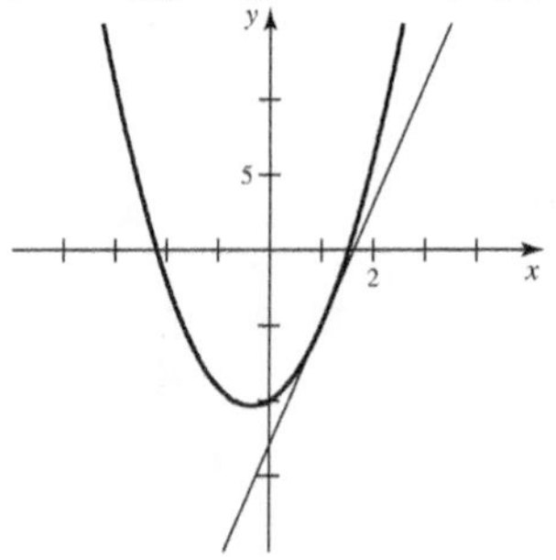

39. a. $f'(x) = 10x - 6$ **b.** $y = 14x - 19$
c.

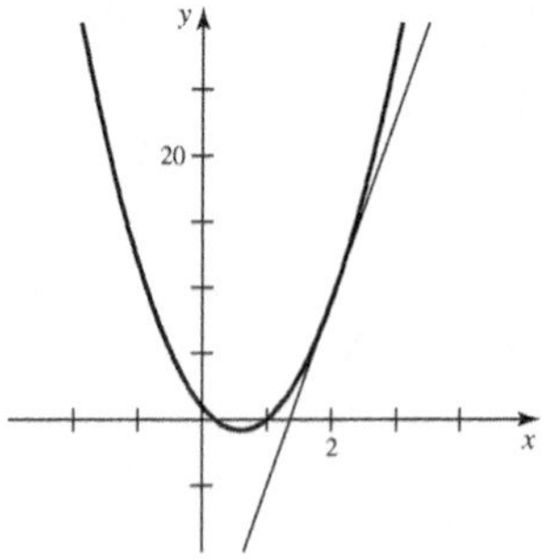

41. a. $2ax + b$ **b.** $8x - 3$ **c.** 5 **43.** $-\frac{1}{4}$ **45.** $\frac{1}{5}$ **47. a.** True **b.** False **c.** True **49. a.** $f'(x) = \dfrac{3}{2\sqrt{3x + 1}}$ **b.** $y = 3x/10 + 13/5$
51. a. $f'(x) = -\dfrac{6}{(3x + 1)^2}$ **b.** $y = -3x/2 - 5/2$ **53. a.** C, D **b.** A, B, E **c.** A, B, E, D, C **55. a.** Approximately 10 kW; approximately −5 kW **b.** $t = 6$ and $t = 18$ **c.** $t = 12$

57. $f(x) = \frac{1}{x+1}$; $a = 2$; $-\frac{1}{9}$ **59.** $f(x) = x^4$; $a = 2$; 32

61. No; f is not defined at $x = 2$. **63.** $a = 4$

65. a.

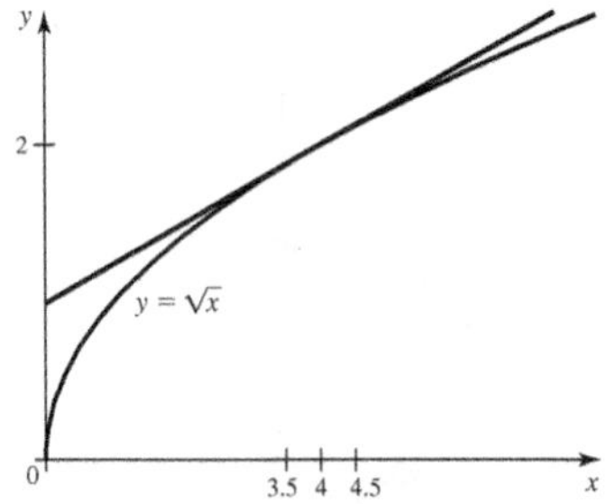

b.

h	Approximation	Error
0.1	0.25002	2.0×10^{-5}
0.01	0.25000	2.0×10^{-7}
0.001	0.25000	2.0×10^{-9}

c. Values of x on both sides of 4 are used in the formula.
d. The centered difference approximations are more accurate than the forward and backward difference approximations.
67. a. 0.39470, 0.41545 **b.** 0.02, 0.0003

Section 3.2 Exercises, pp. 141–143

1. The slope of a curve at a point is independent of the function value at that point. **3.** Yes **5.**

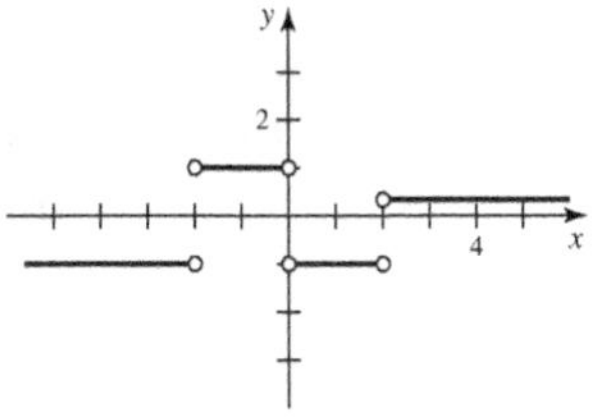

7. a–C; b–C; c–A; d–B **9.** a–D; b–C; c–B; d–A

11.

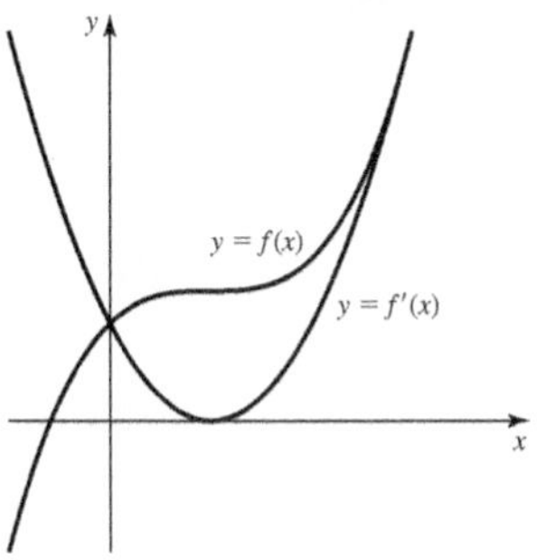

13.

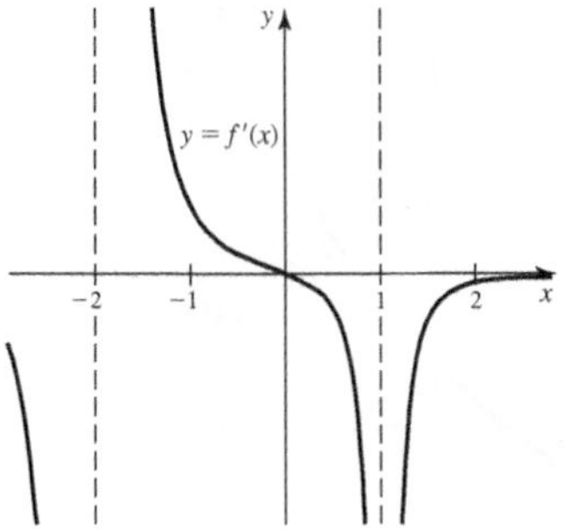

15. a. $x = 1$ **b.** $x = 1, x = 2$ **c.**

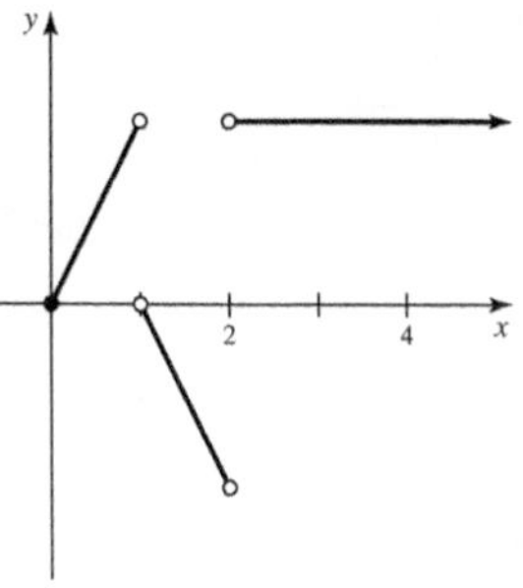

17. a. True **b.** True **c.** False

19. Yes

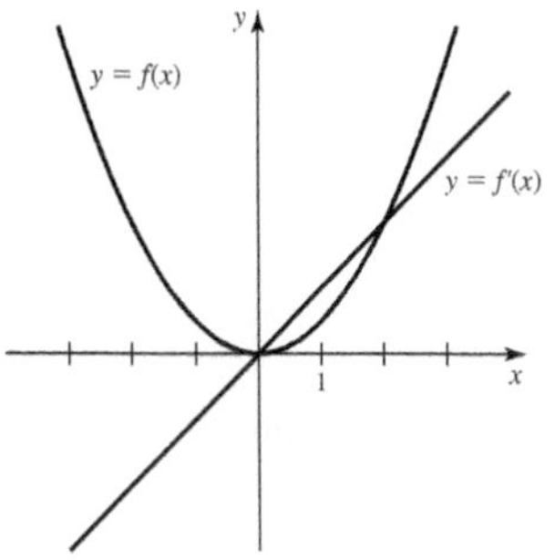

21. $y = -\frac{x}{3} - \frac{2}{3}$

23. $y = \frac{x}{2} + \frac{3}{2}$ **25.** $(1, 2), (5, 26)$ **27.** $(1, 1), \left(-\frac{1}{2}, -2\right)$

29. a. $t = 0$ **b.** Positive **c.** Decreasing
d.

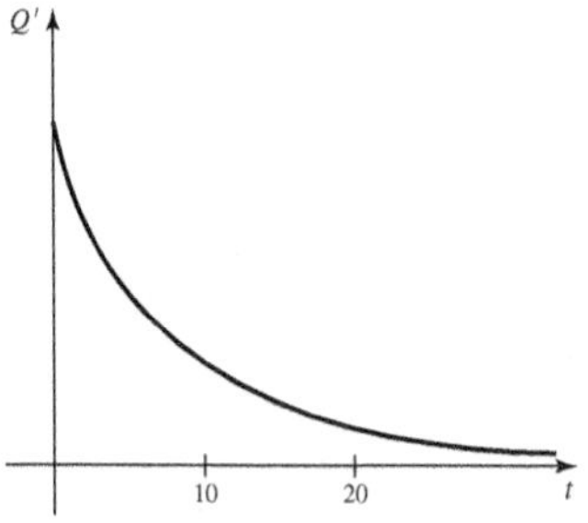

31. b. $f'_+(2) = 1, f'_-(2) = -1$ **c.** f is continuous but not differentiable at $x = 2$.

33. a. Vertical tangent line $x = 2$

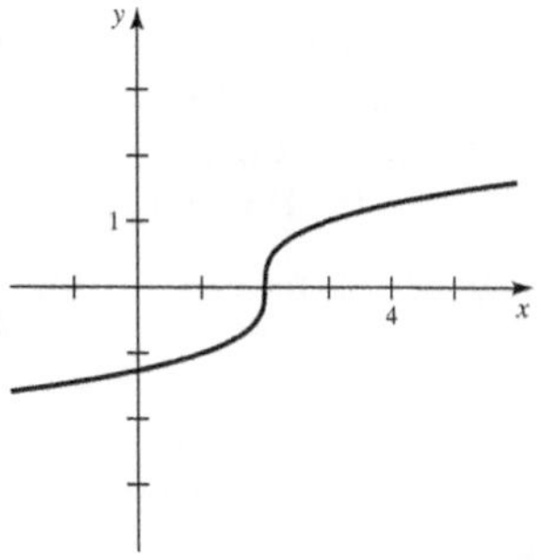

b. Vertical tangent line $x = -1$

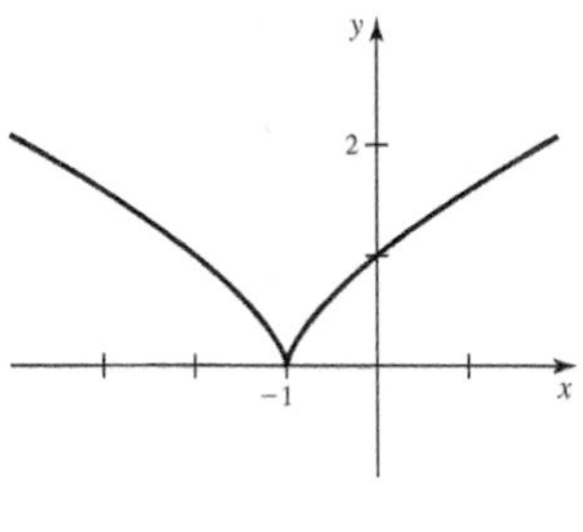

c. Vertical tangent line $x = 4$

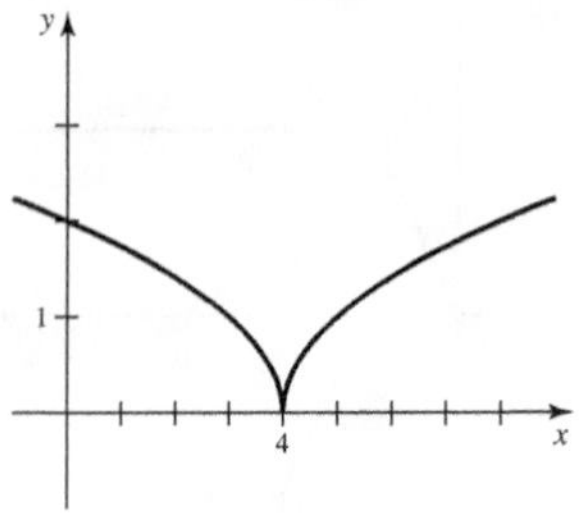

d. Vertical tangent line $x = 0$

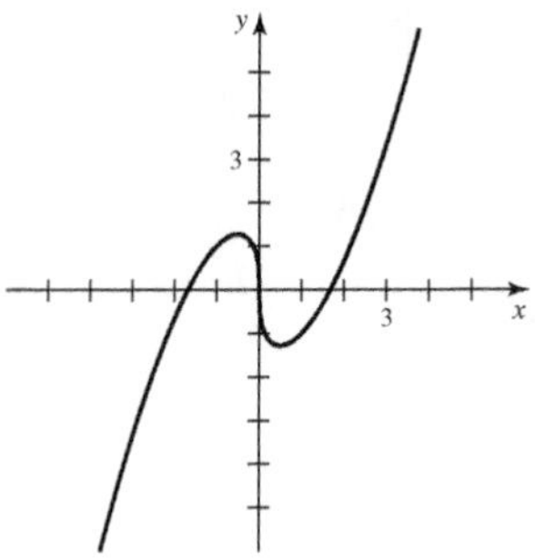

35. $f'(x) = \frac{1}{3}x^{-2/3}$ and $\lim_{x\to 0^-} |f'(x)| = \lim_{x\to 0^+} |f'(x)| = \infty$

37. a.

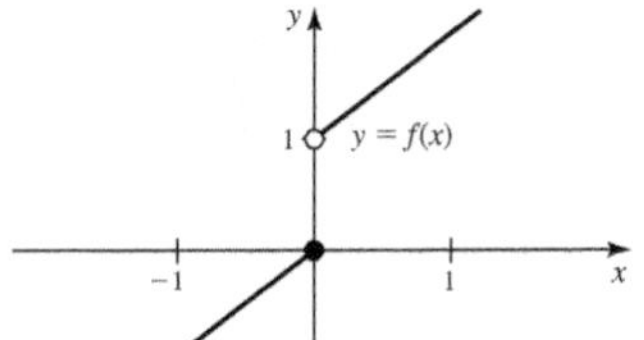

b. 1 **c.** 1 **d.**

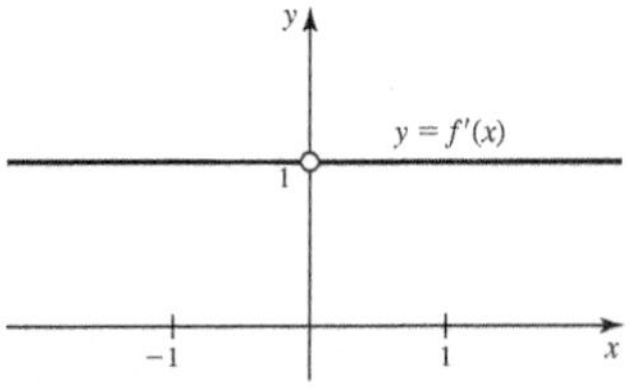

e. f is not differentiable at 0 because it is not continuous at 0.

Section 3.3 Exercises, pp. 150–153

1. Using the definition can be tedious. **3.** $f(x) = e^x$ **5.** Take the product of the constant and the derivative of the function. **7.** $5x^4$ **9.** 0 **11.** 1 **13.** $15x^2$ **15.** 8 **17.** $200t$ **19.** $12x^3 + 7$ **21.** $40x^3 - 32$ **23.** $6w^2 + 6w + 10$ **25.** $18x^2 + 6x + 4$ **27.** $4x^3 + 4x$ **29.** $2w$, for $w \neq 0$ **31.** 1, for $x \neq 1$ **33.** $\frac{1}{2\sqrt{x}}$, for $x \neq a$ **35. a.** $y = -6x + 5$
b.

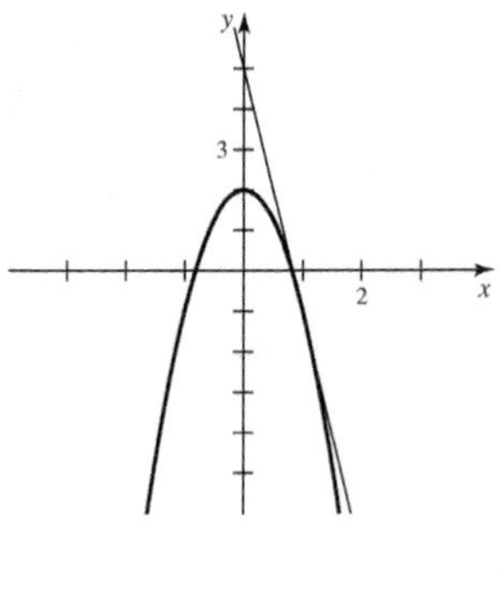

37. a. $y = 3x + 3 - 3\ln 3$ **b.**

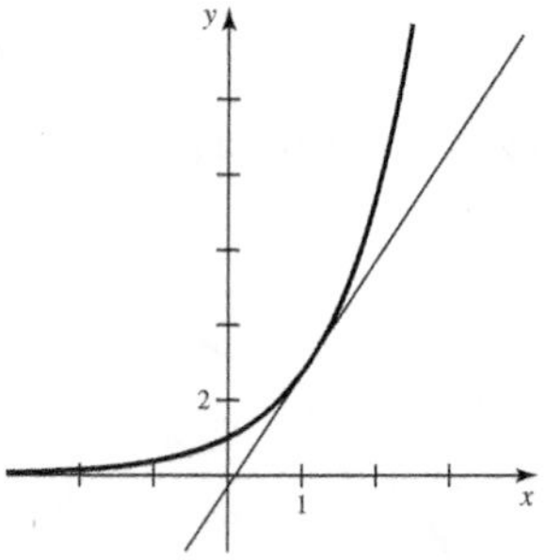

39. a. $x = 3$ **b.** $x = 4$ **41. a.** $(-1, 11), (2, -16)$ **b.** $(-3, -41), (4, 36)$ **43. a.** $(4, 4)$ **b.** $(16, 0)$ **45.** $f'(x) = 20x^3 + 30x^2 + 3$; $f''(x) = 60x^2 + 60x$; $f'''(x) = 120x + 60$
47. $f'(x) = 1; f''(x) = f'''(x) = 0,$ for $x \neq -1$ **49. a.** False **b.** True **c.** False **d.** False **e.** False **51. a.** $y = 7x - 1$ **b.** $y = -2x + 5$ **c.** $y = 16x + 4$ **53.** $b = 2, c = 3$ **55.** -10
57. 4 **59.** 7.5 **61. a.** $f(x) = \sqrt{x}; a = 9$ **b.** $f'(9) = \frac{1}{6}$
63. a. $f(x) = x^{100}$; $a = 1$ **b.** $f'(1) = 100$ **65.** 3 **67.** 1 **69.** $f(x) = e^x$; $a = 0$; $f'(0) = 1$ **71. a.** $d'(t) = 32t$; ft/s; the velocity of the stone **b.** 576 ft; approx. 131 mi/hr
73. a. $A'(t) = -\frac{1}{25}t + 2$ measures the rate at which the city grows in mi^2/yr. **b.** 1.6 mi^2/yr **c.** 1200 people/yr **77. d.** $\frac{n}{2}x^{n/2-1}$
79. c. $2e^{2x}$

Section 3.4 Exercises, pp. 160–162

1. $\frac{d}{dx}(f(x)\,g(x)) = f'(x)\,g(x) + f(x)\,g'(x)$ **3.** $\frac{d}{dx}(x^n) = nx^{n-1}$, for any integer n **5.** $y' = ke^{kx}$, for any real number k
7. $36x^5 - 12x^3$ **9.** $e^t t^4(t + 5)$ **11.** $4x^3$ **13.** $e^w(w^3 + 3w^2 - 1)$
15. a. $6x + 1$ **17. a.** $18y^5 - 52y^3 + 8y$ **19.** $\frac{1}{(x + 1)^2}$
21. $\frac{e^x}{(e^x + 1)^2}$ **23.** $e^{-x}(1 - x)$ **25.** $-\frac{1}{(t - 1)^2}$ **27.** $\frac{e^x(x^2 - 2x - 1)}{(x^2 - 1)^2}$
29. a. $2w$, for $w \neq 0$ **31.** 1, for $x \neq a$ **33. a.** $y = -3x/2 + 17/2$
b.

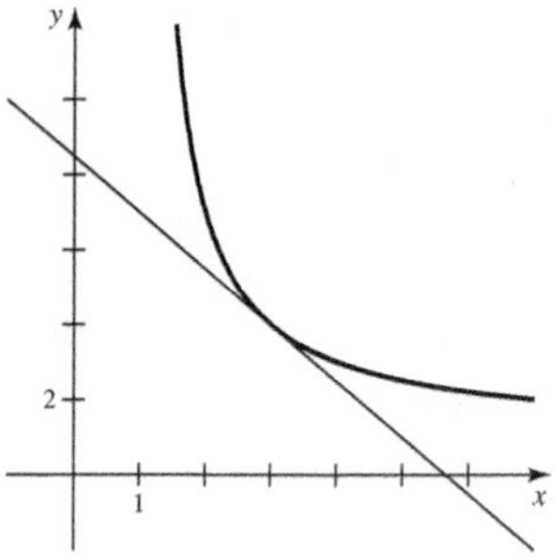

35. a. $y = 3x + 1$ **b.**

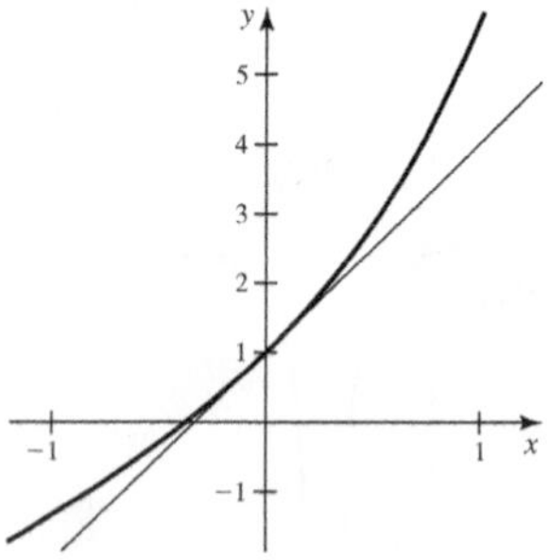

37. $-27x^{-10}$ **39.** $6t - 42/t^8$ **41.** $-3/t^2 - 2/t^3$ **43.** $e^{7x}(7x + 1)$
45. $45e^{3x}$ **47.** $e^{-3x}(1 - 3x)$ **49.** $\frac{2}{3}e^x - e^{-x}$

51. a. $p'(t) = \left(\frac{20}{t+2}\right)^2$ **b.** $p'(5) \approx 8.16$ **c.** $t = 0$
d. $\lim_{t\to\infty} p'(t) = 0$; the population approaches a steady state.
e.

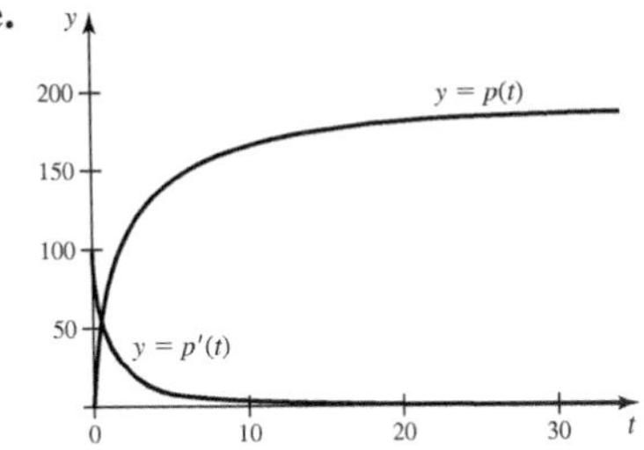

53. a. $Q'(t) = -1.386e^{-0.0693t}$ **b.** -1.386 mg/hr; -1.207 mg/hr **c.** $\lim_{t\to\infty} Q(t) = 0$—eventually none of the drug remains in the bloodstream; $\lim_{t\to\infty} Q'(t) = 0$—the rate at which the body excretes the drug goes to zero over time. **55. a.** $x = -\frac{1}{2}$ **b.** The line tangent to the graph of $f(x)$ at $x = -\frac{1}{2}$ is horizontal. **57.** $\frac{e^x(x^2 - x - 5)}{(x-2)^2}$
59. $\frac{e^x(x^2 + x + 1)}{(x+1)^2}$ **61. a.** False **b.** False **c.** False **d.** True
63. $f'(x) = xe^{3x}(3x + 2)$
$f''(x) = e^{3x}(9x^2 + 12x + 2)$
$f'''(x) = 9e^{3x}(3x^2 + 6x + 2)$
65. $f'(x) = \frac{x^2 + 2x - 7}{(x+1)^2}$; $f''(x) = \frac{16}{(x+1)^3}$
67. $8x - \frac{2}{(5x+1)^2}$ **69.** $\frac{r - 6\sqrt{r} - 1}{2\sqrt{r}(r+1)^2}$
71. $300x^9 + 135x^8 + 105x^6 + 120x^3 + 45x^2 + 15$
73. a. $y = -\frac{108}{169}x + \frac{567}{169}$ **b.**

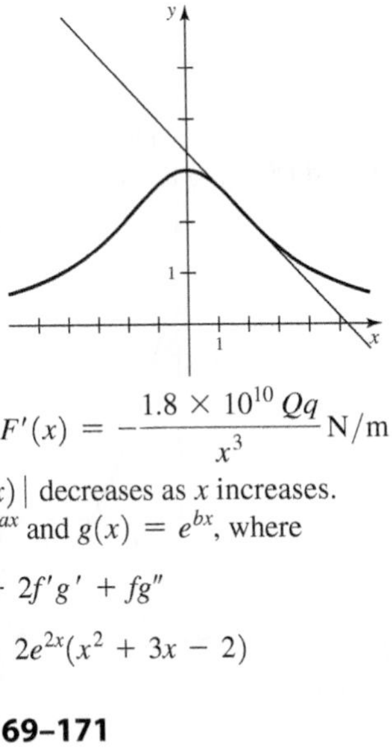

75. $-\frac{3}{2}$ **77.** $\frac{1}{9}$ **79.** $\frac{7}{8}$ **81. a.** $F'(x) = -\frac{1.8 \times 10^{10}\,Qq}{x^3}$ N/m
b. -1.8×10^{19} N/m **c.** $|F'(x)|$ decreases as x increases.
83. One possible pair: $f(x) = e^{ax}$ and $g(x) = e^{bx}$, where $b = \frac{a}{a-1}$, $a \neq 1$ **87.** $f''g + 2f'g' + fg''$
91. a. $f'gh + fg'h + fgh'$ **b.** $2e^{2x}(x^2 + 3x - 2)$

Section 3.5 Exercises, pp. 169–171

1. $\frac{\sin x}{x}$ is undefined at $x = 0$. **3.** The tangent and cotangent functions are defined as ratios of the sine and cosine functions.
5. -1 **7.** 3 **9.** $\frac{7}{3}$ **11.** 5 **13.** 7 **15.** $\frac{1}{4}$ **17.** $\cos x - \sin x$
19. $e^{-x}(\cos x - \sin x)$ **21.** $\sin x + x\cos x$ **23.** $-\frac{1}{1 + \sin x}$
25. $\cos^2 x - \sin^2 x = \cos 2x$ **27.** $-2\sin x\cos x = -\sin 2x$
33. $\sec x\tan x - \csc x\cot x$ **35.** $e^{5x}\csc x(5 - \cot x)$

37. $-\frac{\csc x}{1 + \csc x}$ **39.** $\cos^2 z - \sin^2 z = \cos 2z$ **41.** $2\cos x - x\sin x$
43. $2e^x\cos x$ **45.** $2\csc^2 x\cot x$ **47.** $2(\sec^2 x\tan x + \csc^2 x\cot x)$
49. a. False **b.** False **c.** True **d.** True **51.** a/b **53.** $\frac{3}{4}$
55. 0 **57.** $x\cos 2x + \frac{1}{2}\sin 2x$ **59.** $\frac{1}{2\sin x\cos x - 1}$
61. $\frac{2\sin x}{(1 + \cos x)^2}$ **63. a.** $y = \sqrt{3}x + 2 - \frac{\pi\sqrt{3}}{6}$
b.

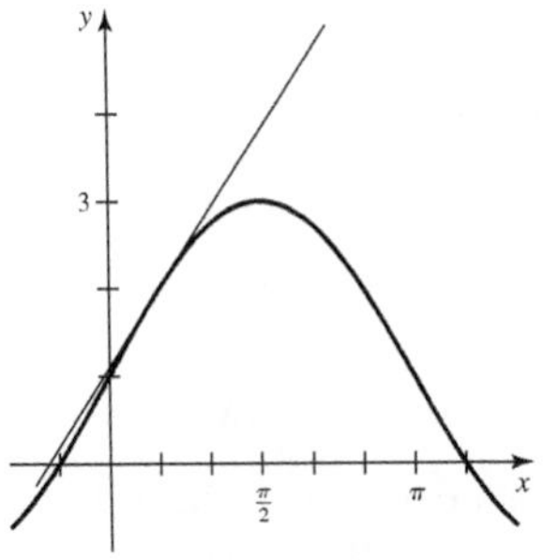

65. a. $y = -2\sqrt{3}x + \frac{2\sqrt{3}\pi}{3} + 1$ **b.**

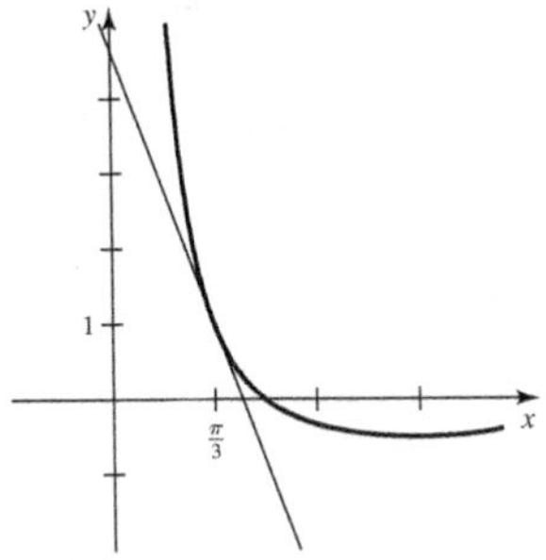

67. $x = 7\pi/6 + 2k\pi$ and $x = 11\pi/6 + 2k\pi$, where k is an integer
69. a.

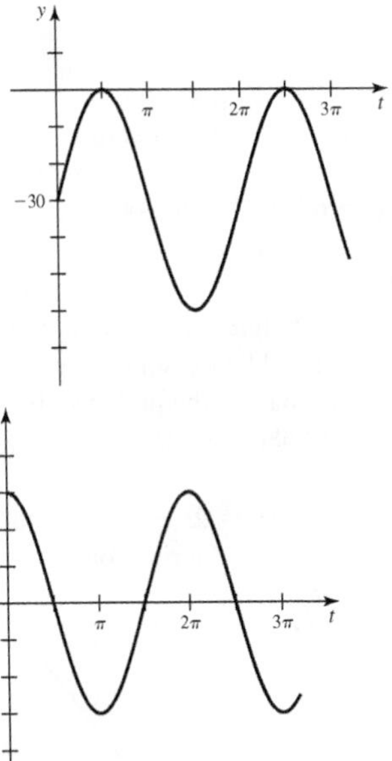

b. $v(t) = 30\cos t$

c.

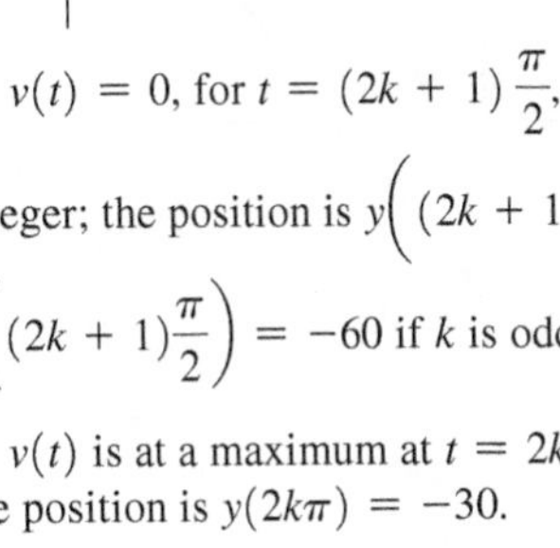

d. $v(t) = 0$, for $t = (2k + 1)\frac{\pi}{2}$, where k is any nonnegative integer; the position is $y\left((2k+1)\frac{\pi}{2}\right) = 0$ if k is even or $y\left((2k+1)\frac{\pi}{2}\right) = -60$ if k is odd.

e. $v(t)$ is at a maximum at $t = 2k\pi$, where k is a nonnegative integer; the position is $y(2k\pi) = -30$.

f. $a(t) = -30 \sin t$

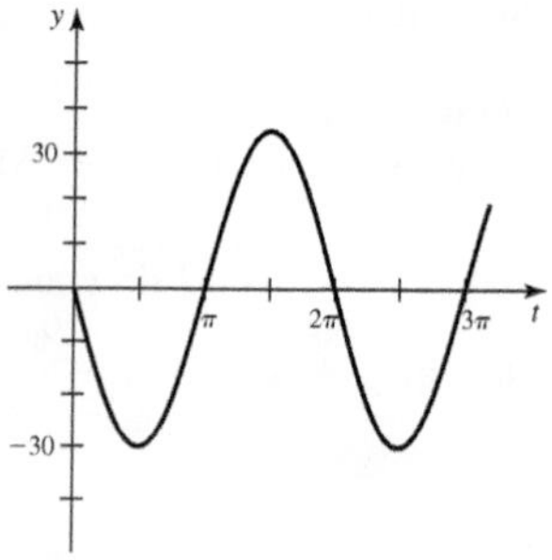

77. $a = 0$ **79. a.** $2 \sin x \cos x$ **b.** $3 \sin^2 x \cos x$ **c.** $4 \sin^3 x \cos x$ **d.** $n \sin^{n-1} x \cos x$; the conjecture is true for $n = 1$. If it holds for $n = k$, then when $n = k + 1$, we have $\frac{d}{dx}(\sin^{k+1} x) = \frac{d}{dx}(\sin^k x \cdot \sin x) = \sin^k x \cos x + \sin x \cdot k \sin^{k-1} x \cos x = (k + 1) \sin^k x \cos x$. **81. a.** $f(x) = \sin x$; $a = \pi/6$ **b.** $\sqrt{3}/2$ **83. a.** $f(x) = \cot x$; $a = \pi/4$ **b.** -2 **85.** Because D is a difference quotient for f (and $h = 0.01$ is small), D is a good approximation to f'. Therefore, the graph of D is nearly indistinguishable from the graph of $f'(x) = \cos x$.

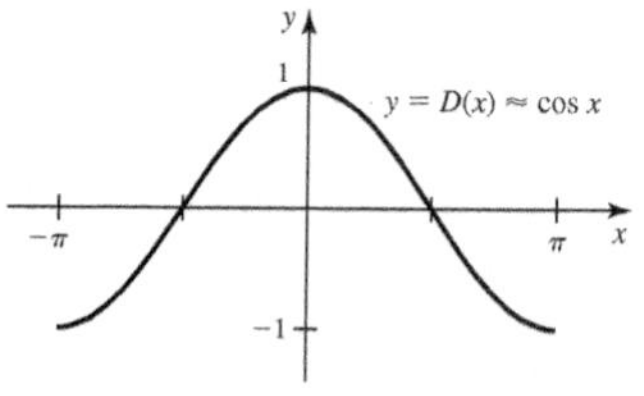

Section 3.6 Exercises, pp. 180–185

1. The average rate of change is $\frac{f(x + \Delta x) - f(x)}{\Delta x}$, whereas the instantaneous rate of change is the limit as Δx goes to zero in this quotient. **3.** Small **5.** If the position of the object at time t is $s(t)$, then the acceleration at time t is $a(t) = d^2 s/dt^2$. **7.** Each of the first 200 stoves costs, on average, \$70 to produce. When 200 stoves have already been produced, the 201st stove costs \$65 to produce.
9. a. 40 mi/hr **b.** 40 mi/hr; yes **c.** −60 mi/hr; −60 mi/hr; south **d.** The police car drives away from the police station going north until about 10:08, when it turns around and heads south, toward the police station. It continues south until it passes the police station at about 11:02 and keeps going south until about 11:40, when it turns around and heads north.
11. a.

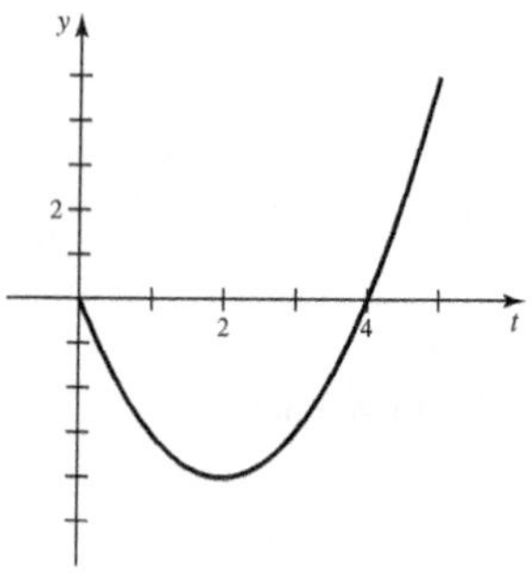

b. $v(t) = 2t - 4$; stationary at $t = 2$, to the right on $(2, 5]$, to the left on $[0, 2)$

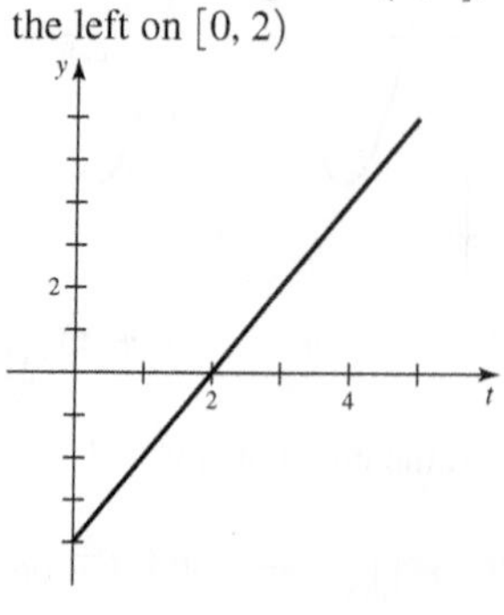

c. $v(1) = -2$ ft/s; $a(1) = 2$ ft/s^2 **d.** $a(2) = 2$ ft/s^2 **e.** $(2, 5]$
13. a.

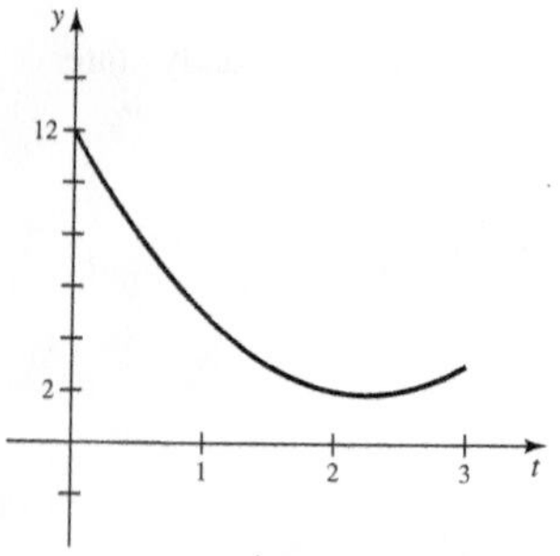

b. $v(t) = 4t - 9$; stationary at $t = \frac{9}{4}$, to the right on $\left(\frac{9}{4}, 3\right]$, to the left on $\left[0, \frac{9}{4}\right)$

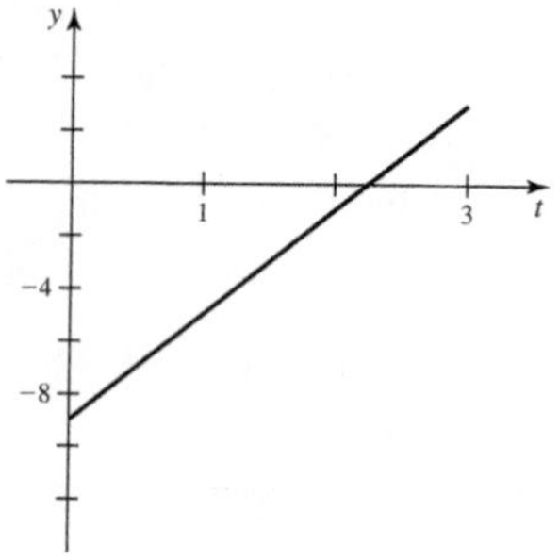

c. $v(1) = -5$ ft/s; $a(1) = 4$ ft/s^2 **d.** $a\left(\frac{9}{4}\right) = 4$ ft/s^2 **e.** $\left(\frac{9}{4}, 3\right]$
15. a.

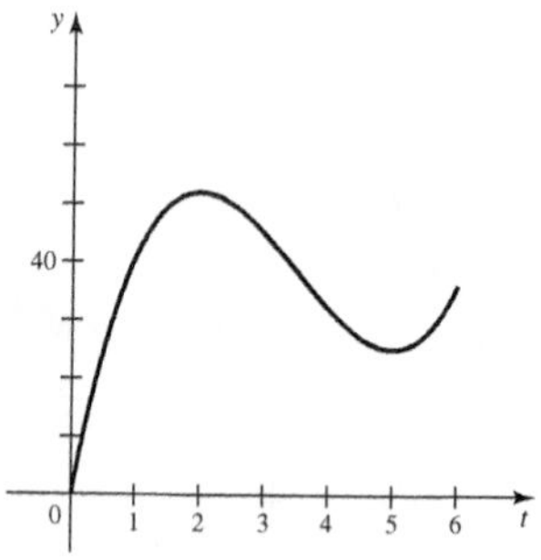

b. $v(t) = 6t^2 - 42t + 60$; stationary at $t = 2$ and $t = 5$, to the right on $[0, 2)$ and $(5, 6]$, to the left on $(2, 5)$

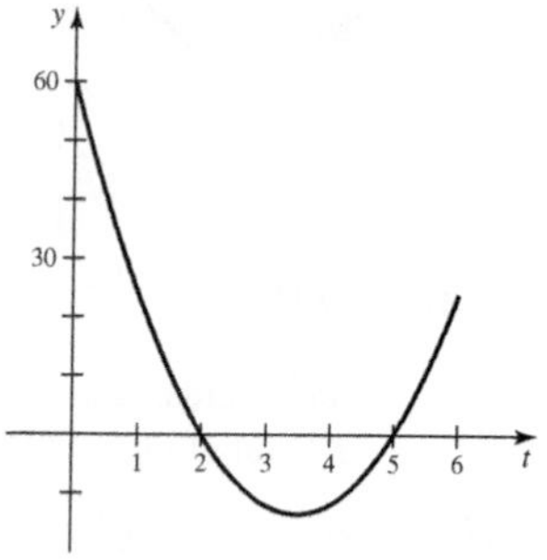

c. $v(1) = 24$ ft/s; $a(1) = -30$ ft/s^2 **d.** $a(2) = -18$ ft/s; $a(5) = 18$ ft/s^2 **e.** $\left(2, \frac{7}{2}\right), (5, 6]$ **17. a.** $v(t) = -32t + 64$ **b.** At $t = 2$ **c.** 96 ft **d.** At $2 + \sqrt{6}$ **e.** $-32\sqrt{6}$ ft/s **f.** $(2, 2 + \sqrt{6})$ **19. a.** 98,300 people/yr in 2005 **b.** 99,920 people/yr in 1997; 95,600 people/yr in 2005 **c.** $p'(t) = -0.54t + 101$; population increased, growth rate is positive but decreasing
21. a. $\overline{C}(x) = \frac{1000}{x} + 0.1$; $C'(x) = 0.1$
b. $\overline{C}(2000) = \$0.60$/item; $C'(2000) = \$0.10$/item
c. The average cost per item when 2000 items are produced is \$0.60/item. The cost of producing the 2001st item is \$0.10.

23. a. $\overline{C}(x) = -0.01x + 40 + 100/x$; $C'(x) = -0.02x + 40$
b. $\overline{C}(1000) = \$30.10/\text{item}$; $C'(1000) = \$20/\text{item}$
c. The average cost per item is about \$30.10 when 1000 items are produced. The cost of producing the 1001st item is \$20.
25. a. 20 **b.** \$20 **c.** $E(p) = \frac{p}{p-20}$ **d.** Elastic for $p > 10$; inelastic for $0 < p < 10$ **e.** 2.5% **f.** 2.5% **27.** $E(p) = -bp$; elastic for $p > \frac{1}{b}$; inelastic for $0 < p < \frac{1}{b}$ **29. a.** False **b.** True **c.** False **d.** True **31.** 240 ft **33.** 64 ft/s **35. a.** $t = 1, 2, 3$
b. It is moving in the positive direction for t in $(0, 1)$ and $(2, 3)$; it is moving in the negative direction for t in $(1, 2)$ and $t > 3$.
c.

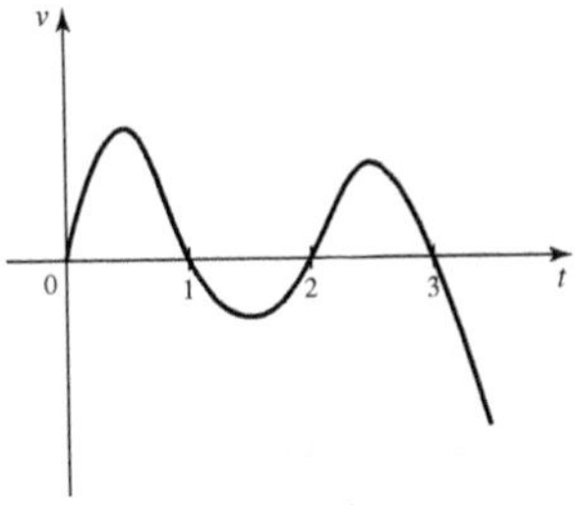

d. $\left(0, \frac{1}{2}\right), \left(1, \frac{3}{2}\right), \left(2, \frac{5}{2}\right), (3, \infty)$

37. a. $P(x) = 0.02x^2 + 50x - 100$
b. $\dfrac{P(x)}{x} = 0.02x + 50 - \dfrac{100}{x}$; $\dfrac{dP}{dx} = 0.04x + 50$
c. $\dfrac{P(500)}{500} = 59.8$; $\dfrac{dp}{dx}(500) = 70$
d. The profit, on average, for each of the first 500 items produced is 59.8; the profit for the 501st item produced is 70.
39. a. $P(x) = 0.04x^2 + 100x - 800$
b. $\dfrac{P(x)}{x} = 0.04x + 100 - \dfrac{800}{x}$; $\dfrac{dp}{dx} = 0.08x + 100$
c. $\dfrac{P(1000)}{1000} = 139.2$; $p'(1000) = 180$
d. The average profit per item for each of the first 1000 items produced is \$139.20. The profit for the 1001st item produced is \$180.
41. a. 1930, 1.1 million people/yr **b.** 1960, 2.9 million people/yr
c. The population was never decreasing.
d. (1905, 1915), (1930, 1960), (1980, 1990)

43. a.

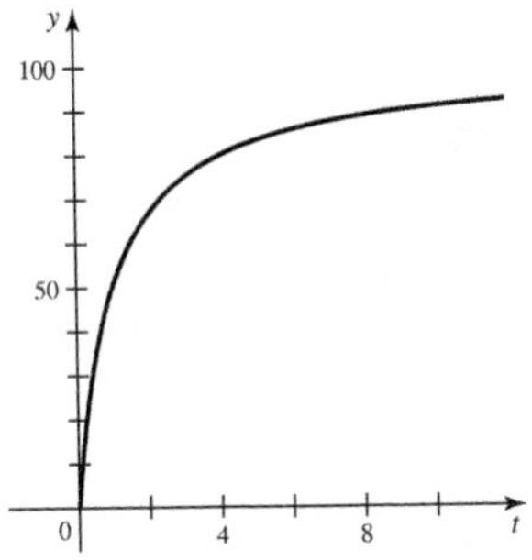

b. $v = \dfrac{100}{(t+1)^2}$

c.

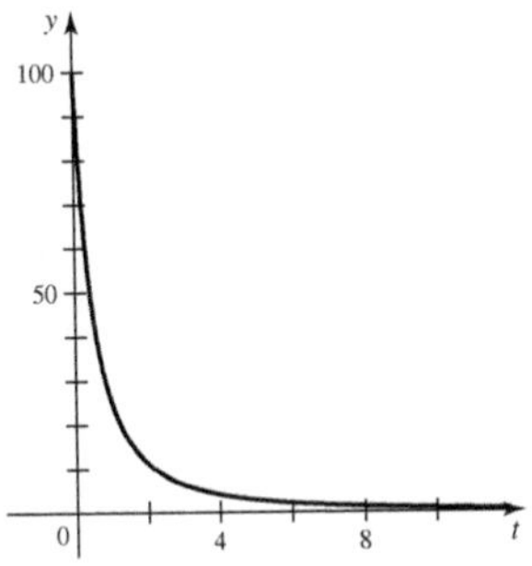

The marble moves fastest at the beginning and slows considerably over the first 5 s. It continues to slow but never actually stops.
d. $t = 4$ s **e.** $t = -1 + \sqrt{2} \approx 0.414$ s

45. a. $C'(x) = -\dfrac{125{,}000{,}000}{x^2} + 1.5$;
$\overline{C}(x) = \dfrac{C(x)}{25{,}000} = 50 + \dfrac{5000}{x} + 0.00006x$

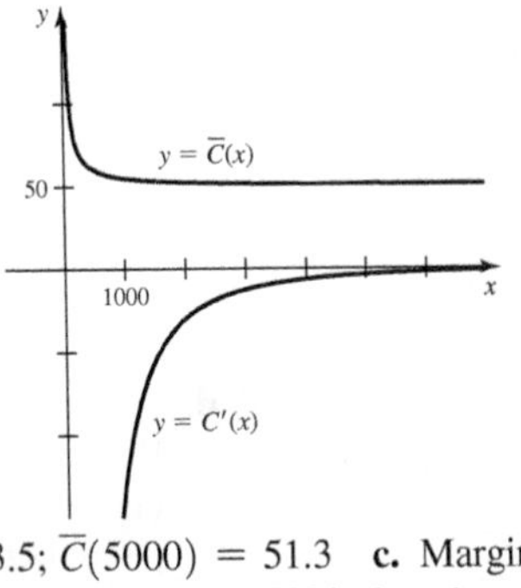

b. $C'(5000) = -3.5$; $\overline{C}(5000) = 51.3$ **c.** Marginal cost: If the batch size is increased from 5000 to 5001, then the cost of producing 25,000 gadgets will *decrease* by about \$3.50. Average cost: When batch size is 5000, it costs \$51.30 *per item* to produce all 25,000 gadgets.
47. a. $R(p) = \dfrac{100p}{p^2 + 1}$

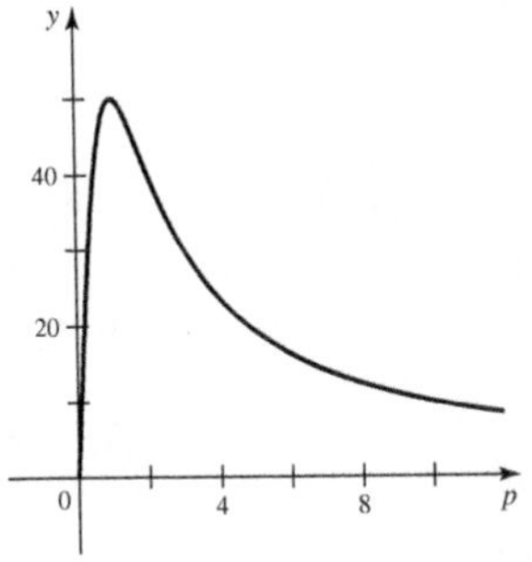

b. $R'(p) = \dfrac{100(1 - p^2)}{(p^2 + 1)^2}$
c. $p = 1$

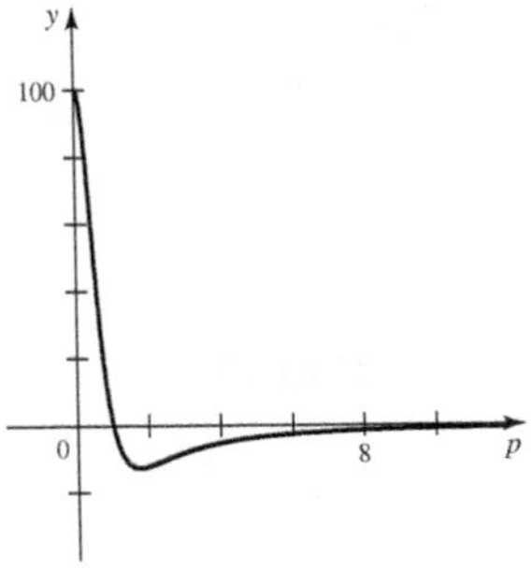

49. a.

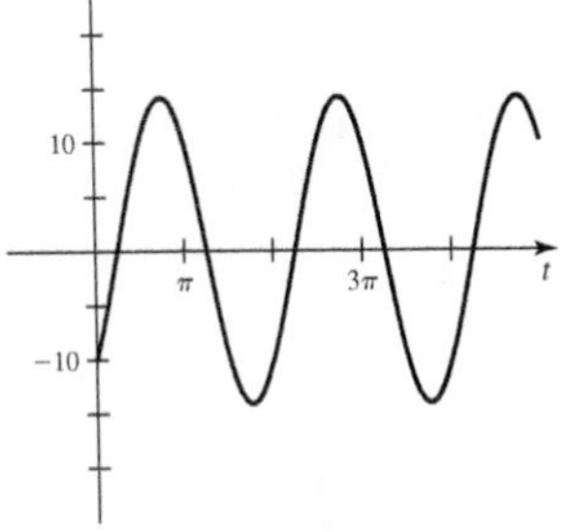

b. $dx/dt = 10 \cos t + 10 \sin t$ **c.** $t = 3\pi/4 + k\pi$, where k is any positive integer **d.** The graph implies that the spring never stops oscillating. In reality, the weight would eventually come to rest.
51. a. Juan starts faster than Jean and opens up a big lead. Then Juan slows down while Jean speeds up. Jean catches up, and the race finishes in a tie. **b.** Same average velocity **c.** Tie **d.** At $t = 2$, $\theta'(2) = \pi/2$ rad/min; $\theta'(4) = \pi$ = Jean's greatest velocity
e. At $t = 2$, $\varphi'(2) = \pi/2$ rad/min; $\varphi'(0) = \pi$ = Juan's greatest velocity

53. a. $v(0) = 4{,}000{,}000\text{ m}^3$

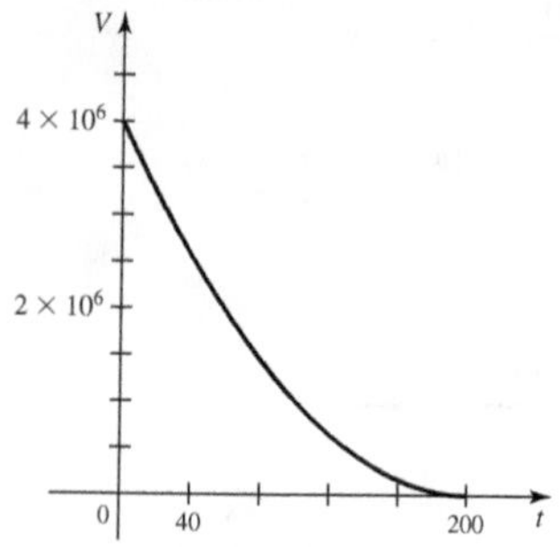

b. 200 hr

c.

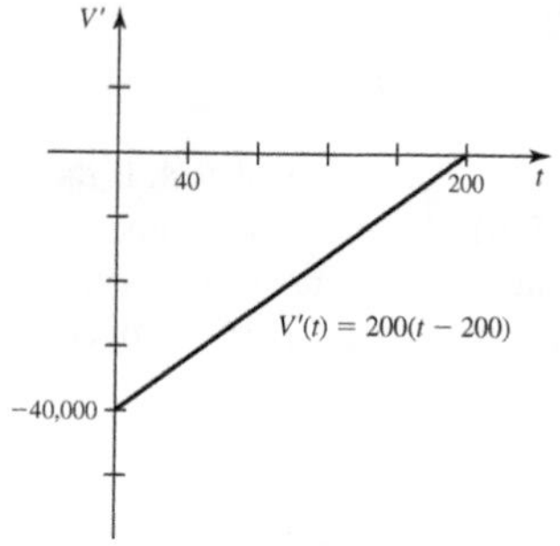

d. The magnitude of the flow rate is greatest (most negative) at $t = 0$ and least (zero) at $t = 200$.

55. a. $v(t) = -15e^{-t}(\sin t + \cos t)$; $v(1) \approx -7.6$ m/s, $v(3) \approx 0.63$ m/s **b.** Down (0, 2.4) and (5.5, 8.6); up (2.4, 5.5) and (8.6, 10) **c.** ≈ 0.65 m/s **57. a.** $-T'(1) = -80, -T'(3) = 80$ **b.** $-T'(x) < 0$ for $0 \le x < 2$; $-T'(x) > 0$ for $2 < x \le 4$ **c.** Near $x = 0$, with $x > 0$, $-T'(x) < 0$, so heat flows toward the end of the rod. Similarly, near $x = 4$, with $x < 4$, $-T'(x) > 0$.

Section 3.7 Exercises, pp. 191–194

1. $\dfrac{dy}{dx} = \dfrac{dy}{du}\cdot\dfrac{du}{dx}$; $\dfrac{d}{dx}(f(g(x))) = f'(g(x))\cdot g'(x)$ **3.** $g(x), x$ **5.** Outer: $f(x) = x^{-5}$; inner: $u = x^2 + 10$ **7.** $30(3x+7)^9$ **9.** $5\sin^4 x\cos x$ **11.** $5e^{5x-7}$ **13.** $\dfrac{x}{\sqrt{x^2+1}}$ **15.** $10x\sec^2(5x^2)$ **17.** $e^x\sec e^x\tan e^x$ **19.** $10(6x+7)(3x^2+7x)^9$ **21.** $\dfrac{5}{\sqrt{10x+1}}$ **23.** $-\dfrac{315x^2}{(7x^3+1)^4}$ **25.** $3\sec(3x+1)\tan(3x+1)$ **27.** $e^x\sec^2 e^x$ **29.** $(12x^2+3)\cos(4x^3+3x+1)$ **31.** $\dfrac{\cos(2\sqrt{x})}{\sqrt{x}}$ **33.** $5\sec x(\sec x + \tan x)^5$ **35. a.** $u = \cos x$, $y = u^3$; $\dfrac{dy}{dx} = -3\cos^2 x\sin x$ **b.** $u = x^3$, $y = \cos u$; $\dfrac{dy}{dx} = -3x^2\sin x^3$ **37. a.** 100 **b.** −100 **c.** −16 **d.** 40 **e.** 40 **39.** −0.297 hPa/min **41.** $y' = 25(12x^5 - 9x^2)(2x^6 - 3x^3 + 3)^{24}$ **43.** $y' = 30(1 + 2\tan x)^{14}\sec^2 x$ **45.** $y' = -\dfrac{\cot x\csc^2 x}{\sqrt{1+\cot^2 x}}$ **47.** $e^x\cos(\sin e^x)\cos e^x$ **49.** $y' = -15\sin^4(\cos 3x)(\sin 3x)(\cos(\cos 3x))$ **51.** $y' = \dfrac{3e^{\sqrt{3x}}}{2\sqrt{3x}}\sec^2 e^{\sqrt{3x}}$ **53.** $y' = \dfrac{1}{2\sqrt{x+\sqrt{x}}}\left(1 + \dfrac{1}{2\sqrt{x}}\right)$ **55.** $y' = f'(g(x^2))g'(x^2)\,2x$ **57.** $\dfrac{5x^4}{(x+1)^6}$ **59.** $xe^{x^2+1}(2\sin x^3 + 3x\cos x^3)$ **61.** $\theta\sec 5\theta(2 + 5\theta\tan 5\theta)$ **63.** $4((x+2)(x^2+1))^3(3x+1)(x+1)$ **65.** $\dfrac{2x^3 - \sin 2x}{\sqrt{x^4 + \cos 2x}}$ **67.** $2(p+\pi)(\sin p^2 + p(p+\pi)\cos p^2)$ **69. a.** True **b.** True **c.** True **d.** False **71.** $2\cos x^2 - 4x^2\sin x^2$ **73.** $4e^{-2x^2}(4x^2-1)$ **75.** $y' = \dfrac{f'(x)}{2\sqrt{f(x)}}$ **77.** $y = -9x + 35$

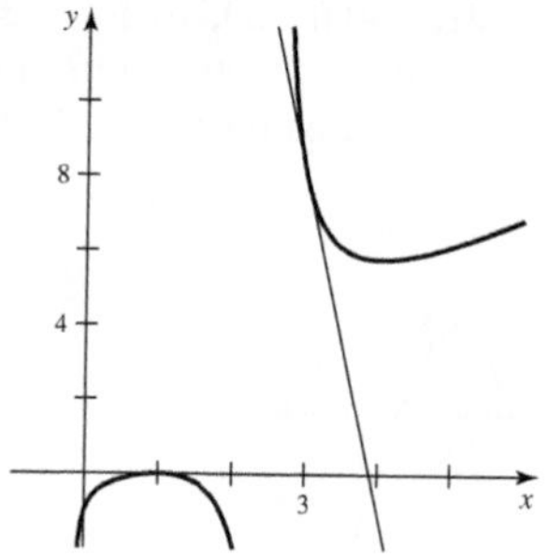

79. a. $h(4) = 9, h'(4) = -6$ **b.** $y = -6x + 33$ **81.** $y = 6x + 3 - 3\ln 3$

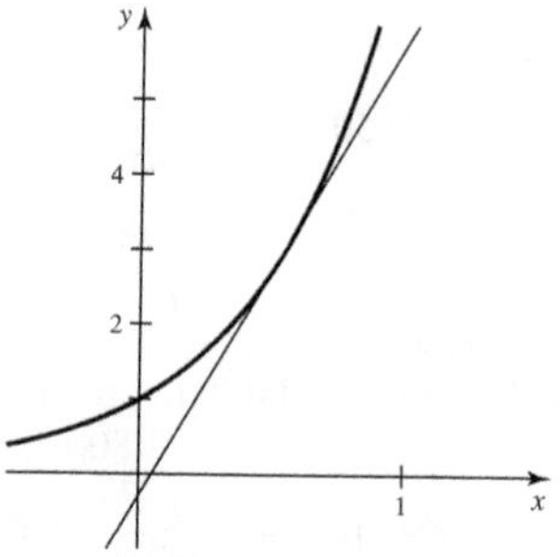

83. a. -3π **b.** -5π **85. a.** $\dfrac{d^2y}{dt^2} = \dfrac{-y_0k}{m}\cos\left(t\sqrt{\dfrac{k}{m}}\right)$ **87. a.**

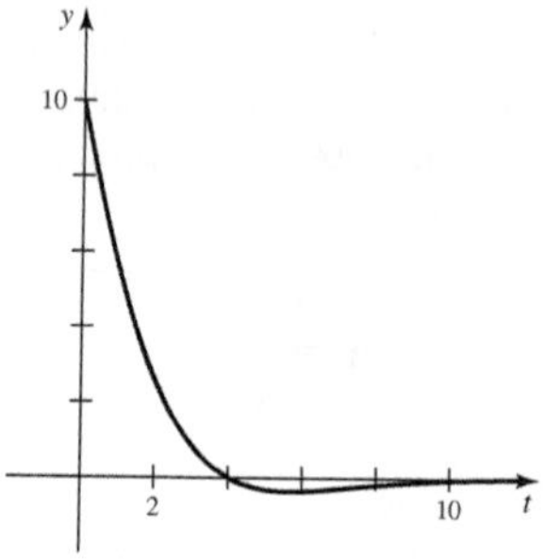

b. $v(t) = -5e^{-t/2}\left(\dfrac{\pi}{4}\sin\dfrac{\pi t}{8} + \cos\dfrac{\pi t}{8}\right)$

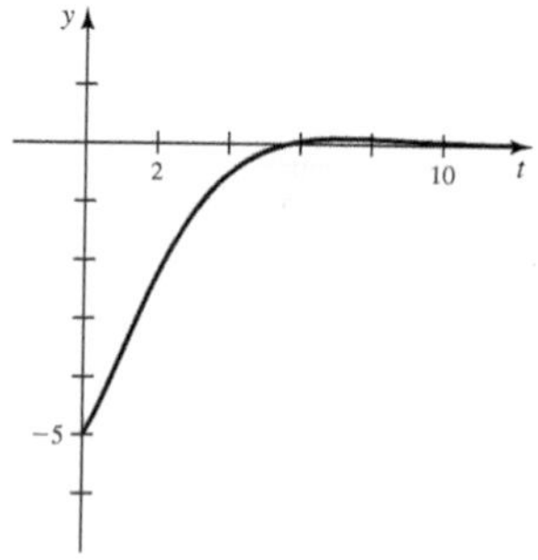

89. a. 10.88 hr **b.** $D'(t) = \frac{6\pi}{365}\sin\left(\frac{2\pi(t + 10)}{365}\right)$
c. 2.87 min/day; on March 1, the length of day is increasing at a rate of about 2.87 min/day.
d.

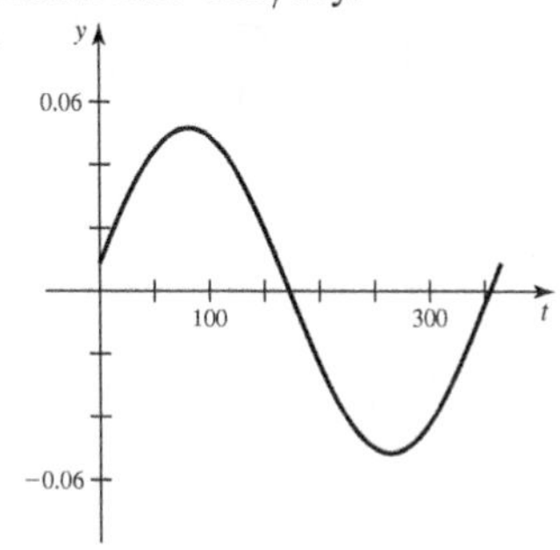

e. Most rapidly; approximately March 22 and September 22; least rapidly: approximately December 21 and June 21

91. a. $E'(t) = 400 + 200\cos\frac{\pi t}{12}$ MW **b.** At noon; $E'(0) = 600$ MW **c.** At midnight; $E'(12) = 200$ MW
d.

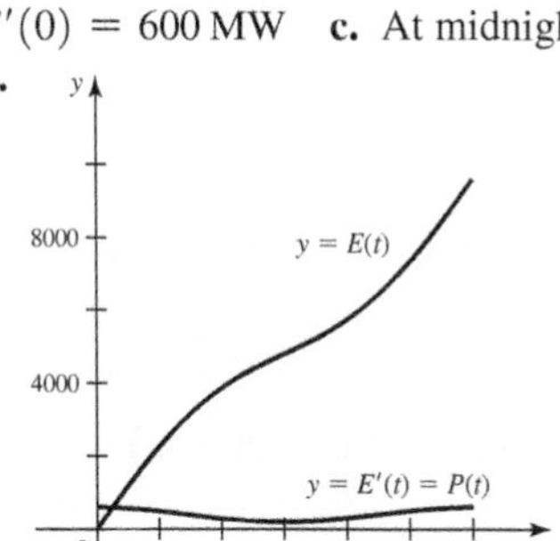

93. a. $f'(x) = -2\cos x\sin x + 2\sin x\cos x = 0$
b. $f(0) = \cos^2 0 + \sin^2 0 = 1$; $f(x) = 1$ for all x; that is, $\cos^2 x + \sin^2 x = 1$ **97. a.** $h(x) = (x^2 - 3)^5$; $a = 2$ **b.** 20 **99. a.** $h(x) = \sin x^2$; $a = \pi/2$ **b.** $\pi\cos(\pi^2/4)$ **101.** $10f'(25)$

Section 3.8 Exercises, pp. 200–202

1. There may be more than one expression for y or y'. **3.** When derived implicitly, dy/dx is usually given in terms of both x and y.
5. a. $-\frac{x^3}{y^3}$ **b.** 1 **7. a.** $\frac{2}{y}$ **b.** 1 **9. a.** $\frac{20x^3}{\cos y}$ **b.** −20
11. a. $-\frac{1}{\sin y}$ **b.** −1 **13.** $\frac{1 - y\cos xy}{x\cos xy - 1}$ **15.** $-\frac{1}{1 + \sin y}$
17. $\frac{1}{2y\sin y^2 + e^y}$ **19.** $\frac{3x^2(x - y)^2 + 2y}{2x}$ **21.** $\frac{13y - 18x^2}{21y^2 - 13x}$
23. $\frac{5\sqrt{x^4 + y^2} - 2x^3}{y - 6y^2\sqrt{x^4 + y^2}}$ **25. a.** $2^2 + 2 \cdot 1 + 1^2 = 7$
b. $y = -5x/4 + 7/2$ **27. a.** $\sin\pi + 5\left(\frac{\pi^2}{5}\right) = \pi^2$
b. $y = \frac{\pi(1 + \pi)}{1 + 2\pi} + \frac{5}{1 + 2\pi}x$
29. a. $\cos\left(\frac{\pi}{2} - \frac{\pi}{4}\right) + \sin\frac{\pi}{4} = \sqrt{2}$ **b.** $y = \frac{x}{2}$
31. $-\frac{1}{4y^3}$ **33.** $\frac{\sin y}{(\cos y - 1)^3}$ **35.** $\frac{4e^{2y}}{(1 - 2e^{2y})^3}$ **37.** $\frac{5}{4}x^{1/4}$
39. $\frac{10}{3(5x + 1)^{1/3}}$ **41.** $-\frac{3}{2^{7/4}x^{3/4}(4x - 3)^{5/4}}$ **43.** $\frac{2}{9x^{2/3}\sqrt[3]{1 + \sqrt[3]{x}}}$

45. $-\frac{1}{4}$ **47.** $-\frac{24}{13}$ **49.** −5 **51. a.** False **b.** True **c.** False **d.** False **53. a.** $y = x - 1$ and $y = -x + 2$
b.

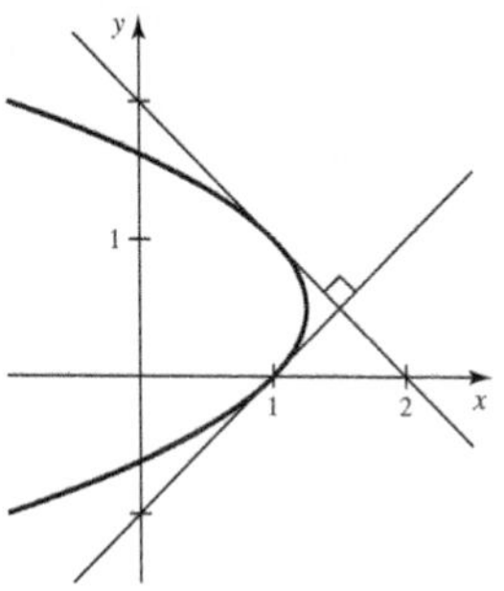

55. a. $y' = -\frac{2xy}{x^2 + 4}$ **b.** $y = \frac{1}{2}x + 2$, $y = -\frac{1}{2}x + 2$
c. $-\frac{16x}{(x^2 + 4)^2}$ **57. a.** $\left(\frac{5}{4}, \frac{1}{2}\right)$ **b.** No
59. Horizontal: $y = -6$, $y = 0$; vertical: $x = 1$, $x = 3$
61. a. $\frac{dy}{dx} = 0$ on the $y = 1$ branch; $\frac{dy}{dx} = \frac{1}{2y + 1}$ on the other two branches. **b.** $f_1(x) = 1$, $f_2(x) = \frac{-1 + \sqrt{4x - 3}}{2}$, $f_3(x) = \frac{-1 - \sqrt{4x - 3}}{2}$
c.

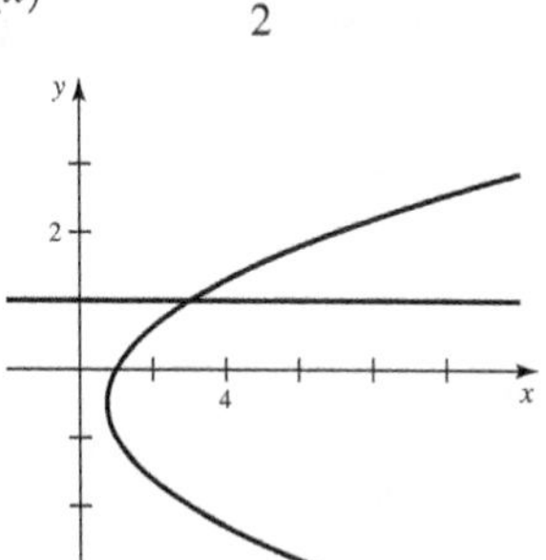

63. a. $\frac{dy}{dx} = \frac{x - x^3}{y}$ **b.** $f_1(x) = \sqrt{x^2 - \frac{x^4}{2}}$; $f_2(x) = -\sqrt{x^2 - \frac{x^4}{2}}$
c.

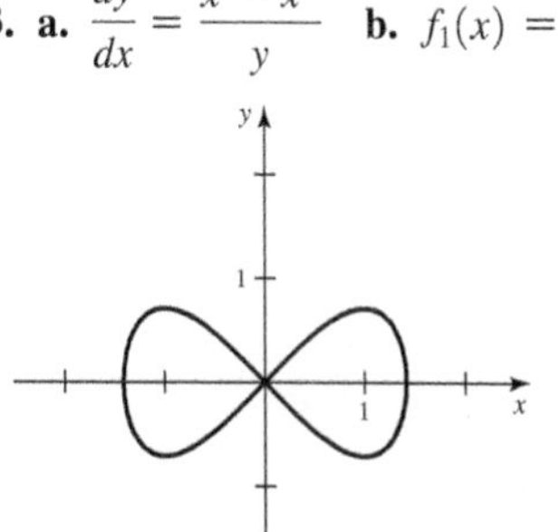

65. $y = \frac{4x}{5} - \frac{3}{5}$

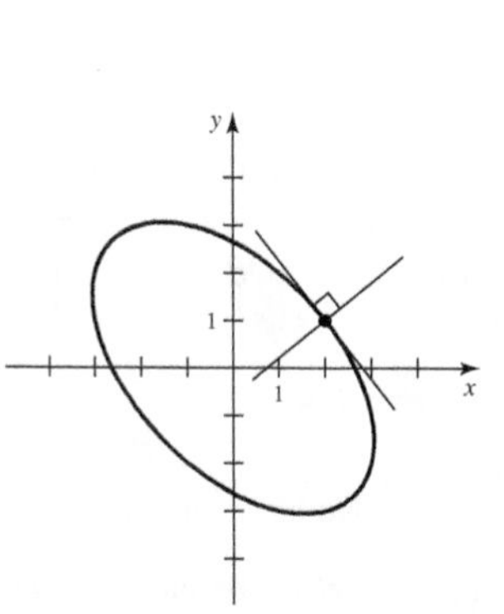

67. $y = -\frac{1 + 2\pi}{5}x + \pi\left(\frac{25 + \pi + 2\pi^2}{25}\right)$

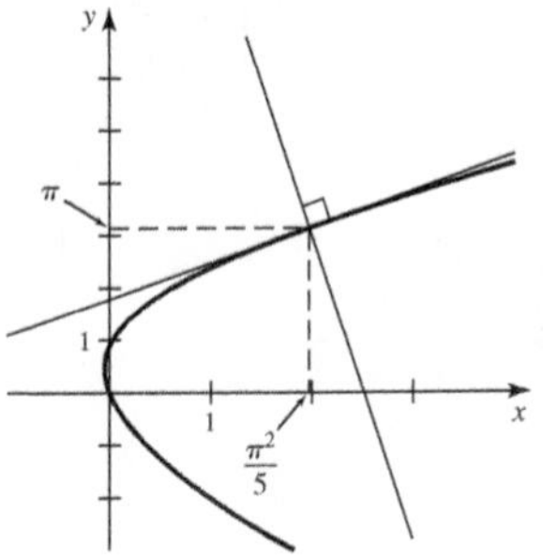

69. $y = -2x + \frac{5\pi}{4}$

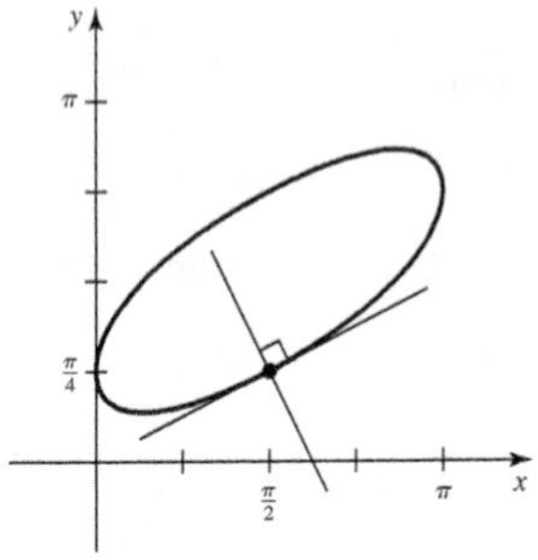

71. a. Tangent line $y = -\frac{9x}{11} + \frac{20}{11}$; normal line $y = \frac{11x}{9} - \frac{2}{9}$

b.

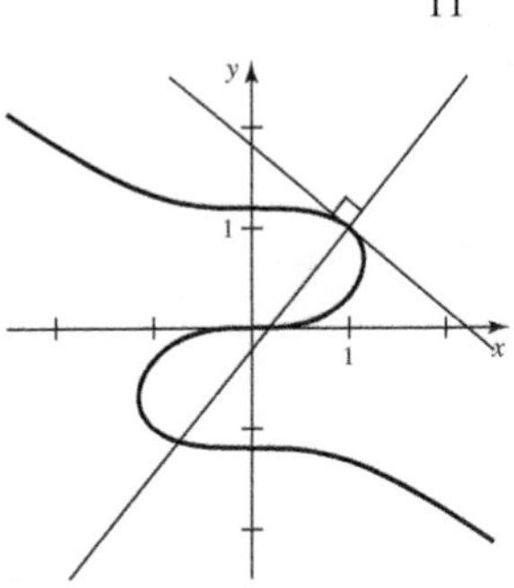

73. a. Tangent line $y = -\frac{x}{3} + \frac{8}{3}$; normal line $y = 3x - 4$

b.

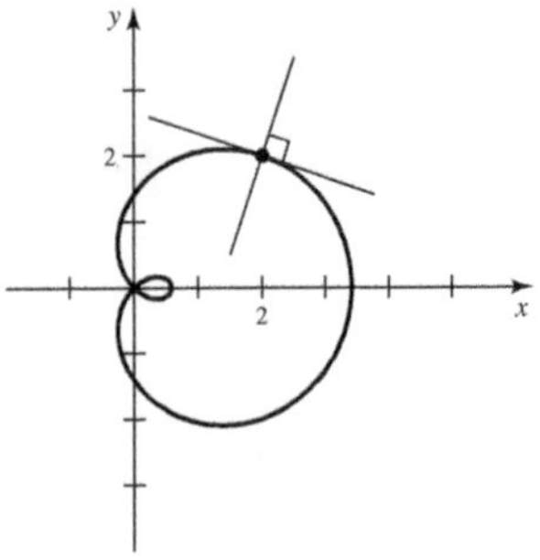

75. a. $\frac{dK}{dL} = -\frac{K}{2L}$ **b.** -4 **77.** $\frac{dr}{dh} = \frac{h - 2r}{h}$; -3

79. Note that for $y = mx$, $dy/dx = m$; for $x^2 + y^2 = a^2$, $dy/dx = -x/y$. **81.** For $xy = a$, $dy/dx = -y/x$. For $x^2 - y^2 = b$, $dy/dx = x/y$. Because $(-y/x) \cdot (x/y) = -1$, the families of curves form orthogonal trajectories. **83.** $\frac{7y^2 - 3x^2 - 4xy^2 - 4x^3}{2y(2x^2 + 2y^2 - 7x)}$

85. $\frac{2y^2(5 + 8x\sqrt{y})}{(1 + 2x\sqrt{y})^3}$ **87.** No horizontal tangent line; vertical tangent lines at $(2, 1)$, $(-2, 1)$ **89.** No horizontal tangent line; vertical tangent lines at $(0, 0)$, $\left(\frac{3\sqrt{3}}{2}, \sqrt{3}\right)$, $\left(-\frac{3\sqrt{3}}{2}, -\sqrt{3}\right)$

Section 3.9 Exercises, pp. 210–213

1. $x = e^y \Rightarrow 1 = e^y y'(x) \Rightarrow y'(x) = 1/e^y = 1/x$

3. $\frac{d}{dx}(\ln kx) = \frac{d}{dx}(\ln k + \ln x) = \frac{d}{dx}(\ln x)$

5. $f'(x) = \frac{1}{x \ln b}$; if $b = e$, then $f'(x) = \frac{1}{x}$. **7.** $f(x) = e^{h(x) \ln g(x)}$

9. $\frac{1}{x}$ **11.** $2/x$ **13.** $\cot x$ **15.** $2/(1 - x^2)$ **17.** $(x^2 + 1)/x + 2x \ln x$

19. $1/(x \ln x)$ **21.** $\frac{1}{x(\ln x + 1)^2}$ **23.** $8^x \ln 8$ **25.** $5 \cdot 4^x \ln 4$

27. $3^x \cdot x^2(x \ln 3 + 3)$ **29.** $1000(1.045)^{4t} \ln(1.045)$

31. a. About 28.7 s **b.** -46.512 s/1000 ft **c.** $dT/da = -2.74 \cdot 2^{-0.274a} \ln 2$

At $t = 8$, $\frac{dT}{da} = -0.4156$ min/1000 ft

$= -24.938$ s/1000 ft.

If a plane travels at 30,000 feet and increases its altitude by 1,000 feet, the time of useful consciousness decreases by about 25 seconds. **33. a.** About 67.19 hr

b. $Q'(12) = -9.815\ \mu\text{Ci/hr}$
$Q'(24) = -5.201\ \mu\text{Ci/hr}$
$Q'(48) = -1.461\ \mu\text{Ci/hr}$

The rate at which iodine-123 leaves the body decreases with time.

35. $2^x \ln 2$ **37.** $e^y y^{e-1}(y + e)$ **39.** $2e^{2\theta}$ **41.** $\frac{\sqrt{x}}{2}(10x - 9)$

43. $\frac{2^x \ln 2}{(2^x + 1)^2}$ **45.** $x^{\cos x - 1}(\cos x - x \ln x \sin x)$; $-\ln(\pi/2)$

47. $x^{\sqrt{x}}\left(\frac{2 + \ln x}{2\sqrt{x}}\right)$; $4(2 + \ln 4)$

49. $\frac{(\sin x)^{\ln x}(\ln(\sin x) + x(\ln x)\cot x)}{x}$; 0

51. $y = x \sin 1 + 1 - \sin 1$ **53.** $y = e^{2/e}$ and $y = e^{-2/e}$

55. $\frac{8x}{(x^2 - 1)\ln 3}$ **57.** $-\sin x(\ln(\cos^2 x) + 2)$ **59.** $-\frac{\ln 4}{x \ln^2 x}$

61. $\frac{(x + 1)^{10}}{(2x - 4)^8}\left(\frac{10}{x + 1} - \frac{8}{x - 2}\right)$ **63.** $2x^{\ln x - 1} \ln x$

65. $\frac{(x + 1)^{3/2}(x - 4)^{5/2}}{(5x + 3)^{2/3}}\left(\frac{3}{2(x + 1)} + \frac{5}{2(x - 4)} - \frac{10}{3(5x + 3)}\right)$

67. $(\sin x)^{\tan x}(1 + (\sec^2 x)\ln \sin x)$ **69. a.** False **b.** False **c.** False **d.** False **e.** True **71.** $-\frac{1}{x^2 \ln 10}$ **73.** $\frac{2}{x}$

75. $3^x \ln 3$ **77.** $\frac{12}{(3x + 1)}$ **79.** $\frac{1}{2x}$

81. $\frac{2}{2x - 1} + \frac{3}{x + 2} + \frac{8}{1 - 4x}$

83. $y = 2$

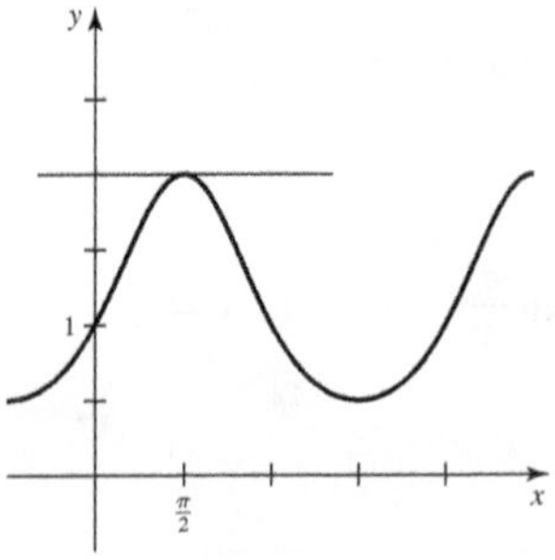

85. $10x^{10x}(1 + \ln x)$ **87.** $x^{\cos x}\left(\frac{\cos x}{x} - (\ln x)\sin x\right)$

89. $\left(1 + \frac{1}{x}\right)^x \left(\ln\left(1 + \frac{1}{x}\right) - \frac{1}{x + 1}\right)$ **91.** $x^{9+x^{10}}(1 + 10 \ln x)$

93. a.

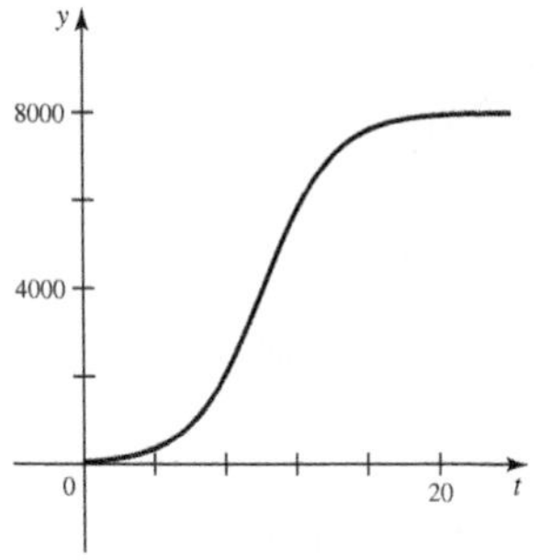

b. $t = 2 \ln 265 \approx 11.2$ years; about 14.5 years
c. $P'(0) \approx 25$ fish/year; $P'(5) \approx 264$ fish/year
d.

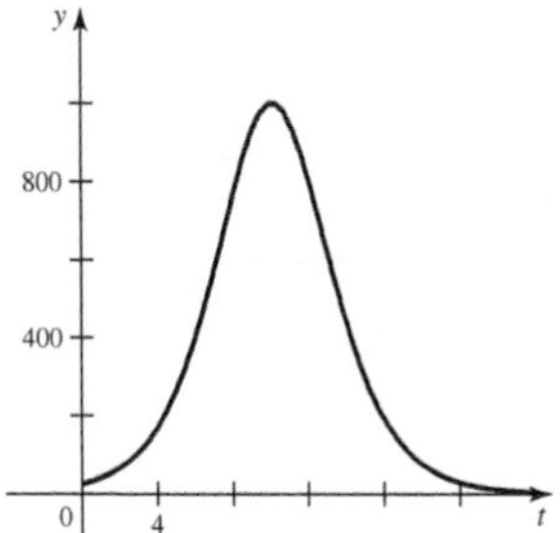

The population is growing fastest after about 10 years.
95. b. $r(11) \approx 0.0133$; $r(21) \approx 0.0118$; the relative growth rate is decreasing. **c.** $\lim_{t \to \infty} r(t) = 0$; as the population gets close to carrying capacity, growth rate approaches zero.
97. a. $A(5) = \$17{,}443$
$A(15) = \$72{,}705$
$A(25) = \$173{,}248$
$A(35) = \$356{,}178$
\$5526.20/year, \$10,054.30/year, \$18,293/year
b. $A(40) = \$497{,}873$
c. $\frac{dA}{dt} = 600{,}000 \ln(1.005)((1.005)^{12t})$
$\approx (2992.5)(1.005)^{12t}$
A increases at an increasing rate. **99.** $p = e^{1/e}$; (e, e) **101.** $1/e$
103. $27(1 + \ln 3)$

Section 3.10 Exercises, pp. 221–223

1. $\frac{d}{dx}(\sin^{-1} x) = \frac{1}{\sqrt{1 - x^2}}$; $\frac{d}{dx}(\tan^{-1} x) = \frac{1}{1 + x^2}$;
$\frac{d}{dx}(\sec^{-1} x) = \frac{1}{|x|\sqrt{x^2 - 1}}$ **3.** $\frac{1}{5}$ **5.** $\frac{1}{4}$ **7.** $\frac{2}{\sqrt{1 - 4x^2}}$
9. $-\frac{4w}{\sqrt{1 - 4w^2}}$ **11.** $-\frac{2e^{-2x}}{\sqrt{1 - e^{-4x}}}$ **13.** $\frac{10}{100x^2 + 1}$
15. $\frac{4y}{1 + (2y^2 - 4)^2}$ **17.** $-\frac{1}{2\sqrt{z}\,(1 + z)}$ **19.** $\frac{1}{|x|\sqrt{x^2 - 1}}$
21. $-\frac{1}{|2u + 1|\sqrt{u^2 + u}}$ **23.** $\frac{2y}{(y^2 + 1)^2 + 1}$
25. $\frac{1}{x|\ln x|\sqrt{(\ln x)^2 - 1}}$ **27.** $-\frac{e^x \sec^2 e^x}{|\tan e^x|\sqrt{\tan^2 e^x - 1}}$
29. $-\frac{e^s}{1 + e^{2s}}$ **31.** $y = x + \frac{\pi}{4} - \frac{1}{2}$ **33.** $y = -\frac{4}{\sqrt{6}}x + \frac{\pi}{3} + \frac{2}{\sqrt{3}}$

35. a. ≈ -0.00055 rad/m
b.

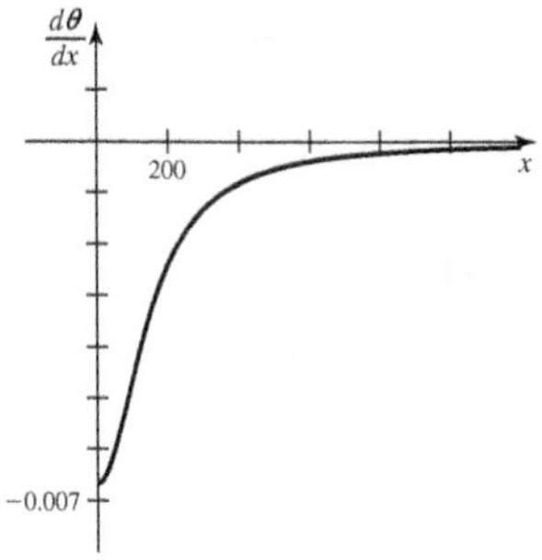

The magnitude of the change in angular size, $|d\theta/dx|$, is greatest when the boat is at the skyscraper (i.e., at $x = 0$).

37. $\frac{1}{3}$ **39.** $-\frac{1}{5}$ **41.** $\frac{1}{2}$ **43.** 4 **45.** $\frac{1}{12}$ **47.** $\frac{1}{4}$ **49.** $\frac{5}{4}$ **51. a.** $\frac{1}{2}$
b. $\frac{2}{3}$ **c.** Cannot be determined **d.** $\frac{3}{2}$ **53. a.** True **b.** False
c. True **d.** True **e.** True
55. a.

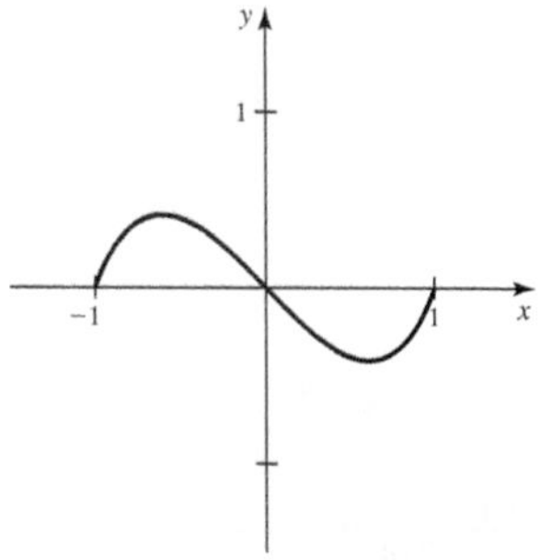

b. $f'(x) = 2x \sin^{-1} x + \frac{x^2 - 1}{\sqrt{1 - x^2}}$

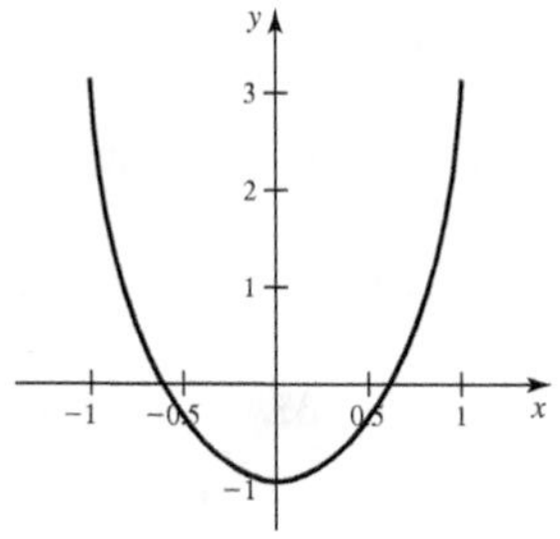

57. a.

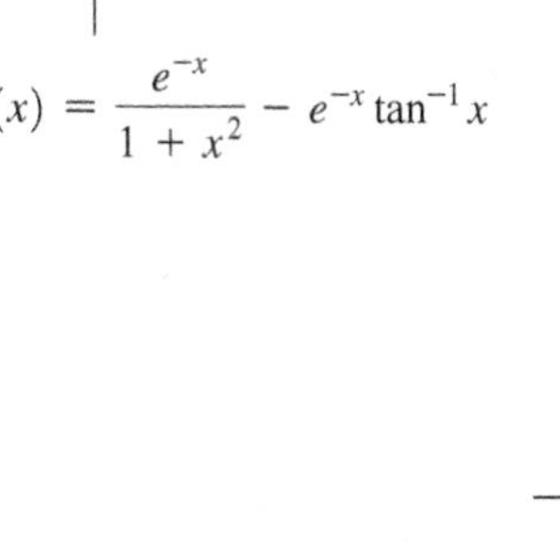

b. $f'(x) = \frac{e^{-x}}{1 + x^2} - e^{-x} \tan^{-1} x$

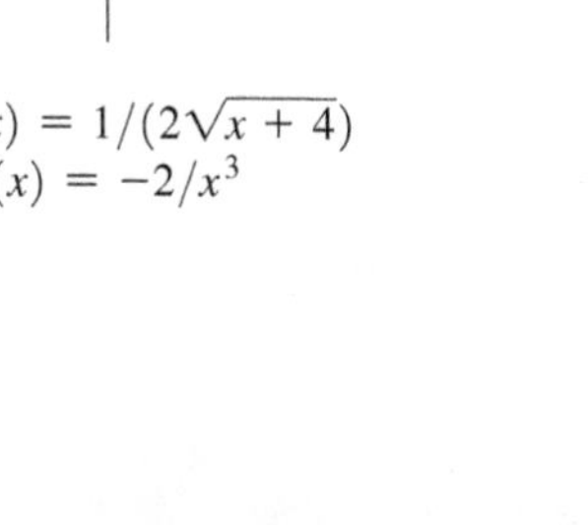

59. $(f^{-1})'(x) = \frac{1}{3}$ **61.** $(f^{-1})'(x) = 1/(2\sqrt{x + 4})$
63. $(f^{-1})'(x) = 2x$ **65.** $(f^{-1})'(x) = -2/x^3$

67. b. $d\theta/d\ell = -0.0041, -0.0289$, and -0.1984
c. $\lim_{\ell \to 10^+} d\theta/d\ell = -\infty$ **d.** The length ℓ is decreasing
69. a. $d\theta/dc = 1/\sqrt{D^2 - c^2}$ **b.** $1/D$ **73.** Use the identity $\cot^{-1} x + \tan^{-1} x = \pi/2$.

Section 3.11 Exercises, pp. 227–231

1. As the side length s of a cube changes, the surface area $6s^2$ changes as well. **3.** The other two opposite sides decrease in length.
5. a. $40\ \text{m}^2/\text{s}$ **b.** $80\ \text{m}^2/\text{s}$
c.

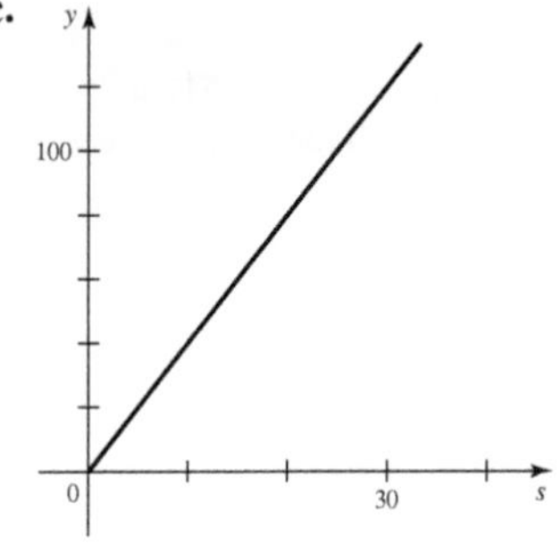

7. a. $4\ \text{m}^2/\text{s}$ **b.** $\sqrt{2}\ \text{m}^2/\text{s}$ **c.** $2\sqrt{2}\ \text{m/s}$ **9. a.** $\frac{1}{4\pi}$ cm/s
b. $\frac{1}{2}$ cm/s **11.** $-40\pi\ \text{ft}^2/\text{min}$ **13.** $\frac{3}{80\pi}$ in/min
17. At the point $\left(\frac{1}{2}, \frac{1}{4}\right)$ **19.** $\frac{1}{500}$ m/min; 2000 min
21. $10 \tan 20°$ km/hr ≈ 3.6 km/hr **23.** $\frac{5}{24}$ ft/s **25.** $-\frac{8}{3}$ ft/s, $-\frac{32}{3}$ ft/s **27.** $2592\pi\ \text{cm}^3/\text{s}$ **29.** $-\frac{8}{9\pi}$ ft/s **31.** $9\pi\ \text{ft}^3/\text{min}$
33. $\frac{2}{5}\ \text{m}^2/\text{min}$ **35.** 57.89 ft/s **37.** 4.66 in/s **39.** $\frac{3\sqrt{5}}{2}$ ft/s
41. ≈ 720.3 mi/hr **43.** 11.06 m/hr **45. a.** 187.5 ft/s
b. 0.938 rad/s **47.** $\frac{d\theta}{dt} = 0.543$ rad/hr
49. $\frac{d\theta}{dt} = \frac{1}{5}$ rad/s, $\frac{d\theta}{dt} = \frac{1}{8}$ rad/s **51.** $\frac{d\theta}{dt} = 0$ rad/s, for all $t \geq 0$
53. -0.0201 rad/s **55. a.** $-\frac{\sqrt{3}}{10}$ m/hr **b.** $-1\ \text{m}^2/\text{hr}$

Chapter 3 Review Exercises, pp. 232–235

1. a. False **b.** False **c.** False **d.** False **e.** True **3. a.** 16
b. $y = 16x - 10$

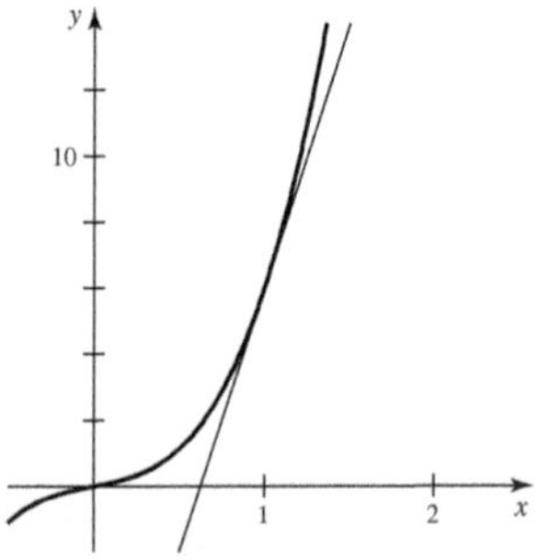

5. a. $-\frac{3}{4}$ **b.** $y = -\frac{3}{4}x + \frac{1}{2}$

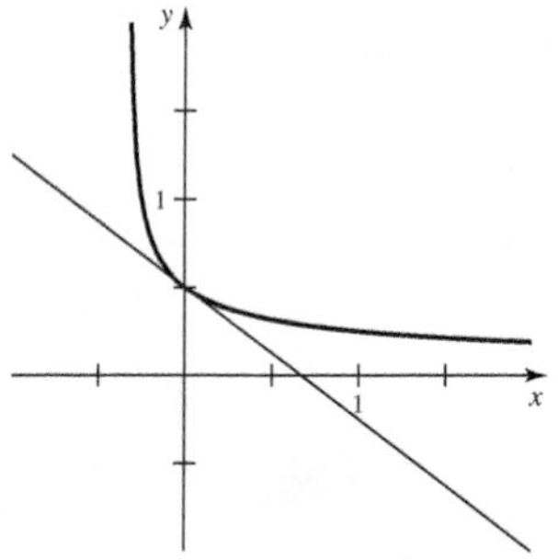

7. a. 2.70 million people/yr **b.** The slope of the secant line through the two points is approximately equal to the slope of that tangent line at $t = 55$. **c.** 2.217 million people/yr **9. a.** 40 m/s
b. 20/3 m/s **c.** 15 m/s **d.**

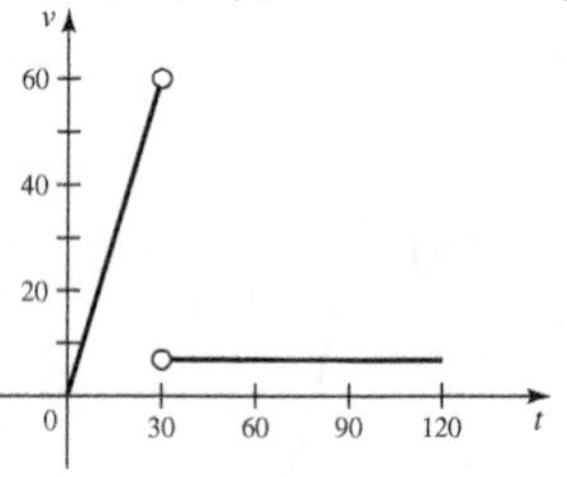

e. The skydiver deployed the parachute.
13.

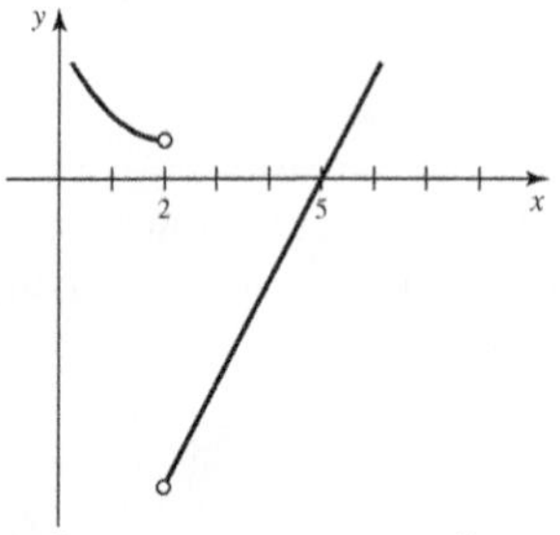

15. $2x^2 + 2\pi x + 7$ **17.** $5t^2 \cos t + 10t \sin t$
19. $(8\theta + 12) \sec^2 (\theta^2 + 3\theta + 2)$ **21.** $\frac{32u^2 + 8u + 1}{(8u + 1)^2}$
23. $(\sec^2 \sin \theta) \cos \theta$ **25.** $\frac{9x \sin x - 2 \sin x + 6x^2 \cos x - 2x \cos x}{\sqrt{3x - 1}}$
27. $(2 + \ln x) \ln x$ **29.** $(2x - 1)\, 2^{x^2 - x} \ln 2$ **31.** $-\frac{1}{|x|\sqrt{x^2 - 1}}$
33. 1 **35.** $\sqrt{3} + \pi/6$ **37.** $\frac{y \cos x}{e^y - 1 - \sin x}$ **39.** $-\frac{xy}{x^2 + 2y^2}$
41. $y = x$ **43.** $y = -\frac{4x}{5} + \frac{24}{5}$ **45.** $x = 4; x = 6$
47. $y' = \frac{\cos \sqrt{x}}{2\sqrt{x}}, y'' = -\frac{\sqrt{x} \sin \sqrt{x} + \cos \sqrt{x}}{4x^{3/2}}$,
$y''' = \frac{3\sqrt{x} \sin \sqrt{x} + (3 - x) \cos \sqrt{x}}{8x^{5/2}}$ **49.** $x^2 f'(x) + 2x f(x)$
51. $\frac{g(x)(xf'(x) + f(x)) - xf(x)g'(x)}{g^2(x)}$ **53. a.** 27 **b.** $\frac{25}{27}$ **c.** 294
d. 1215 **e.** $\frac{1}{9}$ **55.** $f(x) = \tan(\pi\sqrt{3x - 11})$, $a = 5; f'(5) = 3\pi/4$
57. $\frac{6}{13}$ **59.** $(f^{-1})'(x) = -3/x^4$ **61. a.** $(f^{-1})'(1/\sqrt{2}) = \sqrt{2}$
63. a. $\frac{1}{4}$ **b.** 1 **c.** $\frac{1}{3}$ **65. a.** $\overline{C}(3000) = \$341.67$; $C'(3000) = \$280$ **b.** The average cost of producing the first 3000 lawn mowers is \$341.67 per mower. The cost of producing the 3001st lawn mower is \$280. **67. a.** 6550 people/yr
b. $p'(40) = 4800$ people/yr **69.** 50 mi/hr
71. $-5 \sin 65°$ ft/s ≈ -4.5 ft/s **73.** 0.166 rad/s

CHAPTER 4

Section 4.1 Exercises, pp. 242–245

1. f has an absolute maximum at c in $[a, b]$ if $f(x) \le f(c)$ for all x in $[a, b]$. f has an absolute minimum at c in $[a, b]$ if $f(x) \ge f(c)$ for all x in $[a, b]$. **3.** The function must be continuous on a closed interval.

5.

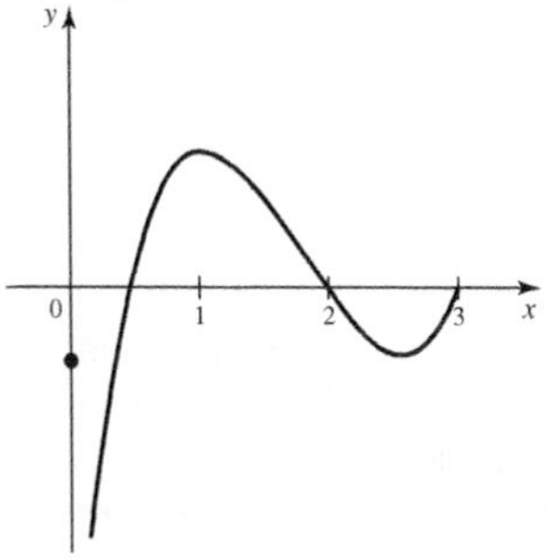

7.

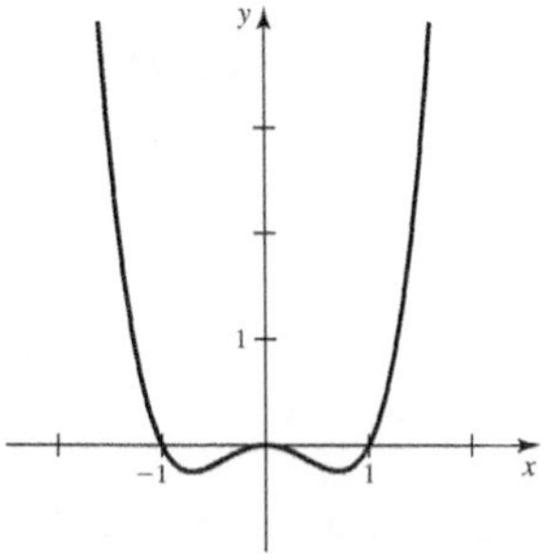

9. Evaluate the function at the critical points and at the endpoints of the interval. **11.** Abs. min at $x = c_2$; abs. max at $x = b$
13. Abs. min at $x = a$; no abs. max **15.** Local min at $x = q, s$; local max at $x = p, r$; abs. min at $x = a$; abs. max at $x = b$
17. Local max at $x = p$ and $x = r$; local min at $x = q$; abs. max at $x = p$; abs. min at $x = b$

19.

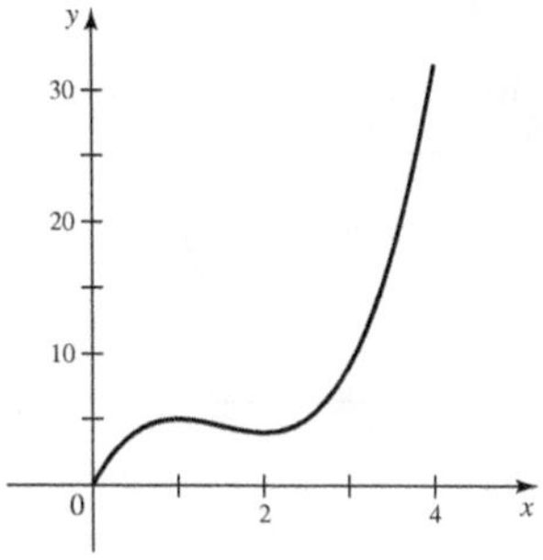

21.

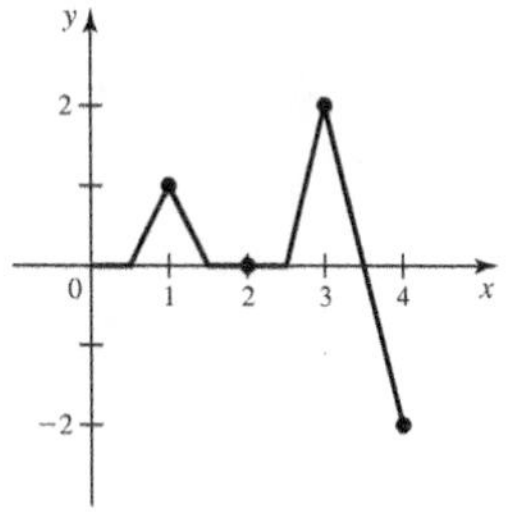

23. a. $x = \frac{2}{3}$ **b.** Local min **25. a.** $x = \pm 3$ **b.** $x = -3$ local max, $x = 3$ local min **27. a.** $x = -\frac{2}{3}, \frac{1}{3}$ **b.** $x = -\frac{2}{3}$ local max, $x = \frac{1}{3}$ local min **29. a.** $x = \pm 1$ **b.** $x = -1$ local min, $x = 1$ local max **31. a.** $x = 0$ **b.** Local min **33. a.** $x = 1$ **b.** local min **35. a.** $x = -\frac{4}{5}, 0$ **b.** $x = -\frac{4}{5}$ local max, $x = 0$ local min **37. a.** $x = 0$ **b.** Abs. max: -1 at $x = 3$; abs. min: -10 at $x = 0$ **c.**

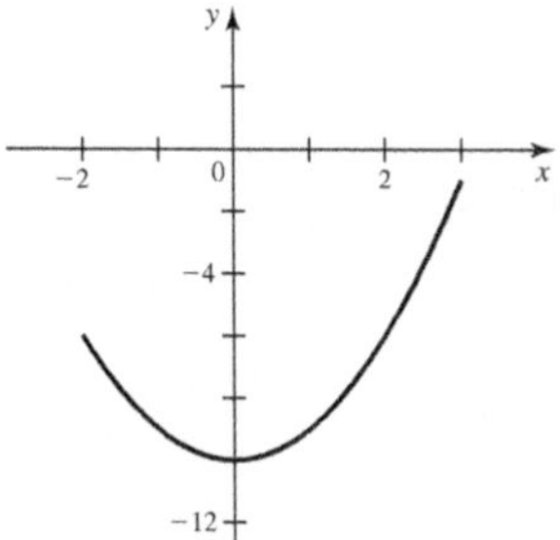

39. a. $x = \pi/2$ **b.** Abs. max: 1 at $x = 0, \pi$; abs. min: 0 at $x = \pi/2$ **c.**

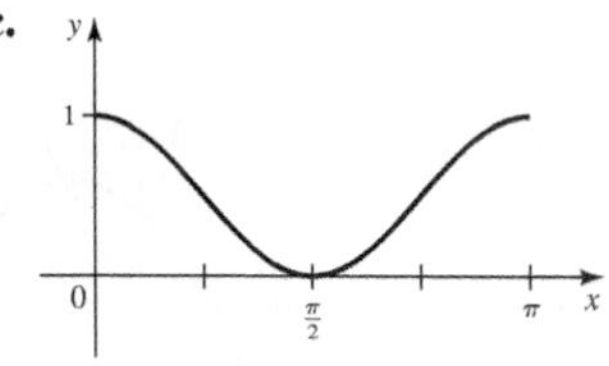

41. a. $x = \pm\pi/6$ **b.** Abs. max: 1 at $x = \pi/6$; abs. min: -1 at $x = -\pi/6$ **c.**

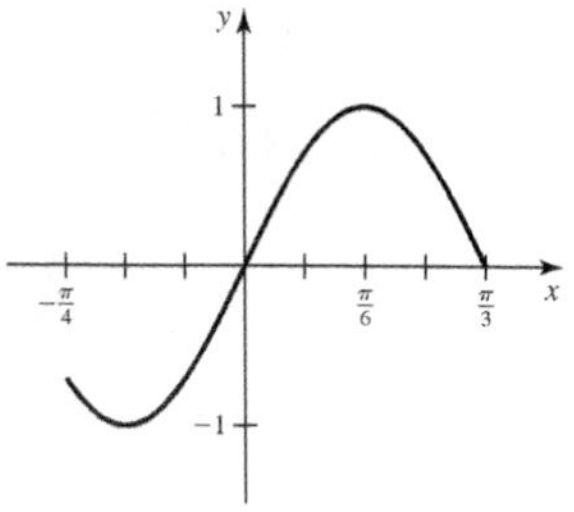

43. a. $x = 1/(2e)$ **b.** Abs. min: $(\sqrt{1/e})^{1/e}$ at $x = 1/(2e)$; abs. max: 2 at $x = 1$ **c.**

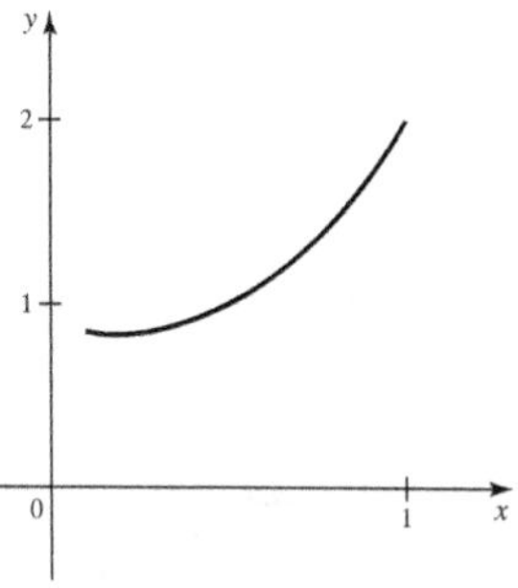

45. a. $x = 1/\sqrt{2}$ **b.** Abs. max: $1 + \pi$ at $x = -1$; abs. min: 1 at $x = 1$ **c.**

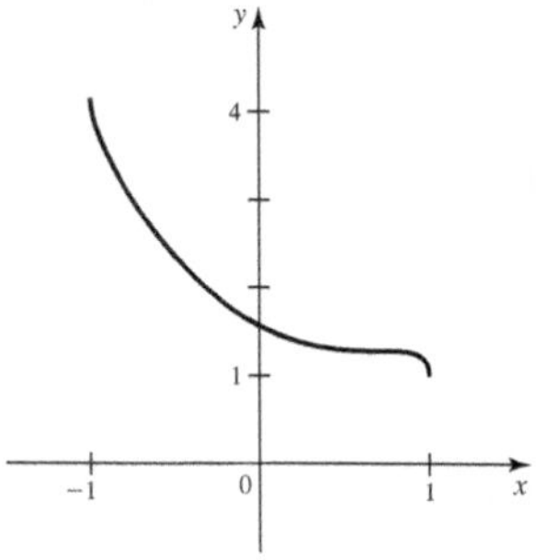

47. a. 1, 4 **b.** Abs. max: 11 at $x = 1$; abs. min: -16 at $x = 4$ **c.**

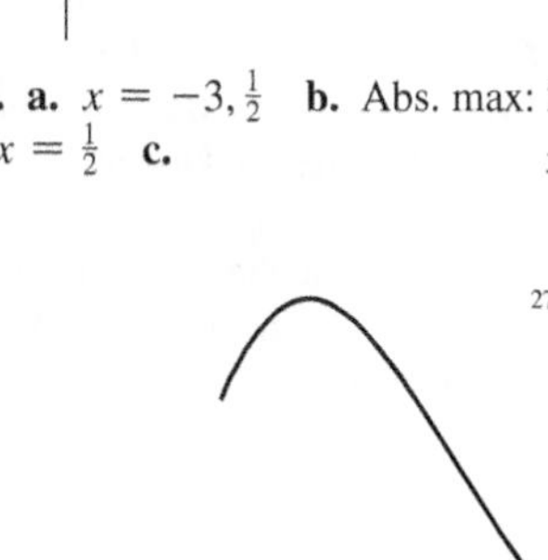

49. a. $x = -3, \frac{1}{2}$ **b.** Abs. max: 27 at $x = -3$; abs. min: $-\frac{19}{12}$ at $x = \frac{1}{2}$ **c.**

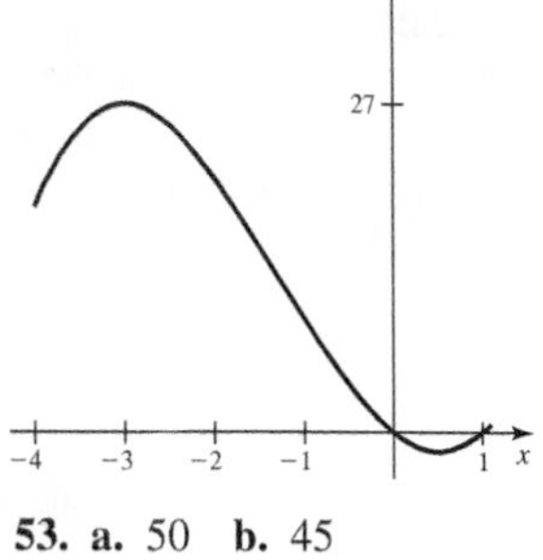

51. $t = 2$ s **53. a.** 50 **b.** 45
55. a. False **b.** False **c.** False **d.** True

57. a. $x = -0.96, 2.18, 5.32$ **b.** Abs. max: 3.72 at $x = 2.18$; abs. min: -32.80 at $x = 5.32$ **c.**

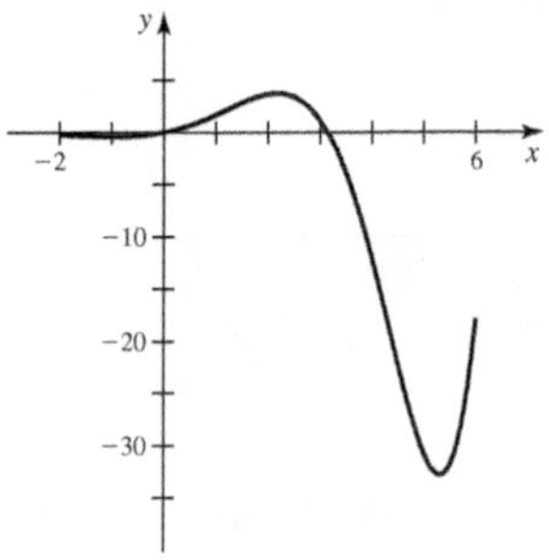

59. a. $x = 0$ **b.** Abs. max: $\sqrt{2}$ at $x = \pm\pi/4$; abs. min: 1 at $x = 0$ **c.**

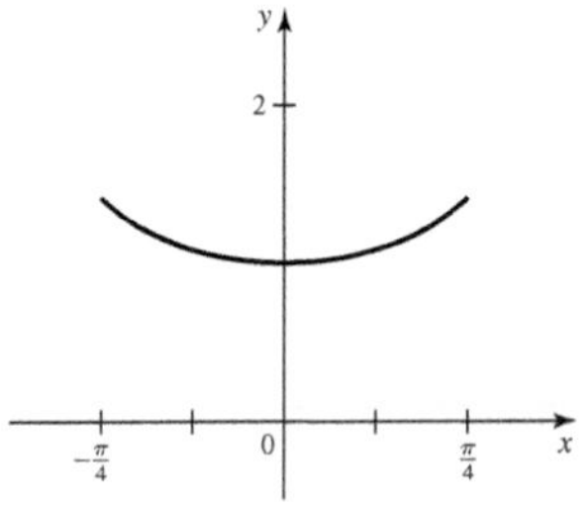

61. a. $x = 0$ and $x = 3$ **b.** Abs. max: $27/e^3$ at $x = 3$; abs. min: $-e$ at $x = -1$ **c.**

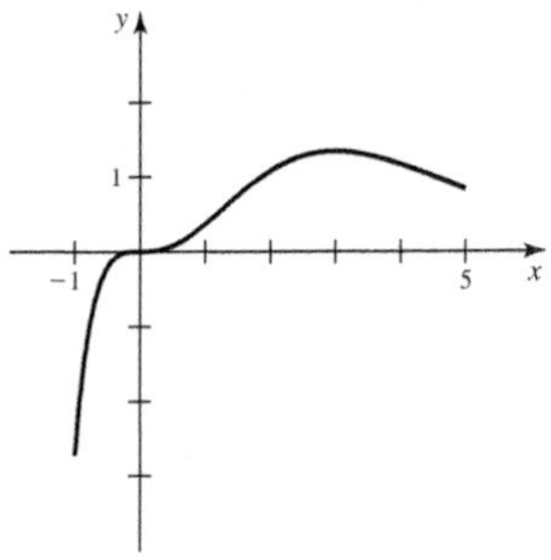

63. a. $x = 8$ **b.** Abs. max: $3\sqrt{2}$ at $x = 6$ and $x = 12$; abs. min: 4 at $x = 8$ **c.**

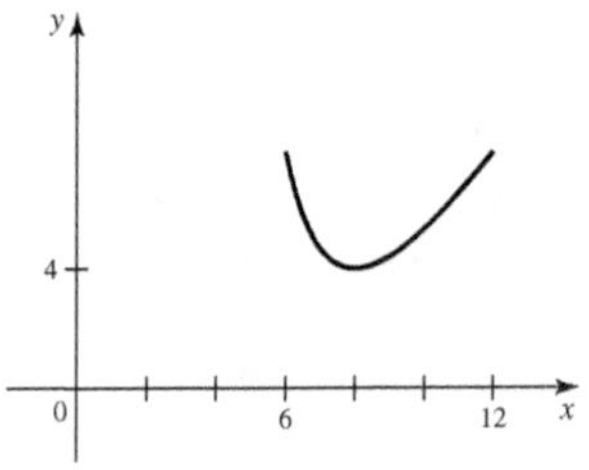

65. If $a \geq 0$, there is no critical point. If $a < 0$, $x = 2a/3$ is the only critical point. **67.** $x = \pm a$ **69. a.** $x = \tan^{-1} 2 + k\pi$, for $k = -2, -1, 0, 1$ **b.** $x = \tan^{-1} 2 + k\pi$, for $k = -2, 0$ correspond to local max; $x = \tan^{-1} 2 + k\pi$, for $k = -1, 1$ correspond to local min. **c.** Abs. max: 2.24; abs. min: -2.24 **71. a.** $x = -\frac{1}{8}$ and $x = 3$ **b.** $x = -\frac{1}{8}$ corresponds to a local min; $x = 3$ is neither **c.** Abs. max: 51.23; abs. min: -12.52 **73. a.** $x = 5 - 4\sqrt{2}$ **b.** $x = 5 - 4\sqrt{2}$ corresponds to a local max. **c.** No abs. max or min **75.** Abs. max: 4 at $x = -1$; abs. min: -8 at $x = 3$

77. a. $T(x) = \dfrac{\sqrt{2500 + x^2}}{2} + \dfrac{50 - x}{4}$ **b.** $x = 50/\sqrt{3}$

c. $T(50/\sqrt{3}) \approx 34.15$, $T(0) = 37.50$, $T(50) \approx 35.36$
d.

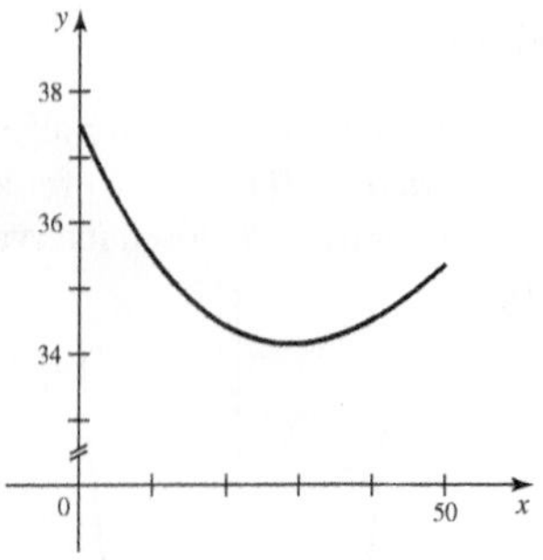

79. a. 1, 3, 0, 1 **b.** Because $h'(2) \neq 0$, h does not have a local extreme value at $x = 2$. However, g may have a local extremum at $x = 2$ (because $g'(2) = 0$). **81. a.** Local min at $x = -c$ **b.** Local max at $x = -c$ **83. a.** $f(x) - f(c) \leq 0$ for all x near c **b.** $\lim_{x\to c^+} \dfrac{f(x) - f(c)}{x - c} \leq 0$ **c.** $\lim_{x\to c^-} \dfrac{f(x) - f(c)}{x - c} \geq 0$ **d.** Because $f'(c)$ exists, $\lim_{x\to c^+} \dfrac{f(x) - f(c)}{x - c} = \lim_{x\to c^-} \dfrac{f(x) - f(c)}{x - c}$. By parts (b) and (c), we must have that $f'(c) = 0$.

Section 4.2 Exercises, pp. 256–260

1. f is increasing on I if $f'(x) > 0$ for all x in I; f is decreasing on I if $f'(x) < 0$ for all x in I. **3.**

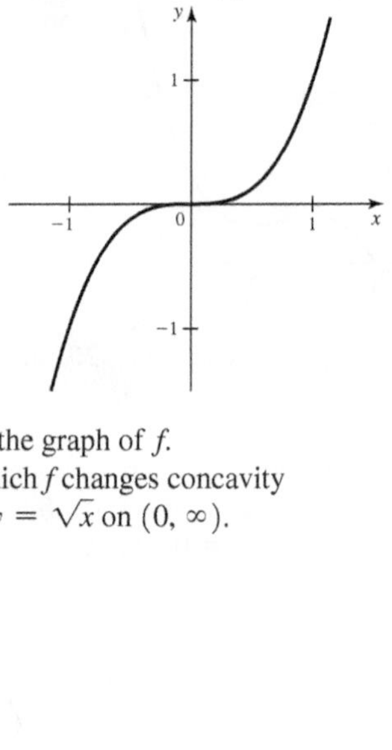

5. The tangent lines lie below the graph of f.
7. A point in the domain at which f changes concavity
9. Yes; consider the graph of $y = \sqrt{x}$ on $(0, \infty)$.
11.

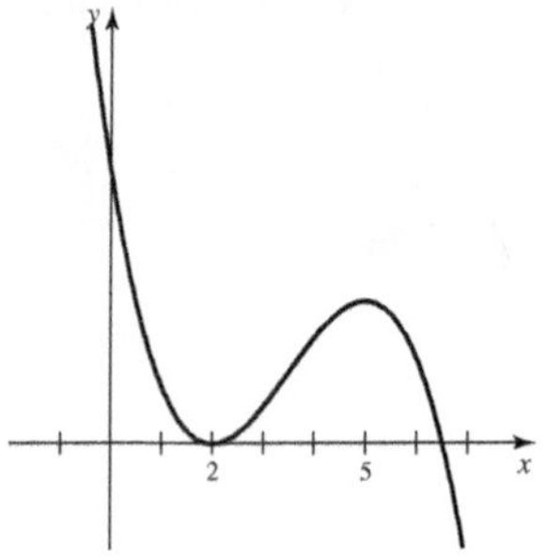

13.

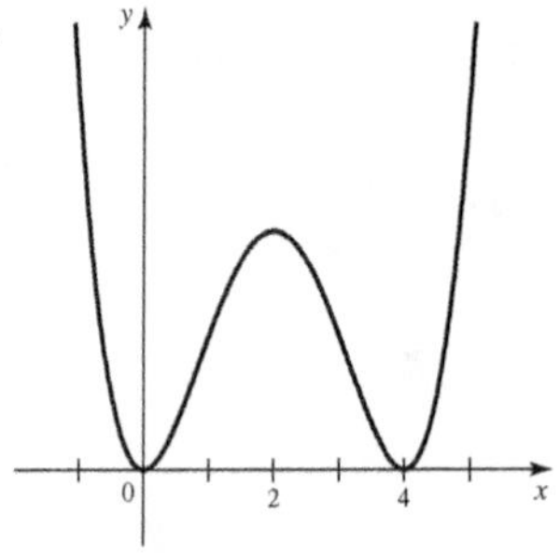

15.

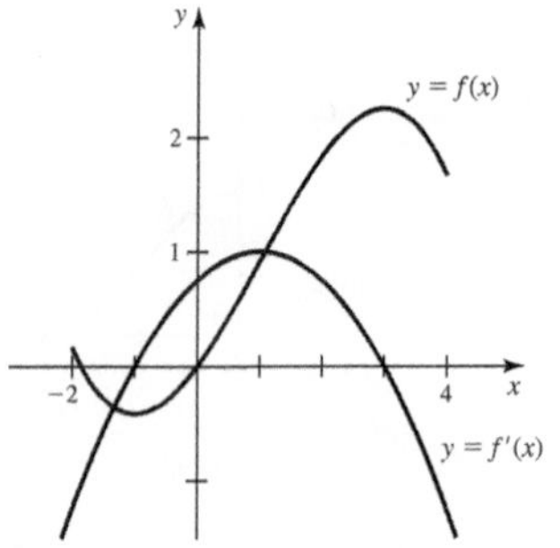

17. Increasing on $(-\infty, 0)$; decreasing on $(0, \infty)$ **19.** Decreasing on $(-\infty, 1)$; increasing on $(1, \infty)$ **21.** Increasing on $(-\infty, 1/2)$; decreasing on $(1/2, \infty)$ **23.** Increasing on $(-\infty, 0)$, $(1, 2)$; decreasing on $(0, 1)$, $(2, \infty)$ **25.** Increasing on $\left(-\frac{1}{\sqrt{e}}, 0\right), \left(\frac{1}{\sqrt{e}}, \infty\right)$; decreasing on $\left(-\infty, -\frac{1}{\sqrt{e}}\right), \left(0, \frac{1}{\sqrt{e}}\right)$ **27.** Increasing on $(-\pi, -2\pi/3)$, $(-\pi/3, 0)$, $(\pi/3, 2\pi/3)$; decreasing on $(-2\pi/3, -\pi/3)$, $(0, \pi/3)$, $(2\pi/3, \pi)$ **29.** Decreasing on $(-\infty, -1)$, $(0, 1)$; increasing on $(-1, 0)$, $(1, \infty)$ **31.** Increasing on $(-\infty, \infty)$ **33.** Decreasing on $(-\infty, 1)$, $(4, \infty)$; increasing on $(1, 4)$ **35.** Increasing on $\left(-\infty, -\frac{1}{2}\right)$, $\left(0, \frac{1}{2}\right)$; decreasing on $\left(-\frac{1}{2}, 0\right)$, $\left(\frac{1}{2}, \infty\right)$ **37.** Increasing on $(-1, 1)$; decreasing on $(-\infty, -1)$, $(1, \infty)$ **39. a.** $x = 0$ **b.** Local min at $x = 0$ **c.** Abs. min: 3 at $x = 0$; abs. max: 12 at $x = -3$ **41. a.** $x = \pm\sqrt{2}$ **b.** Local min at $x = -\sqrt{2}$; local max at $x = \sqrt{2}$ **c.** Abs. max: 2 at $x = \sqrt{2}$; abs. min: -2 at $x = -\sqrt{2}$ **43. a.** $x = \pm\sqrt{3}$ **b.** Local min at $x = -\sqrt{3}$; local max at $x = \sqrt{3}$ **c.** Abs. max: 28 at $x = -4$; abs. min: $-6\sqrt{3}$ at $x = -\sqrt{3}$ **45. a.** $x = 2$ and $x = 0$ **b.** Local max at $x = 0$; local min at $x = 2$ **c.** Abs. min: $-10\sqrt[3]{25}$ at $x = -5$; abs. max: 0 at $x = 0, 5$ **47. a.** $x = e^{-2}$ **b.** Local min at $x = e^{-2}$ **c.** Abs. min: $-2/e$ at $x = e^{-2}$; no abs. max **49.** Abs. max: $1/e$ at $x = 1$ **51.** Abs. min: $36\sqrt[3]{\pi/6}$ at $x = \sqrt[3]{6/\pi}$

53.

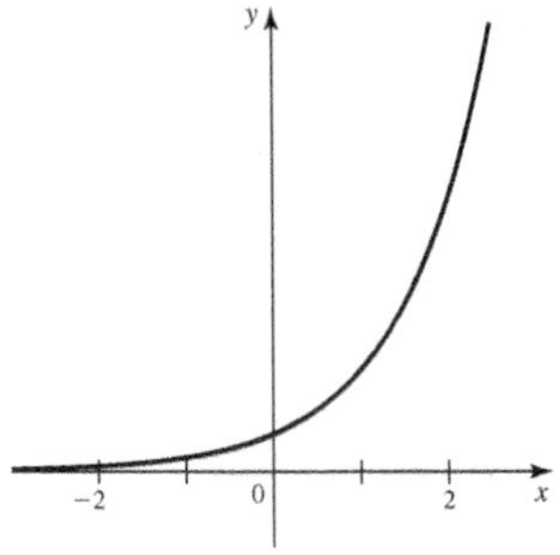

55.

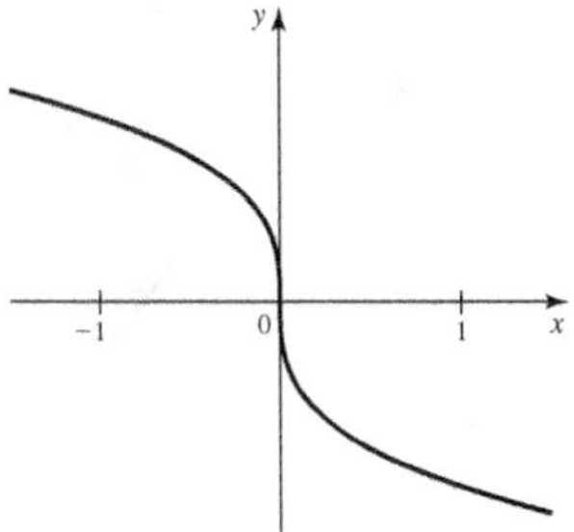

57. Concave up on $(-\infty, 0)$, $(1, \infty)$; concave down on $(0, 1)$; inflection points at $x = 0$ and $x = 1$ **59.** Concave up on $(-\infty, 0)$, $(2, \infty)$; concave down on $(0, 2)$; inflection points at $x = 0$ and $x = 2$ **61.** Concave down on $(-\infty, 1)$; concave up on $(1, \infty)$; inflection point at $x = 1$ **63.** Concave up on $(-1/\sqrt{3}, 1/\sqrt{3})$; concave down on $(-\infty, -1/\sqrt{3})$, $(1/\sqrt{3}, \infty)$; inflection points at $t = \pm 1/\sqrt{3}$ **65.** Concave up on $(-\infty, -1)$, $(1, \infty)$; concave down on $(-1, 1)$; inflection points at $x = \pm 1$ **67.** Concave up on $(0, 1)$; concave down on $(1, \infty)$; inflection point at $x = 1$
69. Concave up on $(0, 2)$, $(4, \infty)$; concave down on $(-\infty, 0)$, $(2, 4)$; inflection points at $x = 0, 2, 4$ **71.** Critical pts. $x = 0$ and $x = 2$; local max at $x = 0$, local min at $x = 2$ **73.** Critical pt. $x = 0$; local max at $x = 0$ **75.** Critical pt. $x = 6$; local min at $x = 6$ **77.** Critical pts. $x = 0$ and $x = 1$; local max at $x = 0$; local min at $x = 1$ **79.** Critical pts. $x = 0$ and $x = 2$; local min at $x = 0$; local max at $x = 2$ **81.** Critical pt. $x = e^5$; local min at $x = e^5$ **83. a.** True **b.** False **c.** True **d.** False **e.** False

85.

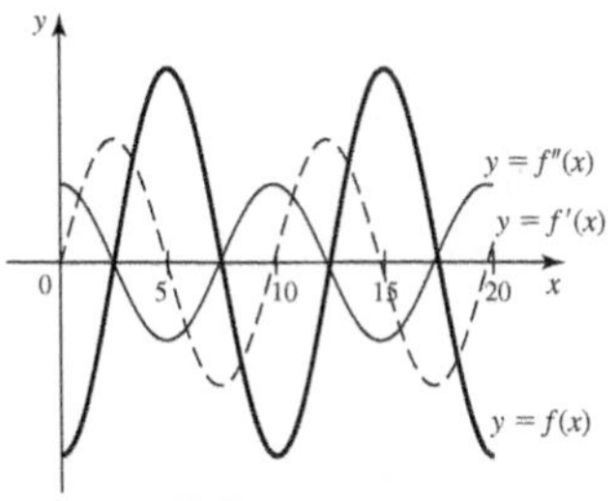

87. a–f–g, b–e–i, c–d–h

89.

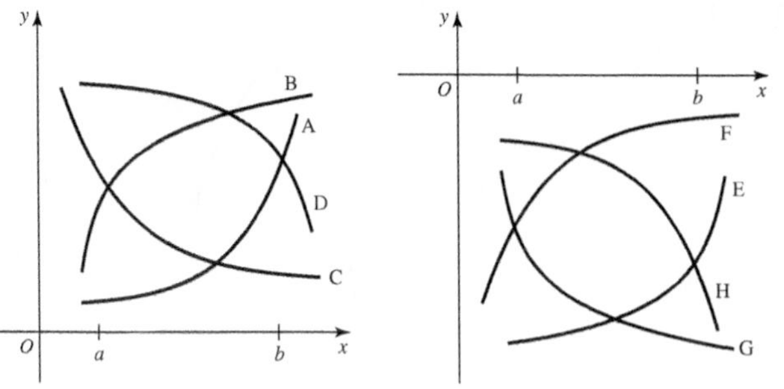

91.

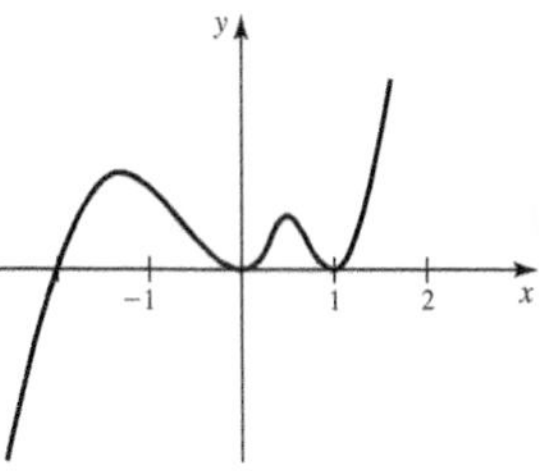

93.

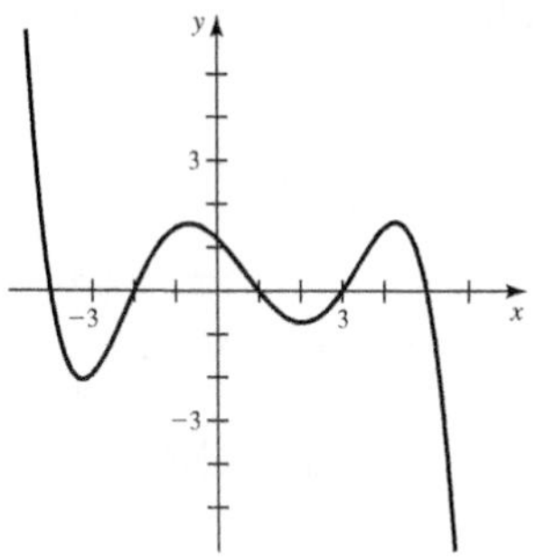

95. a. Increasing on $(-2, 2)$; decreasing on $(-3, -2)$ **b.** Critical pts. $x = -2$ and $x = 0$; local min at $x = -2$; neither a local max nor min at $x = 0$ **c.** Inflection pts. at $x = -1$ and $x = 0$
d. Concave up on $(-3, -1)$, $(0, 2)$; concave down on $(-1, 0)$

e.

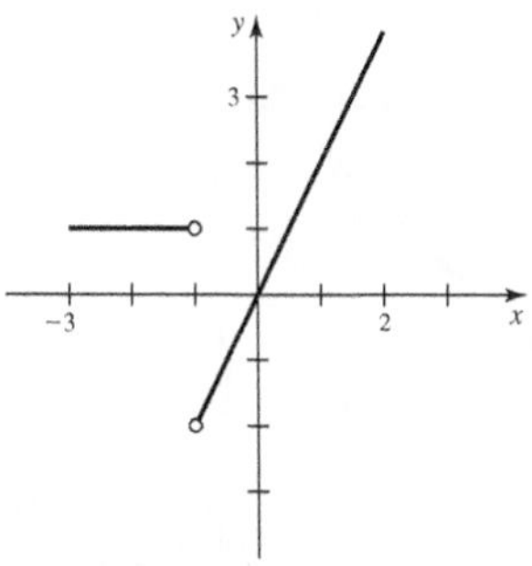

f.

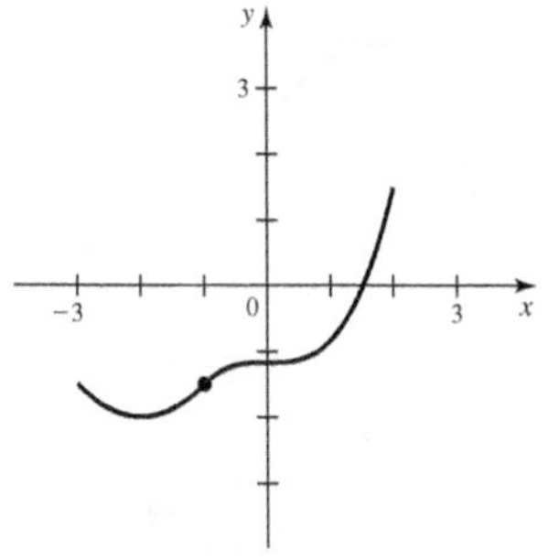

97. Critical pts. $x = -3$ and $x = 4$; local min at $x = -3$; inconclusive at $x = 4$ **99.** No critical pt. **101. a.** $E = \frac{p}{p - 50}$ **b.** -1.4% **c.** $E'(p) = -\frac{ab}{(a - bp)^2} < 0$, for $p \geq 0, p \neq a/b$ **d.** $E(p) = -b$, for $p \geq 0$ **103. a.** 300 **b.** $t = \sqrt{10}$ **c.** $t = \sqrt{b/3}$ **105. a.** $f''(x) = 6x + 2a = 0$ when $x = -a/3$ **b.** $f(-a/3) - f(-a/3 + x) = (a^2/3)x - bx - x^3$; also, $f(-a/3 - x) - f(-a/3) = (a^2/3)x - bx - x^3$

Section 4.3 Exercises, pp. 267–270

1. We need to know on which interval(s) to graph f.
3. No; the domain of any polynomial is $(-\infty, \infty)$; there is no vertical asymptote. Also, $\lim_{x \to \pm\infty} p(x) = \pm\infty$ where p is any polynomial; there is no horizontal asymptote. **5.** Evaluate the function at the critical points and at the endpoints. Then find the largest and smallest values among those candidates.

7.

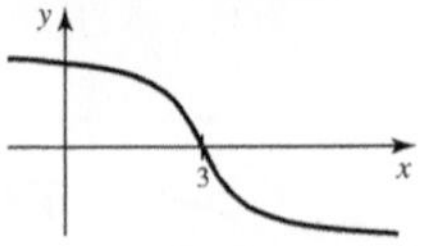

9.

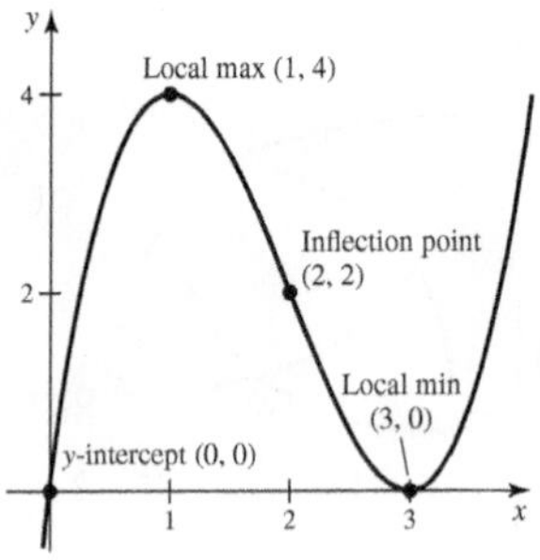

11.

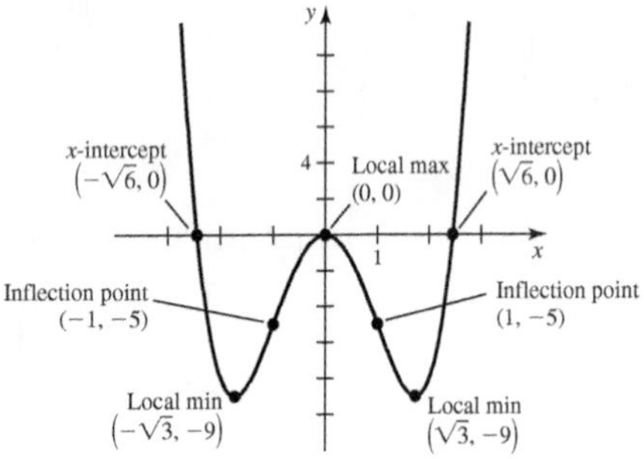

13.

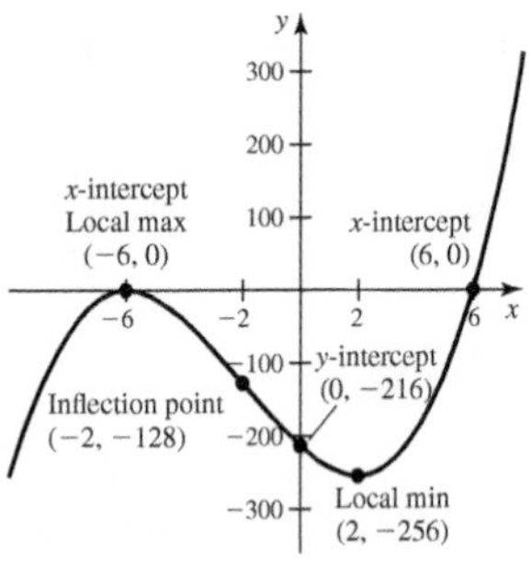

15.

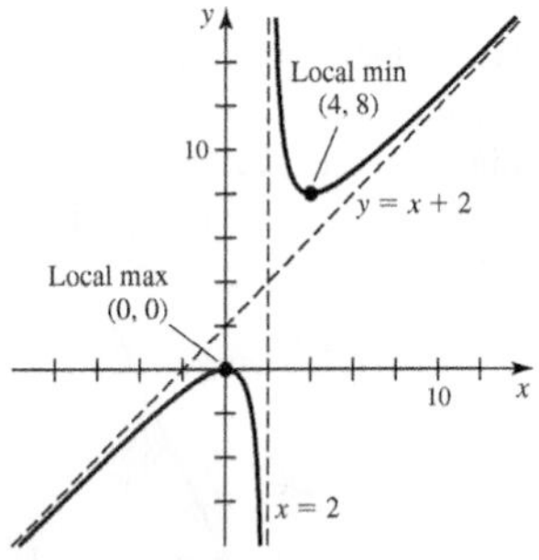

17.

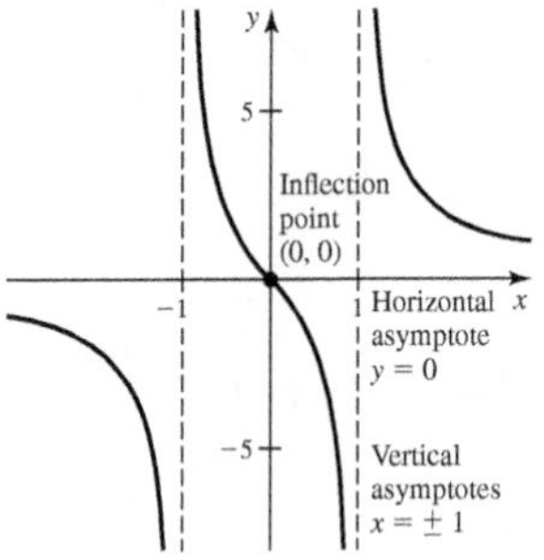

19.

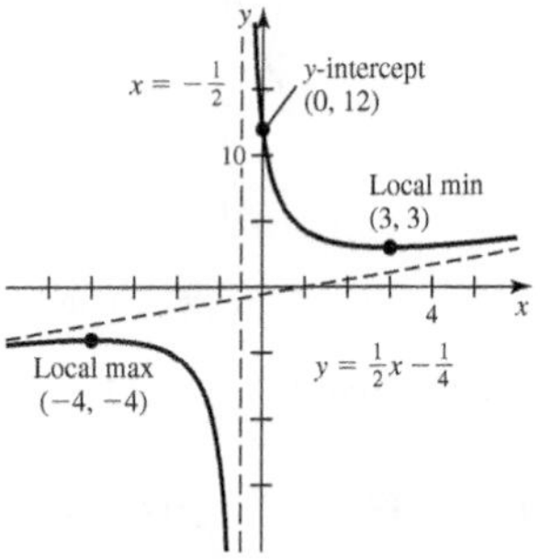

21.

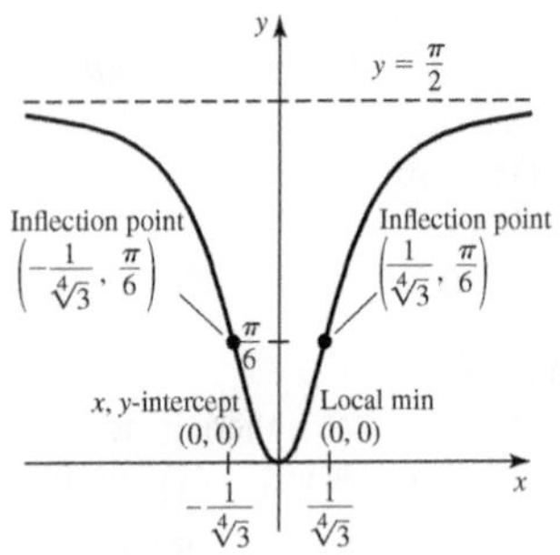

23.

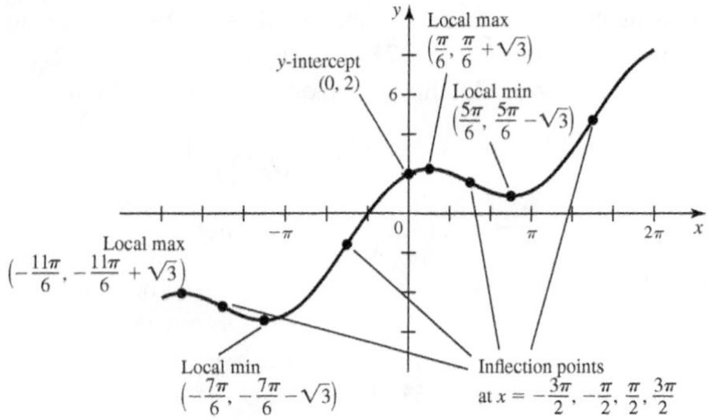

25.

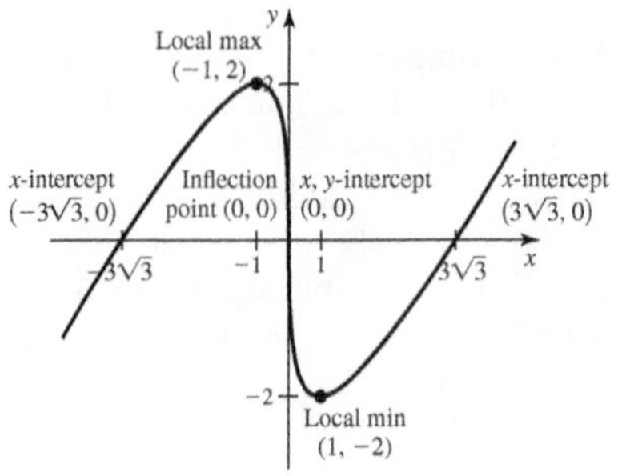

27.

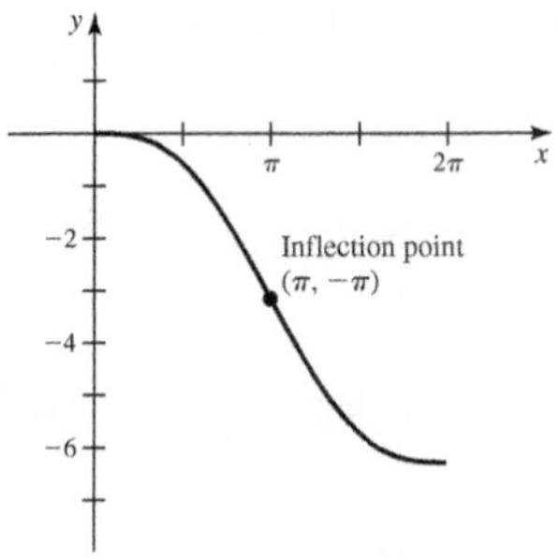

29.

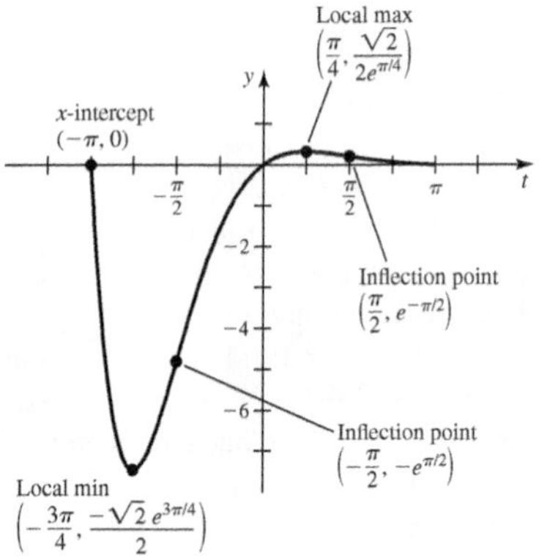

31.

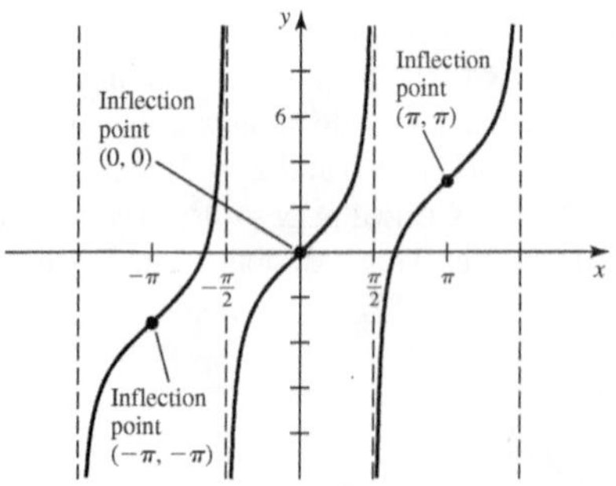

33.

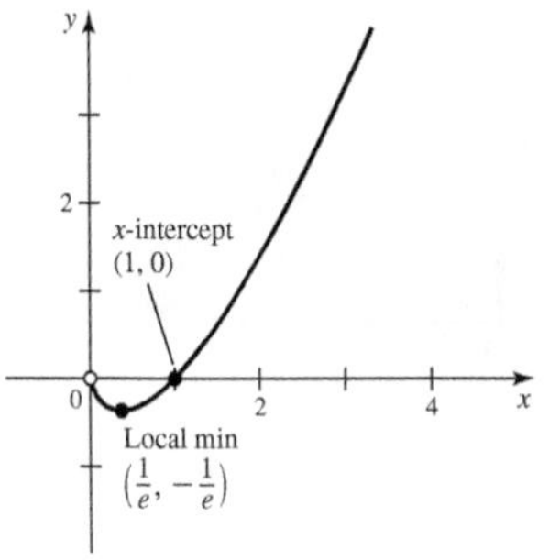

35.

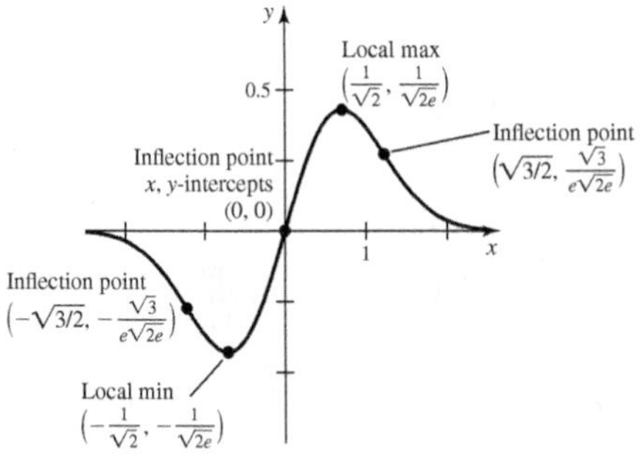

37.

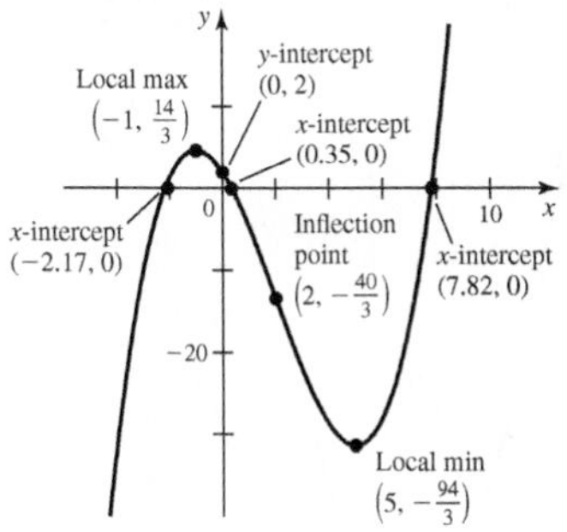

39.

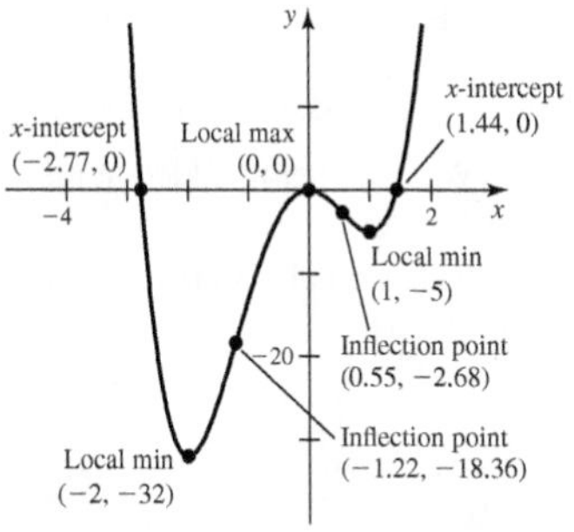

41.

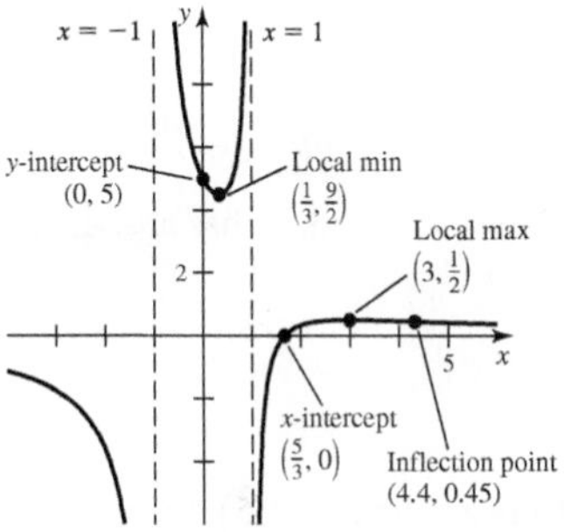

43. a. False **b.** False **c.** False **d.** True

45.

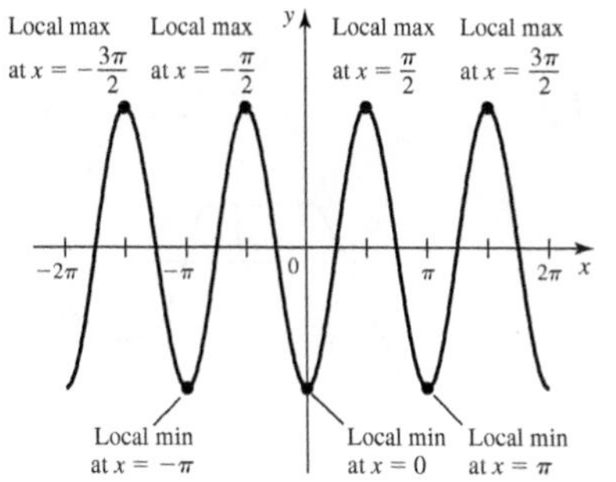

47.

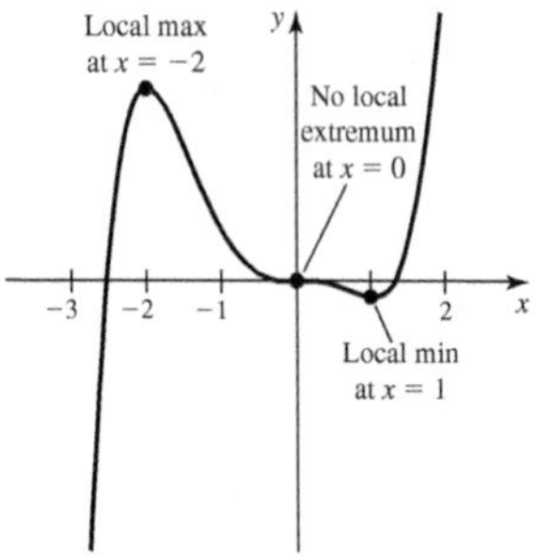

49. Critical pts. at $x = 1, 3$; local max at $x = 1$; local min at $x = 3$; inflection pt. at $x = 2$; increasing on $(0, 1)$, $(3, 4)$; decreasing on $(1, 3)$; concave up on $(2, 4)$; concave down on $(0, 2)$

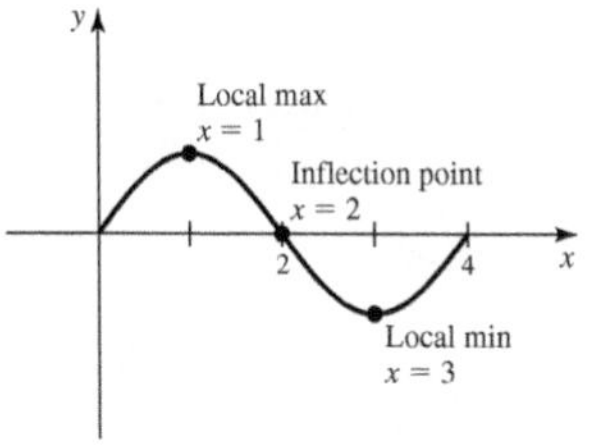

51.

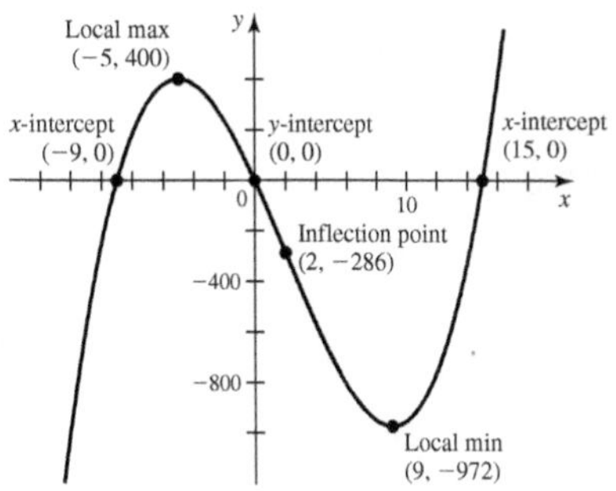

53.

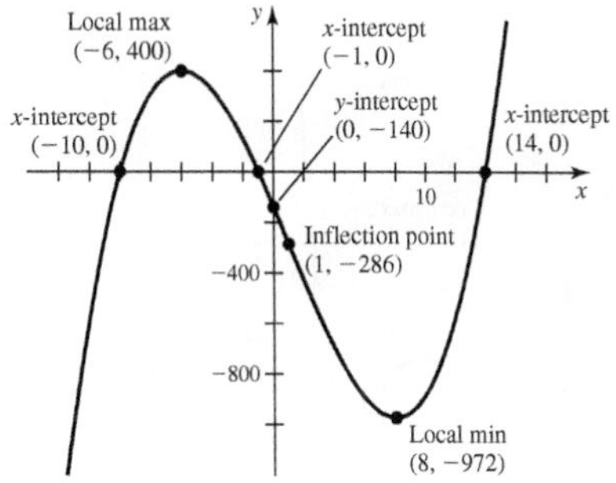

55. Local max of $e^{1/e}$ at $x = e$

57.

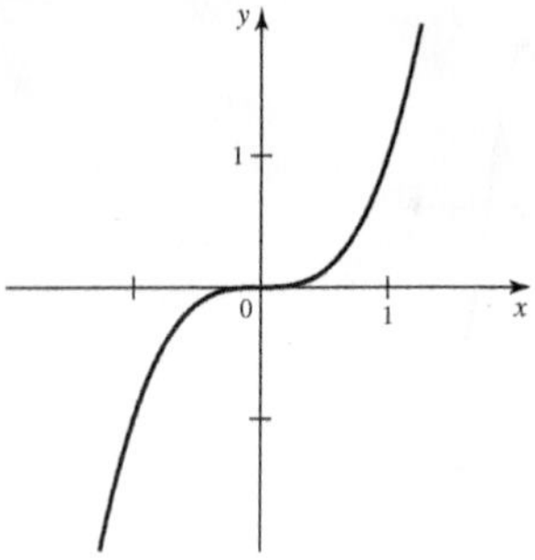

59.

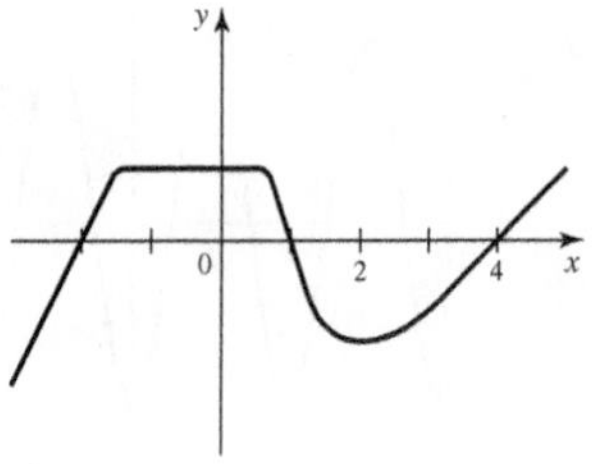

61.

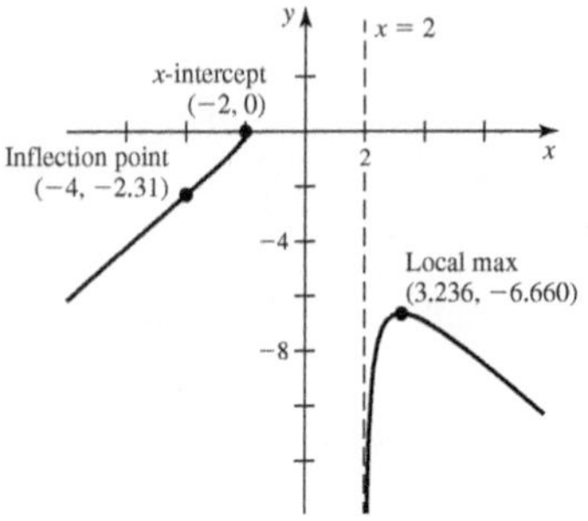

63. a.

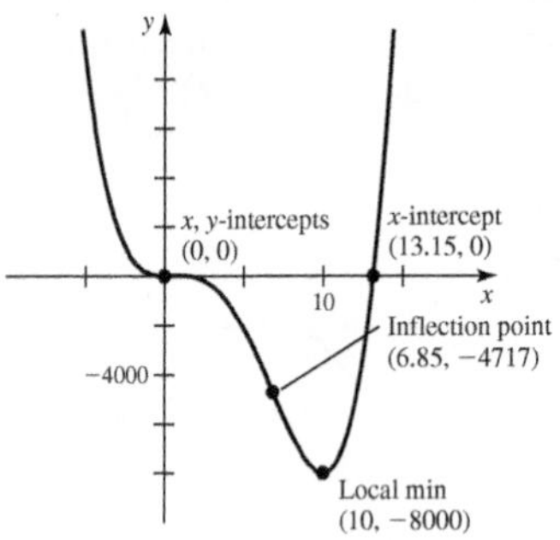

b.

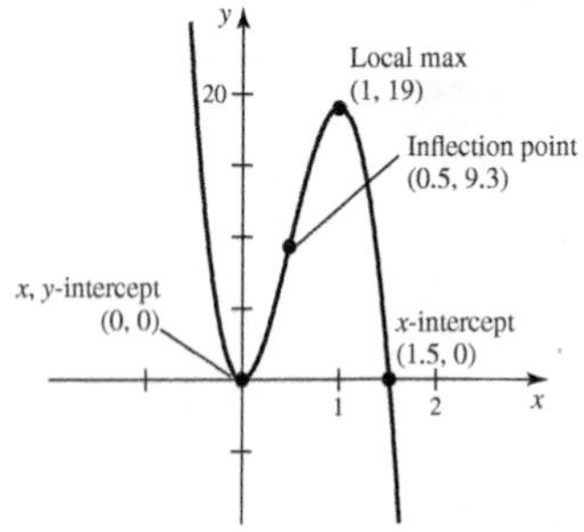

65.

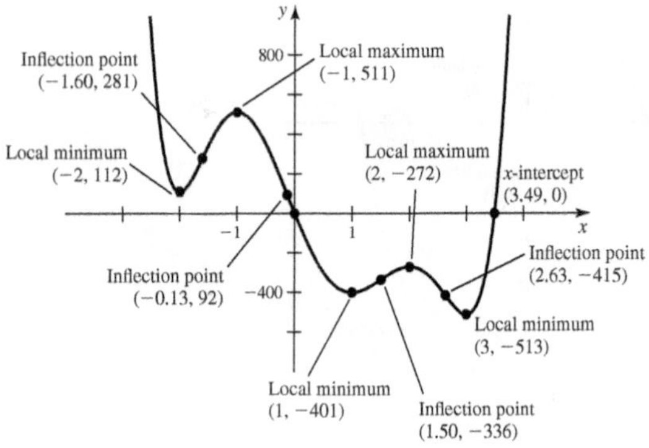

67.

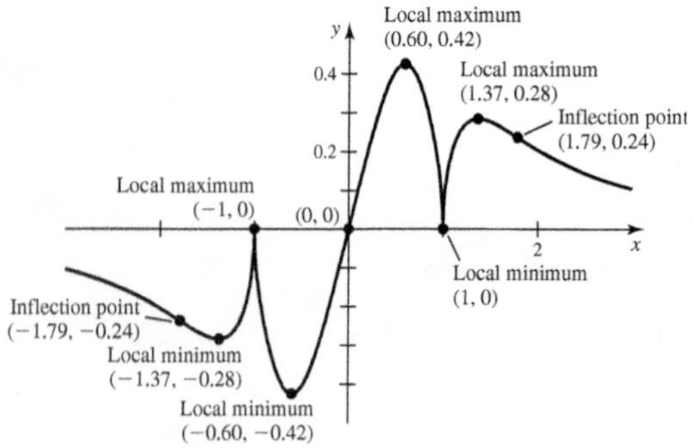

69. a.

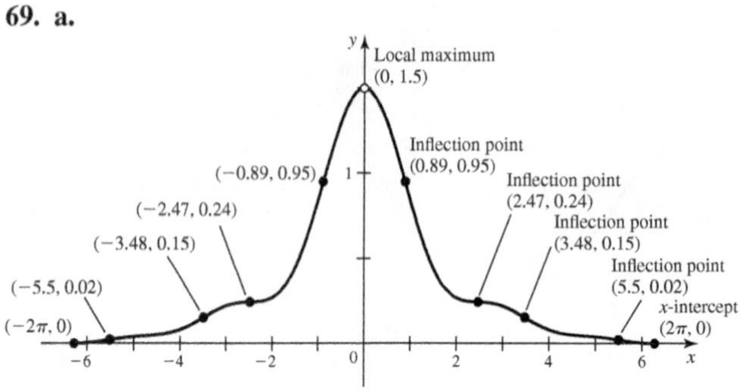

b.

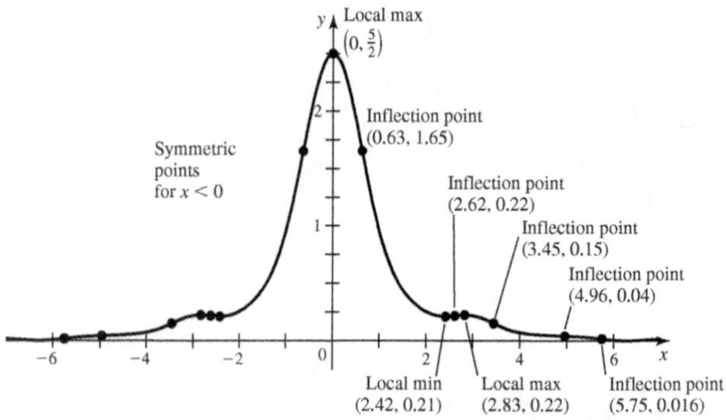

71. (A) a.

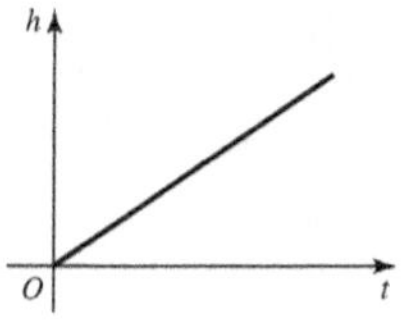

b. Water is being added at all times. **c.** No concavity **d.** h' has an abs. max at all points of $[0, 10]$.

(B) a.

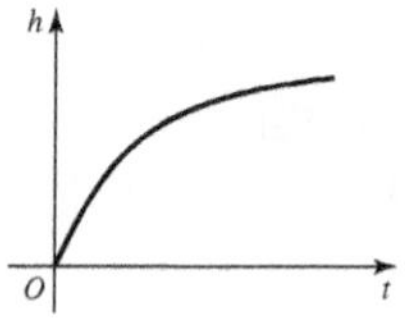

c. Concave down **d.** h' has abs. max at $t = 0$.

(C) a.

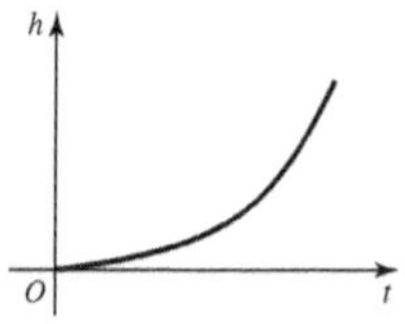

c. Concave up **d.** h' has abs. max at $t = 10$.

(D) a.

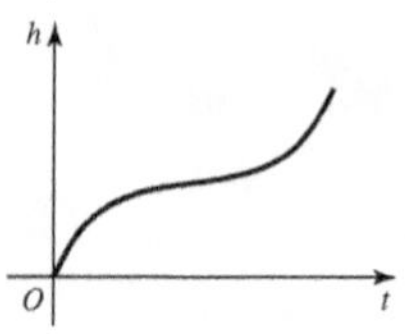

c. Concave up on $(0, 5)$, then concave down on $(5, 10)$; inflection pt. at $t = 5$ **d.** h' has abs. max at $t = 0$ and $t = 10$.

(E) a.

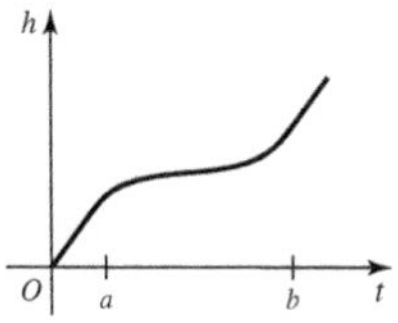

c. First, no concavity; then concave down, no concavity, concave up, and, finally, no concavity **d.** h' has abs. max at all points of an interval $[0, a]$ and $[b, 10]$.

(F) a.

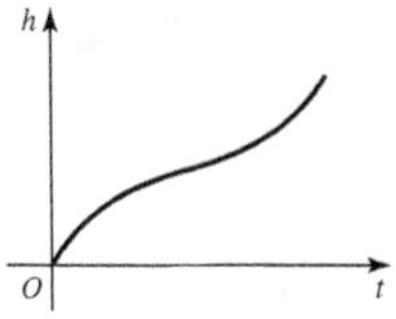

c. Concave down on $(0, 5)$; concave up on $(5, 10)$; inflection pt. at $t = 5$ **d.** h' has abs. max at $t = 0$ and $t = 10$.

73. $f'(0)$ does not exist.

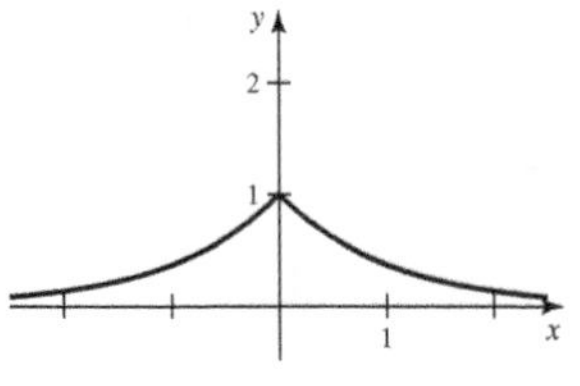

75.

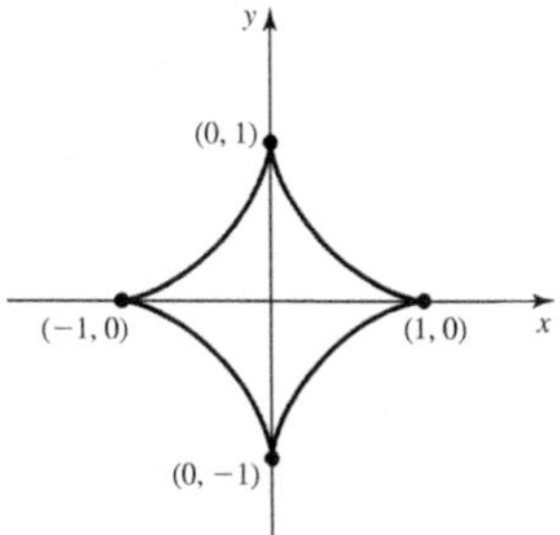

77.

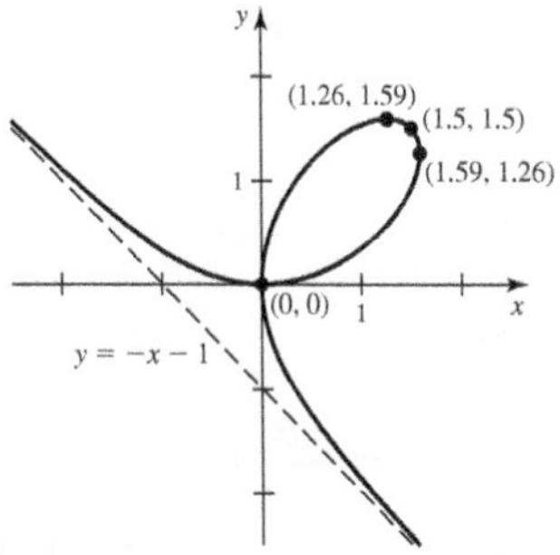

79.

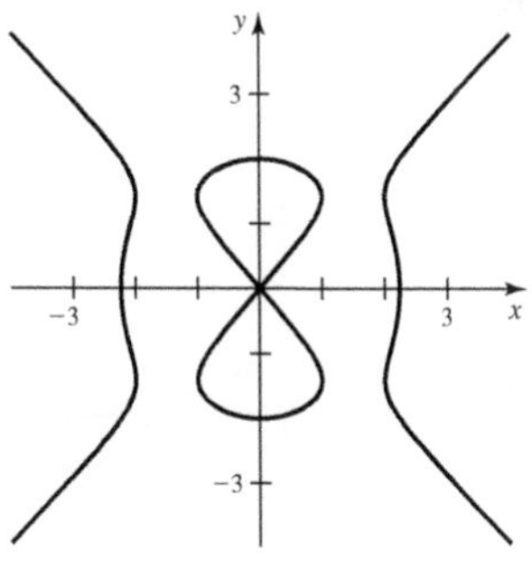

81.

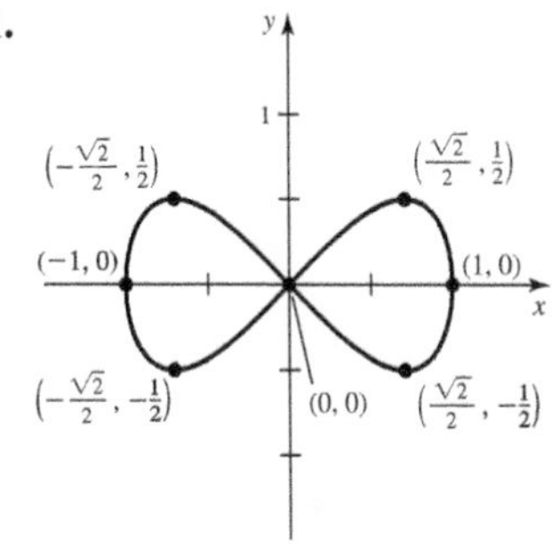

83.

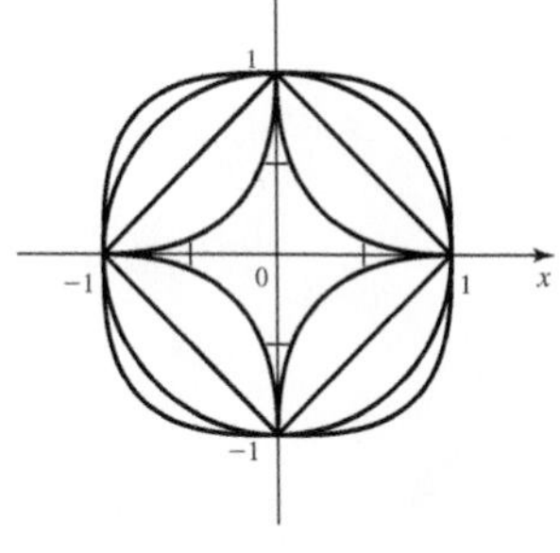

85. a. $\{x: x < a\}$ **b.** $f(a) = 0$, $\lim_{x \to -\infty} f(x) = 0$
c. $f'(x) = (a - x)^{x-1}((a - x)\ln(a - x) - x)$
d. See part (c). **e.** z and $f(z)$ increase as a increases.

87.

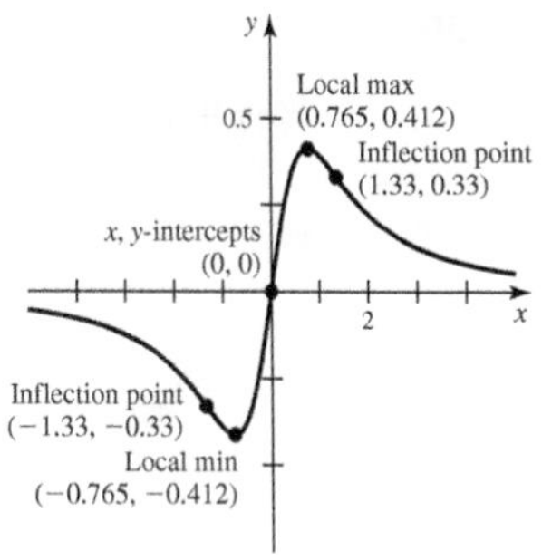

89.

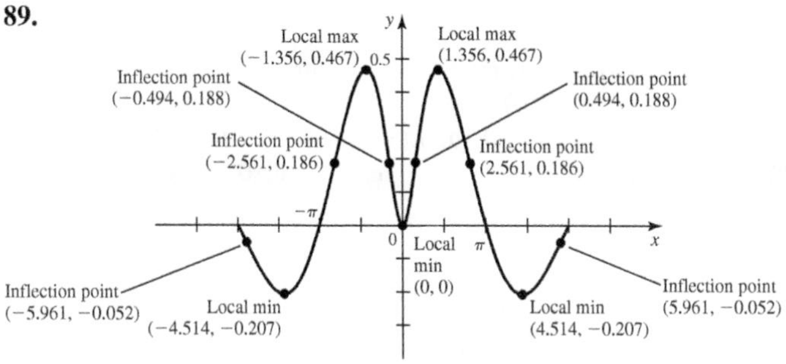

Section 4.4 Exercises, pp. 274–280

1. Objective function, constraint(s) **3.** $Q = x^2(10 - x)$; $Q = (10 - y)^2 y$ **5.** Width $=$ length $= \frac{5}{2}$ m **7.** Width $=$ length $= 10$ **9.** $\frac{23}{2}$ and $\frac{23}{2}$ **11.** $5\sqrt{2}$ and $5\sqrt{2}$ **13.** $x = \sqrt{6}, y = 2\sqrt{6}$ **15.** Length $=$ width $=$ height $= \sqrt[3]{100}$ **17.** $\dfrac{4}{\sqrt[3]{5}}$ ft by $\dfrac{4}{\sqrt[3]{5}}$ ft by $5^{2/3}$ ft **19.** $(5, 15)$, distance ≈ 47.4 **21. a.** A point $8/\sqrt{5}$ mi from the point on the shore nearest the woman in the direction of the restaurant **b.** $9/\sqrt{13}$ mi/hr **23.** 18.2 ft **25.** $\dfrac{10}{\sqrt{2}}$ cm by $\dfrac{5}{\sqrt{2}}$ cm **27.** $h = \dfrac{20}{\sqrt{3}}$; $r = 20\sqrt{\frac{2}{3}}$ **29.** $\sqrt{15}$ m by $2\sqrt{15}$ m **31.** $r/h = \sqrt{2}$ **33.** $r = h = \sqrt[3]{450/\pi}$ m **35.** The point $12/(\sqrt[3]{2} + 1) \approx 5.3$ m from the weaker source **37.** A point $7\sqrt{3}/6$ mi from the point on shore nearest the island, in the direction of the power station **39. a.** $P = 2/\sqrt{3}$ units from the midpoint of the base **41.** $r = \sqrt{6}, h = \sqrt{3}$ **43.** For $L \leq 4r$, max at $\theta = 0$ and $\theta = 2\pi$; min at $\theta = \cos^{-1}(-L/(4r))$ and $\theta = 2\pi - \cos^{-1}(-L/(4r))$. For $L > 4r$, max at $\theta = 0$ and $\theta = 2\pi$; min at $\theta = \pi$. **45. a.** $r = \sqrt[3]{177/\pi} \approx 3.83$ cm; $h = 2\sqrt[3]{177/\pi} \approx 7.67$ cm **b.** $r = \sqrt[3]{177/2\pi} \approx 3.04$ cm; $h = 2\sqrt[3]{708/\pi} \approx 12.17$ cm. Part (b) is closer to the real can. **47.** $\sqrt{30} \approx 5.5$ ft **49.** When the seat is at its lowest point **51.** $r = \sqrt{2}R/\sqrt{3}$; $h = 2R/\sqrt{3}$ **53. a.** $r = 2R/3$; $h = \frac{1}{3}H$ **b.** $r = R/2$; $h = H/2$ **55.** 3:1 **57.** $(1 + \sqrt{3})$ mi ≈ 2.7 mi **59.** You can run 12 mi/hr if you run toward the point 3/16 mi ahead of the locomotive (when it passes the point nearest you). **61. a.** $(-6/5, 2/5)$ **b.** Approx $(0.59, 0.65)$ **c. (i)** $\left(p - \frac{1}{2}, \sqrt{p - \frac{1}{2}}\right)$ **(ii)** $(0, 0)$ **63. a.** 0, 30, 25 **b.** 42.5 mi/hr **c.** The units of $p/g(v)$ are \$/mi and so are the units of w/v. Therefore, $L\left(\dfrac{p}{g(v)} + \dfrac{w}{v}\right)$ gives the total cost of a trip of L miles. **d.** Approx. 62.9 mi/hr **e.** Neither; the zeros of $C'(v)$ are independent of L. **f.** Decreased slightly, to 62.5 mi/hr **g.** Decreased to 60.8 mi/hr **65. b.** Because the speed of light is constant, travel time is minimized when distance is minimized. **67.** Let the angle of the cuts be φ_1 and φ_2, where $\varphi_1 + \varphi_2 = \theta$. The volume of the notch is proportional to $\tan\varphi_1 + \tan\varphi_2 = \tan\varphi_1 + \tan(\theta - \varphi_1)$, which is minimized when $\varphi_1 = \varphi_2 = \dfrac{\theta}{2}$. **69.** $x \approx 38.81, y \approx 55.03$

Section 4.5 Exercises, pp. 288–290

1.

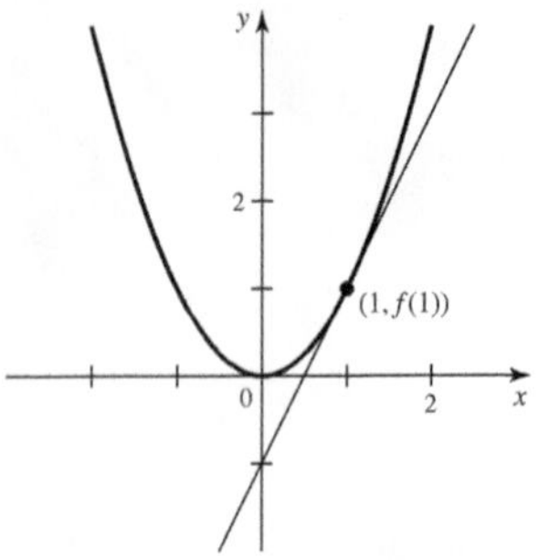

3. $f(x) \approx f(a) + f'(a)(x - a)$

5. $dy = f'(x)\,dx$ **7.** 61 mi/hr; 61.02 mi/hr
9. $L(x) = T(0) + T'(0)(x - 0) = D - (D/60)x = D(1 - x/60)$
11. 84 min; 84.21 min **13. a.** $L(x) = -4x + 16$
b.

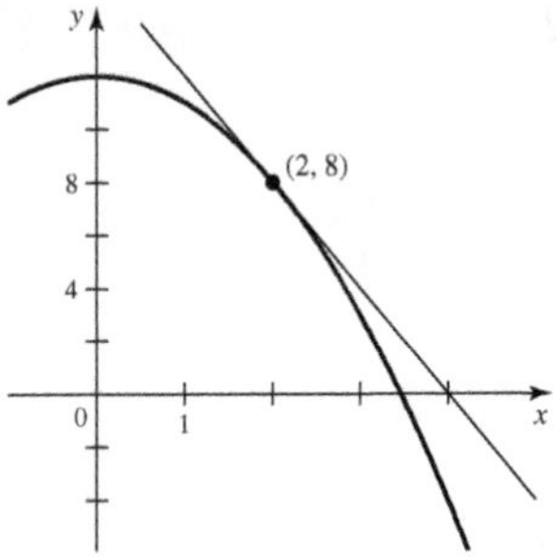

c. 7.6 **d.** 0.13% error

15. a. $L(x) = x$ **b.**

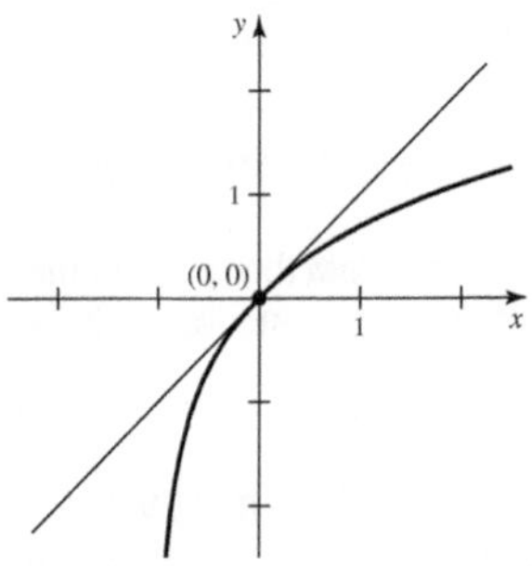

c. 0.9

d. 40% error **17. a.** $L(x) = 1$ **b.**

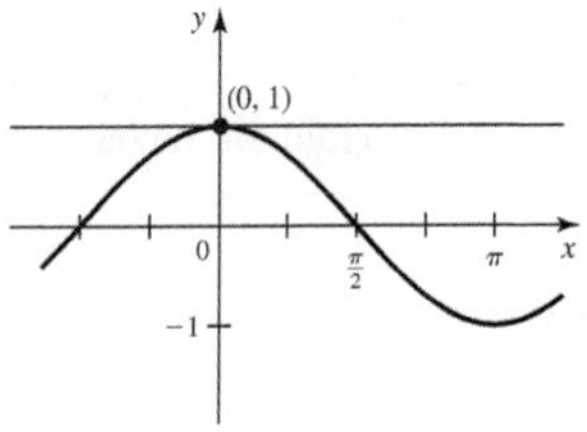

c. 1 **d.** 0.005% error **19. a.** $y = \frac{1}{2} - \frac{x}{48}$
b.

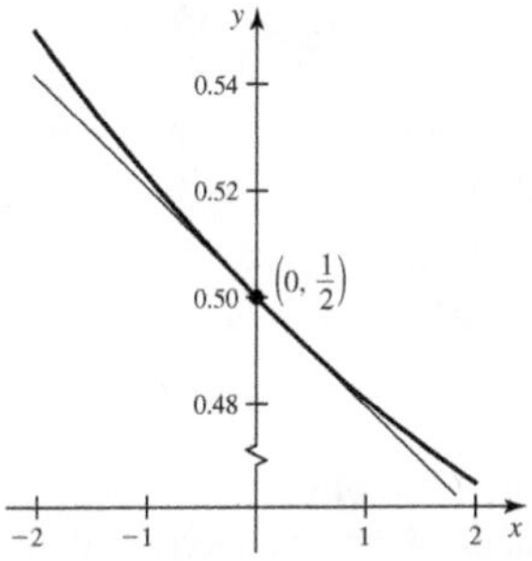

c. 0.5 **d.** 0.003% error

21. $a = 200; \frac{1}{203} \approx 0.004925$ **23.** $a = 144; \sqrt{146} \approx \frac{145}{12}$
25. $a = 1; \ln 1.05 \approx 0.05$ **27.** $a = 0; e^{0.06} \approx 1.06$
29. $a = 512; \frac{1}{\sqrt[3]{510}} \approx \frac{769}{6144} \approx 0.125$

31. a. $L(x) = -2x + 4$ **b.**

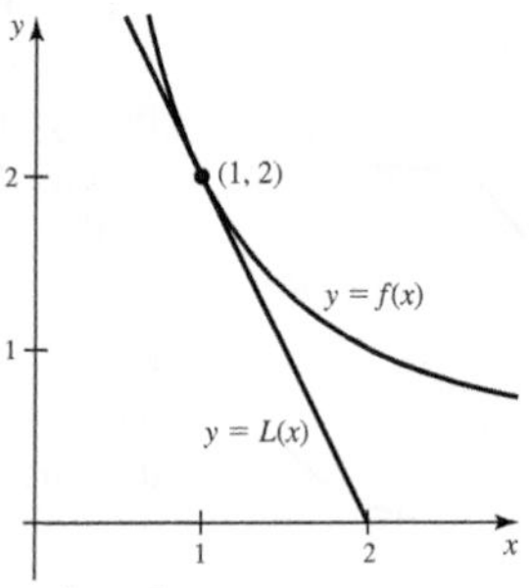

c. Underestimates **d.** $f''(1) = 4 > 0$

33. a. $L(x) = -\frac{1}{2}x + \frac{1}{2}(1 + \ln 2)$ **b.**

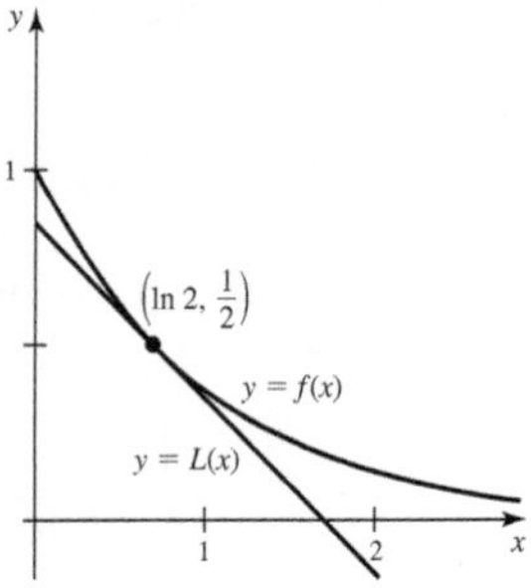

c. Underestimates **d.** $f''(\ln 2) = \frac{1}{2} > 0$ **35.** $\Delta V \approx 10\pi \text{ ft}^3$
37. $\Delta V \approx -40\pi \text{ cm}^3$ **39.** $\Delta S \approx -\frac{59\pi}{5\sqrt{34}} \text{ m}^2$ **41.** $dy = 2\,dx$
43. $dy = -\frac{3}{x^4}\,dx$ **45.** $dy = a \sin x\,dx$ **47.** $dy = (9x^2 - 4)\,dx$
49. $dy = \sec^2 x\,dx$ **51. a.** True **b.** False **c.** True **d.** True
53. 2.7 **55. a.** $L(x) = 1 - x$; **b.**

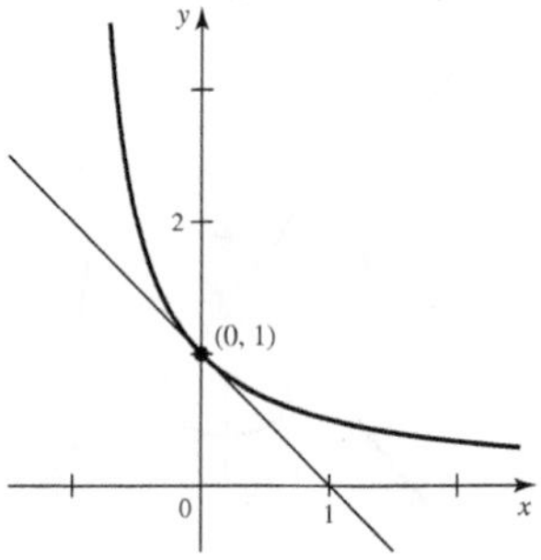

c. $1/1.1 \approx 0.9$ **d.** 1% error **57. a.** $L(x) = 1 - x$
b.

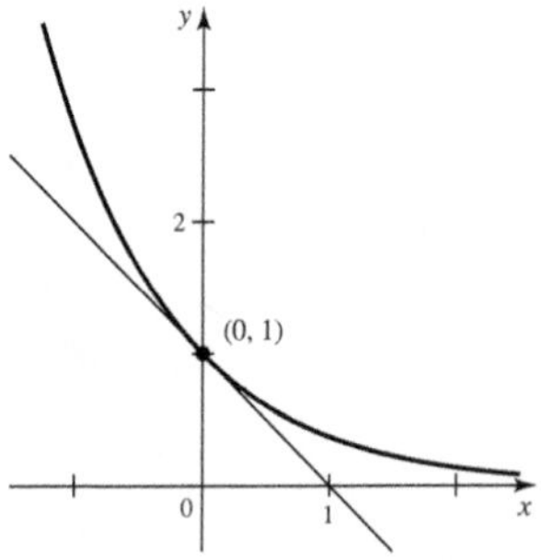

c. $e^{-0.03} \approx 0.97$ **d.** 0.05% error

59. $E(x) \le 1$ when $-7.26 \le x \le 8.26$, which corresponds to driving times for 1 mi from about 53 s to 68 s. Therefore, $L(x)$ gives approximations to $s(x)$ that are within 1 mi/hr of the true value when you drive 1 mi in t seconds, where $53 < t < 68$.

61. $L(x) = 2 + (x - 8)/12$

x	Linear approx.	Exact value	Percent error
8.1	$2.008\overline{3}$	2.00829885	1.7×10^{-3}
8.01	$2.0008\overline{3}$	2.000832986	1.7×10^{-5}
8.001	$2.00008\overline{3}$	2.00008333	1.7×10^{-7}
8.0001	$2.000008\overline{3}$	2.000008333	1.7×10^{-9}
7.9999	$1.999991\overline{6}$	1.999991667	1.7×10^{-9}
7.999	$1.99991\overline{6}$	1.999916663	1.7×10^{-7}
7.99	$1.9991\overline{6}$	1.999166319	1.7×10^{-5}
7.9	$1.991\overline{6}$	1.991631701	1.8×10^{-3}

63. a. f; the rate at which f' is changing at 1 is smaller than the rate at which g' is changing at 1. The graph of f bends away from the linear function more slowly than the graph of g. **b.** The larger the value of $|f''(a)|$, the greater the deviation of the curve $y = f(x)$ from the tangent line at points near $x = a$.

Section 4.6 Exercises, pp. 295–296

1. If f is a continuous function on the closed interval $[a, b]$ and is differentiable on (a, b) and the slope of the secant line that joins $(a, f(a))$ to $(b, f(b))$ is zero, then there is at least one value c in (a, b) at which the slope of the line tangent to f at $(c, f(c))$ is also zero.

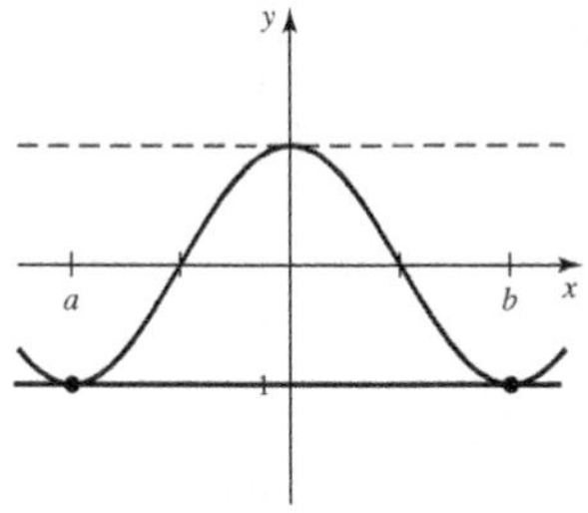

3. $f(x) = |x|$ is not differentiable at 0.
5.

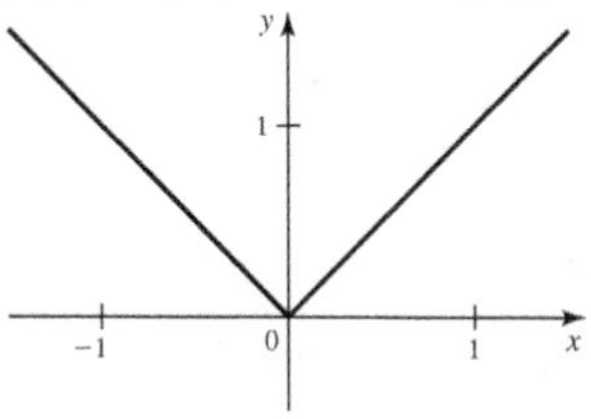

7. $x = \frac{1}{3}$

9. $x = \pi/4$ **11.** Does not apply **13.** $x = \frac{5}{3}$ **15.** Average lapse rate $= -6.3°/\text{km}$. You cannot conclude that the lapse rate at a point exceeds the threshold value. **17. a.** Yes **b.** $c = \frac{1}{2}$
c.

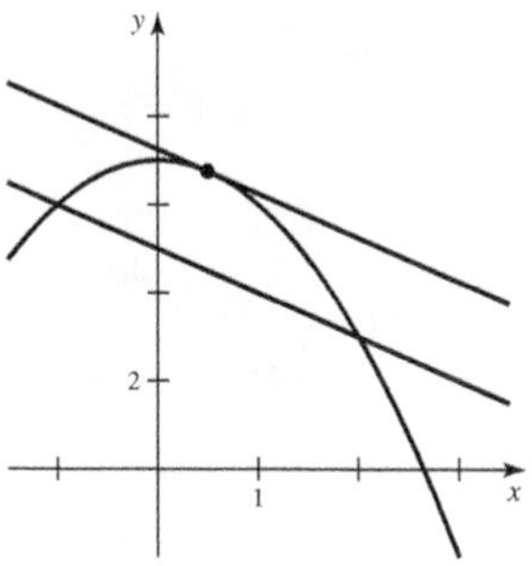

19. a. Yes **b.** $c = \ln\left(\frac{3}{\ln 4}\right)$ **c.**

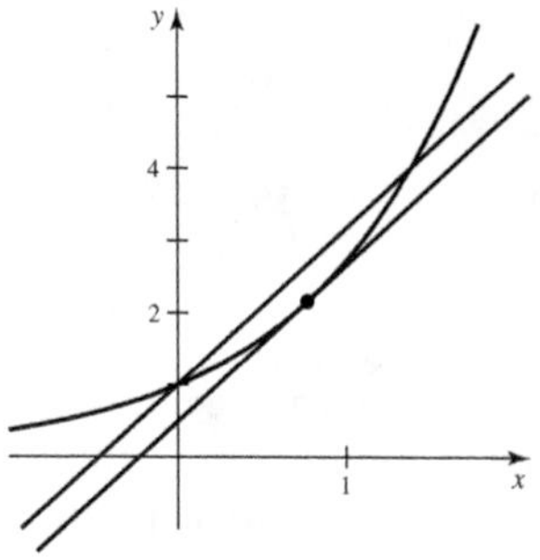

21. a. Yes **b.** $c = \sqrt{1 - 9/\pi^2}$ **c.**

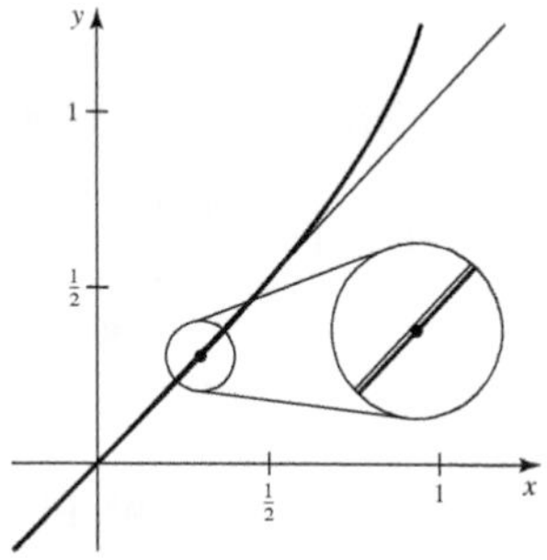

23. a. Does not apply **25. a.** False **b.** True **c.** False
27. h and p **29.**

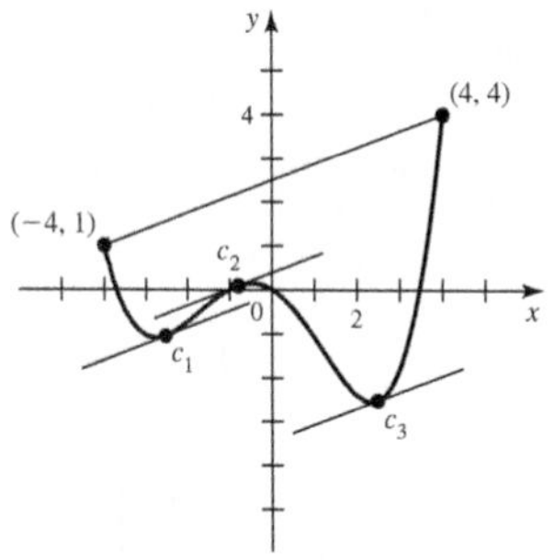

31. No such point exists; function is not continuous at 2.
33. The car's average velocity is $(30 - 0)/(28/60) = 64.3$ mi/hr. By the MVT, the car's instantaneous velocity was 64.3 mi/hr at some time. **35.** Average speed $= 11.6$ mi/hr. By the MVT, the speed was exactly 11.6 mi/hr at least once. By the Intermediate Value Theorem, all speeds between 0 and 11.6 mi/hr were reached. Because the initial and final speed was 0 mi/hr, the speed of 11 mi/hr was reached at least twice. **37.** $\frac{f(b) - f(a)}{b - a} = A(a + b) + B$ and $f'(x) = 2Ax + B$; $2Ax + B = A(a + b) + B$ implies that $x = \frac{a + b}{2}$, the midpoint of $[a, b]$. **39.** $\tan^2 x$ and $\sec^2 x$ differ by a constant; in fact, $\tan^2 x - \sec^2 x = -1$. **41.** Bolt's average speed was 37.58 km/hr, so he exceeded 37 km/hr during the race.
43. b. $c = \frac{1}{2}$

Section 4.7 Exercises, pp. 307–309

1. If $\lim_{x \to a} f(x) = 0$ and $\lim_{x \to a} g(x) = 0$, then we say $\lim_{x \to a} f(x)/g(x)$ is an indeterminate form $0/0$. **3.** Take the limit of the quotient of the derivatives of the functions. **5.** If $\lim_{x \to a} f(x)g(x)$ has the indeterminate form $0 \cdot \infty$, then $\lim_{x \to a}\left(\frac{f(x)}{1/g(x)}\right)$ has the indeterminate form $0/0$ or ∞/∞. **7.** If $\lim_{x \to a} f(x) = 1$ and $\lim_{x \to a} g(x) = \infty$, then $f(x)^{g(x)} \to 1^\infty$ as $x \to a$, which is meaningless; so direct substitution does not work.

9. $\lim_{x\to\infty} \frac{g(x)}{f(x)} = 0$ **11.** $\ln x, x^3, 2^x, x^x$ **13.** -1 **15.** $1/2$ **17.** $1/e$
19. $\frac{12}{5}$ **21.** 4 **23.** $\frac{9}{16}$ **25.** $\frac{1}{2}$ **27.** $1/24$ **29.** 1 **31.** 4 **33.** $-\frac{1}{2}$
35. $1/\pi^2$ **37.** $\frac{1}{2}$ **39.** $-\frac{2}{3}$ **41.** 1 **43.** $\frac{1}{3}$ **45.** 1 **47.** $\frac{7}{6}$ **49.** 1
51. 0 **53.** 0 **55.** 1 **57.** 1 **59.** e **61.** e^a **63.** e^{a+1} **65.** 1
67. e **69.** $e^{0.01x}$ **71.** Comparable growth rates **73.** x^x
75. 1.00001^x **77.** x^x **79.** e^{x^2} **81. a.** False **b.** False **c.** False
d. False **e.** True **f.** True **83.** $\frac{2}{5}$ **85.** $-\frac{9}{4}$ **87.** 0 **89.** $\frac{1}{6}$ **91.** ∞
93. $(\ln 3)/(\ln 2)$ **95.** $\frac{1}{2}$ **97.** $\frac{1}{2}$ **99.** e **101.** $-\frac{1}{3}$
103. a. Approx. 3.43×10^{15} **b.** Approx. 3536 **c.** e^{100}
d. Approx. 163 **105.** 1 **107.** $\ln a - \ln b$

109. b. $\lim_{m\to\infty} (1 + r/m)^m = \lim_{m\to\infty} \left(1 + \frac{1}{(m/r)}\right)^{(m/r)r} = e^r$

111. $\sqrt{a/c}$ **113.** $\lim_{x\to\infty} \frac{x^p}{b^x} = \lim_{t\to\infty} \frac{\ln^p t}{t \ln^p b} = 0$

115. Show $\lim_{x\to\infty} \frac{\log_a x}{\log_b x} = \frac{\ln b}{\ln a} \neq 0.$ **117.** $1/3$

121. a. $b > e$ **b.** e^{ax} grows faster than e^x as $x \to \infty$, for $a > 1$; e^{ax} grows slower than e^x as $x \to \infty$, for $0 < a < 1$.

Section 4.8 Exercises, pp. 316–318

1. Newton's method generates a sequence of x-intercepts of lines tangent to the graph of f to approximate the roots of f.
3. Generally, if two successive Newton approximations agree in their first p digits, then those approximations have p digits of accuracy. The method is terminated when the desired accuracy is reached.

5. $x_{n+1} = x_n - \frac{x_n^2 - 6}{2x_n} = \frac{x_n^2 + 6}{2x_n}$; $x_1 = 2.5, x_2 = 2.45$

7. $x_{n+1} = x_n - \frac{e^{-x_n} - x_n}{e^{-x_n} - 1}$; $x_1 = 0.564382, x_2 = 0.567142$

9.

n	x_n
0	4.000000
1	3.250000
2	3.163462
3	3.162278
4	3.162278
5	3.162278
6	3.162278
7	3.162278
8	3.162278
9	3.162278
10	3.162278

11.

n	x_n
0	1.500000
1	0.101436
2	0.501114
3	0.510961
4	0.510973
5	0.510973
6	0.510973
7	0.510973
8	0.510973
9	0.510973
10	0.510973

13.

n	x_n
0	1.500000
1	1.443890
2	1.361976
3	1.268175
4	1.196179
5	1.168571
6	1.165592
7	1.165561
8	1.165561
9	1.165561
10	1.165561

15. $x \approx 0, 1.895494, -1.895494$
17. $x \approx -2.114908, 0.254102, 1.860806$
19. $x \approx 0.062997, 2.230120$
21. $x \approx 2.798386$
23. $x \approx -0.666667, 1.5, 1.666667$

25. The method converges more slowly for f, because of the double root at $x = 1$.

n	x_n for f	x_n for g
0	2	2
1	1.5	1.25
2	1.25	1.025
3	1.125	1.0003
4	1.0625	1
5	1.03125	1
6	1.01563	1
7	1.00781	1
8	1.00391	1
9	1.00195	1
10	1.00098	1

27. a. True. **b.** False. **c.** False **29.** $x \approx 1.153467, 2.423622, -3.57709$ **31.** $x = 0$ and $x \approx 1.047198$ **33.** $x \approx -0.335408, 1.333057$ **35.** $x \approx 0.179295$ **37.** $x \approx 0.620723, 3.03645$

39.

n	x_n	Error	Residual
0	0.5	0.5	9.8×10^{-4}
1	0.45	0.45	3.4×10^{-4}
2	0.405	0.41	1.2×10^{-4}
3	0.3645	0.36	4.1×10^{-5}
4	0.32805	0.33	1.4×10^{-5}
5	0.295245	0.30	5.0×10^{-6}
6	0.265721	0.27	1.7×10^{-6}
7	0.239148	0.24	6.1×10^{-7}
8	0.215234	0.22	2.1×10^{-7}
9	0.193710	0.19	7.4×10^{-8}
10	0.174339	0.17	2.6×10^{-8}

41. $a = e$ **43. b.** $x \approx 0.142857$ is approximately $\frac{1}{7}$.
45. a. $t = \pi/4$ **b.** $t \approx 1.33897$ **c.** $t \approx 2.35619$
d. $t \approx 2.90977$ **47.** $\lambda = 1.29011, 2.37305, 3.40918$

Section 4.9 Exercises, pp. 327–329

1. The derivative, an antiderivative **3.** $x + C$, where C is an arbitrary constant **5.** $\frac{x^{p+1}}{p+1} + C$, where $p \neq -1$ **7.** $\ln|x| + C$
9. 0 **11.** $x^5 + C$ **13.** $-\frac{1}{2}\cos 2x + C$ **15.** $3 \tan x + C$
17. $y^{-2} + C$ **19.** $e^x + C$ **21.** $\tan^{-1} s + C$ **23.** $\frac{1}{2}x^6 - \frac{1}{2}x^{10} + C$
25. $\frac{8}{3}x^{3/2} - 8x^{1/2} + C$ **27.** $\frac{25}{3}s^3 + 15s^2 + 9s + C$
29. $\frac{9}{4}x^{4/3} + 6x^{2/3} + 6x + C$ **31.** $-x^3 + \frac{11}{2}x^2 + 4x + C$
33. $-x^{-3} + 2x + 3x^{-1} + C$ **35.** $x^4 - 3x^2 + C$
37. $-\frac{1}{2}\cos 2y + \frac{1}{3}\sin 3y + C$ **39.** $\tan x - x + C$
41. $\tan\theta + \sec\theta + C$ **43.** $t^3 + \frac{1}{2}\tan 2t + C$ **45.** $\frac{1}{4}\sec 4\theta + C$
47. $\frac{1}{2}\ln|y| + C$ **49.** $6\sin^{-1}(x/5) + C$ **51.** $\frac{1}{10}\sec^{-1}|x/10| + C$
53. $\frac{1}{5}\sec^{-1}\left|\frac{x}{5}\right| + C$ **55.** $t + \ln|t| + C$ **57.** $e^{x+2} + C$
59. $x^6/6 + 2/x + x - 19/6$ **61.** $\sec v + 1$

63. $2x^4 + 2x^{-1} + 1$ **65.** $y^3 + 5\ln|y| + 2$

67. $f(x) = x^2 - 3x + 4$ **69.** $g(x) = \frac{7}{8}x^8 - \frac{x^2}{2} + \frac{13}{8}$

71. $f(u) = 4\sin u + 2\cos 2u - 3$ **73.** $y(t) = 3\ln|t| + 6t + 2$

75. $y(\theta) = \sqrt{2}\sin\theta + \tan\theta + 1$

77. $f(x) = x^2 - 5x + 4$

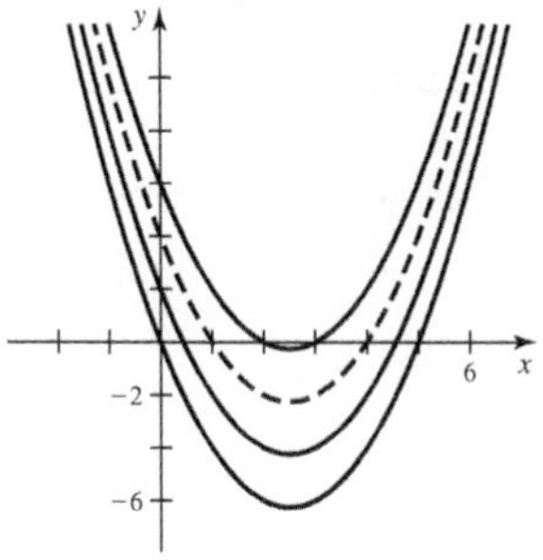

79. $f(x) = \frac{3x^2}{2} - \frac{\cos \pi x}{\pi} + \frac{1 - 3\pi}{\pi}$

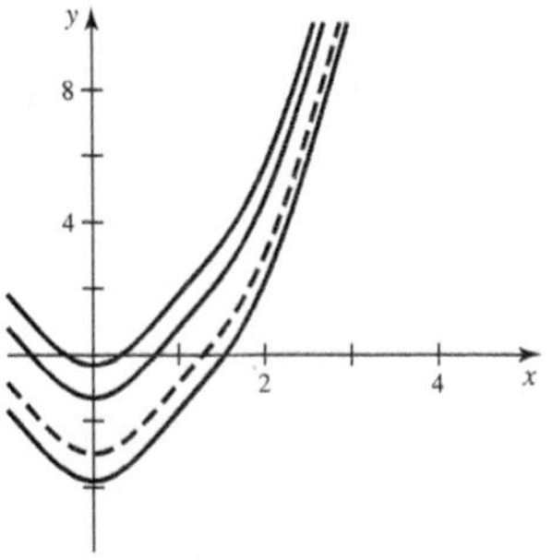

81. $f(t) = \ln t + 4$

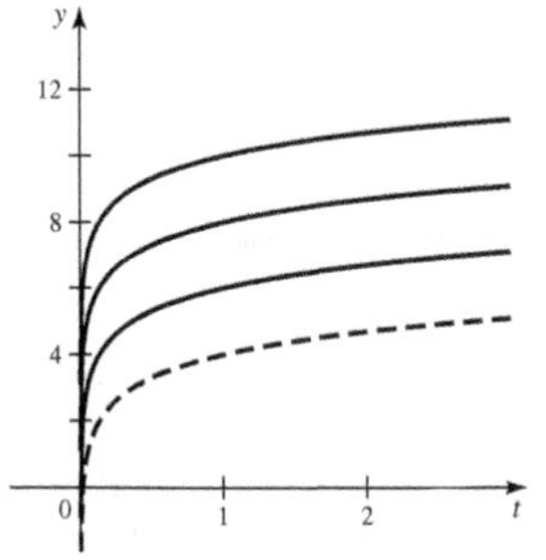

83. $s(t) = t^2 + 4t$

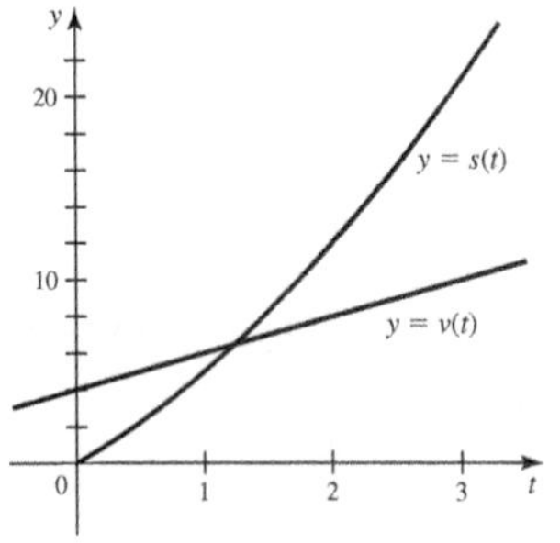

85. $s(t) = \frac{4}{3}t^{3/2} + 1$

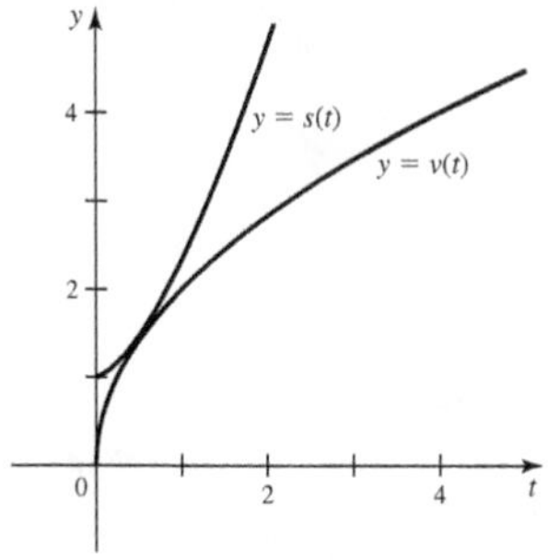

87. $s(t) = 2t^3 + 2t^2 - 10t$

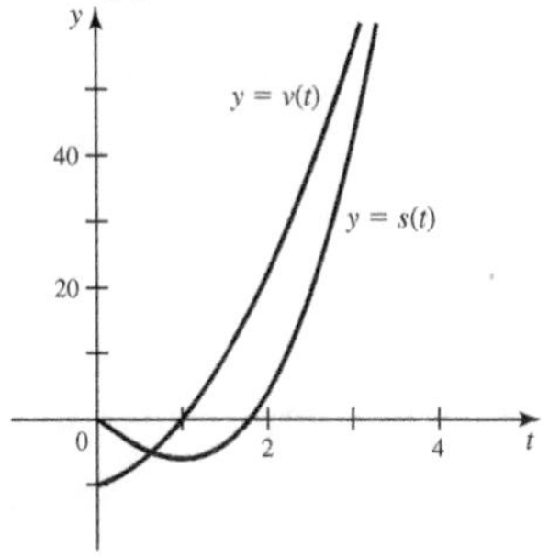

89. $-16t^2 + 20t$ **91.** $\frac{1}{30}t^3 + 1$ **93.** $-\frac{3}{4}\sin 2t + \frac{5}{2}t + 10$

95. Runner A overtakes runner B at $t = \pi/2$.

97. a. $v(t) = -9.8t + 30$ **b.** $s(t) = -4.9t^2 + 30t$

c. 45.92 m at time $t = 3.06$ **d.** $t = 6.12$

99. a. $v(t) = -9.8t + 10$ **b.** $s(t) = -4.9t^2 + 10t + 400$

c. 405.10 m at time $t = 1.02$ **d.** $t = 10.11$ **101. a.** True

b. False **c.** True **d.** False **e.** False **103.** $(e^{2x} + e^{-2x})/4 + C$

105. $-\cot\theta + 2\theta^3/3 - 3\theta^2/2 + C$ **107.** $\ln|x| + 2\sqrt{x} + C$

109. $\frac{4}{15}x^{15/2} - \frac{24}{11}x^{11/6} + C$ **111.** $F(x) = -\cos x + 3x + 3 - 3\pi$

113. $F(x) = 2x^8 + x^4 + 2x + 1$ **115. a.** $Q(t) = 10t - t^3/30$ gal

b.

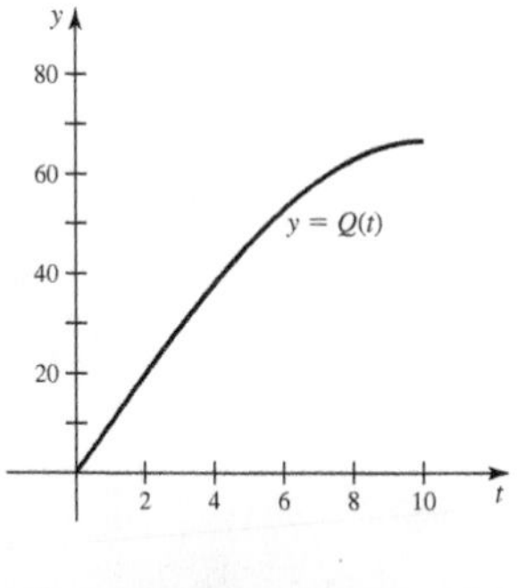

c. $\frac{200}{3}$ gal

117. $\int \sin^2 x\, dx = x/2 - (\sin 2x)/4 + C$;

$\int \cos^2 x\, dx = x/2 + (\sin 2x)/4 + C$

Chapter 4 Review Exercises, pp. 330–332

1. a. False **b.** False **c.** True **d.** True **e.** True **f.** False

3.

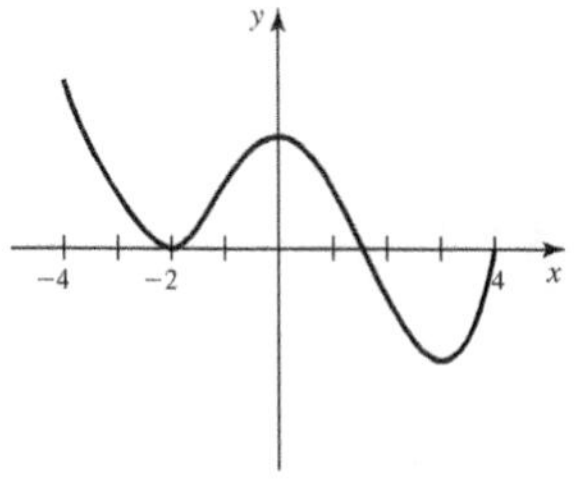

5.

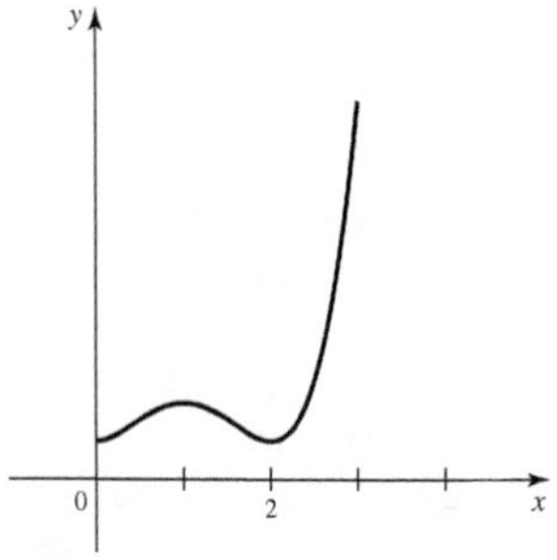

7. $x = 3$ and $x = -2$; no abs. max or min

9. $x = 1/e$; abs. min at $(1/e, 10 - 2/e)$

11.

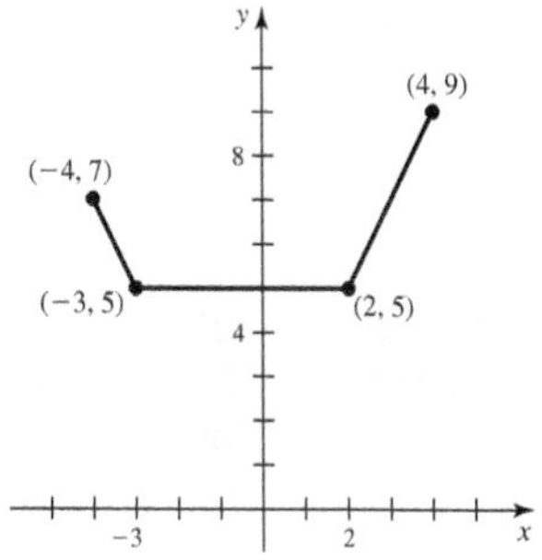

Critical pts.: all x in the interval $[-3, 2]$; abs. max at $(4, 9)$; abs. and local min at $(x, 5)$ for all x in $[-3, 2]$; local max at $(x, 5)$ for all x in $(-3, 2)$

13.

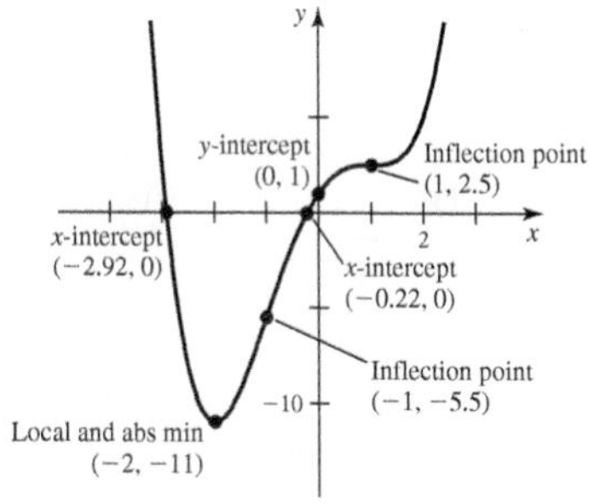

15.

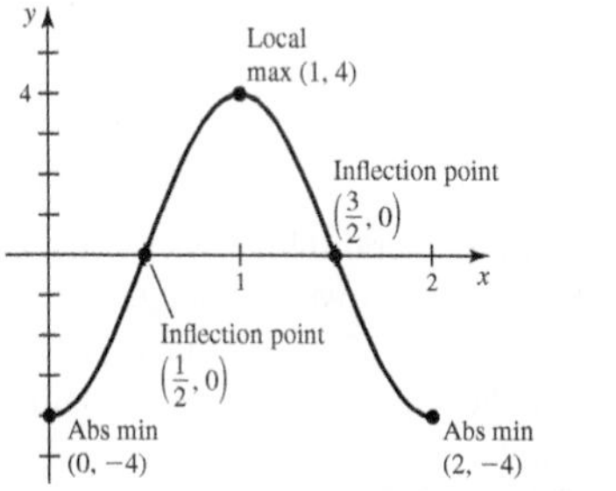

17.

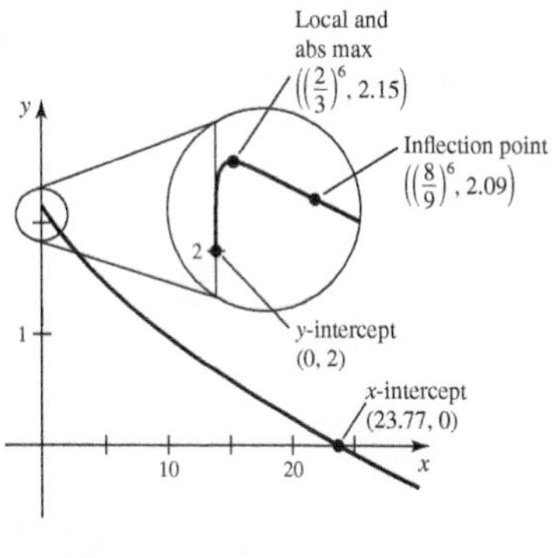

19.

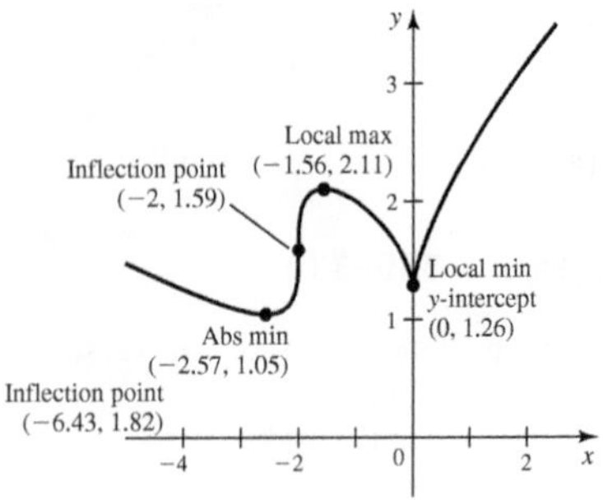

21. $r = 4\sqrt{6}/3$; $h = 4\sqrt{3}/3$ **23.** $x = 7, y = 14$
25. $p = q = 5\sqrt{2}$ **27. a.** $L(x) = \frac{2}{9}x + 3$
b. $\frac{85}{9} \approx 9.44$; overestimate
29. $f(x) = 1/x^2$; $a = 4$; $1/4.2^2 \approx 9/160 = 0.05625$
31. $\Delta h \approx -112$ ft **33. a.** $\frac{100}{9}$ cells/week **b.** $t = 2$ weeks
35. $-0.434259, 0.767592, 1$ **37.** $0, \pm 0.948683$ **39.** 0 **41.** 12
43. $\frac{2}{3}$ **45.** ∞ **47.** 0 **49.** 1 **51.** 0 **53.** 1 **55.** 1 **57.** $1/e^3$
59. 1 **61.** $x^{1/2}$ **63.** $\sqrt{x}$ **65.** 3^x **67.** Comparable growth rates
69. $\frac{4}{3}x^3 + 2x^2 + x + C$ **71.** $-\frac{1}{x} + \frac{4}{3}x^{-3/2} + C$
73. $\theta + \frac{1}{3}\sin 3\theta + C$ **75.** $\frac{1}{2}\sec 2x + C$ **77.** $12 \ln|x| + C$
79. $\tan^{-1} x + C$ **81.** $\frac{4}{7}x^{7/4} + \frac{2}{7}x^{7/2} + C$
83. $f(t) = -\cos t + t^2 + 6$
85. $h(x) = \frac{x}{2} - \frac{1}{4}\sin 2x + \frac{1}{2} + \frac{\sin 2}{4}$
87. $v(t) = -9.8t + 120$; $s(t) = -4.9t^2 + 120t + 125$
The rocket reaches a height of 859.69 m at time $t = 12.24$ s and then falls to the ground, hitting at time $t = 25.49$ s. **89.** 1; 1
91. 0 **93.** $\lim_{x\to 0^+} f(x) = 1$; $\lim_{x\to 0^+} g(x) = 0$

CHAPTER 5

Section 5.1 Exercises, pp. 343–347

1.

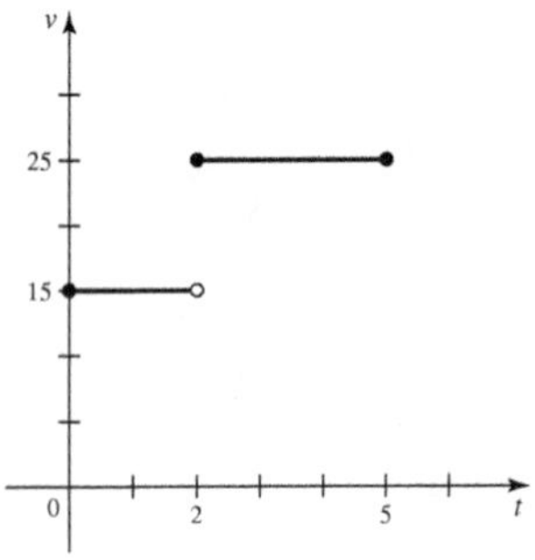

Displacement = 105 m

3. Subdivide the interval $[0, \pi/2]$ into several subintervals, which will be the bases of rectangles that fit under the curve. The heights of the rectangles are computed by taking the value of $\cos x$ at the right-hand endpoint of each base. We calculate the area of each rectangle and add them to get a lower bound on the area.
5. 0.5; 1, 1.5, 2, 2.5, 3; 1, 1.5, 2, 2.5; 1.5, 2, 2.5, 3; 1.25, 1.75, 2.25, 2.75
7. Underestimate; the rectangles all fit under the curve.
9. a. 67 ft **b.** 67.75 ft **11.** 40 m **13.** 2.78 m
15. 148.96 mi **17.** 20; 25

19. a. c.

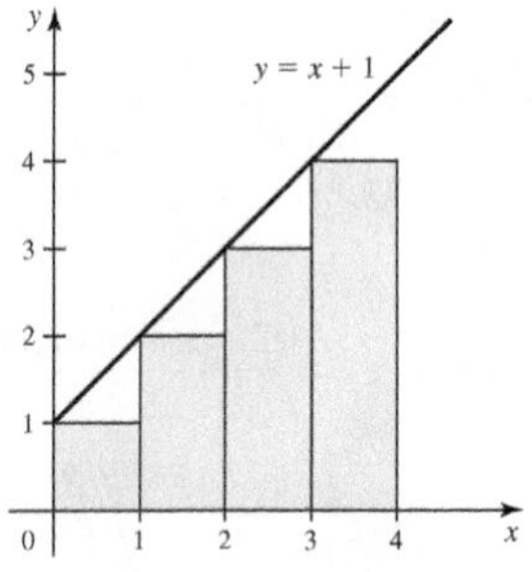

Left Riemann sum underestimates area.

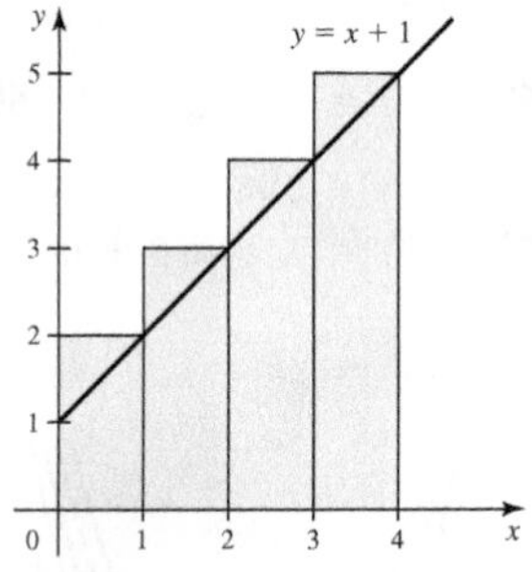

Right Riemann sum overestimates area.

b. $\Delta x = 1$; $x_0 = 0, x_1 = 1, x_2 = 2, x_3 = 3, x_4 = 4$ **d.** 10, 14
21. a. c.

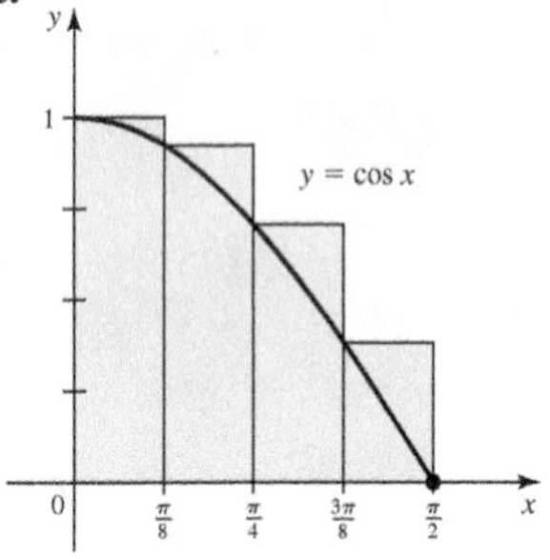

Left Riemann sum overestimates area.

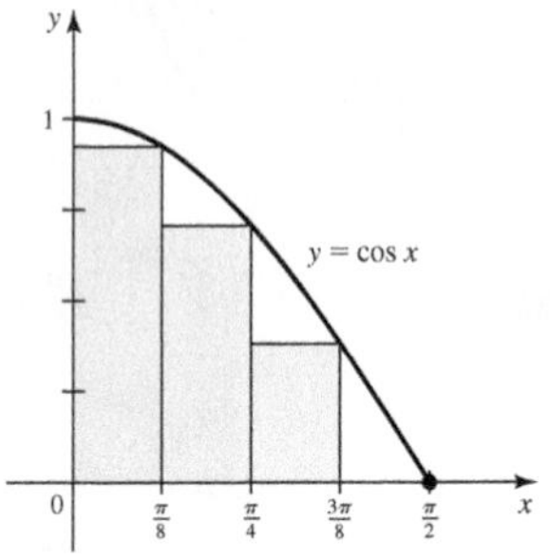

Right Riemann sum underestimates area.

b. $\Delta x = \pi/8$; $0, \pi/8, \pi/4, 3\pi/8, \pi/2$ **d.** 1.18; 0.79
23. a. c.

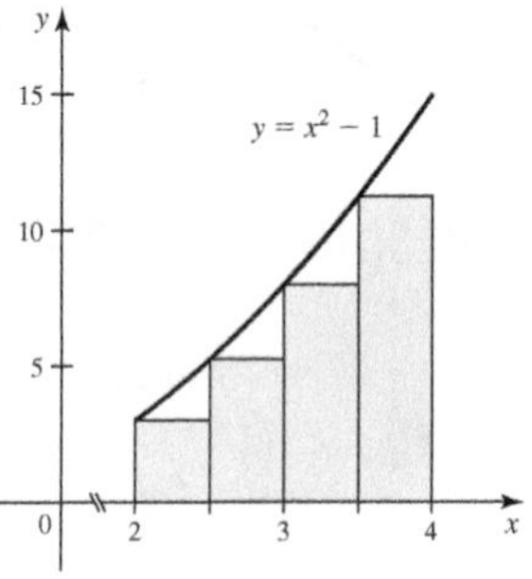

Left Riemann sum underestimates area.

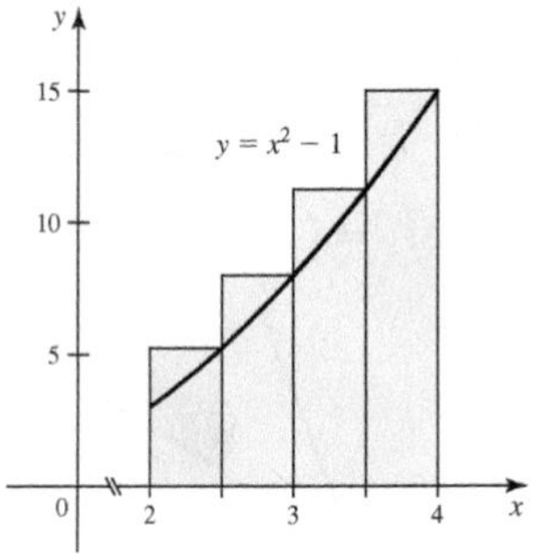

Right Riemann sum overestimates area.

b. $\Delta x = 0.5$; 2, 2.5, 3, 3.5, 4 **d.** 13.75; 19.75
25. a. c.

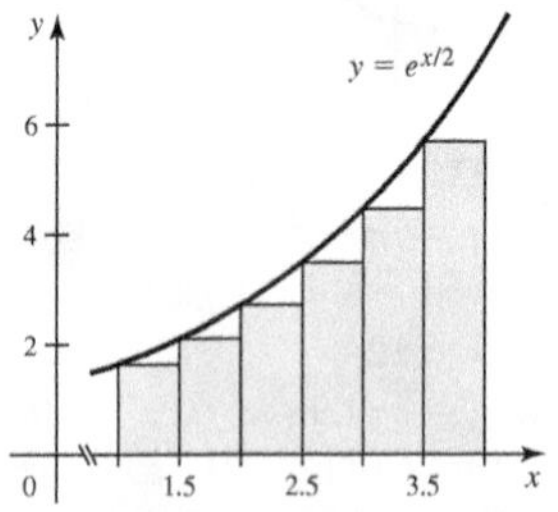

Left Riemann sum underestimates area.

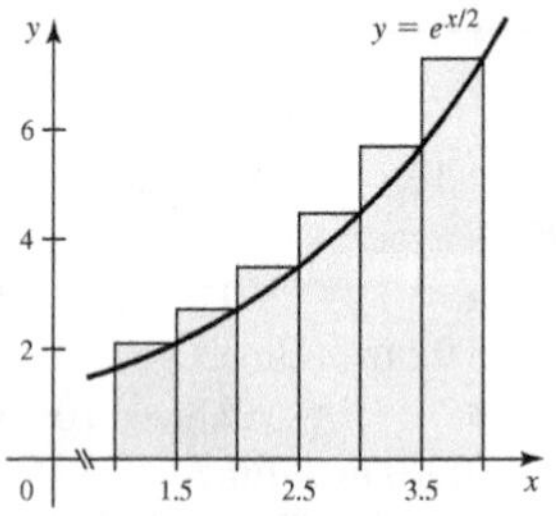

Right Riemann sum overestimates area.

b. $\Delta x = 0.5$; $x_0 = 1, x_1 = 1.5, x_2 = 2, x_3 = 2.5, x_4 = 3, x_5 = 3.5, x_6 = 4$ **d.** 10.11, 12.98 **27.** 670
29. a. c.

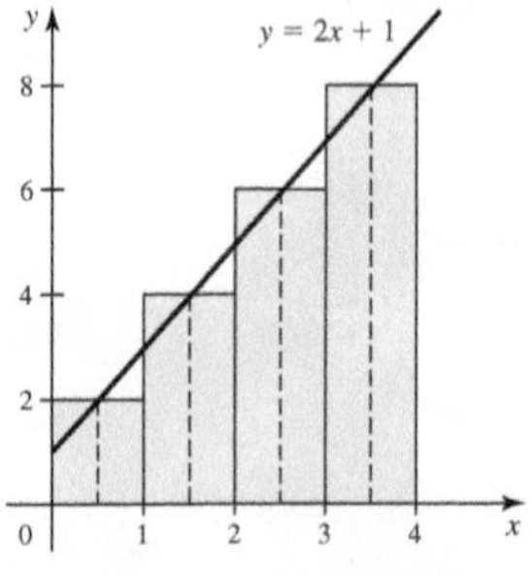

b. $\Delta x = 1$; 0, 1, 2, 3, 4
d. 20

31. a. c.

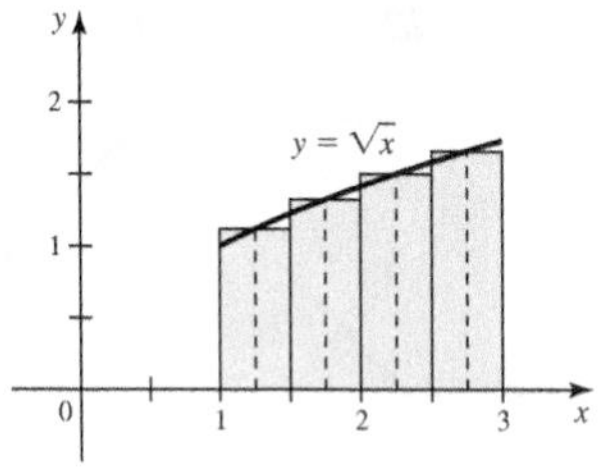

b. $\Delta x = \frac{1}{2}$; $1, \frac{3}{2}, 2, \frac{5}{2}, 3$ **d.** 2.80

33. a. c.

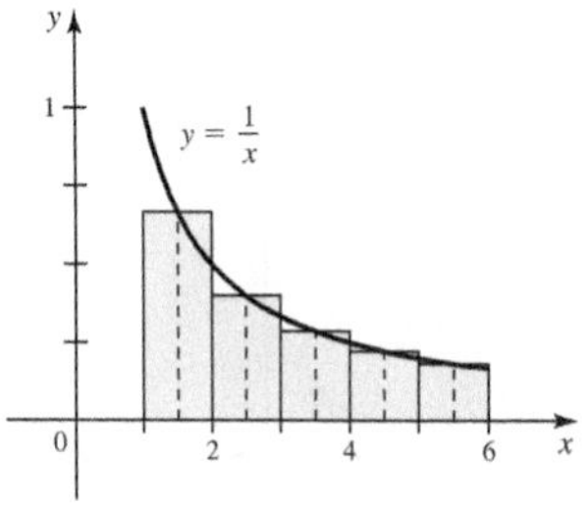

b. $\Delta x = 1$; 1, 2, 3, 4, 5, 6 **d.** 1.76

35. 5.5, 3.5 **37. b.** 110, 117.5 **39. a.** $\sum_{k=1}^{5} k$ **b.** $\sum_{k=1}^{6} (k+3)$ **c.** $\sum_{k=1}^{4} k^2$ **d.** $\sum_{k=1}^{4} \frac{1}{k}$ **41. a.** 55 **b.** 48 **c.** 30 **d.** 60 **e.** 6 **f.** 6 **g.** 85 **h.** 0 **43. a.** Left: $\frac{1}{10}\sum_{k=1}^{40}\sqrt{\frac{k-1}{10}} \approx 5.23$; right: $\frac{1}{10}\sum_{k=1}^{40}\sqrt{\frac{k}{10}} \approx 5.43$; midpoint: $\frac{1}{10}\sum_{k=1}^{40}\sqrt{\frac{2k-1}{20}} \approx 5.34$ **b.** $\frac{16}{3}$ **45. a.** Left: $\frac{1}{15}\sum_{k=1}^{75}\left(\left(\frac{k+29}{15}\right)^2 - 1\right) \approx 105.17$; right: $\frac{1}{15}\sum_{k=1}^{75}\left(\left(\frac{k+30}{15}\right)^2 - 1\right) \approx 108.17$; midpoint: $\frac{1}{15}\sum_{k=1}^{75}\left(\left(\frac{2k+59}{30}\right)^2 - 1\right) \approx 106.66$ **b.** 106.7

47.

n	Right Riemann sum
10	10.56
30	10.65
60	10.664
80	10.665

The sums approach $\frac{32}{3}$.

49.

n	Right Riemann sum
10	5.655
30	6.074
60	6.178
80	6.205

The sums approach approximately 6.2. The actual limit is 2π.

51.

n	Right Riemann sum
10	1.0844
30	1.0285
60	1.0143
80	1.0107

The sums approach 1.

53. a. True **b.** False **c.** True

55. $\sum_{k=1}^{50}\left(\frac{4k}{50} + 1\right)\cdot\frac{4}{50} = 12.16$

57. $\sum_{k=1}^{32}\left(3 + \frac{2k-1}{8}\right)^3 \cdot \frac{1}{4} \approx 3639.1$

59. Right; $[1, 5]$; 4

61. Midpoint; $[2, 6]$; 4

63. a.

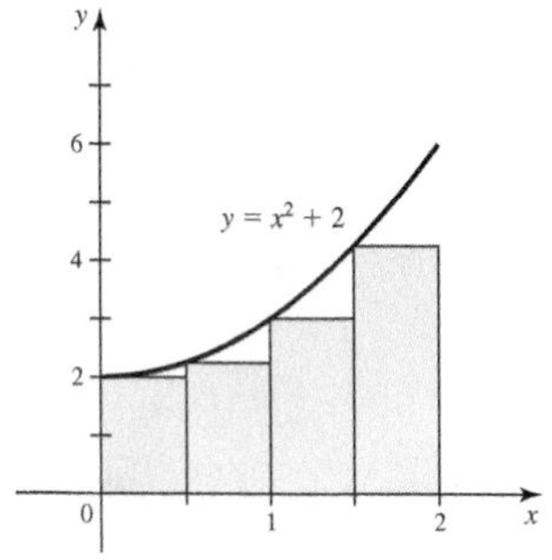

Left Riemann sum is $\frac{23}{4} = 5.75$.

b.

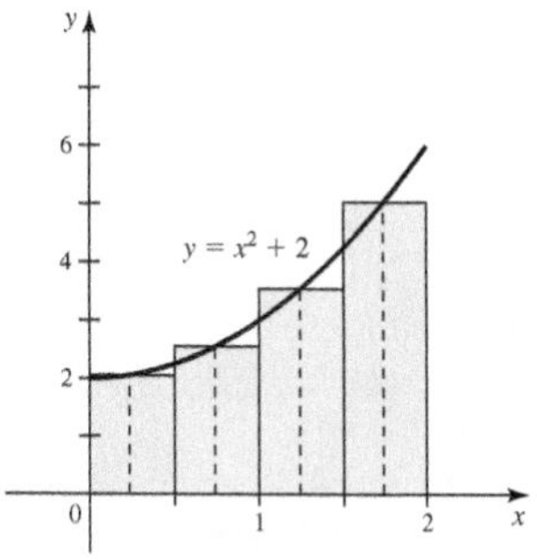

Midpoint Riemann sum is $\frac{53}{8} = 6.625$.

c.

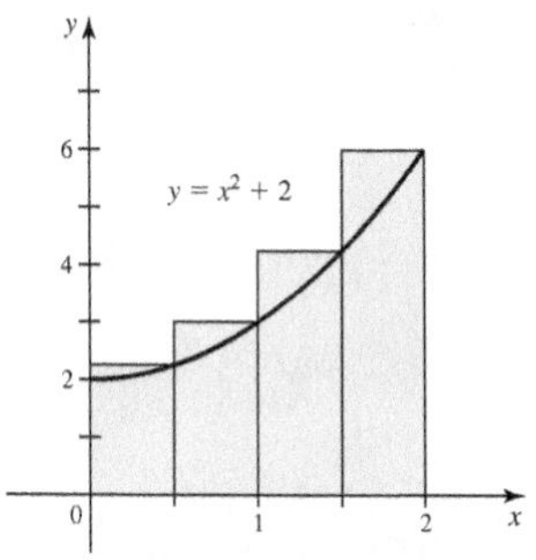

Right Riemann sum is $\frac{31}{4} = 7.75$.

65. Left sum: 34; right sum: 24 **67. a.** The object is speeding up on the interval $(0, 1)$, moving at a constant rate on $(1, 3)$, slowing down on $(3, 5)$, and moving at a constant rate on $(5, 6)$. **b.** 30 m **c.** 50 m **d.** $s(t) = 30 + 10t$ **69. a.** 14.5 g **b.** 29.5 g **c.** 44 g **d.** $x = \frac{19}{3}$ cm **71.** $s(t) = \begin{cases} 30t & \text{if } 0 \le t \le 2 \\ 50t - 40 & \text{if } 2 < t \le 2.5 \\ 44t - 25 & \text{if } 2.5 < t \le 3 \end{cases}$

73.

n	Midpoint Riemann sum
16	0.503906
32	0.500977
64	0.500244

The sums approach 0.5.

75.

n	Midpoint Riemann sum
16	4.7257
32	4.7437
64	4.7485

The sums approach 4.75.

79. Underestimates for decreasing functions, independent of concavity; overestimates for increasing functions, independent of concavity.

Section 5.2 Exercises, pp. 358–361

1. The difference between the area bounded by the curve above the x-axis and the area bounded by the curve below the x-axis **3.** When the function is nonnegative on the entire interval; when the function has negative values on the interval **5.** Both integrals equal 0. **7.** The length of the interval $[a, a]$ is $a - a = 0$, so the net area is 0. **9.** $\frac{a^2}{2}$

11. a.

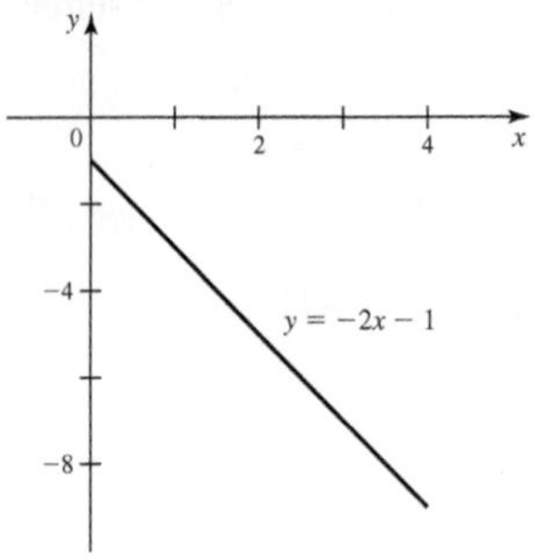

b. −16, −24, −20

13. a.

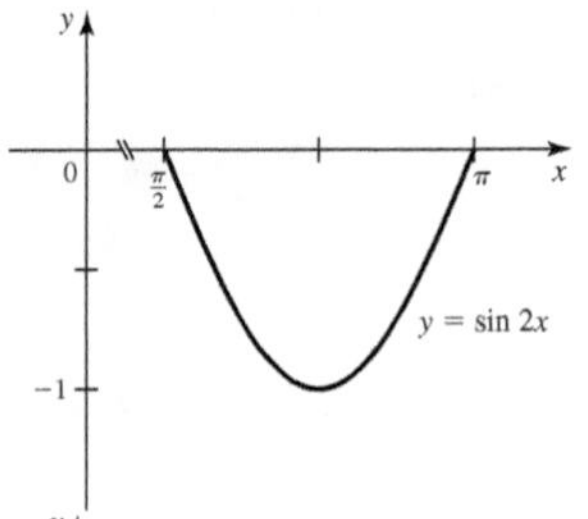

b. −0.948, −0.948, −1.026

15. a.

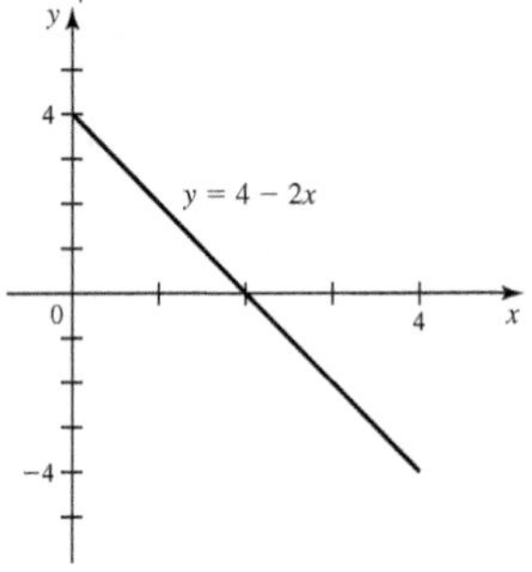

b. 4, −4, 0 **c.** Positive contribution on $[0, 2)$; negative contribution on $(2, 4]$

17. a.

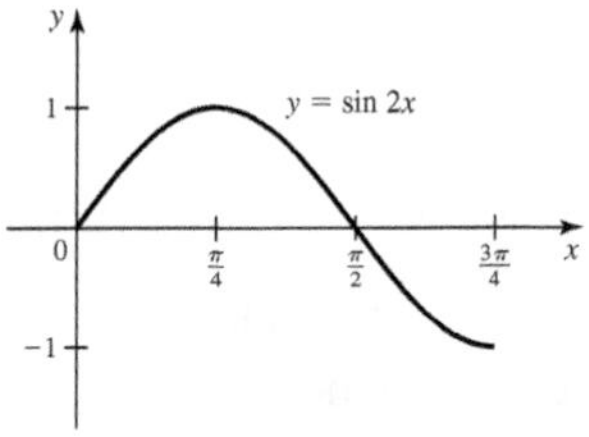

b. 0.735, 0.146, 0.530 **c.** Positive contribution on $(0, \pi/2)$; negative contribution on $(\pi/2, 3\pi/4]$.

19. a.

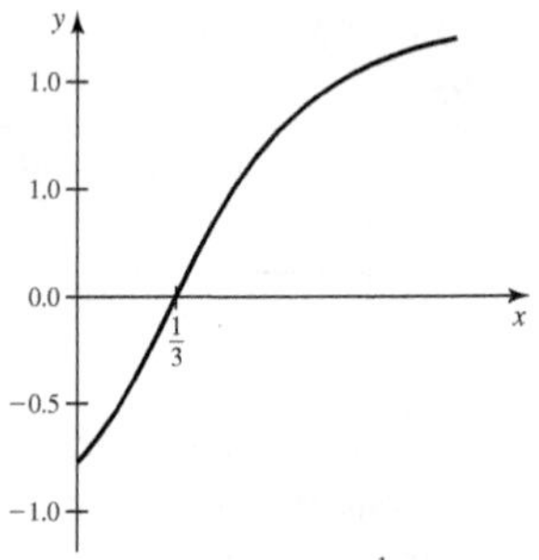

b. 0.082; 0.555; 0.326

c. Positive contribution on $(\frac{1}{3}, 1]$; negative contribution on $[0, \frac{1}{3})$

21. $\int_0^2 (x^2 + 1)\, dx$ **23.** $\int_1^2 x \ln x\, dx$

25. 16

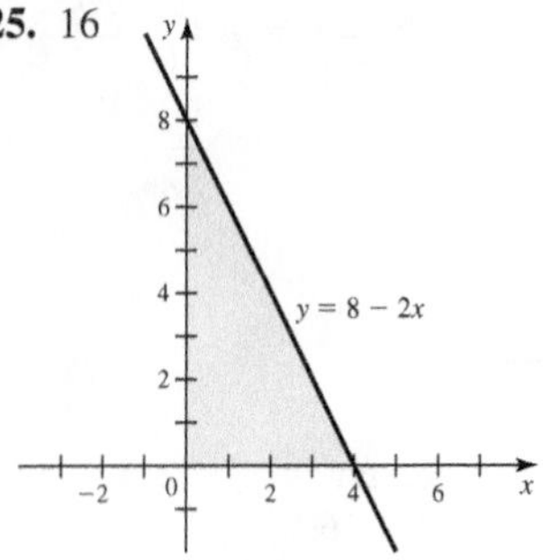

27. $-\frac{5}{2}$

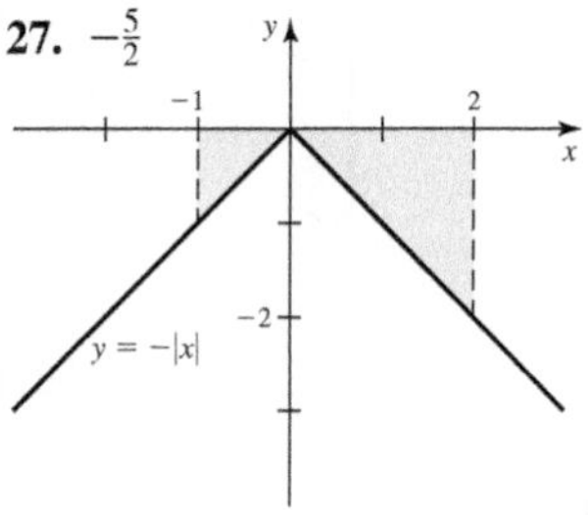

29. 4π

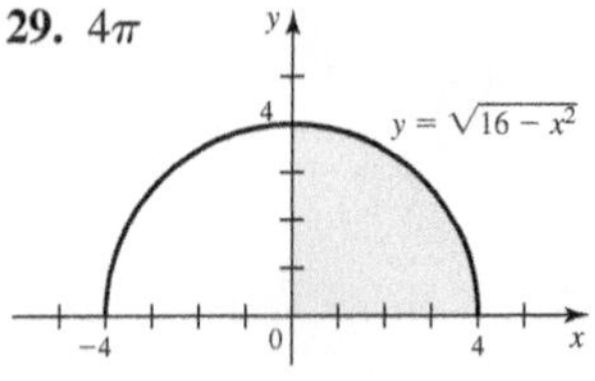

31. 26

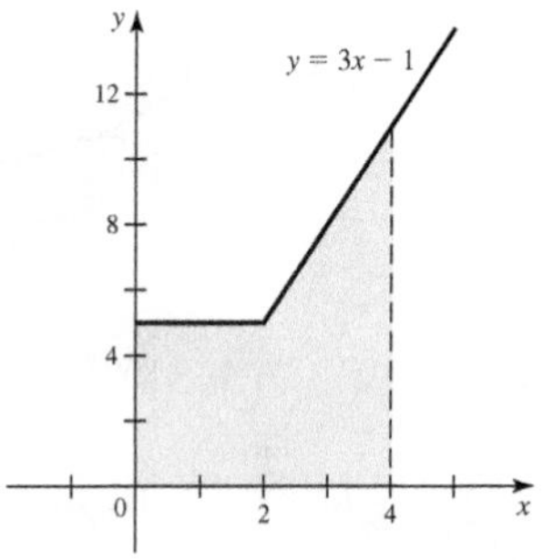

33. 16 **35.** 6 **37.** π **39.** -2π **41. a.** −32 **b.** $-\frac{32}{3}$ **c.** −64 **d.** Not possible **43. a.** 10 **b.** −3 **c.** −16 **d.** 3 **45. a.** $\frac{3}{2}$ **b.** $-\frac{3}{4}$ **47.** 6 **49.** 104 **51.** 18 **53. a.** True **b.** True **c.** True **d.** False **e.** False

55. a.

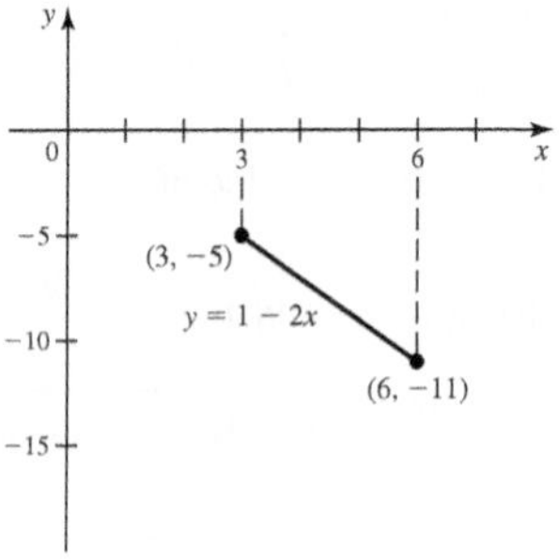

b. $\Delta x = \frac{1}{2}$; 3, 3.5, 4, 4.5, 5, 5.5, 6 **c.** −22.5; −25.5 **d.** The left Riemann sum overestimates the integral; the right Riemann sum underestimates the integral.

57. a.

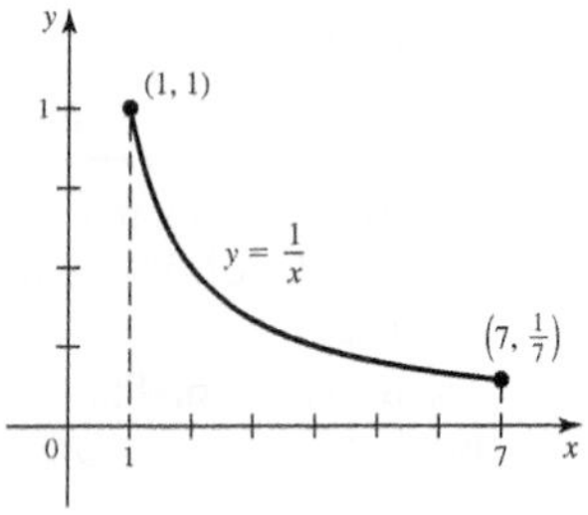

b. $\Delta x = 1$; 1, 2, 3, 4, 5, 6, 7 **c.** $\frac{49}{20}$; $\frac{223}{140}$ **d.** The left Riemann sum overestimates the integral; the right Riemann sum underestimates the integral.

59. a. Left: $\sum_{k=1}^{20}\left(\left(\frac{k-1}{20}\right)^2 + 1\right)\cdot\frac{1}{20} = 1.30875$;

right: $\sum_{k=1}^{20}\left(\left(\frac{k}{20}\right)^2 + 1\right)\cdot\frac{1}{20} = 1.35875$;

left: $\sum_{k=1}^{50}\left(\left(\frac{k-1}{50}\right)^2 + 1\right)\cdot\frac{1}{50} = 1.3234$;

right: $\sum_{k=1}^{50}\left(\left(\frac{k}{50}\right)^2 + 1\right)\cdot\frac{1}{50} = 1.3434$;

left: $\sum_{k=1}^{100}\left(\left(\frac{k-1}{100}\right)^2 + 1\right)\cdot\frac{1}{100} = 1.32835$;

right: $\sum_{k=1}^{100}\left(\left(\frac{k}{100}\right)^2 + 1\right)\cdot\frac{1}{100} = 1.33835$ **b.** $\frac{4}{3}$

61. a. Left: $\sum_{k=1}^{20} \cos^{-1}\left(\frac{k-1}{20}\right)\frac{1}{20} = 1.03619;$

right: $\sum_{k=1}^{20} \cos^{-1}\left(\frac{k}{20}\right)\frac{1}{20} = 0.95765;$

left: $\sum_{k=1}^{50} \cos^{-1}\left(\frac{k-1}{50}\right)\frac{1}{50} = 1.01491;$

right: $\sum_{k=1}^{50} \cos^{-1}\left(\frac{k}{50}\right)\frac{1}{50} = 0.983494;$

left: $\sum_{k=1}^{100} \cos^{-1}\left(\frac{k-1}{100}\right)\frac{1}{100} = 1.00757;$

right: $\sum_{k=1}^{100} \cos^{-1}\left(\frac{k}{100}\right)\frac{1}{100} = 0.99186$ **b.** 1.

63. a. $\frac{3}{n}\sum_{k=1}^{n} \sqrt{2\left(1+\left(k-\frac{1}{2}\right)\frac{3}{n}\right)}$

b.

n	Midpoint Riemann sum
20	9.33380
50	9.33341
100	9.33335

Estimate: $\frac{28}{3}$

65. a. $\frac{4}{n}\sum_{k=1}^{n} \left(4\left(k-\frac{1}{2}\right)\frac{4}{n} - \left(\left(k-\frac{1}{2}\right)\frac{4}{n}\right)^2\right)$

b.

n	Midpoint Riemann sum
20	10.6800
50	10.6688
100	10.6672

Estimate: $\frac{32}{3}$

67. a. 15 **b.** 5 **c.** 3 **d.** −2 **e.** 24 **f.** −10

69.

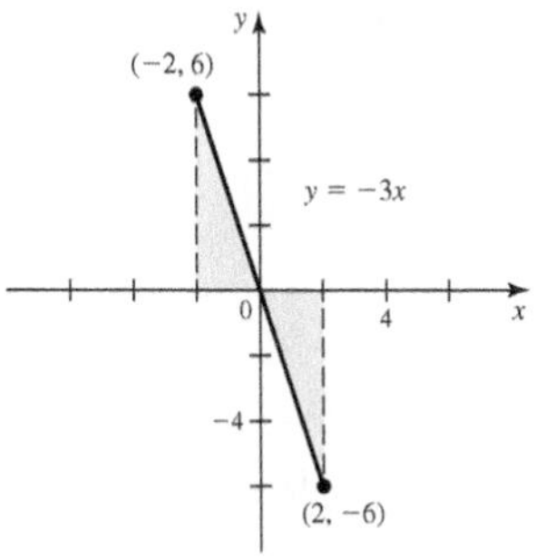

The area is 12; the net area is 0.

71.

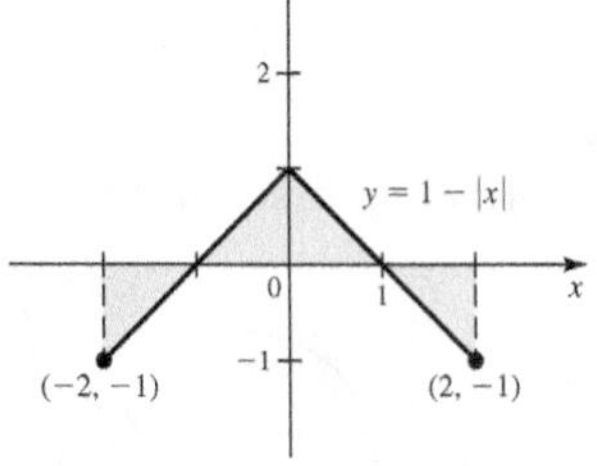

The area is 2; the net area is 0.

73. 17 **75.** $25\pi/2$ **77.** 25 **79.** 35 **83.** For any such partition on $[0, 1]$, the grid points are $x_k = k/n$, for $k = 0, 1, \ldots, n$. That is, x_k is rational for each k so that $f(x_k) = 1$, for $k = 0, 1, \ldots, n$. Therefore, the left, right, and midpoint Riemann sums are $\sum_{k=1}^{n} 1 \cdot (1/n) = 1$.

Section 5.3 Exercises, pp. 373–376

1. A is an antiderivative of f; $A'(x) = f(x)$

3. Let f be continuous on $[a, b]$. Then $\int_a^b f(x)\,dx = F(b) - F(a)$, where F is any antiderivative of f. **5.** Increasing **7.** The derivative of the integral of f is f, or $\frac{d}{dx}\left(\int_a^x f(t)\,dt\right) = f(x)$. **9.** $f(x), 0$

11. a. 0 **b.** −9 **c.** 25 **d.** 0 **e.** 16

13. a. $A(x) = 5x$ **b.** $A'(x) = 5$

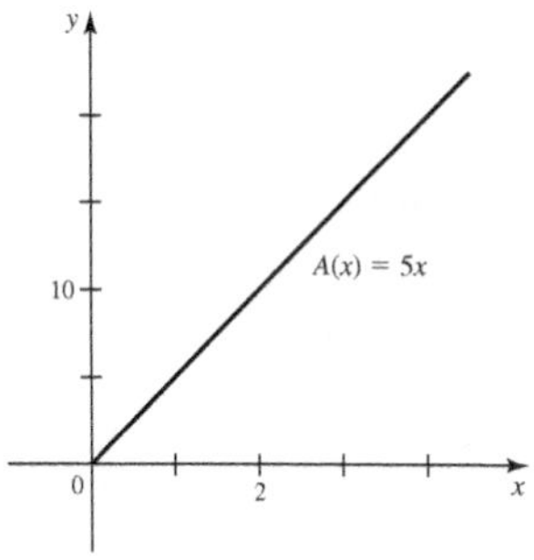

15. a. $A(x) = 5x + 25$ **b.** $A'(x) = 5$

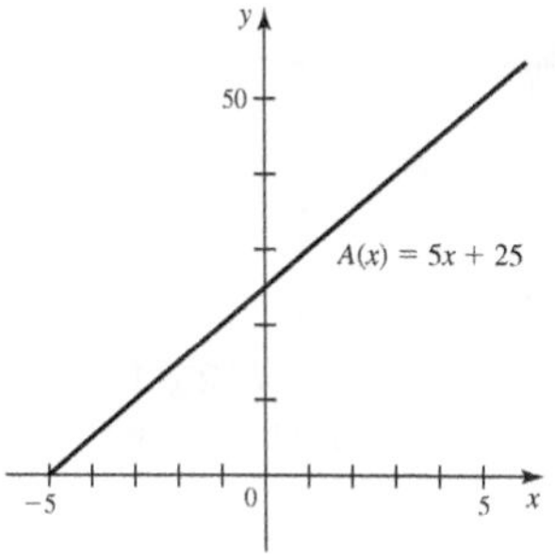

17. a. $A(2) = 2, A(4) = 8; A(x) = \frac{1}{2}x^2$ **b.** $F(4) = 6, F(6) = 16;$ $F(x) = \frac{1}{2}x^2 - 2$ **c.** $A(x) - F(x) = \frac{1}{2}x^2 - \left(\frac{1}{2}x^2 - 2\right) = 2$

19. a.

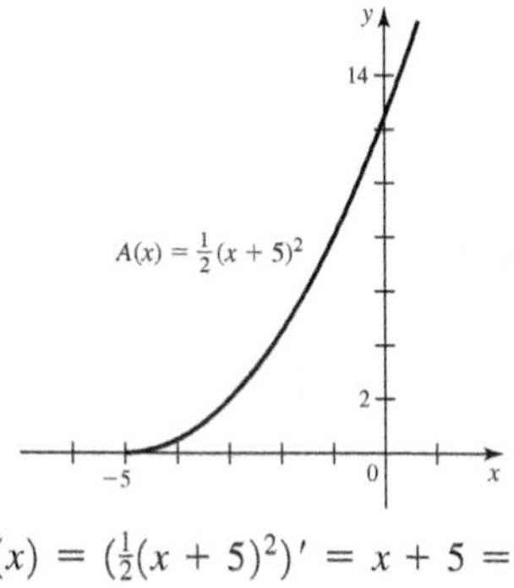

b. $A'(x) = \left(\frac{1}{2}(x+5)^2\right)' = x + 5 = f(x)$

21. a.

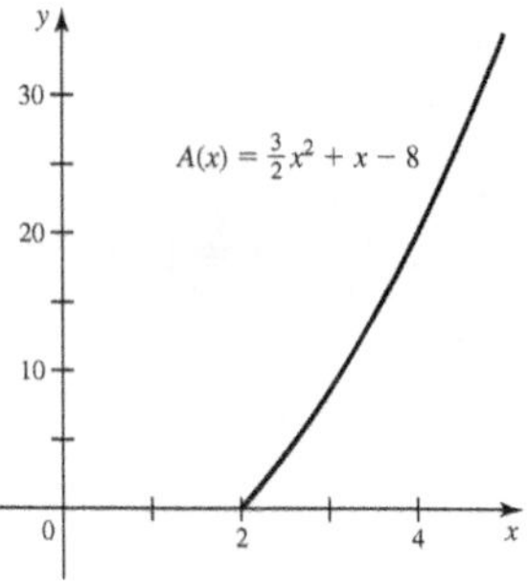

b. $A'(x) = \left(\frac{3}{2}x^2 + x - 8\right)' = 3x + 1 = f(x)$ **23.** $\frac{7}{3}$

25. $-\frac{125}{6}$

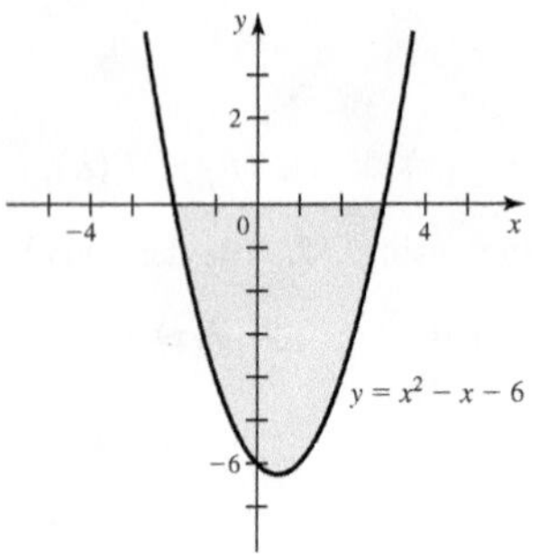

27. $-\frac{10}{3}$

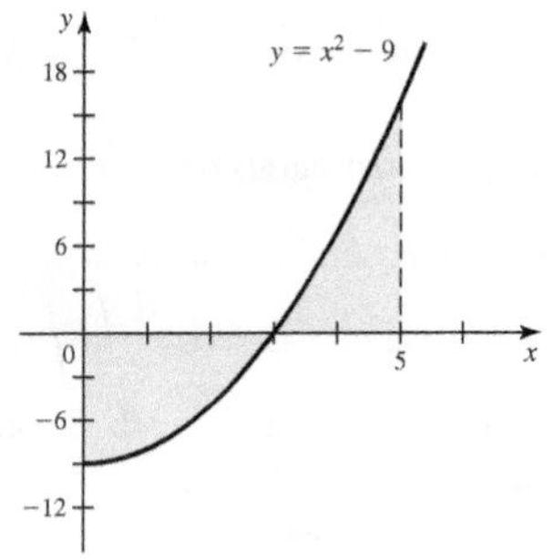

29. 16 **31.** $\frac{7}{6}$ **33.** 8 **35.** $-\frac{32}{3}$ **37.** $-\frac{5}{2}$ **39.** 1 **41.** $-\frac{3}{8}$
43. $\frac{9}{2}$ **45.** $3 \ln 2$ **47.** $\sqrt{2}/4$ **49.** $\pi/12$
51. (i) $\frac{14}{3}$ (ii) $\frac{14}{3}$

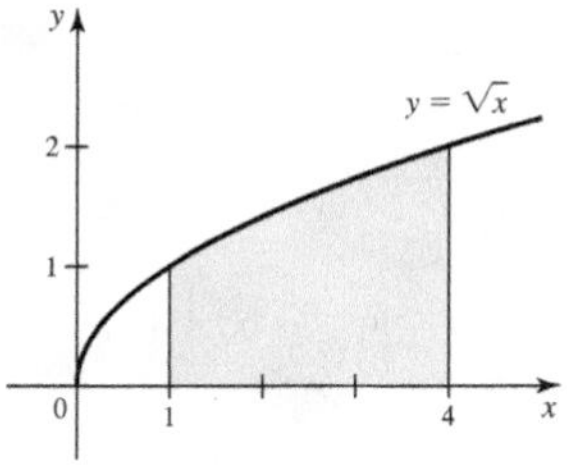

53. (i) -51.2 (ii) 51.2

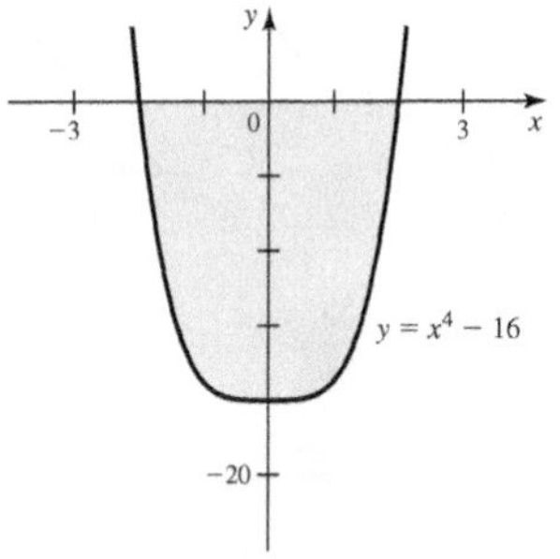

55. $\frac{94}{3}$ **57.** $\ln 2$ **59.** 2 **61.** $x^2 + x + 1$
63. $3/x^4$ **65.** $-\sqrt{x^4 + 1}$ **67.** $2\sqrt{1 + x^2}$ **69.** a–C, b–B, c–D, d–A
71. a. $x = 0, x \approx 3$ **b.** Local min at $x \approx 1.5$; local max at $x \approx 8.5$
c.

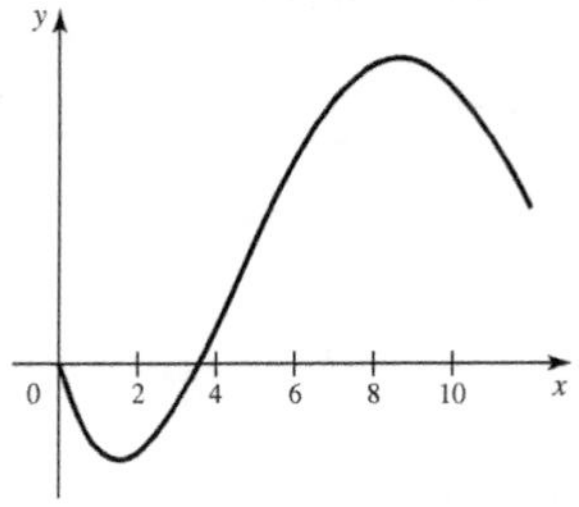

73. a. $x = 0, 10$ **b.** Local max at $x = 5$
c.

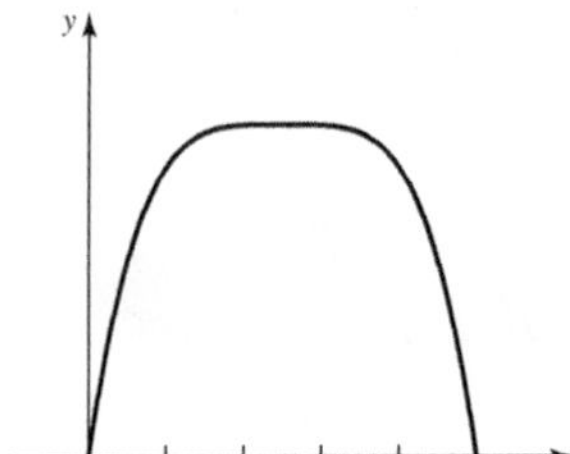

75. $-\pi, -\pi + \frac{9}{2}, -\pi + 9, 5 - \pi$ **77. a.** $A(x) = e^x - 1$
b.

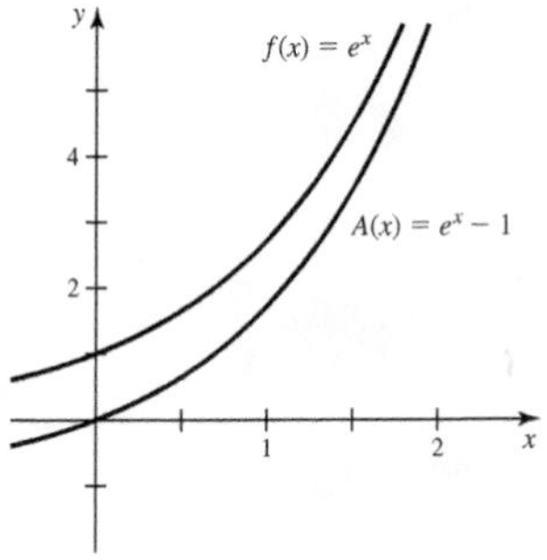

c. $A(\ln 2) = 1$; $A(\ln 4) = 3$

79. a. $A(x) = \dfrac{1}{\pi} \sin \pi x$

b.

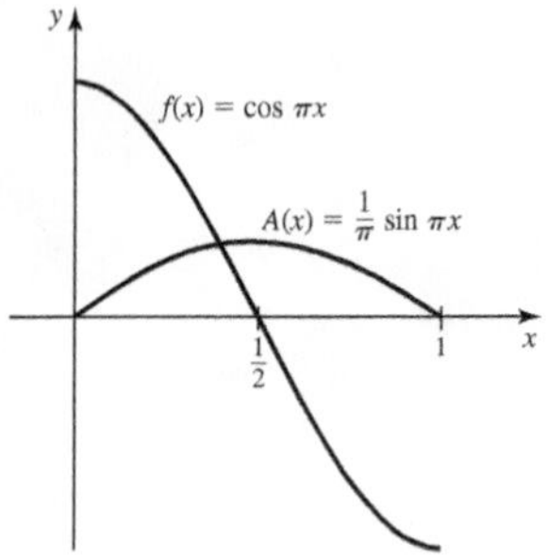

c. $A\left(\dfrac{1}{2}\right) = \dfrac{1}{\pi}$; $A(1) = 0$

81. a.

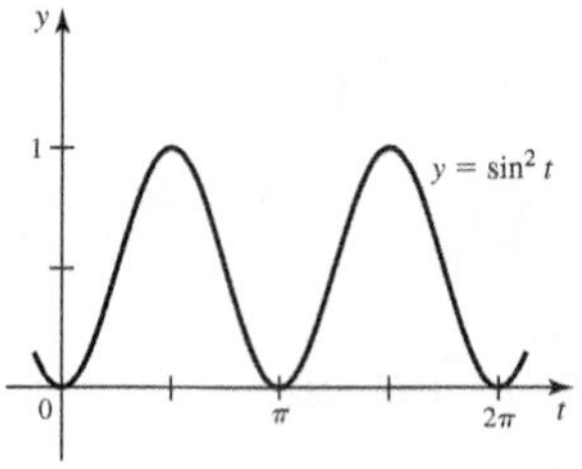

b. $g'(x) = \sin^2 x$

c.

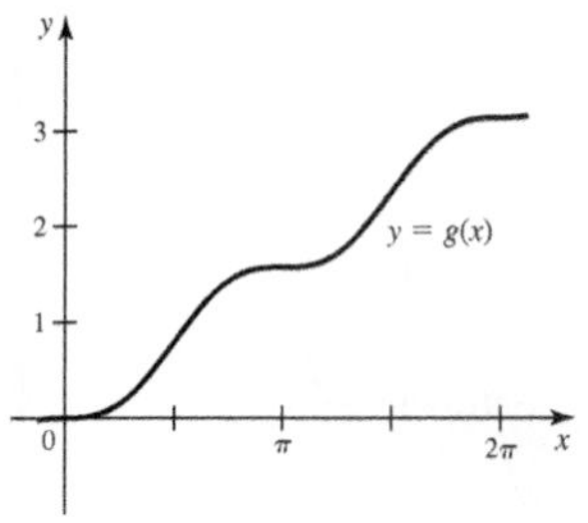

83. a.

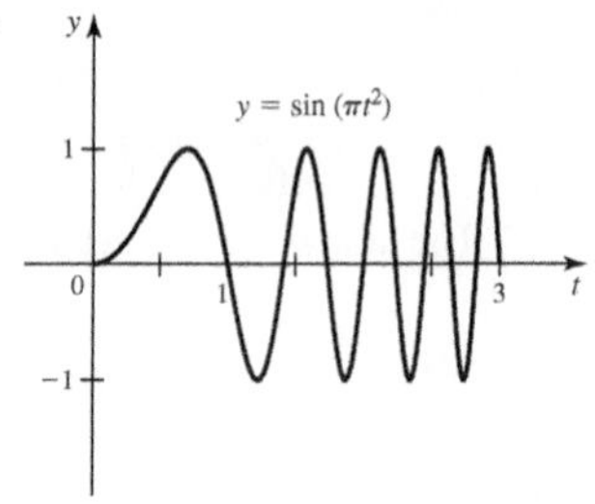

b. $g'(x) = \sin(\pi x^2)$

c.

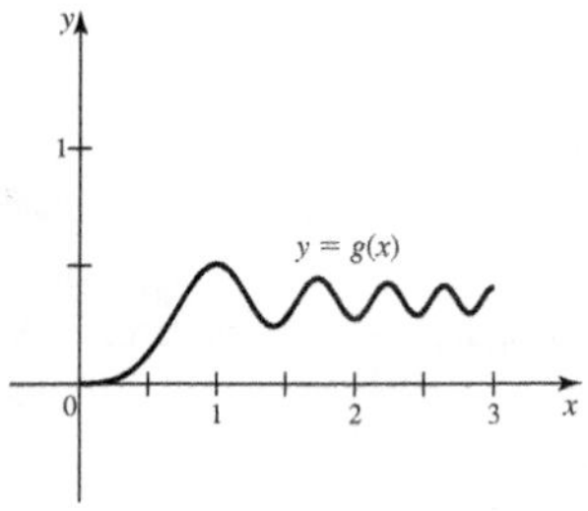

85. a. True **b.** True **c.** False **d.** True **e.** True **87.** $\frac{2}{3}$ **89.** 1
91. $\frac{45}{4}$ **93.** $\frac{3}{2} + 4 \ln 2$
95.

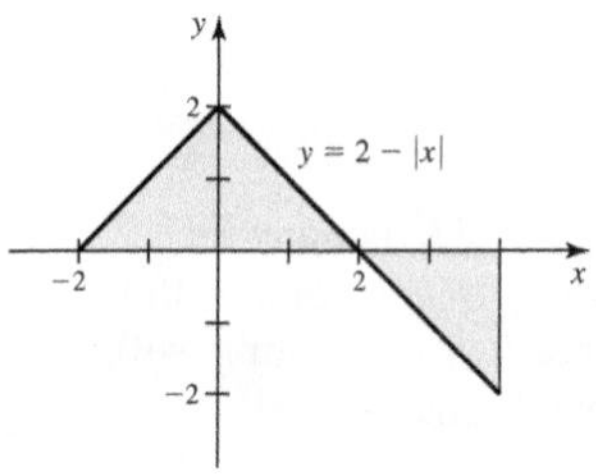

Area = 6

97.

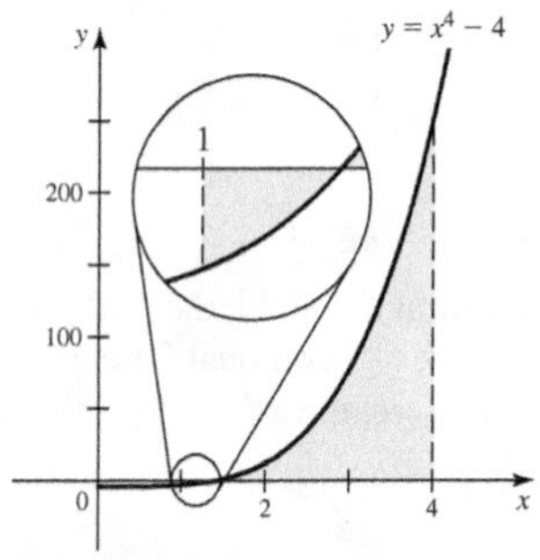

Area ≈ 194.05

99. $f(8) - f(3)$ **101.** $-(\cos^4 x + 6)\sin x$ **103.** $\frac{9}{t}$

105. a.

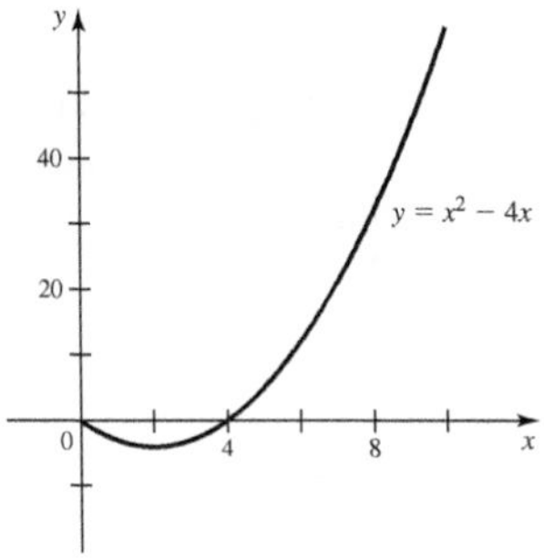

b. $b = 6$ **c.** $b = \frac{3a}{2}$

107. 3 **109.** $f(x) = -2\sin x + 3$ **111.** $\pi/2 \approx 1.57$

113. $(S'(x))^2 + \left(\frac{S''(x)}{2x}\right)^2 = (\sin x^2)^2 + \left(\frac{2x\cos x^2}{2x}\right)^2$
$= \sin^2 x^2 + \cos^2 x^2 = 1$

115. c. The summation relationship is a discrete analog of the Fundamental Theorem. Summing the difference quotient and integrating the derivative over the relevant interval give the difference of the function values at the endpoints.

Section 5.4 Exercises, pp. 381–384

1. If f is odd, the regions between f and the positive x-axis and between f and the negative x-axis are reflections of each other through the origin. Therefore, on $[-a, a]$, the areas cancel each other. **3.** Even; even **5.** If f is continuous on $[a, b]$, then there is a c in (a, b) such that $f(c) = \frac{1}{b-a}\int_a^b f(x)\,dx$. **7.** 0 **9.** $\frac{1000}{3}$ **11.** $-\frac{88}{3}$ **13.** 0 **15.** 0

17. 0

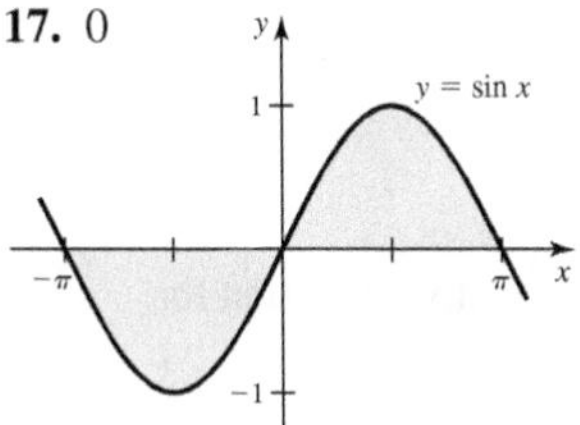

19. 0

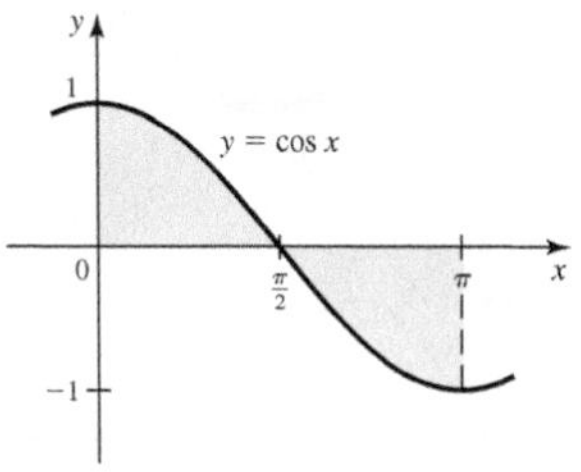

21. 0

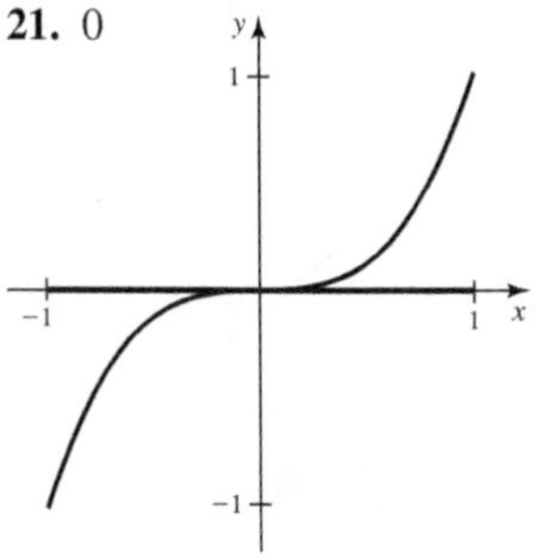

23. $\frac{\pi}{4}$

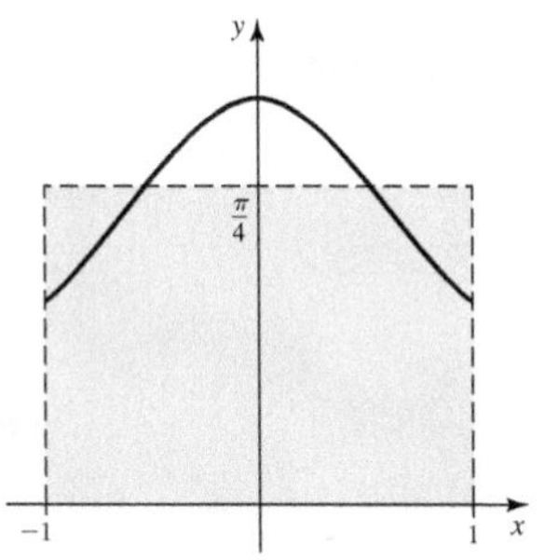

25. $1/(e - 1)$

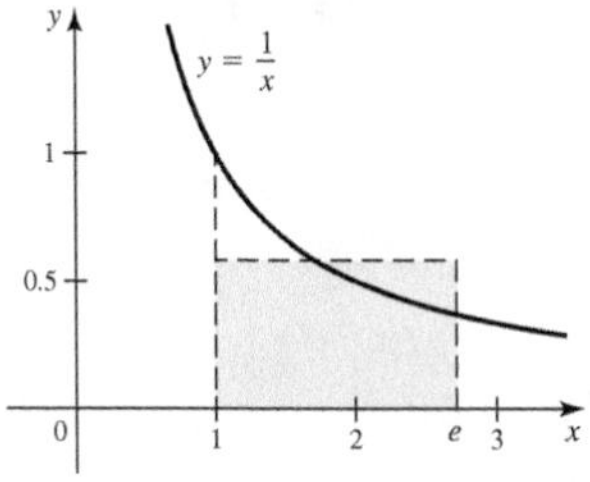

27. $2/\pi$

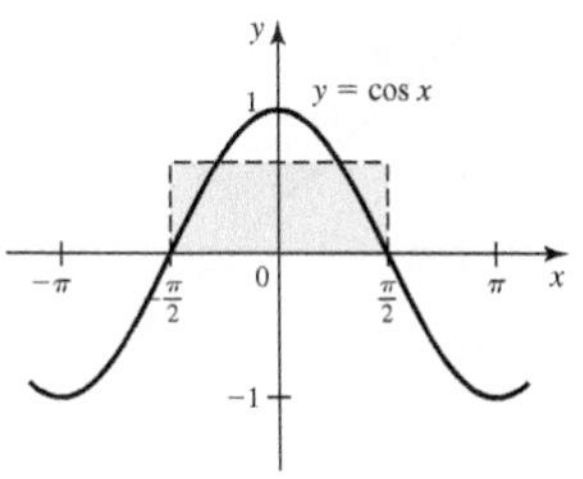

29. $1/(n + 1)$

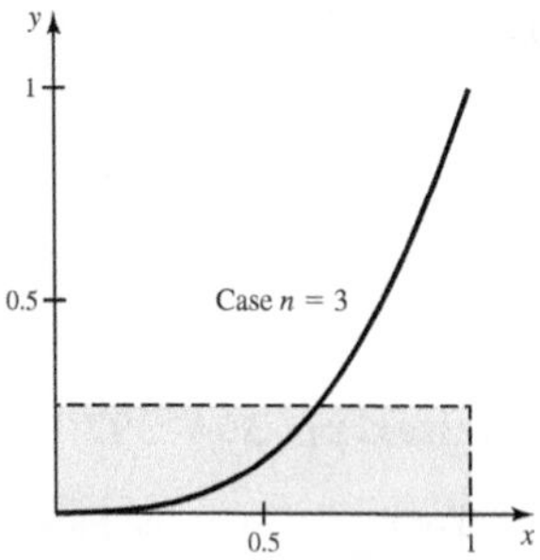

31. 2000 **33.** $20/\pi$ **35.** 2 **37.** $a/\sqrt{3}$ **39.** $c = \pm\frac{1}{2}$
41. a. True **b.** True **c.** True **d.** False **43.** 2 **45.** 0
47. 420 ft **51. a.** 9 **b.** 0 **53.** $f(g(-x)) = f(g(x)) \Rightarrow$ the integrand is even; $\int_{-a}^{a} f(g(x))\,dx = 2\int_0^a f(g(x))\,dx$
55. $p(g(-x)) = p(g(x)) \Rightarrow$ the integrand is even; $\int_{-a}^{a} p(g(x))\,dx = 2\int_0^a p(g(x))\,dx$ **57. a.** $a/6$
b. $(3 \pm \sqrt{3})/6$, independent of a **61.** $c = \sqrt[4]{12}$

65.

Even	Even
Even	Odd

Section 5.5 Exercises, pp. 390–393

1. The Chain Rule **3.** $u = g(x)$ **5.** We let a become $g(a)$ and b become $g(b)$. **7.** $\frac{x}{2} + \frac{\sin 2x}{4} + C$ **9.** $\frac{(x+1)^{13}}{13} + C$

11. $\frac{(2x+1)^{3/2}}{3} + C$ **13.** $\frac{(x^2+1)^5}{5} + C$ **15.** $\frac{1}{4}\sin^4 x + C$

17. $\frac{(x^2-1)^{100}}{100} + C$ **19.** $-\frac{(1-4x^3)^{1/2}}{3} + C$ **21.** $\frac{(x^2+x)^{11}}{11} + C$

23. $\frac{(x^4+16)^7}{28} + C$ **25.** $\frac{\sin^{-1} 3x}{3} + C$ **27.** $\frac{(x^6-3x^2)^5}{30} + C$

29. $\frac{1}{2}\tan^{-1} 2x + C$ **31.** $2\sec^{-1} 2x + C$
33. $\frac{2}{3}(x-4)^{1/2}(x+8) + C$ **35.** $\frac{3}{5}(x+4)^{2/3}(x-6) + C$
37. $\frac{3}{112}(2x+1)^{4/3}(8x-3) + C$ **39.** $\frac{7}{2}$ **41.** $\frac{1}{3}$ **43.** $(e^9 - 1)/3$
45. $\sqrt{2} - 1$ **47.** $\frac{\pi}{6}$ **49.** $\frac{1}{2}\ln 17$ **51.** $\frac{\pi}{9}$ **53.** π

55. $\frac{\theta}{2} - \frac{1}{4}\sin\left(\frac{6\theta+\pi}{3}\right) + C$ **57.** $\frac{\pi}{4}$ **59.** $\ln\frac{9}{8}$ **61. a.** True
b. True **c.** False **d.** False **e.** False **63.** $\frac{1}{10}\tan 10x + C$
65. $\frac{1}{2}\tan^2 x + C$ **67.** $\frac{1}{7}\sec^7 x + C$ **69.** $\frac{1}{3}$ **71.** $\frac{3}{4}(4 - 3^{2/3})$
73. $\frac{32}{3}$ **75.** $-\ln 3$ **77.** $\frac{1}{7}$ **79.** 1 **81.** $\frac{64}{5}$ **83.** $\frac{2}{3}$; constant

85. a. π/p **b.** 0 **87. a.** 160 **b.** $\frac{4800}{49} \approx 98$

c. $\Delta p = \int_0^T \frac{200}{(t+1)^r}\,dt$; decreases as r increases **d.** $r \approx 1.28$
e. As $t \to \infty$, the population approaches 100. **89.** $2/\pi$

93. One area is $\int_4^9 \frac{(\sqrt{x}-1)^2}{2\sqrt{x}}\,dx$. Changing variables by letting $u = \sqrt{x} - 1$ yields $\int_1^2 u^2\,du$, which is the other area. **95.** $7297/12$

97. $\frac{(f^{(p)}(x))^{n+1}}{n+1} + C$ **99.** $\frac{2}{15}(3 - 2a)(1 + a)^{3/2} + \frac{4}{15}a^{5/2}$

101. $\frac{1}{3}\sec^3\theta + C$ **103. a.** $I = \frac{1}{8}x - \frac{1}{32}\sin 4x + C$ **b.** $I = \frac{1}{8}x - \frac{1}{32}\sin 4x + C$

107. $\dfrac{4}{3}(-2 + \sqrt{1+x})\sqrt{1+\sqrt{1+x}} + C$

109. $\dfrac{32}{105}$ **111.** $-4 + \sqrt{17}$

Chapter 5 Review Exercises, pp. 394–397

1. a. True **b.** False **c.** True **d.** True **e.** False **f.** True **g.** True **3. a.** 8.5 **b.** -4.5 **c.** 0 **d.** 11.5 **5.** 4π **7. a.** $1((3\cdot 2 - 2) + (3\cdot 3 - 2) + (3\cdot 4 - 2)) = 21$ **b.** $\sum_{k=1}^{n} \frac{3}{n}\left(3\left(1 + \frac{3k}{n}\right) - 2\right)$ **c.** $\frac{33}{2}$ **9.** $-\frac{16}{3}$ **11.** 56

13. $\int_0^4 (1 + x^5)\,dx = \dfrac{2060}{3}$ **15.** $\frac{212}{5}$ **17.** 20 **19.** $x^9 - x^7 + C$ **21.** $\frac{7}{6}$ **23.** $\frac{\pi}{6}$ **25.** 1 **27.** $\frac{\pi}{2}$ **29.** $\frac{1}{3}\ln\frac{9}{2}$ **31.** $\frac{256}{3}$ **33.** 8 **35.** $-\dfrac{4}{15}; \dfrac{4}{15}$ **37. a.** 20 **b.** 0 **c.** 80 **d.** 10 **e.** 0 **39.** 18 **41.** 10 **43.** Not enough information **45.** Displacement $= 0$; distance $= 20/\pi$ **47. a.** $5/2, c = 3.5$ **b.** $3, c = 3$ and $c = 5$ **49.** 24 **51.** $f(1) = 0$; $f'(x) > 0$ on $[1, \infty)$; $f''(x) < 0$ on $[1, \infty)$

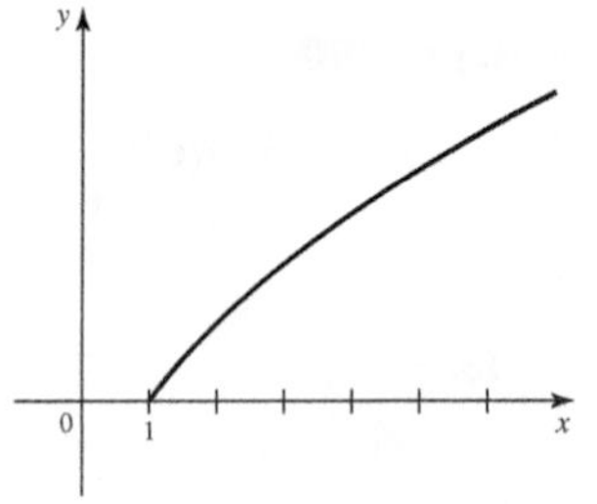

53. a.

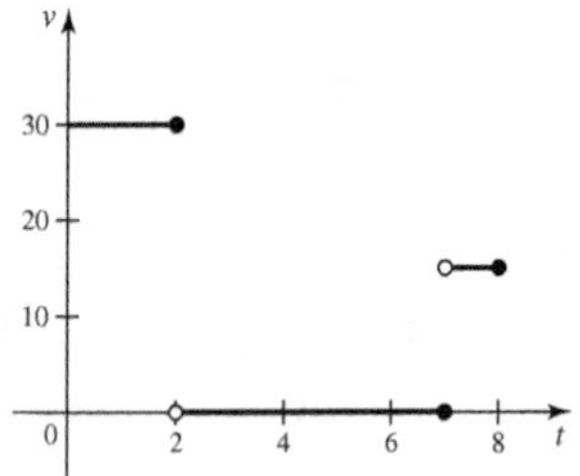

b. 75 **c.** The area is the distance the diver ascends.

55. a. $\dfrac{3}{2}, \dfrac{5}{6}$ **b.** x **c.** $\dfrac{1}{2}x^2$ **d.** $-1, \dfrac{1}{2}$ **e.** 1, 1 **f.** $\dfrac{3}{2}$ **57.** e^4

63. $\cos\dfrac{1}{x} + C$ **65.** $\ln|\tan^{-1} x| + C$ **67.** $\ln(e^x + e^{-x}) + C$ **69.** Differentiating the first equation gives the second equation; no. **71. a.** Increasing on $(-\infty, 1)$ and $(2, \infty)$; decreasing on $(1, 2)$ **b.** Concave up on $(\frac{13}{8}, \infty)$; concave down on $(-\infty, \frac{13}{8})$ **c.** Local max at $x = 1$; local min at $x = 2$ **d.** Inflection point at $x = \frac{13}{8}$

CHAPTER 6

Section 6.1 Exercises, pp. 407–411

1. The position $s(t)$ is the location of the object relative to the origin. The displacement is the change in position between time $t = a$ and $t = b$. The distance traveled between $t = a$ and $t = b$ is $\int_a^b |v(t)|\,dt$, where $v(t)$ is the velocity at time t. **3.** The displacement between $t = a$ and $t = b$ is $\int_a^b v(t)\,dt$. **5.** $Q(t) = Q(0) + \int_0^t Q'(x)\,dx$ **7. a.** $[0, 1), (3, 5)$ **b.** -4 mi **c.** 26 mi **d.** 6 mi **e.** 6 mi on the positive side of the initial position

9. a.

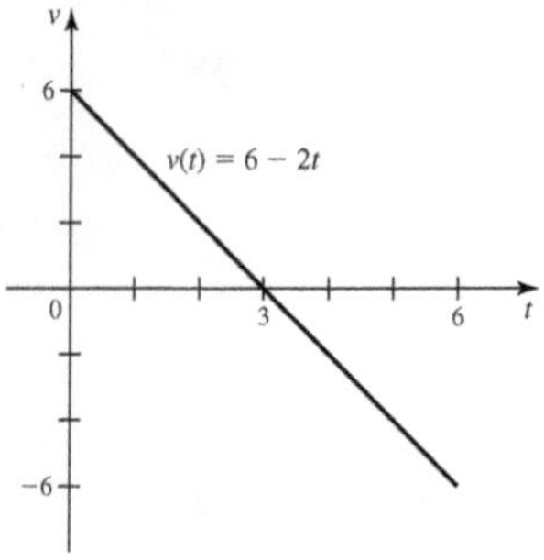

Positive direction for $0 \le t < 3$; negative direction for $3 < t \le 6$ **b.** 0 **c.** 18 m

11. a.

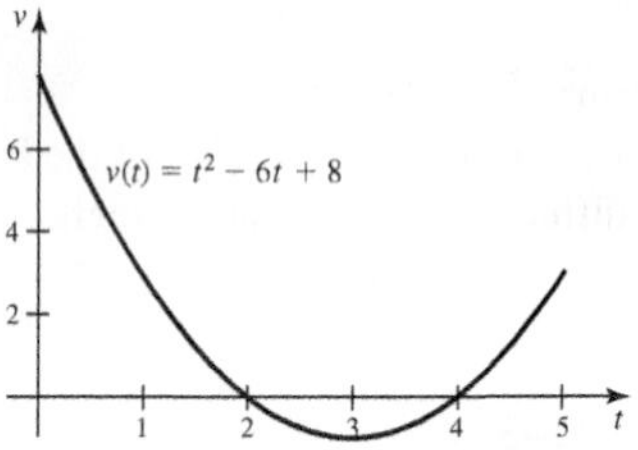

Positive direction for $0 \le t < 2$ and $4 < t < 5$; negative direction for $2 < t < 4$ **b.** $20/3$ m **c.** $28/3$ m

13. a.

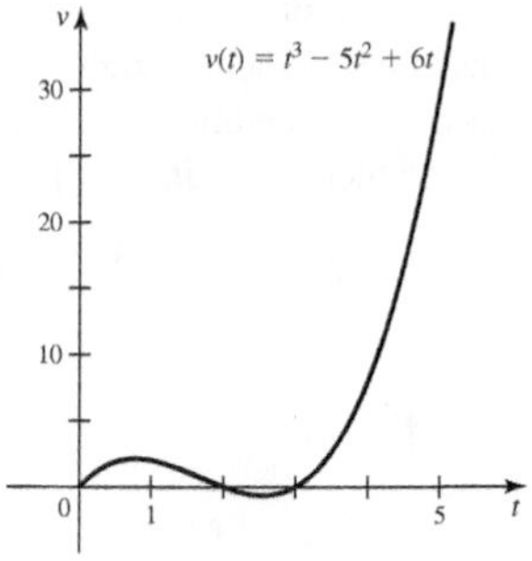

Positive direction for $0 < t < 2$ and $3 < t < 5$; negative direction for $2 < t < 3$ **b.** $\dfrac{275}{12}$ m **c.** $\dfrac{95}{4}$ m

15. a.

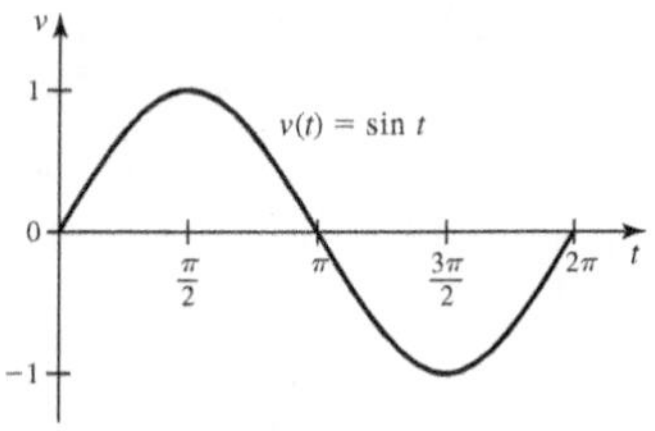

Positive direction for $0 < t < \pi$; negative direction for $\pi < t < 2\pi$

b. $s(t) = 2 - \cos t$ **c.**

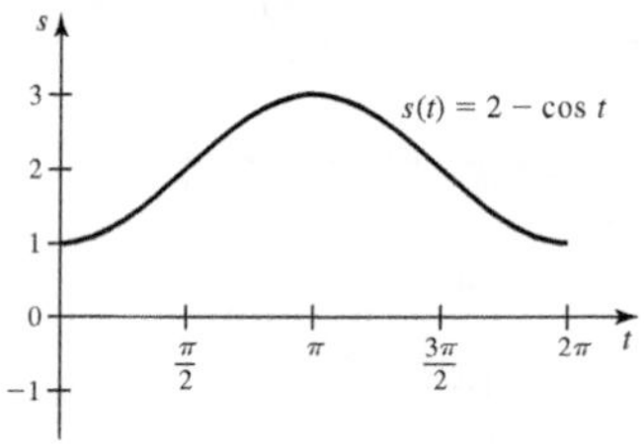

17. a.

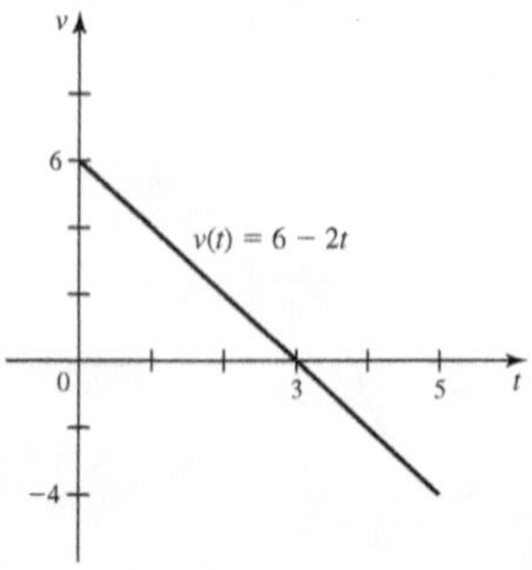

Positive direction for $0 \le t < 3$; negative direction for $3 < t \le 5$

b. $s(t) = 6t - t^2$ **c.**

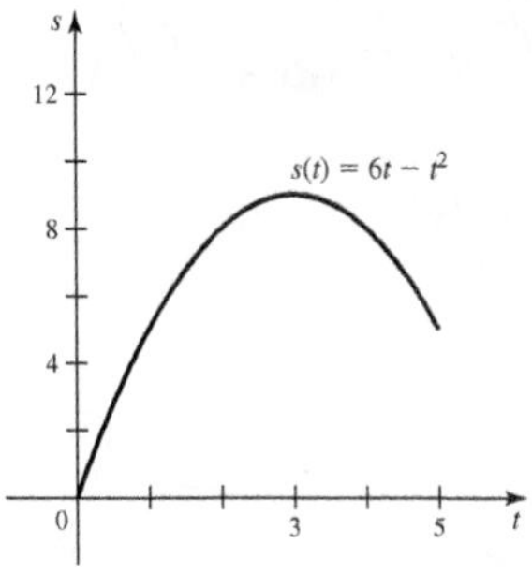

19. a.

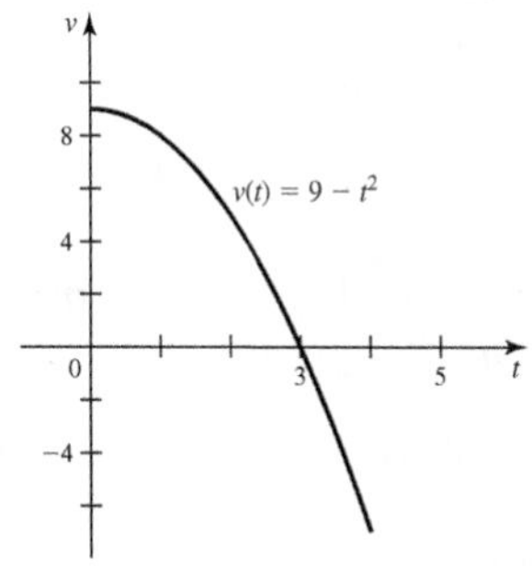

Positive direction for $0 \le t < 3$; negative direction for $3 < t \le 4$

b. $s(t) = 9t - \frac{t^3}{3} - 2$ **c.**

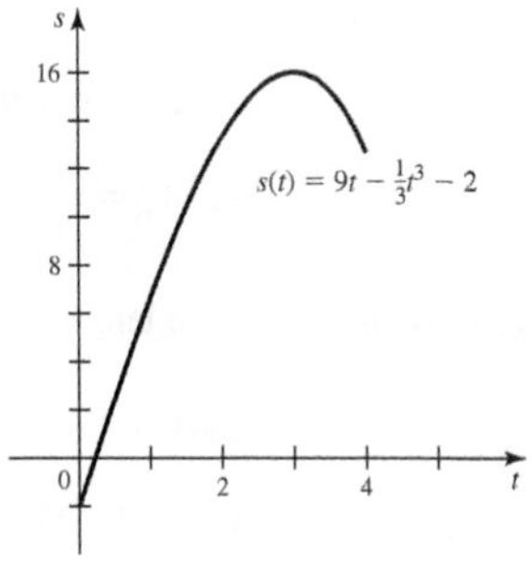

21. a. $s(t) = 2 \sin \pi t$ **b.**

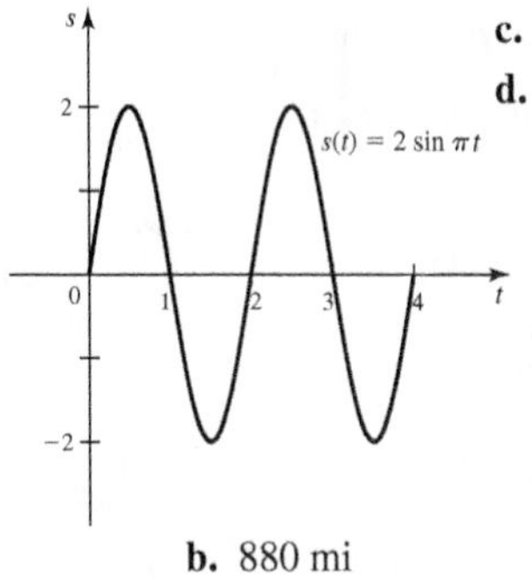

c. $\frac{3}{2}, \frac{7}{2}, \frac{11}{2}$
d. $\frac{1}{2}, \frac{5}{2}, \frac{9}{2}$

23. a. $s(t) = 10t(48 - t^2)$

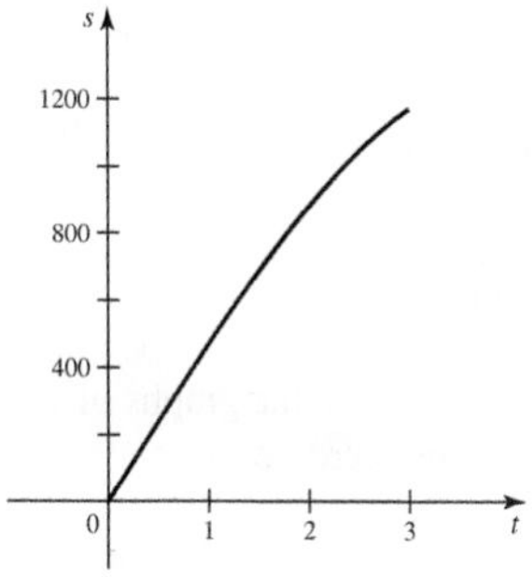

b. 880 mi
c. $\frac{2720\sqrt{6}}{9} \approx 740.29$ mi

25.

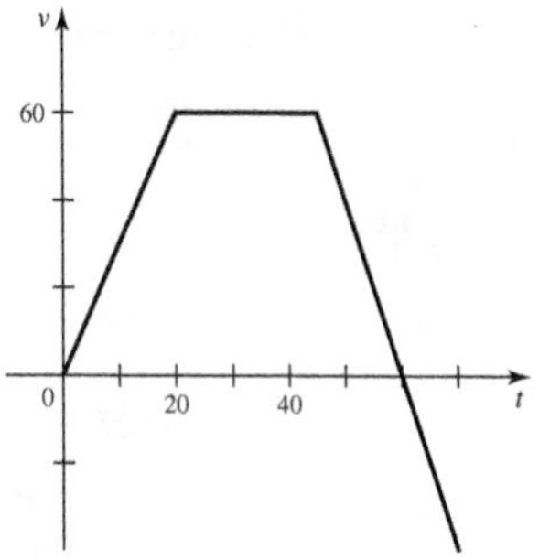

a. Velocity is a maximum for $20 \le t \le 45$; $v = 0$ at $t = 0$ and $t = 60$ **b.** 1200 m **c.** 2550 m **d.** 2100 m

27. $v(t) = -32t + 70$; $s(t) = -16t^2 + 70t + 10$
29. $v(t) = -9.8t + 20$; $s(t) = -4.9t^2 + 20t$
31. $v(t) = -\frac{1}{200}t^2 + 10$; $s(t) = -\frac{1}{600}t^3 + 10t$
33. $v(t) = \frac{1}{2}\sin 2t + 5$; $s(t) = -\frac{1}{4}\cos 2t + 5t + \frac{29}{4}$

35.

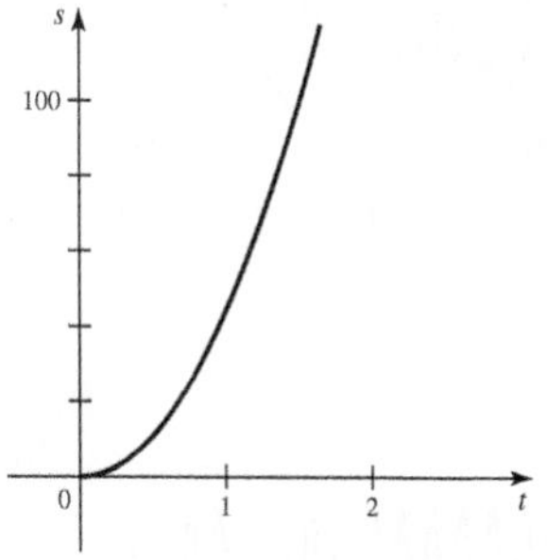

a. $s(t) = 44t^2$
b. 704 ft
c. $\sqrt{30} \approx 5.477$ s
d. $\frac{5\sqrt{33}}{11} \approx 2.611$ s
e. Approximately 180.023 ft

37. 6.154 mi; 1.465 mi **39. a.** 27,250 barrels **b.** 31,000 barrels **c.** 4000 barrels **41. a.** 2639 people **b.** $P(t) = 250 + 20t^{3/2} + 30t$ people **43. a.** 1897 cells; 1900 cells **b.** $N(t) = -400e^{-0.25t} + 1900$ **45. a.** \$96,875 **b.** \$86,875 **47. a.** \$69,583.33 **b.** \$139,583.33 **49. a.** False **b.** True **c.** True **d.** True **51. a.** 3 **b.** $\frac{13}{3}$ **c.** 3

d. $s(t) = \begin{cases} -\frac{t^2}{2} + 2t, & 0 \le t \le 3 \\ \frac{3t^2}{2} - 10t + 18, & 3 < t \le 4 \\ -t^2 + 10t - 22, & 4 < t \le 5 \end{cases}$

53. $\frac{2}{3}$ **55.** $\frac{25}{3}$ **57. a.**

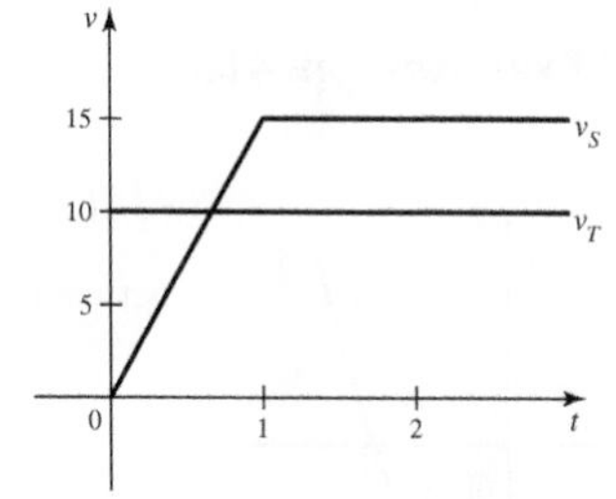

b. Theo **c.** Sasha **d.** Theo hits the 10-mi mark before Sasha; Sasha and Theo hit the 15-mi mark at the same time; Sasha hits the 20-mi mark before Theo. **e.** Sasha **f.** Theo

59. a. Abe initially runs into a headwind; Bess initially runs with a tailwind.

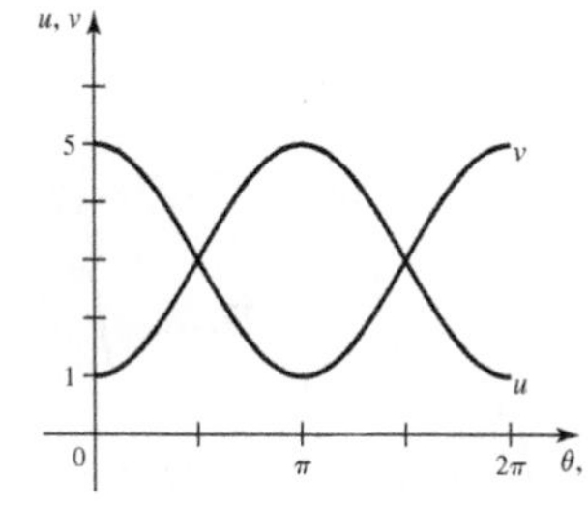

b. 3 mi/hr for both runners **c.** $\pi\sqrt{5}/25$ hr for both runners

61. a. $\dfrac{10^7(1 - e^{-kt})}{k}$ **b.** $\dfrac{10^7}{k}$ = total number of barrels of oil extracted if the nation extracts the oil indefinitely where it is assumed that the nation has at least $\dfrac{10^7}{k}$ barrels of oil in reserve **c.** $k = \dfrac{1}{200} = 0.005$ **d.** Approximately 138.6 yr

63. a. $\dfrac{120}{\pi} + 40 \approx 78.20\ \text{m}^3$ **b.** $Q(t) = 20\left(t + \dfrac{12}{\pi}\sin\left(\dfrac{\pi}{12}t\right)\right)$

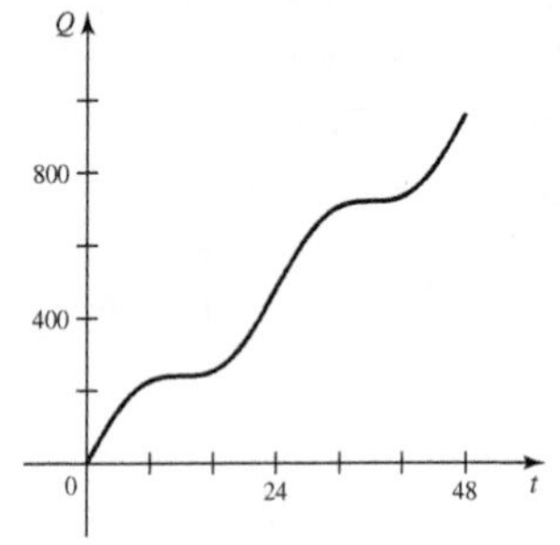

c. Approximately 122.6 hr

65. a. $V(t) = 5 + \cos\dfrac{\pi t}{2}$

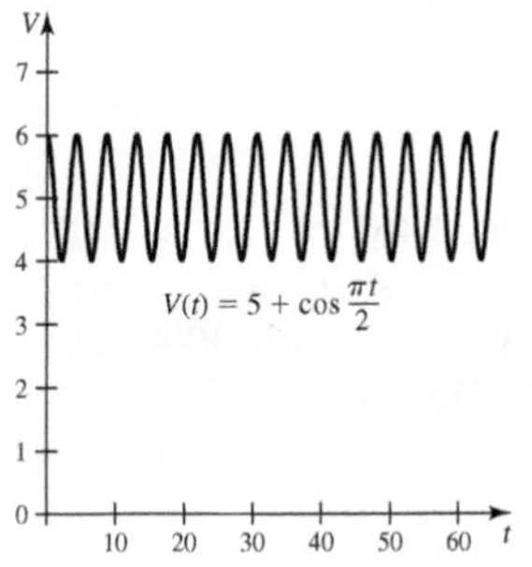

b. 15 breaths/min **c.** 2 L, 6 L

67. a. 7200 MWh or 2.592×10^{13} J **b.** 16,000 kg; 5,840,000 kg **c.** 450 g; 164,250 g **d.** About 1500 turbines

69. $\displaystyle\int_a^b f'(x)\,dx = f(b) - f(a) = g(b) - g(a) = \int_a^b g'(x)\,dx$

Section 6.2 Exercises, pp. 416–420

1.

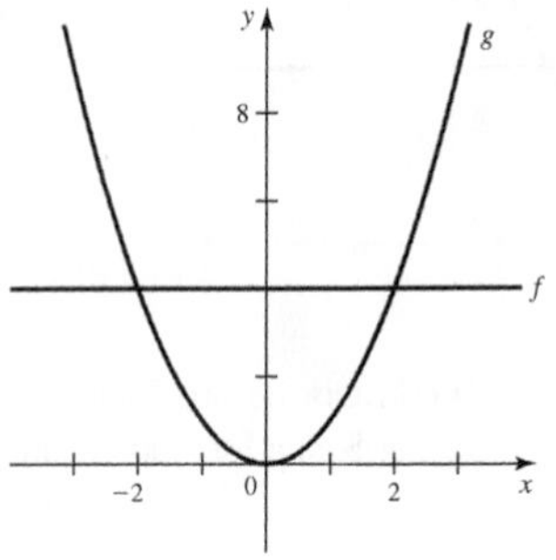

$\displaystyle\int_{-2}^{2}(f(x) - g(x))\,dx$ is the area between these curves.

3. See solution to Exercise 1. **5.** $\dfrac{9}{2}$ **7.** $\dfrac{5}{2} - \dfrac{1}{\ln 2}$ **9.** $\dfrac{25}{2}$ **11.** $\dfrac{81}{32}$ **13.** $\pi - 2$ **15.** $2 - \sqrt{2}$ **17.** $\frac{1}{2} + \ln 2$ **19.** $\dfrac{7}{3}$ **21.** 3 **23.** 2 **25.** $\dfrac{125}{2}$ **27. a.** $\displaystyle\int_{-\sqrt{2}}^{-1}(2 - x^2)\,dx + \int_{-1}^{0}(-x)\,dx$

b. $\displaystyle\int_{-1}^{0}(y + \sqrt{y + 2})\,dy$

29. a. $\displaystyle 2\int_{-3}^{-2}\sqrt{x + 3}\,dx + \int_{-2}^{6}\left(\sqrt{x + 3} - \frac{x}{2}\right)dx$

b. $\displaystyle\int_{-1}^{3}(2y - (y^2 - 3))\,dy$

31. 9

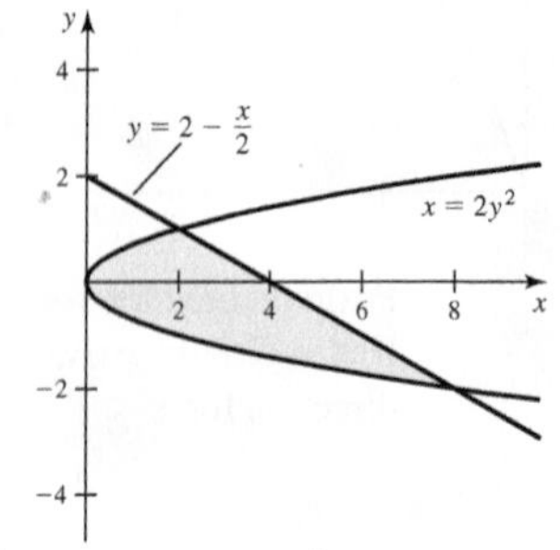

33. $\frac{64}{5}$ **35.** $\ln 2$ **37.** $\frac{5}{24}$ **39. a.** False **b.** False **c.** True **41.** $\frac{1}{6}$ **43.** $\frac{9}{2}$ **45.** $\frac{32}{3}$ **47.** $\frac{63}{4}$ **49.** $\frac{15}{8} - 2\ln 2$

51. a. Area $(R_1) = \dfrac{p - 1}{2(p + 1)}$ for all positive integers p; area $(R_2) = \dfrac{q - 1}{2(q + 1)}$ for all positive integers q; they are equal. **b.** R_1 has greater area. **c.** R_2 has greater area. **53.** $\dfrac{17}{3}$ **55.** $\dfrac{81}{2}$ **57.** $\dfrac{n - 1}{2(n + 1)}$ **59.** $A_n = \dfrac{n - 1}{n + 1}$; $\lim_{n\to\infty} A_n = 1$; the region approximates a square with side length of 1. **61.** $k = 1 - \dfrac{1}{\sqrt{2}}$ **63.** $k = \dfrac{1}{2}$ **65. a.** The lowest p% of households owns exactly p% of the wealth for $0 \le p \le 100$. **b.** The function must be one-to-one and its graph must lie below $y = x$ because the poorest p% cannot own more than p% of the wealth. **c.** $p = 1.1$ is most equitable; $p = 4$ is least equitable. **e.** $G(p) = \dfrac{p - 1}{p + 1}$ **f.** $0 \le G \le 1$ for $p \ge 1$ **g.** $\dfrac{5}{18}$ **67.** −1 **69.** $\frac{4}{9}$ **71. a.** $F(a) = ab^3/6 - b^4/12$; $F(a) = 0$ if $a = b/2$ **b.** Because $A'(b/2) = 0$ and $A''(b/2) > 0$, A has a minimum at $a = b/2$. The maximum value of $b^4/12$ occurs if $a = 0$ or $a = b$.

73. a.

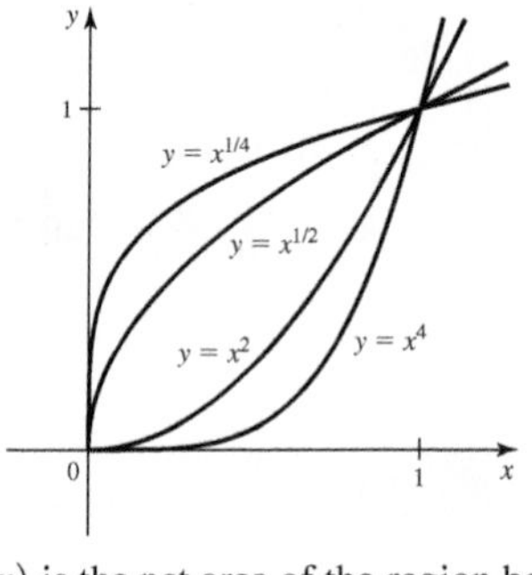

b. $A_n(x)$ is the net area of the region between the graphs of f and g from 0 to x. **c.** $x = n^{n/(n^2-1)}$; the root decreases with n.

Section 6.3 Exercises, pp. 429–433

1. $A(x)$ is the area of the cross section through the solid at the point x.

3. $\displaystyle\int_0^2 \pi(4x^2 - x^4)\,dx$ **5.** The cross sections are disks, and $A(x)$ is the area of a disk. **7.** $\dfrac{64}{15}$ **9.** 1 **11.** $\dfrac{1000}{3}$ **13.** $\dfrac{\pi}{3}$ **15.** $\dfrac{16\sqrt{2}}{3}$ **17.** 36π **19.** $\dfrac{15\pi}{32}$ **21.** $\dfrac{\pi^2}{2}$ **23.** $\dfrac{\pi^2}{6}$ **25.** $\dfrac{\pi^2}{2}$

27. $32\pi/3$ **29.** $5\pi/6$ **31.** $117\pi/5$ **33.** $(4\pi - \pi^2)/4$ **35.** 54π **37.** $64\pi/5$ **39.** $32\pi/3$ **41.** Volumes are equal. **43.** x-axis

45. $\frac{\pi}{6}$ **47.** $2\pi(8 + \pi)$ **49.** $(6\sqrt{3} - 2\pi)\pi$ **51.** 4π

53. a. False **b.** True **c.** True **55.** $\pi \ln 3$ **57.** $\frac{\pi}{2}(e^4 - 1)$

59. $49\pi/2$ **61.** Volume $(S) = 8\pi a^{5/2}/15$; volume $(T) = \pi a^{5/2}/3$

63. a.

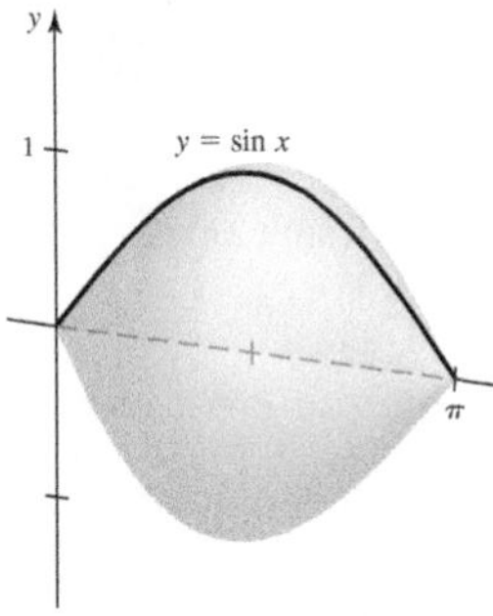

b.

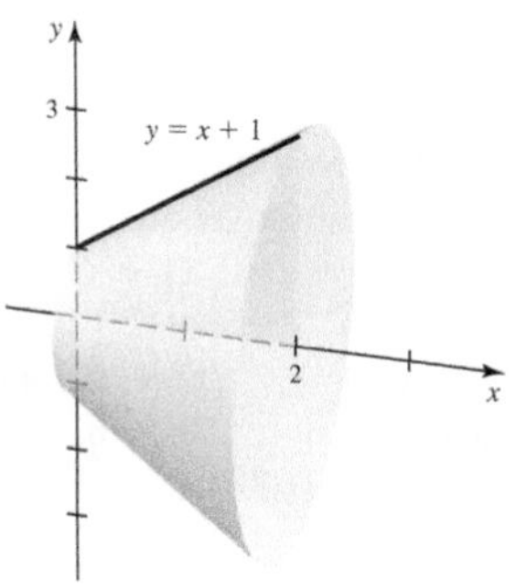

65. a. $\frac{1}{3}V_C$ **b.** $\frac{2}{3}V_C$ **67.** $24\pi^2$ **69. b.** $2/\sqrt{\pi}$ m

Section 6.4 Exercises, pp. 442–445

1. $\int_a^b 2\pi x(f(x) - g(x))\,dx$ **3.** x; y **5.** $\frac{\pi}{6}$ **7.** $\pi \ln 5$ **9.** π

11. $\frac{\pi}{5}$ **13.** π **15.** 8π **17.** $\frac{32\pi}{3}$ **19.** $\frac{2\pi}{3}$ **21.** $\frac{81\pi}{2}$ **23.** 90π

25. π **27.** 24π **29.** 54π **31.** $\frac{16\sqrt{2}\,\pi}{3}$ **33.** $\frac{11\pi}{6}$ **35.** $\frac{23\pi}{15}$

37. $\frac{52\pi}{15}$ **39.** $\frac{36\pi}{5}$ **41.** $\frac{4\pi}{15}$; shell method **43.** $\frac{8\pi}{27}$; shell method **45.** $\pi(\sqrt{e} - 1)^2$; shell method **47.** $\frac{\pi}{9}$; washer method

49. a. True **b.** False **c.** True **51.** $4\pi \ln 2$ **53.** $2\pi e(e - 1)$ **55.** $16\pi/3$ **57.** $608\pi/3$ **59.** $\pi/4$ **61.** $\pi/3$

63. a. $V_1 = \frac{\pi}{15}(3a^2 + 10a + 15)$ $V_2 = \frac{\pi}{2}(a + 2)$

b. $V(S_1) = V(S_2)$ for $a = 0$ and $a = -\frac{5}{6}$ **67.** $\frac{\pi h^2}{3}(24 - h)$

69. $24\pi^2$ **73.** 10π **75. a.** $27\sqrt{3}\pi r^3/8$ **b.** $54\sqrt{2}/(3 + \sqrt{2})^3$ **c.** $500\pi/3$

Section 6.5 Exercises, pp. 450–451

1. Determine whether f has a continuous derivative on $[a, b]$. If so, calculate $f'(x)$ and evaluate the integral $\int_a^b \sqrt{1 + f'(x)^2}\,dx$.

3. $\int_{-2}^{5} \sqrt{1 + 9x^4}\,dx$ **5.** $\int_0^2 \sqrt{1 + 4e^{-4x}}\,dx$ **7.** $4\sqrt{5}$ **9.** $8\sqrt{65}$

11. 168 **13.** $\frac{4}{3}$ **15.** $\frac{123}{32}$ **17. a.** $\int_{-1}^{1} \sqrt{1 + 4x^2}\,dx$ **b.** 2.96

19. a. $\int_1^4 \sqrt{1 + \frac{1}{x^2}}\,dx$ **b.** 3.34 **21. a.** $\int_3^4 \sqrt{\frac{4x - 7}{4x - 8}}\,dx$ **b.** 1.08

23. a. $\int_0^{\pi} \sqrt{1 + 4\sin^2 2x}\,dx$ **b.** 5.27 **25. a.** $\int_1^{10} \sqrt{1 + 1/x^4}\,dx$

b. 9.15 **27.** $7\sqrt{5}$ **29.** $\frac{123}{32}$ **31. a.** False **b.** True **c.** False **33. a.** $f(x) = \pm 4x^3/3 + C$ **b.** $f(x) = \pm 3\sin 2x + C$ **35.** $y = 1 - x^2$ **37.** Approximately 1326 m **39. a.** $L/2$ **b.** L/c

Section 6.6 Exercises, pp. 457–459

1. 15π **3.** Evaluate $\int_a^b 2\pi f(x)\sqrt{1 + f'(x)^2}\,dx$ **5.** $156\sqrt{10}\pi$

7. $\frac{2912\pi}{3}$ **9.** $\frac{53\pi}{9}$ **11.** $\frac{\pi}{8}(16 + e^8 - e^{-8})$ **13.** $\frac{275\pi}{32}$

15. $\frac{9\pi}{125}\,\text{m}^3$ **17.** $\frac{\pi}{9}(17^{3/2} - 1)$ **19.** $15\sqrt{17}\,\pi$

21. a. False **b.** False **c.** True **d.** False **23.** $\frac{48{,}143\pi}{48}$

25. $\frac{1{,}256{,}001\pi}{1024} \approx 3853.36$ **27. b.** Approximately 7.21

29. b. Approximately 3.84 **31.** $\frac{12\pi a^2}{5}$ **35. a.** $\frac{6}{a}$ **b.** $\frac{3}{a}$

c. $\frac{3}{2a} + \frac{3a}{2\sqrt{a^2 - 1}}\sin^{-1}\left(\frac{\sqrt{a^2 - 1}}{a}\right)$ **d.** The sphere **e.** A sphere **37. a.** $c^2 A$ **b.** A

Section 6.7 Exercises, pp. 467–471

1. 150 g **3.** 25 J **5.** Different volumes of water are moved different distances. **7.** 39,200 N/m^2 **9.** $\pi + 2$ **11.** 3 **13.** $(2\sqrt{2} - 1)/3$ **15.** 10 **17.** 9 J **19. a.** $k = 150$ **b.** 12 J **c.** 6.75 J **d.** 9 J **21. a.** 112.5 J **b.** 12.5 J **23. a.** 31.25 J **b.** 312.5 J **25. a.** 625 J **b.** 391 J **27.** 1.15×10^7 J **29.** 3.94×10^6 J **31. a.** $66{,}150\pi$ J **b.** No **33. a.** 2.10×10^8 J **b.** 3.78×10^8 J **35. a.** 32,667 J **b.** Yes **37.** 7.70×10^3 J **39.** 1.47×10^7 N **41.** 2.94×10^7 N **43.** 6533 N **45.** 8×10^5 N **47.** 6737.5 N **49. a.** True **b.** True **c.** True **d.** False **51. a.** Compared to a linear spring $F(x) = 16x$, the restoring force is less for large displacements. **b.** 17.87 J **c.** 31.6 J **53.** 0.28 J **55. a.** 8.87×10^9 J **b.** $500\,GMx/(R(x + R)) = (2 \times 10^{17})x/(R(x + R))$ J **c.** GMm/R **d.** $v = \sqrt{2GM/R}$ **57. a.** 22,050 J **b.** 36,750 J **61.** Left: 16,730 N; right: 14,700 N **63. a.** Yes **b.** 4.296 m

Section 6.8 Exercises, pp. 480–481

1. $D = (0, \infty), R = (-\infty, \infty)$ **3.** $\frac{4^x}{\ln 4} + C$

5. $e^{x \ln 3}, e^{\pi \ln x}, e^{(\sin x)(\ln x)}$ **7.** 3 **9.** $\cos(\ln x)/x, x > 0$

11. $-\frac{5}{x(\ln 2x)^6}$ **13.** $6(1 - \ln 2)$ **15.** $\frac{3}{8}$ **17.** $\frac{1}{2}\ln(4 + e^{2x}) + C$

19. $\frac{1}{\ln 2} - \frac{1}{\ln 3}$ **21.** $4 - \frac{4}{e^2}$ **23.** $2e^{\sqrt{x}} + C$ **25.** $\ln|e^x - e^{-x}| + C$

27. $\frac{99}{10\ln 10}$ **29.** 3 **31.** $\frac{6^{x^3+8}}{3\ln 6} + C$ **33.** $4^{2x+1}x^{4x}(1 + \ln 2x)$

35. $(\ln 2)\,2^{x^2+1}x$ **37.** $2(x + 1)^{2x}\left(\frac{x}{x + 1} + \ln(x + 1)\right)$

39. $y^{\sin y}\left(\cos y \ln y + \frac{\sin y}{y}\right)$ **41. a.** True **b.** False **c.** False **d.** False **e.** False

43.

h	$(1 + 2h)^{1/h}$	h	$(1 + 2h)^{1/h}$
10^{-1}	6.1917	-10^{-1}	9.3132
10^{-2}	7.2446	-10^{-2}	7.5404
10^{-3}	7.3743	-10^{-3}	7.4039
10^{-4}	7.3876	-10^{-4}	7.3905
10^{-5}	7.3889	-10^{-5}	7.3892
10^{-6}	7.3890	-10^{-6}	7.3891

$\lim_{h\to 0}(1 + 2h)^{1/h} = e^2$

45.

x	$\frac{2^x - 1}{x}$	x	$\frac{2^x - 1}{x}$
10^{-1}	0.71773	-10^{-1}	0.66967
10^{-2}	0.69556	-10^{-2}	0.69075
10^{-3}	0.69339	-10^{-3}	0.69291
10^{-4}	0.69317	-10^{-4}	0.69312
10^{-5}	0.69315	-10^{-5}	0.69314
10^{-6}	0.69315	-10^{-6}	0.69315

$\lim_{x \to 0} \frac{2^x - 1}{x} = \ln 2$

47. a. No **b.** No **49.** $\frac{\ln p}{p-1}, 0$ **51.** $-20xe^{-10x^2}$

53. $-(1/x)^x(1 + \ln x)$ **55.** $\left(-\frac{4}{x+4} + \ln\left(\frac{x+4}{x}\right)\right)\left(1 + \frac{4}{x}\right)^x$

57. $-\sin(x^{2\sin x})\,x^{2\sin x}\left(\frac{2\sin x}{x} + 2\cos x \ln x\right)$ **59.** $-\frac{1}{9^x \ln 9} + C$

61. $\frac{10^{x^3}}{3\ln 10} + C$ **63.** $\frac{3 \cdot 3^{\ln 2} - 1}{\ln 3}$ **65.** $\frac{32}{3}$ **67.** $\frac{1}{3}\ln\frac{65}{16}$

69. $\frac{1}{2}(\ln 2 + 1) \approx 0.85$

73. $\ln 2 = \int_1^2 \frac{dt}{t} < L_2 = \frac{5}{6} < 1$

$\ln 3 = \int_1^3 \frac{dt}{t} > R_7$

$= 2\left(\frac{1}{9} + \frac{1}{11} + \frac{1}{13} + \frac{1}{15} + \frac{1}{17} + \frac{1}{19} + \frac{1}{21}\right) > 1$

Section 6.9 Exercises, pp. 488–490

1. The relative growth is constant. **3.** The time it takes a function to double in value **5.** $T_2 = (\ln 2)/k$ **7.** Compound interest, world population **9.** $\frac{df}{dt} = 10.5; \frac{dg}{dt} \cdot \frac{1}{g} = \frac{10e^{t/10}}{100e^{t/10}} = \frac{1}{10}$
11. $P(t) = 90{,}000e^{t \ln 1.024}$ people with $t = 0$ in 2010; 2039
13. $P(t) = 50{,}000e^{0.1t \ln 1.1}$ people; 60,500
15. $p(t) = 100e^{t \ln 1.03}$ dollars with $t = 0$ in 2005; \$146.85
17. a. $T_2 \approx 87$ yr, 2050 pop $\approx$ 425 million **b.** $T_2 \approx 116$ yr, 2050 pop $\approx$ 393 million; $T_2 \approx 70$ yr, 2050 pop $\approx$ 460 million
19. About 33 million **21.** $H(t) = 800e^{t \ln 0.97}$ homicides with $t = 0$ in 2010; 2019 **23.** $a(t) = 20e^{(t/36)\ln 0.5}$ mg with $t = 0$ at midnight; 15.87 mg; 119.6 hr $\approx$ 5 days **25.** $P(t) = 9.94e^{(t/10)\ln 0.994}$ in millions with $t = 0$ in 2000; 9.82 million; the population decline may stop if the economy improves. **27.** 18,928 ft; 125,754 ft
29. 1.055 billion yr **31. a.** False **b.** False **c.** True **d.** True **e.** True **33.** If $A(t) = A_0e^{kt}$ and $A(T) = 2A_0$, then $e^{kt} = 2$ and $T = (\ln 2)/k$. Therefore, the doubling time is a constant.
35. a. Bob; Abe **b.** $y = 4\ln(t+1)$ and $y = 8 - 8e^{-t/2}$; Bob

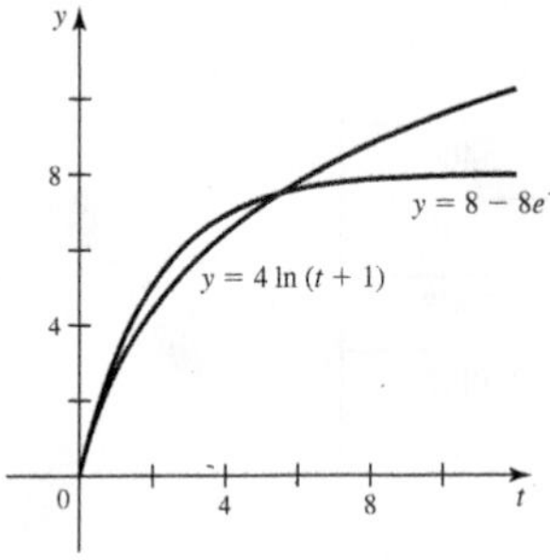

37. 10.034%; no **39.** 1.3 s **41.** 1044 days **43.** \$50
45. $k = \ln(1 + r)$; $r = 2^{(1/T_2)} - 1$; $T_2 = (\ln 2)/k$

Section 6.10 Exercises, pp. 502–506

1. $\cosh x = \frac{e^x + e^{-x}}{2}$; $\sinh x = \frac{e^x - e^{-x}}{2}$ **3.** $\cosh^2 x - \sinh^2 x = 1$
5. $\sinh^{-1} x = \ln(x + \sqrt{x^2 + 1})$ **7.** Evaluate $\sinh^{-1}\frac{1}{5}$.
9. $\int \frac{dx}{16 - x^2} = \frac{1}{4}\coth^{-1}\frac{x}{4} + C$ when $|x| > 4$; in this case, the values in the interval of integration $6 \le x \le 8$ satisfy $|x| > 4$.
23. $2\cosh x \sinh x$ **25.** $2\tanh x \operatorname{sech}^2 x$ **27.** $-2\tanh 2x$
29. $2x\cosh 3x(3x\sinh 3x + \cosh 3x)$ **31.** $(\sinh 2x)/2 + C$
33. $\ln(1 + \cosh x) + C$ **35.** $x - \tanh x + C$
37. $(\cosh^4 3 - 1)/12 \approx 856$ **39.** $\ln(5/4)$
41. $(x^2 + 1)/(2x) + C$ **43. a.** The values of $y = \coth x$ are close to 1 on $[5, 10]$. **b.** $\ln(\sinh 10) - \ln(\sinh 5) \approx 5.0000454$; $|\text{error}| \approx 0.0000454$
45.

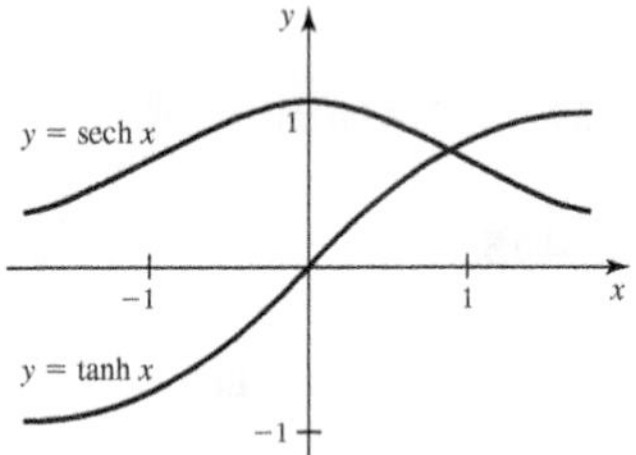

a. $x = \sinh^{-1} 1 = \ln(1 + \sqrt{2})$ **b.** $\pi/4 - \ln\sqrt{2} \approx 0.44$
47. $4/\sqrt{16x^2 - 1}$ **49.** $2v/\sqrt{v^4 + 1}$ **51.** $\sinh^{-1} x$
53. $\frac{1}{2\sqrt{2}}\coth^{-1}\left(\frac{x}{2\sqrt{2}}\right) + C$ **55.** $\tanh^{-1}(e^x/6)/6 + C$
57. $-\operatorname{sech}^{-1}(x^4/2)/8 + C$ **59.** $\sinh^{-1} 2 = \ln(2 + \sqrt{5})$
61. $-(\ln 5)/3 \approx -0.54$
63. $3\ln\left(\frac{\sqrt{5} + 2}{\sqrt{2} + 1}\right) = 3(\sinh^{-1} 2 - \sinh^{-1} 1)$
65. $\frac{1}{15}\left(17 - \frac{8}{\ln(5/3)}\right) \approx 0.09$
67. a. sag $= f(50) - f(0) = a(\cosh(50/a) - 1) = 10$; now divide by a. **b.** $t \approx 0.08$ **c.** $a = 10/t \approx 125$; $L = 250\sinh(2/5) \approx 102.7$ ft **69.** $\lambda \approx 32.81$ m
71. When $d/\lambda < 0.05$, $2\pi d/\lambda$ is small. Because $\tanh x \approx x$ for small values of x, $\tanh(2\pi d/\lambda) \approx 2\pi d/\lambda$; therefore,

$$v = \sqrt{\frac{g\lambda}{2\pi}\tanh\left(\frac{2\pi d}{\lambda}\right)} \approx \sqrt{\frac{g\lambda}{2\pi} \cdot \frac{2\pi d}{\lambda}} = \sqrt{gd}.$$

$v = \sqrt{gd}$ is a function of depth alone; when depth d decreases, v also decreases. **73. a.** False **b.** False **c.** False **d.** True **e.** False
75. a. 1 **b.** 0 **c.** Undefined **d.** 1 **e.** 13/12 **f.** 40/9
g. $\left(\frac{e^2 + 1}{2e}\right)^2$ **h.** Undefined **i.** $\ln 4$ **j.** 1 **77.** $x = 0$
79. $x = \pm\tanh^{-1}(1/\sqrt{3}) = \pm\ln(2 + \sqrt{3})/2 \approx \pm 0.658$
81. $\tan^{-1}(\sinh 1) - \pi/4 \approx 0.08$ **83.** Applying l'Hôpital's Rule twice brings you back to the initial limit; $\lim_{x \to \infty} \tanh x = 1$ **85.** $2/\pi$
87. 1 **89.** $-\operatorname{csch} z + C$ **91.** $\ln\sqrt{3} \cdot \ln(4/3) \approx 0.158$
93. $12(3\ln(3 + \sqrt{8}) - \sqrt{8}) \approx 29.5$ **95. a.** ≈ 360.8 m **b.** first 100 m: $t \approx 4.72$ s, $v_{av} \approx 21.2$ m/s; second 100 m: $t \approx 2.25$ s, $v_{av} \approx 44.5$ m/s **97. a.** $\sqrt{mg/k}$ **b.** $35\sqrt{3} \approx 60.6$ m/s
c. $t = \sqrt{\frac{m}{kg}}\tanh^{-1}(0.95) = \frac{1}{2}\sqrt{\frac{m}{kg}}\ln 39$ **d.** ≈ 736.5 m
109. $\ln(21/4) \approx 1.66$

Chapter 6 Review Exercises, pp. 507–510

1. a. True **b.** True **c.** True **d.** False **e.** False **f.** False **g.** True **3.** $s(t) = 20t - 5t^2$; displacement $= 20t - 5t^2$;

$$D(t) = \begin{cases} 20t - 5t^2 & \text{if } 0 \le t < 2 \\ 5t^2 - 20t + 40 & \text{if } 2 \le t \le 4 \end{cases}$$

5. a. $v(t) = -\dfrac{8}{\pi}\cos\dfrac{\pi t}{4}$; $s(t) = -\dfrac{32}{\pi^2}\sin\dfrac{\pi t}{4}$

b. Min value $= -\dfrac{32}{\pi^2}$; max value $= \dfrac{32}{\pi^2}$ **c.** 0; 0 **7. a.** $R(t) = 3t^{4/3}$

b. $R(t) = \begin{cases} 3t^{4/3} & \text{if } 0 \le t \le 8 \\ 2t + 32 & \text{if } t > 8 \end{cases}$ **c.** $t = 59$ min

9. a.

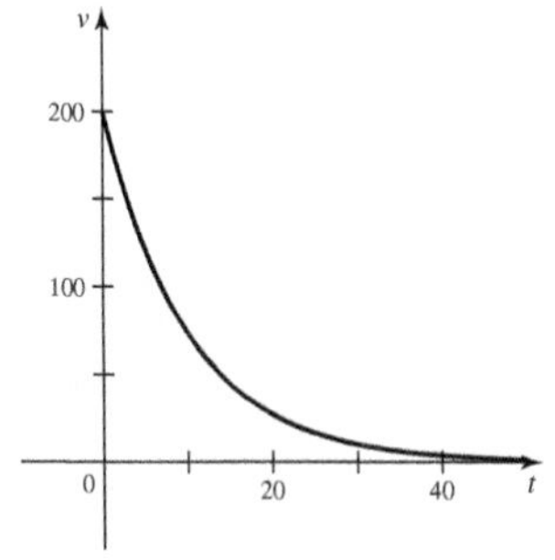

b. $10 \ln 4 \approx 13.86$ s

c. $s(t) = 2000(1 - e^{-t/10})$ **d.** No

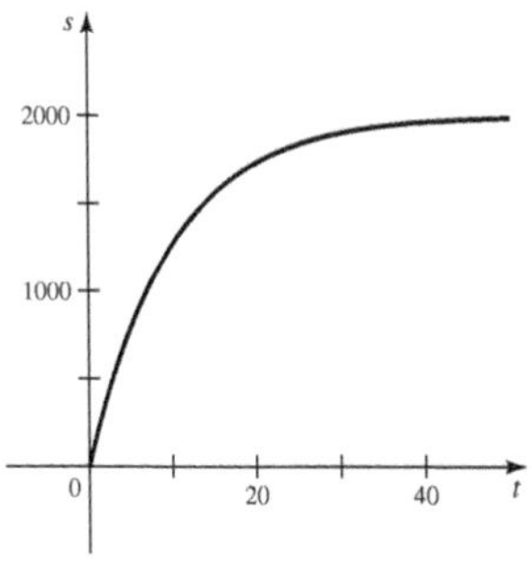

11. a. $s_{\text{Tom}}(t) = -10e^{-2t} + 10$
$s_{\text{Sue}}(t) = -15e^{-t} + 15$

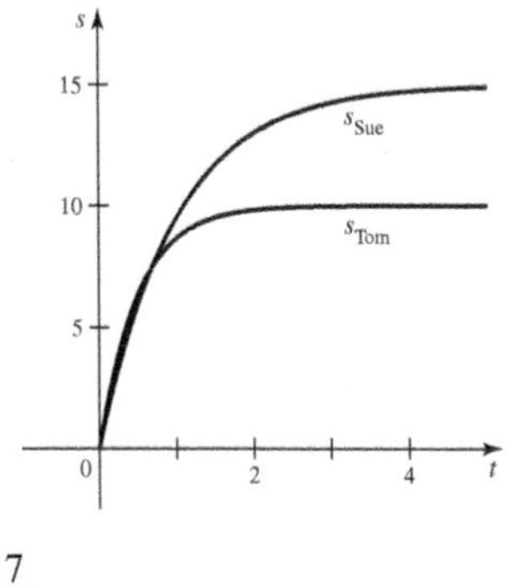

b. $t = 0$ and $t = \ln 2$ **c.** Sue **13.** $\dfrac{7}{3}$

15. R_1: 17/6; R_2: 47/6; R_3: 11/2 **17.** 8 **19.** 1 **21.** $\dfrac{1}{3}$ **23.** $\dfrac{5}{6}$

25. $\dfrac{8}{15}$ **27.** $\dfrac{8\pi}{5}$ **29.** $\pi(e - 1)^2$ **31.** π **33.** $\dfrac{512\pi}{15}$

35. About $y = -2$: 80π; about $x = -2$: 112π

37. a. V_y **b.** V_y

c. $V_x = \begin{cases} \pi\left(\dfrac{a^{1-2p} - 1}{1 - 2p}\right) & \text{if } p \ne 1/2 \\ \pi \ln a & \text{if } p = 1/2 \end{cases}$

d. $V_y = \begin{cases} 2\pi\left(\dfrac{a^{2-p} - 1}{2 - p}\right) & \text{if } p \ne 2 \\ 2\pi \ln a & \text{if } p = 2 \end{cases}$

39. $c = 5$ **41.** 1 **43.** $2\sqrt{3} - \dfrac{4}{3}$

45. $\sqrt{b^2 + 1} - \sqrt{2} + \ln\left(\dfrac{(\sqrt{b^2 + 1} - 1)(1 + \sqrt{2})}{b}\right)$; $b \approx 2.715$ **47. a.** 9π **b.** $\dfrac{9\pi}{2}$ **49. a.** $\dfrac{263{,}439\pi}{4096}$ **b.** $\dfrac{483}{64}$

c. $\dfrac{\pi}{8}(84 + \ln 2)$ **d.** $\dfrac{264{,}341\pi}{18{,}432}$ **51.** $\left(450 - \dfrac{450}{e}\right)$ g

53. a. 562.5 J **b.** 56.25 J **55.** 5.2×10^7 J **57.** ln 4

59. $\frac{1}{2}\ln(x^2 + 8x + 25) + C$

61. $\cosh^{-1}(x/3) + C = \ln(x + \sqrt{x^2 - 9}) + C$

63. $\tanh^{-1}(1/3)/9 = (\ln 2)/18 \approx 0.0385$ **65.** 48.37 yr

67. Local max at $x = -\frac{1}{2}(\sqrt{5} + 1)$; local min at $x = \frac{1}{2}(\sqrt{5} - 1)$; inflection points at $x = -3$ and $x = 0$; $\lim\limits_{x\to-\infty} f(x) = 0$; $\lim\limits_{x\to\infty} f(x) = \infty$

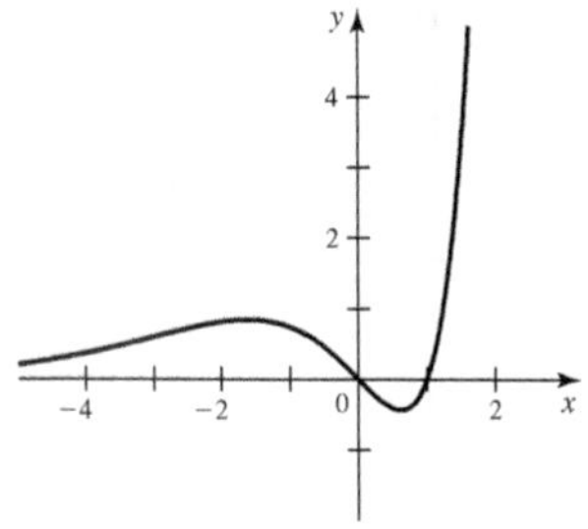

69. a.

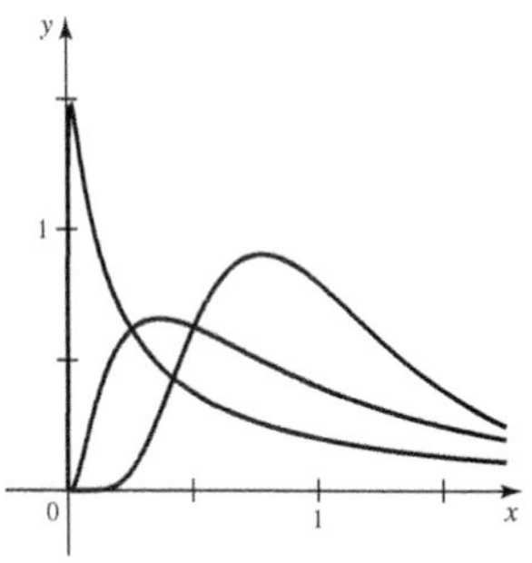

b. $\lim\limits_{x\to 0} f(x) = 0$

d. $f(x^*) = \dfrac{1}{\sqrt{2\pi}}\dfrac{e^{\sigma^2/2}}{\sigma}$ **e.** $\sigma = 1$

71. a. $\cosh x$ **b.** $\operatorname{sech} x(1 - x\tanh x)$

73. $L(x) = \frac{5}{3} + \frac{4}{3}(x - \ln 3)$; $\cosh 1 \approx 1.535$

APPENDIX A

Exercises, pp. 1157–1158

1. The set of real numbers greater than -4 and less than or equal to 10; $(-4, 10]$;

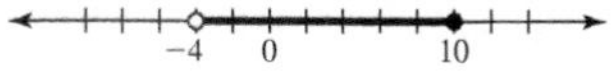

3. $|x| = \begin{cases} x & \text{if } x \ge 0 \\ -x & \text{if } x < 0 \end{cases}$ **5.** $2x - 4 \ge 3$ or $2x - 4 \le -3$

7. Take the square root of the sum of the squares of the differences of the x- and y-coordinates. **9.** $y = \sqrt{36 - x^2}$

11. $m = \dfrac{y + 2}{x - 4}$ or $y = m(x - 4) - 2$ **13.** They are equal.

15. 4 **17.** $4uv$ **19.** $-\dfrac{h}{x(x + h)}$ **21.** $(y - y^{-1})(y + y^{-1})$

23. $u = \pm\sqrt{2}, \pm 3$ **25.** $3x^2 + 3xh + h^2$

27. $(1, 5)$

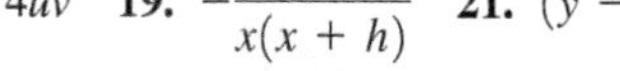

29. $(-\infty, 4] \cup [5, 6)$

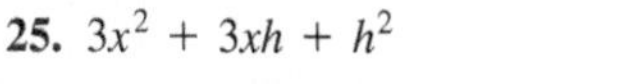

31. $\{x: x < -4/3$ or $x > 4\}$; $\left(-\infty, -\frac{4}{3}\right) \cup (4, \infty)$

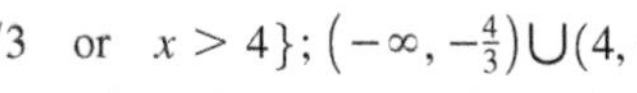

33. $\{x: -2 < x < -1 \text{ or } 2 < x < 3\}; (-2, -1) \cup (2, 3)$

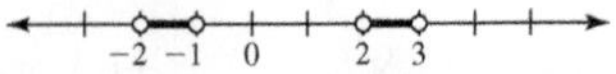

35. $y = 2 - \sqrt{9 - (x + 1)^2}$

37. $y = \frac{5}{3}x + 4$

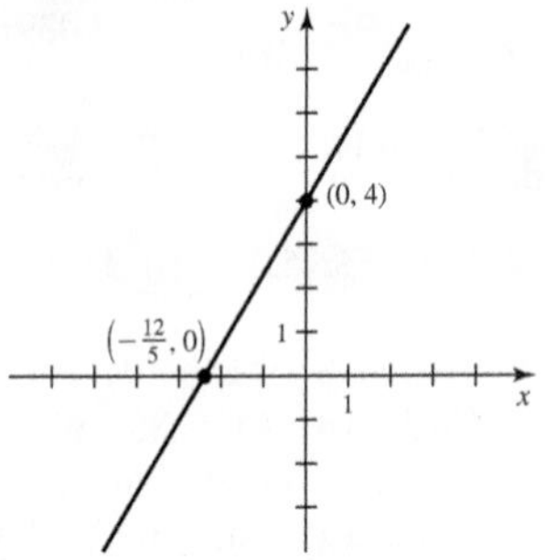

39. $y = \frac{4}{5}x - 4$

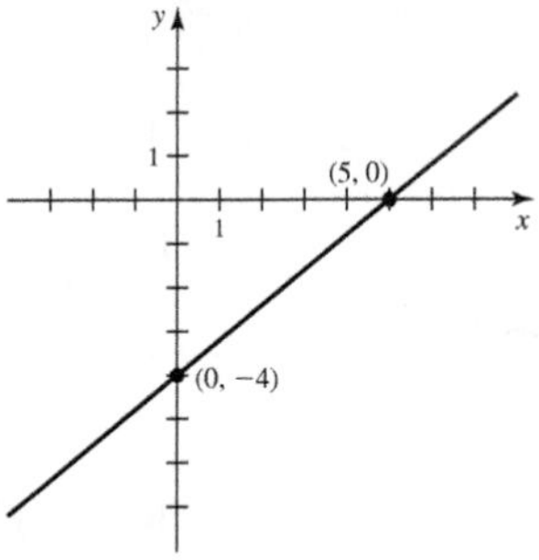

41. $x + 2y = 24$

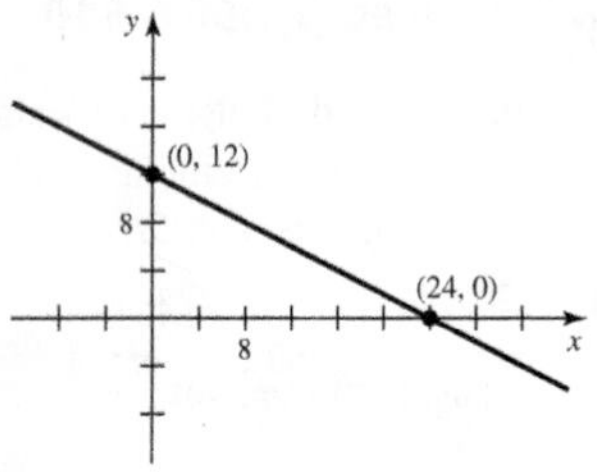

43. $y = \frac{1}{3}x - 7$ **45.** **a.** False **b.** True **c.** False **d.** False **e.** False **f.** True **g.** False **47.** $\{x: |x - 1| \geq 3\}$

49.

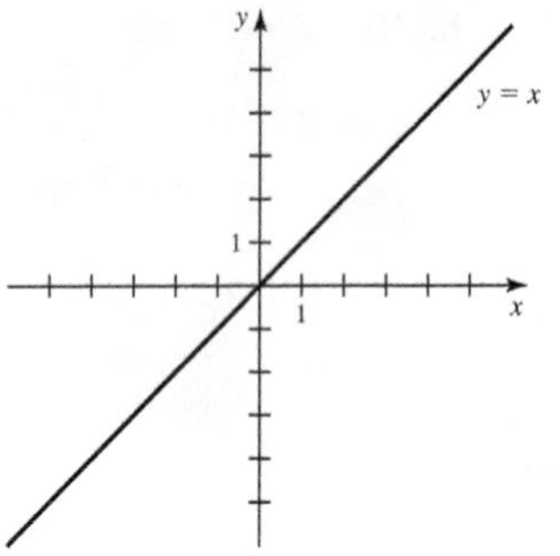

Index

Note: Page numbers in *italics* indicate figures, "t" indicated a table, "e" indicates an exercise, and GP indicates Guided Projects.

A

B

D

E

F

G

H

I

J

K

L

N

O

P

Q

R

U

TABLE OF INTEGRALS

Substitution Rule	Integration by Parts
$\int f(g(x))g'(x)\,dx = \int f(u)\,du \quad (u = g(x))$	$\int u\,dv = uv - \int v\,du$
$\int_a^b f(g(x))g'(x)\,dx = \int_{g(a)}^{g(b)} f(u)\,du$	$\int_a^b uv'\,dx = uv\Big\|_a^b - \int_a^b vu'\,dx$

Basic Integrals

1. $\int x^n\,dx = \frac{1}{n+1}x^{n+1} + C;\ n \neq -1$

2. $\int \frac{dx}{x} = \ln|x| + C$

3. $\int \cos ax\,dx = \frac{1}{a}\sin ax + C$

4. $\int \sin ax\,dx = -\frac{1}{a}\cos ax + C$

5. $\int \tan x\,dx = \ln|\sec x| + C$

6. $\int \cot x\,dx = \ln|\sin x| + C$

7. $\int \sec x\,dx = \ln|\sec x + \tan x| + C$

8. $\int \csc x\,dx = -\ln|\csc x + \cot x| + C$

9. $\int e^{ax}\,dx = \frac{1}{a}e^{ax} + C$

10. $\int b^{ax}\,dx = \frac{1}{a\ln b}b^{ax} + C;\ b > 0, b \neq 1$

11. $\int \ln x\,dx = x\ln x - x + C$

12. $\int \log_b x\,dx = \frac{1}{\ln b}(x\ln x - x) + C$

13. $\int \frac{dx}{\sqrt{a^2 - x^2}} = \sin^{-1}\frac{x}{a} + C$

14. $\int \frac{dx}{x^2 + a^2} = \frac{1}{a}\tan^{-1}\frac{x}{a} + C$

15. $\int \frac{dx}{x\sqrt{x^2 - a^2}} = \frac{1}{a}\sec^{-1}\left|\frac{x}{a}\right| + C$

16. $\int \sin^{-1}x\,dx = x\sin^{-1}x + \sqrt{1 - x^2} + C$

17. $\int \cos^{-1}x\,dx = x\cos^{-1}x - \sqrt{1 - x^2} + C$

18. $\int \tan^{-1}x\,dx = x\tan^{-1}x - \frac{1}{2}\ln(1 + x^2) + C$

19. $\int \sec^{-1}x\,dx = x\sec^{-1}x - \ln(x + \sqrt{x^2 - 1}) + C$

20. $\int \sinh x\,dx = \cosh x + C$

21. $\int \cosh x\,dx = \sinh x + C$

22. $\int \operatorname{sech}^2 x\,dx = \tanh x + C$

23. $\int \operatorname{csch}^2 x\,dx = -\coth x + C$

24. $\int \operatorname{sech} x \tanh x\,dx = -\operatorname{sech} x + C$

25. $\int \operatorname{csch} x \coth x\,dx = -\operatorname{csch} x + C$

26. $\int \tanh x\,dx = \ln\cosh x + C$

27. $\int \coth x\,dx = \ln|\sinh x| + C$

28. $\int \operatorname{sech} x\,dx = \tan^{-1}\sinh x + C = \sin^{-1}\tanh x + C$

29. $\int \operatorname{csch} x\,dx = \ln|\tanh(x/2)| + C$

Trigonometric Integrals

30. $\int \cos^2 x\,dx = \frac{x}{2} + \frac{\sin 2x}{4} + C$

31. $\int \sin^2 x\,dx = \frac{x}{2} - \frac{\sin 2x}{4} + C$

32. $\int \sec^2 ax\,dx = \frac{1}{a}\tan ax + C$

33. $\int \csc^2 ax\,dx = -\frac{1}{a}\cot ax + C$

34. $\int \tan^2 x\,dx = \tan x - x + C$

35. $\int \cot^2 x\,dx = -\cot x - x + C$

36. $\int \cos^3 x\,dx = -\frac{1}{3}\sin^3 x + \sin x + C$

37. $\int \sin^3 x\,dx = \frac{1}{3}\cos^3 x - \cos x + C$

38. $\int \sec^3 x\,dx = \frac{1}{2}\sec x \tan x + \frac{1}{2}\ln|\sec x + \tan x| + C$

39. $\int \csc^3 x\,dx = -\frac{1}{2}\csc x \cot x - \frac{1}{2}\ln|\csc x + \cot x| + C$

40. $\int \tan^3 x\,dx = \frac{1}{2}\tan^2 x - \ln|\sec x| + C$

41. $\int \cot^3 x\,dx = -\frac{1}{2}\cot^2 x - \ln|\sin x| + C$

42. $\int \sec^n ax \tan ax\,dx = \frac{1}{na}\sec^n ax + C;\ n \neq 0$

43. $\int \csc^n ax \cot ax\,dx = -\frac{1}{na}\csc^n ax + C;\ n \neq 0$

44. $\int \frac{dx}{1 + \sin ax} = -\frac{1}{a}\tan\left(\frac{\pi}{4} - \frac{ax}{2}\right) + C$

45. $\int \frac{dx}{1 - \sin ax} = \frac{1}{a}\tan\left(\frac{\pi}{4} + \frac{ax}{2}\right) + C$

46. $\int \frac{dx}{1 + \cos ax} = \frac{1}{a}\tan\frac{ax}{2} + C$

47. $\int \frac{dx}{1 - \cos ax} = -\frac{1}{a}\cot\frac{ax}{2} + C$

48. $\int \sin mx \cos nx\,dx = -\frac{\cos(m+n)x}{2(m+n)} - \frac{\cos(m-n)x}{2(m-n)} + C;\ m^2 \neq n^2$

49. $\int \sin mx \sin nx\,dx = \frac{\sin(m-n)x}{2(m-n)} - \frac{\sin(m+n)x}{2(m+n)} + C;\ m^2 \neq n^2$

50. $\int \cos mx \cos nx\,dx = \frac{\sin(m-n)x}{2(m-n)} + \frac{\sin(m+n)x}{2(m+n)} + C;\ m^2 \neq n^2$

Reduction Formulas for Trigonometric Functions

51. $\int \cos^n x\,dx = \frac{1}{n}\cos^{n-1} x \sin x + \frac{n-1}{n}\int \cos^{n-2} x\,dx$

52. $\int \sin^n x\,dx = -\frac{1}{n}\sin^{n-1} x \cos x + \frac{n-1}{n}\int \sin^{n-2} x\,dx$

53. $\int \tan^n x\,dx = \frac{\tan^{n-1} x}{n-1} - \int \tan^{n-2} x\,dx;\ n \neq 1$

54. $\int \cot^n x\,dx = -\frac{\cot^{n-1} x}{n-1} - \int \cot^{n-2} x\,dx;\ n \neq 1$

55. $\int \sec^n x\,dx = \frac{\sec^{n-2} x \tan x}{n-1} + \frac{n-2}{n-1}\int \sec^{n-2} x\,dx;\ n \neq 1$

56. $\int \csc^n x\,dx = -\frac{\csc^{n-2} x \cot x}{n-1} + \frac{n-2}{n-1}\int \csc^{n-2} x\,dx;\ n \neq 1$

57. $\int \sin^m x \cos^n x\,dx = -\frac{\sin^{m-1} x \cos^{n+1} x}{m+n} + \frac{m-1}{m+n}\int \sin^{m-2} x \cos^n x\,dx;\ m \neq -n$

58. $\int \sin^m x \cos^n x\,dx = \frac{\sin^{m+1} x \cos^{n-1} x}{m+n} + \frac{n-1}{m+n}\int \sin^m x \cos^{n-2} x\,dx;\ m \neq -n$

59. $\int x^n \sin ax\,dx = -\frac{x^n \cos ax}{a} + \frac{n}{a}\int x^{n-1} \cos ax\,dx;\ a \neq 0$

60. $\int x^n \cos ax\,dx = \frac{x^n \sin ax}{a} - \frac{n}{a}\int x^{n-1} \sin ax\,dx;\ a \neq 0$

Integrals Involving $a^2 - x^2$; $a > 0$

61. $\int \sqrt{a^2 - x^2}\,dx = \frac{x}{2}\sqrt{a^2 - x^2} + \frac{a^2}{2}\sin^{-1}\frac{x}{a} + C$

62. $\int \frac{dx}{x\sqrt{a^2 - x^2}} = -\frac{1}{a}\ln\left|\frac{a + \sqrt{a^2 - x^2}}{x}\right| + C$

63. $\int \frac{dx}{x^2\sqrt{a^2 - x^2}} = -\frac{\sqrt{a^2 - x^2}}{a^2 x} + C$

64. $\int x^2\sqrt{a^2 - x^2}\,dx = \frac{x}{8}(2x^2 - a^2)\sqrt{a^2 - x^2} + \frac{a^4}{8}\sin^{-1}\frac{x}{a} + C$

65. $\int \frac{\sqrt{a^2 - x^2}}{x^2}\,dx = -\frac{1}{x}\sqrt{a^2 - x^2} - \sin^{-1}\frac{x}{a} + C$

66. $\int \frac{x^2}{\sqrt{a^2 - x^2}}\,dx = -\frac{x}{2}\sqrt{a^2 - x^2} + \frac{a^2}{2}\sin^{-1}\frac{x}{a} + C$

67. $\int \frac{dx}{a^2 - x^2} = \frac{1}{2a}\ln\left|\frac{x + a}{x - a}\right| + C$

Integrals Involving $x^2 - a^2$; $a > 0$

68. $\int \sqrt{x^2 - a^2}\,dx = \frac{x}{2}\sqrt{x^2 - a^2} - \frac{a^2}{2}\ln\left|x + \sqrt{x^2 - a^2}\right| + C$

69. $\int \frac{dx}{\sqrt{x^2 - a^2}} = \ln\left|x + \sqrt{x^2 - a^2}\right| + C$

70. $\int \frac{dx}{x^2\sqrt{x^2 - a^2}} = \frac{\sqrt{x^2 - a^2}}{a^2 x} + C$

71. $\int x^2\sqrt{x^2 - a^2}\,dx = \frac{x}{8}(2x^2 - a^2)\sqrt{x^2 - a^2} - \frac{a^4}{8}\ln\left|x + \sqrt{x^2 - a^2}\right| + C$

72. $\int \frac{\sqrt{x^2 - a^2}}{x^2}\,dx = \ln\left|x + \sqrt{x^2 - a^2}\right| - \frac{\sqrt{x^2 - a^2}}{x} + C$

73. $\int \frac{x^2}{\sqrt{x^2 - a^2}}\,dx = \frac{a^2}{2}\ln\left|x + \sqrt{x^2 - a^2}\right| + \frac{x}{2}\sqrt{x^2 - a^2} + C$

74. $\int \frac{dx}{x^2 - a^2} = \frac{1}{2a}\ln\left|\frac{x - a}{x + a}\right| + C$

75. $\int \frac{dx}{x(x^2 - a^2)} = \frac{1}{2a^2}\ln\left|\frac{x^2 - a^2}{x^2}\right| + C$

Integrals Involving $a^2 + x^2$; $a > 0$

76. $\int \sqrt{a^2 + x^2}\, dx = \frac{x}{2}\sqrt{a^2 + x^2} + \frac{a^2}{2} \ln (x + \sqrt{a^2 + x^2}) + C$

77. $\int \frac{dx}{\sqrt{a^2 + x^2}} = \ln (x + \sqrt{a^2 + x^2}) + C$

78. $\int \frac{dx}{x\sqrt{a^2 + x^2}} = \frac{1}{a} \ln \left| \frac{a - \sqrt{a^2 + x^2}}{x} \right| + C$

79. $\int \frac{dx}{x^2\sqrt{a^2 + x^2}} = -\frac{\sqrt{a^2 + x^2}}{a^2 x} + C$

80. $\int x^2\sqrt{a^2 + x^2}\, dx = \frac{x}{8}(a^2 + 2x^2)\sqrt{a^2 + x^2} - \frac{a^4}{8} \ln (x + \sqrt{a^2 + x^2}) + C$

81. $\int \frac{\sqrt{a^2 + x^2}}{x^2}\, dx = \ln |x + \sqrt{a^2 + x^2}| - \frac{\sqrt{a^2 + x^2}}{x} + C$

82. $\int \frac{x^2}{\sqrt{a^2 + x^2}}\, dx = -\frac{a^2}{2} \ln (x + \sqrt{a^2 + x^2}) + \frac{x\sqrt{a^2 + x^2}}{2} + C$

83. $\int \frac{\sqrt{a^2 + x^2}}{x}\, dx = \sqrt{a^2 + x^2} - a \ln \left| \frac{a + \sqrt{a^2 + x^2}}{x} \right| + C$

84. $\int \frac{dx}{(a^2 + x^2)^{3/2}} = \frac{x}{a^2\sqrt{a^2 + x^2}} + C$

85. $\int \frac{dx}{x(a^2 + x^2)} = \frac{1}{2a^2} \ln \left(\frac{x^2}{a^2 + x^2} \right) + C$

Integrals Involving $ax \pm b$; $a \neq 0, b > 0$

86. $\int (ax + b)^n\, dx = \frac{(ax + b)^{n+1}}{a(n + 1)} + C;\ n \neq -1$

87. $\int (\sqrt{ax + b})^n\, dx = \frac{2}{a} \frac{(\sqrt{ax + b})^{n+2}}{n + 2} + C;\ n \neq -2$

88. $\int \frac{dx}{x\sqrt{ax - b}} = \frac{2}{\sqrt{b}} \tan^{-1} \sqrt{\frac{ax - b}{b}} + C;\ b > 0$

89. $\int \frac{dx}{x\sqrt{ax + b}} = \frac{1}{\sqrt{b}} \ln \left| \frac{\sqrt{ax + b} - \sqrt{b}}{\sqrt{ax + b} + \sqrt{b}} \right| + C;\ b > 0$

90. $\int \frac{x}{ax + b}\, dx = \frac{x}{a} - \frac{b}{a^2} \ln |ax + b| + C$

91. $\int \frac{x^2}{ax + b}\, dx = \frac{1}{2a^3}((ax + b)^2 - 4b(ax + b) + 2b^2 \ln |ax + b|) + C$

92. $\int \frac{dx}{x^2(ax + b)} = -\frac{1}{bx} + \frac{a}{b^2} \ln \left| \frac{ax + b}{x} \right| + C$

93. $\int x\sqrt{ax + b}\, dx = \frac{2}{15a^2}(3ax - 2b)(ax + b)^{3/2} + C$

94. $\int \frac{x}{\sqrt{ax + b}}\, dx = \frac{2}{3a^2}(ax - 2b)\sqrt{ax + b} + C$

95. $\int x(ax + b)^n\, dx = \frac{(ax + b)^{n+1}}{a^2} \left(\frac{ax + b}{n + 2} - \frac{b}{n + 1} \right) + C;\ n \neq -1, -2$

96. $\int \frac{dx}{x(ax + b)} = \frac{1}{b} \ln \left| \frac{x}{ax + b} \right| + C$

Integrals with Exponential and Trigonometric Functions

97. $\int e^{ax} \sin bx\, dx = \frac{e^{ax}(a \sin bx - b \cos bx)}{a^2 + b^2} + C$

98. $\int e^{ax} \cos bx\, dx = \frac{e^{ax}(a \cos bx + b \sin bx)}{a^2 + b^2} + C$

Integrals with Exponential and Logarithmic Functions

99. $\int \frac{dx}{x \ln x} = \ln |\ln x| + C$

100. $\int x^n \ln x\, dx = \frac{x^{n+1}}{n + 1} \left(\ln x - \frac{1}{n + 1} \right) + C;\ n \neq -1$

101. $\int xe^x\, dx = xe^x - e^x + C$

102. $\int x^n e^{ax}\, dx = \frac{1}{a} x^n e^{ax} - \frac{n}{a} \int x^{n-1} e^{ax}\, dx;\ a \neq 0$

103. $\int \ln^n x\, dx = x \ln^n x - n \int \ln^{n-1} x\, dx$

Miscellaneous Formulas

104. $\int x^n \cos^{-1} x\, dx = \frac{1}{n + 1} \left(x^{n+1} \cos^{-1} x + \int \frac{x^{n+1} dx}{\sqrt{1 - x^2}} \right);\ n \neq -1$

105. $\int x^n \sin^{-1} x\, dx = \frac{1}{n + 1} \left(x^{n+1} \sin^{-1} x - \int \frac{x^{n+1}\, dx}{\sqrt{1 - x^2}} \right);\ n \neq -1$

106. $\int x^n \tan^{-1} x\, dx = \frac{1}{n + 1} \left(x^{n+1} \tan^{-1} x - \int \frac{x^{n+1}\, dx}{x^2 + 1} \right);\ n \neq -1$

107. $\int \sqrt{2ax - x^2}\, dx = \frac{x - a}{2}\sqrt{2ax - x^2} + \frac{a^2}{2} \sin^{-1} \left(\frac{x - a}{a} \right) + C;\ a > 0$

108. $\int \frac{dx}{\sqrt{2ax - x^2}} = \sin^{-1} \left(\frac{x - a}{a} \right) + C;\ a > 0$

GRAPHS OF ELEMENTARY FUNCTIONS

Linear functions

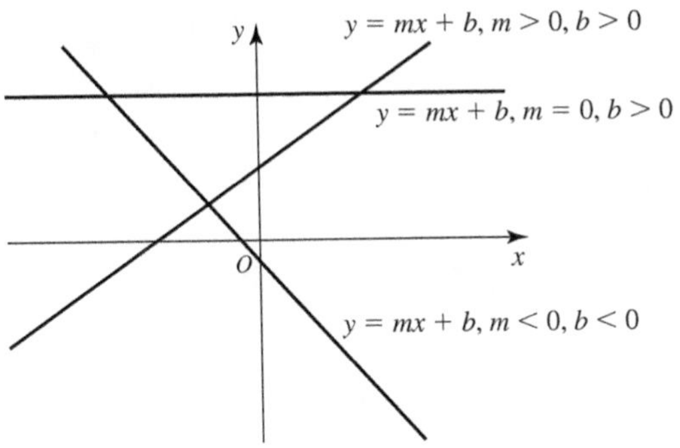

Quadratic functions

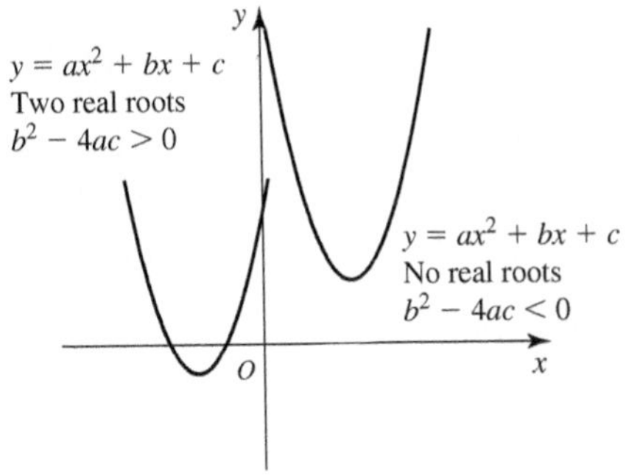

Positive even powers

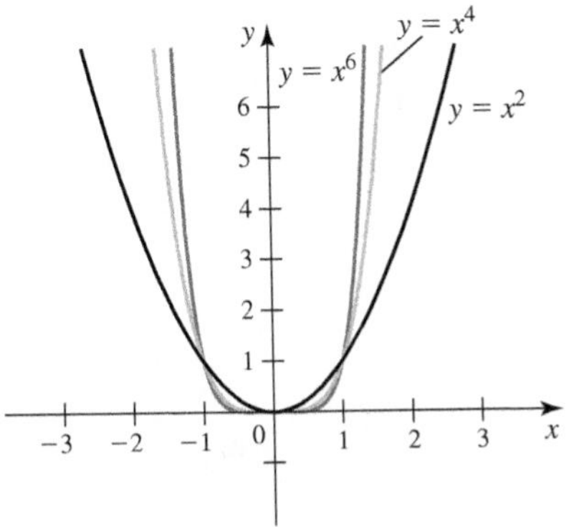

Positive odd powers

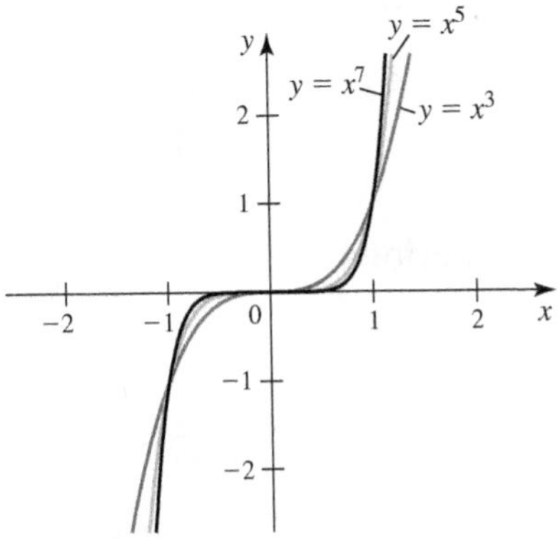

Negative even powers

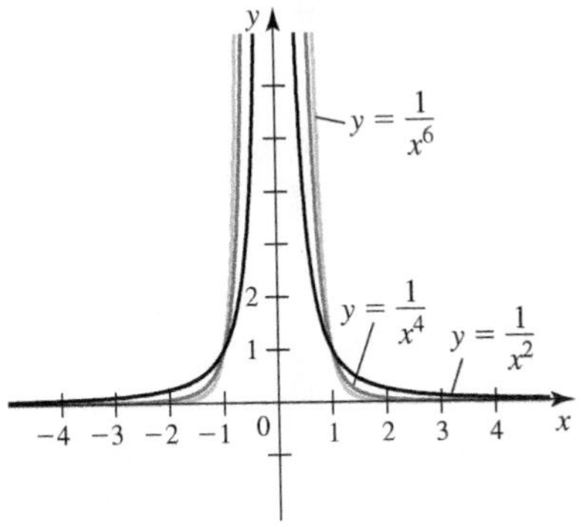

Negative odd powers

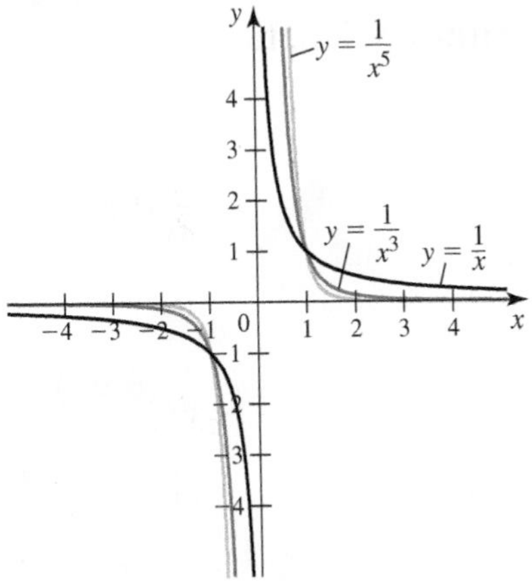

Exponential functions

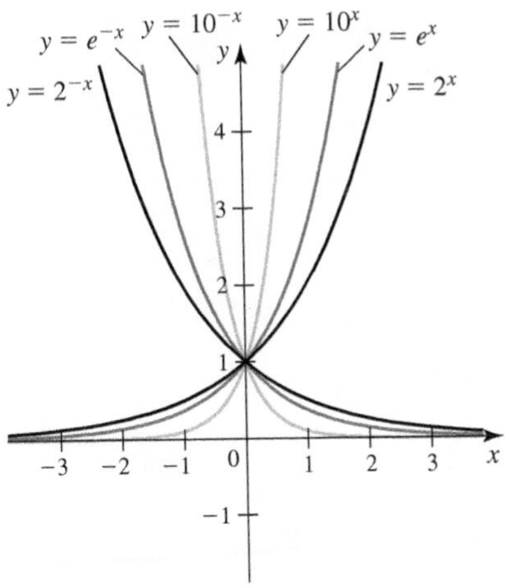

Natural logarithmic and exponential functions

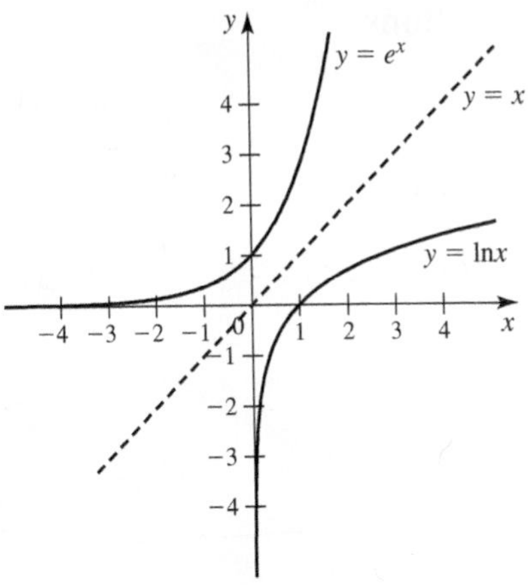

DERIVATIVES

General Formulas

$$\frac{d}{dx}(c) = 0$$

$$\frac{d}{dx}(cf(x)) = cf'(x)$$

$$\frac{d}{dx}(f(x) + g(x)) = f'(x) + g'(x)$$

$$\frac{d}{dx}(f(x) - g(x)) = f'(x) - g'(x)$$

$$\frac{d}{dx}(f(x)g(x)) = f'(x)g(x) + f(x)g'(x)$$

$$\frac{d}{dx}\left(\frac{f(x)}{g(x)}\right) = \frac{g(x)f'(x) - f(x)g'(x)}{(g(x))^2}$$

$\frac{d}{dx}(x^n) = nx^{n-1}$, for real numbers n

$$\frac{d}{dx}[f(g(x))] = f'(g(x)) \cdot g'(x)$$

Trigonometric Functions

$$\frac{d}{dx}(\sin x) = \cos x$$

$$\frac{d}{dx}(\cos x) = -\sin x$$

$$\frac{d}{dx}(\tan x) = \sec^2 x$$

$$\frac{d}{dx}(\cot x) = -\csc^2 x$$

$$\frac{d}{dx}(\sec x) = \sec x \tan x$$

$$\frac{d}{dx}(\csc x) = -\csc x \cot x$$

Inverse Trigonometric Functions

$$\frac{d}{dx}(\sin^{-1} x) = \frac{1}{\sqrt{1 - x^2}}$$

$$\frac{d}{dx}(\cos^{-1} x) = -\frac{1}{\sqrt{1 - x^2}}$$

$$\frac{d}{dx}(\tan^{-1} x) = \frac{1}{1 + x^2}$$

$$\frac{d}{dx}(\cot^{-1} x) = -\frac{1}{1 + x^2}$$

$$\frac{d}{dx}(\sec^{-1} x) = \frac{1}{|x|\sqrt{x^2 - 1}}$$

$$\frac{d}{dx}(\csc^{-1} x) = -\frac{1}{|x|\sqrt{x^2 - 1}}$$

Exponential and Logarithmic Functions

$$\frac{d}{dx}(e^x) = e^x$$

$$\frac{d}{dx}(b^x) = b^x \ln b$$

$$\frac{d}{dx}(\ln |x|) = \frac{1}{x}$$

$$\frac{d}{dx}(\log_b x) = \frac{1}{x \ln b}$$

Hyperbolic Functions

$$\frac{d}{dx}(\sinh x) = \cosh x$$

$$\frac{d}{dx}(\cosh x) = \sinh x$$

$$\frac{d}{dx}(\tanh x) = \text{sech}^2 x$$

$$\frac{d}{dx}(\coth x) = -\text{csch}^2 x$$

$$\frac{d}{dx}(\text{sech}\, x) = -\text{sech}\, x \tanh x$$

$$\frac{d}{dx}(\text{csch}\, x) = -\text{csch}\, x \coth x$$

Inverse Hyperbolic Functions

$$\frac{d}{dx}(\sinh^{-1} x) = \frac{1}{\sqrt{x^2 + 1}}$$

$$\frac{d}{dx}(\cosh^{-1} x) = \frac{1}{\sqrt{x^2 - 1}} \quad (x > 1)$$

$$\frac{d}{dx}(\tanh^{-1} x) = \frac{1}{1 - x^2} \quad (|x| < 1)$$

$$\frac{d}{dx}(\coth^{-1} x) = \frac{1}{1 - x^2} \quad (|x| > 1)$$

$$\frac{d}{dx}(\text{sech}^{-1} x) = -\frac{1}{x\sqrt{1 - x^2}} \quad (0 < x < 1)$$

$$\frac{d}{dx}(\text{csch}^{-1} x) = -\frac{1}{|x|\sqrt{1 + x^2}} \quad (x \neq 0)$$

FORMS OF THE FUNDAMENTAL THEOREM OF CALCULUS

Fundamental Theorem of Calculus	$\int_a^b f'(x)\,dx = f(b) - f(a)$
Fundamental Theorem of Line Integrals	$\int_C \nabla f \cdot d\mathbf{r} = f(B) - f(A)$ (A and B are the initial and final points of C.)
Green's Theorem	$\iint_R (g_x - f_y)\,dA = \oint_C f\,dx + g\,dy$ $\iint_R (f_x + g_y)\,dA = \oint_C f\,dy - g\,dx$
Stokes' Theorem	$\iint_S (\nabla \times \mathbf{F}) \cdot \mathbf{n}\,dS = \oint_C \mathbf{F} \cdot d\mathbf{r}$
Divergence Theorem	$\iiint_D \nabla \cdot \mathbf{F}\,dV = \iint_S \mathbf{F} \cdot \mathbf{n}\,dS$

FORMULAS FROM VECTOR CALCULUS

Assume $\mathbf{F}(x, y, z) = f(x, y, z)\,\mathbf{i} + g(x, y, z)\,\mathbf{j} + h(x, y, z)\,\mathbf{k}$, where f, g, and h are differentiable on a region D of $\mathbb{R}^3$.

Gradient: $\nabla f(x, y, z) = \dfrac{\partial f}{\partial x}\mathbf{i} + \dfrac{\partial f}{\partial y}\mathbf{j} + \dfrac{\partial f}{\partial z}\mathbf{k}$

Divergence: $\nabla \cdot \mathbf{F}(x, y, z) = \dfrac{\partial f}{\partial x} + \dfrac{\partial g}{\partial y} + \dfrac{\partial h}{\partial z}$

Curl: $\nabla \times \mathbf{F}(x, y, z) = \begin{vmatrix} \mathbf{i} & \mathbf{j} & \mathbf{k} \\ \dfrac{\partial}{\partial x} & \dfrac{\partial}{\partial y} & \dfrac{\partial}{\partial z} \\ f & g & h \end{vmatrix}$

$\nabla \times (\nabla f) = \mathbf{0}$ $\qquad \nabla \cdot (\nabla \times \mathbf{F}) = 0$

$\mathbf{F}$ conservative on $D \Leftrightarrow \mathbf{F} = \nabla \varphi$ for some potential function φ

$\Leftrightarrow \oint_C \mathbf{F} \cdot d\mathbf{r} = 0$ over closed paths C in D

$\Leftrightarrow \int_C \mathbf{F} \cdot d\mathbf{r}$ is independent of path for C in D

$\Leftrightarrow \nabla \times \mathbf{F} = \mathbf{0}$ on D